Restaurant
Guide 2002

AA **Lifestyle Guides**

Produced by AA Publishing

OS Ordnance Survey This product includes mapping data licensed from Ordnance Survey® with the permission of the Controller of Her Majesty's Stationery Office. © Crown copyright 2001. All rights reserved. Licence number 399221

Northern Ireland mapping reproduced by permission of the Director and Chief Executive, Ordnance Survey of Northern Ireland, acting on behalf of the Controller of Her Majesty's Stationery Office © Crown copyright 2001. Permit No. 1674

Republic of Ireland mapping based on Ordnance Survey Ireland by permission of the Government. Permit No. MP006701 © Government of Ireland.

Maps prepared by the Cartographic Department of The Automobile Association

Cover illustration by Sue Climpson, Whitchurch, England
Design by Nautilus Design UK Ltd, Basingstoke, Hampshire

Cover photo by Prisma/Foodpix

Cartoons by Larry. Additional photographs provided courtesy of Shaun Hill

Photographs in the gazetteer provided by the establishments.
Special thanks to: Fairyhill, Swansea (p6)

Advertisement Sales: advertisingsales@theaa.com
Editorial: lifestyleguides@theaa.com

Typeset/Repro Anton Graphics, Andover, Hampshire

Printed and bound in Italy by Rotolito, Lombarda SpA

Restaurant assessments and rosette awards are based on reports of visits carried out anonymously by the AA's Hotel and Restaurant Inspectors. Although our Inspectors are a highly trained and very experienced team of professional men and women, it must be stressed that the opinions expressed are only opinions, based on the experience of one or more particular occasions, and assessments are therefore to some extent necessarily subjective and may not reflect or dictate a reader's own opinion on another occasion. See page 16 for a clear explanation of how, based on our Inspectors' inspection experiences, establishments are graded. If the meal or meals experienced by an Inspector or Inspectors during an inspection or inspections fall between award levels the restaurant concerned may be awarded the lower of any award levels considered applicable.

Restaurant descriptions have been contributed by the following team of writers: Jon Boden, Linda Edge, Martin Greaves, Manisha Gambhir Harkins, David Hancock, Alex Hayward, Robert Hayward, Julia Hynard, Denise Laing, Nick Priestland, Allen Stidwell, Jo Sturges, Jenny White.

A CIP catalogue record for this book is available from the British Library

Published by AA Publishing, which is a trading name of Automobile Association Developments Limited whose registered office is
Millstream, Maidenhead Road, Windsor, Berkshire, SL4 5GD

Registered number 1878835.

ISBN 0749 53110X

Published in the USA
by AAA

Contents

How to Use this Guide 4

Features
  Don't Get Fooled Again - *Simon Wright* 8

  Meanwhile in the Kitchen - *Shaun Hill* 10

  AA Chefs' Chef 2002
  Heston Blumenthal interviewed 12

The AA Wine Awards 14

Rosette Awards Explained 16

The Top Ten Per Cent 17

County Map 24

The Restaurant Guide - Ten Years On 26

Restaurants

Restaurant of the Year-England 27

England 28

Channel Islands 561

Isle of Man 574

Restaurant of the Year-Scotland 575

Scotland 576

Restaurant of the Year-Wales 669

Wales 670

Northern Ireland 712

Republic of Ireland Listings 718

Location Maps 722

London Maps 739

Index of Restaurants .742

How to Use
this Guide

Welcome to the *2002 edition of The Restaurant Guide*. You'll find a few changes in this year's model beginning with the editorial article on page 8 and an insight into life behind the kitchen door from Shaun Hill on page 10.

Our *Restaurants of the Year* for 2002 can be found at the front of the England, Scotland and Wales sections and the eagle-eyed amongst you will notice that London (Central and Greater) now takes its alphabetical place in the guide.

With our annual *Wine Awards* we highlight the top wine lists in the country (including those with strengths in specific areas) and name the overall winners for England, Scotland and Wales.

On Page 12 you will find an interview with the winner of *Chefs' Chef 2002* – the result of our annual poll of all the chefs featured in this guide.

Most importantly, at the back of the book, you'll find the *readers' report form* that is your opportunity to pass on comments and recommendations. Your contributions (growing in volume every year) are invaluable. Please keep them coming.

SAMPLE ENTRY

ANY TOWN   *MAP* 5 TL03 ——④

❶— **Any Restaurant**   ❷——**NEW** ◎◎ —③   ⑤

High Street SX0 2QQ ——⑥

Converted 16th-century farmhouse with a pleasant, relaxed style and friendly young staff. Local produce is an important part of menus here, and a spring meal began with oak-smoked salmon (they have their own smoke house), followed by Welsh Black beef. Desserts are straightforward, allowing flavours to shine through, the inspector was enthusiastic about an assiette of chocolate which included a 'meltingly delicious' fondant. The wine list has a good selection of wines by the glass, and the New World is a particular strength.

Tel: 02228 5557833
Fax: 02228 5557834 ——⑦
E-mail: test@btnet.co.uk ——⑧
Chef(s): The Chefs ——⑨
Owner(s): The Owners
Cost: *Alc* £42.50, set-price ——⑩
L £21.50. H/wine £14.50 ☺☺
Times: Noon-2pm 7-9.30pm.——⑪
Closed D Sun, all Mon
Additional: Children 12yrs+ ——⑫
Seats: 50 ——⑬
Style: Classic/country house ——⑭
Smoking: No smoking in ——⑮
dining room
Civil licence: 100 ——⑯

⑰— **Accommodation:** 24 ★ ★
⑱— **Directions:** 1.5 miles from Any town

See sample entry opposite for numbers:

1 Establishments are listed in country and county order, by town, and then alphabetically within that town. There is also an index by establishment name. In London central restaurants are listed in order of postal districts and then alphabetically.

2 **NEW** indicates an entry new to the Guide this year.

3 ◉ The AA Rosette Award. Every restaurant included has been awarded one or more rosettes, up to a maximum of five. See page 16 for a clear explanation of how they are graded.

4 The map number. In the London section, each restaurant has a map reference number to help locate its approximate position on the Central or Greater London maps at the end of the Guide. In the remainder of the Guide, the map references refer to the 16-page atlas. First is the map page number, followed by the National Grid Reference. To find the location, read the first figure horizontally and the second figure vertically within the lettered square.

5 Indicates that the establishment is a winner of an AA Wine Award. See page 14 for further details.

6 The establishment's address and postcode

7 Indicates an establishment which responded '50% or more' when asked what percentage of their ingredients are organically sourced.

8 E-mail addresses may be subject to change during the currency of the guide.

9 The names of the chef(s) and owner(s). These are as up-to-date as we could make them at the time of going to press, but changes in personnel often occur, and may affect both the style and the quality of the restaurant.

10 Alc (A la carte) is the average cost of a 3-course meal for one person, including coffee and service but not wine. Set-price lunch and dinner menus come next. The cost of the house wine or one of the cheaper wines on the list follows. Prices quoted are a guide only, and are subject to change without notice. ☺ Indicates that the restaurant have told us they offer a 2-course lunch for under £15 and ☺ where they offer a 3-course dinner for under £25 a head (excluding wine).

11 The opening and closing times of the restaurant, and the days of the week the restaurant is closed, together with seasonal closures. Note that opening times are liable to change without notice. It is always a good idea to telephone any establishment which you are intending to visit to avoid disappointment.

⑫ Additional information e.g. whether: in addition to meals in the restaurant, bar meals are served at lunch and/or dinner; Sunday lunch is served; Children are welcome, any age limitations are specified. Vegetarian - as most places have a vegetarian choice we have only indicated where we have been told that this is not available, or only by prior arrangement. It is always a good idea to check with the establishment to ensure that no one is disappointed.

⑬ The number of seats in the restaurant. Not all restaurants will take private parties, the number given is for the maximum number of people in a party. Jacket and tie is preferred in a few restaurants, and this is specified.

⑭ We asked establishments to choose two words from a selection, or come up with their own, in order to indicate the style of the restaurant.

⑮ Establishments that do not allow smoking in the dining room may allow it elsewhere, in a lounge or bar, for instance. If you are a smoker, it is worth checking beforehand.

⑯ Civil Wedding Licence - establishments which are licensed for civil weddings have told us the maximum number of guests they can accommodate for the ceremony. Please note, in Scotland a licence is not required for religious ceremonies at any location.

⑰ Accommodation: the number of rooms is shown, together with how many are en suite. If the establishment is in either of the AA's accommodation schemes the rating is also shown. See panel below for further details.

⑱ Directions are given wherever they have been supplied by the proprietor.

All establishments take major credit cards, except where we specify otherwise
'Telephone for further details' appears where an establishment has not supplied us with current details.

All AA recognised accommodation has been assessed under quality standards agreed between the AA, the English Tourism Council and the RAC and given a classification that is based on an overnight 'mystery guest' visit by one of our highly qualified inspectors. This means that whether you choose to stay in a country farmhouse or a luxury five-star hotel, you can be sure of its quality and service.

For hotels, star ratings from one to five symbolise the level of service, range of facilities and quality of guest care that you can expect. Hotels are required to meet progressively higher standards as they move up the scale from one to five stars. A small number of hotels are awarded the AA Red Star Award for outstanding quality. These hotels are indicated with red instead of black stars. For Bed & Breakfast accommodation (guest houses, farmhouses and inns), ratings from one to five diamonds reflect visitors' expectations where quality is seen as more important than facilities and services.

Detailed information on both star and diamond ratings is available at www.theAA.com/hotels.

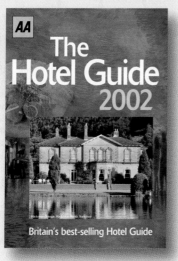
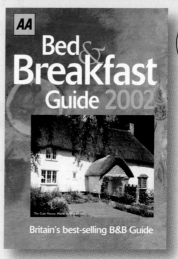

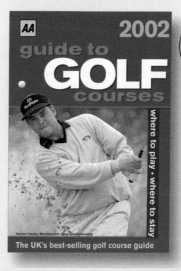

Don't Get *Fooled Again*

I don't find it difficult to stand up for restaurateurs. I used to be one so I guess you could almost call it self-defence. Not that I feel any need to be an advocate for the restaurant trade, it's just that doing what I do, people tend to air their grievances when I'm around. As Shaun Hill's article illustrates, there is a world of difference between the experience of the customers and those behind the scenes - so a little added understanding of the realities doesn't go amiss.

Take the price for instance, particularly at the top end of the market. How can any restaurant justify charging an amount of money for a single dinner that would otherwise buy a week's shopping? Well, I think it's possible. You are paying for intricate food that needs an almighty brigade of chefs to prepare it and uses frighteningly expensive ingredients. Couple this with the kind of highly demarcated sleek service that calls for a swathe of well-trained bodies and it's not that hard to work out where the fat end of your 70-odd quid is headed. Now whether or not you think the end result is worth all this trouble and expense is a different question again, but a portion of the populace clearly think so and, as long as they're getting what they pay for, fair enough.

The difficulty comes when people either feel duped - what was promised hasn't been delivered - or that they've been treated like an idiot. Now this is something I can't, and wouldn't want, to defend. It does happen, and you'll be glad to know that restaurant guide editors are not discriminated against in this respect. Take this exchange that took place in London, mid-2001, at a restaurant that delivers the kind of bill that can keep you entertained all the way home. I had, very politely, sent back a bottle of wine:

"The wine isn't 100% sir, but there isn't anything actually wrong with it."

"I don't understand?"

"It's not perfect sir, but then...I can find no fault with it. Nevertheless, because you are not happy with it, I will change the bottle."

Great stuff isn't it? I'd willingly stump up for more dialogue like this, I mean Franz Kafka made a career out of it. They must be paying him well because this man could have been a lawyer.

The new bottle arrives, compared to the first one the wine is shinier, deeper in colour and the musty aroma of the first has been replaced by a lively scent of red fruit. There is absolutely zero comparison between the two.

"There is a slight difference sir, a nuance."

Right, "a nuance", the sort of fine distinction that would measure the gap between George W Bush and Fidel Castro, summer in San Francisco and winter in Wales, chalk and cheese. You could hardly get a cigarette paper between them, really.

What was the waiter, sorry sommelier, up to? In the end, he was happy to change the bottle (with the kind of mark-up on this list it was hardly going to make much difference) and he accepted there was at least something wrong with it, so why the nit-picking?

If this had, otherwise, been a happy meal experience, I guess this incident would have been little more than an

interesting interlude. In fact, on that evening at least, it seemed to typify the whole ethos of the venue. Smug, self-satisfied and trading on its reputation. The fact that the place remained packed was disconcerting, a case of The Emperor's Old Clothes I suspect.

It's not an isolated case and neither is it restricted to the crustier, classical end of the trade. Take this experience on arriving at a modish, design-led, gastrodome.

"Do you have a table for four?"

"Have you booked?"

"No, I'm afraid not."

"You should have."

"Well I did call several times this afternoon but could only get a recorded message."

"That is because we are so busy sir."

"But do you have a table?"

"Yes."

Life's too short surely? I wanted a table, the restaurant had one available; a perfect match I would have thought.

Let's be clear, these are the exceptions rather than the rule. Many restaurants provide exemplary levels of hospitality and do everything they can to make the customer feel at ease. Most, at the very least, ensure that guests feel their custom is valued. Nevertheless, a tedious snobbery still persists amongst certain elements of the restaurant trade and it tends to surface in places that can do the talk but not the walk.

Perhaps this is the root of the problem. Too often, the fundamentals - top class raw materials, simple accurate cooking, enthusiastic intelligent service - seem to be given less priority than posturing in areas that don't have any real impact on the quality of eating out.

Menus are a prime example. How often have you come across flowery descriptions for the utterly prosaic? Where for instance did roquette come from? What's wrong with plain rocket? What on earth is a breath of coulis? Almost as annoying are the attempts to describe the association between the ingredients on the plate. Whether it's in terms of geography (since when did food go to sleep on a bed of anything?) or relationships (I once saw, for instance – "a marriage of chocolate fondant and a sweetened beetroot sauce" – a recipe for an early divorce if ever I saw one).

And these overwrought descriptions often come hand in hand with similarly elaborate script. Swirls and curls of frantic typeface adding a further layer of obscurity. The reality of course, is that all this convoluted presentation adds up to one half of a pretty reliable equation. Let's call it the Law of Gastronomic Relativity – an overcomplicated menu that misses the point equals overcomplicated food that misses the point. Not exactly Einstein I know, but true nevertheless.

In the final account, none of this does the kitchen any favours. It's about expectation. If you give the audience the impression they're going to get Jools Holland and you serve up Les Dawson, then you're asking for trouble.

I'm not advocating that we all join the awkward squad. Although the relationship between the restaurant and the customer is ultimately defined by money (and this is where it differs from cooking for friends at home – most of us tend not to charge our friends) it shouldn't be adversarial. It's an association that we should approach with benevolence, understanding and even a willingness to forgive. But we should also demand honesty and respect. Most of all, when we encounter restaurants puffed up with self-importance and pretension we should have the confidence to take up our silver toothpicks and prick them hard.

Simon Wright - Editor

Meanwhile
in the kitchen

While you're enjoying a top class meal in the serenity of the dining room, there's a quite different scenario unfolding on the other side of the kitchen door. **Shaun Hill** invites us behind the scenes at his acclaimed restaurant The Merchant House in Ludlow.

The door that divides the kitchen from the dining room separates more than just the kitchen smells from the sensitivities of those dining. There's a dramatic difference in atmosphere too, for the diners do not see the kitchen hurly-burly and the chefs do not see those who pay to eat their food. The contrast is what gives a Fawlty Towers feel to the arrangement when things don't run as expected.

Wonderful food rarely goes hand in hand with serenity in the kitchen. The suave affability of the maitre d' and his crew are far removed from the clatter and earthy terminology of the busy commercial kitchen just a few feet away and traditionally the cooks and waiters have been deadly enemies. George Orwell's stint as washer-up in a Paris hotel kitchen before the war was painfully well observed and perceptive. He saw the waiters as snobs, envious of the clientele, and the cooks as macho and vain, spotting even then the basic problem with the art of

> *" the chef's difficulties have always been self-inflicted "*

food presentation, that the more positioned and elaborated a dish was, the more fingers and pieces of kitchen cloth it would have seen. Time has seen an improvement in relations between cook and waiter but there is still an element of truth in his observation concerning the plate decoration. But the chef's difficulties have always been self-inflicted.

The evening's menu, the device that offers whatever choice, stimulation and interest there is to those dining, also dictates the workload and possible pitfalls for those cooking. The line between what is possible and what will cause deep stress is a fine one and it is paradoxical that an ambitious chef will always offer the combination of dishes that tests the kitchen to its limits.

It's a large part of the excitement of restaurant cooking, you see, the sub-theatrical atmosphere, the nervous tension masked by swagger, and the constant checking and rechecking of mise en place – all those little containers of chopped shallots, peeled tomato, reduced veal stock and suchlike - and the knowledge that it could all go horribly wrong today even if it went like clockwork yesterday. The job would be boring if it were easy or predictable and the large drink that signals the close of another mealtime would just be booze rather than fair reward for the battle fought and won. We revel in the speed and urgency of it all and are elated beyond what's sensible when things go well.

The mealtime service at the Merchant House starts with all these contradictions. I type the menu with two fingers, check the spelling for glaring mistakes, check the dishes for contrast, so that cheese, parsley, garlic or cream doesn't figure in every dish bar the puds. Lastly, I check the names of those expected that evening in case there is someone we know, a regular face that has particular preferences. Mentally, I guess which dishes will be popular and which not. Regularly I get it wrong.

The kitchen door closes as the first diners arrive and from then on, adrenalin will carry everything through until the last order leaves the kitchen. Our waitress will change her expression from admiration to sympathy as she flashes into the kitchen with the first order for four – four different starters and four different main courses – and the race to have starters cooked and ready simultaneously in about fifteen minutes time begins.

The age-old antipathy between kitchen and dining room has no place here. I'm the only kitchen crew and Anja, my wife, not only runs the service with Saskia, our waitress, but also bakes the bread and makes most of the puddings. A fit of pique from me would leave me rather isolated. I don't see the diners but get constant feedback on each table's progress from them both. This and a careful if swift inspection of the returning plates will tell you more than any tour of the tables, fishing for compliments and interrupting people's conversation. The dining room atmosphere loosens up with the steady intake of food and drink, and the kitchen atmosphere becomes more intense as main courses for one table arrive at the point they should be served before the diners are ready to eat them, starters for the next three tables are ready to go out and there is no room

> **" I guess which dishes will be popular and which not. Regularly I get it wrong "**

on my stove to start cooking the next order until something moves toward the dining room. Saskia comes in to tell me that the party of six would like a birthday cake afterwards. I tell her to get knotted and she heads back to their table to express the chef's apologies that there will not be time to bake one.

The last main course goes. I have been reasonably happy with the food and the world seems a fine place. I don the my Marigolds and attempt to restore the cooker to its former pristine self. I will make a large drink for Anja and myself and try to persuade Saskia to have one as well, to make amends for any unintended snarling during the evening.

In the dining room everyone has slowed up, sipping coffee and relaxed. When they all head back home, we will have a snack of bread and cheese and open a bottle of wine. The atmosphere will then be the same in both halves of the restaurant and tomorrow's menu will need a little thought. It may be hectic but it is never dull.

Shaun Hill's most recent book *Cooking At The Merchant House* is published by Conran Octopus. Price £20.

MEANWHILE IN THE KITCHEN

Chefs' Chef 2002

Heston Blumenthal

What is Chefs' Chef?

The one decided by the chefs themselves. A unique poll of around 1,800 of the country's top chefs to find out which of their peers have most impressed them in the past 12 months.

Previous winners were Jean-Christophe Novelli, Gordon Ramsay, Kevin Viner, Rick Stein, and Marco Pierre White (who in a special poll last year was voted Chefs' Chef of the Decade).

Heston Blumenthal reckons he has seen the future of cooking and its name is Molecular Gastronomy but, as Simon Wright finds out, far from blinding us with science, his passion is to demystify the kitchen.

New Clear Cuisine

The Fat Duck isn't an obvious venue for insurrection. For a start, it's in the Berkshire village of Bray. Expensively sedate, rarely disturbed by anything more than the lapping of the Thames and home of that most reassuring embodiment of classic culinary tradition - Michel Roux's Waterside Inn. From the outside, the restaurant is unassuming, discreet and entirely respectful of its neighbourhood. A simple sign hangs above the heavy wooden door, which although there is still an hour until lunch, I find to be hospitably ajar. Inside there has been a fairly recent and impressive transformation. New tables and seating have brought higher comfort levels and the most radical development is that the toilets are now inside the building. In fact the toilets are the most obvious manifestation of cutting edge technology. They are round you see, designed by Phillipe Starck and, according to the chef, possessing of a peculiar design characteristic that will only be fully apparent to men (you'll have to find out for yourselves). As I arrive the carpet is undergoing a thorough vacuuming and the day's clean linen is being delivered. Boxes of fresh produce can be seen being carried in through the back entrance and one or two of the kitchen team drift past in pristine whites. Other than an unusually relaxed and good-humoured atmosphere, there is little that wouldn't be found in any serious restaurant of its type. There is also little to suggest that this might well be the setting for the biggest revolution in cooking since the rise of Nouvelle Cuisine.

Heston Blumenthal deposits himself on the sofa, bringing with him a bottle of mineral water from which he will swig regularly and enthusiastically (later a concerned member of the waiting staff will bring him a glass – "do you want people to think you were brought up badly?"). The water is necessary. He talks freely with an infectious enthusiasm and you get the feeling that sometimes he can barely contain himself. His honesty is captivating, there is a complete lack of pretension and the tone is crusading, driven by belief and an unsullied sense of wonder.

The passion for cooking captured him in his mid-teens when his father's business took off and the family found themselves with the resources to travel to France. "My parents weren't gourmets or anything but my mother had read about this restaurant, we went and I was immediately captivated." Tellingly, perhaps, it was the theatricality of the experience that had him spellbound. "We sat outside with the cicadas singing and the waiters pouring the sauces, my jaw literally dropped...."

The journey from there to the opening of the Fat Duck in 1996 has the makings of a small legend. Every year he saved assiduously for a two-week pilgrimage to France where he would visit the top restaurants making comparisons and learning by example. "I might do a brûlée and do it thirty times. Somewhere, logged in my mind was the best one I had ever eaten, I had to get to that one as a foundation." That he also read voraciously is apparent from his encyclopaedic knowledge of culinary history. Every now and then he illustrates a point with a reference from for instance, 15th-century France (to which I nod sagely whilst wondering where on earth I can look it up).

He cites this "thirst for knowledge" and "burning desire to improve" at least half a dozen times during our conversation and this is the real heartbeat of his cooking style. The now famous crab and smoked bacon ice creams are not the expression of a simple desire to be different or to show off but of a "why not?" attitude coupled with an analytical approach to why certain flavours work together and how our senses interpret the experience of eating.

Some of this, he ventures, may have been forced upon him. In the early days of the Fat Duck his domestic oven only had one temperature, a discipline that forced him to think hard about what was actually going on in the cooking process. It was just another spark that set him on a course of discovery that now seems to be expanding into all sorts of areas at an exponential rate. "The doors are just opening" he implores, " a whole new gastronomy is ahead that's not even been touched".

Looking for innovative possibilities is not new to his cooking but some recent relationships with academics and industrial scientists have been a further revelation and convinced him that the possibilities are immense. He talks of them as kindred souls, headed in the same direction, but coming along entirely different paths. "When I first rang up Peter (Barham, a physicist at Bristol University) I said "I think you don't need salt in the water to keep your veg green," I got half my reasons right and half were a bit misplaced and he

went 'Eureka! A chef that understands'." This initial contact led him to fertile meetings with food technologists and visits to Firmenich, the flavouring company, in Geneva. "That was just like Charlie and the Chocolate Factory, Christmas! These weren't people in white coats who just wanted to change food on paper, they really are enthusiasts."

I ask him if he's worried about taking the magic away from cooking, deconstructing it to the point of extinction. "No, it's about understanding the magic and using what you find to make more magic, new magic, better magic." He agrees that in the final summation it's all about quality. "There are health issues and there are moral issues" (he says that for him, the jury's still out on GM foods and he wouldn't use them) "but those things aside it's about the quality of what you eat."

We talk at length about food as entertainment. It is after all the one discipline that involves all five senses and although we seldom talk about it this way, it can move you in the same way as other arts. "Childhood flavours, ever eaten something and it takes you right back to childhood? A specific time and place? I want to do that. It's like the pigeon jelly we serve. I wanted to create the jelly and cream feeling I had as a child. The heat of the mouth melts the jelly and this is coated in the crab or langoustine cream replicating the effect."

Where does he see all this being worked into the culture of cooking? "It should simplify, demystify. It's not about recipes, it's about understanding. There's so much work to be done, so much information to be sifted but the broader it becomes the more accessible it becomes. Maybe five years down the line, maybe longer, it could be having an impact across the board at any level, we could be using it in the home."

As I leave he gives me a 30-page read-out that gives a chemical break-down of cocoa and caviar which shows that they have key components in common. Earlier I'd been served an as yet experimental disk of white chocolate, studded with caviar. I was taken aback to find that the two flavours, rather than fighting it out as expected, had merged perfectly. Now I have an inkling, at least, as to why. Molecular gastronomy is on the way.

His honesty is captivating, there is a complete lack of pretension and the tone is crusading, driven by belief and an unsullied sense of wonder

The AA *wine awards*

Sponsored by T&W wines, the AA Wine Awards recognise some of the finest wine lists in the country. As well as the overall winners for England, Scotland and Wales we shortlist around 25 finalists who are indicated throughout the guide together with a selection of specialist lists singled out for their excellence in a particular field.

This year, a second round selection process asked entrants to pair wines from their own list with a menu composed by chefs Raymond Blanc and Gary Jones from Le Manoir Aux Quat' Saisons. Below is the menu, with wine selections from this year's overall winner, The Fat Duck at Bray.

Canapés
Beaumont des Crayèles Cuvée Prestige NV

Essence of Tomato with its own Sorbet with Pressed Tomatoes
Amontillado Fino Alberto Lorente Piaget Lustau

Cannelloni of Scottish Langoustine with Tarragon Scented Sabayon
Tokay Pinot Gris 1997 Vielles Vignes Domaine Sorg

Poached Truffle Breast of Landes Chicken steamed in a "Papillotte", Wild Mushrooms and a Port Wine Sauce
Gevrey Chambertin 1997 Domaine Rousseau

Hot Chocolate Fondant with bitter Almond Crème and Pistachio Ice Cream
Montbazillac Chateau Tirecul La Gravières 1994

Coffee & Petits Fours
Vielle Prune Reserve L.O.R Louis Rocque

Wine Award for England and Overall Winner - **The Fat Duck, Berkshire**

The overall winner receives a week long expenses paid visit to the vineyard of **Willi Opitz** the award-winning producer of Austrian dessert wines.

AA Wine Award for Wales - **Fairyhill, Swansea**

Wine Award for Scotland - **The Peat Inn, Fife**

Finalists
Hotel Du Vin & Bistro, Bristol
The Old Bridge Hotel, Cambridge
Riber Hall, Derbyshire
Corse Lawn House Hotel, Gloucestershire
New Mill, Hampshire
Mandarin Oriental Hyde Park, London
Pétrus, London
Restaurant Gordon Ramsay, London
Roussillon, London
The Capital, London
Le Meridien Piccadilly -
The Oak Room, London
Merchant House, Shropshire
Little Barwick House, Somerset
The Cottage in the Wood Hotel, Worcestershire
Yorke Arms, Yorkshire
Braidwoods, N Ayrshire
Old Monastery Restaurant, Moray
Kinnaird, Perth & Kinross
Ynyshir Hall, Ceredigion
Bodysgallen Hall Hotel, Conwy
Plas Bodegroes, Gwynedd
Llangoed Hall, Powys

Specialist Winners
Best American List- The Vineyard, Berkshire
Best Alsace List- Gidleigh Park, Devon
Best Italian List- Alloro, London
Best Regional French List-
Club Gascon, London
Best Value List- Gilbey's, London
Best Indian List- Zaika, London
Best Short List-
Hart's Restaurant, Nottinghamshire
Best Half Bottle List-
Le Manoir Aux Quat' Saisons, Oxfordshire
Best Organic List- Terre á Terre, East Sussex
Best Pub List- Angel Inn, North Yorkshire
Best Brasserie List-
Tower Restaurant, Edinburgh
Best South African List-
Champany Inn, West Lothian

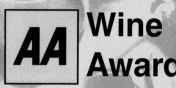

AA Rosette Awards

How the AA assesses restaurants for Rosette Awards

The AA's rosette award scheme was the first nation-wide scheme for assessing the quality of food served by restaurants and hotels. The rosette scheme is an award scheme, not a classification scheme and although there is necessarily an element of subjectivity when it comes to assessing taste, we aim for a consistent approach to our awards throughout the UK. It is important, however, to remember that many places serve enjoyable food but do not qualify for an AA award.

Our awards are made solely on the basis of a meal visit or visits by one or more of our hotel and restaurant inspectors who have an unrivalled breadth and depth of experience in assessing quality. They award rosettes annually on a rising scale of one to five.

So what makes a restaurant worthy of a Rosette Award?

For our inspectors the top and bottom line is the food. The taste of the food is what counts for them, and whether the dish successfully delivers to the diner what the menu promises. A restaurant is only as good as its worst meal. Although presentation and competent service should be appropriate to the style of the restaurant and the quality of the food, they cannot affect the rosette assessment as such, either up or down.

The following summaries attempt to explain what our inspectors look for, but are intended only as guidelines. The AA is constantly reviewing its award criteria and competition usually results in an all-round improvement in standards, so it becomes increasingly difficult for restaurants to reach award level.

One rosette

At the simplest level, one rosette, the chef should display a mastery of basic techniques and be able to produce dishes of sound quality and clarity of flavours, using good, fresh ingredients.

Two rosettes

To gain two rosettes, the chef must show greater technical skill, more consistency and judgement in combining and balancing ingredients and a clear ambition to achieve high standards. Inspectors will look for evidence of innovation to test the dedication of the kitchen brigade, and the use of seasonal ingredients sourced from quality suppliers.

Three rosettes

This award takes a restaurant into the big league, and, in a typical year, fewer than 10 per cent of restaurants in our scheme achieve this distinction. Expectations of the kitchen are high, and inspectors find little room for inconsistencies. Exact technique, flair and imagination will come through in every dish, and balance and depth of flavour are all-important.

Four rosettes

This is an exciting award because, at this level, not only should all technical skills be exemplary, but there should also be daring ideas, and they must work. There is no room for disappointment. Flavours should be accurate and vibrant.

Five rosettes

This award is the ultimate awarded only when the cooking is at the pinnacle of achievement. Technique should be of such perfection that flavours, combinations and textures show a faultless sense of balance, giving each dish an extra dimension. The sort of cooking that never falters and always strives to give diners a truly memorable taste experience.

KITCHEN

The Top Ten Per Cent

Each year all the restaurants in the AA Restaurant Guide are awarded a specially commissioned plate that marks their achievement in gaining one or more AA Rosettes. The plates represent a partnership between the AA and Villeroy & Boch two quality brands working together to recognise high standards in restaurant cooking.

ROSETTE AWARD

AA

2001

AA Rosette Award for
Culinary Excellence

Villeroy & Boch
1748

Restaurants awarded three, four or five AA Rosettes represent the Top Ten Per Cent of the restaurants in this guide. The pages that follow list those establishments that have attained this special status

Villeroy & Boch
1748

Villeroy & Boch

1748

Over 250 Years of Excellence

As Europe's best selling tableware brand, Villeroy & Boch obviously has a strong brand heritage in manufacturing top quality tableware. However, many people are not aware that Villeroy & Boch is also able to apply all of its design expertise in tabletop manufacturing to offer an extensive range of cutlery, crystal and accessories.

Villeroy & Boch's ranges are designed to cater for everybody's lifestyles and have been categorised to reflect people's diverse interests. Perfect for elegant country living, or for those aspiring to a rural lifestyle, the House & Garden collection is typified by traditional shapes and floral decoration.

Kimono Bone China

Equally there are those who prefer a more formal look and for whom dining with guests is an occasion to celebrate. For them we have developed the Chateau collection of elegant bone china ranges.

Popular for family life is the Switch collection, the ultimate in mix and match for informal dining. You can put a stamp of individuality on your dinner service as you select patterns to co-ordinate to your preferred taste and this collection is as stylish as it is practical and affordable.

Marking a new direction for Villeroy & Boch, the newly introduced Metropolitan collection allows shape and texture to create the story. The Metropolitan collection was introduced to meet the needs of the more design-conscious consumer who aspires to 'loft living' simplicity. As people are becoming more adventurous with the food they serve, so too they are looking for more unusual ways in which to present their creations and traditional plate designs simply don't meet the mark. Picture how dramatic small antipasti dishes drizzled in olive oil or Thai skewered prawns could look when served on an attractive dish or unusual platter. The New Wave design in pure white fine china typifies this design innovation with a shape that resembles a flag waving in the wind.

Mankai Glasses

VILLEROY & BOCH

Twist by Villeroy & Boch

LONDON

Restaurant Gordon Ramsay,
68 Royal Hospital Road, SW3
020 7352 4441

ENGLAND

BERKSHIRE
The Fat Duck
High Street, BRAY, SL6 2AQ
01628 580333

DEVON
Gidleigh Park, CHAGFORD,
TQ13 8HH
01647 432367

OXFORDSHIRE
Le Manoir Aux Quat' Saisons,
GREAT MILTON, OX44 7PD
01844 278881

SCOTLAND

HIGHLAND
Altnaharrie Inn,
ULLAPOOL,   IV26 2SS
01854 633230

LONDON

John Burton-Race at The
Landmark,
The Landmark Hotel,
222 Marylebone Road,
NW1
020 7723 7800

Mandarin Oriental Hyde Park,
66 Knightsbridge, SW1X
020 7235 2000

Pétrus,
33 St James Street, SW1
020 7930 4272

Aubergine,
11 Park Walk, SW10
020 7352 3449

Putney Bridge,
The Embankment, SW15
020 8780 1811

Le Gavroche Restaurant,
43 Upper Brook Street, W1Y
020 7408 0881

Pied á Terre
34 Charlotte Street, W1P
020 7636 1178

ENGLAND

BERKSHIRE
Waterside Inn, Ferry Road,
BRAY, SL6 2AT
01628 620691

CUMBRIA
Michael's Nook
Country House Hotel,
GRASMERE, LA22 9RP
015394 35496

GLOUCESTERSHIRE
Le Champignon Sauvage
Restaurant,
24 Suffolk Road, CHELTENHAM,
GL50 2AQ
01242 573449

Lords of the Manor,
UPPER SLAUGHTER, GL54 2JD
01451 820243

HEREFORDSHIRE
Castle House Hotel,
Castle Street, HEREFORD, HR1 2NW
01432 356321

La Rive,
Bridge Street, HEREFORD, HR4 9DG
01432 349008

LINCOLNSHIRE
Winteringham Fields,
WINTERINGHAM, DN15 9PF
01724 733096

RUTLAND
Hambleton Hall,
Hambleton, OAKHAM, LE15 8TH
01572 756991

SOMERSET
Restaurant Lettonie,
35 Kelston Road, BATH, BA1 3QH
01225 446676

REPUBLIC OF IRELAND

DUBLIN
Patrick Guilbaud at
The Merrion Hotel,
Upper Merrion Street, DUBLIN
01 6030600

LONDON

EC1
Gaudi Restaurante,
63 Clerkenwell Road
020 7608 3220

EC4
City Rhodes Restaurant,
1 New Street Square
020 7583 1313

SW1
Drones,
1 Pont Street
020 7233 5955

Roussillon,
16 St Barnabas Street
020 7730 5550

Sheraton Park Tower,
101 Knightsbridge
020 7235 8050

La Tante Claire at The Berkeley,
Wilton Place, Knightsbridge
020 7235 6000

Zafferano,
15 Lowndes Street
020 7235 5800

SW17
Chez Bruce,
2 Bellevue Road,
Wandsworth Common
020 8672 0114

SW3
Floriana,
15 Beauchamp Place
020 7838 1500

The Capital,
Basil Street, Knightsbridge
020 7589 5171

Zaika,
257-259 Fulham Road
020 7351 7823

W1
Restaurant 1837 at Brown's,
Albemarle Street, Mayfair
020 7408 1837

Chez Nico,
90 Park Lane
020 7409 1290

The Dorchester, The Oriental,
Park Lane
020 7629 8888

L'Escargot - Picasso Room,
48 Greek Street
020 7439 7474

Hakkasan,
8 Hanway Place
020 7927 7000

L'Odeon,
65 Regent Street
020 7287 1400

Le Meridien Piccadilly,
The Oak Room,
21 Piccadilly
0870 400 8400

Lindsay House Restaurant,
21 Romilly Street
020 7439 0450

Mirabelle,
56 Curzon Street
020 7499 4636

Nobu,
Old Park Lane
020 7447 4747

Orrery,
55-57 Marylebone High Street
020 7616 8000

Quo Vadis,
26-29 Dean Street
020 7437 9585

The Square,
6-10 Bruton Street
020 7495 7100

W6
River Café,
Thames Wharf Studios, Rainville
Road, Hammersmith
020 7386 4200

W8
The Belvedere,
Abbotsbury Road, Holland House,
Holland Park
020 7602 1238

Royal Garden Hotel,
2-24 Kensington High Street
020 7937 8000

W14
Chinon Restaurant,
23 Richmond Way
020 7602 5968

WC2
The Savoy, The River Room
Strand
020 7836 4343

ENGLAND

BERKSHIRE
Fredrick's Hotel,
Shoppenhangers Road,
MAIDENHEAD, SL6 2PZ
01628 581000

The Vineyard at Stockcross,
Stockcross, NEWBURY, RG20 8JU
01635 528770

BRISTOL
Harveys Restaurant,
12 Denmark Street, BRISTOL,
BS1 5DQ
0117 927 5034

BUCKINGHAMSHIRE
Hartwell House,
Oxford Road, AYLESBURY, HP17 8NL
01296 747444

Cliveden, Waldo's,
TAPLOW, SL6 0JF
01628 668561

CAMBRIDGESHIRE
The Pink Geranium,
Station Road, MELBOURN, SG8 6DX
01763 260215

CHESHIRE
The Chester Grosvenor,
Eastgate, CHESTER, CH1 1LT
01244 324024

CORNWALL & ISLES OF SCILLY
Well House Hotel,
St Keyne, LISKEARD, PL14 4RN
01579 342001

Seafood Restaurant,
PADSTOW, PL28 8BY
01841 532700

St Martin's on the Isle,
Lower Town, ST MARTIN'S,
TR25 0QW
01720 422090

Hotel Tresanton
Lower Castle Road, ST MAWES,
TR2 5DR
01326 270055

CUMBRIA
Sharrow Bay Country House Hotel,
Sharrow Bay, HOWTOWN, CA10 2LZ
017684 86301

Rampsbeck Country House Hotel,
WATERMILLOCK, CA11 0LP
017684 86442

Gilpin Lodge Country House Hotel,
Crook Road, WINDERMERE,
LA23 3NE
015394 88818

Holbeck Ghyll Country House
Hotel,
Holbeck Lane, WINDERMERE,
LA23 1LU
015394 32375

DERBYSHIRE
Fischer's Baslow Hall,
Calver Road, BASLOW, DE45 1RR
01246 583259

The Old Vicarage,
Ridgeway Moor, RIDGEWAY,
S12 3XW
0114 2475814

DEVON
The Carved Angel,
2 South Embankment,
DARTMOUTH, TQ6 9BH
01803 832465

Michael Caines at The Royal
Clarence,
Cathedral Yard, EXETER, EX1 1HD
01392 319955

The Horn of Plenty,
GULWORTHY, PL19 8JD
01822 832528

Arundell Arms,
LIFTON, PL16 0AA
01566 784666

Pophams,
Castle Street, WINKLEIGH,
EX19 8HQ
01837 83767

DORSET
Summer Lodge,
EVERSHOT,
DT2 0JR
01935 83424

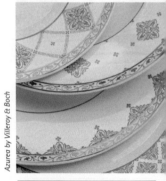

Azurea by Villeroy & Boch

COUNTY DURHAM
Seaham Hall Hotel,
Lord Byron's Walk, SEAHAM,
SR7 7AG
0191 5161400

GLOUCESTERSHIRE
Buckland Manor,
BUCKLAND, WR12 7LY
01386 852626

The Bacchanalian
Hotel on the Park,
38 Evesham Road, CHELTENHAM,
GL52 2AH
01242 518898

The Greenway,
Shurdington, CHELTENHAM
GL51 4UG
01242 862352

Lower Slaughter Manor,
LOWER SLAUGHTER, GL54 2HP
01451 820456

947AD at The Royalist,
Digbeth Street,
STOW-ON-THE-WOLD, GL54 1BN
01451 830670

The Close Hotel,
8 Long Street, TETBURY, GL8 8AQ
01666 502272

GREATER LONDON
Chapter One, Farnborough
Common, Locksbottom, BROMLEY,
BR6 8NF
01689 854848

GREATER MANCHESTER
Juniper,
21 The Downs, ALTRINCHAM,
WA14 2QD
0161 929 4008

HAMPSHIRE
36 On The Quay,
47 South Street, EMSWORTH,
PO10 7EG
01243 375592

The Three Lions,
Stuckton, FORDINGBRIDGE, SP6 2HF
01425 652489

Le Poussin at Parkhill,
Beaulieu Road, LYNDHURST,
SO43 7FZ
023 8028 2944

Chewton Glen Hotel,
Christchurch Road,
NEW MILTON, BH25 6QS
01425 275341

Old Manor House Restaurant,
21 Palmerston Street, ROMSEY,
SO51 8GF
01794 517353

The Chesil Rectory,
1 Chesil Street, WINCHESTER,
SO23 0HU
01962 581555

KENT
Read's Restaurant,
Macknade Manor,
Canterbury Road, FAVERSHAM,
ME13 8XE
01795 535344

Sandgate Hotel et Restaurant
La Terrasse,
The Esplanade, Sandgate,
FOLKESTONE, CT20 3DY
01303 220444

LANCASHIRE
Northcote Manor,
Northcote Road, LANGHO, BB6 8BE
01254 240555

Paul Heathcote's Restaurant,
104-106 Higher Road, LONGRIDGE,
PR3 3SY
01772 784969

LINCOLNSHIRE
Harry's Place,
17 High Street, Great Gonerby,
GRANTHAM, NG31 8JS
01476 561780

NORFOLK
Morston Hall,
Morston, Holt, BLAKENEY,
NR25 7AA
01263 741041

Adlard's Restaurant,
79 Upper St Giles Street, NORWICH,
NR2 1AB
01603 633522

OXFORDSHIRE
Studley Priory,
HORTON-CUM-STUDLEY, OX33 1AZ
01865 351203

La Gousse d'Ail,
268 Woodstock Road, OXFORD,
OX32 7NW
01865 311936

SHROPSHIRE
Hibiscus,
17 Corve Street, LUDLOW, SY8 1DA
01584 872325

Merchant House,
62 Lower Corve Street, LUDLOW,
SY8 1DU
01584 875438

Mr Underhills Restaurant,
Dinham Weir, LUDLOW, SY8 1EH
01584 874431

Overton Grange Hotel,
Hereford Road, LUDLOW, SY8 4AD
01584 873500

Sol Restaurant,
82 Wyle Cop, SHREWSBURY,
SY1 1UT
01743 340560

Old Vicarage Hotel,
WORFIELD, WV15 5JZ
01746 716497

SOMERSET
Bath Priory,
Weston Road, BATH, BA1 2XT
01225 331922

The Royal Crescent Hotel,
16 Royal Crescent, BATH, BA1 2LS
01225 823333

Homewood Park Hotel,
HINTON CHARTERHOUSE, BA2 7TB
01225 723731

Andrews on the Weir,
Porlock Weir, PORLOCK, TA24 8PB
01643 863300

Charlton House,
Charlton Road, SHEPTON MALLET,
BA4 4PR
01749 342008

Castle Hotel,
Castle Green, TAUNTON, TA1 1NF
01823 272671

Little Barwick House,
Barwick Village, YEOVIL, BA22 9TD
01935 423902

STAFFORDSHIRE
Old Beams Restaurant with Rooms,
Leek Road, WATERHOUSES,
ST10 3HW
01538 308254

SUFFOLK
Hintlesham Hall Hotel,
HINTLESHAM, IP8 3NS
01473 652334

French Garden by Villeroy & Boch

SURREY
Pennyhill Park Hotel &
Country Club,
London Road, BAGSHOT, GU19 5EU
01276 471774

Michels' Restaurant,
13 High Street, RIPLEY, GU23 6AQ
01483 224777

SUSSEX, EAST
One Paston Place,
1 Paston Place, BRIGHTON,
BN2 1HA
01273 606933

Röser's Restaurant,
64 Eversfield Place, HASTINGS &
ST LEONARDS, TN37 6DB
01424 712218

SUSSEX, WEST
Gravetye Manor Hotel,
EAST GRINSTEAD, RH19 4LJ
01342 810567

South Lodge Hotel,
Brighton Road, LOWER BEEDING,
RH13 6PS
01403 891711

Alexander House Hotel,
East Street, TURNERS HILL,
RH10 4QD
01342 714914

WARWICKSHIRE
Mallory Court Hotel,
Harbury Lane, Bishop's Tachbrook,
ROYAL LEAMINGTON SPA,
CV33 9QB
01926 330214

WEST MIDLANDS
Birmingham Marriott Hotel,
12 Hagley Road, Five Ways,
BIRMINGHAM, B16 8SJ
0121 452 1144

Nuthurst Grange
Country House Hotel,
Nuthurst Grange Lane,
HOCKLEY HEATH, B94 5NL
01564 783972

WIGHT, ISLE OF
George Hotel,
Quay Street, YARMOUTH, PO41 0PE
01983 760331

WILTSHIRE
Old Rectory,
CRUDWELL, SN16 9EP
01666 577194

Manor House Hotel,
CASTLE COMBE, SN14 7HR
01249 782206

Howard's House Hotel,
Teffont Evias, SALISBURY, SP3 5RJ
01722 716392

WORCESTERSHIRE
Croque-en-Bouche Restaurant,
221 Wells Road, Malvern Wells,
MALVERN, WR14 4HF
01684 565612

YORKSHIRE, NORTH
Middlethorpe Hall Hotel,
Bishopthorpe Road, Middlethorpe,
YORK, YO23 2GB
01904 641241

CHANNEL ISLANDS

JERSEY
Longueville Manor Hotel
ST SAVIOUR, JE2 7WF
01534 725501

SCOTLAND

ABERDEENSHIRE
Darroch Learg Hotel, Braemar Road,
BALLATER, AB35 5UX
013397 55443

ARGYLL & BUTE
Isle of Eriska,
Eriska, Ledaig, ERISKA, PA37 1SD
01631 720371

Airds Hotel,
PORT APPIN, PA38 4DF
01631 730236

AYRSHIRE, NORTH
Braidwoods,
Drumastle Mill Cottage, DALRY,
KA24 4LN
01294 833544

AYRSHIRE, SOUTH
Lochgreen House, Monktonhill
Road, Southwood, TROON,
KA10 7EN
01292 313343

DUMFRIES & GALLOWAY
Kirroughtree House,
Minnigaff, NEWTON STEWART,
DG8 6AN
01671402141

DUNBARTONSHIRE, WEST
Cameron House Hotel
BALLOCH, G83 8QZ
01389 755565

EDINBURGH, CITY OF
The Sheraton Grand Hotel,
Festival Square, EDINBURGH,
EH3 9SR
0131 229 9131

FIFE
Cellar Restaurant
24 East Green, ANSTRUTHER,
KY10 3AA
01333 310378

Ostlers Close Restaurant,
Bonnygate, CUPAR, KY15 4BU
01334 655574

The Peat Inn, PEAT INN, KY15 5LH
01334 840206

HIGHLAND
Arisaig House,
Beasdale, ARISAIG, PH39 4NR
01687 450622

The Three Chimneys,
COLBOST, Isle of Skye, IV55 8ZT
01470 511258

Inverlochy Castle Hotel,
Torlundy, FORT WILLIAM, PH33 6SN
01397 702177

The Cross,
Tweed Mill Brae, Ardbroilach Road,
KINGUSSIE, PH21 1TC
01540 661166

Boath House,
Auldearn, NAIRN, IV12 5TE
01667 454896

PERTH & KINROSS
Auchterarder House,
AUCHTERARDER, PH3 1DZ
01764 663646

Kinloch House Hotel,
BLAIRGOWRIE, PH10 6SG
01250 884237

Kinnaird,
Kinnaird Estate, DUNKELD, PH8 0LB
01796 482440

STIRLING
Roman Camp Country House Hotel,
CALLANDER, FK17 8BG
01877 330003

WALES

CEREDIGION
Ynyshir Hall,
EGLWYSFACH, SY20 8TA
01654 781209

CONWY
Tan-y-Foel Country House Hotel,
Capel Garmon, BETWS-Y-COED,
LL26 0RE
01690 710507

The Old Rectory Country House,
Llanrwst Road, Llansanffraid Glan
Conwy, CONWY, LL28 5LF
01492 580611

St Tudno Hotel, The Promenade,
LLANDUDNO, LL30 2LP
01492 874411

GWYNEDD
Hotel Maes y Neuadd, TALSARNAU,
LL47 6YA
01766 780200

POWYS
Carlton House Hotel,
Dolycoed Road, LLANWRTYD WELLS,
LD5 4RA
01591 610248

SWANSEA
Fairyhill,
REYNOLDSTON, SA3 1BS
01792 390139

NORTHERN IRELAND

BELFAST
Restaurant Michael Deane,
38/40 Howard Street, BELFAST,
BT1 6PD
028 90331134

DOWN
Shanks
The Blackwood, Crawfordsburn
Road, BANGOR, BT19 1GB
028 91853313

REPUBLIC OF IRELAND

CORK
Longueville House Hotel,
MALLOW,
022 47156

DONEGAL
Harvey's Point Country Hotel,
Lough Eske, DONEGAL
073 22208

DUBLIN
Fitzwilliam Hotel,
St Stephens Green, DUBLIN
01 478000

The Hibernian Hotel,
Eastmoreland Place, Ballsbridge,
DUBLIN
01 6687666

GALWAY
Ardagh Hotel & Restaurant,
Ballyconnely Road,
CLIFDEN
095 21384

Rock Glen Country House Hotel
CLIFDEN
095 21035

KERRY
Park Hotel Kenmare,
KENMARE
064 41200

Aghadoe Heights Hotel,
KILLARNEY
064 31766

KILDARE
The Kildare Hotel & Country Club,
STRAFFAN
01 6017200

LIMERICK
Dunraven Arms Hotel,
ADARE
061 396633

AA Hotel Booking Service

Telephone: 0870 5050505
e-mail: accommodation@aabookings.com
24 hours a day 7 days a week

www.theAA.com/hotels

Tell us where you want to go and we'll help you find a place to stay.

From a rustic farm cottage to a smart city centre hotel even a cosy weekend for two - we can accommodate you.

www.theAA.com/latebeds

Latebeds, a new online service that offers you reduced-price late deals on hotels and B&Bs.

You can find a last-minute place to stay and then book it online in an instant.

Choose from 8,000 quality-rated hotels and B&Bs in the UK and Ireland.
Why not book on-line at www.theAA.com/hotels

County Map

The county map shown here will help you identify the counties within each country. You can look up each county in the guide using the county names at the top of each page. To find towns featured in the guide use the atlas pages and the index at the back of the book.

England	**Scotland**	**Wales**
1 Bedfordshire	17 City of Glasgow	26 Blaenau Gwent
2 Berkshire	18 Clackmannanshire	27 Bridgend
3 Bristol	19 East Ayrshire	28 Caerphilly
4 Buckinghamshire	20 East Dunbartonshire	29 Denbighshire
5 Cambridgeshire	21 East Renfrewshire	30 Flintshire
6 Greater Manchester	22 Perth & Kinross	31 Merthyr Tydfil
7 Herefordshire	23 Renfrewshire	32 Monmouthshire
8 Hertfordshire	24 South Lanarkshire	33 Neath Port Talbot
9 Leicestershire	25 West Dunbartonshire	34 Newport
10 Northamptonshire		35 Rhondda Cynon Taff
11 Nottinghamshire		36 Torfaen
12 Rutland		37 Vale of Glamorgan
13 Staffordshire		38 Wrexham
14 Warwickshire		
15 West Midlands		
16 Worcestershire		

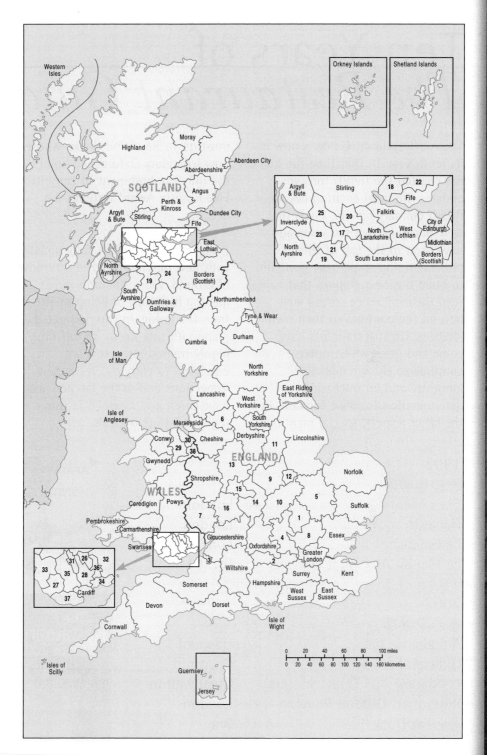

Western
Isles

Highland

Moray

Aberdeen City

Aberdeenshire

SCOTLAND

Angus

Perth &
Kinross

Dundee City

Argyll
& Bute

Stirling

Fife

East
Lothian

North
Ayrshire

19

24

Borders
(Scottish)

South
Ayrshire

Dumfries &
Galloway

Northumberland

Isle
of Man

Cumbria

Durham

Tyne & Wear

North
Yorkshire

Lancashire

West
Yorkshire

East Riding
of Yorkshire

Isle of
Anglesey

Merseyside

6

South
Yorkshire

Conwy

30

Cheshire

Derbyshire

Lincolnshire

29

38

11

Gwynedd

ENGLAND

13

WALES

Shropshire

9

12

Norfolk

Ceredigion

Powys

15

14

10

5

Suffolk

Pembrokeshire

16

7

Carmarthenshire

Swansea

Gloucestershire

3

1

8

Essex

Cardiff

4

Oxfordshire

2

Greater
London

Wiltshire

Surrey

Kent

Somerset

Hampshire

West
Sussex

East
Sussex

Devon

Dorset

Isle of
Wight

Cornwall

Isles of
Scilly

Orkney Islands

Shetland Islands

Argyll
& Bute

Stirling

18

22

Fife

Inverclyde

25

20

Falkirk

City of
Edinburgh

23

17

North
Lanarkshire

West
Lothian

Midlothian

North
Ayrshire

21

19

South Lanarkshire

Borders
(Scottish)

31

26

32

33

35

36

27

28

34

37

Cardiff

0   20   40   60   80   100 miles
0 20 40 60 80 100 120 140 160 kilometres

Guernsey

Jersey

Ten Years of
The Restaurant Guide

The AA Restaurant Guide is now in its tenth year. In that time the guide has charted the trends through perhaps the most exciting decade in British culinary history. Chefs that were barely known ten years ago have risen to the top of their profession and some have gone on to build business empires that have seen their influence spread well beyond the confines of their own kitchens. Great restaurants have come and gone whilst others continue to show remarkable longevity and an unceasing determination to move forward. In the latter respect, special mention must go to Raymond Blanc, whose now legendary Oxfordshire hotel is the only establishment to carry its Five Rosette Award through the decade.

Every year the guide is fully updated with new descriptions and a turnover of around 500 restaurants either gaining inclusion or being omitted from the guide. In carrying out this mammoth task up to 30 full-time highly trained inspectors are employed to carry out restaurant inspections and in the last ten years have eaten and assessed in the region of 45,000 meals.

1992
◉◉◉◉◉

Chez Nico	-	London
Harvey's	-	London
Le Gavroche	-	London
Le Manoir Aux Quat' Saisons	-	Great Milton

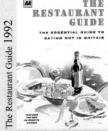

2002
◉◉◉◉◉

Altnaharrie Inn	-	Ullapool
Gidleigh Park	-	Chagford
Le Manoir Aux Quat' Saisons	-	Great Milton
Restaurant Gordon Ramsay	-	London
The Fat Duck	-	Bray

Pétrus

Waiting lists for the top London restaurants may have shortened somewhat but getting a table at Pétrus still requires either serious forethought or extreme perseverance. It's not difficult to work out why. Although the menu offers the kind of elegant French cooking that can be found elsewhere in the capital, the consistency, precision and attention to detail in evidence has few peers. The room – long narrow and brooding – has an air of sobriety about it that has the effect, intentional or otherwise, of throwing the brightness and vivacity of the cooking into even greater relief. The service too, is correct, attentive and not without humour but is hardly likely to become a focal point of the experience. Given the location, the quality and the presence of incidentals (amuse, pre-dessert, petits fours) prices can be viewed as restrained in respect of both the three-course carte and the seven-course tasting menu.

Perhaps the most consistent characteristic of any meal here is the startling lightness of touch that defines almost every dish. Flavours vary from the interstellar to the barely traceable, but they are balanced with the obvious understanding and intelligence that has led, for instance, to a starter of pan-fried sweetbreads with pickled vegetables, new potatoes and a soya vinaigrette being described as "just perfection". Fish, and in particular shellfish are spectacularly good whether it's a ravioli of lobster with sautéed langoustine, celeriac purée, asparagus and shellfish vinaigrette or "an inspired combination" of sautéed scallops with tortellini of leek and onion, ginger and horseradish cream. Meat dishes can sound quite familiar in conception but be a revelation in their execution. The likes of canon of lamb with potato fondant, braised onions, shallot purée and tarragon jus or Bresse pigeon with braised fennel hearts, creamed cabbage, sautéed gnocchi and Madeira truffle sauce have both proved exceptional. The agile approach is perhaps most evident in the desserts where a delicate assiette of passion fruit and honeycomb or a crème brûlée with roasted strawberries, plum, almond sponge and strawberry sauce have both won excited praise. The wine list offers the breadth and weight expected at this level and does feature some bins of character at the lower end of the price range.

33 St James' Street, LONDON   **MAP D3**
SW1 1HD
Tel: 020 7930 4272
Fax: 020 7930 9702
Chef: Marcus Wareing
Owners: Marcus Wareing, Gordon Ramsay
Cost: *Alc* £55, set-price L £30/D £65. H/wine £18
Times: Noon-2.30pm /6.45-10.45pm. Closed Sun, L Sat, Xmas, BHs
Additional: Children 5yrs+. Vegetarian dishes by prior notice only
Seats: 50
Style: Modern, chic
Smoking: No pipes, no cigars, air conditioning
Directions: Nearest Tube: Green Park

BEDFORDSHIRE

BEDFORD

Map 5 TL04

Knife & Cleaver

A 17th century country inn with an elegant conservatory restaurant. A meal begins in the cosy bar, delightfully furnished with Jacobean panelling. The large, exuberant menu travels as far as Thailand but also reworks ideas from closer to home such as fillet of Welsh beef with creamed leeks, Stilton mousse and port sauce.

Directions: Just off A6, 5 miles S of Bedford. Follow brown tourist signs from A6. Opposite church in village

The Grove, Houghton Conquest, MK45 3LA
Tel: 01234 740387
Fax: 01234 740900
e info@knifeandcleaver.com
Chef(s): Chris Bishopp
Owner(s): Mrs P & Mr D Loom
Cost: Set price L £14.95-£19.95/ D £20-£25.50. ☺ ☺ H/wine £10.50
Times: noon-2.30pm/7-9.30pm. Closed L Sat, D Sun, 26-30 Dec, BHs-dinner only
Additional: Sunday L. Bar food. Children welcome
Seats: 65. Private dining room 12. Jacket and tie preferred
Style: Victorian, conservatory
Smoking: No smoking in dining room; Air conditioning
Accommodation: 9 rooms (9 en suite)
♦♦♦♦

Woodlands Manor

Set in a country house hotel, this pretty blue and yellow restaurant reflects the French influences in its cooking. The imaginative menu might include breast of chicken with magret of duck or tian of aubergine and goats cheese. Expect carefully prepared, well presented food with all the trimmings, including intermediate courses, complimentary sorbet and petits fours.

Green Lane, Clapham, MK41 6EP
Tel: 01234 363281
Fax: 01234 272390
e woodlands.manor@pageant.co.uk
Chef(s): Rae Johnson
Cost: *Alc* £32.50, set price L £9.95-£14.95/D £32.50-£37.50. ☺ H/wine £12.50
Times: 12.30-2pm/7.30-9.45pm. Closed L Sat
Additional: Sunday L. Bar food. Children welcome
Seats: 65. Private dining room 40. Jacket and tie preferred
Style: Traditional French
Smoking: No smoking in dining room
Civil licence: 60
Accommodation: 33 rooms (33 en suite) ★★★
Directions: From A6 to Clapham turn R into Green Ln

FLITWICK

Map 4 TL03

Menzies Flitwick Manor

A gem of a Georgian mansion set in extensive parkland. The restaurant overlooks the garden and is decorated in warm,

Church Road, MK45 1AE
Tel: 01525 712242
Fax: 01525 718753

inviting colours, with well-spaced tables allowing plenty of privacy in which to enjoy the quality cooking. Modern British in style with a sprinkling of European flavours, dishes might include roast 'tronçon' of brill on a nest of spinach with field mushroom essence or a duet of lamb with herb de Provence jus. The fresh breads and saucing are particularly fine, as is the formal but friendly service. An ample wine list carries a number of heavyweights along with more contemporary New World choices.

e flitwick@menzies-hotels.co.uk
Chef(s): Richard Salt
Cost: Alc £42, set price L £25.50.
H/wine £19.50
Times: Noon-1.30pm/7-9.30pm.
Additional: Sunday L. Children welcome. Vegetarian by request only
Seats: 50. Private dining room 16. Jacket and tie preferred
Style: Traditional, Country-House
Smoking: No smoking in dining room
Civil licence: 50
Accommodation: 17 rooms (17 en suite) ★ ★ ★
Directions: M1 J12, through Westoning. On approaching Flitwick take 1st left into Church Road. Manor 200yds on L

MILTON ERNEST
Map 4 TL05

The Strawberry Tree   NEW

18th-century thatched cottage replete with inglenook fires and low beams. Modern flavours greet guests in the restaurant in the guise of wild mushroom tortellini on a bed of spinach and Puy lentil sauce with truffle oil, for example. Good produce is at the heart of this operation with organically grown herbs and veg in season and free-range plus rare-breed meat and poultry.

Seats: 22. Private dining room 8. **Style:** Modern
Smoking: No smoking in dining room
Directions: M1 J13. 4 miles N of Bedford on A6

3 Radwell Rd, MK44 1RY
Tel: 01234 823633
Fax: 01234 825976
e strawtree@lineone.net
Chef(s): Jason & Andrew Bona
Owner(s): John & Wendy Bona
Cost: Alc £35, set price D £34.
H/wine £12
Times: Noon-1.30pm/7-9pm.
Closed Mon, Tue, L Sat, D Sun
Additional: Sunday L. Children welcome

WOBURN
Map 4 SP93

Paris House Restaurant

Built in 1878 for the Paris exhibition then dismantled and re-erected in the Woburn parkland that is the ideal backdrop for this mock Tudor property. The interior tends towards the floral, with crisp linen, silver cutlery and polished glassware. The emphasis is on classical French cuisine menu descriptions that come straight to the point (confit of duck in orange sauce, fillet of lamb with rosemary, fillet of beef in red wine and shallot sauce) and there is accurate execution to match. Red mullet with saffron sauce and an exemplary tarte tatin have both impressed.

Seats: 48. Private dining room 16
Style: Classic French
Directions: M1 J13. From Woburn take A4012 Hockliffe, 1.75 miles out of Woburn village on the L

Woburn Park, MK17 9QP
Tel: 01525 290692
Fax: 01525 290471
e gailbaker@parishouse.co.uk
Chef(s): Peter Chandler
Owner(s): Mr P Chandler
Cost: Alc £46.50, set price L £25/D £46.50-£50. H/wine £15
Times: Noon-2pm/7-10pm.
Closed Mon, D Sun, Feb
Additional: Sunday L. Children welcome

England

BERKSHIRE

ASCOT
Map 4 SU96

Royal Berkshire Hotel

Originally built for the Churchill family, this hotel is peacefully located in 14 acres of grounds. Décor in the restaurant blends bold yellow walls and uplighters with white napery and high backed chairs, creating a modern country house atmosphere. The menu follows suit, offering classics alongside modern dishes such as seared magret of duck with violet mash and glazed Japanese artichokes.

Smoking: No smoking in dining room
Civil licence: 90
Accommodation: 63 rooms (63 en suite) ★★★★
Directions: From A30 towards Bagshot turn R opposite Wentworth Club onto A329, 2m, Hotel entrance on R

London Road, Sunninghill, SL5 0PP
Tel: 01344 623322
Fax: 01344 627100
Chef(s): Danny Driscoll
Owner(s): Jarvis Hotel Plc
Cost: Alc £40, set price L £27.50/ D £29.50. ☺ H/wine £18
Times: Noon-2pm/7-10pm. Closed L Sat
Additional: Sunday L. Bar food. Children welcome
Seats: 38. Private dining room 90. Jacket and tie preferred
Style: Traditional

BRACKNELL
Map 4 SU86

Coppid Beech

Never a dull moment at this chalet-style complex with its health club, ski slope, ice rink, nightclub and bierkeller. There's also a choice of restaurants: the Brasserie and the fine-dining Rowans. The latter is a bright air-conditioned room with a central gazebo fromagiare, a timber ceiling and inverted 'ice-capped' chandeliers. Two menus, one fixed-price, one à la carte, offer some imaginative and fairly elaborate dishes. Char-grilled supreme of corn-fed chicken, set on a wild mushroom and thyme crumble and served with a light apple and onion soubise, are examples of some accurate cooking, with varied textures and delicate flavours.

Civil licence: 150
Accommodation: 205 rooms (205 en suite) ★★★★
Directions: From M4 J10, follow A329(M) to 1st exit. At roundabout take 1st exit to Binfield; hotel 300 metres on R

John Nike Way, RG12 8TF
Tel: 01344 303333
Fax: 01344 301200
🖂 welcome@coppid-beech-hotel.co.uk
Chef(s): Neil Thrift/Paul Zolik
Owner(s): Nike Group Hotels Ltd
Cost: Alc £35, set price L £19.50/ D £23.95. ☺ H/wine £12.50
Times: Noon-2.30pm/7-10pm.
Additional: Sunday L. Bar food. Children welcome
Seats: 120. Private dining room 40. Jacket and tie preferred
Style: Traditional, Formal
Smoking: No-smoking area; no cigars; Air conditioning

Stirrups Country House

As the name suggests, this restaurant has a rustic feel, with bare beams, a real fire and polished wood tables. The contemporary style menu caters for most tastes: dishes include grills, vegetarian options and exciting combinations such as supreme of red snapper in cajun spices on a bed of gingered sweet potatoes served with coconut, lemongrass and quick fried Chinese leaves.

Maidens Green, RG42 6LD
Tel: 01344 882284
Fax: 01344 882300
e reception@stirrupshotel.co.uk
Chef(s): Stuart Hooker
Owner(s): Mr C Reed
Cost: *Alc* £22, set price L £22/D £22.
☺ H/wine £10.25
Times: Noon-2pm/7-10pm.
Additional: Sunday L. Bar food.
Children welcome
Seats: 48. Private dining room 100
Style: Traditional
Smoking: No smoking in dining room;
Air conditioning
Civil licence: 50
Accommodation: 29 rooms (29 en
suite) ★ ★ ★
Directions: 3 miles N of Bracknell on
B3022 towards Windsor

BRAY   Map 4 SU97

Chauntry House

This smart, traditional country house hotel is located in the middle of the village, tucked between St Michael's church and the cricket club. The country charm of the setting is reflected in the pretty restaurant, which overlooks the garden. The menu offers classic combinations with a modern twist. Dishes might include roast marinated venison loin with braised savoy cabbage, figs tart and red wine sauce or seared fillet of sea bass on a salted cod brandade with trompettes mushroom, glazed vegetables and clams emulsion. Desserts include old favourites and modern treats such as caramelised banana terrine with dark rum and a glazed Malibu sabayon.

Chef(s): Jean De La Rouziere
Owner(s): Alan Moxon, Luis Carvahlo
Cost: *Alc* £35, set price L £19.50/D £30-£35. ☺ H/wine £14
Times: Noon-3pm/7-11pm. Closed 26 Dec – 3 Jan
Additional: Sunday L. Children welcome
Seats: 40. Private dining room 20
Style: Country-House
Smoking: No smoking in dining room
Civil licence: 55
Accommodation: 15 rooms (15 en suite) ★ ★ ★
Directions: From M4 J8/9 take A308 (Windsor). L on B3028.
Into Bray & hotel 100yds on R.

SL6 2AB
Tel: 01628 673991
Fax: 01628 773089
e res@chauntryhouse.com

The Fat Duck

Berkshire

Nigel Sutcliffe
General Manager

A first visit to the Fat Duck is something that sticks in the memory. It's the kind of place guaranteed to excite hyperbole and even those who are deeply sceptical of what they have heard of Heston Blumenthal's cooking are invariably won over. It's easy to lose perspective when confronted by the pyrotechnic aspects of the menu. Yes, it is arguably the "most exciting, interesting, imaginative and daring" food in the country but this is also cooking that is "technically close to perfect" and whilst you may well leave amazed, you're likely to be well satisfied too. Nevertheless, there is an extra degree of theatre and entertainment that sets this apart from any other restaurant in the country. The venue itself has received a comprehensive makeover with comfort levels rising accordingly and an understated elegance imbued by pale blue walls and flashes of colour from some bold abstract paintings. It's a warm and accessible space and there's a similar ethic apparent amongst the front of house staff, who enthuse rather than lecture and offer service that is consistently relaxed and accommodating. The menu is now structured into a series of mini-courses with choices at third, fourth and sixth courses only. First up though is likely to be a palette cleanser along the lines of a frothy and light 'vodka sour' flavoured with green tea and lime which may be followed by the pea purée, pigeon jelly and crab cream amuse which has become something of a staple of the menu. A second amuse might comprise Pommery mustard ice cream served with a red cabbage gazpacho and amongst the starter choices might be an "awesome" langoustine with pig's trotter and truffle. Mains have included petit salé of duck, green coffee sauce, pommes purée "genius in its simplicity" and a now familiar dish of sweetbreads cooked in salt crust with hay, crusted with pollen, cockles a al plancha and parsnip purée. As for the desserts an outrageous reworking of the stereotypical breakfast (smokey bacon and egg ice cream, pain perdu, tomato jam) which turned out to be "a revelation" and importantly "memorable for all the right reasons". Remarkably, this is still a young restaurant.

As The Fat Duck has matured, so has the wine list. From Alsace to California there is strength in depth from across the globe and not one bin that could be described as a passenger. The incomparable range of sherries has been noted before, but the depth in Rhône, Bordeaux and the remarkable selection from less celebrated areas such as Languedoc Roussillon are equally impressive. Mark-ups are not restrained for a restaurant of this standing and there is an inspired collection of digestifs too.

High Street, BRAY SL6 2AQ **MAP 4 SU97**
Tel: 01628 580333
Fax: 01628 776188
Chef: Heston Blumenthal
Owners: Heston & Zanna Blumenthal
Cost: Alc £56 Set price L £25.50
H/wine £16
Times: Noon-2pm/7-9.30pm.
Closed D Sun, all Mon, 2 wks at Xmas
Additional: Sunday L. Children welcome
Seats: 45
Style: Chic, minimalist
Smoking: Air Conditioning
Directions: M4 J8/9 (Maidenhead) take
A308 towards Windsor, turn L into Bray.
Restaurant in centre of village on L.

BRAY *Continued*   Map 4 SU97

Monkey Island Hotel

This hotel really is on an island. Reached by footbridge or boat, its willow lined grounds are occupied by wandering peacocks and an army of rabbits. The menu sets out to please everyone, with dishes ranging from classic (pan fried calves' liver with bacon) to international (cajun seabass with Asian greens).

Seats: 80. Private dining room 120
Style: Classic
Smoking: No smoking in dining room; Air conditioning
Civil licence: 120
Accommodation: 26 rooms (26 en suite) ★ ★ ★ ★
Directions: M4 J8/9, A308 towards Windsor, before flyover turn L towards Bray Village, then follow signs

Old Mill Lane, SL6 2EE
Tel: 01628 623400
Fax: 01628 784732
e monkeyisland@btconnect.com
Chef(s): David Bilsland
Owner(s): Metropolitan Hotels International
Cost: *Alc* £40. H/wine £18
Times: 12.30-2.30pm/7-10pm
Additional: Sunday L. Bar food. Children welcome

Waterside Inn

"Serene" was the first word that came into the mind of one correspondent in respect of a first visit to this justly celebrated institution. Who could argue, weather allowing, a glass of champagne and canapés by the Thames has got to be amongst the most sublime preludes to any meal. The feeling of harmony extends well beyond initial impressions though because, above all, this remains a restaurant that knows exactly what it stands for and has no hang-ups about keeping pace with fad or fashion. There is of course no need, the Waterside is not short of supporters, the ambition is to satisfy the customer rather than any guidebook and the menu is thus built to accommodate the wants and moods of the clientele rather than to push them in a particular direction. It is the delightfully simple but penetratingly accurate dishes such as a velvety cream of shellfish soup with an oyster or a "sparklingly intense" game consommé with mushroom ravioli that really impress. Of course, this is still the most classic of French cuisine and dishes like pike quenelle with langoustine tails would be gloriously hard to find elsewhere in the UK. The refinement and clarity of flavours evident in, for instance, cassolette of langoustine and scallops with wild mushrooms and a juniper berry nage or grilled rabbit fillets with celeriac and glazed chestnuts is the key to cooking of this nature. Recent visits have found that this precision still sets the place apart from others of its type. It may not be setting the pace, but then, that really isn't the point.

Ferry Road, SL6 2AT
Tel: 01628 620691
Fax: 01628 784710
e waterinn@aol.com
Chef(s): Michel Roux, Mark Dodson, Alain Roux
Owner(s): Michel Roux
Cost: *Alc* £88.60, set price L £33.50-£73.50/D £73.50. H/wine £20-£25
Times: Noon-1.30pm/7-9.30pm. Closed Mon-Tue, D Tue ex Jun-Aug, 26 Dec-31 Jan
Additional: Sunday L. Children 12yrs+
Seats: 75. Private dining room 8. Jacket and tie preferred
Style: Classic
Smoking: No pipes or cigars
Civil licence: 70
Accommodation: 9 rooms (9 en suite)
Directions: M4 J8/9, A308 then B3028 to Bray. Restaurant clearly signed

COOKHAM   Map 4 SU88

Malik's   NEW

What a find! A creeper covered red brick building nestling at the heart of the picturesque village, offering superior Indian dining in plush contemporary surroundings. The menu features many interesting options but also caters for those just looking for carefully prepared, accurately cooked old favourites. If you have difficulty choosing between the many tempting starters the sampler option might appeal - with tandoori skewered prawns

High Street,
SL6 9SF
Tel: 01628 520085
Fax: 01628 529321
Chef(s): Shahinkhan & Nurul Islam
Owner(s): Malik Ahmed & Mujibur Rahman

COOKHAM *Continued*

Map 4 SU88

being singled out for praise. For a real revelation try the Sikandri lamb main - marinated for forty-eight hours and roasted to produce a super-intense depth of flavour.

Malik's

Cost: *Alc* £20, set price Sun L £9.95/ D £25-£30. ☺ ☺ H/wine £13.95
Times: noon-2.30pm/6-11pm. Closed 25 Dec
Additional: Sunday L. Children welcome
Seats: 70. Private dining room 30
Style: Classic Country-House
Smoking: No-smoking area; no cigars
Directions: M4 J7, take A4 towards Maidenhead, 2 miles

COOKHAM DEAN

Map 4 SU88

Inn on The Green

A lovely extended village pub full of log fires, squashy armchairs and newspapers. The restaurant is in a small room off the main bar and serves an adventurous menu, full of European flavours. A meal might include chicken liver and foie gras parfait followed by medallions of venison, with a vegetable barley risotto finished with a raspberry glaze.

The Old Cricket Common, SL6 9NZ
Tel: 01628 482638
Fax: 01628 487474
e reception@theinnonthegreen.com
Chef(s): Derek Moran
Owner(s): Sphere Restaurants Ltd
Cost: *Alc* £28.95, set price L £17.95-£29.95/D £17.95-£29.95. ☺ ☺
H/wine £11.50
Times: noon-3pm/7-midnight. Closed 1-8 Jan
Additional: Sunday L. Bar food L. Children welcome
Seats: 60 (120 summer). Private dining room 34
Style: Country-House
Smoking: No pipes. **Civil licence:** 34
Accommodation: 8 rooms (8 en suite)
◆◆◆◆
Directions: From Marlow or Maidenhead follow Cookham Dean signs. In Cookham Dean turn into Hills Lane; into National Trust road by War Memorial

HURST

Map 4 SU77

Castle Restaurant

This impressive building (once a run down pub) has been restored to its former glory, with wood panelled walls, exposed fireplaces and a section of Saxon wattle and daub. The restaurant occupies two cosy ground floor rooms and a larger room upstairs, with rush matting and a high beamed ceiling. The menu is an exciting modern affair, drawing ideas from around the world. Dishes might range from roast fillet of Scotch

Church Hill,
RG10 0SJ
Tel: 0118 934 0034
Fax: 0118 934 0334
e info@castlerestaurant.co.uk
Chef(s): Damian Broom
Owner(s): Anthony Edwards & Amanda Hill

beef, braised cheek and red wine sauce to tranche of baby brill with roast salsify, glazed seaweed and thyme scented chicken jus.

Cost: *Alc* £37.75, set price L £20/ D £34.50. ☺ H/wine £12.25
Times: Noon-2.30pm/7-10pm. Closed Mon, D Sun, 26 Dec
Additional: Sunday L. Children welcome
Seats: 70. Private dining room 40

Style: Chic. **Smoking:** No-smoking area
Directions: 10 mins from M4 Junction 10

MAIDENHEAD

Map 4 SU88

Fredrick's Hotel

🦀🦀🦀
Shoppenhangers Road, SL6 2PZ
Tel: 01628 581000
Fax: 01628 771054
e reservations@fredricks-hotel.co.uk
Chef(s): Brian Cutler
Owner(s): F W Losel
Cost: *Alc* £53, set price L £29.50/ D £38.50. H/wine £16
Times: Noon-2pm/7-9.45pm. Closed L Sat, 24 Dec-3 Jan
Additional: Sunday L. Bar food L. Children welcome
Seats: 60. Private dining room 130
Style: Classic
Smoking: No cigars; Air conditioning
Civil licence: 120
Accommodation: 37 rooms (37 en suite) ★ ★ ★ ★

There's nothing discreet or understated about Fredrick's, and that includes the food. From the plush and showy décor to those 'naughty but nice' touches of luxury that crop up throughout a meal, this is a venue where a dash of theatre enlivens the dining experience. It's all slightly larger than life, and the regulars - wealthy business and leisure clients - like it that way. That's not to say the food is pretentious or flashy: modern French and British rethinking of classical dishes produces the likes of plump juicy scallops and chicory tatin, and a rump of lamb with girolle mushrooms, and potato and parsnip gâteau judged 'as good as it gets'. Short set menus support the *carte*, with choices like grilled skate and squid starter, and strips of venison fillet with foie gras and forest mushrooms. The exceptional staff really are a major plus, and the short wine list has its pedigree bins.

Directions: From M4 J8/9 take A404(M), then turning for Cox Green/White Waltham. L into Shoppenhangers Lane. Restaurant on R

England

MAIDENHEAD *Continued*   Map 4 SU88

Ye Olde Bell

In an idyllic village outside Maidenhead, a 17th-century inn now much expanded. Some international influences on the modern British repertoire, such as warm salad (duck, rocket, watercress, toasted pine nuts), and noisettes of lamb with mint tart, along with the traditional trolley roasts. Classic desserts like tarte tatin, and eager to please staff.

Hurley, SL6 5LX
Tel: 01628 825881
Fax: 01628 825939
Telephone for further details

MARSH BENHAM   Map 4 SU46

Red House

This attractive rural inn is now more restaurant than pub, with food served in the congenial bar as well the bright country house dining room. Various menus offer tasty modern European cuisine - wild mushroom risotto, duck with Provençal vegetables, cod with mustard lentils and cappuccino crème brûlée. Quick friendly service and a summer terrace are further charms.

Seats: 60
Style: French
Smoking: No smoking in dining room
Directions: 400yds off A4, 5 miles from Hungerford; 3 miles from Newbury

RG20 8LY
Tel: 01635 582017
Fax: 01635 581621
e redhouse@ukonline.co.uk
Chef(s): Jerry Nonnessin & Jerome Leopold
Owner(s): Tricrane Ltd.
Cost: A/c £22.50, set price L £11.95/D £15. ☺ ☺ H/wine £11.95
Times: Noon-2pm/7-10pm. Closed Mon, D Sun
Additional: Sunday L. Bar food L. Children 6 yrs+

NEWBURY   Map 4 SU46

Donnington Valley Hotel

This sumptuously furnished modern hotel stands on its own 18 hole golf course. The light and airy restaurant is decorated in creams and greens, with stainless steel balconies and smart, white clothed tables. It overlooks the golf course, outside water feature and gardens. The modern menu offers some familiar combinations (char grilled calves' liver with bacon; rib eye steak with fries) and a variety of interesting international dishes such as Californian salad or mussels with lemon grass, ginger, coriander and saffron cream. The proprietor's passion for wine is evident in the well-chosen wine list.

Accommodation: 58 rooms (58 en suite) ★ ★ ★ ★
Directions: Exit M4 J13, take A34 S/bound and exit Donnington Castle sign. Turn R, then L at next junction. Hotel 1mile on R

Old Oxford Road, Donnington, RG14 3AG
Tel: 01635 551199
Fax: 01635 551123
e general@donningtonvalley.co.uk
Chef(s): Kelvin Johnson
Owner(s): Sir Peter Michael
Cost: Set price L £18/D £25. H/wine £11.50
Times: Noon-2pm/7-9pm.
Additional: Sunday L. Bar food. Children welcome
Seats: 120. Private dining room 130
Style: Modern
Smoking: No smoking in dining room
Civil licence: 85

Regency Park Hotel

@@

Bowling Green Road, Thatcham,
RG18 3RP
Tel: 01635 871555
Fax: 01635 871571
Chef(s): Paul Green
Owner(s): Pedersen Caterers
Cost: *Alc* £34.45, set price L
£15.50/D £19.50. H/wine £12.25
Times: Noon-2pm/7-10pm.
Additional: Sunday L. Bar food.
Children welcome
Seats: 100. Private dining room 140
Style: Contemporary
Smoking: No smoking in dining room

The water feature in the landscaped gardens provides a tranquil
backdrop at the Watermark restaurant. Designer Italian
furniture and pastel shades set the tone of this stylish modern
venue. The simply presented food is contemporary and with an
individual touch. Starters may be flash-fried king scallop with a
leek timbale or wild mushroom consommé with tarragon and
shallot dumplings. Among main courses are saffron risotto
galette with roasted vegetables in green salsa and pan-fried
medallions of veal in parsnip crêpes with nut-brown butter.
One menu favourite is fillet of Dover sole filled with asparagus
mousse and served with a tomato hollandaise.

Accommodation: 82 rooms (82 en suite) ★★★★
Directions: From Thatcham A4, towards Newbury, turn R into
Northfield Road, then L at mini-rdbt. Hotel is on R

The Vineyard at Stockcross

@@@

Stockcross, RG20 8JU
Tel: 01635 528770
Fax: 01635 528398
 general@the-vineyard.co.uk
Chef(s): Billy Reid
Owner(s): Sir Peter Michael
Cost: *Alc* £47, set price L £23/D £47.
H/wine £12
Times: Noon-2pm/7-10pm.
Closed Xmas

A little bit of London in the Home Counties, mixed with a dash
of California - particularly prevalent on a show-case wine list -
are essential ingredients of the remarkable venture that has
blossomed at the Vineyard. Dubbed "A restaurant with room to
stay", it is all that and more, yet cedes pride of place to Billy
Reid's oft-inspired cooking that is supported by exemplary
standards of comfort and service. In the split-level restaurant,
with its unifying theme of a fine steel balustrade depicting an
endless winding grapevine, a successful blend of uncomplicated

England

NEWBURY *Continued* — Map 4 SU46

menus, prime ingredients and technical wizardry delivers memorable dining moments. The menu - accurately described as Fusion - produces safe yet accomplished options, of which black pudding beignet in light batter on potato purée and topped with lightly scalded scallops, followed by succulent, lightly smoked beef fillet dressed with a medley of fungi and light port reduction are typical. To round off, the champagne jelly - light, soft and set over a bed of red fruits compôte - is to die for.

Directions: From M4 J13 take A34 Newbury bypass S-bound, 3rd exit and at rdbt turn R. At 2nd rdbt take 2nd exit to Stockcross, 0.6 mile on R

Additional: Sunday L. Children welcome
Seats: Private dining room 60
Style: Classic French
Smoking: No-smoking area; no cigars
Civil licence: 60
Accommodation: 31 rooms (31 en suite) ★ ★ ★ ★ ★

PANGBOURNE — Map 4 SU67

Copper Inn

RG8 7AR
Tel: 0118 984 2244
Fax: 0118 984 5542
📧 manager@copper-inn.co.uk
Chef(s): John Sherry
Owner(s): Mr. F Phillips
Cost: *Alc* £30, set price L £18. ☺ ☺
H/wine £13.95
Times: Noon-2.30pm/7-9.30pm.
Additional: Sunday L. Bar food. Children welcome. Vegetarian by request only
Seats: 60. Private dining room 8
Style: French
Smoking: No-smoking area; no cigars
Civil licence: 80

This attractive Tudor style hotel is an easy place to relax, with courteous staff and a smart restaurant whose white walls provide the perfect backdrop for tapestries, oil paintings and classic linen covered tables. The kitchen makes good use of fresh ingredients, local where possible. Dishes range from classic to modern, drawing ideas from all over the world but favouring France: a meal might begin with thinly sliced salmon marinated in fresh lime and ginger, served with mango and coriander salsa before progressing to Thames valley venison with a caramelised onion and Dijon mustard tart.

Accommodation: 22 rooms (22 en suite) ★ ★ ★
Directions: 5 miles from M4 J12, at junction of A329 Reading/Oxford and A340; next to parish church

READING — Map 4 SU77

Millennium Madejski Hotel   NEW

An easy, mellow atmosphere at this landmark new hotel, part of the Reading Madejski football stadium. The place oozes style, from the Atrium's 10ft-high water sculpture and 1.5 litre jugs of cocktails to the restaurant's twisted willow table decorations. Pre-course surprises like lobster bisque set the palate tingling, and the classical menu (with Sevruga caviar at £79 for two and glass of champagne thrown in) does not

Madejski Stadium, RG2 0FL
Tel: 0118 925 3500
Fax: 0118 925 3501
📧 sales.reading@mill-cop.com
Chef(s): Jamie Halliday
Owner(s): Madejski Hotel Co.
Cost: *Alc* £40, set price D £40.
H/wine £13

disappoint. Fish and meat are equally represented, and for that touch of theatre choose Chateaubriand or Dover sole cooked at your table. The plump wine list with in-depth choice also scores highly.

Accommodation: 140 rooms (140 en suite) ★ ★ ★ ★
Directions: 2 miles from Reading town centre, 1mile from M4 J11

Times: Dinner only, 7-10pm. Closed Sun, Xmas & New Year
Additional: Children 12yrs+
Seats: 55. Jacket and tie preferred
Style: Modern, Formal
Smoking: No-smoking area; Air conditioning

SONNING   Map 4 SU77

The French Horn

Delightful riverside setting with 'Wind in the Willows' style views of the tree lined infant Thames. This is no hotel dining room: The French Horn is a foodie destination and has enjoyed a faultless reputation for successful, ambitious cooking for decades. Of the three menus available at dinner, two are variations or tasters of the *carte*, a French scripted journey through the classics. Dishes might include Lobster Thermidor, garlic roasted lamb or monkfish in a fresh mussel sauce. Attractive presentation, quality ingredients and skilful cooking make this a successful formula whose authenticity is enhanced by the efficient French staff.

Smoking: No pipes; Air conditioning
Accommodation: 20 rooms (20 en suite) ★ ★ ★
Directions: M4 J8/9 & A4, village centre, on the river

RG4 6TN
Tel: 0118 969 2204
Fax: 0118 944 2210
✉ thefrenchhorn@compuserve.com
Chef(s): Gille Company
Owner(s): Mr Emmanuel
Cost: *Alc* £55, set price L £22.50/ D £35. H/wine £17
Times: Noon-4.30pm/7pm-midnight. Closed Good Friday, 1 Jan
Additional: Sunday L. Children 3yrs+
Seats: 60. Private dining room 24. Jacket and tie preferred
Style: Formal, French

STREATLEY   Map 4 SU58

Swan Diplomat Hotel

The Racing Swan restaurant has been completely refurbished with a red and blue colour scheme inspired by the Henley Regatta. It is located on the banks of the Thames, and the restaurant's undressed windows take full advantage of the river views and the old college barge moored to the side of the hotel. An all-day *carte* from 10am to 10pm offers a wide choice of dishes demonstrating technical skill and an eye for seasonality. Highlights have included a cracking piece of cod, pan-fried with scallops, baby leeks and chive butter sauce, served with simple new potatoes.

High Street, RG8 9HR
Tel: 01491 878800
Fax: 01491 872554
✉ sales@swan-diplomat.co.uk
Chef(s): Lee Vincent
Cost: *Alc* £29. ☺ ☺ H/wine £13.50
Times: Noon-2pm/7-10pm. Closed L Mon-Sat
Additional: Sunday L. Bar food. Children welcome
Seats: 70. Private dining room 20
Style: Modern Country-House
Smoking: No pipes
Civil licence: 100
Accommodation: 46 rooms (46 en suite) ★ ★ ★ ★
Directions: Follow A329 from Pangbourne, on entering Streatley turn R at traffic lights. The hotel is on L before bridge

England

WINDSOR

Map 4 SU97

Aurora Garden Hotel

Bolton Avenue, SL4 3JF
Tel: 01753 868686
Fax: 01753 831394
e aurora@auroragarden.co.uk
Chef(s): Denton Robinson
Owner(s): Karen Castle
Cost: *Alc* £22.50, set price L £9.50/
D £15.95. ☺ ☺ H/wine £10.95
Times: Noon-2pm/7-10pm.
Closed L Sat, 25 – 31 Dec
Additional: Sunday L. Bar food.
Children welcome
Seats: 45. Private dining room 80.
Jacket and tie preferred
Style: Traditional, Country-House
Smoking: No smoking in dining room
Civil licence: 60
Accommodation: 19 rooms (19 en
suite) ★ ★
Directions: From M4 take A308
(Staines); at 3rd rdbt take 3rd exit
(Bolton Ave). Hotel is 500yds on R

A privately run hotel close to the town centre and Windsor Great Park. The conservatory restaurant is a relaxing setting for a meal, with lovely night time views of the illuminated water gardens. The menu favours classic combinations such as loin of lamb with redcurrant jus or supreme of chicken with Puy lentil jus and smoked bacon.

Castle Hotel

In the immediate vicinity of Windsor Castle is this ambitious hotel restaurant looking onto the high street. The menu offers a selection of modish, modern British cuisine along the lines of roast pigeon breast served on a wild risotto cake, or roast sole fillet with saffron and dill crushed potatoes.

Additional: Sunday L. Bar food L. Children welcome
Seats: 50. Private dining room 300
Style: Traditional
Smoking: No smoking in dining room; Air conditioning
Civil licence: 100
Accommodation: 111 rooms (111 en suite) ★ ★ ★
Directions: In town centre opposite Guildhall

High Street, SL4 1LJ
Tel: 0870 4008300
Fax: 01753 830244
e heritagehotelswindsor.
castle@forte-hotels.com
Chef(s): Andrew Barrass
Owner(s): Forte Hotels
Cost: *Alc* £35, set price L £13.95-
£15.95/D £25-£27.95. ☺ ☺
H/wine £13.50
Times: Noon-2pm/7-10pm

Sir Christopher Wren Hotel

The original home of celebrated architect Sir Christopher Wren, this hotel enjoys an idyllic location on the banks of the Thames. The smart, sophisticated restaurant is decorated in Art Deco style and has lovely views of the river. The inspiring menu makes it hard to choose between familiar dishes (traditional Chateaubriand with fresh vegetables and béarnaise sauce) and international dishes such as roast fillet of lamb with a spicy couscous and ratatouille millefeuille, dressed with garlic snails. Service is so attentive and professional that every guest feels like the most important person in the room.

Smoking: No smoking in dining room; Air conditioning
Civil licence: 90
Accommodation: 85 rooms (85 en suite) ★ ★ ★

Thames Street, SL4 1PX
Tel: 01753 861354
Fax: 01753 860172
e wrens@wrensgroup.com
Chef(s): Philip Wild
Owner(s): The Wrens Hotel Group
Cost: Set price L £23.75/D £23.75. ☺
H/wine £16
Times: 12.30-2.30pm/6.30-10pm.
Additional: Sunday L. Bar food L.
Children welcome. Vegetarian by
request only
Seats: 60. Private dining room 90.
Jacket and tie preferred
Style: Modern

WINKFIELD

Map 4 SU97

Rose & Crown

Two-hundred-year-old building with beams and low ceilings, now housing a 36-seater restaurant and extended bar. In effect an archetypal British pub complete with cheery atmosphere. Cooking is simple and robust - deep-fried goats' cheese with tomato salsa, and guinea fowl with honey glaze and apple sauce are typical.

Seats: 36
Style: Traditional. **Smoking:** No pipes
Accommodation: 2 rooms
Directions: M3 J3 from Ascot racecourse on A332, take 2nd exit from Heatherwood Hospital rdbt, then 2nd L

Woodside, Windsor Forest, SL4 2DP
Tel: 01344 882051
Fax: 01344 885346
Chef(s): Ahmed Bassaid
Owner(s): Mr & Mrs Morris
Cost: Alc £24.50, set price L
£12.50/D £24.50. ☺ ☺ H/wine £9.50
Times: noon-2.30pm/7-9.30pm.
Closed D Sun & Mon
Additional: Sunday L. Bar food.
Children 7yrs+. Vegetarian by request only

YATTENDON

Map 4 SU57

Royal Oak

The Square, RG18 0UG
Tel: 01635 201325
Fax: 01635 201926
Chef(s): Jason Gladwyn
Owner(s): Regal Corus
Cost: Alc £40, set price D £38.
H/wine £12
Times: Noon-2pm/7pm-10pm.
Closed L Mon-Sat , D Sun
Additional: Sunday L. Bar food.
Children welcome
Seats: 26. Private dining room 10
Style: Chic
Smoking: No smoking in dining room
Accommodation: 5 rooms (5 en suite)
★ ★
Directions: M4 J12, follow signs to Pangbourne, L to Yattendon. Royal Oak in village centre

In 1644, Oliver Cromwell reportedly dined here before the battle of Newbury. Today, the pretty, red brick building is an immaculate country house hotel. Although the bar remains, the emphasis is now on food. The low ceilinged restaurant is decorated in modern country pub style, with creamy yellow walls and framed botanical prints. Cooking is classically based, with the occasional modern twist. A meal might include a starter of mussels cooked in curried spices with coconut milk, followed by pan fried calves' liver and bacon with creamy mash and onion marmalade. Good wine list.

The finest wine lists

The AA wine awards recognise some of the finest wine lists in the country. As well as the winners for England, Scotland and Wales you will find this symbol throughout the guide indicating those restaurants who reached the final shortlist and others that were recognised for their excellence in specialist areas. The AA wine awards are sponsored by T&W wines of Thetford.

BRISTOL

Bells Diner

Moroccan and African influences alongside a more familiar
repertoire of red onion and goats' cheese tart, and seared sea
bass at this quiet backstreet restaurant with a relaxed, trendy
atmosphere. Spicy Cornish crab tagliatelle (delicious), home-
made breads, and lemon peel parfait are highly recommended,
dinner is particularly strong.

1 York Road, Montpellier, BS6 5QB
Tel: 0117 924 0357
Fax: 0117 924 4280
Telephone for further details

Blue Goose Restaurant

The open kitchen and the modern, brightly-coloured interior
give this restaurant a lively feel. The menu has some interesting
dishes such as whole roasted glazed quail served with tropical
Miami salsa and a quenelle of creamed goats' cheese or, for
dessert, pineapple tarte Tatin with cracked black pepper,
rhubarb soup and rosemary ice cream.

Style: Informal, Modern
Smoking: Air conditioning
Directions: From city centre, A38 N (Stokes Croft) approx 2
miles to Horfield. On L corner of Ash & Gloucester Roads

344 Gloucester Road, Horfield,
BS7 8TP
Tel: 0117 942 0940
Fax: 0117 944 4033
Chef(s): Andress Ostenfield
Cost: Set price D £18.50.
H/wine £11.50
Times: D only, 6.30pm-midnight.
Closed Sun, BHs
Additional: Children welcome
Seats: 70

Bristol Marriott City Centre

An authentic English dining room complete with oak-panelled
walls and white linen cloths, serving modern British cooking.
Standards occasionally drift, but rack of lamb has been a tasty,
tender main course. A mainly French wine list, and puddings
like Baileys bavarois are a decided success.

Lower Castle Street, BS1 3AD
Tel: 0117 929 4281
Fax: 0117 927 6377
Telephone for further details

Bristol Marriott Royal Hotel

Proof that grand hotel dining still exists outside of London.
Eating out of this type is all about a sense of occasion, and here
the key ingredients (silky service, tricksy but consistent cooking

College Green, BS1 5TA
Tel: 0117 925 5100
Fax: 0117 925 1515
✉ bristol.royal@marriotthotels.co.uk
Chef(s): Giles Stonehouse
Owner(s): Whitbread Hotel Co
Cost: Alc £38, set price D £35
Times: Dinner only, 7.30-10.30pm.
Closed Sun, BHs
Additional: Children welcome
Seats: 72. Private dining room. Jacket
and tie preferred
Style: Classic, Formal
Smoking: No-smoking area; no cigars;
Air conditioning
Civil licence: 200
Accommodation: 242 rooms (242 en
suite) ★★★★
Directions: Next to the cathedral by
the village green on Park Street

England

and an imposing dining room) are all in place. Not surprising perhaps, to find that the style favours the classical French, but other influences (witness Dublin Bay prawns on black rice with a Thai lemon sauce) are not excluded. There's a welcome lightness of touch throughout, whether in a carefully sculpted magret of duck with duck liver parfait and an aubergine gâteau or in a dessert of iced amaretto parfait with blackcurrant sauce. Excellent breads (carved from the trolley of course) deserve a special mention.

Glass Boat Restaurant

Not actually a boat but close to afloat with huge windows looking out over the River Avon. A great venue and some good, modish and Mediterranean tinged cooking accurately executed. Puds are a particular strength and the wine list offers some character at reasonable mark-ups.

Welsh Back, BS1 4SB
Tel: 0117 929 0704
Fax: 0117 929 7338
🄴 ellie@glassboat.co.uk
Chef(s): Michael Karlson
Owner(s): Arne Ringer
Cost: Alc £30, set price D £18.95.
☺ ☺ H/wine £10.50
Times: Noon-2.30pm/6-11pm.
Closed Sun, L Sat, 25-26 Dec, 1 Jan
Additional: Children welcome
Seats: 120. Private dining room 40
Style: Classic
Smoking: No-smoking area; no pipes;
Air conditioning
Civil licence: 80
Directions: Moored below Bristol
Bridge in the old centre of Bristol

Harveys Restaurant

12 Denmark Street,
BS1 5DQ
Tel: 0117 927 5034
Fax: 0117 927 5001
Chef(s): Daniel Galmiche
Owner(s): Allied Domecq
Cost: Alc £45. ☺ H/wine £14
Times: Noon-2pm/7-10pm.
Closed Sun, L Sat, 1 wk Feb,
2 wks Aug, BHs

No gastronomic tour of the south west's first city should be complete without a visit to the medieval, barrel-vaulted cellars - once part of a monastery - that have been the headquarters of Harveys, the wine and sherry shippers, since 1796. Today's restaurant and wine vaults owe their contemporary style to Sir Terence Conran's 1960s re-vamp that remains as ever, distinctively ageless. Food overall is contemporary in style although there are ample classics like smoked salmon with

England

BRISTOL *Continued* Map 3 ST57

caviar cream and Scottish beef fillet with truffle mash and red wine jus. The kitchen copes manfully with up-to-date renditions, based on the best fresh seasonal produce in the likes of langoustine mille-feuille with caramelised cauliflower purée and crab essence, pan-roast Cornish sea bass with candied tomato and olives or organic farmed lamb loin with garlic, rosemary and anchovies. Amongst the desserts a highlight is a "Geometry" of excellent bitter chocolate mousse and griottines that is a triumph of composition and balance in anyone's book.

Additional: Children welcome
Seats: 60. Private dining room 40
Style: Contemporary
Smoking: No-smoking area; no pipes; Air conditioning
Directions: City centre off Unity St at bottom of Park St, opposite City Hall and Cathedral; follow signs for Harveys Wine Museum

Hotel du Vin & Bistro

This third property in one of Britain's most exciting and innovative hotel groups maintains the high standards for which they are already renowned. The atmospheric bistro features dark wooden floorboards, wine ephemera and yellow 'tobacco stained' walls. Cooking is unfussy, using quality ingredients to produce dishes such as roast salmon with creamed cabbage and thyme jus or Angus steak with chips.

Style: Traditional, Bistro-Style
Smoking: No cigars; Air conditioning
Accommodation: 40 rooms (40 en suite) ★ ★ ★ ★
Directions: From M4 J19, M32 into Bristol. With 'Bentalls' on L take R lane at next lights. Turn R onto opposite side of carriageway. Hotel easily visible, 200yds in side road

The Sugar House,
Narrow Lewins Mead,
BS1 2NU
Tel: 0117 925 5577
Fax: 0117 925 1199
📧 info@bristol.hotelduvin.co.uk
Chef(s): Andy Clarke
Owner(s): Robin Hutson,
Gerard Basset
Cost: *Alc* £35. ☺
Times: Noon-2pm/6-10pm.
Additional: Sunday L. Children welcome
Seats: 85. Private dining room 72

Howards Restaurant

This bistro style restaurant occupies two adjoining dock side houses, close to the city centre and the SS Great Britain. The interior is nicely decked out with wood panelling, striped wallpaper and a small bar area. A popular venue with plenty of loyal customers, it offers a relaxed, friendly atmosphere and plenty of imaginative cooking. An emphasis is placed on high quality, fresh ingredients (fish is delivered daily from Cornwall). A meal might include warm wood pigeon and smoked bacon salad followed by fillet of salmon with a chilli and dill dressing, served on a bed of leeks with large prawns.

1a-2a Avon Crescent,
Hotwells, BS1 6XQ
Tel: 0117 926 2921
Fax: 0117 925 5585
Chef(s): David Short
Owner(s): Mr C Howard
Cost: *Alc* £25, set price L £12.50/
D £15. ☺ ☺ H/wine £9.95
Times: noon-2pm/7-11pm.
Closed Sun, L Sat, Bhs
Additional: Children welcome
Seats: 60. Private dining room 27
Style: Traditional, French
Smoking: No-smoking area; no cigars
Directions: 5 mins from city centre following signs for M5/Avonmouth. On the dockside over a small bridge, close to SS of Great Britain

Markwicks

This cooly elegant restaurant is located in the vaults of a former bank. The décor could be described as 'Provence meets modern England in an Art Deco setting' and achieves a peaceful, relaxed ambience in which to enjoy the classically based menu. A meal might include Provençal fish soup followed by roast squab pigeon with pancetta, baby leeks and a red wine and shallot sauce. Desserts follow suit, offering accomplished versions of favourites such as lemon meringue pie or hot rhubarb crumble. The lengthy, well chosen wine list is a joy to read, offering tasting notes and details about the origins of each wine.

Smoking: No cigars
Directions: Top end of Corn St beneath Commercial Rooms

43 Corn Street, BS1 1HT
Tel: 0117 926 2658
Fax: 0117 926 2658
Chef(s): Stephen Markwick
Owner(s): Stephen & Judy Marwick
Cost: Alc £32.50, set price D £25.
☺ ☺ H/wine £14.50
Times: Noon-2pm/7-10pm.
Closed Sun, L Sat, 1wk Xmas, BHs, 1wk Easter, last 2wks Aug
Additional: Children welcome
Seats: 24. Private dining room 16
Style: Classic, Chic

Red Snapper Restaurant

A jazzy, bistro style restaurant with red and yellow walls and ceilings. Tucked away in a mainly residential area, it's well worth tracking down, but make sure you've booked in advance. The menu blends British and European influences, placing an emphasis on fish dishes such as grilled ling fillet with Puy lentils and bacon or lemon sole with capers and fennel.

Additional: Children welcome. **Seats:** 68
Style: Chic, Minimalist. **Smoking:** No cigars
Directions: Telephone for directions.

1 Chandos Road, Redland, BS6 6PG
Tel: 0117 973 7999
Fax: 0117 923 7999
e redsnapper@cix.co.uk
Chef(s): John Raines
Owner(s): John & Joanna Raines
Cost: Set price L £14. ☺ ☺ H/wine £10
Times: Noon-2pm/7-10pm.
Closed L Mon, 10 days at Xmas, Jun

Riverstation

Since it opened four years ago, Riverstation has gone from strength to strength, delivering consistently high quality, good value food. It is divided into two main areas: downstairs, a relaxed bar/bistro offers light snacks and salads, whilst upstairs the restaurant provides a more formal setting. The modern menu offers something for everyone. Familiar dishes such as grilled steak with chips and béarnaise might feature alongside a European influenced roast pigeon with root vegetable gratin, griottines and rosemary jus or an Oriental style seared tea smoked swordfish with pak choi, noodles, ginger and soy. The wine list is equally impressive.

Style: Modern, Minimalist. **Smoking:** No-smoking area
Directions: Telephone for directions

The Grove BS1 4RB
Tel: 0117 914 4434
Fax: 0117 934 9990
e relax@riverstation.co.uk
Chef(s): Peter Taylor, Simon Green
Owner(s): S Bell, J Payne, M Hall, P Taylor
Cost: Alc £28, set price L £14.75. ☺ ☺ H/wine £10
Times: Noon-2.30pm/6-10.30pm.
Closed Xmas
Additional: Sunday L. Children welcome
Seats: 120

Severnshed

When Isambard Kingdom Brunel designed the industrial Severnshed, he probably never envisaged serving food there. However, with mainly organic produce and inspiration from around the world with strong Middle Eastern influences, the 'shed' is now a restaurant with an unusual menu. Using a wood-burning oven a variety of breads are baked twice daily, while desserts are light and fruity.

Smoking: No smoking in dining room
Directions: Telephone for directions

The Grove, Harbourside, BS1 4RB
Tel: 0117 925 1212
Cost: Alc £21.50, set price L £8.95-9.95. ☺ ☺ H/wine £9.95
Times: Noon-3pm/6.30-11pm.
Additional: Sunday L. Bar food. Children welcome
Style: Chic, Informal

England

BRISTOL *Continued*

Map 3 ST57

Tico Tico

NEW

Popular neighbourhood restaurant, bistro-style, with a variety of influences apparent in the menu - Chinese spices, Thai fragrances and marinades from the Middle East to Jamaica. It is open for dinner only and booking is essential Friday and Saturday. A main course of chargrilled brochette of red snapper has found favour, served with a coconut milk, lime and coriander curry sauce.

Seats: 45. Private dining room 12
Style: Modern Bistro-Style
Smoking: No-smoking area; no cigars
Directions: Telephone for directions

24 Alma Vale Road, Clifton, BS8 2HY
Tel: 01179 238700
Fax: 01179 741533
Chef(s): A Kendall
Owner(s): A Kendall
Cost: *Alc* £23, set price D £17.50. ☺
H/wine £12.95
Times: Dinner only, 7pm-Midnight.
Closed Sun & Mon, 23 Dec – 4 Jan
Additional: Children welcome

BUCKINGHAMSHIRE

AYLESBURY

Map 4 SP81

Hartwell House

The rat race seems a long way from this utterly magnificent stately home-turned hotel, where every aid to relaxation and de-stressing is on offer. The former refuge of Louis XVIII is as elaborate as you might expect, and the high-ceilinged restaurant, with its calming yellow walls and shimmering drapes, promotes a sense of well-being. No doubt inspired by the surroundings, the cuisine is equally impressive: take starters like carpaccio of venison, home-made smoked chicken and spring onion sausage, and wood pigeon with marinated forest mushrooms and truffle vinaigrette from the bill of fare. Other highlights have included, seared halibut fillet on crushed anchovy potatoes, monkfish medallions wrapped in Parma ham, and local pheasant with fondant potatoes. Chocolate fondant with peppermint ice cream has been described as 'devilishly good', and rich, mellow coffee follows.

Oxford Road, HP17 8NL
Tel: 01296 747444
Fax: 01296 747450
e info@hartwell-house.com
Chef(s): Daniel Richardson
Owner(s): Jonathan Thompson
Cost:, set price L £22.50-£29.50/
D £46 ☺ H/wine £14.90
Times: 12.30-1.45pm/7.30-9.45pm.
Additional: Sunday L. Children 8yrs+.
Vegetarian by request only
Seats: 56. Private dining room 30.
Jacket and tie preferred
Style: Modern British
Smoking: No smoking in dining room;
no cigars
Accommodation: 46 rooms (46 en
suite) ★ ★ ★ ★
Directions: 2m SW of Aylesbury on
A418

BUCKINGHAM

Map 4 SP63

Villiers Hotel, Henry's Restaurant

Henry's Restaurant overlooks the cobble courtyard of this historic coaching inn that was a haven for Oliver Cromwell and co back in the 17th-century. A spacious and traditional looking hotel dining room is home to some contemporary cooking that has a largely French flavour but ranges from robust country style (pork medallions with honeyed apples and brie) to Mediterranean and Eastern flourishes (marinated tuna in teriyaki and ginger with a seaweed salad). Fish is treated with sensitivity in the likes of monkfish with fennel rösti and a star anise sauce. Puds such as exotic fruits in apple jelly with pineapple tempura and a caramel sauce show some genuine imagination.

3 Castle Street, MK18 1BS
Tel: 01280 822444
Fax: 01280 822113
e reception@villiers-hotels.co.uk
Chef(s): Paul Stopps
Owner(s): Dawn Park Ltd
Cost: *Alc* £26, set price L £16.25/
D £24.75. ☺ ☺ H/wine £10.95
Times: Noon-2.30pm/7-10pm. Closed
L Mon-Sat, D Sun, 26 Dec, 1 Jan
Additional: Sunday L. Bar food.
Children welcome
Seats: 55. Private dining room 20

Style: Quintessentially English
Smoking: No cigars; Air conditioning
Civil licence: 150
Accommodation: 46 rooms (46 en suite) ★ ★ ★
Directions: Town centre – Castle Street is to the R of Town Hall near main square

BURNHAM

Map 4 SU98

Burnham Beeches

Traditional hotel restaurant in an attractive Georgian mansion. The menu is modern British in style, delivering sensible but nevertheless interesting combinations such as braised rump of lamb with a pink lentil and bacon casserole or breast of chicken with Somerset brie and potato rösti. Desserts (especially those with pastry) are a great strength.

Seats: 70. Private dining room 140
Style: Country-House
Smoking: No smoking in dining room. **Civil licence:** 140
Accommodation: 82 rooms (82 en suite) ★ ★ ★
Directions: Off A355, via Farnham Royal roundabout

Grove Road, SL1 8DP
Tel: 01628 429955
Fax: 01628 603994
Chef(s): Dave Pay
Cost: A/c £22.50, set price L £17.50/D £22.50. ☺ ☺
H/wine £14.95
Times: Noon-2pm/7-10pm.
Closed L Sat
Additional: Sunday L. Bar food L. Children welcome

Grovefield Hotel

Once the country retreat of John Fuller (of the well known brewing family), Grovefield is now an elegant modern hotel. The restaurant overlooks spacious grounds and serves an appealing selection of classical and modern European cooking. Dishes might include lamb shank with a herb pommes purée or supreme of chicken with ceps risotto and a tarragon creme sauce.

Taplow Common Road, SL1 8LP
Tel: 01628 603131
Fax: 01628 668078
✉ info@grovefield-macdonald-hotels.co.uk
Chef(s): R Shrewsbury
Cost: A/c £25, set price L £18-£25/D £25-£35. ☺ H/wine £14.50
Times: Noon-3pm/7-10pm.
Closed L Sat
Additional: Sunday L. Bar food. Children welcome
Seats: 60. Private dining room 50. Jacket and tie preferred
Style: Country-house
Smoking: No smoking in dining room
Civil licence: 150
Accommodation: 40 rooms (40 en suite) ★ ★ ★
Directions: Telephone for directions

England

DINTON

Map 4 SP71

La Chouette

The proprietor of this Belgian restaurant is also its chef, barman and waiter, he manages all these roles in his own inimitable style. The room is decorated with pictures of birds of prey (la chouette means owl), with tables decked out in pink and white linen. Whitewashed walls and low, timbered ceilings add to the charm of the place. The menu makes impressive use of the freshest ingredients, from fish (fillet of sea bass in a chablis sauce) to game (pheasant with chicory). Should you have difficulty choosing, it also offers helpful descriptive comments such as '100% Belgian'.

Style: Country-House
Smoking: No cigars
Directions: On A418 at Dinton

Westlington Green,
Nr Aylesbury, HP17 8UW
Tel: 01296 747422
Fax: 01296 747422
Chef(s): Frederic Desmette
Owner(s): Frederic Desmette
Cost: Alc £30, set price L £10-£36.50/D £28.50-£36.50. ☺
H/wine £11.50
Times: Noon-2pm/7-9pm.
Closed Sun, D Sat
Additional: Children welcome.
Vegetarian by request only
Seats: 35

GREAT MISSENDEN

Map 4 SP80

Bert's Restaurant   NEW

Polished floorboards, sunshine colours and a courtyard garden reflect the Spanish and Italian nationalities of the owners, as do the modern Mediterranean dishes on the menu - perhaps linguine with tiger prawns or organic salmon with braised fennel, red onions and tomato bisque. Only the patio heaters remind you this is Britain.

Style: Modern, Mediterranean
Smoking: No-smoking area; no cigars
Directions: On B485 towards Chesham, 1 mile from junction with A413. By junction with Kings Lane

Chesham Road, Hyde End,
HP16 0QT
Tel: 01494 865625
Fax: 01494 866406
Chef(s): Mark Fox
Owner(s): Adrian & Susy Bertorelli
Cost: Alc £25, set price L £15. ☺ ☺
H/wine £10.95
Times: 12.30-2.30pm/7-10pm.
Closed Sun & Mon, L Sat, All Bhs
Additional: Children 7+ at D
Seats: 70. Private dining room 30

HADDENHAM

Map 4 SP70

Green Dragon

8 Churchway,
HP17 8AA
Tel: 01844 291403
Fax: 01844 299532
📧 paul.berry4@virgin.net
Chef(s): Paul Berry
Owner(s): Peter Moffat, Paul Berry
Cost: Alc £23. ☺ ☺ H/wine £10.95

A cheerful pub restaurant with yellow and blue décor, a relaxed atmosphere and friendly, cheerful service. Consistency is evident in both produce and execution, resulting in dishes such as confit duck with honey and black pepper on pineapple chutney and nicely balanced Cornish sea bass on braised fennel with orange and juniper berries. Thai coconut and basil cream sauce accompanies fresh steamed mussels; walnuts, raisins and peppercorns are used to good effect with grilled sirloin steak; and mascarpone ice cream is a happy partner to the warm Belgian chocolate tart.

Smoking: No-smoking area; no cigars
Directions: From M40 take A329 towards Thame, then A418. Turn 1st R after entering Haddenham

Times: Noon-2pm/6.30-9.30pm. Closed D Sun
Additional: Sunday L. Bar food L. Children welcome
Seats: 55. Private dining room 18
Style: Classic, Bistro-style

IVINGHOE
Map 4 SP91

The King's Head

A 17th-century black and white former inn, set among the few houses that make up Ivinghoe. Old-fashioned values and theatricality are maintained with elegant silver service and flambé work. There is a battalion of professional staff and ducks are carved at the table in three minutes flat. The *carte* and fixed-price menus are similarly traditional with a few concessions to current trends.

LU7 9EB
Tel: 01296 668264
Fax: 01296 668107
Chef(s): Patrick O'Keeffe
Owner(s): Granada Forte
Cost: *Alc* £45, set price L £14.50-£28.75/D £28.75. ☺ H/wine £17.95
Times: 12.30-2pm/7.30-9.30pm. Closed D Sun
Additional: Sunday L. Children welcome. Vegetarian by request only
Seats: 55. Private dining room 40. Jacket and tie preferred
Style: Chic & Traditional
Smoking: No smoking in dining room; Air conditioning
Directions: From M25 J20. Take A41(M) towards Tring. Turn R, B488 (Ivinghoe). Hotel on R at junction with B489

LONG CRENDON
Map 4 SP60

The Angel Restaurant

47 Bicester Road, HP18 9EE
Tel: 01844 208268
Fax: 01844 202497
Chef(s): Trevor Bosch
Owner(s): Trevor Bosch & Angela Good
Cost: *Alc* £25. ☺ ☺ H/wine £12.50

This old pub has evolved into a serious restaurant, but diners can still enjoy a pint of real ale with a meal. The interior includes wattle and daub walls, rag washed paintwork and an eclectic mix of furnishings, from chesterfield sofas to sturdy oak tables. A daily changing fish specials board combines the

LONG CRENDON *Continued*　　　　Map 4 SP60

freshest ingredients with flavours from the Mediterranean and the Pacific Rim, whilst the standard menu ensures that neither the vegetarian nor the traditionalist is overlooked: dishes might include roasted highland beef with Yorkshire pudding or mushroom and asparagus millefeuille in a roast garlic and tarragon sauce.

Accommodation: 3 rooms (3 en suite)
Directions: Beside B4011, 2 miles north west of Thame

Times: Noon-3pm/7-10pm.
Closed D Sun
Additional: Sunday L. Bar food.
Children welcome
Seats: 75. Private dining room 14
Style: Chic
Smoking: No-smoking area;
Air conditioning

MARLOW　　　　Map 4 SU88

Danesfield House

A sumptuous house and gardens, dating back to the nineteenth century. The gaping fireplace, ornate oak panelling and equally elaborate plasterwork create a superbly dramatic scene in the Oak restaurant, whilst the adjoining conservatory offers views of topiary in the gardens and the Thames beyond. Dishes are Classically British and French in style, making good use of seasonal and regional produce. A meal might include galantine of foie gras and morel mushrooms followed by saddle of rabbit stuffed with langoustines and glazed baby onions. A list of almost three hundred wines leaves few countries untouched

Henley Road, SL7 2EY
Tel: 01628 891010
Fax: 01628 890408
e sales@danesfieldhouse.co.uk
Chef(s): Michael MacDonald
Cost: *Alc* £47, set price L £26.50/
D £39.50
Times: Noon-2.30pm/7-10pm.
Additional: Sunday L. Bar food.
Children 4 yrs+. Vegetarian by request only
Seats: 45. Private dining room 120.
Jacket and tie preferred
Style: Classic, Country-House
Smoking: No smoking in dining room
Civil licence: 120
Accommodation: 87 rooms (87 en suite) ★ ★ ★ ★
Directions: M4 J8/9 to Marlow. 2m from Marlow on A4155

The Compleat Angler

Marlow Bridge, SL7 1RG
Tel: 0870 4008100
Fax: 01628 485388
Chef(s): Alan Swinson, Dean Timpson
Owner(s): Heritage Hotels (Forte)
Cost: *Alc* £50, set price L £21.50-
£59/D £34.50-£59. H/wine £18.50
Times: 12.30-2.30pm/7-10pm.
Additional: Sunday L. Bar food.
Children welcome
Seats: 80. Private dining room 110.
Jacket and tie preferred
Style: Classic Formal
Smoking: No smoking in dining room
Civil licence: 100

Located at the point where the Thames crashes over Marlow Weir, the plush Riverside restaurant is one of two eating options at this Georgian hotel. Views of the rushing water and the occasional pane of stained glass lend a distinctive character to an otherwise traditional setting (white linen, heavy curtains and fresh flowers). The menu is mostly British, with a few guest stars from Europe, such as crab tortellini or Quail and foie gras raviolo. A broad selection of fine wines completes an enjoyable experience, offering new world choices alongside plenty of European greats.

Accommodation: 65 rooms (65 en suite) ★★★★
Directions: From M4 J8/9 or M40 J4 take A404. Hotel is on south bank of river by bridge

TAPLOW

Map 4 SU98

Cliveden, Waldo's Restaurant

Cliveden Estate, SL6 0JF
Tel: 01628 668561
Fax: 01628 661837
Owner(s): Cliveden Ltd
Cost: Alc £58, set price D £84 (9 courses). H/wine £25
Times: Dinner only, 7.30-9.30pm. Closed Mon, Sun, Late Dec-1st Feb
Additional: Children 12yrs+
Seats: 24. Private dining room 12. Jacket and tie preferred
Style: Classic Country-House
Smoking: No smoking in dining room; Air conditioning
Civil licence: 200

STOP PRESS Change of Chef

The menu quotes Virginia Woolf on the imperative of dining well, and her exhortation has been well absorbed by this plush basement restaurant. The atmosphere is intimate, with only nine tables, and smacks of the gentleman's club, but there's nothing traditional about the food. Expect imaginative flights of fancy anchored securely to brilliant technique, and you won't be surprised. Hand-dived scallop with pea risotto and ventreche bacon, carpaccio of tuna, oriental crab salad and coriander tuille, and game sausage and coleslaw with red onion and mustard dressing show the flair of the starter range. Chargrilled beef fillet with confit tarragon potatoes and wild mushrooms drew oodles of praise for its harmony of flavours, while Earl Grey roasted Trelough duck with lentils, potato and duck rillette, baby spinach and red wine jus is another example of innovation. Assiette of chocolate created a new benchmark for desserts, and the petit fours are to die for.

Accommodation: 38 rooms (38 en suite) ★★★★★
Directions: On B476, 2 miles N of Taplow

Cliveden, The Terrace Dining Room

Even Cliveden's name implies a 'rather grand affair' and those looking for an opulent, stately home will certainly not be disappointed. Cliveden is a Home Counties fixture with meticulous, formal gardens and a splendid dining room, complete with ornate cornices and gargantuan windows overlooking a terrace. Expect an atmosphere to match its

Cliveden Estate, SL6 0JF
Tel: 01628 668561
Fax: 01628 661837
Owner(s): Cliveden Ltd
Cost: Alc £55, set price L £21.50-£26/D £48-£58. H/wine £19-£22
Times: 12.30-2.30pm/7-9.30pm

STOP PRESS Change of Chef

TAPLOW *Continued*   Map 4 SU98

Cliveden, The Terrace
Dining Room

surroundings, but with friendly staff who do their best to make people comfortable. A long *carte* may offer moist and tender duck confit or well-executed foie gras parfait, although accompanying flavours could use more precise balancing at times. Pleasant spiced pears and Armagnac and prune parfait round off a meal nicely.

Accommodation: 38 rooms (38 en suite) ★ ★ ★ ★ ★
Directions: On B476, 2 miles N of Taplow

Additional: Sunday L. Children welcome
Seats: 75. Private dining room 60. Jacket and tie preferred
Style: Traditional, Country Style
Smoking: No smoking in dining room; Air conditioning
Civil licence: 200

CAMBRIDGESHIRE

CAMBRIDGE   Map 5 TL45

Cambridge Quy Mill

This rustic old watermill comes complete with a ghost and is divided into formal and informal eating areas. Similarly, the menu is split into a 'blackboard' section (lots of favourites, from pies to tagliatelli) and a speciality menu (thoroughly British in style, with Scottish salmon, Barbary duck and fillet of beef). There's a nice range of sticky puddings too.

Directions: Turn off A14 at junction E of Cambridge onto B1102 for 50yds, hotel entrance opposite church

Newmarket Road, Stow Cum Quy, CB5 9AG
Tel: 01223 293383
Fax: 01223 293770
🇪 cambridgequy@bestwestern.co.uk
Chef(s): Paul Freakley
Owner(s): David Monroe
Cost: *Alc* £25, set price L £15/D £20. ☺ ☺ H/wine £10.50
Times: Noon-2.30pm/7-9.45pm. Closed 27-31 Dec
Additional: Sunday L. Bar food. Children welcome
Seats: 48
Style: Rustic
Smoking: No-smoking area; no cigars
Civil licence: 80
Accommodation: 24 rooms (24 en suite) ★ ★ ★

Midsummer House

Midsummer Common, CB4 1HA
Tel: 01223 369299
Fax: 01223 302672
Chef(s): Daniel Clifford
Owner(s): Mr R Morgan
Cost: A/c £46, set price L £20/D £42.
☺ H/wine £15.95
Times: Noon-2pm/7-10pm. Closed
Mon, L Sat, D Sun, 2wks from 26
Dec, 9-16 Apr, 2wks from 20 Aug
Additional: Sunday L. Children
welcome
Seats: 50. Private dining room 20
Style: Modern, French
Smoking: No-smoking area; no pipes

Even when the sun doesn't shine into the conservatory that dominates this restaurant, a bright interior and some vivacious Mediterranean influenced cooking mean you won't go short of warmth and radiance. A demi-tasse of punchy gazpacho might set the tone for a salad of crunchy leaves with ample shavings of Parmesan and a great truffle vinaigrette. Freshness and simplicity are the key and the likes of roast salmon with tagliatelle of vegetables and a lemongrass beurre blanc show what can be achieved with this intelligent approach. Amongst the puds, raspberry soufflé has been noted as a highlight.

Civil licence: 50
Directions: Park in Pretoria Rd, off Chesterton Road, then walk across footbridge to restaurant

22 Chesterton Road

Expect a leisurely meal at this converted Victorian house. The restaurant appeals to town and gown, offering a short, balanced menu with an optional fish course (maybe grilled tuna on wilted greens), and a wine list of some quality. Provençale tart has been deemed a winner, along with roast pork with black pudding, and confit of duck.

Additional: Children 10yrs+
Seats: 26. Private dining room 12
Style: Modern
Smoking: Air conditioning
Directions: Telephone for directions

22 Chesterton Road, CB4 3AX
Tel: 01223 351880
Fax: 01223 323814
📧 davidcarter@restaurant22.co.uk
Chef(s): Ian Reinhardt &
Martin Cullum
Owner(s): Mr D Carter
Cost: A/c £26.50/D £24.50. ☺
H/wine £10.25
Times: Dinner only, 7-9.45pm.
Closed Sun & Mon, Xmas &
New Year

DUXFORD   Map 5 TL44

Duxford Lodge

Le Paradis restaurant is decorated in mellow style with plenty of mirrors and bird prints gracing the patterned wallpaper. The cooking is modern British with Gallic influences, as is the service provided by the friendly team of British and French staff. Well spaced tables and fresh flowers add to an easy relaxed atmosphere. A meal begins with appetisers in the lounge bar, where numerous aircraft prints might inspire a visit to the nearby air museum. The menu delivers high quality

Ickleton Road,
CB2 4RU
Tel: 01223 836444
Fax: 01223 832271
📧 duxford@btclick.com
Chef(s): Antonello Carta
Owner(s): Mr & Mrs R Craddock
Cost: A/c £36, set price L £13.99-
£21.24/D £25-£32.50. ☺ H/wine £10

DUXFORD *Continued*   Map 5 TL44

Duxford Lodge Hotel

ingredients in dishes such as terrine of confit chicken and foie gras followed by roast Gressingham duck with Szechuan tuile and Madeira jus.

Times: Noon-2.15pm/7-9.30pm.
Closed L Sat, 26-30 Dec
Additional: Sunday L. Bar food.
Children welcome
Seats: 44. Private dining room 27
Style: Traditional, Country-House

Smoking: No-smoking area; no cigars; Air conditioning
Accommodation: 15 rooms (15 en suite) ★★★
Directions: M11 J10, take A505 E, then 1st R to Duxford; take R fork at T-junction, entrance 70 yards on L

ELY   Map 5 TL58

The Anchor Inn   NEW

With stunning views over the New Bedford River, there is a rustic country feel to this inn enhanced by the gas lamp lighting and heavy wooden furniture. Honest flavours and good quality ingredients result in a moist, tasty shredded duck starter. A succulent cod fillet with crisp skin, a velvety white wine sauce and garlic mash has made an excellent main course.

Seats: 70. **Style:** Rustic, Traditional
Smoking: No-smoking area; no pipes
Accommodation: 2 rooms (2 en suite) ♦♦♦♦
Directions: Signposted off B1381 in Sutton Village, 7 miles W of Ely via A142

Sutton Gault, Sutton, CB6 2BD
Tel: 01353 778537
Fax: 01353 776180
🅴 anchor@sutton-gault.freeserve.co.uk
Chef(s): Martin Russell, Gareth Williams, Edward Parker
Owner(s): Robin & Heather Moore
Cost: *Alc* £24, set price L £7.95-£16.50. ☺ ☺ H/wine £11.95
Times: Noon-3.30pm/7-11pm.
Additional: Sunday L. Bar food L. Children welcome. Vegetarian by request only

Old Fire Engine House

An informal 'family home' atmosphere sets the scene for honest, British cooking of a consistently high standard. Dishes might include rabbit with mustard and parsley or stuffed leg of pork with apple sauce. Nobody leaves feeling hungry, because guests are always offered more meat or fish. Vegetarians can choose any two dishes from a list of around fifteen.

Style: Traditional, Rustic
Smoking: No-smoking area; no cigars
Directions: Facing St Mary's Chuch in town centre

25 Saint Mary's Street, CB7 4ER
Tel: 01353 662582
Fax: 01353 668364
Chef(s): Terri Kindred
Owner(s): Mr & Mrs M R Jarman
Cost: *Alc* £25. ☺ H/wine £9
Times: 12.15-2pm/7.15-9pm. Closed D Sun, BHs, 2 wks from 24 Dec
Additional: Sunday L. Children welcome
Seats: 36. Private dining room 22

FOWLMERE
Map 5 TL44

The Chequers Inn Restaurant

SG8 7SR
Tel: 01763 208369
Fax: 01763 208944
Chef(s): Louis Gambie
Owner(s): Mr N S Rushton
Cost: *Alc* £18.30. ☺ ☺ H/wine £9.30
Times: Noon-2pm/7-10pm.
Closed 25 Dec
Additional: Sunday L. Bar food.
Children welcome
Seats: 30. Private dining room 24
Style: Modern
Smoking: No cigars
Directions: Between Royston and
Cambridge, B1368 turn off A10

A loyal following for this restaurant, suitably attracted to its
wide range of dishes and imaginative vegetarian items. In the
restored surroundings of the sixteenth century coaching inn,
treat yourself to beautifully tender full-flavoured grilled lamb
cutlets served on a creamed mint and caper sauce for a real
earthy and full-flavoured experience.

HUNTINGDON
Map 4 TL27

Old Bridge Hotel

An 18th-century former private bank that overlooks the river
Ouse and offers food in a modern idiom, picked-and-mixed
from both restaurant and lounge menus. Tuna carpaccio with
fierce tomato and chilli sorbet and monkfish in Parma ham for
fish lovers and black pudding with mashed potato, bacon and
apple - followed perhaps by breast of Goosnargh duck with
turnip gratin and pak choi - indicate a thoughtful approach,
marred just occasionally by over-zealous seasoning. Stars on the
dining menu include veal sweetbreads on a potato galette, and
roast pheasant with mashed parsnip and braised endive: an
apricot soufflé was adjudged well worth the wait.

Accommodation: 24 rooms (24 en suite) ★ ★ ★
Directions: Off A1 near junction with A1/M1 link and
A604/M11

PE29 3TQ
Tel: 01480 424300
Fax: 01480 411017
e oldbridge@huntsbridge.co.uk
Chef(s): Martin Lee
Owner(s): J Hoskins, Martin Lee
Cost: *Alc* £23, set price L £19. ☺ ☺
H/wine £11
Times: Noon-2.30pm/6-10pm.
Additional: Sunday L. Bar food.
Children welcome
Seats: 40. Private dining room 20
Style: Modern
Smoking: No smoking in dining room
Civil licence: 80

KEYSTON
Map 4 TL07

Pheasant Inn

Having built a hefty reputation for fine food at the likes of
Lords of the Manor, Clive Dixon might seem an unlikely name
to associate with a thatched pub in the languid village of
Keyston. As someone renowned for his commitment to using
top-notch raw materials it's a happy position to be in and the
results are apparent in cooking that is refined but not over-
fussy. Look out for "super" pasta in a beef ravioli with truffled
spring cabbage, and excellent caramelised apple tart.

Smoking: No-smoking area; no pipes
Directions: 0.5 mile off A14, clearly signposted

PE18 0RE
Tel: 01832 710241
Fax: 01832 710340
Chef(s): Clive Dixon
Owner(s): John Hoskins
Cost: *Alc* £23.95, set price L £13.50.
☺ ☺ H/wine £11.90
Times: Noon-2pm/6.30-10pm.
Additional: Sunday L. Children
welcome
Seats: 100
Style: Rustic, Formal

LITTLE SHELFORD

Map 5 TL45

Sycamore House

NEW

Close to academia but in a village setting, this delightfully converted old pub offers a perfect escape from the crowds. Intimate and friendly with low ceilings and beams, its short punchy menu is surprisingly varied. Expect, perhaps, crab risotto cake, and a decent steak and kidney pud with cep gravy, or roast partridge with apple, cream and Calvados.

Smoking: No smoking in dining room
Directions: From M11 J11 take A10 then 1st Left through Hauxton to Little Shelford. Approx 2 miles from motorway

1 Church Street, CB2 5HG
Tel: 01223 843396
Chef(s): Michael Sharpe
Owner(s): Michael & Susan Sharpe
Cost: Set price D £23.50. ☺
H/wine £9.95
Times: Dinner only, 7.30-9pm.
Closed Sun-Mon, Xmas
Additional: Children 12yrs+
Seats: 24
Style: Traditional French-Style

MADINGLEY

Map 5 TL36

Three Horseshoes Restaurant

Picturesque thatched inn close to the village cricket pitch with an attractive conservatory restaurant. Such a quintessentially English village setting does not preclude innovation. A modish, internationally influenced kitchen offers up the likes of buffalo mozzarella salad with purple figs, rocket, basil and pomegranate.

Additional: Sunday L. Bar food. Children welcome
Seats: 55. **Smoking:** No smoking in dining room
Directions: 1.5 miles from M11 J13, 2 miles W of Cambridge

High Street, CB3 8AB
Tel: 01954 210221
Fax: 01954 212043
Chef(s): Richard Stokes
Owner(s): Huntsbridge
Cost: *Alc* £25, set price L £25-£35/
D £35. ☺ ☺ H/wine £10
Times: Noon-2pm/6.30-9.30pm.
Closed D Sun

MELBOURN

Map 5 TL34

Pink Geranium

Station Road, SG8 6DX
Tel: 01763 260215
Fax: 01763 262110
Chef(s): Mark Jordan
Owner(s): Mr L Champion
Cost: *Alc* £40, set price L £18/
D £30-£55. ☺ H/wine £11.50
Times: Noon-2pm/7-9.30pm.
Closed Mon, D Sun, 25-26 Dec, 1 Jan
Additional: Sunday L. Children welcome
Seats: 60. Private dining room 14
Style: Traditional
Smoking: No smoking in dining room
Directions: On A10 between Royston and Cambridge. In centre of village, opposite church

Pink it most certainly is. The interior is almost shockingly so, but fortunately the food can still shine through, and although value for money has been questioned, many of the dishes really hit the spot. An "electric" example of the latter being a guinea fowl and foie gras terrine dressed with smoked belly pork, haricot blanc and artichoke, together with oozing quails eggs. Similar praise for chicken with sweetbreads and wild mushrooms, buttered cabbage and a Madeira cream sauce where the leg came boned out and stuffed with the sweetbreads and mushrooms and the accompaniments (roasted shallots and garlic, excellent fondant potato) were excellent. Overall, it's an honest and robust style that runs to desserts along the lines of an "outstanding" thin apple tart with rum and raisin ice cream. Well chosen wine list with a good range of half bottles.

Sheene Mill

This 17th century water mill has been transformed into a fashionable hotel, run by TV chef Steven Saunders and his wife. The restaurant features Moroccan slate floors, blue furnishings, yellow walls and a baby grand piano. Dishes are bang up to date, making good use of seasonal and organic products such as free range lamb (wrapped in pancetta and served with swede fondant, wilted spinach and tomato fondue) or organic chicken (roasted with lemon and rosemary then served with creamed potatoes and braised leeks). An interesting, wide ranging menu that lives up to the promise of the surroundings.

Station Road, SG8 6DX
Tel: 01763 261393
Fax: 01763 261376
e steven@stevensaunders.co.uk
Chef(s): Steven Saunders, Chris Driver
Owner(s): Mr & Mrs S Saunders
Cost: *Alc* £30, set price L £14-£18/ D £20-£25. ☺ ☺ H/wine £10
Times: Noon-2.30pm/7-10pm.
Closed D Sun, 26 Dec
Additional: Sunday L. Bar food.
Children welcome
Seats: 110
Style: Modern, Chic
Smoking: No-smoking area; no cigars;
Air conditioning
Civil licence: 125
Accommodation: 9 rooms (9 en suite)
Directions: Take 2nd exit from A10 Melbourn by-pass signed Melbourn. Sheene Mill is 300yds down Station Road on R

PETERBOROUGH   Map 4 TL19

Orton Hall

A formal dining experience on offer in the oak-panelled restaurant of this 16th-century country house hotel. Diced vegetables with a chilli dressing gives extra zip to a starter of "perfectly cooked" pan-fried scallops. Rack of lamb, cooked pink, is served on an intensely flavoured aubergine and tomato risotto. Puds have included a creditable chocolate assiette.

Orton Longueville, PE2 7DN
Tel: 01733 391111
Fax: 01733 231912
e reception@ortonhall.co.uk
Chef(s): Kevin Wood
Owner(s): Abacus Hotels
Cost: *Alc* £31.95, set price D £21.50.
☺ H/wine £10.50
Times: 12.30-2pm/7-9.30pm.
Closed L Mon-Sat
Additional: Sunday L. Children welcome
Seats: 34. Private dining room 40.
Jacket and tie preferred
Style: Classic Country-House
Smoking: No smoking in dining room; no cigars
Civil licence: 100
Accommodation: 65 rooms (65 en suite) ★★★
Directions: Telephone for directions

England

SIX MILE BOTTOM

Map 5 TL55

Swynford Paddocks

An elegant English country house where Lord Byron wrote many of his works (and also found time to seduce his half-sister). A fairly eclectic menu with a global twist offers everything from sturdy soups (broccoli and rocket with Rocquefort) through Mediterranean style salad to a tarte Tatin of red onions with toasted pine nuts and a sun-dried tomato coulis. Some robust mains have included fillet of beef sliced on truffled mash with a red wine sauce.

Style: Traditional
Smoking: No smoking in dining room
Civil licence: 60
Accommodation: 15 rooms (15 en suite) ★★★
Directions: On A1304, 6 miles SW of Newmarket

CB8 0UE
Tel: 01638 570234
Fax: 01638 570283
e info@swynfordpaddocks.com
Chef(s): Patrick Collins
Owner(s): Peter Bottomley
Cost: Alc £33.75. H/wine £14.80
Times: Noon-2.30pm/7-9.30pm.
Closed L Sat, 1 wk after Xmas
Additional: Sunday L. Bar food.
Children welcome. Vegetarian by request only
Seats: 25. Private dining room 20

STILTON

Map 5 TL18

Bell Inn

Located just minutes from the motorway in the lovely village of Stilton (of cheese fame), this 16th-century coaching inn is said to have served as a hiding place for Dick Turpin. Inside, beamed ceilings, log fires and a galleried restaurant create an

appropriately rustic setting. The cooking mixes modern and traditional influences to good effect: a meal might include chicken livers with toasted brioche and red onion marmalade followed by braised blade of beef with creamed celeriac, roasted shallots and red wine jus. Finish with a choice from the imaginative dessert menu or Long Clawston Stilton with home baked plum bread.

Great North Road, PE7 3RA
Tel: 01733 241066
Fax: 01733 245173
e reception@thebellstilton.co.uk
Chef(s): Gavin Sansom
Owner(s): Mr L A McGivern
Cost: Set price L £15/D £22.50. ☺ ☺
H/wine £10.60
Times: Noon-2pm/6.30-9.30pm.
Closed L Sat, 25 Dec
Additional: Sunday L. Bar food.
Children 5yrs+
Seats: 60. Private dining room 20
Style: Classic
Smoking: No-smoking area; no pipes
Civil licence: 90
Accommodation: 19 rooms (19 en suite) ★★★
Directions: From A1(M) J16 follow signs to Stilton. Hotel on High Street in centre of village

WANSFORD

Map 4 TL09

Haycock Hotel

An attractive 17th-century hotel and inn, set beside the river. The interesting menu includes plenty of favourites, such as fish and chips or superior roasts, alongside a weekly changing selection of specials. More imaginative in style, these might include cajun sausage with Mexican salsa sauce or baked cod on salsify, potatoes and mustard lentils.

PE8 6JA
Tel: 01780 782223
Fax: 01780 783031
Chef(s): Neil Smith
Cost: Alc £20.50, set price L £16.95/D £16.95. ☺ ☺
H/wine £13.95

Times: 12.30-2pm/6.30-10pm.
Closed D 25 & 31 Dec,
Additional: Sunday L. Bar food.
Children welcome
Seats: 100. Private dining room 12
Style: Bistro
Smoking: No smoking in dining room
Civil licence: 100
Accommodation: 50 rooms (50 en suite) ★★★

Directions: In village centre between A1 and A47

WISBECH Map 5 TF40

Crown Lodge

An intimate, bistro style restaurant in a popular hotel, this is a comfortable environment in which to enjoy an exciting selection of modern and traditional British food. Dishes might include roast beef with herb pudding, fondant potatoes and a whisky and horseradish sauce or sautéed scampi tails flamed in brandy with a light mustard cheese sauce.

Downham Road, Outwell,
PE14 8SE
Tel: 01945 773391
Fax: 01945 772668
e crownlodgehotel@hotmail.com
Chef(s): Mick Castell
Owner(s): Mr W J Moore
Cost: Alc £28. ☺ ☺ H/wine £8.50
Times: Noon-2pm/6.30-9.30pm.
Closed 25-26 & 31 Dec, 1 Jan
Additional: Sunday L. Bar food.
Children welcome
Seats: 40. Private dining room 35
Style: Modern
Smoking: No smoking in dining room
Accommodation: 10 rooms (10 en suite) ★★
Directions: 5 miles SE of Wisbech on A1122, close to junction with A1101

CHESHIRE

ALDERLEY EDGE Map 7 SJ87

Alderley Edge Hotel

Split-level conservatory restaurant offering some adventurous cuisine. An eclectic menu with varied influences offers the likes of sautéed calves' liver with sweet and sour onions, marjoram and aged balsamico. Desserts are a strength with hot banana and caramel soufflé with vanilla ice cream a highlight. Top quality produce is used in crafting the dishes and there is a careful eye to presentation. Service is very professional, both attentive and dedicated. *continued*

Macclesfield Road,
SK9 7BJ
Tel: 01625 583033
Fax: 01625 586343
e sales@alderley-edge-hotel.co.uk
Chef(s): Duncan Poyser
Owner(s): Mr A Kurcer
Cost: Alc £40, set price L £15.50/ D £26.50. H/wine £12.95

England

ALDERLEY EDGE *Continued*   Map 7 SJ87

Alderley Edge Hotel

Times: Noon-2pm/7.30-10pm.
Closed 1 Jan
Additional: Sunday L. Bar food.
Children welcome
Seats: 80. Private dining room 100.
Jacket and tie preferred
Style: Classic, Formal
Smoking: No pipes; Air conditioning
Civil licence: 100
Accommodation: 46 rooms (46 en
suite) ★ ★ ★
Directions: A538 to Alderley Edge,
then B5087 Macclesfield road

ALSAGER   Map 7 SJ75

Manor House Hotel

A fascinating blend of the old and the new, a modern hotel built around an old farmhouse, with the original beams retained as a feature of the restaurant and bars. Much imagination goes into the food, which is based on skilful working of quality ingredients.

From the four-course set menu expect starters like warm pan-seared tandoori chicken, or fillet of peppered smoked mackerel, then poached salmon and sole roulé, or honey-roast Gressing-ham duck. Otherwise there's herb-crusted Cornish crab cakes, flash roast loin of lamb, and lemon and vanilla crème brûlée, say, or brandy snap basket with ice cream and berries to finish.

⊛⊛
Audley Road, ST7 2QQ
Tel: 01270 884000
Fax: 01270 882483
e mhres@compasshotels.co.uk
Chef(s): Ian Turner
Owner(s): Compass Hotels Ltd
Cost: *Alc* £26.50, set price L
£13.95/D £21.50. ☺ ☺
H/wine £10.95
Times: Noon-2pm/7.15-9.30pm.
Closed L Sat, D Sun
Additional: Sunday L. Bar food.
Children welcome
Seats: 75. Private dining room 150.
Style: Traditional, Country-House
Smoking: No smoking in dining room
Civil licence: 100
Accommodation: 57 rooms (57 en
suite) ★ ★ ★
Directions: M6 J16, then A500
towards Stoke-on-Trent. After 0.5 mile
take 1st slip road, Alsager, L at top,
2 miles, hotel on L before village

BOLLINGTON   Map 7 SJ97

Mauro's Restaurant

A glass fronted Italian restaurant on the main road through the village of Bollington, well established and popular with the locals. Décor is bright and fresh with a pleasant Mediterranean feel to it and the menu is typically Italian, with cooking uncomplicated and rustic, using well-sourced ingredients. A la *carte* plus a table d'hôte at lunch and weekday evenings are both on offer. A first course of bruschetta al fungi, has been noted as simple but effective with deep earthy flavours, similar praise for a main course of polpettone divitello (minced veal with pistachio,

⊛⊛
88 Palmerston Street,
SK10 5PW
Tel: 01625 573898
Fax: 01625 572800
Chef(s): Vincenzo Mauro
Owner(s): Mr V & Mrs G Mauro
Cost: *Alc* £25, set price L £11.60/
D £12.80. ☺ ☺ H/wine £10.50
Times: Noon-2pm/7-10pm.
Closed Sun, Mon, L Sat, 25-26 Dec

mushrooms and mozzarella cheese with a light wine sauce). Good puds and real Italian coffee.

Directions: Situated on the main street of the village, at the Pott Shrigley end. 4 miles from Macclesfield

Additional: Bar food L. Children welcome
Seats: 49
Style: Classic Italian
Smoking: No cigars

CHESTER
Map 7 SJ46

The Chester Crabwall Manor

Parkgate Road, Mollington, CH1 6NE
Tel: 01244 851666
Fax: 01244 851400
e crabwallmanor@
marstonhotels.com
Chef(s): Paul Murfitt
Owner(s): Marston Hotels
Cost: Alc £45, set price L £35/D £35. H/wine £13.95
Times: Noon-2pm/7-9.30pm.
Additional: Sunday L. Bar food. Children welcome
Seats: 100. Private dining room 80. Jacket and tie preferred
Style: Classic, Formal

First mentioned in the Domesday Book, this re-built manor house hotel dates from the 17th century and stands in 11 acres of mature wooded grounds. An impressive, castle-like building, it is crammed with modern day comforts but still manages to retain its period charm. The conservatory restaurant serves an imaginative menu, full of ideas from France, Italy and Britain. A meal might include lobster tortellini with carrot linguini, lettuce and herb boullion followed by saddle of rabbit with sage gnocchi, panchetta, roasted leeks and tarragon jus. A team of French staff provide professional, friendly service.

Smoking: No smoking in dining room; Air conditioning
Civil licence: 100
Accommodation: 48 rooms (48 en suite) ★ ★ ★ ★
Directions: From A56 take A5117 then A540. Hotel set back from A540, N of Chester

Chester Grosvenor

Eastgate, CH1 1LT
Tel: 01244 324024
Fax: 01244 313246

A quintessentially English hotel beside the old Roman wall, an icon of hospitality and excellence equally popular with tourists and local business people. The small dining room is classical in style, lightened by a glass atrium with an orange tree growing beneath. Matching this grand setting is an impressive range of dishes in which lavish ingredients are integrated with immense skill, and served with friendly expertise. A special dish - perhaps "Bresse" pigeon with braised greens and fois gras cream - extends the set menu, where grilled rabbit with leek Flamiche and langoustines, or hot pork cheek with foie gras and apples are likely starters. Then look for osso bucco with sweetbread minestrone, sea bass with fondued crab and basil tortellini, or perhaps poulet de Bresse with mushrooms, sweet chicory and Madeira. Puddings are pretty hot too, with the likes of blackberry and apple with schnapps Moscovite, and there's an awesome wine list.

England

CHESTER *Continued*   Map 7 SJ46

Accommodation: 85 rooms (85 en suite) ★★★★★
Directions: City Centre adjacent to the Eastgate Clock and Roman Walls

Craxton Wood

For **Craxton Wood** *see* entry under Puddington, Cheshire

CREWE   Map 7 SJ75

Crewe Hall

A magnificent stately home whose elaborate interior is a true reflection of Victorian ostentation. Expect bright colours, ornate wooden panelling and extravagantly moulded ceilings. The restaurant combines all these features, throwing in a couple of huge fireplaces for good measure. The equally varied menu offers a modern take on many classic dishes. These might include supreme of chicken with a pickled walnut and black pepper corn crust or pan fried Gressingham duck with bacon and leek mash and a sweet honey jus. Desserts range from imaginative (deep fried chocolate ravioli) to traditional (sticky toffee pudding).

Civil licence: 200
Accommodation: 25 rooms (25 en suite) ★★★★
Directions: From M6 J16 take A500 towards Crewe. At rdbt take A5020. At next rdbt take 1st exit to hotel

Chester Grosvenor Hotel

e chesgrov@chestergrosvenor.co.uk
Chef(s): Simon Radley
Cost: *Alc* £54.50, set price L £30/ D £48. H/wine £13.75
Times: Noon-2.30pm/7-9.30pm. Closed Mon, D Sun, 25 Dec-22 Jan except New Year's Eve
Additional: Sunday L. Children welcome. Vegetarian by request only
Seats: 45. Private dining room 240. Jacket and tie preferred
Style: Classic, Formal
Smoking: No smoking in dining room; no cigars; Air conditioning
Civil licence: 150

Weston Road, CW1 6UZ
Tel: 01270 253333
Fax: 01270 253322
e reservations@crewehall.com
Chef(s): Jonathan File
Owner(s): Mr P Humphreys
Cost: *Alc* £38.50, set price L £19.95/D £34.50. ☺ ☺
H/wine £13.95
Times: Noon-2pm/7-9.30pm.
Additional: Sunday L. Bar food. Children welcome
Seats: 60. Private dining room 200. Jacket and tie preferred
Style: Modern
Smoking: No smoking in dining room

HANDFORTH   Map 7 SJ88

Belfry House

The gourmet menu of this sophisticated Art Deco restaurant shows much flair and imagination (melon and summer fruit minestrone). Careful preparation of good raw materials succeeds in bringing out the full flavour of the produce in dishes such as rack of lamb with fresh and vibrant vegetables.

Seats: 110. Private dining room 40. Jacket and tie preferred
Style: Classic, French
Civil licence: 150
Accommodation: 80 rooms (80 en suite) ★ ★ ★ ★
Directions: A34 to Handforth, at end of village

Stanley Road, SK9 3LD
Tel: 0161 437 0511
Fax: 0161 499 0597
e office@belfryhousehotel.co.uk
Chef(s): Martin Thompson
Owner(s): Mr P T Heywood
Cost: Alc £35, set price L £16.50-£18/D £19.95-£32. ☺ ☺
H/wine £14.50
Times: 12.30-2.30pm/7-10pm.
Additional: Sunday L. Bar food. Children welcome

KNUTSFORD   Map 7 SJ77

Cottons Hotel

A window seat in the Magnolia restaurant will get you views of the gardens and the lake. The menu is a lively, upbeat range of dishes in the broadly modern British mould with the likes of terrine of tomatoes with goats' cheese, really fresh roast cod and red pepper meringue with red fruits.

Seats: 70. Private dining room 20. Jacket and tie preferred
Style: Traditional
Smoking: No smoking in dining room
Civil licence: 180
Accommodation: 99 rooms (99 en suite) ★ ★ ★ ★
Directions: From M6 J19/A556 (Stockport). Turn R at lights (A50 to Knutsford). Hotel 1.5 miles on R

Manchester Road,
WA16 0SU
Tel: 01565 650333
Fax: 01565 755351
e cottons@shireinns.co.uk
Chef(s): Adrian Sedden
Owner(s): Shire Inns
Cost: Alc £32, set price L £12.95.☺
H/wine £13.95
Times: Noon-2.30pm/7-9.45pm.
Closed L Sat (L Sun unless over 30),
L BHs
Additional: Bar food. Children welcome

Mere Court

Built in Edwardian times as a wedding gift, this sophisticated country house hotel stands in seven acres of mature gardens and parkland. The restaurant is decorated in traditional, elegant style and offers a wide selection of modern European cooking. Dishes might include grilled chicken on herb risotto or escalope of salmon on aubergine caviar, saffron and tarragon velouté.

Warrington Road, Mere,
WA16 0RW
Tel: 01565 831000
Fax: 01565 831001
e sales@merecourt.co.uk
Chef(s): Stephen Price
Owner(s): Mr & Mrs Hampson
Cost: Alc £31, set price L £14.95-£17.95/D £22.50-£25.50. ☺ ☺
H/wine £14.95
Times: Noon-2pm/7-10pm.
Closed L Sat
Additional: Sunday L. Bar food. Children welcome. Vegetarian by request only
Seats: 40. Private dining room 90
Style: Country House
Smoking: No smoking in dining room
Civil licence: 80
Accommodation: 37 rooms (37 en suite) ★ ★ ★ ★
Directions: Telephone for directions

NANTWICH

Map 7 SJ65

Rookery Hall

Main Road, Worleston, CW5 6DQ
Tel: 01270 610016
Fax: 01270 626027
e rookery@arcadianhotels.co.uk
Chef(s): Craig Grant
Owner(s): Hand Picked
Hotels/Arcadian
Cost: A/c £37.50, set price L £15/
D £28. ☺ ☺ H/wine £13.50
Times: Noon-2pm/7-10pm.
Closed L Sat
Additional: Sunday L. Bar food.
Children welcome
Seats: 36. Private dining room 40
Style: Classic Country-House
Smoking: No smoking in dining room

A dramatic, dark stoned Georgian mansion set in 38 acres of Cheshire countryside. The dining room is equally imposing: an ornate plasterwork ceiling, shining wood panels and candlelight provide the perfect backdrop for a leisurely meal. The menu throws together ideas from around the world, creating interesting dishes such as pan fried bream on coriander risotto with deep fried cucumber and a lemongrass butter sauce. The addition of several vegetarian options and one or two more traditional dishes ensures that everybody is happy - as does the list of 110 wines.

Civil licence: 65. **Accommodation:** 45 rooms (45 en suite) ★ ★ ★
Directions: On B5074 N of Nantwich, 1.5 miles on R towards Worleston

PRESTBURY

Map 7 SJ87

White House Restaurant

SK10 4DG
Tel: 01625 829376
Fax: 01625 828627
e info@thewhitehouse.uk.com
Chef(s): Ryland Wakeham,
Mark Cunniffe
Owner(s): Mr. R J Wakeham
Cost: A/c £29.95, set price L £14.95-
£16.90/D £17.95-£20.45. ☺ ☺
H/wine £13.95
Times: Noon-2pm/7-10pm.
Closed L Mon, D Sun, 25 Dec
Additional: Sunday L. Bar food L.
Children welcome
Seats: 70. Private dining room 40
Style: Modern
Smoking: No cigars
Accommodation: 11 rooms (11 en
suite)
Directions: Village centre on A538 N
of Macclesfield

Don't believe the old fashioned exterior - this is a stylish, modern restaurant full of coloured glass and artful lighting. The equally up-to-date menu offers a colourful blend of classic and international ideas. Whet your appetite with canapés in the bar before progressing to an imaginative starter such as pan seared scallops on a coulis of aromatic cauliflower and mango-chilli

England

salsa. Main courses follow suit, offering dishes such as tortilla wraps with baba ghanoush, char grilled peppers, feta cheese and mint alongside restyled favourites - perhaps roast baby chicken stuffed with sage and apple and served with cranberry, sage and balsamic jus.

PUDDINGTON
Map 7 SJ37

Craxton Wood

Set in attractive grounds, this rambling, whitewashed house has been extensively upgraded and extended since it was built over 100 years ago. The restaurant combines soft colours with rich fabrics and classic white table linen to create an elegant, relaxed setting - part of which occupies a conservatory with pretty garden views. The menu offers plenty of favourites (grilled Dover sole; chicken Caesar salad; Aberdeen Angus steak) alongside modern dishes such as sweet potato and spinach soup or langoustine and prawn tagliatelli with a hint of chilli. Among the desserts, look out for the theatrical (and very successful) crêpe suzette, flambéed at your table.

Civil licence: 300
Accommodation: 73 rooms (73 en suite) ★ ★ ★ ★
Directions: From end of M56 (westbound) take A5117 (Queensferry), R at 1st rdbt onto A540 (Hoylake). Hotel 200yds after next traffic lights

Parkgate Road, Ledsham CH66 9PB
Tel: 0151 347 4000
Fax: 0151 347 4040
e info@craxton.macdonald.co.uk
Chef(s): Ian Cobham
Owner(s): MacDonalds Hotels Plc
Cost: Alc £30, set price L £16.50/ D £27.50
Times: 12.30-2pm/7-9.45pm. Closed L Sat
Additional: Sunday L. Bar food L. Children welcome
Seats: 104. Private dining room 40. Jacket and tie preferred
Style: Modern
Smoking: No smoking in dining room; Air conditioning

SANDIWAY
Map 7 SJ67

Nunsmere Hall

Classic country house package at Nunsmere with a terrific setting and the expansive grandeur of public rooms in which to take pre and post dinner drinks. A restrained atmosphere offers few interruptions and a genuinely peaceful atmosphere. Formal

Tarporley Road, CW8 2ES
Tel: 01606 889100
Fax: 01606 889055
e reservations@nunsmere.co.uk
Chef(s): John Tamila
Owner(s): Mr & Mrs M S McHardy
Cost: Alc £38, set price L £25 H/wine £16.60
Times: Noon-2pm/7-10pm.
Additional: Sunday L. Bar food L. Children 12yrs+
Seats: 60. Private dining room 45. Jacket and tie preferred
Style: Country House, Traditional
Smoking: No smoking in dining room
Accommodation: 36 rooms (36 en suite) ★ ★ ★

service of some upbeat, busy cooking, which might offer a tatin of shallot and figs with salsa verde and an accompanying leaf salad with Parmesan as a starter. Highlights have included tenderloin of pork wrapped in pancetta with tarragon risotto and a lemon tart with a "superb" chocolate truffle mousse.

Directions: From M16 J19 take A56 for 9 miles. Turn L onto A49 towards Tarporley. Hotel 1 mile on L

WARRINGTON

Map 7 SJ68

Daresbury Park

Cool and contemporary, the Cheshire Room is the more formal of two eating options at this extravagantly refurbished hotel. Begin your evening in the smart bar area, where drinks are brought to your table, before progressing to the split level

dining room for a meal full of old favourites: typical dishes include lobster thermidor, beef stroganoff, chicken Kiev and grilled steak. Polished, friendly service adds to the air of luxury created by smooth wooden floors, warm, modern lighting and luxury fabrics in shades of gold, red and green.

Chester Road, Daresbury, WA4 4BB
Tel: 01925 267331
Fax: 01925 265615
e daresburyparksalesmanager@
dever-hotels.com
Chef(s): David Chapman
Owner(s): De Vere Group Plc
Cost: Alc £28. ☺ ☺ H/wine £10.95
Times: Dinner only, 7-10pm.
Closed Sun-Mon
Additional: Sunday L. Bar food.
Children welcome
Seats: 60. Private dining room 300
Style: Modern, Bistro-Style
Smoking: No-smoking area; Air
conditioning
Civil licence: 250
Accommodation: 181 rooms (181 en
suite) ★★★★
Directions: M56 J11 onto A56 to
Warrington. Just on L off roundabout

Hanover International

Located in a charming village in the heart of the Cheshire countryside, this large modern hotel provides a peaceful haven not far from the motorway. The elegant Harlequin restaurant serves an extensive selection of dishes, ranging from British favourites (roasted fillet steak; rack of lamb) to European classics such as Greek salad or tagliatelli with olive oil and seafood.

Directions: M56 J10, follow A49 signed Warrington, R towards Appleton Thorn at 1st lights, hotel 200yds on R

Stretton Road, Stretton,
WA4 4NS
Tel: 01925 730706
Fax: 01925 730740
e hotel@park-royal-int.co.uk
Chef(s): Tom Rogers
Cost: Alc £30, set price L £13.45/
D £18.85. ☺ ☺ H/wine £10
Times: Noon-2.30pm/7.00pm-
10.00pm.
Additional: Sunday L. Bar food.
Children welcome
Seats: 125. Private dining room 42
Style: Traditional
Smoking: No-smoking area; Air
conditioning
Civil licence: 400
Accommodation: 140 rooms (140 en
suite) ★★★★

England

Rockfield Hotel

Unless we've missed something, Anglo-Swiss cuisine doesn't have a wealth of practitioners in the UK. Step forward this family run hotel offering the likes of Basel onion soup and pork schnitzel as well as a range of steaks and more traditional British dishes in the aptly named Swiss Restaurant.

Seats: 70. **Style:** Classic
Smoking: No smoking in dining room. **Civil licence:** 60
Accommodation: 12 rooms (12 en suite)
Directions: From M6 J20, A50, forks with A56. 1.5miles L in Victoria Rd, R in 60yds

Alexandra Road, WA4 2EL
Tel: 01925 262898
Fax: 01925 263343
e rockfieldhotel@btinternet.com
Chef(s): Thomas Zuger
Owner(s): Thomas & Esther Zuger
Cost: Alc £18, set price L £12.50/ D £16.50. ☺ ☺ H/wine £9.95
Times: Noon-2pm/7pm-midnight. Closed D Sun
Additional: Sunday L. Children welcome

WILMSLOW   Map 7 SJ88

Mottram Hall Hotel

Named after the reclusive Nathaniel Booth who built the Hall in 1650, Nathaniel's restaurant is one of the newest additions to this popular country hotel. Decorated in warm contemporary colours and offering friendly, relaxed service, it's the perfect backdrop for a selection of modern European dishes such as roast rump of lamb with garlic and rosemary jus or fillet steak on fondant potato with wild mushrooms and Bordeaux jus.

Seats: 140. Private dining room. Jacket and tie preferred
Style: Chic, Modern
Smoking: No smoking in dining room
Civil licence: 180. **Accommodation:** 132 rooms ★★★★

Wilmslow Road, Mottram St Andrews, Prestbury SK10 4QT
Tel: 01625 828135
Fax: 01625 828950
e dmh.sales@devere-hotels.com
Chef(s): Mark Fletcher
Cost: Alc £26, set price L £26/D £26. ☺ ☺ H/wine £16
Times: Noon-2pm/7-10pm. Closed L Sat
Additional: Sunday L. Bar food. Children welcome. Vegetarian by request only

Stanneylands Hotel

A traditional hotel set in attractive gardens. Its elegant mahogany panelled restaurant is a comfortable, spacious place

to eat and offers an interesting choice of dishes, ranging from traditional favourites to more imaginative contemporary dishes. A dinner menu might include starters of Dublin Bay prawns and roasted goats' cheese followed by main courses such as sea bass poached in tomato consommé or roasted partridge with game chips and bread sauce. Whilst thought clearly goes into the cooking, vegetable accompaniments are not always tailored to individual dishes. Meals are rounded off by good coffee and truffles.

Stanneylands Road, SK9 4EY
Tel: 01625 525225
Fax: 01625 537282
e reservations@stanneylands.co.uk
Chef(s): Martin Swindley
Owner(s): Mr L Walshe
Cost: Alc £30, set price L £16-£18.50/D £23.50-£26. ☺ ☺ H/wine £12.95
Times: Noon-2.30pm/7-9.30pm. Closed D Sun
Additional: Sunday L. Bar food. Children welcome
Seats: 60. Private dining room 120
Style: Country-house, Modern
Smoking: No-smoking area
Civil licence: 80
Accommodation: 32 rooms (32 en suite) ★★★
Directions: From M5 J5 follow signs for Wilmslow/Moss Nook. At traffic lights turn R, through Styal, L at Handiforth sign, follow into Stanneylands Rd

CORNWALL & ISLES OF SCILLY

England

BRYHER
Map 2 SW17

Hell Bay Hotel

Despite the name, this is a haven of peace with lovely sea views. The restaurant has a rustic feel (exposed beams and brickwork) and serves a variety of European style dishes. Although the cooking sometimes lacks refinement, the many simple, but effective, fish dishes on the menu are a real strength.

Seats: 54. **Style:** Country House
Smoking: No smoking in dining room
Accommodation: 17 rooms (17 en suite) ★ ★ ★
Directions: By boat from main island of St Mary's

◉
TR23 0PR
Tel: 01720 422947
Fax: 01720 423004
🄴 hellbay@aol.com
Chef(s): Graham Shone, Hayley Spink
Cost: Alc £27.50. ☺ H/wine £9.50
Times: D only 7-8.45pm.
Closed Oct-Mar
Additional: Bar food L. Children 6yrs+

BUDE
Map 2 SS20

Atlantic House

This relaxed, personally run hotel is set in a quiet area overlooking the beach, just a few minutes walk from the town centre. The restaurant serves an imaginative, well balanced menu. A meal might include warm goats' cheese and raspberry timbale followed by fillet of salmon with cheesy polenta, sweet chilli sauce and Mexican salsa.

Seats: 50. **Style:** Traditional
Smoking: No smoking in dining room
Accommodation: 15 rooms (15 en suite) ★ ★
Directions: From M5 J31, follow A30 past Okehampton. Then A386 (Bude) to join A3072 (Holsworthy & Bude)

◉
17-18 Summerleaze Crescent, EX23 8HJ
Tel: 01288 352451
Fax: 01288 356666
🄴 enq@atlantichousehotel.co.uk
Chef(s): Nick & Jeannie Cole
Owner(s): Nick & Jeannie Cole
Cost: Set price D £16. ☺ H/wine £7.45
Times: 12.30-1.30pm/6.30-8pm.
Closed Nov-Feb
Additional: Bar food L. Children welcome

CALLINGTON
Map 2 SX36

Thyme & Plaice

Once a baker's shop, the Thyme & Plaice now has more ambitious leanings though not just towards the ocean as the name implies. A comfortable, welcoming seating area complete with blazing fire opens onto the dining room, an intimate space where large tables are well spaced to give a feeling of privacy. Good value menus offer a choice of modern British dishes from a variety of sources: roast Gressingham duck with red wine and port, fillet of Cornish beef with a Madeira and peppercorn sauce, and monkfish and salmon with a sorrel butter sauce show the range.

Directions: From the direction of Plymouth into Callington town centre, L at lights and R into Church Street.

◉◉
3 Church Street, PL17 7RE
Tel: 01579 384933
Fax: 01579 384933
🄴 thymplaice@aol.com
Chef(s): Anton Buttery
Owner(s): Anton & Gail Buttery
Cost: Alc £27, set price D £22.95 (6 courses). ☺ H/wine £8.65
Times: Dinner only, 7.30pm-midnight. Closed Sun-Wed
Additional: Children 8yrs+
Seats: 20
Style: Modern, Chic
Smoking: No-smoking area

CONSTANTINE
Map 2 SW72

Trengilly Wartha Inn

A popular and busy country inn hotel located in a designated area of outstanding natural beauty. The restaurant is decorated in warm yellows and pale blues, and looks onto attractive

◉◉
Nancenoy, TR11 5RP
Tel: 01326 340332
Fax: 01326 340332
🄴 trengilly@compuserve.com

gardens. An impressive selection of Cornish produce is given an imaginative, modern treatment in dishes such as beef fillet with a pickled walnut crust, chestnut mushroom sauce and creamed potatoes or Guinea fowl stuffed with chilli and cranberries, served with a Cumberland sauce and dauphinoise potatoes. In addition to the numerous dishes on the restaurant menu, guests are invited to select any of the fish dishes available in the bar.

Accommodation: 8 rooms (7 en suite) ★ ★
Directions: In Constantine village turn L at top of hill, follow signs for Gweek, 1 mile out of village turn L, follow hotel signs

Chef(s): Mike Maguire
Owner(s): Mr & Mrs Logan, Mr & Mrs Maguire
Cost: Set price D £27.50
H/wine £10.70
Times: Dinner only, 7.30-9.30pm. Closed 25 Dec, 31 Dec
Additional: Bar food. Children welcome
Seats: 28
Style: Modern

CONSTANTINE BAY — Map 2 SW87

Treglos Hotel

Owned by the same family for 34 years, Treglos Hotel has plenty of loyal customers. Its restaurant is decorated in an unfussy, traditional style and serves food to match: a meal might include baked huss, followed by 'succulent' partridge served on roast parsnips with a Victoria plum and Armagnac jus. The seaside setting delivers gorgeous views and great fish.

Seats: 100. Private dining room 20. Jacket and tie preferred
Style: Traditional, Country-House
Smoking: No smoking in dining room; Air conditioning
Accommodation: 44 rooms (44 en suite) ★ ★ ★
Directions: Take B3276 (Constantine Bay). At village stores turn R, hotel is 50 yards on L

PL28 8JH
Tel: 01841 520727
Fax: 01841 521163
e enquiries@treglos-hotel.co.uk
Chef(s): Paul Becker
Owner(s): Mr & Mrs J Barlow
Cost: Alc £32, set price L £12.50-£15/ D £24.75. ☺ ☺ H/wine £12.50
Times: 12.15-2.15pm/7.30-8.45pm. Closed Closed mid Nov-beginning March
Additional: Sunday L. Bar food. Children 7yrs+ at D

FALMOUTH — Map 2 SW83

Royal Duchy Hotel

Situated on the sea front, just a short walk from the town centre, this welcoming hotel enjoys spectacular views across the bay. Where better to enjoy these than in the restaurant, an attractive, formal room decorated in rich shades of red and cream. The interesting selection of dishes might include roasted veal sweetbreads with chestnut purée and basil beurre blanc or grilled salmon with creamed leeks and Champagne butter sauce. Desserts range from sticky toffee pudding to red wine fruit jelly. Meals are accompanied by the sound of the harp or by the resident pianist at the grand piano.

Cliff Road, TR11 4NX
Tel: 01326 313042
Fax: 01326 319420
e info@royalduchy.co.uk
Chef(s): Dez Turland
Owner(s): Brend Hotel Group
Cost: Set price L £9.95-£11.50/ D£22. ☺ ☺ H/wine £8.95
Times: 12.30-2.30pm/7-9pm.
Additional: Sunday L. Bar food L. Children welcome
Seats: 100. Private dining room 15. Jacket and tie preferred
Style: Traditional, Formal
Smoking: No pipes
Civil licence: 150
Accommodation: 43 rooms (43 en suite) ★ ★ ★ ★
Directions: Hotel is at Castle end of Promenade

FOWEY

Map 2 SX15

Food for Thought

Clear flavours tantalise the palate, and simple, unfussy cooking offers a refreshing experience at this beamed waterside restaurant. Set on the quayside next to a fish and chip shop, it has been part of local scene for over 20 years. The food is thoroughly contemporary, focusing on specialities from the River Fowey, and leaning away from meat with only a couple of carnivorous choices. Rendezvous of red mullet, turbot, scallops and sea bass with a saffron and mussel cream sauce is a typical main dish. Good value mainly French wines and decent house choices. Pleasant staff give a well-choreographed service, and create a relaxed and cheerful atmosphere.

The Quay, PL23 1AT
Tel: 01726 832221
Fax: 01726 832077
Telephone for further details

Fowey Hall

Hanson Drive, PL23 1ET
Tel: 01726 833866
Fax: 01726 834100
e info@foweyhall.com
Chef(s): Tony Duce
Owner(s): Mr. N Dickinson & Mr. N Chapman
Cost: Alc £32, set price D £29.50.
☺ ☺ H/wine £13.50
Times: Noon-2pm/7.30-9.30pm.
Additional: Sunday L. Bar food. Children welcome
Seats: 30. Private dining room 20
Style: Modern
Smoking: No smoking in dining room

The dining room of this listed mansion enjoys stunning views across the English Channel. An attractive, wood panelled room, it offers the choice of a daily changing restaurant menu and an à la *carte* on which local Cornish produce is styled with modern British and Mediterranean influences. Dishes might include honey glazed duck breast with braised lentils and vanilla sauce or fillet of beef with Provençale vegetables. Also available is an impressive range of seafood dishes, such as oak smoked salmon with lemon or Fowey river oysters with cracked pepper. These can be ordered as starters or main courses.

Civil licence: 100
Accommodation: 25 rooms (25 en suite) ★ ★ ★
Directions: Into town centre, pass school on R, 400 mtrs turn R onto Hanson Drive

Fowey Hotel

A large white building standing proudly above the estuary, The Fowey is a classic example of a Victorian grand hotel. The restaurant is exactly as you'd expect: beautiful views, chandeliers, rich red carpets and heavily draped curtains. The menu is more of a surprise, offering modern, European style dishes alongside the expected favourites such as grilled meats or lemon sole with mash. The continental influence extends to the desserts, which might include strawberry parfait or banana

The Esplanade,
PL23 1HX
Tel: 01726 832551
Fax: 01726 832125
e fowey@richardsonhotels.co.uk
Chef(s): Jason White
Owner(s): Keith Richardson
Cost: Alc D £25.50, set price L £14.
☺ ☺ H/wine £13.50

delice, but you'll also encounter treats from closer to home such as Cornish ice cream served in a brandy snap basket with Cornish clotted cream.

Smoking: No smoking in dining room
Accommodation: 30 rooms (30 en suite) ★ ★ ★
Directions: From A390 take B3269 for approx 5m, follow signs for Fowey continue along Pavillion Road for 0.75mile. 2nd R

Times: Noon-2.30pm/7-9pm
Additional: Sunday L. Bar food L. Children welcome
Seats: 70. Jacket and tie preferred
Style: Modern, Classic

GILLAN   Map 2 SW52

Tregildry Hotel

From its peaceful, unspoilt location Tregildry is blessed with beautiful sea and riverside views. The 10 table dining room caters mainly for residents, though non-residents will be accepted if a table is free. Decorated in Mediterranean style, it's the perfect place to enjoy the views and an innovative selection of food. The daily changing menu can be relied upon for familiar dishes (steak and fries; rack of lamb with apple and parsnip mash) as well as modern creations such as roast fillet of cod with a parsley and parmesan crust served with avocado and chilli compôte.

Accommodation: 10 rooms (10 en suite) ★ ★
Directions: A3083 from Helston (Lizard Road), take 1st L for St Keverne. Follow signs for Manaccan and Gillan

TR12 6HG
Tel: 01326 231378
Fax: 01326 231561
e trgildry@globalnet.co.uk
Owner(s): Huw & Lynne Phillips
Cost: Set price D £24. ☺
H/wine £11.75
Times: Dinner only, 7-8.45pm. Closed Nov-Feb
Additional: Children 8 yrs+
Seats: 30
Style: Modern, Chic
Smoking: No smoking in dining room
Chef(s): Huw Phillips

HELSTON   Map 2 SW62

Nansloe Manor

A haven of tranquillity and understated elegance, this Georgian grade II property dates back to 1735. The gracious lounge and dining room typify the high standards of presentation throughout the hotel. Imaginative cuisine is a priority: a meal might begin with Cornish smoked salmon bisque seared with a crispy chorizo beignet, before progressing to a main course of slow braised Moroccan spiced lamb shank with chick pea, coriander seed and spring onion mash. Desserts are equally exciting, and might include lemon and tarragon scented pannacotta with red fruit compôte and Pernod syrup. Don't forget to explore the grounds, which include a wonderful walled garden.

Smoking: No smoking in dining room
Accommodation: 7 rooms (6 en suite) ★ ★
Directions: 300yds from junction of A394 & A3083

Meneage Road, TR13 0SB
Tel: 01326 574691
Fax: 01326 564680
e info@nansloe-manor.co.uk
Chef(s): Howard Ridden
Owner(s): The Ridden Family
Cost:-£12.95-£23.95. ☺ ☺
H/wine £10.95
Times: Noon-1.30pm/7-8.30pm. Closed L Mon-Sat
Additional: Sunday L. Bar food L. Children 10yrs+
Seats: 40. Private dining room 40. Jacket and tie preferred
Style: Traditional, Country-House

LISKEARD   Map 2 SX26

Well House Hotel

Nestling in a Cornish valley, this hotel restaurant has the pick of the finest produce from both sea and land. Not surprisingly, then, the daily-changing menus pay tribute to the fruits of each, featuring perhaps locally-landed turbot and sole, scallops and sea bass alongside fillet of beef, spiced pheasant breast and roast canon of lamb. Sensitive cooking is apparent in the light

St Keyne, PL14 4RN
Tel: 01579 342001
Fax: 01579 343891
e wellhse@aol.com
Chef(s): Mathew Corner
Owner(s): Mr N Wainford, Ione Nurdin

England

LISKEARD *Continued* Map 2 SX26

treatment of, for instance, red mullet fillets with ratatouille and balsamic syrup with breast of Gressingham duck on spicy red cabbage with confit leg on rösti and sausage on mash, being cited as a great combination for a recent main dish. Desserts range from hot chocolate fondant with vanilla ice cream to hot Grand Marnier soufflé with chocolate sauce, while apple and Calvados tart with star anise ice cream was a big hit. A mainly Burgundy/Bordeaux wine list with some aged clarets is moving towards the New World.

Directions: At St Keyne Church follow signs to St Keyne Well, the restaurant is 0.5 mile further

Cost: *Alc* £30, set price L & D
£23.50-£32.50. H/wine £10.50
Times: 12.30-2pm/7-9pm.
Additional: Sunday L.
Children 8yrs+ at D
Seats: 32
Style: Modern
Smoking: No smoking in dining room
Accommodation: 9 rooms (9 en suite)
★ ★

MARAZION Map 2 SW53

Mount Haven Hotel

Former coaching inn looking out on St Michael's Mount. The split-level restaurant is in the baronial hall style but the cooking has a contemporary edge. Seafood from nearby Newlyn features daily in dishes like fresh crab soup, and steamed sea bass scented with chilli, coriander and lemon grass.

Turnpike Road, TR17 0DQ
Tel: 01736 710249
Fax: 01736 711658
📧 mounthaven@compuserve.com
Chef(s): Stewart Mitchell
Owner(s): Mr & Mrs JA James
Cost: *Alc* £24.50, set price D £21.50.
☺ H/wine £9.50
Times: Noon-2pm/7-9pm. Closed L
Mon-Sat, Xmas, D Mar-Sep
Additional: Sunday L. Bar food.
Children welcome
Seats: 50. Jacket and tie preferred
Style: Baronial Hall
Smoking: No smoking in dining room
Accommodation: 17 rooms (17 en suite) ★ ★
Directions: Through village to end of built-up area

MAWNAN SMITH Map 2 SW72

Budock Vean-
The Hotel on the River

Occasional forays into exciting terrain enliven the traditional cooking at this peaceful hotel beside the Helford River. Expect salmon, chilli and coriander fishcakes, duo of turbot and bass with dill butter sauce, and pear and frangipane tart. Verdant views over the garden to the golf course are a pleasant distraction.

TR11 5LG
Tel: 01326 252100
Fax: 01326 250892
Telephone for further details

Trelawne Hotel

TR11 5HS
Tel: 01326 250226
Fax: 01326 250909
Telephone for further details

Superb views of the coastline from St Mawes to the Lizard can be relished from this friendly informal hotel, popular with many returning guests. The restaurant is reassuringly traditional, and pleasant staff keep things ticking over efficiently. Some delicate and imaginative touches are evident from a talented kitchen staff, as in poppy seed tartlet with mackerel, coriander sabayon and red onion compôte, and lemon and ginger sorbet. Seared salmon and scallops with asparagus spears, truffle and saffron butter was an ambitious main course that didn't quite meet expectations. A wide-ranging wine list, and some delicious petit fours.

MOUSEHOLE   Map 2 SW42

Cornish Range

6 Chapel Street, TR19 6SB
Tel: 01736 731488
Fax: 01736 732255
e ryfox@compuserve.com
Chef(s): David Rashleigh
Owner(s): Mr A Ryan
Cost: A/c £23.50. ☺ ☺ H/wine £9.95
Times: Dinner only, 7-9.30pm.
Closed L Mon-Sat in summer, all day Mon-Wed in winter
Additional: Sunday L in winter.
Children welcome
Seats: 50
Style: Modern Chic
Smoking: No-smoking area; no cigars
Accommodation: 3 rooms (3 en suite)
Directions: Mousehole is 3 miles S from Penzance, via Newlyn

Here's a restaurant with a truly great atmosphere, positive service and vibrant colour - on the plate as well as on the walls that are lined with contemporary artwork. An amusing range of cocktails is offered while you check out the menu. Expect sea-fresh fish from Newlyn and a strong Mediterranean influence.

England

MOUSEHOLE *Continued*   Map 2 SW42

Old Coastguard Inn

There are fantastic views across the sub-tropical gardens to the sea from this attractive modern brasserie. Fresh local produce features on a menu divided between seafood, meats, and a section of salads, pasta and risotto. Typical options are mixed fish grill, fillet steak with a shallot potato rösti, and a Newlyn crab salad with guacamole and chilli potatoes.

The Parade, TR19 6PR
Tel: 01736 731222
Fax: 01736 731720
e bookings@oldcoastguardhotel. co.uk
Chef(s): Keith Terry, Mary Kitchen, Steven Coyne
Owner(s): P S Wood, A W Treloar
Cost: *Alc* £20. ☺ ☺ H/wine £8.50
Times: Noon-3pm/6.30-11pm. Closed 25 Dec
Additional: Sunday L. Bar food. Children welcome
Seats: 80
Style: Modern Bistro
Smoking: No-smoking area
Accommodation: 22 rooms (21 en suite) ★★
Directions: From Penzance take coast road through Newlyn. Inn 1st large building on L on entering village, just after public car park

---

MULLION   Map 2 SW61

Mullion Cove   NEW

Sunsets are a speciality with stunning views over the bay from the Atlantic dining room. Although there are some more prosaic dishes on the menu, there are some interesting and adventurous combinations. Avocado might come with baked tomatoes, red peppers and a rocket and pine kernel salad, poached breast of chicken stuffed with tapenade and served with a piquant caper sauce. Expect the likes of pistachio crème brûlée amongst the desserts.

Smoking: No smoking in dining room
Accommodation: 30 rooms (30 en suite) ★★★
Directions: Telephone for directions

Nr Helston, TR12 7EP
Tel: 01326 240328
Fax: 01326 240998
e mullion.cove@btinternet.com
Chef(s): Melanie Rosevear
Owner(s): Jane Davis & Clive Wilkinson
Cost: *Alc* £19.50, set price D £19.50
Times: Dinner only, 7-8.45pm
Additional: Bar food. Children 7yrs+
Seats: 70
Style: Traditional

NEWQUAY   Map 2 SW86

Corisande Manor

Benefitting from direct access to Gannel Sands, this friendly Victorian hotel stands in three acres of grounds, yet within easy access of the town centre. Each evening, a short menu offers an innovative choice of dishes, supported by an extensive, well chosen wine list. A meal might include broad bean soup and a main course of chicken with grapes and cream.

Style: Traditional, Country-House
Smoking: No smoking in dining room
Accommodation: 12 rooms (12 en suite) ★★
Directions: Off the main road, down the Pentire headland, left at Newquay Nursing Home into Pentire Crescent, then R into Riverside Avenue

Riverside Avenue, Pentire, TR7 1PL
Tel: 01637 872042
Fax: 01637 874557
e relax@corisande.com
Chef(s): Chris Grant
Owner(s): Mr & Mrs D Grant
Cost: Set price D £22. ☺ H/wine £10
Times: D only, at 8pm
Additional: Children welcome. Vegetarian by request only
Seats: 20

Porth Veor Manor

Splendid coastal views from every window put you in a relaxed frame of mind. Dishes are not too taxing either, with well conceived combinations and some accurate cooking. Expect to find the likes of carrot and courgette timbale, steamed cod with spinach risotto and lime butter, and sultana and butterscotch pudding.

Seats: 60. **Style:** Modern Country-House
Smoking: No smoking in dining room
Accommodation: 22 rooms (22 en suite) ★ ★
Directions: Leave Newquay on A3058. After 1mile turn L onto B3276 (Padstow Coast Rd). Hotel is on L at bottom of hill

Porth Way, TR7 3LW
Tel: 01637 873274
Fax: 01637 851690
e booking@porthveor.co.uk
Chef(s): Elizabeth Slyfield
Owner(s): Mr P G Harknett
Cost: Alc £19.95, set price D £12.95-£15.95. ☺ ☺ H/wine £9.95
Times: Dinner only, 7-9pm
Additional: Lunch by prior arrangement only. Bar food L. Children welcome

---

PADSTOW   Map 2 SW97

Brocks

Located just off the harbourside, this first floor restaurant offers a friendly welcome and plenty of robust, gutsy cooking. A high beamed ceiling, bright rag washed walls and seagrass floors lend an air of Provence to the setting. The menu includes a great value set meal alongside à la *carte* dishes such as sautéed foie gras with caramelised apples and calvados jus or grilled sea bass on pesto mash with tapenade. You could round the meal off with British farmhouse cheese or desserts such as Mississipi mud pie with clotted cream. The kitchen delivers all promised flavours, creating a vibrant, enjoyable experience.

Directions: Follow one-way around harbour. Past bandstand on left

The Strand, PL28 8AJ
Tel: 01841 532565
e brockx@compuserve.com
Chef(s): Carl Hamilton
Owner(s): Tim & Hazel Brocklebank
Cost: Alc £25, set price D £21.50.
☺ ☺ H/wine £12.50
Times: 12.30-2pm/7-9.30pm.
Closed Sun, L Mon, 5 Jan-5 Feb
Additional: Children welcome
Seats: 40. Private dining room 30
Style: Classic, French
Smoking: No smoking in dining room

Margot's

This bistro succeeds admirably in its mission to provide 'fresh food and friendly service in a relaxed setting'. A small room filled with work by local artists, it serves classic and modern dishes such as rack of lamb with a herb crust or hot pot of mussels and tiger prawns with leeks, ginger and new potatoes. Best to book.

Seats: 25. **Style:** Bistro Style.
Smoking: No smoking in dining room
Directions: Telephone for directions

11 Duke Street, PL28 8AB
Tel: 01841 533441
e oliveradrian@hotmail.com
Chef(s): Adrian Oliver
Owner(s): Adrian & Julie Oliver
Cost: Set price D £24.95. ☺
H/wine £9.95
Times: Dinner only, 7-9pm.
Closed Mon-Tue, Nov, Jan,
restricted opening Dec
Additional: Children welcome

Old Custom House Inn, Pescadou Restaurant

This charming harbourside inn is popular with locals and visitors alike. The restaurant is a bright, modern room whose open kitchen produces mouthwatering seafood such as moules marinière or roasted plaice with lemon and herbs. Meaty alternatives might include grilled entrecôte steak with salsa verdi and chips.

Smoking: No smoking in dining room; Air conditioning
Accommodation: 24 rooms (24 en suite) ★ ★ ★
Directions: From Wadebridge take A389 (Padstow). Take 2nd R after Padstow School, round sharp bend at bottom of hill. Inn is opposite entrance to harbour car park

South Quay, PL28 8ED
Tel: 01841 532359
Fax: 01841 533372
e oldcustomhouse@
westcountryhotelrooms.co.uk
Chef(s): Gareth Eddy
Owner(s): St Austell Brewery Co Ltd.
Cost: Alc £25. ☺ ☺ H/wine £8
Times: Noon-3pm/7-9.30pm.
Closed Xmas
Additional: Sunday L. Children 8 yrs+
Seats: 60
Style: Modern, Bistro-Style

PADSTOW *Continued*   Map 2 SW97

St Petroc's House

A delightful period property near the harbour, run by the famous Rick Stein. The bistro offers French cooking of a simpler style than his Seafood Restaurant. A meal might include moules marinière followed by plaice with leeks, bacon and mint. Meat dishes - such as roast partridge with sauerkraut and red wine jus - are also available.

Seats: 34. Private dining room 12. **Style:** Bistro-Style
Smoking: No smoking in dining room; Air conditioning
Accommodation: 13 rooms (13 en suite) ◆◆◆◆
Directions: Follow one-way around harbour, 1st L, situated on R

4 New Street, PL28 8EA
Tel: 01841 532700
Fax: 01841 532942
e reservations@rickstein.com
Chef(s): Alistair Clive
Owner(s): Rick Stein
Cost: *Alc* £25.50, set price L £19.
H/wine £14.95
Times: Noon-1.30pm/7-9.30pm.
Closed Mon, 1 May, 1 wk Xmas
Additional: Sunday L. Bar food.
Children welcome

The Seafood Restaurant

Although Rick Stein continues to cast his net ever further, the Seafood Restaurant seems to remain his anchor. Balancing a media career and a kitchen is a tough act, but here we have an unusually neat symbiosis typified by a menu that draws inspiration from recent travels (shark vindaloo being a witty example). The great strength, of course, is in the quality of the fish and in a kitchen that has the confidence to keep it simple. The likes of grilled Padstow lobster with fines herbes, pan-fried skate au poivre with béarnaise and crab and gruyere tart concentrate on getting the basics right with, in the latter case, excellent pastry and ultra-fresh crab. The quayside location serves to emphasise the straight from the sea philosophy and staff dispense breezy service amongst the, inevitably packed, tables. An extensive wine list is selected with care and an eye for character.

Directions: A389 towards Padstow, R after 3 miles at T-junct. R to centre (signed). Restaurant on Riverside

PL28 8BY
Tel: 01841 532700
Fax: 01841 533574
e reservations@rickstein.com
Chef(s): Rick Stein
Owner(s): R & J Stein
Cost: *Alc* £45, set price L £30.50/
D £37. H/wine £14.95
Times: Noon-1.30pm/7-10pm.
Closed 1wk Xmas, 1 May
Additional: Sunday L. Children 3yrs+
Seats: 104
Style: Modern
Smoking: Air conditioning
Accommodation: 13 rooms (13 en suite) ◆◆◆◆◆

PENZANCE   Map 2 SW43

Harris' Restaurant

Friendly and intimate setting tucked away in the centre of town. Perhaps unsurprisingly local fish features strongly on the menu - simply cooked with considered restraint. Meat eaters - fear not! Wild venison cooked to perfection demonstrates real dexterity in the kitchen.

Additional: Bar food L. Children welcome. Vegetarian by request only
Seats: 40
Smoking: No smoking in dining room

46 New Street, TR18 2LZ
Tel: 01736 364408
Fax: 01736 333273
e harriss.restaurant@lineone.net
Chef(s): Roger Harris
Owner(s): Roger & Anne Harris
Cost: *Alc* £26. ☺ ☺
H/wine £12.50
Times: L from Noon, D from 7pm.
Closed Sun, 3 wks winter, 25-26 Dec,
1 Jan

PORT GAVERNE   Map 2 SX08

Port Gaverne Hotel

Set in a spectacular little cove and retaining its flagged floors, beamed ceilings and steep stairways, this is a charming place to

PL29 3SQ
Tel: 01208 880244
Fax: 01208 880151

England

dine. The menu has a traditional feel and features plenty of local produce. Starters might include chicken liver pâté, whilst main courses such as beef stroganoff are accompanied by pleasing selections of fresh vegetables. Well balanced wine list.

Seats: 40
Style: Traditional
Smoking: No smoking in dining room; no cigars
Accommodation: 16 rooms (16 en suite) ★ ★
Directions: Signposted from B3314, 2 miles from Delabole

e pghotel@telinco.co.uk
Chef(s): Ian Brodey
Owner(s): Midge Ross
Cost: ☺ ☺ H/wine £7.85
Times: Noon-2.30pm/7-9.30pm.
Closed L Mon-Sat, early Jan-mid Feb
Additional: Sunday L. Bar food.
Children 7yrs+

PORTHLEVEN   Map 2 SW62

Critchards Seafood Restaurant

Three-hundred year old converted mill offering a relaxed Mediterranean ambience and multi-national cuisine. Fighting-fresh fish from Newlyn forms the basis of some interesting dishes with a Pacific Rim twist.

Seats: 44
Style: Traditional, Spanish
Smoking: No smoking in dining room
Accommodation: 2 rooms (2 en suite)
Directions: Overlooking the harbour

The Harbour Head, TR13 9JA
Tel: 01326 562407
Fax: 01326 564444
Chef(s): Jo Critchard
Owner(s): Steve & Jo Critchard
Cost: Alc £22.50. ☺ H/wine £11.95
Times: Dinner only, 6.30-9.30pm.
Closed Sun, Jan
Additional: Children 5yrs+

PORT ISAAC   Map 2 SW98

The Castle Rock Hotel

A stylish, modern restaurant with beautiful views over cliffs to the sea. The menu offers plenty of favourites (pork chop with veg and mash; salmon with herb and garlic butter), but also includes vibrant international dishes such as a whole roasted mackerel stuffed with Thai red chilli paste and rice.

Seats: 40. Private dining room 30
Style: Afro-Mediterranean
Smoking: No smoking in dining room
Accommodation: 18 rooms (18 en suite) ★ ★
Directions: From A39 take B3314, then B3267 to top of Port Isaac

4 New Road, PL29 3SB
Tel: 01208 880300
Fax: 01208 880219
e info@castlerockhotel.co.uk
Chef(s): Carron Smith
Owner(s): Mr & Mrs J Henderson
Cost: Alc £18. ☺ ☺ H/wine £9.25
Times: 12.30-2.30pm/6.30-11pm.
Additional: Sunday L. Bar food.
Children welcome. Vegetarian by request only

PORTREATH   Map 2 SW64

Tabb's Restaurant

Rustic restaurant in a single storey stone building. From the aromatic home-baked bread to the carefully prepared desserts the quality is consistent and the flavours are full. Main courses range from pan-fried chicken livers in a cream, onion and sherry sauce to a vegetable pilaff with fresh ginger, lemongrass and garlic

Additional: Sunday L. Children welcome
Seats: 35
Style: Classic, Rustic
Smoking: No smoking in dining room
Directions: In the centre of the village under the viaduct

Railway Terrace,
TR16 4LD
Tel: 01209 842488
Fax: 01209 842488
Chef(s): Nigel Tabb
Owner(s): Nigel & Melanie Tabb
Cost: Alc £26.50, set price L
£13.50/D £15. ☺ ☺ H/wine £9.95
Times: 12.15-1.45pm/7-late.
Closed Tue, L Mon, Wed-Sat,
2wks Jan & Nov

England

PORTSCATHO
Map 2 SW83
Rosevine Hotel

A pianist plays throughout dinner in this smart, spacious dining room whilst impeccable staff serve course after course of confident, interesting cooking. The style is modern, with influences from Britain and France. 'Excellent' appetisers might include duck mousse on filo tartlet or smoked salmon with quail's eggs. Flavours are skilfully (sometimes surprisingly) combined, as in a starter of French onion and cider soup or a main course of sea bass cooked with herbs to bring out its 'tremendous flavour'.

TR2 5EW
Tel: 01872 580206
Fax: 01872 580230
e info@makepeacehotels.co.uk
Chef(s): Keith Makepeace/
Didier Bienaime
Owner(s): The Makepeace Family
Cost: Alc £20, set price L £20/D £30.
☺ H/wine £15
Times: Noon-3pm/7.15-9.30pm.
Closed Nov-Feb (open for Xmas)
Additional: Sunday L. Bar food L.
Children welcome
Seats: 50. Jacket and tie preferred
Style: Classic
Smoking: No smoking in dining room
Accommodation: 17 rooms (17 en suite) ★ ★ ★
Directions: Off A3078, hotel signed on R, 2 miles after Ruan High Lanes

RUAN HIGH LANES
Map 2 SW93
The Hundred House   NEW

Expect tablecloths and cushions in this homely country house where unfussy, English food is the order the day. The setting is peaceful and pretty, whilst the menu makes good use of local produce, including Cornish new potatoes, local meats, fresh fish from Mevagissey and, of course, clotted cream.

TR2 5JR
Tel: 01872 501336
Fax: 01872 501151
Chef(s): Kitty Eccles
Owner(s): Mr & Mrs J M Eccles
Cost: Alc £25, set price D £25.
H/wine £10
Times: Dinner only, at 7.30pm.
Closed Nov-Feb
Additional: Children 8yrs+.
Vegetarian by request only
Seats: 24. Jacket and tie preferred
Style: Modern Country-house
Smoking: No smoking in dining room
Accommodation: 10 rooms (10 en suite) ★ ★
Directions: On A3078, 4 miles after Tregony on R

ST AUSTELL
Map 2 SX05
Carlyon Bay Hotel

Renowned for its leisure facilities and set in 250 acres of grounds, this hotel continues to have a loyal following. The

Sea Road, Carlyon Bay, PL25 3RD
Tel: 01726 812304
Fax: 01726 814938

restaurant makes the most of its cliff top position, offering superb views across the bay. Typical dishes include noisette of English lamb with tomato and rosemary or roast beef with red wine and tarragon jus. Service is formal and efficient.

 info@carlyonbay.co.uk
Chef(s): Paul Leakey
Owner(s): PR Brend Hoteliers Ltd.
Cost: Alc £24, set price L £12/D £24.
☺ ☺ H/wine £9.75
Times: 12.30-2pm/7-9pm
Additional: Sunday L. Bar food.
Children welcome
Seats: 120. Private dining room 60.
Jacket and tie preferred
Style: Classic, Traditional
Smoking: Air conditioning
Civil licence: 150
Accommodation: 73 rooms (72 en suite) ★ ★ ★ ★
Directions: A390 towards St Austell; from town follow Charlestown then Carlyon Bay/Crinnis. Hotel at end of Sea Road

---

ST IVES   Map 2 SW54

Carbis Bay Hotel

Overlooking the sea, the spacious dining room has a traditional atmosphere. The menu combines the traditional, such as pheasant consommé with julienne vegetables, with the modern, in grilled open mushrooms with sweet peppers and bacon in a curry sabayon. Locally caught fish also features as in braised brill with orange and basil sauce and, for dessert, try white chocolate and champagne terrine.

Smoking: No smoking in dining room
Accommodation: 35 rooms (35 en suite) ★ ★ ★
Directions: Telephone for directions

Carbis Bay, TR26 2NP
Tel: 01736 795311
Fax: 01736 797677
 carisbayhotel@talk21.com
Cost: Alc £30, set price D £24. ☺
H/wine £9.95
Times: Dinner only, 6-8.30pm
Additional: Bar food L
Seats: 120
Style: Classical, French

Garrack Hotel

Burthallan Lane, Higher Ayr,
TR26 3AA
Tel: 01736 796199
Fax: 01736 798955
 garrack@accuk.co.uk
Chef(s): Ben Reeve
Owner(s): Michael, Stephen & France Kilby

This family owned hotel stands in two acres of grounds overlooking Porthmeor beach. The traditional style dining room stretches into a bright conservatory and offers plenty of lovely views. The lengthy menu is full of international flavours but makes good use of local ingredients including lamb (roasted and served with a crispy red onion and garlic pudding), Dover Sole (baked and topped with white crab meat and garlic

ST IVES *Continued*   Map 2 SW54

crouton crust) and at least four different lobster dishes. Finish with a home-made dessert such as ice cream made to the chef's own recipe. The smart staff provide genuinely friendly service.

Style: Classic, informal
Smoking: No smoking in dining room
Accommodation: 18 rooms (18 en suite) ★ ★ ★
Directions: Follow signs for 'Porthmeor Beach and Car Parks'

Cost: *Alc* £26, set price D £23.50. ☺
H/wine £8.97
Times: Dinner only, at 7pm
Additional: L by arrangement only.
Bar food. Children welcome
Seats: 48. Jacket and tie preferred

Pedn-Olva Hotel

'Pedn-Olva' means 'lookout on the headland' and has been a registered navigational mark since the 19th century. The Mediterranean style restaurant makes the most of the wonderful sea views. Its daily changing menu includes modern dishes such as pan fried duck breast with cider and honey fumet or oven baked plaice and John Dory on a shellfish cream.

Seats: 80. Private dining room 20
Style: Mediterranean
Smoking: No smoking in dining room
Accommodation: 30 rooms (30 en suite) ★ ★
Directions: Take A30 to Hayle, then A3074 to St Ives. Sharp R at bus station, into railway station car park, down steps to hotel

West Porthminster Beach,
TR26 2EA
Tel: 01736 796222
Fax: 01736 797710
📧 pedn-olvahotel@
cornwall-county.com
Chef(s): Colin Hankin
Owner(s): Mr D London
Cost: *Alc* £23.50, set price L £16/
D £22. ☺ ☺ H/wine £9.95
Times: Noon-2.30pm/6.30-9.30pm.
Additional: Sunday L. Bar food L.
Children welcome

Porthminster Beach Restaurant

Enjoy stunning sea views from this restaurant at the end of Porthminster beach. The décor has a Mediterranean feel, with ceramic tiled floors and modern artwork on whitewashed walls. The equally vibrant menu includes plenty of seafood. Dishes might include grilled cod with wilted spring greens, white wine and bay leaf or Moroccan nut crusted lamb fillet with spiced coriander couscous.

Directions: Telephone for directions

Porthminster, TR26 2EB
Tel: 01736 795352
Fax: 01736 795352
Chef(s): Simon Morgan, Simon Pellow
Cost: *Alc* £28. ☺ ☺ H/wine £9
Times: Noon-4pm/7-10pm.
Additional: Children welcome
Seats: 80
Style: Modern, Mediterranean
Smoking: No smoking in dining room

ST KEYNE   Map 2 SX26

The Old Rectory

Hideaway haven for lovers of good food and rolling English countryside. Peaceful, civilised and intimate the kind of place that you walk into and somehow know that the pan fried loin of local venison will be cooked pretty close to perfection, hot banana soufflé will be fluffy and light with a striking burst of banana. Even details such as the petits fours show careful thought and originality. The wine list also benefits from the personal interest of the proprietor embracing the best of New World offerings and with a choice of nine house wines.

Style: Traditional Country-House
Smoking: No smoking in dining room
Accommodation: 6 rooms (6 en suite) ★ ★
Directions: 3 miles from Liskeard on B3254

PL14 4RL
Tel: 01579 342617
Fax: 01579 342293
📧 savillelyons@freenet.co.uk
Chef(s): Glen Gatland
Owner(s): B Saville, M Lyons
Cost: *Alc* £28, set price D £25-
£28.50. H/wine £9.80
Times: Dinner only, 7.30-9pm.
Closed Dec-Jan
Additional: Children 16yrs+.
Vegetarian by request only
Seats: 16. Jacket and tie preferred

England

ST MARTIN'S   Map 2 SW28

St Martin's on the Isle

A splendid "get away from it all" hotel that continues to impress with its service and quality of cuisine. In the Tean restaurant, adorned with paintings by local artists, prime window seats have views out over the harbour. Following a day of relaxation or

Lower Town, TR25 0QW
Tel: 01720 422092
Fax: 01720 422298
e stay@stmartinshotel.co.uk
Chef(s): Stuart Eddy
Owner(s): Peter Sykes
Cost: Set price D £35
Times: Noon-2pm/7-9pm.
Closed Nov-Mar
Additional: Bar food L.
Children 12yrs+
Seats: 60
Smoking: No smoking in dining room
Civil licence: 60
Accommodation: 30 rooms (30 en suite) ★ ★ ★

walking, dinner chosen from a nightly-changing menu has an understated style typical of the island's character. Complex dishes might include venison medallion with salsify and foie gras ravioli followed by poached turbot fillet on asparagus mousse with mushroom and scallop cappuccino sauce. Dishes recommended for those preferring more simple food are clearly marked - perhaps fresh grilled sardine fillets or local crab soup followed by chicken cocotte with thyme gravy. There are some elaborate marriages in the flavour of desserts such as red-currant and blueberry tartlet with lavender crème brûlée. Wines are spot on, with a fine reserve list of French vintages.

Directions: By helicopter or steamship from Penzance to St Mary's. Flights from Bristol, Exeter, Newquay or Land's End. Then 25-min launch transfer to St Martin's

ST MARY'S   Map 2 SW28

Star Castle

Once the officers' mess of this 16th-century castle, this dining room retains a huge fireplace, bare stone walls and a beamed ceiling. The menu has an international feel, offering dishes such as Moroccan lamb, stuffed peppers with ratatouille or sirloin of beef with a sun dried tomato and tarragon crust.

Seats: 95. Jacket and tie preferred
Style: Traditional, Country-House
Smoking: No smoking in dining room
Accommodation: 34 rooms (34 en suite) ★ ★ ★
Directions: Flights available from Lands End, Plymouth, Exeter, Bristol & Southampton. Helicopter or ferry from Penzance. Hotel taxi meets all guests from airport or quay

The Garrison, TR21 0JA
Tel: 01720 423342/422317
Fax: 01720 422343
e recept@starcastlescilly.demon. co.uk
Chef(s): Christopher Evans
Owner(s): John & Mary Nicholls
Cost:-£26.50. ☺ H/wine £10.25
Times: Noon-2.30pm/6.30-8.30pm
Closed Mid Oct-Mid Mar
Additional: Bar food L. Children 5yrs+

ST MAWES

Map 2 SW83

Hotel Tresanton

Lower Castle Road, TR2 5DR
Tel: 01326 270055
Telephone for further details

The charming terraces at this restaurant have a distinctly Mediterranean flavour, with their potted palms and wicker chairs looking out across the sea - a popular spot for a pre- or post-dinner drink or coffee. The modern British food also has leanings towards a sunnier clime, and specialises in the fruits of the ocean. A beautifully fresh, chunky carpaccio of tuna with panzarella salad (cubed bread, tomatoes, olives and garlic) hit the spot recently, while chargrilled pigeon with celeriac remoulade was succulent and simple. Roast suckling pig with crisp crackling, roasted apples, fennel and pumpkin, and roast lemon sole with crushed new potatoes, savoy cabbage and salsa verde were also perfectly-timed main courses using top quality ingredients. Amongst the desserts expect poached nectarine with crème chiboust, and pear crème brûlée. Good espresso and cappuccino.

Idle Rocks Hotel   NEW

Harbour Side, TR2 5AN
Tel: 01326 270771
Fax: 01326 270062
🄴 idlerocks@richardsonhotels.co.uk
Chef(s): Alan Vickops, Mark Griffiths
Owner(s): E K Richardson
Cost: Alc £28.95. ☺ H/wine £14.95
Times: noon-3pm/7-9.35pm.
Additional: Bar food L.
Children welcome at L
Seats: 60. Jacket and tie preferred
Style: Classic, French
Smoking: No smoking in dining room
Accommodation: 28 rooms (28 en suite) ★★★
Directions: Telephone for directions

Fantastic location, overlooking the quayside to the sea beyond. This is Modern English cuisine featuring excellent local fish and seafood from nearby Falmouth on a daily changing menu. Elaborate descriptions may hint at a slight tendency to over-

embellish such excellent raw materials, but in fact the basics are done well (an excellent fillet of sea bass for instance). A good range of in-house breads gets things off on the right note. Pan-fried lamb's liver served with grain mustard, potato purée and roasted shallots with rosemary jus feature amongst the starters, once again making use of excellent local produce. A relatively formal and restrained atmosphere.

Rising Sun Hotel

TR2 5DJ
Tel: 01326 270233
Fax: 01326 270198
🄴 therisingsun@btclick.com
Chef(s): Ann Long
Owner(s): Mr R J Milan
Cost: Set price D £24.50. ☺ ☺
H/wine £10.50

Popular with artists and the yachting fraternity, the pretty harbour of St Mawes is the perfect setting for this charming, convivial hotel. The bar and brasserie are a focal point of village life, offering an imaginative daily menu that makes good use of local seafood. Dishes might include roast cod on vegetable casserole or fillet steak with sherry and cream.

Seats: 50. Jacket and tie preferred
Style: Modern Country-House
Smoking: No smoking in dining room
Accommodation: 9 rooms (9 en suite) ★★
Directions: On harbour front

Times: Noon-2pm/7-9pm. Closed L
Mon-Sat, 1 month from 10 Jan
Additional: Sunday L. Bar food.
Children 8yrs+

ST MELLION   Map 2 SX36

St Mellion International

A purpose built hotel, golfing and leisure complex surrounded by 140 acres of land and two 18-hole golf courses. The restaurant offers an innovative menu that makes good use of local specialist suppliers. Dishes might include roast Barbary duck with stir-fried vegetables, toasted sesame seeds and teryaki dressing or fillet of Cornish beef with Stilton mousseline, red cabbage and a Madeira jus.

Style: Traditional, Formal
Smoking: No smoking in dining room; Air conditioning
Civil licence: 120
Accommodation: 39 rooms (39 en suite) ★★★
Directions: On A388 about 4 miles N of Saltash

PL12 6SD
Tel: 01579 351351
Fax: 01579 350537
✉ stmellion@americangolfuk.com
Chef(s): Ian Crook
Cost: Alc £30, set price L £14/D £25.
☺ ☺ H/wine £10.95
Times: Noon-2pm/7-9.30pm.
Closed L Mon-Sat, Xmas, New Year
Additional: Sunday L. Bar food L.
Children welcome
Seats: 60. Private dining room.
Jacket and tie preferred

TALLAND BAY   Map 2 SX25

Talland Bay Hotel

Quiet and refined, this hotel dining room is characterised by oak panelling, log fires and, at night, by candlelight. In the day substitute beautiful sea views. Seafood is a feature, including fresh lobster and crab available at 24 hours' notice, alongside the likes of roast rack of Cornish lamb. Trad service is provided by attentive staff.

Style: Traditional Country-House
Smoking: No smoking in dining room
Accommodation: 22 rooms (22 en suite) ★★★
Directions: From Plymouth take A38 to Looe, then towards Polperro. 1mile ignoring 1st sign for Talland Bay, a further mile to crossroads, follow sign for hotel

PL13 2JB
Tel: 01503 272667
Fax: 01503 272940
✉ tallandbay@aol.com
Chef(s): Mathew Read
Owner(s): Mr & Mrs B Rosier
Cost: Alc £33.50, set price L £12.50/D £23. ☺ ☺ H/wine £11
Times: 12.30-2pm/7.30-9pm.
Closed Jan
Additional: Bar food L. Children welcome
Seats: 40

TINTAGEL   Map 2 SX08

Trebrea Lodge

18th-century manor house with stunning views over Tintagel and the Cornish coastline. Decorated and furnished in period style, the dining room is oak panelled and candlelit, with linen covered tables. The set dinner menu (no choices) might include cream of artichoke soup followed by sea trout with Hollandaise sauce.

Style: Classic, Country-House
Smoking: No smoking in dining room
Accommodation: 7 rooms (7 en suite) ★★
Directions: From centre of Tintagel take B3263 towards Bocastle. Turn R at RC church and R at top of Trenale Lane

Trenale, PL34 0HR
Tel: 01840 770410
Fax: 01840 770092
Chef(s): Sean Devlin
Owner(s): John Charlick & Sean Devlin
Cost: Set price D £24. ☺
H/wine £9.75
Times: Dinner only, 8-10pm.
Closed Jan
Additional: Children 12yrs+.
Vegetarian by request only
Seats: 14

TRESCO

Map 2 SW17

Island Hotel

A magnificent island setting and stunning gardens are just two of many reasons for visiting this splendid hotel. Local fish and shellfish are staples on the regularly changing menus, and spectacular sea views are sure to enhance any meal in the pleasant sunny restaurant.

TR24 0PU
Tel: 01720 422883
Fax: 01720 423008
Telephone for further details

New Inn

Dazzlingly bright restaurant with paintings of sun drenched gardens hopefully reflecting the views from the window (well at least they can guarantee sun of some sort). An eclectic, modern menu might include mains of poached wild Cornish sea bass, or baked avocado filled with ratatouille niçoise. Some enterprising desserts have included fresh strawberries set in Champagne jelly with black pepper and vanilla ice cream.

Style: Modern
Smoking: No smoking in dining room
Accommodation: 14 rooms (14 en suite) ★ ★
Directions: 250yds from the harbour (private island, contact hotel for details)

TR24 0QQ
Tel: 01720 422844
Fax: 01720 423200
📧 newinn@tresco.co.uk
Chef(s): Craig Fowler
Owner(s): Mr R Dorrien-Smith
Cost: Alc £26.50, set price D £26.50. H/wine £10.50
Times: Dinner only, 7-8.30pm
Additional: Bar food. Children welcome
Seats: 40

TRURO

Map 2 SW84

Alverton Manor

Formerly a convent, this impressive sandstone property stands in six acres of grounds, within easy walking distance of the city centre. Stylish public areas include the former chapel (now a function room), a library, and, of course, the elegant restaurant. Here the à la *carte* and fixed price menus offer a familiar

selection of classics and international style dishes. Starters could include home made tomato soup or strips of chicken and stir fried vegetables in oriental sauce, whilst main courses might feature chargrilled steak with a rösti and stilton sauce or oven baked salmon with Mediterranean salsa.

Tregolls Road, TR1 1ZQ
Tel: 01872 276633
Fax: 01872 222989
📧 reception@alvertonmanor co.uk
Chef(s): Robert Brandreth, Mark Oldham
Owner(s): Mr M Sagin
Cost: Alc £30, set price L from £7.95/ D £23.50. ☺ ☺ H/wine £10
Times: 11.45am-1.45pm/7-9.30pm
Additional: Sunday L. Children welcome
Seats: 50. Private dining room 120. Jacket and tie preferred
Style: Traditional, Country-house
Smoking: No smoking in dining room
Civil licence: 120
Accommodation: 34 rooms (34 en suite) ★ ★ ★
Directions: From Truro by-pass, take A39 to St Austell. Just past church on L

England

VERYAN
Map 2 SW93

Nare Hotel

Carne Beach, TR2 5PF
Tel: 01872 501279
Fax: 01872 501856
Telephone for further details

Care and courtesy in the best country house traditions are part of the package at this delightful seaside hotel. Another major attraction is the traditionally-based cuisine which includes superb local seafood (the lobster comes highly recommended). The restaurant overlooks the ocean on three sides, and the fiercely-loyal clientele rightly appreciate both the views and the cooking. Successful dishes have included timbale of crab with coriander and pesto, and duckling with orange-infused jus ('at long last, duck cooked exactly as it should be!'). Silver service, desserts from the trolley, and several château-bottled clarets and good glasses.

Directions: Through village passing New Inn on L, continue 1 mile to sea

CUMBRIA

ALSTON
Map 12 NY74

Lovelady Shield House

CA9 3LF
Tel: 01434 381203
Fax: 01434 381515
Telephone for further details

Set high in the Pennines, a charming hotel in four acres of natural grounds with a trout stream. The kitchen seeks out good local produce for the daily-changing menu, with limited choice including pot of spiced Cornish crab with feta cheese, roasted loin of Mansergh Hall lamb, and French treacle tart with crème fraîche.

 Indicates a restaurant that has told us that 50% or more of their ingredients are organically sourced

Prices quoted in the guide are for guidance only and are subject to change without notice

AMBLESIDE

Map 7 NY30

Drunken Duck Inn

Inventive food in a busy pub restaurant. The building dates back over 400 years, and the log fires and oak beams define the

atmosphere. While the restaurant is more formal than the bar, the food is the same in both - perhaps lightly poached langoustines with lemon, garlic and coriander, and noisettes of lamb with wonderful parsnip dauphinoise.

Barngates, LA22 0NG
Tel: 015394 36347
Fax: 015394 36781
e info@drunkenduckinn.co.uk
Chef(s): Nick Foster
Owner(s): Stephanie Barton
Cost: *Alc* £23. ☺ ☺ H/wine £10.50
Times: Noon-2.30pm/6-9pm.
Closed 25 Dec
Additional: Sunday L. Bar food.
Children welcome
Seats: 42
Style: Modern & Traditional
Smoking: No smoking in dining room
Accommodation: 11 rooms (11 en suite) ♦♦♦♦
Directions: Take A592 from Kendal, follow signs for Hawkshead, in 2.5miles sign for inn on R. 1 mile up hill

Fisherbeck Hotel

This homely hotel enjoys lovely views of Loughrigg and the surrounding fells. The dining room offers a varied, well-priced menu which makes good use of local ingredients. A meal might include smoked venison terrine with plum chutney followed by honey glazed duck breast with red cabbage, crushed potatoes, beetroot and orange bouillabaisse.

Style: Modern & Traditional
Smoking: No smoking in dining room
Accommodation: 18 rooms (18 en suite) ★★
Directions: Telephone for directions

Lake Road, LA22 0DH
Tel: 015394 33215
Fax: 015394 33600
Chef(s): Joe Hargreaves
Owner(s): Joe Hargreaves
Cost: Set price D £21.95. ☺ ☺
H/wine £8.95
Times: Dinner only, 7pm-late.
Closed 26 Dec for 4 wks
Additional: Sunday L. Bar food.
Children 5yrs+
Seats: 44

Nanny Brow Country House

Elegant décor and beautiful lakeland views are matched-up with exquisitely presented and locally sourced dishes. Surroundings and service may be traditional but this is exciting modern cooking. Risotto of fresh crab can be followed by seared salmon with garden vegetables and a fresh pea and truffle sauce, or alternatively, lamb sourced from the owner's own flock of Romney sheep. A special meal might be rounded off with a nougat glace in the company of an excellent, tangy passion fruit sorbet. Great petits fours too.

Directions: 1.5m from Ambleside on A593 towards Coniston

Clappersgate, LA22 9NF
Tel: 015394 32036
Fax: 015394 32450
Telephone for further details

Regent Hotel

A welcoming holiday hotel situated close to Waterhead Bay.
The contemporary style dining room overlooks the award-
winning flower courtyard and offers imaginative, modern dishes
such as cod fillet with clam, shallot and celery fricassée and
poached egg or corn fed guinea fowl with blood orange,
oregano and panchetta casserole and roasted root vegetables.

Additional: Bar food L. Children 6yrs+
Seats: 60. **Style:** Modern.
Smoking: No smoking in dining room
Accommodation: 30 rooms (30 en suite) ★★★
Directions: 1 mile S of Ambleside at Waterhead Bay

Waterhead Bay, LA22 0ES
Tel: 015394 32254
Fax: 015394 31474
e info@regentlakes.co.uk
Chef(s): Michael Wilson
Owner(s): Vogue Leisure Ltd.
Cost: Set price D £19.50-£21.50. ☺
H/wine £11.95
Times: Noon-2pm/7-9pm.
Closed Xmas

APPLEBY-IN-WESTMORLAND   Map 12 NY62

Appleby Manor
Country House   NEW

Family-run hotel providing a true country house dining
experience, yet in a relaxed environment. The abundance of
malt whiskies may be reason enough to visit, but the views of
the Cumbrian Fells from the oak panelled dining room and
satisfying food make the trip really enjoyable. Locally
influenced dishes include Wensleydale cheese soufflé and
braised shank of Dales lamb.

Style: Country-House
Smoking: No smoking in dining room
Accommodation: 30 rooms (30 en suite) ★★★
Directions: From M6 J40 take A66 for Scotch Corner. (12 miles)
Take turn for Appleby. Manor 1.5 miles on the R

Roman Road, CA16 6JB
Tel: 017683 51571
Fax: 017683 52888
e reception@applebymanor.co.uk
Chef(s): David Farrar
Owner(s): Dunbobbin Family
Cost: Alc £25, set price L £14.50. ☺
☺ H/wine £13.95
Times: Noon-2pm/7pm-9pm
Additional: Sunday L. Children
welcome
Seats: 65. Private dining room 20

Tufton Arms

Classic cooking allows the ingredients to speak for themselves
in this smart conservatory restaurant. The lunch menu includes
fish, char-grilled meats, pasta and vegetarian options, whilst the
evening menu delivers expertly done favourites such as
'unmissable' sautéed chicken livers, grilled Dover sole or roast
rack of lamb with red onion marmalade.

Market Square, CA16 6XA
Tel: 017683 51593
Fax: 017683 52761
e info@tuftonarmshotel.co.uk
Chef(s): David Milsom
Owner(s): Mr W D Milsom
Cost: Set price D £23. ☺ ☺
H/wine £9.95
Times: Noon-2pm/7-9pm.
Additional: Sunday L. Bar food.
Children welcome
Seats: 75. Private dining room 100
Style: Traditional
Civil licence: 100
Accommodation: 21 rooms (21 en
suite) ★★★
Directions: In centre of Appleby on
B6260, 12 miles from M6 J38

England

BASSENTHWAITE
Map 11 NY23

Armathwaite Hall

CA12 4RE
Tel: 017687 76551
Fax: 017687 76220
e reservations@armathwaite-hall.com
Chef(s): Kevin Dowling
Cost: Alc £45, set price L £17.95/ D £36.95. H/wine £14
Times: 12.30-1.45pm/7.30-9.30pm.
Additional: Sunday L. Bar food L. Children welcome
Seats: 100. Private dining room 25. Jacket and tie preferred
Style: Country-house, Traditional
Smoking: No smoking in dining room
Civil licence: 100

An impressive 17th-century mansion that stands amid 400 acres of parkland in the shadow of Skiddaw and was described by Hugh Walpole as "perfect and irresistible" and retains its timeless appeal in panelled day-rooms with splendid open fires. Serious food options tend to be confined to the six-course, fixed price dinner: king prawns with tropical fruit salsa, beef consommé, fish courses such as salmon with anchovies and caviar, then perhaps fillet steak topped with seared scallops. Light chocolate truffle cake topped with a coffee sabayon mousse precedes strong, flavourful coffee and petits fours. Well-supervised, attentive service.

Accommodation: 42 rooms (42 en suite) ★ ★ ★ ★
Directions: From M6 J40 take A66 to Keswick then A591 towards Carlisle. Turn L by Castle Inn, 8miles to hotel

BORROWDALE
Map 11 NY21

Borrowdale Gates Country House

CA12 5UQ
Tel: 017687 77204
Fax: 017687 77254
e hotel@borrowdale-gates.com
Chef(s): Michael Heathcote
Owner(s): Mr & Mrs T Parkinson

Classic Lake District dining, mixing trad service, a well-dressed dining room and panoramic views of the lake. The four or five-course fixed-price dinner has dishes rotating on a nightly basis. The selected main course came together well, a dish of pan-

England

fried escalope of calves' liver set on a haggis potato purée with red onion tarte tatin, grilled pancetta and Madeira jus. The impressive menu of beautifully kept cheeses is well worth considering as an alternative or in addition to dessert.

Smoking: No smoking in dining room
Accommodation: 29 rooms (29 en suite) ★ ★ ★
Directions: B5289 from Keswick after 4 miles turn R over bridge to Grange. Hotel 400yds on R

Cost: Set price L £15.75/D £32.50.
☺ H/wine £13.50
Times: 12.15-1.30pm/7-8.45pm.
Closed Jan
Additional: Sunday L. Bar food L.
Children 7yrs+
Seats: 60. Jacket and tie preferred
Style: Country-house

BRAMPTON

Map 12 NY56

Farlam Hall

Hallbankgate, CA8 2NG
Tel: 016977 46234
Fax: 016977 46683
e farlamhall@dial.pipex.com
Chef(s): Barry Quinion
Owner(s): Quinion & Stevenson families
Cost: Set price D £32.50.
H/wine £13.75
Times: Dinner only, 8-8.30pm.
Closed 25-30 Dec
Additional: Children 5yrs+
Seats: 40. Private dining room 20.
Jacket and tie preferred
Style: Traditional, Country-house
Smoking: No cigars
Accommodation: 12 rooms (12 en suite) ★ ★ ★
Directions: On A689, 2.5miles SE of town. Not in Farlam Village

This family run country house dates back as far as 1428 and stands in extensive landscaped grounds. Lovingly restored throughout, the dining room retains plenty of imposing elegance, with huge windows looking over Victorian gardens to the ornamental lake. The menu offers a good balance of classics (beef Wellington; roasted pheasant with chestnut and onion stuffing) and internationally influenced dishes such as Lancashire guinea fowl pan fried with Chinese five spice and served on sweet potato mash with a plum and ginger sauce. A formal but friendly restaurant providing an authentic English country house experience.

CARLISLE

Map 11 NY35

Magenta's

18 Fisher Street, CA3 8RH
Tel: 01228 546363
Fax: 01228 546363
Chef(s): Chris & Paul Taylor
Owner(s): Chris & Paul Taylor, Alison Watkin
Cost: Alc £24.50, set price D £19. ☺
H/wine £12.95
Times: Dinner only, 7-9.30pm.
Closed Sun-Mon. Summer holiday closure
Additional: Children welcome
Seats: 32
Style: Minimalist, Modern

CARLISLE *Continued*
Map 11 NY35   *Magenta's*

Real excitement, genuine flair and a contemporary feel to this basement restaurant that offers such rare delights as crispy pig trotters (stuffed with chicken and wild mushrooms). Descend through alley and steps into the white washed, arched cellar space to encounter tender rib-eye of beef with a sauce of lip-smacking braised oxtail, crisp fillet of sea bass with ratatouille and squid rings and a lively lemon tart. Attention to details such as the excellent bread is worthy of additional praise.

Smoking: No smoking in dining room
Directions: M6 J44 – Carlisle city centre roundabout take 3rd exit and 1st L. R at box junction. Follow road around onto Fisher St; restaurant on L

CARTMEL
Map 7 SD37

Aynsome Manor Hotel

An elegant old manor house with views of the Norman priory, meadows and woods. The menu changes daily and makes good use of local seasonal produce: a meal might include smoked salmon and Cornish crab fishcakes followed by pan fried Cartmel pheasant breast wrapped in Cumbrian air dried ham and served with a pear and Calvados gravy.

Style: Country-House
Smoking: No smoking in dining room
Accommodation: 12 rooms (12 en suite) ★ ★
Directions: Leave A590 signed Cartmel. Hotel is 0.5 mile N of Cartmel village on R

LA11 6HH
Tel: 015395 36653
Fax: 015395 36016
e info@aynsomemanorhotel.co.uk
Chef(s): Nicholas Stopford
Owner(s): P A Varley
Cost: Set price L £14/D £19-£23.
☺ ☺ H/wine £11.50
Times: L at 1pm/7-8.30pm.
Closed L Mon-Sat, D Sun (ex residents), 2-28 Jan
Additional: Sunday L. Children 5yrs+
Seats: 28. Jacket and tie preferred

Uplands Hotel

The natural charm of Tom and Diana Peters allied to the stylish, relaxed country house setting makes this a pretty irresistible package. The simple, honest cooking isn't designed to dazzle but with consistent use of good quality ingredients and intelligent cooking, it is likely to leave you quietly impressed. Typical of the style might be fresh langoustine tails in a pleasingly light, chive cream sauce and supremely tender loin of lamb might come with a caper jus. Dessert could include a chocolate mousse with Grand Marnier. The wine list covers most bases and is fairly marked-up.

Accommodation: 5 rooms (5 en suite) ♦♦♦♦♦
Directions: 1 mile up road signed Grange opposite Pig & Whistle pub in Cartmel

Haggs Lane, LA11 6HD
Tel: 015395 36248
Fax: 015395 36848
e uplands@kencomp.net
Chef(s): Tom Peter
Owner(s): Tom & Diana Peter
Cost: Set price L £16/D £29.50.
H/wine £11.90
Times: 12.30 for 1pm/7.30 for 8pm.
Closed Mon, L Tue-Wed, Jan-Feb
Additional: Sunday L. Children 8yrs+
Seats: 28. Jacket and tie preferred
Style: Modern, Country-house
Smoking: No smoking in dining room

CROOKLANDS   Map 7 SD58

Crooklands Hotel

A charming, quirky hotel whose interior includes bare stone walls and exposed beams. The Hayloft restaurant is crammed full of farming memorabilia and fascinating curios - the perfect environment in which to enjoy a traditional style menu. Dishes include favourites such as bangers and mash, Irish stew and sirloin steak.

Style: English, European
Smoking: No-smoking area; Air conditioning
Accommodation: 30 rooms (30 en suite) ★ ★ ★
Directions: 1.5 miles from M6 J36, 4 miles from Kendal on A65

LA7 7NW
Tel: 015395 67432
Fax: 015395 67525
e crooklands_hotel@postmaster.co.uk
Chef(s): Colin Scott
Owner(s): Mr & Mrs Connor
Cost: Alc £20. ☺ H/wine £9.95
Times: Dinner only, 7-9pm.
Closed Sun-Mon, 26 Dec
Additional: Sunday L. Bar food L.
Children welcome
Seats: 50. Private dining room 80

CROSTHWAITE   Map 11 SD49

The Punchbowl Inn

LA8 8HR
Tel: 015395 68237
Fax: 015395 68875
e enquiries@punchbowl.fsnet.co.uk
Chef(s): Steven Doherty
Owner(s): Mrs Doherty
Cost: Alc £20, set price L £10.95.
☺ ☺ H/wine £12
Times: Noon-2pm/6-9pm.
Closed Mon, D Sun,
Nov-Mar, 25 Dec
Additional: Sunday L. Children
welcome
Seats: 60
Style: Traditional, country pub
Smoking: No smoking in dining room
Accommodation: 3 rooms
Directions: M6 J36 (Kendal). L onto
A540 (Barrow). R at Jaguar dealership
and follow A5074 until Crosthwaite
sign. Top of lane on L next to church

More of a restaurant than a pub, this 17th-century coaching inn features low beamed ceilings and three open fires. The modern menu draws inspiration from around the world, with dishes ranging from seared salmon fillet with whole wheat noodles and a soy, ginger and spring onion sauce to braised shank of lamb on grain mustard mashed potatoes with a minted lemon sauce. Equally impressive desserts might include spiced poached pear or warm lemon cake with home-made lemon curd and blackcurrant sorbet. The relaxing atmosphere is enhanced by a team of attentive, friendly staff.

GRANGE-OVER-SANDS   Map 7 SD47

Clare House

Lakeland hotel dining room, of the crocheted tablemat and silver cutlery variety, offering stunning views and a fixed-price five-course menu. Simple successes have included a warm salad of mixed leaves, crispy pancetta and sautéed Jerusalem artichokes and turkey saltimbocca with sweet potato mash and a good cranberry and orange relish. Sticky toffee pudding with home-made butterscotch ice cream has been highlighted.

Accommodation: 17 rooms (16 en suite) ★
Directions: From M6 take A590 then B5277 to Grange-over-Sands Park. Road follows the shore line. Hotel on L

Park Road, LA11 7HQ
Tel: 015395 33026
e ajread@clarehouse.fsbusiness.co.uk
Chef(s): Andrew Read, Mark Johnston
Owner(s): Mr & Mrs D S Read
Cost: Set price D £22.50. ☺
H/wine £10
Times: Dinner only, 6.45-7.15pm.
Closed Dec-Apr
Additional: Children welcome
Seats: 32. **Style:** Classic
Smoking: No smoking in dining room

England

GRASMERE

Map 11 NY30

Gold Rill Hotel

With its Lake District location and reputation for steamed puddings, the Gold Rill Hotel has a winning formula. Formal service accompanies a traditional four-course menu with all the extras for which regulars clamber. The food is generally appealing, but the kitchen's strength lies in simple dishes. Try favourites like the sugar-baked ham and steamed mincemeat roly-poly.

Style: Modern, Traditional
Smoking: No smoking in dining room; Air conditioning
Accommodation: 28 rooms (28 en suite) ★ ★ ★
Directions: M6 J36 then A590/A591: Red Bank Road is in centre of village opposite St Oswalds Church. Hotel 200yds on L

Red Bank Road, LA22 9PU
Tel: 015394 35486
Fax: 015394 35486
e enquiries@gold-rill.com
Chef(s): Ian Thompson
Owner(s): Paul Jewsbury
Cost: Set price D £22
Times: Dinner only, 7.30-8.30pm.
Closed 2 wks before Xmas. 2 wks mid Jan
Additional: Bar food L. Children welcome. Vegetarian by request only
Seats: 60. Jacket and tie preferred

Grasmere Hotel

Attentive and hospitable service creates a good atmosphere at this family run hotel. Set in secluded gardens beside the River Rothay, its attractive dining room offers pretty views and a menu full of carefully prepared favourites such as Guinea fowl supreme or roast beef with Yorkshire pudding and pan gravy.

Seats: 24. Private dining room 24. Jacket and tie preferred
Style: Traditional
Smoking: No smoking in dining room; Air conditioning
Accommodation: 12 rooms (12 en suite) ★ ★
Directions: Off A591 close to village centre

Broadgate, LA22 9TA
Tel: 015394 35277
Fax: 015394 35277
e enquiries@grasmerehotel.co.uk
Chef(s): Gretchen Riley
Owner(s): Mr P Riley
Cost: Set price D £15-£18.50. ☺
H/wine £10
Times: Dinner only, 7-8.30pm.
Closed Jan
Additional: Bar food D.
Children 9 yrs+

The Jumble Room Café NEW

Langdale Road, LA22 0QF
Tel: 015394 35188
Fax: 015394 36088
e thejumbleroom@which.net
Chef(s): Chrissy Hill, Trudy Clay, Paul McDougal
Owner(s): Andrew & Chrissy Hill
Cost: Alc £20 H/wine £8.95
Times: 10.30am-5pm/6.30-10.30pm.
Closed Tue, D Mon & Wed, 25-26 Dec
Additional: Sunday L.
Children welcome
Seats: 28
Style: Bistro, Italian
Smoking: No smoking in dining room
Directions: Telephone for directions

Tiny, bright orange and decorated with everything from soft toys to newspaper cuttings, the Jumble Room is a fun, arty affair. The chatty menu might include Thai chicken salad, mushroom stroganoff, fish and chips or Italian meatballs. Food is mostly organic, as is the interesting selection of wine and beer.

Michael's Nook
Country House Hotel

LA22 9RP
Tel: 015394 35496
Fax: 015394 35645
e m-nook@wordsworth-grasmere.
co.uk
Chef(s): Michael Wignall
Owner(s): Mr R Gifford
Cost: Set price L £37.50/D £48.
H/wine £18
Times: 12.30-1pm/7.30-8.30pm.
Additional: Sunday L. Children 7yrs+.
Vegetarian by request only
Seats: 50. Jacket and tie preferred
Style: Classic, Country-house
Smoking: No smoking in dining room
Civil licence: 30
Accommodation: 14 rooms (14 en
suite) ★ ★ ★
Directions: On N Side of Grasmere
from A591, turn uphill at The Swan,
bear L for 400yds

There's no two ways about it, a visit to Michael's Nook is not an experience you forget in a hurry. The fine Victorian country house with its imposing mahogany panelling and wealth of period pieces is the backdrop for some outstanding cooking by Michael Wignall and his team. There is an element of drama at work and proceedings commence in the drawing room where tiny, intricate canapés (guinea fowl samosa, foie gras boudin, goats cheese millefeuille) are served. Their delicacy is a pretty accurate trailer for what's to come with every element of the meal studiously assembled and – as is crucial with such an approach – pinpoint accurate. It is the depth and clarity of flavour that can really make your day though. Michael Wignall sets his sights high and given the level of ambition it is amazing that he rarely slips up. Take for example a starter of generously stuffed ravioli of scallops and lobster with ultra-delicate pasta and plump shellfish or sea bass with an "ecstacy inducing" white bean and truffle foam. Roast quail has come with ravioli of spinach and seared foie gras and lamb with "the most tender" baby artichokes and puy lentils. Take a dessert like lemon assiette (no less than five micro-variations on the lemon theme) and there is a danger of sensory overload. Yes, there is a lot happening on the plate and nine times out of ten that isn't such a good thing. Here we have the exception.

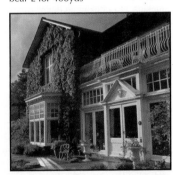

Rothay Garden Hotel

Broadgate, LA22 9RJ
Tel: 015394 35334
Fax: 015394 35723
Telephone for further details

On the edge of an unspoilt Cumbrian village, this Lakeland-stone property is surrounded by typically magnificent views of

GRASMERE *Continued*   Map 11 NY30

the fells. Two large conservatories house the restaurant, and a
miniature sample of each dish is displayed at the entrance.
Highlights of a recent meal included roast fillet of Cumbrian
fell beef with a red wine jus, mushroom and shallot ragout,
Kenyan beans and cocotte potatoes. Other dishes might be
asparagus and spring vegetable feuilleté with chive butter sauce,
cream of vegetable soup, and warm raspberry soufflé with
strawberry compôte. Self-service coffee in the lounge with petit
fours, and an enthusiastic wine list has several glasses.

White Moss House

This traditional Lakeland house (once bought by Wordsworth
for his son) is a haven of relaxation. The dining room looks
onto the front garden, with Rydal Water in the distance. Dishes
make good use of local produce such as Lakeland mallard
(roasted with sage and onion stuffing) or guinea fowl (with Puy
lentils and dry cider). Desserts include nursery style sticky
puddings.

Style: Traditional, Country-House
Smoking: No smoking in dining room
Accommodation: 8 rooms (8 en suite) ★
Directions: On A591 between Grasmere and Ambleside
opposite Rydal Water

Rydal Water, LA22 9SE
Tel: 015394 35295
Fax: 015394 35516
e sue@whitemoss.com
Chef(s): Peter Dixon,
Robert Simpson
Owner(s): Peter & Sue Dixon
Cost: Set price D £30. H/wine £10.95
Times: Dinner only, 8pm.
Closed Sun, Dec & Jan
Additional: Children welcome.
Vegetarian by request only
Seats: 18

Wordsworth Hotel

LA22 9SW
Tel: 015394 35592
Fax: 015394 35765
e enquiry@wordsworth-grasmere.
co.uk
Chef(s): Bernard Warne
Cost: Set price L £19.50-£24.50/
D £31.50-£39.50. ☺ H/wine £14.50
Times: 12.30-2pm/7-9.30pm.
Additional: Sunday L. Bar food L.
Children welcome at L and early
evening
Seats: 65. Private dining room 20.
Jacket and tie preferred
Style: Modern, French
Civil licence: 110

A busy hotel in the heart of Grasmere village, The Wordsworth
stands next to the churchyard in which its namesake is buried.
Decorated throughout in traditional, floral fabrics, it offers a
relaxing atmosphere and lovely Lakeland views. A good
selection of modern and traditional food is served in the
conservatory style restaurant, where a meal might include local
trout ravioli with a chive infused beurre blanc followed by a
main course of Scotch beef with braised red cabbage and a red
wine shallot jus. An elegant setting with attentive service and
relaxing views of the garden.

Accommodation: 37 rooms (36 en suite) ★ ★ ★ ★
Smoking: No smoking in dining room; Air conditioning
Directions: From Ambleside follow A591 N to Grasmere. Hotel
is in town centre next to the church

HAWKSHEAD

Map 7 SD39

Highfield House

This country house hotel enjoys one of the most stunning panoramas in the Lake District. It also has a growing reputation for its simple, honest cooking. A meal in the cheerful dining room might include chicken liver parfait with tomato chutney and Cumberland sauce followed by pan fried sirloin steak with a rich red wine mushroom and tomato sauce.

Smoking: No smoking in dining room
Accommodation: 11 rooms (11 en suite) ★ ★
Directions: From Ambleside take A593 south and turn L at Clappersgate onto B5286 to Hawkshead. Turn R onto B5285, hotel up hill on L

Hawkshead Hill, LA22 0PN
Tel: 015394 36344
Fax: 015394 36793
e rooms@highfield-hawkshead.com
Chef(s): Jason Spedding
Owner(s): Geoff & Kay Todd
Cost: Set price L £18/D £25. ☺ ☺
H/wine £11.50
Times: Noon-2pm/7-9pm.
Additional: Sunday L. Children 7 yrs+
Seats: 22
Style: Modern, Country-house

HOWTOWN

Map 12 NY41

Sharrow Bay

For over half a century the epitome of fine hotel keeping, in a magnificent situation overlooking Lake Ullswater, Sharrow Bay is justly lauded for its traditional Country House values combined with an understated opulence that creates a unique and special environment. The dining-room is pure theatre; part stage-set with lots of gilt and glamour and part floor-show carefully stage-managed with complete professionalism. In well-worked styles that echo the philosophy of "gentle cooking" inspired by the late Francis Coulson, the kitchen produces food of pristine quality that scores highly for being neither overworked nor too elaborate. Terrine of venison, pork and pistachio nuts makes an impressive start with its contrasting textures and bold flavour, followed by a daily soup that might be creamy sweet potato flavoured to perfection. To follow, duck breast marinated in soy sauce, sesame oil and honey provides a touch of the exotic and beef fillet with roasted vegetables is stunningly tender. Francis's Old English Regency syllabub served with Katherine Adair's shortbread hearts serves as a nostalgic way to round off a fine dinner.

Directions: From Pooley Bridge fork right by church towards Howtown. At crossroads turn R and follow lakeside road for 2 miles

Sharrow Bay, CA10 2LZ
Tel: 017684 86301
Fax: 017684 86349
e enquiries@sharrow-bay.com
Chef(s): Johnne Martin & Colin Akrigg
Owner(s): Brian Sack
Cost: Set price L £30-£36.25/ D £47.25. H/wine £15.75
Times: 1 for 1.30pm/8 for 8.30pm. Closed Dec-Mar
Additional: Sunday L. Children 13yrs+. Vegetarian by request only
Seats: 55. Jacket and tie preferred
Style: Classic, Country-house
Smoking: No smoking in dining room; Air conditioning
Civil licence: 35
Accommodation: 26 rooms (23 en suite) ★ ★ ★

England

KENDAL   Map 7 SD59

The Castle Green

The Greenhouse Restaurant offers views of Kendal Castle and the Lakeland Fells from its new conservatory extension. Cooking is modern by design with imaginative combinations making good use of fresh seasonal produce. A fish course of linguini, fresh lobster and langoustine worked well with a roasted red pepper. A rich chocolate marquis with kumquat marmalade was equally well conceived.

Smoking: No smoking in dining room. **Civil licence:** 300
Accommodation: 99 rooms (99 en suite) ★★★
Directions: From M6 J37 to Kendal (5 miles). Hotel 1st on R approaching Kendal

LA9 6RG
Tel: 01539 734000
Fax: 01539 735522
e reception@castlegreen.co.uk
Chef(s): John Adler-Connor
Owner(s): James Alexander
Cost: Set price L £21.95/D £21.95.
☺ H/wine £9.95
Times: Noon-10pm
Additional: Sunday L. Bar food.
Children welcome
Seats: 100
Style: Modern

KESWICK   Map 11 NY22

Dale Head Hall

A 16th-century house surrounded by trees on the shore of Lake Thirlmere. The restaurant is a smart, carpeted room and offers a short but inspiring menu of modern dishes - perhaps goats' cheese and black pepper fondant on basil and onion toast followed by roast chicken breast with rösti, sautéed spinach and chilli jam. A lengthy, well-chosen wine list completes an enjoyable experience.

Style: Country-House
Smoking: No smoking in dining room
Accommodation: 14 rooms (14 en suite) ★★★
Directions: 12 miles from M6 J40, between Keswick and Grasmere

Lake Thirlmere, CA12 4TN
Tel: 017687 72478
Fax: 017687 71070
e onthelakeside@dale-head-hall.
co.uk
Chef(s): Caroline Bonkenburg
Owner(s): Mr & Mrs A Lowe
Cost: Set price D £30
Times: Dinner only, 7.30-8pm.
Closed Jan
Additional: Children 10yrs+.
Vegetarian by request only
Seats: 18. Private dining room 12.
Jacket and tie preferred

Highfield Hotel

Situated in a park with stunning views of the mountains beyond, Highfield Hotel is the epitome of Victorian elegance. The relaxed restaurant offers some surprisingly modern dishes such as venison on a parsnip and potato rösti with beetroot and liquorice sauce. Those with more traditional tastes can request gravy with their main course, or opt for favourites such as sirloin steak.

Seats: 40. **Style:** Classic, Traditional
Smoking: No smoking in dining room
Accommodation: 18 rooms (18 en suite) ★★
Directions: From M6 J40 follow A66 towards Keswick

The Heads, CA12 5ER
Tel: 017687 72508
Fax: 017687 80634
e highfieldkeswick@talk21.com
Chef(s): Ashley Whittaker
Owner(s): Derek & Celia Kitchinsman
Cost: Set price L £12/D £19.50. ☺ ☺
H/wine £9.50
Times: Noon-1.30pm/6-8.30pm.
Closed Dec-Jan (ex Xmas & New Year)
Additional: Sunday L. Bar food L.
Children 8yrs+. Vegetarian by request only

Horse & Farrier Inn

This smart, stylish inn offers value for money and an exciting menu: traditional dishes include roast lamb shank and grilled entrecôte of beef, but the intrepid foodie might be enticed by seared scallops with black pudding or pavé of salmon served on chorizo and wild mushroom casserole. A skilled team ensure that even the complex dishes are a success.

Style: Traditional. **Smoking:** No smoking in dining room
Accommodation: 9 rooms (9 en suite) ★★
Directions: Telephone for directions

Threlkeld, CA12 4SQ
Tel: 017687 79688
Chef(s): Garth Wilson
Owner(s): Jennings Bros Plc
Cost: Alc £25. ☺ ☺ H/wine £8.95
Times: Noon-2pm/6.30-9.30pm.
Additional: Sunday L. Bar food.
Children welcome
Seats: 45

Kings Head

Thirlspot, Thirlmere, CA12 4TN
Tel: 017687 72393
Fax: 017687 72309
Telephone for further details

An elegant dining room at this traditional inn, renowned for its creative handling of fresh local and seasonal produce. The menu provides a clear indication that the chef has a classical background, and this experience is adapted to more modern dishes. The set menu changes daily, offering four choices at each level. Pithivier of duck confit with onion marmalade (delectable) was an example of perfect seasoning and a light touch, and seared Shetland scallops with linguini and coriander beurre blanc combined absolute freshness with careful cooking. Trio of chocolate desserts is an accomplished pudding, and it all comes at reasonable prices.

Underscar Manor

Applethwaite, CA12 4PH
Tel: 017687 75000
Fax: 017687 74904
Telephone for further details

Make your way up the long drive and prepare yourself for some remarkable architecture. A mid-Victorian mansion built in the Italianate style with arched windows and a campanile. The cooking is along fairly modish lines with some Mediterranean influences apparent in dishes like seared tuna (accurately done for once) with sun dried tomatoes and salsa. More traditional dishes too as in pan fried steak of English spring lamb with a mint and port sauce or Barbary duck with a juniper and orange sauce. Amongst the puds, expect the likes of a chocolate and orange mousse gateau with white chocolate and vodka sorbet.

KIRKBY LONSDALE   Map 7 SD68

Hipping Hall   **NEW**

Cowan Bridge, LA6 2JJ
Tel: 015242 71187
Fax: 015242 72452
e hippinghal@aol.com
Chef(s): Jean Skelton
Owner(s): Mr & Mrs Skelton
Cost: Alc £25. ☺ H/wine £11
Times: Dinner only, 6.30-10pm.
Closed Feb
Additional: Children welcome
Seats: 14. Private dining room 12

With luck, non-residents will soon be able to experience a meal in this attractive 15th-century house. Furnished in smart but rustic style, its classic menu has a strong French accent: chicken might come in Chardonnay sauce; steak with red wine and peppercorns. Cowan Bridge is a picturesque setting, famous as the place where the Brontë sisters attended the not so lovely clergy daughters' school.

Style: Country-House
Smoking: No smoking in dining room
Accommodation: 6 rooms (6 en suite) ★
Directions: Telephone for details

England

MUNGRISDALE   Map 11 NY33
The Mill Hotel

CA11 0XR
Tel: 017687 79659
Fax: 017687 79155
Chef(s): Eleanor Quinlan
Owner(s): Mr & Mrs R T Quinlan
Cost: Set price D £27.50. ☺
H/wine £9.75
Times: Dinner only, 7-8pm
Closed Nov-Feb
Additional: Children welcome.
No credit cards accepted
Seats: 20
Style: Country-house
Smoking: No smoking in dining room
Accommodation: 7 rooms (5 en suite)
★
Directions: Mungrisdale is signed on
A66, mid way between Penrith and
Keswick. Hotel 2 miles N of A66

Totally isolated amid the stunning scenery of the North Lakes, this former mill cottage offers plenty of period charm: the interior includes low ceilings, cosy lounges and a plethora of books, antiques and paintings. Dinner includes imaginative dishes such as Jamaican black eye bean hot pot or pan fried sea bass with salsa verdi.

NEAR SAWREY   Map 7 SD39
Sawrey House Country Hotel

LA22 0LF
Tel: 015394 36387
Fax: 015394 36010
e enquiries@sawrey-house.com
Chef(s): Nigel Skinkis
Owner(s): Mr C Whiteside
Cost: Set price D £29.50.
H/wine £11.95
Times: Dinner only, 7.30-8pm.
Closed Jan
Additional: Children 10yrs+.
Vegetarian by request only
Seats: 30
Style: Country-house
Smoking: No smoking in dining room;
Air conditioning

Views from this restaurant are as prettily pastoral as you might expect in the heart of Beatrix Potter country. The chef sticks to the English theme but is not afraid to add a modern flourish. The result is an exciting selection of dishes, all freshly made with real flair. Dinner is a six-course affair, and might include Jerusalem artichoke soup with girolles and a hint of truffle oil, a 'perfect' risotto of peppers, pecorino cheese and gazpacho, and a main course of seared salmon with tarragon and potatoes. The atmosphere is informal and the service well paced but relaxed.

Accommodation: 11 rooms (11 en suite) ♦♦♦♦♦
Directions: From Ambleside A593 S. L at Clappersgate onto B5286 towards Hawkshead then take B5285 towards Sawrey/Ferry. Hotel 1.5 miles on R

NETHER WASDALE   Map 6 NY10

Low Wood Hall

First there is the view - Whinn Rigg and Orton Fell framing a tranquil haven of woodland and landscaped gardens. Happily, the food doesn't pale by comparison, think baked fillet of beautifully fresh turbot with a smoked salmon and basil crust in a light white wine and shallot sauce.

Seats: 30. Private dining room 15
Style: Country-house
Smoking: No smoking in dining room
Accommodation: 12 rooms (12 en suite) ★★
Directions: Exit A595 at Gosforth & bear L for Wasdale, after 3 miles turn R for Nether Wasdale

CA20 1ET
Tel: 019467 26100
Fax: 019467 26111
e reservations@lowwoodhall.co.uk
Chef(s): Frederick Williams
Owner(s): Mr & Mrs A Olney
Cost: Set price D £17.95. ☺
H/wine £10.45
Times: Dinner only, 7-9.30pm.
Closed Sun
Additional: Children welcome

NEWBY BRIDGE   Map 7 SD38

Lakeside Hotel

It's hard to concentrate on pre-dinner drinks when the conservatory looks onto Lake Windermere. Rather simple canapés may do little to distract you from the breathtaking views, but in the main restaurant the menu impresses with its use of local produce in classical dishes such as Graythwaite wood pigeon, or roast Lakeland lamb. A vegetarian menu is available on request.

Style: Classic Country-House
Smoking: No smoking in dining room; Air conditioning
Civil licence: 100
Accommodation: 80 rooms (80 en suite) ★★★★
Directions: M6 J36 follow A590 to Newby Bridge, R over bridge, follow Hawkshead Road for 1 mile

Lakeside, LA12 8AT
Tel: 015395 31207
Fax: 015395 31699
e sales@lakesidehotel.co.uk
Chef(s): Duncan Collinge,
Paul Waring
Owner(s): Mr N R Talbot
Cost: Alc £25, set price L £15-£25/
D £35. ☺ ☺ H/wine £15
Times: Noon-3pm/7-9.30pm.
Additional: Sunday L. Bar food L.
Children welcome
Seats: 70. Private dining room 28.
Jacket and tie preferred

TEBAY   Map 12 NY53

Westmorland Hotel

Breathtaking Lakeland scenery provides the backdrop for this split-level, open-plan restaurant, which has a warm Mediterranean feel. True to theme, the menu offers a mix of modern Southern European dishes and local specialities, utilising mainly local produce. Roasted Mediterranean vegetables feature alongside marinated rump of Lakeland lamb and tomato and spinach risotto tart.

Style: Classic, Traditional
Smoking: No smoking in dining room; Air conditioning
Civil licence: 120
Accommodation: 53 rooms (53 en suite) ★★★

Orton, CA10 3SB
Tel: 015396 24351
Fax: 015396 24354
e westmoorlandhotel@aol.com
Chef(s): Lee Braithwaite
Cost: Alc £22. ☺ H/wine £12.50
Times: Dinner only, 7-9pm
Additional: Bar food. Children welcome
Seats: 120. Private dining room 126

TEMPLE SOWERBY   Map 12 NY62

Temple Sowerby House

An ancient farmhouse used as a trading post before the Knights Templar settled nearby, and now a comfortable hotel with a terrific atmosphere. Candlelit dining is the form, and the

CA10 1RZ
Tel: 017683 61578
Fax: 017683 61958
e stay@temple-sowerby.com

England

cooking is reliably good: pan-fried rib-eye beef , warm vegetable terrine, and steamed salmon with monkfish mousse are made with great care.

Style: Traditional, Country-house
Smoking: No smoking in dining room
Accommodation: 13 rooms (13 en suite) ★ ★ ★
Directions: On A66, 5 miles E of Penrith in village centre

Chef(s): Richard Axford
Owner(s): Paul & Julie Evans
Cost: *Alc* £30. H/wine £14.75
Times: Dinner only, 7-9pm
Seats: 24. Private dining room 30

TROUTBECK   Map 7 NX40

Broadoaks Country House

A lovingly restored Victorian house whose many charms include richly patterned rugs on polished wood floors, real fires and a music room complete with Bechstein piano. The dining room is stunning with its specially made red wallpaper, but despite the historical setting the menu feels modern: dishes might include local partridge roasted with root vegetables and served with spicy raisin couscous.

Style: Modern
Smoking: No smoking in dining room
Civil licence: 60
Accommodation: 12 rooms (12 en suite)
Directions: From Kendal take A591 to Windermere. Then A592 towards Troutbeck. Hotel on R

Bridge Lane, Troutbeck,
LA23 1LA
Tel: 015394 45566
Fax: 015394 88766
e trev@broadoaksF9.co.uk
Chef(s): J Pavelyn, T Baxton
Owner(s): Mr & Mrs T Pavelyn
Cost: *Alc* £32, set price D £35. ☺ ☺
H/wine £11.50
Times: D only, 6.30-8.30pm
Additional: Sunday L. Bar food L.
Children 5 yrs+
Seats: 40. Private dining room 26.
Jacket and tie preferred

Queens Head

An Elizabethan four poster bed serves as the bar and focal point of this old coaching house. Real fires, stone floors and beamed ceilings send the charm rating off the scale. You can dine downstairs or in the old mayor's parlour on the first floor - the menu is the same in both. Expect old favourites (lamb shank served on garlic mash with a selection of 'good, crisp, perfectly seasoned' veg), alongside the odd modern dish such as fillet of pork marinated in soy and ginger, with couscous and a coconut cream.

Smoking: No-smoking area
Accommodation: 15 rooms (15 en suite) ◆◆◆◆
Directions: On A592, approx 2 miles from Windermere

Town Head, Troutbeck,
LA23 1PW
Tel: 015394 32174
Fax: 015394 31938
e enquiries@queensheadhotel.com
Chef(s): Wallace Drumond
Owner(s): M Stewardson & J Sherratt
Cost: *Alc* £18.75, set price L
£15.50/D £15.50. ☺ ☺ H/wine £9.95
Times: Noon-2pm/6.30-9pm.
Closed 25 Dec
Additional: Sunday L. Bar food.
Children welcome

WATERMILLOCK   Map 12 NY42

Leeming House

A stunning location in 20 acres of mature wooded gardens, with the Peak District National Park and Ullswater as a backdrop. The restaurant has a classy feel, full of rich colours and ornate mouldings. The imaginative, European style cooking can lead to some audacious combinations, but the dessert menu is full of happy marriages such as a lovely apricot and almond tart.

CA11 0JJ
Tel: 0870 4008131
Fax: 017684 86443
e heratigehotels_ullswater.
leeming_house@forte-hotels.com
Chef(s): Adam Marks
Owner(s): Heritage Hotels

Cost: Set price L £15-£18/D £29.50.
☺ H/wine £14.95
Times: Noon-2pm/7-9pm.
Additional: Sunday L. Bar food L.
Children welcome
Seats: 60. Private dining room 24
Style: Country-House, Traditional
Smoking: No smoking in dining room
Civil licence: 30
Accommodation: 40 rooms (40 en suite) ★ ★ ★
Directions: M6 J40. 8miles from motorway and Penrith

Old Church Hotel

An idyllic setting on the edge of Lake Ulswater with a dining room that looks out over the gardens, mountains and lake. Daily three course menu offering a choice of simple, freshly prepared dishes. Grilled goats' cheese salad with orange and walnut dressing and sautéed chicken breast with a basil and tomato sauce are typical of the style. Friendly attentive service.

Old Church Bay, CA11 0JN
Tel: 017684 86204
Fax: 017684 86368
Telephone for further details

Rampsbeck Hotel

CA11 0LP
Tel: 017684 86442
Fax: 017684 86688
e enquiries@rampsbeck.fsnet.co.uk
Chef(s): Andrew McGeorge
Owner(s): Mr & Mrs T Gibb
Cost: Set price L £25/D £31.
H/wine £11.25
Times: Noon-1.15pm/7-8.15pm.
Closed 8 Jan-9 Feb
Additional: Sunday L. Bar food L.
Children 7yrs+
Seats: 40. Private dining room 15.
Jacket and tie preferred
Style: Traditional Country-house
Smoking: No smoking in dining room
Accommodation: 20 rooms
(20 en suite) ★ ★ ★

Spectacular views across Ullswater almost in themselves justify a special visit to the elegant and spacious dining-room of this family-run 18th-century country house. Yet even in this context it remains well worthwhile to concentrate on the fine-tuned cooking on the fixed-price lunch and dinner menus that take a no-nonsense approach to quality, fresh local ingredients and presentation. A precisely poached courgette flower with delicate pepper mousse, ratatouille dressing and perfectly seared hand-dived scallops being fairly typical examples. Red cep soup or lemon sorbet may pave the way for main dishes such as fillet of Scottish salmon with asparagus, champagne cream sauce and puréed potatoes or roast veal fillet and sweetbreads with celeriac, galette potato and Madeira sauce. Baked pear wrapped in sable pastry with prune-and-armagnac ice cream, or a contemporary semi-freddo apple brûlée served on shredded macaroon, round off cooking characterised by style and sensitivity.

Directions: M6 J40, A592 to Ullswater, R at lakes edge. Hotel 1.25 miles

England

WINDERMERE

Map 7 SD49

Beech Hill Hotel

Newby Bridge Road,
LA23 3LR
Tel: 015394 42137
Fax: 015394 43745
e beechhill@richardsonhotels.co.uk
Chef(s): Adrian Law
Owner(s): Mr E K Richardson
Cost: Set price L £12.95/D £29.50.
☺ ☺ H/wine £12.95
Times: Noon-2.30pm/7-9.30pm
Additional: Sunday L. Bar food.
Children welcome
Seats: 100. Private dining room 100
Style: Classic, Traditional
Smoking: No smoking in dining room;
Air conditioning
Civil licence: 100
Accommodation: 58 rooms (58 en
suite) ★★★
Directions: On A592, Newby Bridge
4 miles from Windermere

The sofas in the lounge might tempt you to savour drinks, olives and views of Lake Windermere for longer than you planned, but the elegant restaurant will reward you for moving. More lovely views, good service and imaginative cooking complete a memorable experience. Dishes might include roast lemon sole with courgette spaghetti or seared pork with oyster mushrooms and Tarragon jus.

Fayrer Garden House

Lyth Valley Road, Bowness on
Windermere, LA23 3JP
Tel: 015394 88195
Fax: 015394 45986
e lakescene@fayrergarden.com
Chef(s): Edward Wilkinson
Owner(s): Mr & Mrs Garside
Cost: Set price L £13.50/D £24-
£29.95. ☺ ☺ H/wine £12.50
Times: Noon-2pm/7-8.30pm.
Closed L Mon-Sat
Additional: Sunday L. Bar food L.
Children 5yrs+
Seats: 60. Private dining room 20
Style: Modern, Country-house
Smoking: No smoking in dining room;
Air conditioning
Accommodation: 18 rooms (18 en
suite) ★★★
Directions: On A5074, 1 mile from
town centre

A pretty turn of the century country house situated high above the lake away from the hubbub of Bowness. The panelled hall leads into a cosy sitting room and a conservatory restaurant. Richly furnished with high backed chairs, pink clothed tables and Tiffany lamps, it provides lovely views of Lake Windermere and the fells. The menu reveals flair and imagination: a meal might begin with a starter of wild boar and pheasant boudin, followed by herb roasted loin of Cumbrian pork with a filo basket of steamed veg with cider cream sauce.

England

Gilpin Lodge

Crook Road, LA23 3NE
Tel: 015394 88818
Fax: 015394 88058
e hotel@gilpin-lodge.co.uk
Chef(s): Grant Tomkins
Owner(s): John & Christine Cunliffe
Cost: *Alc* £21, set price D £35. ☺
H/wine £12.50
Times: Noon-2.30pm/7-9pm
Additional: Sunday L. Bar food L.
Children 7yrs+
Seats: 55. Private dining room 28
Style: Traditional, Country-house
Smoking: No smoking in dining room
Accommodation: 14 rooms (14 en
suite) ★ ★ ★
Directions: M6 J36 & A590, then
B5284 for 5 miles

Surprisingly spacious and unfailingly elegant within, Victorian Gilpin Lodge, just 100 years old, makes both an ideal touring base and a home-from-home for those wishing to relax in front of an open fire, while its reputation for service and personal attention is legion. In an intimate dining-room comprising three inter-linked rooms four-course menus are changed nightly, providing interesting, creative dishes based on classical concepts in modern combinations. Delicious canapés and home-baked breads form the curtain raiser to multi-choice starters embracing seared scallops with brandade of salmon and herb oil and roast pigeon on creamed baby leeks with ceps and Madeira sauce. Following a choice of soup (pea and broad bean with white truffle that caresses the palette) or ballotine of dressed Scottish salmon, main dishes might be beef fillet, puréed shallots, Savoy cabbage, rösti potato and red wine sauce or roast guinea fowl with thyme and pancetta risotto and game sauce. Desserts can be equally involved, with savouries and a cheese plate as alternatives or supplementary. Daily lunch is a somewhat simpler affair.

Holbeck Ghyll

Holbeck Lane,
LA23 1LU
Tel: 015394 32375
Fax: 015394 34743
e accommodation@holbeck-
ghyll.co.uk
Chef(s): David McLauglin
Owner(s): David & Patricia Nicholson

The former hunting lodge of Lord Lonsdale, who purchased this Victorian property in 1888 has established itself as a Country House of high repute since passing into present ownership just 100 years later. Its magnificent location overlooking Lake Windermere and the Langdale Fells is unsurpassed; its cosy lounges, panelled dining-room and the

England

newer terrace room that opens onto an al fresco summer patio all offer a share of the spectacular views. Thus it is easy for dinner to become a memorable event, starting with canapés in the lounge before relaxing in appreciation of service that is both professional and knowledgeable. Strong French influences on the menu produce an appetiser of Jerusalem artichoke velouté with truffle oil and crème fraîche preceding boudin of duck with a well-balanced shallot and balsamic dressing - laid on leaves from their own herb garden - and followed by perfectly cooked veal loin presented on butternut squash and girolles, with mouth-watering cherry clafoutis in a fine pastry with home-made almond ice cream to round off.

Directions: 3 miles N of Windermere on A591. Turn R into Holbeck Lane. Hotel is 0.5 mile on L

Cost: Set price L £25/D £47.50. H/wine £17.95
Times: 12.30-2pm/7-9.30pm
Additional: Bar food L. Children 8yrs+
Seats: 40. Private dining room 20. Jacket and tie preferred
Style: French, Country-house
Smoking: No smoking in dining room
Civil licence: 65
Accommodation: 20 rooms (20 en suite) ★ ★ ★

Jerichos

Subtle lighting and an open kitchen add an air of theatre to a meal in this thoroughly modern restaurant. The menu offers some risky sounding combinations but flavours prove to be balanced and well matched. A meal might begin with a starter of pan fried chicken liver, black pudding and chorizo salad with feta cheese, pickled beetroot, garlic mayonnaise and virgin olive oil viniagrette. Main courses include poached fillet of sea bass on spring onion, ginger and new potato stir fry with confit of spiced tomatoes and black olive tapenade. The friendly staff provide super service.

Style: Traditional
Smoking: No smoking in dining room
Directions: M6 J36, then A591. In town centre

Birch Street, LA23 1EG
Tel: 015394 42522
Fax: 015394 42522
e enquiries@jerichos.co.uk
Chef(s): Chris Blaydes, Sarah Connolly
Owner(s): Mr & Mrs C Blaydes
Cost: *Alc* £23.50. ☺ H/wine £12.50
Times: Dinner only, 6.45-9.30pm. Closed Mon, Sun (Jan-Mar) 2 wks end Nov, 1st wk Dec, 25-26 Dec, 1 Jan
Additional: Children 12yrs+
Seats: 36. Private dining room 24

Langdale Chase Hotel

The carved fireplaces, oak panelling and unique galleried staircase of this imposing mansion are offset by terraced gardens and views of lake Windermere. The menu is British based but roams through most of Europe, sometimes picking up a few too many souvenirs on the way (as in a strongly flavoured starter of scallops on couscous with peppers and proscuitto chips). However, dishes such as medallions of wild venison accompanied by celeriac mash, parsnips and roasted chestnuts are impressive and well suited to the setting. Desserts range from fruity to creamy but if you can't choose, go for the Grande Assiette (a mixture of all).

Civil licence: 130
Accommodation: 27 rooms (27 en suite) ★ ★ ★
Directions: 2 miles S of Ambleside and 3 miles N of Windermere

Langdale Chase, LA23 1LW
Tel: 015394 32201
Fax: 015394 32604
Chef(s): Wendy Lindars
Owner(s): Mr T G Noblett
Cost: *Alc* £29, set price L £15.95/ D £29. ☺ ☺ H/wine £12.50
Times: Noon-2pm/7-9pm.
Additional: Sunday L. Bar food. Children welcome
Seats: 80. Private dining room 28
Style: Classic
Smoking: No smoking in dining room; Air conditioning

Lindeth Fell Hotel

Edwardian country house with stunning views over the garden, Lake Windermere and Coniston mountains from a formal dining room. Dinner is a fixed-price, five-course affair with a choice of two or three honestly cooked dishes at each course.

Lyth Valley Road, Bowness-on-Windermere, LA23 3JP
Tel: 015394 43286
Fax: 015394 47455

This might amount to, cheese and herb soufflé, soup, baked cod with basil mash, steamed syrup sponge, and cheeses.

Directions: 1m S of Bowness-on-Windermere on A5074

 kennedy@lindethfell.co.uk
Chef(s): Stewart Marsden,
Wayne Tarney
Owner(s): Pat & Diana Kennedy
Cost: Alc £12, set price L £12/D £23.
☺ ☺ H/wine £8.50
Times: 12.30-1.30pm/7.30-8.30pm.
Closed L Mon-Sat
Additional: Sunday L. Bar food L.
Children 7yrs+
Seats: 36. Private dining room . Jacket
and tie preferred
Style: Modern, Country-house
Smoking: No smoking in dining room
Accommodation: 14 rooms (14 en
suite) ★ ★

Linthwaite House

This could be one of the most impressive locations in the Lake District. Whilst the 14 acres of hilltop grounds include a fishing tarn and stunning views of Lake Windermere, the hotel offers a traditional but stylish hideaway, full of character and comfy chairs. The restaurant is adorned with mirrors of every shape and size and offers a well-balanced, classically based menu. Main courses might include char-grilled escalopes of pork with roasted root vegetables and a port wine jus or supreme of corn fed chicken with a sauce of ceps and lentils.

⊛⊛
Crook Road, LA23 3JA
Tel: 015394 88600
Fax: 015394 88601
 admin@linthwaite.com
Owner(s): Mike Bevans
Cost: Set price L £15.95/D £39. ☺ ☺
Times: 12.30-1.30pm/7.15-9pm.
Additional: Sunday L. Bar food L.
Children 7yrs+ at D
Seats: 60. Private dining room 25
Style: Classic, Country-house
Smoking: No smoking in dining room
Civil licence: 55
Accommodation: 26 rooms (26 en
suite) ★ ★ ★
Directions: Take 1st L off A591 at
rdbt NW of Kendal (B5284). Follow
for 6 miles, hotel is 1 mile after
Windermere Golf Club on L

STOP PRESS Change of Chef

Low Wood Hotel

A popular hotel with good food in the restaurant. Fricassée of lobster and scallops in chervil beurre blanc with citrus gremolata, Cumbrian fell-bred beef fillet served on spinach purée with wild mushroom and Madeira jus and rhubarb crème brûlée served with local Grasmere gingerbread are just some examples from the menu.

Smoking: No smoking in dining room
Civil licence: 250
Accommodation: 114 rooms (114 en suite) ★ ★ ★
Directions: M6 J36, A590, A591 to Ambleside. Hotel on R

⊛
LA23 1LP
Tel: 015394 33338
Fax: 015394 34072
 lowwood@e.l.h.co.uk
Chef(s): Paul Ray, Steve Morris
Owner(s): English Lakes Hotels
Cost: Set price D £21.50. ☺
Times: D only 7-9.45pm.
Additional: Children welcome
Seats: 125. Private dining room 40
Style: Traditional, Formal

England

Miller Howe

Rayrigg Road, LA23 1EY
Tel: 015394 42536
Fax: 015394 45664
 lakeview@millerhowe.com
Chef(s): Susan Elliott
Owner(s): Charles Garside
Cost: Set price L £17.50-£19.95/
D £39.50. ☺ H/wine £17.50
Times: 12.30-1.30pm/D at 8pm.
Closed 2 wks Jan
Additional: Sunday L. Children 8yrs+
Seats: 64. Private dining room 30.
Jacket and tie preferred
Style: Country-house
Smoking: No smoking in dining room;
Air conditioning
Civil licence: 64
Accommodation: 12 rooms (12 en
suite) ★ ★
Directions: On A592, between
Windermere & Bowness

Set in magnificent landscaped gardens with stunning views of
Lake Windermere, this elegant hotel offers a choice of
sumptuous lounges in which to study the menu and enjoy pre-
dinner drinks with canapés. The lights in the Italianate dining
room are theatrically dimmed at dinner in anticipation of a
menu whose daring combinations range from fillet of venison
with horseradish cream and red wine bitter chocolate liquorice
sauce to roast fillet of halibut smeared with curry essence and
served on caramelised mushrooms with a vanilla Sauternes
sauce. At the end of the meal, the chef tours the tables to check
on guests' satisfaction.

Storrs Hall

Storrs Park, Bowness-on-Windermere,
LA23 3LG
Tel: 015394 47111
Fax: 015394 47555
 reception@storrshall.co.uk
Chef(s): Michael Dodds
Owner(s): Mr Hindle & Mr Liyock
Cost: Set price L £17.50/
D £35. ☺ H/wine £14.75
Times: 12.30-1.30pm/7-9pm
Additional: Sunday L. Bar food L
Seats: 64. Jacket and tie preferred
Style: Classic

An elegant Grade II listed Georgian house with commanding
views over Lake Windermere. Sumptuous furnishings,
fascinating antiques and bold colours create an air of distinction
which is carried through into the Terrace restaurant, where
diners can enjoy views of the lake and a classically based menu.
Dishes might include roast rack of Lakeland lamb or slow
roasted mallard duck.

Smoking: No smoking in dining room
Civil licence: 60
Accommodation: 23 rooms (23 en suite) ★ ★ ★
Directions: On A592, 2 miles S of Bowness on the Newby
Bridge Road

Wild Boar Hotel

Crook, LA23 3NF
Tel: 015394 45225
Fax: 015394 42498
Telephone for further details

A traditional coaching inn boasting a smart comfortable
restaurant. The well-constructed *carte* may include a game
terrine with home-made chutney and warm brioche, a fricassée
of asparagus, button mushrooms and artichokes or braised
shank of Lakeland lamb with garlic and rosemary.

Directions: 2.5 miles S of Windermere. Take B5284 towards
Crook. Hotel on R after 3.5 miles

DERBYSHIRE

ASHBOURNE
Map 7 SK14

Callow Hall

Mappleton Road,
DE6 2AA
Tel: 01335 300900
Fax: 01335 300512
e reservations@callowhall.co.uk
Chef(s): David & Anthony Spencer
Owner(s): David, Dorothy &
Anthony Spencer
Cost: Alc £39, set price L £20.50/
D £38. H/wine £11.95
Times: 12.30-2pm/7.30-11pm.
Closed L Mon-Sat, D Sun
(ex residents), 25-26 Dec
Additional: Sunday L. Children
welcome
Seats: 70. Private dining room 40.
Jacket and tie preferred

This delightful, creeper clad Victorian house stands in a 44 acre estate with views over Bentley Brook and the Dove Valley. The country style interior includes tapestries, fresh flowers and an inviting dining room with rich red walls and a real fire. Appropriately enough for such a traditional setting, the cooking favours tried and tested combinations - perhaps guinea fowl with lemon and tarragon cream sauce or fillet of cod with crushed sweet potato, cream sauce and basil oil. The lengthy wine list (over 100 bins) covers France particularly well.

Style: Classic, Country-House
Smoking: No smoking in dining room
Accommodation: 16 rooms (16 en suite) ★★★
Directions: 0.75mile from Ashbourne; A515 (Buxton), sharp L by Bowling Green Pub, 1st R Mappleton Road

ASHFORD-IN-THE-WATER
Map 7 SK17

Riverside House Hotel

Fennel Street, DE45 1QF
Tel: 01629 814275
Fax: 01629 812873
e riversidehouse@enta.net
Chef(s): John Whelan
Owner(s): Mr J Lamb
Cost: Alc £39.95, set price L £26.95-
£35/D £39.95-£49. H/wine £16
Times: Noon-2pm/7-9.30pm
Additional: Sunday L. Bar food.
Children 12yrs+
Seats: 40. Private dining room 30
Style: Modern, Country-house
Smoking: No smoking in dining room
Accommodation: 15 rooms (15 en
suite) ★★★
Directions: 2 miles from Bakewell on
A6. In Ashford next to Sheepwash
Bridge

An immaculate hotel, parts of which date back to 1630. Located in the centre of the village beside the River Wye, it is surrounded by peaceful, mature gardens and offers guests a

England

plush, idiosyncratic taste of country life. The chef cooks to a high standard, producing plenty of restyled classics such as slow cooked belly of organic pork with sage potatoes, celeriac purée and parsnip crisps or partridge filled with foie gras and truffle mousse. The menu also includes imaginative desserts (perhaps butterscotch rice puding brûlée with eucalyptus honey ice cream) and a mouthwatering cheese course.

BAKEWELL
Map 8 SK26

Renaissance Restaurant

Interesting antiques, mustard coloured walls and chairs of various colours create a stylish, relaxed atmosphere in this converted barn. A popular, authentic French restaurant, it offers effortless classics complemented by a good (mostly French) wine list. A meal might include 'fisherman's net' soup topped with smoked salmon soufflé, followed by lamb cutlets with lentils.

Style: Chic, French
Smoking: No smoking in dining room
Directions: From Bakewell rdbt in town centre take A6 Buxton exit. 1st R into Bath Street (one-way)

Bath Street, DE45 1BX
Tel: 01629 812687
Chef(s): E Piedaniel
Owner(s): E Piedaniel
Cost: Alc £26, set price L £21.95/ D £21.95. ☺ ☺ H/wine £10.99
Times: Noon-2pm/7-10pm.
Closed Mon, D Sun, 2wk Jan, 2wk Aug
Additional: Sunday L. Bar food L. Children welcome
Seats: 50. Private dining room 25

Rutland Arms Hotel

This historic listed building is home to the invention of the Bakewell Pudding. The Four Seasons restaurant is traditional in style, with a profusion of clocks on display. Bakewell pudding is, of course, a feature of the table d'hôte menu, served with crème anglaise. Starter options might include confit of rabbit saddle, honey-roasted poussin, mixed seafood casserole and vegetable tempura.

Style: Classic
Smoking: No smoking in dining room
Accommodation: 35 rooms (35 en suite) ★ ★ ★
Directions: On A6 in Bakewell centre opposite war memorial. Parking opposite side entrance

The Square, DE45 1BT
Tel: 01629 812812
Fax: 01629 812309
✉ rutland@bakewell.demon.co.uk
Chef(s): Benjamin Olley
Owner(s): Mr P Feather
Cost: Set price L £9.95/D £19.50-£22.50. ☺ ☺ H/wine £10
Times: Noon-2.15pm/7-9.30pm.
Additional: Sunday L. Bar food. Children welcome
Seats: 40. Private dining room 25. Jacket and tie preferred

BASLOW
Map 8 SK27

Fischer's Baslow Hall

Dining is a truly memorable experience at this Grade II listed Derbyshire mansion house that stands in five acres of gardens at the edge of the Chatsworth Estate. The interior makes lavish use of dramatic fabrics in its elegant, high-ceilinged rooms with open fires to warm the lounge and fine appointments that lend the dining-room a touch of class. To this, Max Fischer brings his own unique talents. His cooking according to the seasons makes very best use of such local produce as Derbyshire spring lamb, Chatsworth venison and wild hare alongside the bought-in luxuries of foie gras and truffles. Some of his results on the plate are little short of stunning; epitomised by crab and lobster ravioli with a faultless seafood sauce and such signature dishes as char-grilled duck sausage on cannellini bean panaché with an

Calver Road, DE45 1RR
Tel: 01246 583259
Fax: 01246 583818
Chef(s): Max Fischer
Owner(s): Mr M & Mrs S Fischer
Cost: Set price L £24-£48. H/wine £13
Times: Noon-1.30pm/7-9.30pm.
Closed L Sat, D Sun (ex residents), 25 & 26 Dec
Additional: Sunday L. Children 12yrs+
Seats: 40. Private dining room 24. Jacket and tie preferred

apple jus reduction and slow-braised suckling pork served with a stuffed trotter of morels, pease pudding and wilted spring greens. Max's dessert assiette, exhibiting the full cross-section of available menu specialities, is certainly not to be missed.

Style: Formal, Country-house
Smoking: No smoking in dining room
Civil licence: 40
Accommodation: 11 rooms (11 en suite) ★ ★

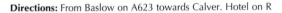

Directions: From Baslow on A623 towards Calver. Hotel on R

BELPER
Map 8 SK34

Makeney Hall

Choose to dine in the airy conservatory overlooking gorgeous gardens, or an oak-panelled restaurant dominated by a massive restored fireplace. Either way the food at this plush country house hotel is well worth sampling, and includes some distinctive flavours. Try the likes of spicy Thai-style prawn fishcakes, and pink roasted rump of lamb. Look out for desserts that may raise a few eyebrows!

Smoking: No smoking in dining room; Air conditioning
Civil licence: 140
Accommodation: 45 rooms (45 en suite) ★ ★ ★
Directions: Join A6 N of Derby & turn R into Milford. Hotel is 0.25 mile, just passed Garden Centre

Makeney, Milford, DE56 0RS
Tel: 01332 842999
Fax: 01332 842777
Chef(s): Martyn Yates
Cost: Alc £30, set price L £11.95-£15.95/D £18-£24.50. ☺ ☺
H/wine £12.50
Times: Noon-2.30pm/7-11pm. Closed L Sat
Additional: Sunday L.
Children welcome
Seats: 60. Private dining room
Style: Traditional, Country-house

BUXTON
Map 7 SK07

Best Western
Lee Wood Hotel

The hotel's Garden Room restaurant is a large and attractive conservatory overlooking the gardens, where (conditions allowing) you can dine by starlight. Good use is made of local produce, and comforting English dishes are spiced up with an imaginative approach. A mini plate of fish and chips with mushy peas has been declared "a winner", as was a starter of sausage, Bury black pudding and bacon terrine. Greatest praise has been reserved though, for a main course of fresh and bright white sea bass served in a mussel stew with terrific depth of flavour .

Accommodation: 40 rooms (40 en suite) ★ ★ ★
Directions: Follow A5004 Long Hiill to Whaley Bridge. Hotel approx 200 metres beyond the Devonshire Royal Hospital on L

 ⊛⊛
The Park, SK17 6TQ
Tel: 01298 23002
Fax: 01298 23228
 e leewoodhotel@btinternet.com
Chef(s): Chris Bates
Owner(s): Mr J C Millican
Cost: Alc £26, set price D £24.50-£30.
☺ ☺ H/wine £11.50
Times: Noon-2pm/7.15-9.30pm.
Additional: Sunday L. Bar food.
Children welcome
Seats: 80. Private dining room 60
Style: Traditional, Conservatory
Smoking: No smoking in dining room
Civil licence: 120

DARLEY ABBEY

Map 8 SK33

Darleys Restaurant

Darley Abbey Mill,
DE22 1DZ
Tel: 01332 364987
Fax: 01332 541356
e davidpinchbeck@hotmail.com
Chef(s): Kevin Stone, Gavin Allcock
Owner(s): David & Gillian Pinchbeck
Cost: Set price L £14.50/D £22.
☺ ☺ H/wine £14
Times: Noon-2pm/6.30-10pm.
Closed D Sun, BHs
Additional: Sunday L.
Children welcome
Seats: 70
Style: Minimalist

Smack on the River Derwent - a plush modern restaurant offering a menu of bright brasserie style dishes. Friendly and efficient staff deliver punchy starters along the lines of seared peppered tuna with salad niçoise and duck terrine with wild mushrooms. Mains tend to the hearty in combinations like rump of lamb with a red wine and garlic jus and good fondant potatoes or Gressingham duck with more wild mushrooms, berries and a Madeira sauce. Typical of the puds - a hot chocolate fondant with an ultra-rich white chocolate ice cream or warm gingerbread with caramel sauce and marmalade ice cream.

Smoking: No smoking in dining room; Air conditioning
Directions: A6 N from Derby, 2miles, village signposted

DERBY

Map 8 SK33

Menzies Mickleover Court

An unusual circular hotel with glass lift, and plenty of brass and marble in the bright Brasserie. The *carte* is partly available as a short fixed-price menu, with dishes like smoked duck and ham terrine with gooseberry chutney and garlic brioche, and slow-cooked belly of pork with egg-noodle stir-fry and chilli jam. Upstairs the Italian bistro offers a popular alternative.

Style: Modern
Smoking: No-smoking area; no pipes; Air conditioning
Civil licence: 140
Accommodation: 100 rooms (100 en suite) ★ ★ ★ ★
Directions: From Mickleover take A516 (Uttoxeter). Hotel is L of 1st rdbt

Etwall Road, Mickleover, DE3 5XX
Tel: 01332 521234
Fax: 01332 521238
e info@menzies-hotel.co.uk
Chef(s): Martin Clayton
Owner(s): Menzies Hotels Plc
Cost: *Alc* £22, set price L £14.95.
☺ ☺ H/wine £11.95
Times: 12.30-2.30pm/7-10pm
Additional: Sunday L. Bar food.
Children welcome
Seats: 100. Private dining room 150

HATHERSAGE

Map 8 SK28

The George at Hathersage

Charlotte Brontë used to visit this inn and set *Jane Eyre* in Hathersage, renaming it Morton after the landlord of the George. Today, beamed ceilings and blazing fires create the perfect backdrop for an inspired selection of food. Dishes range

Main Road, S32 1BB
Tel: 01433 650436
Fax: 01433 650099
e info@george-hotel.net
Chef(s): Ben Handley

from British (home-made fish and chips) to Oriental (crispy aromatic belly pork with watercress salad and sweet and sour tomatoes), with a good range of meat, vegetable and fish options. Ingredients are high quality and flavours well balanced. Warm home-made breads, quality coffee and attentive service complete a satisfying experience.

Civil licence: 90
Accommodation: 19 rooms (19 en suite) ★ ★ ★
Directions: In village centre on A625

Owner(s): Eric Marsh
Cost: *Alc* £22. ☺ ☺ H/wine £12.50
Times: 10am-2.30pm/7-10pm.
Additional: Sunday L. Bar food L. Children welcome
Seats: 45. Private dining room 90
Style: Modern, Country house
Smoking: No smoking in dining room

MATLOCK
Map 8 SK35

Riber Hall

DE4 5JU
Tel: 01629 582795
Fax: 01629 580475
e info@riber-hall.co.uk
Chef(s): John Bradshaw
Owner(s): Alex Biggin
Cost: Set price L £13-£16/ D £28.50-£34. ☺ H/wine £14.95
Times: Noon-1.30pm/7-late
Additional: Sunday L. Bar food L. Children welcome. Vegetarian by request only
Seats: 60. Private dining room 30. Jacket and tie preferred
Style: Traditional, Country-house
Smoking: No smoking in dining room

Elizabethan manor house in tranquil countryside high above Matlock, its lounges and dining-room tastefully appointed with period furnishings. The quality of ingredients and execution remain consistent on a menu founded, in classical French tradition, on well-tried, familiar dishes. Saffron risotto and baby fennel with perfect king scallops to start, and braised oxtail and roasted onions with roast fillet of beef typify the style. Praiseworthy warm chocolate pudding with dark and white Belgian chocolate sauces stood out; fine dining that complements the excellent wine list and attentive service.

Civil licence: 40
Accommodation: 14 rooms (14 en suite) ★ ★ ★
Directions: 1 mile up Alders Lane & Carr Lane, off A615 at Tansley

MELBOURNE
Map 8 SK32

The Bay Tree

Everybody seems at peace with the world in this comfortable, popular and friendly establishment. At a recent meal the fresh, tender calamari was juicy and served with sweet chilli dip, while the main course of sea bass with crab mash was perfectly cooked. The wonderfully orangey iced Grand Marnier mousse completed a delightful meal in a relaxed atmosphere.

4 Potter Street, DE73 1DW
Tel: 01332 863358
Fax: 013332 865545
Telephone for further details

RIDGEWAY

Map 8 SK48

The Old Vicarage

Ridgeway Moor, S12 3XW
Tel: 0114 2475814
Fax: 0114 2477079
Telephone for further details

There is an appealing richness and opulence associated with this fine country house and the luxurious sofas where you have your pre-dinner drink are an invitation to relax. The butter yellow colouring of the dining room is set off by carefully chosen paintings and a view of the gardens. The set-price menu, which has a steep price tag, commences with canapés that can best be described as delectable flavour bombs. A precisely seasoned bouche of wild mushroom tartlet could be the opening gambit on a selection from the four-course menu with its lively seasonal dishes. Showing clever touches and subtle flavouring were roast breast of Gressingham duck suffused with sage leaf, accompanied by confit of the leg on noodles with crispy skin. The braised oxtail main course had cinnamon glazed root vegetables and mash - the latter, a chef's favourite. The high quality wine list has 15 half bottles for experimentation.

RISLEY

Map 8 SK43

Risley Hall

Dating back to the 11th century, this impressive manor house stands in beautiful listed gardens. Dinner is served in a selection of country house style dining rooms, and begins with simple but successful canapés such as stuffed cherry tomatoes or a mini kebab. The imaginative, classically based menu might include roast John Dory with braised endive and emulsion of tarragon or pigeon with caramelised parsnips and chocolate sauce. The wine list is well priced and offers a good range of bottles from Europe and the New World. Don't miss the tasty selection of petits fours with coffee.

Style: Traditional, Country-House
Smoking: No smoking in dining room
Civil licence: 120
Accommodation: 36 rooms (36 en suite) ★★★
Directions: From M1 J25 take Sandiacre exit, L at T-junct, 0.5 mile on L

Derby Road, DE72 3SS
Tel: 0115 939 9000
Fax: 0115 939 7766
e enquiries@risley.co.uk
Chef(s): Paul Halifax
Owner(s): Mr M Crosbie
Cost: Alc £35, set price L £16.95-£27.50/D £22.50-£35. ☺ ☺
H/wine £12.95
Times: Noon-2.30pm/7-9.30pm.
Closed D Sun, 25 Dec evening, 31 Dec evening
Additional: Sunday L.
Children welcome
Seats: 80. Private dining room 24.
Jacket and tie preferred

ROWSLEY
Map 8 SK26

East Lodge

A sedate country house hotel situated in ten acres of attractive grounds and gardens. The recently refurbished restaurant does a good line in Sunday lunches and Derbyshire cream teas, but also offers an appealing mixture of traditional favourites (fillet steak garni; roasted noisettes of lamb) and modern combinations such as monkfish and scallops with chilli noodles and tomato salsa.

DE4 2EF
Tel: 01629 734474
Fax: 01629 733949
e info@eastlodge.com
Chef(s): Russell Hayes
Owner(s): Elyzian Hospitality Ltd
Cost: *A/c* £23, set price L £14/
D £23-£26. ☺ ☺ H/wine £10.95
Times: Noon-2pm/7-9pm.
Additional: Sunday L. Bar food L.
Children 5 yrs+
Seats: 60. Private dining room 40
Style: Country-house

Smoking: No smoking in dining room; Air conditioning
Civil licence: 100
Accommodation: 15 rooms (15 en suite) ★ ★ ★
Directions: Hotel drive access on A6, 5 miles from Matlock and 3 miles from Bakewell

SOUTH NORMANTON
Map 8 SK45

Renaissance Derby/Nottingham Hotel

Handy for the likes of Alton Towers and Chatsworth House, and minutes from the M1. The formal hexagonal restaurant with white timbered ceiling serves tasty, well-made food including some yummy desserts. Expect penne with onion, gorgonzola and cream, smoked haddock with creamy mustard sauce, and a calorific rum and dark chocolate truffle.

Carter Lane East,
DE55 2EH
Tel: 01773 812000
Fax: 01773 580032
Telephone for further details

DEVON

ASHBURTON
Map 3 SX77

Agaric
NEW

In relaxed informal surroundings stylishly decked with wooden tables and floors, choose from consistently well made dishes for the friendly staff to deliver to you. Start with celeriac and hazelnut soup before roast brill steak with marinated fennel and peppers, which might be followed by poached pear with vanilla syrup and blackberry liqueur sauce.

30 North Street,
TQ13 7QD
Tel: 01364 654478
Chef(s): Nick Coiley
Owner(s): Mr N Coiley &
Miss S Crossley
Cost: *A/c* £28.35, set price L
£22.50/D £27.50. ☺ ☺ H/wine £9.95
Times: Noon-3pm/7-9.30pm.
Closed Mon-Tue, D Sun, Xmas,
2 wks Jan
Additional: Sunday L. Children
welcome

Seats: 30
Style: Modern Chic
Smoking: No smoking in dining room
Directions: On North Street opposite the Town Hall. Ashburton is off A38 between Exeter and Plymouth

England

AXMINSTER

Map 3 SY29

Fairwater Head Hotel

Views over the Axe valley greet visitors to this country house hotel. Dishes in the friendly restaurant make good use of local produce and range from understated (sirloin steak with a light ale sauce) to elaborate - perhaps seared venison steaks in pomme mousseline studded with black pepper and encompassed by an orange scented carrot and cranberry coulis.

Seats: 40. Private dining room 10. Jacket and tie preferred
Style: Traditional, Country-House
Smoking: No smoking in dining room
Accommodation: 20 rooms (20 en suite) ★ ★ ★
Directions: Turn off B3165 (Crewkerne to Lyme Regis Road) hotel signposted to Hawkchurch

Hawkchurch, EX13 5TX
Tel: 01297 678349
Fax: 01297 678459
e reception@fairwaterhead.demon.co.uk
Chef(s): Ian Carter, Paul Swingler
Owner(s): Mrs J Lowe,
Mrs & Mrs Austin
Cost:, set price L £13.50/D £23.50.
☺ ☺ H/wine £10
Times: Noon-1.45pm/7-8.30pm.
Closed Jan
Additional: Sunday L. Bar food L.
Children welcome. Vegetarian by request only

Lea Hill Hotel

This delightful thatched Devon longhouse (parts of which date back to the 1300s) houses an atmospheric, bare beamed restaurant. The chef makes good use of local produce and cooks with composure, aesthetic precision and deftness. Meals begin with a good selection of canapés before progressing to starters such as fresh local rabbit with soft fried polenta chips, braised beetroot and home grown horseradish or home-made salmon and lobster ravioli. Main courses might include roast venison with potato rösti and pears poached in Beaujolais or ballontine of lamb with roasted shallots, parsnip crisps and a red wine and redcurrant veal jus.

Accommodation: 11 rooms (11 en suite) ★ ★
Directions: From Axminster follow A358 towards Chard. After 2 miles turn L to Smallridge and follow signs to Membury. 0.5 mile on R after village

Membury, EX13 7AQ
Tel: 01404 881881
Fax: 01404 881890
e reception@leahillhotel.co.uk
Chef(s): James Hubbard
Owner(s): Mr & Mrs C Hubbard
Cost: Set price D £26.50. H/wine £13
Times: Dinner only, 7-9pm.
Closed Sun, 3 Jan-mid Mar
Additional: Children 12yrs+.
Vegetarian by request only
Seats: 30. Private dining room 12.
Jacket and tie preferred
Style: Traditional, Country-house
Smoking: No smoking in dining room

BARNSTAPLE

Map 2 SS53

Halmpstone Manor

This historical manor, now a country-house hotel, is set in its own gardens off a country lane amid rolling farmland. Dinner in the panelled and candlelit restaurant is a five-course affair with no choice until dessert, which follows a selection of cheeses. A soup might start things off - carrot and coriander, say, or, in season, asparagus - followed by something fishy such as Clovelly scallops with a cream and white wine sauce, or sea bass with herbs. Lamb or beef might figure as main courses; otherwise there could be chicken breast with duxelle, or guinea fowl roasted with lime, accompanied by as many as five vegetables. Finish with apple crumble and local clotted cream, before rounding things off with coffee and mints.

Directions: From Barnstaple take A377 to Bishop's Tawton. At end of village turn L for Cobbaton; sign on R

Bishop's Tawton, EX32 0EA
Tel: 01271 830321
Fax: 01271 830826
e jane@halmpstonemanor.co.uk
Chef(s): Jane Stanbury
Owner(s): Mr & Mrs Stanbury
Cost: Set price L £30/D £30.
☺ H/wine £9.95
Times: Dinner only, 7-9pm.
L by arrangement. Closed Nov, Feb
Additional: Children 12yrs+
Seats: 24. Jacket and tie preferred
Style: Country-House
Smoking: No smoking in dining room
Accommodation: 5 rooms (5 en suite)
★ ★

Royal & Fortescue Hotel, The Bank

It is a sign of the times that right in the heart of town what was once a bank is now a restaurant. The ornate plasterwork ceiling

Boutport Street, EX31 1HG
Tel: 01271 324446
Fax: 01271 342289

and oak-panelled walls give the restaurant a very grand air. The menu is brasserie-style ranging from baguettes to specials such as roast Barbary duck with rich orange sauce and fillet Rossini.

Accommodation: 50 rooms (50 en suite) ★ ★ ★
Directions: A361 into Barnstaple, along Barbican Rd signposted town centre; turn R into Queens St & L (one way) Boutport St. Hotel on L

Chef(s): Peter Horn
Cost: Alc £20. H/wine £9.75
Times: 10am-10pm. Closed Sun
Additional: Children welcome
Style: Informal, Bistro-Style

BIDEFORD   Map 3 SS42

Yeoldon Country House

Victorian country house overlooking the river Torridge. Soyer's restaurant is named after famous Victorian chef Alexis Soyer, and is full of antiquarian cookery books. Despite this, the menus have a modern feel. Dishes might include pan fried skate wing with capers and nut brown lemon butter or supreme of chicken wrapped in bacon and glazed with stilton.

Style: Modern, Country-House
Smoking: No smoking in dining room
Accommodation: 10 rooms (10 en suite) ★ ★
Directions: From Barnstaple take A39 towards Bideford. Take 3rd R into Durrant Lane. Hotel 0.25mile

Durrant Lane, Northam, EX39 2RL
Tel: 01237 474400
Fax: 01237 476618
e yeoldonhouse@aol.com
Chef(s): Brian Steele
Owner(s): Brian & Jennifer Steele
Cost: Set price D £21.50. ☺
H/wine £10.50
Times: Dinner only, 7-8.30pm.
Closed Xmas
Additional: Bar food L.
Children welcome
Seats: 30

BOVEY TRACEY   Map 3 SX87

Edgemoor Hotel

Haytor Road,
Lowerdown Cross, TQ13 9LE
Tel: 01626 832466
Fax: 01626 834760
e edgemoor@btinternet.com
Chef(s): Edward Elliott
Owner(s): Rod & Pat Day
Cost: Set price L £16.95/D £24.50.
☺ ☺ H/wine £8.45
Times: Noon-3pm/7-11pm.
Closed 1 wk at New Year
Additional: Sunday L. Bar food.
Children 10yrs+
Seats: 30
Style: Traditional, Country-house
Smoking: No smoking in dining room

This country house hotel stands on the edge of Dartmoor in two acres of peaceful gardens and grounds. The traditionally decorated restaurant offers a monthly changing menu as well as a selection of daily specials. Modern British in style, the cooking makes good use of local ingredients: dishes might include fillet of lamb with roast garlic, rosemary and sherry jus or guinea fowl with a forcemeat fritter and a dark smoked bacon sauce. Good sized portions, quality ingredients and clear flavours keep numerous regular customers satisfied. Service is friendly, relaxed and efficient.

Accommodation: 16 rooms (16 en suite) ★ ★ ★
Directions: From A38 take A382 (Drumbridges). Cross first mini rdbt & turn L at 2nd rdbt. Bear L towards Haytor. Hotel 0.25 mile on R

England

BRANSCOMBE
Map 3 SY18

The Masons Arms

A charming 14th-century inn just half a mile from the sea in the picturesque village of Branscombe. The oak-beamed restaurant serves an appealing selection of traditional and modern dishes: a meal might include smoked salmon roulade followed by pan-fried medallions of pork with an apple and cider sauce.

Seats: 30. Private dining room 12
Style: Traditional, Rustic
Smoking: No smoking in dining room
Accommodation: 28 rooms (25 en suite) ★★
Directions: Turn off A3052 (Exeter to Lyme Regis) and follow road through Branscombe

EX12 3DJ
Tel: 01297 680300
Fax: 01297 680500
✉ reception@masonsarms.co.uk
Chef(s): Stephen Tipper
Owner(s): Murray Inglis
Cost: Set price D £24. ☺ ☺
H/wine £11
Times: Noon-2pm/7-9pm
Additional: Sunday L. Bar food.
Children 10+

BRIXHAM
Map 3 SX95

Maypool Park

A welcoming, family run hotel set at the head of a wooded valley and bordering the estate of the late Agatha Christie. The house is an attractive, stone built building whose restaurant offers interesting dishes such as pheasant with caramelised apple and a light cream sauce with a hint of curry, or avocado stuffed with pepper and mushroom.

Maypool, Galmpton, TQ5 0ET
Tel: 01803 842442
Fax: 01803 845782
✉ peacock@maypoolpark.co.uk
Chef(s): Andrew Peacock
Owner(s): Ms F Peacock
Cost: Set price L £12.50/D £21.50.
☺ ☺ H/wine £8.95
Times: Noon-2pm/7-8.30pm.
Closed L Mon-Sat
Additional: Sunday L.
Children 12yrs+
Seats: 35
Style: Country-House
Smoking: No smoking in dining room
Accommodation: 10 rooms (10 en suite) ★★
Directions: Turn off A3022 at Churston into Manor Vale Road for Maypool, pedestrian ferry and Greenway Quay and continue for 2 miles

Quayside Hotel

Seafront freshness in evidence at this harbourside hotel. Discreet lighting creates an intimate atmosphere in which local

41-49 King Street, TQ5 9TJ
Tel: 01803 855751
Fax: 01803 882733
✉ quayside.hotel@virgin.net
Chef(s): Owain Rees
Owner(s): Mr & Mrs C F Bowring
Cost: Alc £25. ☺ H/wine £10
Times: Dinner only, 6.30-10.30pm.
Additional: Children 14yrs+
Seats: 40. Private dining room 18
Style: Modern
Smoking: No smoking in dining room
Accommodation: 29 rooms (29 en suite) ★★★
Directions: From Exeter take A380 towards Torquay, then A3022 to Brixham

England

produce is simply presented to allow the flavours to speak for themselves. Seafood is a strength (it would be a bit embarrassing if it wasn't) with full flavoured Dover sole with basil and tomato being a notable example.

BROADHEMBURY
Map 3 ST10

Drewe Arms

An old thatched pub in a delightful Devon village, oozing character with log fires, flag-stoned floors and lots of intimate nooks and crannies. Popular locally for its atmosphere and seafood, and the blackboard shows dishes like scallops with mango chutney sauce, brill with horseradish hollandaise, and baked figs with Amaretto ice cream.

EX14 0NF
Tel: 01404 841267
Fax: 01404 841267
Telephone for further details

BURRINGTON
Map 3 SS61

Northcote Manor

Located amid beautiful grounds, this gabled manor is an idyllic place to dine. The Manor House restaurant offers an imaginative menu, giving a modern twist to many classic European recipes. Starters might include a risotto of panchetta, asparagus and Parmesan or a terrine of confit chicken and foie gras, whilst main courses range from salmon, scallop and langoustine broth with courgettes and a caviar ravioli to rump of lamb with creamed lentils, buttered Savoy cabbage and a rosemary jus. Desserts might include iced raspberry parfait or dark chocolate marquise with chocolate sorbet. A friendly, relaxing experience.

Civil licence: 50
Accommodation: 11 rooms (11 en suite) ★ ★ ★
Directions: Do not enter Burrington Village. Follow A377 (Barnstaple-Crediton road). Entrance opposite Portsmouth Arms railway station and pub

EX37 9LZ
Tel: 01769 560501
Fax: 01769 560770
 rest@northcotemanor.co.uk
Chef(s): Chris Dawson
Owner(s): David Boddy
Cost: Alc £37.50, set price L £19.50/ D £37.50-£49 H/wine £15
Times: Noon-2pm/7-9.30pm. L by prior arrangement only
Additional: Sunday L. Bar food L. Children 10yrs+. Vegetarian by request only
Seats: 34. Private dining room 14. Jacket and tie preferred
Style: Country-house
Smoking: No smoking in dining room

CHAGFORD
Map 3 SX78

Gidleigh Park

Michael Caines' achievements at Gidleigh Park are quite remarkable. The last couple of years have seen him expand his

TQ13 8HH
Tel: 01647 432367
Fax: 01647 432574
 gidleighpark@gidleigh. co.uk
Chef(s): Michael Caines
Owner(s): Paul & Kay Henderson
Cost: Alc £65, set price L £38-£70/ D £65-£70 H/wine £20
Times: 12.30-2pm/7-9pm
Additional: Sunday L. Bar food L. Children 7yrs+.
Vegetarian by request only
Seats: 35. Jacket and tie preferred
Style: Country-house
Smoking: No smoking in dining room
Accommodation: 15 rooms (15 en suite) ★ ★ ★

CHAGFORD *Continued*

Map 3 SX78

Gidleigh Park

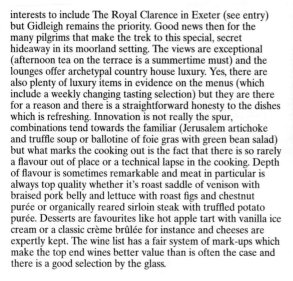

interests to include The Royal Clarence in Exeter (see entry) but Gidleigh remains the priority. Good news then for the many pilgrims that make the trek to this special, secret hideaway in its moorland setting. The views are exceptional (afternoon tea on the terrace is a summertime must) and the lounges offer archetypal country house luxury. Yes, there are also plenty of luxury items in evidence on the menus (which include a weekly changing tasting selection) but they are there for a reason and there is a straightforward honesty to the dishes which is refreshing. Innovation is not really the spur, combinations tend towards the familiar (Jerusalem artichoke and truffle soup or ballotine of foie gras with green bean salad) but what marks the cooking out is the fact that there is so rarely a flavour out of place or a technical lapse in the cooking. Depth of flavour is sometimes remarkable and meat in particular is always top quality whether it's roast saddle of venison with braised pork belly and lettuce with roast figs and chestnut purée or organically reared sirloin steak with truffled potato purée. Desserts are favourites like hot apple tart with vanilla ice cream or a classic crème brûlée for instance and cheeses are expertly kept. The wine list has a fair system of mark-ups which make the top end wines better value than is often the case and there is a good selection by the glass.

Directions: From Chagford Square turn R at Lloyds Bank into Mill Street, after 150 yards R fork, straight across crossroads into Holy Street. Restaurant is in 1.5 miles

Mill End Hotel

Peace, quiet and relaxation are the hallmarks of this charming hotel, located in the Dartmoor National Park. A good location for fishing, walking or just relaxing, the elegantly decorated building includes a dining room with views of the working water wheel. The menu gives a modern twist to classic English ingredients such as Medallions of beef pan fried with paprika cream and mushroom sauce or breast of chicken with black pudding mousse, celeriac purée and a cranberry, rosemary and red wine jus. An interesting, varied wine list and plenty of local specialities (clotted cream, cheese, ice cream) complete an enjoyable experience.

Smoking: No smoking in dining room
Accommodation: 16 rooms (16 en suite) ★ ★ ★
Directions: From A382 (Moretonhampstead) – don't turn into Chagford at Sandy Park

Dartmoor National Park, Sandy Park, TQ13 8JN
Tel: 01647 432282
Fax: 01647 433106
🄴 millendhotel@talk21.com
Chef(s): Alan Lane
Owner(s): Keith Green
Cost: *Alc* £27.50, set price L £17.50-£24.50/D £27.50-£34.50.
H/wine £11.50
Times: Noon-3pm/7.30-11pm.
Additional: Sunday L. Bar food L. Children 10 yrs+
Seats: 42. Jacket and tie preferred
Style: Classic, Country-house

22 Mill Street

Petite shop fronted restaurant that retains plenty of Dartmoor character (granite fireplaces for instance) whilst being modishly decorated in blazing bright yellow. The atmosphere is relaxed and informal with a healthy local following attracted by some of the best cooking in the area. The style is not too elaborate with some punchy flavours and an emphasis on getting the best out of some good quality ingredients. "Excellent" scallops come with judiciously spiced chick peas and roast fillet of cod with ravioli of ceps and a velouté of Jerusalem artichoke. There's a welcome lightness of touch apparent in the desserts with a vanilla crème brûlée coming with sweet strawberries and honeycomb.

22 Mill Street, TQ13 8AW
Tel: 01647 432244
Fax: 01647 433101
Telephone for further details

England

CHITTLEHAMHOLT
Map 3 SS62

Highbullen Hotel

This Victorian Gothic mansion stands on high ground between the Mole and Taw valleys, surrounded by wooded parkland containing a golf course, croquet lawn and swimming pool. The simply decorated restaurant (cane chairs, floral curtains, soft pink linen) offers a selection of traditional favourites - perhaps steak and kidney pie, beef stroganoff or grilled calves' liver with bacon and onions.

Smoking: No-smoking area
Accommodation: 37 rooms (37 en suite) ★ ★ ★
Directions: From M5 J27 take A361 to South Molton, then B3226(Crediton rd); after 5.2miles turn R to Chittlehamholt. Hotel 0.5 mile beyond village

EX37 9HD
Tel: 01769 540561
Fax: 01769 540492
e highbullen@sosi.net
Chef(s): Colette Potter
Owner(s): Hugh & Pam Neil
Cost: A/c £25, set price L £15/D £25.
☺ H/wine £12
Times: Noon-2pm/7-9pm
Additional: Bar food L.
Children 8yrs+
Seats: 80
Style: Classic, Traditional

CLOVELLY
Map 2 SS32

Red Lion Hotel

18th-century inn located at the water's edge, busy by day and tranquil by night. The restaurant is friendly, relaxed and decorated in rustic style - the perfect setting in which to sample imaginatively prepared local ingredients such as sea bass with new potatoes and seafood sauce or rump steak with fondant potato and red onion marmalade.

Style: Traditional, Rustic
Smoking: No smoking in dining room
Accommodation: 11 rooms (11 en suite)
Directions: M5 J27. Leave A39 at Clovelly Cross onto B3237. At bottom of hill take 1st L by white railings to harbour

The Quay, EX39 5TF
Tel: 01237 431237
Fax: 01237 431044
e redlion@clovelly.co.uk
Chef(s): Michael Corbett
Owner(s): Clovelly Estate Co Ltd
Cost: Set price D £25. H/wine £8.60
Times: Dinner only, 7-10.30pm
Additional: Bar food. Children welcome
Seats: 40

COLYFORD
Map 3 SY29

Swallows Eaves

Lovely, 1930's wisteria-cloaked hotel with a graceful and traditional dining room. A short menu places the emphasis on quality as opposed to quantity with good locally sourced ingredients and clear flavours. Simple but effective cooking is represented by an "excellent" chicken liver salad and salmon with grain mustard and lime.

Seats: 16. Jacket and tie preferred
Style: Traditional
Smoking: No smoking in dining room
Accommodation: 8 rooms (8 en suite) ★ ★
Directions: In the centre of the village on A3082

Swan Hill Road,
EX24 6QJ
Tel: 01297 553184
Fax: 01297 553574
Chef(s): Jane Beck
Owner(s): Mr & Mrs J Beck
Cost: Set price D £23. ☺
H/wine £10.95
Times: Dinner only, 7-8.30pm.
Closed Dec-Feb
Additional: Children 14yrs+.
Vegetarian by request only

DARTMOUTH
Map 3 SX85

Carved Angel Restaurant

This eyecatching building, adorned with heraldic designs, houses an equally memorable restaurant. The Carved Angel is a long standing attraction of Dartmouth, but its reputation continues to improve as well as endure. The assured modern

2 South Embankment,
TQ6 9BH
Tel: 01803 832465
Fax: 01803 835141
e enquiries@thecarvedangel.com

England

DARTMOUTH *Continued* Map 3 SX85

cooking makes use of the finest ingredients, delivering a vibrant, well judged mixture of textures and flavours. Canapés and imaginative breads (perhaps "utterly moreish" ham and

cheese) set the scene and are followed by starters such as braised oxtail ravioli with truffled parsnip purée or seared scallops with artichoke cream and trompettes. Main courses range from pan fried bream with crab risotto and shellfish sauce to roast partridge with ceps and beetroot gravy, whilst vegetarians are kept happy by dishes such as millefeuille of cumin roast vegetables and creamed cabbage. The desserts are equally inspiring, and might include crème brûlée with mulled fruits or spiced banana tatin with toffee ripple ice cream.

Carved Angel Restaurant

Chef(s): David Jones
Owner(s): Paul Roston, Peter Gorton
Cost: *Alc* £28.50/D £39.50. ☺
H/wine £17
Times: 12.30-2.30pm/7-9.30pm.
Closed L Mon, D Sun, 3 days Xmas
Additional: Sunday L. Children
10 yrs+ at D
Seats: 50. Private dining room 15
Style: Modern, Classic
Smoking: No smoking in dining room
Directions: Dartmouth centre, on the water's edge.

Hooked

The oldest working building in the town, with windows taken from a Spanish galleon. A contemporary style interior includes terracotta walls, cane chairs and neatly clothed tables. As the name suggests, it is predominantly a fish restaurant - and one that makes imaginative use of the genre. A meal might include assorted sushi with pickled ginger and wasabi followed by roasted halibut with a mini 'fish pie' and an asparagus and morel velouté. Those who don't fancy fish can enjoy favourites such as fillet of Aberdeen Angus with rösti potato and Brouilly braised button vegetables. Service is friendly and efficient.

5 Higher Street,
TQ6 9RB
Tel: 01803 832022
Fax: 01803 832022

📧 hookedthefish@hotmail.com
Chef(s): Paul Micklewright
Owner(s): Mark & Lyn Coxon
Cost: *Alc* £25, set price L £14.50. ☺ ☺ H/wine £10
Times: Noon-2pm/7-9pm. Closed Sun, L Mon, D Mon (out of season), Xmas, Jan
Additional: Children 10 yrs+. Vegetarian by request only
Seats: 50. Private dining room 14
Style: Ecclectic
Smoking: No cigars
Directions: From A38, through Totnes, to Dartmouth. Past Naval College towards town centre. Take 3rd R to T-junction, then R, 1st L, 1st L again. Restaurant on L

England

EXETER

Map 3 SX99

Barton Cross Hotel

Huxham, Stoke Canon,
EX5 4EJ
Tel: 01392 841245
Fax: 01392 841942
✉ bartonxhuxham@aol.com
Chef(s): Paul Bending
Owner(s): Brian Hamilton
Cost: *Alc* £20, set price L £20.50-
£27.50/D £20.50-£27.50.
☺ H/wine £9.25
Times: Dinner only, 6.30pm-midnight
Additional: Children welcome
Seats: 50. Private dining room 15
Style: Classic, Country-house

The charm of the 17th century blends perfectly with the luxury of the 21st century at this lovely country hotel. Traditional comforts are much in evidence in the dining room, where fine classical British and French cooking is presented on a fixed-price menu. Seasonal starters like warm seafood tart on a spring salad with lemon and chives, and duck confit on a bed of braised green lentils and topped with griddled foie gras might precede noisettes of Devonshire lamb wrapped in basil mousse, served with dauphinoise potatoes, topped with a small tart of lambs' kidneys. Plenty of vegetarian choice too.

Smoking: No smoking in dining room
Accommodation: 9 rooms (9 en suite) ★ ★ ★
Directions: 0.5 mile off A396 at Stoke Canon, 3m N of Exeter

Hotel Barcelona   NEW

Magdalen Street, EX2 4HY
Tel: 01392 281010
Fax: 01392 281001
✉ info@hotelbarcelona-uk.com
Chef(s): Michael Feild
Owner(s): Alias Hotels Plc
Cost: *Alc* £25. ☺ ☺ H/wine £10.50
Times: Noon-2pm/7-10pm
Additional: Sunday L. Children
welcome
Seats: 72. Private dining room 18
Style: Modern, Chic
Smoking: No smoking in dining room;
Air conditioning
Accommodation: 46 rooms (46 en
suite) ★ ★ ★ ★
Directions: Telephone for directions

Café Paradiso no less. Hotel Barcelona like its Cheltenham sibling (Hotel Kandinsky, see entry) has its tongue firmly in its cheek with big top design and a plethora of off the wall objets d'art. The food is fun too but it's also very good. Authentic pizza and creditable pasta sit alongside a brasserie-style menu offering rack of lamb with balsamic vinegar and thyme and a good fondant-style chocolate pudding.

EXETER *Continued*   Map 3 SX99

Lord Haldon Hotel   NEW

Family-run hotel with exquisite views over some of the most picturesque countryside in Devon. Some accomplished cooking with obvious ambition offering starters such as scallops with basil risotto or red onion tart and mains along the lines of crispy fillet of salmon with an orange butter sauce. Pineapple tarte tatin stands out amongst the desserts.

Smoking: No smoking in dining room
Civil licence: 120
Accommodation: 19 rooms (19 en suite) ★ ★ ★
Directions: Telephone for details

Dunchideock, EX6 7YF
Tel: 01392 832483
Fax: 01392 833765
e lordhaldon@eclipse.co.uk
Chef(s): Andrew Shortman
Owner(s): Mr Preece
Cost: *Alc* £24.50, set price L £14.90
Times: Noon-1.45pm/7-9.30pm.
Additional: Sunday L. Bar food.
Children welcome
Seats: 60. Private dining room 25.
Jacket and tie preferred

Michael Caines at
The Royal Clarence

An Exeter landmark, opposite the cathedral and housed in a building dating back to the 14th century. The Royal Clarence has been transformed under the tutelage of Gidleigh Park's Michael Caines into a buzzing venue containing a traditional tavern, stylish café-bar and a stunningly smart and colourful dining-room that is a showcase for his boundless imagination and masterful cooking. Served in a casual atmosphere results are always enjoyable and often inspired. A seafood starter of prawns, monkfish, salmon and scallops features risotto at its best on a vegetable nage with shaved Parmesan; roast loin of venison with tasty morsels of pork belly, chestnut purée and juniper jus on a bed of cabbage strikes the right note in terms of flavour and balance; while to round off, vanilla mousse, light as a feather, with spiced preserved fruits exhibits close control of advanced techniques. Arranged by grape variety, the global wine list benefits from the sommelier's careful annotation and slick service.

Cathedral Yard, EX1 1HD
Tel: 01392 310031
Fax: 01392 310032
e tables@michaelcaines.com
Chef(s): Jean-Marc Zanetti
Owner(s): Michael Caines
Cost: *Alc* £25, set price L £17.
☺ ☺ H/wine £13
Times: Noon-2.30pm/7-10pm.
Closed D Xmas
Additional: Sunday L. Bar food L.
Children welcome
Seats: 76. Private dining room 50
Style: Modern
Smoking: No smoking in dining room;
Air conditioning. **Civil licence:** 50
Accommodation: 56 rooms (56 en suite) ★ ★ ★
Directions: Opposite Cathedral

Queens Court Hotel   NEW

The Olive Tree Restaurant styles itself as Mediterranean and has a menu to match. Bright, upbeat cooking with some good use of local raw materials (pan-fried Brixham Bay scallops with tagliatelle, asparagus and a saffron oil dressing) and consistently

Bystock, EX4 4HY
Tel: 01392 272709
Fax: 01392 491390
e enquiries@queenscourt-hotel.co.uk
Chef(s): Robert Drakett

lively flavours. Alongside the lighter, southern European offerings are some heftier dishes such as fillet of Cornish beef with a chive potato cake and confit of red cabbage with a red wine jus.

Style: Modern, French
Smoking: No smoking in dining room
Accommodation: 18 rooms (18 en suite) ★ ★ ★
Directions: 5 miles from M5, town centre, near clocktower rdbt

Owner(s): Mr & Mrs Clark
Cost: *Alc* £22. ☺ ☺ H/wine £10
Times: Noon-3pm/7-10.30pm.
Closed L Sun, 1st wk Jan
Additional: Bar food.
Children welcome
Seats: 26. Private dining room 20

St Olaves Hotel & Restaurant

Mary Arches Street, EX4 3AZ
Tel: 01392 217736
Fax: 01392 413054
e info@olaves.co.uk
Chef(s): Graham Beal
Owner(s): Mr & Mrs Hughes
Cost: *Alc* £25, set price L £17.50/
D £17.50. ☺ H/wine £11.50
Times: Noon-2pm/7-9.30pm.
Closed L Sat
Additional: Sunday L. Bar food.
Children welcome
Seats: 45. Private dining room 12
Style: Traditional
Smoking: No smoking in dining room

Situated just a short walk from the medieval centre of Exeter, St Olave's Court is a surprisingly peaceful hotel standing in its own walled garden. The intimate Golsworthy's restaurant has the feel of a smart, understated living room, complete with mantel clock and oil paintings. The food is traditional but has some interesting modern touches: a menu might include carpaccio of beef, roasted partridge on a red onion tarte tatin, and poached turbot with roasted salsify. At times the cooking lacks vibrancy but dishes are well matched to the season and desserts are often imaginative.

Civil licence: 120
Accommodation: 15 rooms (15 en suite) ★ ★ ★
Directions: Follow signs to city centre, then 'Mary Arches P'. Hotel is opposite car park entrance

GULWORTHY   Map 2 SX47

Horn of Plenty

As its name suggests, this small, elegantly appointed hotel with breathtaking views of the Tamar Valley has for a decade now successfully assumed the mantle of its first mentor, Sonia Stephenson, who arguably pioneered the concept of a restaurant-with-rooms. Even the locally baked bread is based on her original recipe, while constant bedroom improvements have kept the entire operation well abreast of the times. As chef and co-proprietor, Peter Gorton enthuses at the consistent standards the restaurant is acclaimed for with good reason. Ever-friendly service helps to create a pleasant and relaxed atmosphere in which to enjoy cooking that is safe on choice yet full of thoughtfully balanced flavours. Pan-fried scallops with carrot and star anise sauce and Oriental duck salad with

PL19 8JD
Tel: 01822 832528
Fax: 01822 832528
e enquiries@thehornofplenty.co.uk
Chef(s): Peter Gorton
Owner(s): Mr & Mrs P Roston &
Mr P Gorton
Cost: Set price L £23.50/D £40.
H/wine £15
Times: Noon-2pm/7-9pm.
Closed L Mon, 24-26 Dec
Additional: Sunday L.
Children 10 yrs+ at D

England

GULWORTHY *Continued*   Map 2 SX47   *Horn of Plenty*

shiitaki mushrooms and spring onion oil precede venison medallions, cranberry relish and poached red wine pear, and grilled turbot with braised red cabbage and mustard sauce. Similarly well crafted is a dessert of hot rice pudding fritters with pineapple salsa and coconut sorbet - an indulgence to be savoured in these splendid surroundings.

Seats: 60. Private dining room 16. Jacket preferred
Style: Country-house
Smoking: No smoking in dining room
Civil licence: 150
Accommodation: 10 rooms (10 en suite) ★ ★ ★

Directions: 3 miles from Tavistock on A390. Turn R at Gulworthy cross, follow signposted

HAYTOR VALE   Map 3 SX77

Rock Inn

A charming coaching inn dating back to the 1750s, Rock Inn offers a hearty menu full of favourites such as steak and kidney suet pudding or a superior chicken curry. More unusual dishes include braised wild boar in an apple and fresh sage sauce or local ostrich, braised and served in a rich red wine, cranberry and orange sauce.

Seats: 25. **Style:** Classic, Traditional
Smoking: No smoking in dining room
Accommodation: 9 rooms (9 en suite) ★ ★
Directions: In Haytor on A3387, 3 miles from A382

TQ13 9XP
Tel: 01364 661305
Fax: 01364 661242
e rockinn@eclipse.co.uk
Chef(s): Ian Nixon
Owner(s): Mr C Graves
Cost: *Alc* £21. ☺ ☺ H/wine £9.95
Times: Noon-2.30pm/6.30-9.30pm.
Closed 25 Dec
Additional: Sunday L. Bar food.
Children welcome

HEDDON'S MOUTH   Map 3 SS64

Heddon's Gate Hotel

A gong summons diners at 8pm prompt, and with six courses ahead it's best to begin with a hearty appetite. The classy restaurant overlooks scenic Exmoor, but concentration is better focused on the local ingredients and cleverly juggled flavours in, maybe, soft and smooth duck liver, bacon and Armagnac parfait, and moist chicken breast with tarragon sauce. Leave room for handmade chocolates.

Smoking: No smoking in dining room
Accommodation: 14 rooms (14 en suite) ★ ★
Directions: A39 from Lynton. After 4 miles R towards Martinhoe/Woody Bay. First L after 0.5 mile, follow signs to Hunters Inn/Heddon's Mouth. Hotel on R

EX31 4PZ
Tel: 01598 763313
Fax: 01598 763363
e info@hgate.co.uk
Chef(s): Robert Deville
Owner(s): Robert Deville
Cost: *Alc* £26. ☺ H/wine £9.20
Times: Dinner only, 7pm-8pm.
Closed Nov-Mar
Additional:. Vegetarian not available
Seats: 30. Jacket and tie preferred
Style: Traditional, Country-house

England

HONITON
Map 3 SY19

Combe House at Gittisham

Gittisham EX14 3AD
Tel: 01404 540400
Fax: 01404 46004
🅴 stay@thishotel.com
Chef(s): Philip Leach
Owner(s): Ken & Ruth Hunt
Cost: *Alc* £31.50, set price L
£16.50/D £28.50-£31.50.
☺ H/wine £15.50
Times: Noon-2pm/7-9.30pm.
Additional: Sunday L. Children
welcome
Seats: 60. Private dining room 48
Style: Modern
Smoking: No smoking in dining room

An Elizabethan mansion set in no less than 3,500 acres with idyllic woodland views. The cooking has a contemporary edge though and starters might included seared chicken livers with a truffle and wild mushroom risotto. Highlights also include roasted breast and confit leg of duck with gingered cabbage and thyme and orange jus and a rich chocolate tart with raspberry sorbet. The countryside location is much in evidence with extensive use of local produce and the ancient underground cellars allow for an extensive and varied selection of wines

Civil licence: 100
Accommodation: 15 rooms (15 en suite) ★ ★ ★
Directions: From M5 J28 take A373 to Honiton. Then from A30, W of Honiton, follow signs for Gittisham. Hotel signposted

ILSINGTON
Map 3 SX77

The Ilsington Country House

This peaceful hotel stands in extensive well-kept grounds on the southern slopes of Dartmoor. The traditional style dining room

Ilsington Village, TQ13 9RR
Tel: 01364 661452
Fax: 01364 661307
🅴 hotel@ilsington.co.uk
Chef(s): Mike O'Donnell
Owner(s): Tim & Maura Hassell
Cost: Set price L £13.50/D £24.95.
☺ ☺ H/wine £9.95
Times: Noon-2pm/6.30-9pm.
Additional: Sunday L. Bar food.
Children welcome
Seats: 40. Private dining room 32
Style: Traditional, Country-house
Smoking: No smoking in dining room
Accommodation: 25 rooms (25 en
suite) ★ ★ ★
Directions: From M5 take A38 to
Plymouth. Exit at Newton Abbot turn,
then 3rd exit from rdbt to Ilsington,
then 1st R and hotel 5 miles on after
Post Office

provides a relaxing setting in which to enjoy the surprisingly modern cooking. Dishes might include seared tuna on a warm fennel and mouli salad or local lamb with roasted plum tomato and rosemary mousseline.

IVYBRIDGE Map 3 SX66

Glazebrook House

A friendly Victorian country house on the slopes of the Dartmoor National Park, where fresh local produce is transformed into enjoyable Anglo-French dishes. Expect the likes of fillet of beef with roasted shallots on a Madeira wine sauce, and medallions of venison on a parsnip and garlic mash with a port wine and juniper sauce. Amongst the puds brioche with soft fruit and clotted cream stands out.

Style: Modern
Smoking: No-smoking area; Air conditioning
Accommodation: 11 rooms (11 en suite) ★ ★
Directions: From A38, between Ivybridge and Buckfastleigh, follow 'Hotel' signs to South Brent.

South Brent, TQ10 9JE
Tel: 01364 73322
Fax: 01364 72350
Chef(s): David Merriman
Owner(s): Mr & Mrs Heard
Cost: Alc £30, set price L £19.50-£27/D £19.50-£27. ☺ H/wine £10
Times: 12.30-2pm/7-8.30pm.
Closed Sun
Additional: Bar food.
Children welcome. Vegetarian by request only
Seats: 60. Private dining room 12.
Jacket and tie preferred

KINGSBRIDGE Map 3 SX74

Buckland-Tout-Saints

A beautifully proportioned Queen Anne manor house standing in its own grounds, with elegant wood-panelled rooms. One of these is the intimate restaurant, where imaginative, even adventurous cooking disavows the formal surroundings. The likes of smoked duck breast with rocket and pine nuts with raspberry dressing and plum compôte testifies to refined kitchen skills, as does baked red mullet with mousseline of truffles, spinach and basil concasse and sauce vierge. Desserts are another demonstrable strength, as in warm chocolate tart stuffed with fennel confit and sorbet with chocolate sauce, and warm exotic fruit salad with spice en croute and coconut brioche.

Civil licence: 100
Accommodation: 10 rooms (10 en suite) ★ ★ ★
Directions: 3 miles NE of Kingsbridge off A381. Through village to Goveton, 500yds past church

Goveton, TQ7 2DS
Tel: 01548 853055
Fax: 01548 856261
buckland@tout-saints.co.uk
Chef(s): Jean-Philippe Bidart
Owner(s): Mr & Mrs Trumble
Cost: Alc £30, set price L £18/D £25-£35. ☺ ☺ H/wine £9.75
Times: Noon-1.45pm/7-9pm.
Closed 15 Jan-5 Feb
Additional: Sunday L. Bar food L.
Children welcome. Vegetarian by request
Seats: 40. Private dining room 18
Style: Classic, Country-House
Smoking: No smoking in dining room

KINGSKERSWELL Map 3 SX86

Pitt House Restaurant

A chocolate box style thatched Devon cottage with low beams, a wood burning stove and an oak panelled ceiling in the dining room. The cooking is honest and unfussy, making impressive use of local ingredients. Dishes might include roasted local lamb with a redcurrant and red wine gravy or braised Gressingham duck with Burgundy wine and thyme jus.

Style: Traditional
Smoking: No smoking in dining room
Directions: From Newton Abbot take Torquay road, 1st R, follow road to junction & turn L, parish church on R. Take 1st R, restaurant 50yds on L

2 Church End Road, TQ12 5DS
Tel: 01803 873374
Chef(s): Vanessa Rogers
Owner(s): Mr & Mrs J Rogers
Cost: Set price D £25. H/wine £12.95
Times: Noon-3pm/7-11pm.
Closed Mon, L Tue & Sat, D Sun-Mon, Xmas, 2 wks Jan, 2 wks Aug
Additional: Sunday L.
Children 10yrs+
Seats: 30. Private dining room 12.
Jacket and tie preferred

LEWDOWN

Map 2 SX48

Lewtrenchard Manor

A stone manor house built in around 1600, this hotel lives up to the promise of its beautiful exterior and country garden setting. Every room reveals more antique furniture and magnificent wood panelling. The food is equally impressive, combining high quality ingredients with international flavours. A meal might include roasted pigeon breast with stuffed baby cabbage, pomme galette and foie gras, followed by braised pork cheek with star anise, lardons of pancetta and a parsley jus. Influences from further afield are evident in dishes such as cumin crusted lamb with fruit and nut couscous and a cucumber raita.

Civil licence: 60
Accommodation: 9 rooms (9 en suite) ★ ★ ★
Directions: Take A30 for Lewdown, after 6 miles turn L at signpost for Lewtrenchard. Follow signs for 0.75 mile

EX20 4PN
Tel: 01566 783256
Fax: 01566 783332
e s&j@lewtrendchard.co.uk
Chef(s): Jason Hornbuckle
Owner(s): Mr & Mrs J Murray
Cost: Alc £32, set price L £32/D £32.
☺ H/wine £12
Times: Noon-1.30pm/7-9pm.
Additional: Sunday L. Bar food.
Children 8yrs+
Seats: 35. Private dining room 16.
Jacket and tie preferred
Style: Formal, Country-House
Smoking: No smoking in dining room

LIFTON

Map 2 SX38

Arundell Arms

PL16 0AA
Tel: 01566 784666
Fax: 01566 784494
e reservations@arundellarms.com
Chef(s): Philip Burgess,
Nick Shopland
Owner(s): Anne Vossbark
Cost: Alc £37.50, set price L £22/
D £30. ☺ ☺ H/wine £11
Times: 12.30-2pm/7.30-9.30pm
Additional: Sunday L. Bar food.
Children welcome
Seats: 70. Private dining room 24
Smoking: No smoking in dining room
Accommodation: 27 rooms (27 en suite) ★ ★ ★

Delightful 18th-century former coaching inn with a newly-revamped restaurant introducing a modern dimension to a traditional hotel. Bright overhead spotlights place the cooking under the glare, and highlight some exceptional dishes from the varied menu. Spiced fillet of red mullet with celeriac, bacon and basil relish was one such recent starter, while tournedos of Devon beef with creamed leeks, pan-fried chicken liver and a rich red wine ands thyme sauce came a close second, with its rich flavours and tender meat. Desserts range from poached fruits through rum and raisin pudding to chocolate mousse with a coffee bean sauce and a selection of cheeses, and a meal finishes with a cafetière of filter coffee and chocolate truffles. Service from an experienced and efficient young staff is in keeping with the new crisp atmosphere of the dining room.

Directions: Just off A30 in village of Lifton

England

LIFTON *Continued* Map 2 SX38

Tinhay Mill Restaurant NEW

Tinhay, PL16 0AJ
Tel: 01566 784201
Chef(s): Margaret Wilson
Owner(s): Mr P & Mrs M Wilson
Cost: *Alc* £23.50, set price £23.50. ☺
H/wine £5.25
Times: Dinner only, 7-9.30pm.
Closed D Sun & Mon
Additional: Children 12yrs+
Seats: 30. Private dining room 26.
Jacket and tie preferred
Style: Classic, Country-house
Smoking: No smoking in dining room
Accommodation: 3 rooms (3 en suite)
◆◆◆◆
Directions: Telephone for directions

Village restaurant in a 15th-century house with beamed ceilings, white walls and inglenook fireplaces. Set-price and *carte* menus are offered, and an interesting selection of reasonably priced wines. Fresh local produce brings plenty of flavour to the well-balanced dishes - terrine of salmon and spinach, tender rack of lamb with a plum, rosemary and Madeira sauce, and a Japonaise strawberry gateau.

LYDFORD Map 2 SX58

Dartmoor Inn

EX20 4AY
Tel: 01822 820221
Fax: 01822 820494
Chef(s): Philip Burgess & Ian Brown
Owner(s): Karen & Philip Burgess,
Anne Voss-Bark
Cost: *Alc* £23.75, set price L £14.75/
D £19.75-£23. ☺ ☺ H/wine £11.75
Times: Noon-2.15pm/6.30-10pm.
Closed Mon, D Sun
Additional: Sunday L. Bar food.
Children 5yrs+ Fri-Sat D
Seats: 65. Private dining room 20
Style: Rustic
Smoking: No smoking in dining room
Directions: On A386, Tavistock to
Okehampton road

The sheer enthusiasm of the Burgess family is palpable at this affectionately restored 16th-century coaching inn. The cooking continues to be rustic in style and there is an honesty to dishes like a mighty slow roast lamb shank with citrus sauce that can only bring a warmth to your heart and a smile to your lips. Some of the rough edges have been smoothed and there is now more dexterity in evidence in those concoctions that require that approach - a starter of chicken and spinach terrine for instance. Puds also tend to be robust with the likes of a chocolate and raspberry tart or baked ricotta cheesecake with pine nuts and a Jasmine scented winter fruit compote.

LYNMOUTH

Map 3 SS74

Rising Sun

A former smugglers inn with whitewashed walls and a thatched roof, nestling beside the harbour. The interior is just as you'd hope: crooked ceilings, thick walls and uneven oak floors. Occupying several buildings, the hotel incorporates Shelley's Cottage, in which the poet is believed to have spent his honeymoon in 1812. The restaurant offers a good selection of modern dishes, all confidently done with well-balanced flavours. A meal might include pan fried scallops with saffron couscous, beetroot crisps and a light curry oil followed by pan fried fillet of Devon beef with sautéed asparagus tips, wild mushrooms and roast mushroom jus.

Accommodation: 16 rooms (16 en suite) ★ ★
Directions: M5 J23 (Minehead). Take A39 to Lynmouth. Opposite the harbour

Harbourside, EX35 6EQ
Tel: 01598 753223
Fax: 01598 753480
e risingsunlynmouth@easynet.co.uk
Chef(s): Steven Batchelor
Owner(s): H Jeune
Cost: *Alc* £30, set price L £15.95/ D £19.95. ☺ ☺ H/wine £10.95
Times: Noon-2pm/7-9.30pm.
Additional: Sunday L. Bar food. Children 7yrs+
Seats: 32
Style: Modern
Smoking: No smoking in dining room

MARTINHOE

Map 3 SS64

Old Rectory Hotel

Located just 500 yards from the coastal footpath, the Old Rectory provides the ideal base from which to explore Exmoor. The dining room is a traditionally styled room (grandfather clock, patterned carpet, polished tables) and provides a spacious, candlelit setting for a meal. Dishes might include chicken breast with apple and Devon Blue sauce or roast fillet of lamb with leek sauce.

Style: Country-House
Smoking: No smoking in dining room; no cigars
Accommodation: 8 rooms (8 en suite) ★ ★
Directions: M5 J27 onto A361, R onto A399 Blackmore Gate, R onto A39 Parracombe. At Martinhoe Cross, 3rd road on L to Woody Bay/Martinhoe

EX31 4QT
Tel: 01598 763368
Fax: 01598 763567
e reception@oldrectoryhotel.co.uk
Chef(s): Enid Richmond
Owner(s): Christopher & Enid Richmond
Cost: Set price D £27. H/wine £9.50
Times: Dinner only, 7.30-8pm.
Closed Dec-Feb (Opening times vary in Mar & Nov)
Additional: Children 14 yrs+.
Vegetarian by request only
Seats: 20

MORETONHAMPSTEAD

Map 3 SX78

Blackaller Hotel

A 17th-century woollen mill sitting peacefully beside the River Bovey. An inglenook fireplace is a striking feature of the dining room, where British dishes like whole grilled Mediterranean prawns, and roast salmon fillet on rocket leaves, are served in the evening.

North Bovey, TQ13 8QY
Tel: 01647 440322
Fax: 01647 440322
Telephone for further details

Manor House

Classy Victorian hotel with lovely views over Dartmoor National Park. Good-looking food and variety are obvious strengths. Vegetarians too, will be happy with their choices. Don't skip the homemade, flavoured rolls and for the carnivore,

TQ13 8RE
Tel: 01647 440355
Fax: 01647 440961
e reception.manorhouse @principalhotels.co.uk

England

MORETONHAMPSTEAD *Continued*   Map 3 SX78

the meaty game terrine. Peanut butter ice cream and a good range of petits fours are a hit with diners.

Seats: 150. Private dining room 120. Jacket and tie preferred.
Style: Classic, Traditional
Smoking: No smoking in dining room. **Civil licence:** 120
Accommodation: 90 rooms (90 en suite) ★ ★ ★ ★
Directions: 2miles from Moretonhamstead towards Princetown on B3212

Chef(s): David Berry
Owner(s): Principle Hotels
Cost: *Alc* £30, set price L £12.95/ D £23. ☺ ☺ H/wine £13.50
Times: 12.30-2pm/7-9.30pm.
Additional: Sunday L. Bar food. Children welcome

PARKHAM   Map 2 SS32

Penhaven Country Hotel

Badger-watching is a nocturnal attraction at this comfortable 17th-century hotel, while the midday and evening lure is certainly the food. Vegetarians are particularly welcomed, while dishes like mashed prawns on toast with sesame seeds and a spicy dip, and pan-fried wild boar loin steak with a honey and cranberry sauce cater splendidly for the rest.

Seats: 45. **Smoking:** No-smoking area
Accommodation: 12 rooms (12 en suite) ★ ★ ★
Directions: From A39 at Horns Cross, follow signs to Parkham and turn L after church

Rectory Lane, EX39 5PL
Tel: 01237 451711
Fax: 01237 451878
📧 reception@penhaven.co.uk
Chef(s): Richard Copp
Owner(s): Mr & Mrs Wade
Cost: *Alc* £23, set price L £11.95/ D £16.50. ☺ ☺ H/wine £12.95
Times: 12.15-1.30pm/7.15-9pm.
Closed L Mon-Sat
Additional: Children 10yrs+

PLYMOUTH   Map 2 SX45

Boringdon Hall

There's an elegant air of faded glory to this Elizabethan manor house, with the gallery restaurant - which overlooks the great hall - being a suitably grand place to dine. The British based menu might include honey glazed duck breast with an orange marmalade sauce or chicken supreme with mango, prawns and a white wine butter sauce.

Civil licence: 120
Accommodation: 40 rooms (40 en suite) ★ ★ ★
Directions: From A38 to Marsh Mills Rdbt, follow signs for Plympton, dual carriageway to small island. L over bridge follow brown tourist signs

Colebrook, Plympton, PL7 4DP
Tel: 01752 344455
Fax: 01752 346578
Chef(s): Jamie Symons
Cost: *Alc* £30, set price L £12/ D £24.95. ☺ ☺ H/wine £14
Times: Noon-2pm/7-9.30pm.
Closed L Mon-Sat
Additional: Sunday L. Bar food. Children welcome
Seats: 50. Private dining room 25
Style: Country-house
Smoking: No smoking in dining room

Chez Nous

13 Frankfort Gate, PL1 1QA

After 20 years, Jacques Marchal's resolutely French restaurant retains its cosy bistro feel and that blackboard menu (pretty much illegible without 20/20 vision!). Incongruously located in a small pedestrian square of Plymouth's post war reconstruction, but cross the threshold and you're entering French territory. High quality ingredients are seriously and professionally cooked, the menu is large (for a one-man band), and the repertoire does not change radically from year to year, although dishes come and go from day to day as supplies are marshalled. The style is light, fish and shellfish, as one would expect, are especial strengths (scallops with ginger, and glow in the dark white turbot with a herby pepper crust). Offal too is worth a second look, (excellent lamb's sweetbreads with Madeira). Susanne Marchal keeps every thing ship shape front of house and it is a pleasure to eat here, there is indeed a true sense of 'chez-nous'.

Tel: 01752 266793
Fax: 01752 266793
Chef(s): Jacques Marchal
Owner(s): J A Marchal
Cost: Alc £37.50, set price L £37.50/ D £37.50. H/wine £10.50
Times: 12.30-11.30pm/7-10.30pm. Closed Sun, Mon, 3 wks Feb, 3 wks Sep
Additional: Children 10yrs+. Vegetarian with 24hrs notice
Seats: 28
Style: French
Smoking: No pipes

Directions: Frankfort Gate is a pedestrianised street between Western Approach & Market Avenue

Duke of Cornwall Hotel

16th-century coaching inn with a Gothic feel: the large restaurant features a massive chandelier hanging from a domed ceiling. The menu is more up to date, with dishes such as crab cake or braised pheasant making good use of Westcountry produce. Skilfully handled desserts might include crème brûlée tart with fruit compôte.

Seats: 80. Private dining room 30
Style: Classic. **Smoking:** No smoking in dining room
Civil licence: 300
Accommodation: 71 rooms (71 en suite) ★ ★ ★
Directions: City centre, follow signs 'Pavilions', hotel road is opposite

Millbay Road, PL1 3LG
Tel: 01752 275850
Fax: 01752 275854
e duke@bhere.co.uk
Chef(s): Darren Kester
Owner(s): Chris Chapman
Cost: Alc £19.50, set price L £15/ D £19.50. ☺ ☺ H/wine £10.75
Times: Dinner only, 7-10pm
Additional: Bar food. Children welcome

Kitley House Hotel

Yealmpton, PL8 2NW
Tel: 01752 881555
Fax: 01752 881667
e reservations@kitleyhousehotel.com
Chef(s): Vivien Marshall
Owner(s): Mr A Huckerby
Cost: Alc £24.50, set price L £14.50/ D £24.50. ☺ ☺ H/wine £12.95
Times: 12.30-2.30pm/7-9.30pm.
Additional: Sunday L. Bar food. Children welcome
Seats: 40. Private dining room 20. Jacket and tie preferred
Style: Country-house
Smoking: No smoking in dining room
Civil licence: 100
Accommodation: 20 rooms (20 en suite) ★ ★ ★

A mile long tree lined drive leads to this grade one listed Tudor revival house. The restaurant is housed in the former library, whose deep red walls still contain recesses filled with books. The imaginative menu might include duck breast on cassis sauce with black pudding mash or grilled medallion of beef fillet glazed with boursin cheese with a wild mushroom and truffle sauce.

Directions: From Plymouth take A379 (Kingsbridge). Entrance between villages of Brixton & Yealmpton on R (10 mins)

England

Langdon Court

Once owned by Henry VIII, there is history at every turn at Langdon Court with many original features interwoven with contemporary improvements. In the elegant restaurant choose, perhaps, pan-fried medallions of beef fillet with rich pâté and red wine sauce or roasted baby poussin set on a cherry stuffing and glazed with a spring onion sauce. Don't forget to allow a small space for a speciality Devon creamery ice cream or one of chef's own puddings.

Down Thomas, PL9 0DY
Tel: 01752 862358
Fax: 01752 863428
e enquiries@langdoncourt.co.uk
Chef(s): Steve Dyer, Chris Aldridge, Andy Stevens-Lock
Owner(s): Sheila Barnes, Alan & Ann Cox
Cost: *Alc* £24. ☺ ☺ H/wine £8.50
Times: Noon-2pm/7-9.30pm. Closed D Sun
Additional: Sunday L. Bar food. Children welcome
Seats: 60. Private dining room 25. Jacket and tie preferred
Style: Country-house
Smoking: No smoking in dining room
Civil licence: 80
Accommodation: 18 rooms (18 en suite) ★★
Directions: From A379 at Elburton, follow brown tourist signs.

Tanners Restaurant

Plymouth's oldest building has many charms: a simple interior, stone floors, a water well and (most importantly) consistently good cooking. The excellent value menu offers classic combinations such as roast chicken supreme stuffed with garlic and herbs or steamed hake with chive butter sauce, but also includes contemporary dishes - perhaps pepper and bean sprout spring roll with a balsamic dressing or risotto of mussels with vermouth sauce and crispy leeks. Ingredients are local and of the highest quality - just one more reason for this restaurant's ever growing popularity.

Directions: Town centre. Behind St Andrews Church on Royal Parade

Prysten House, Finewell Street, PL1 2AE
Tel: 01752 252001
Fax: 01752 252105
Chef(s): Christopher & James Tanner
Owner(s): Christopher & James Tanner
Cost: Set price L £15.50/D £22.50-£27.50. ☺ ☺ H/wine £10.50
Times: Noon-2.30pm/7-9.30pm. Closed Sun-Mon, Xmas, 31 Dec, 1st 2 wks Jan
Additional: Children 12yrs+
Seats: 45
Style: Traditional
Smoking: No smoking in dining room

ROCKBEARE
Map 3 SY09

The Jack In The Green

EX5 2EE
Tel: 01404 822240
Fax: 01404 823445
e info@jackinthegreen.uk.com
Chef(s): Matthew Mason
Owner(s): Paul Parnell
Cost: Set price L £19/D £19. ☺ ☺
H/wine £9.50
Times: 11am-2pm/6-9.30pm.
Closed 25 Dec-1 Jan
Additional: Sunday L. Bar food.
Children welcome

This popular pub takes its name from the pagan figure who presided over spring fertility rituals. The menu is appropriately in tune with the seasons but does not restrict itself to British traditions. Dishes might include seared salmon with coriander and chick pea curry or loin of pork wrapped in pancetta with roquefort and lemon. Staff are 'excellent'.

Seats: 60. Private dining room 30. **Style:** Modern
Smoking: No-smoking area; Air conditioning
Directions: Situated 5 miles E of Exeter. From M5 J29 take old A30 towards Honiton. Take turn to Rockbeare on R

SALCOMBE
Map 3 SX73

Soar Mill Cove Hotel

Soar Mill Cove, Marlborough, TQ7 3DS
Tel: 01548 561566
Fax: 01548 561223
e info@makepeacehotels.co.uk
Chef(s): Keith Makepeace
Owner(s): Mr & Mrs K Makepeace
Cost: Set price L £27.90/D £34
Times: Noon-3pm/7.15-9.30pm.
Closed 2 Jan-8 Feb
Additional: Sunday L. Bar food L. Children welcome. Vegetarian by request only
Seats: 50. Private dining room 22
Style: Classic, Country-house
Smoking: No smoking in dining room

Justifiably popular with the locals, this restaurant enjoys spectacular views down the cove to the sea. Inside, comfortable armchairs and a log fire create a relaxing atmosphere. A meal might begin with cocktails in the lounge, followed by canapés and an amuse bouche such as cheese and leek tartlet. Thanks to the coastal setting, the modern British menu includes an impressive choice of fresh fish, such as bass fillet on pumpkin purée with fresh mussels, but meats are also local wherever possible: the 'superb' North Devon fillet (from a breed of cattle reared opposite the hotel) is well worth sampling.

Accommodation: 21 rooms (21 en suite) ★ ★ ★
Directions: A381 to Salcombe, through village follow signs to sea.

Tides Reach Hotel

South Sands, TQ8 8LJ
Tel: 01548 843466
Fax: 01548 843954
e enquirie@tidesreach.com
Chef(s): Finn Ibsen
Owner(s): Pat, Roy & John Edwards
Cost: Set price L £16.50/D £30. ☺
H/wine £13.75

Despite its size, this modern hotel retains a friendly, personal feel, largely because of the quality service provided by the proprietors and their staff. The Garden Room is a bright, conservatory style restaurant, with lovely views of palm filled gardens and the sea beyond. A solid base of traditional dishes and a smattering of modern, international flavours give the menu a broad appeal. Local ingredients are used wherever possible, as in a starter of half a Salcombe lobster with three

SALCOMBE *Continued*   Map 3 SX73

bean salad, cherry tomatoes and basil dressing. Lovely seaside location with a sandy beach only yards away.

Smoking: No smoking in dining room
Accommodation: 35 rooms (35 en suite) ★ ★ ★
Directions: Take cliff road towards sea and Bolt Head

Times: 12.15-2pm/7-9pm.
Closed Dec, Jan
Additional: Sunday L. Bar food L.
Children 8yrs+
Seats: 80. Jacket and tie preferred
Style: Modern, Formal

SAUNTON   Map 2 SS43

Preston House

Built as a Victorian summer retreat, this is still the perfect place to enjoy views of Barnstaple bay. The dining room offers traditional combinations such as Welsh lamb with rosemary jus alongside more imaginative dishes - perhaps deep fried monkfish tails with spiced vegetable salad and a lime and cumin mayonnaise.

Smoking: No smoking in dining room
Accommodation: 12 rooms (12 en suite) ★ ★
Directions: From Barnstaple on A361 follow signs to Braunton. In Braunton turn L at traffic lights. Signed Saunton/Croyde. Hotel 4 miles on the R

EX33 1LG
Tel: 01271 890472
Fax: 01271 890555
e prestonhouse-saunton@zoom.co.uk
Chef(s): Kevin Little
Owner(s): Jan Poole
Cost: Set price D £25-£30.
H/wine £11.95
Times: Dinner only, 7pm-8.30pm.
Closed Jan
Additional: Children 15yrs+
Seats: 30. Jacket and tie preferred
Style: Traditional

SIDMOUTH   Map 3 SY18

Brownlands Hotel

Originally built as the retirement home of Victorian astronomer Sir Norman Lockyer, Brownlands offers beautiful views over the wooded slopes of Salcombe hill to Sidmouth and the sea. The smart dining room is a relaxing place to enjoy old favourites (breaded lamb cutlets; griddled salmon), or to sample modern dishes such as pan fried sausage with bubble and squeak and red onion.

Smoking: No smoking in dining room
Accommodation: 14 rooms (14 en suite) ★ ★
Directions: From A3052 turn R past Blue Bull Inn onto Fortescue Rd. Hotel 1 mile

Sid Road, EX10 9AG
Tel & Fax: 01395 513053
e brownlandshotel@virgin.net
Chef(s): Laurence Barber, Janice May
Owner(s): Peter, Diane,
Steven Kendall-Tordy
Cost: Set price £22. ☺ ☺
H/wine £9.95
Times: Noon-7-8pm. Closed Nov-Mar
Additional: Bar food L.
Children 8yrs+
Seats: 35. Jacket and tie preferred
Style: Classic, Traditional

Riviera Hotel

Elegance and traditional comforts are thriving at this coastal Regency hotel, and nowhere more so than in the restaurant.

The Esplanade, EX10 8AY
Tel: 01395 515201
Fax: 01395 577775
e enquiries@hotelriviera.co.uk
Chef(s): Mark Leavers,
Christian Miguel
Owner(s): Peter Wharton
Cost: *Alc* £28.50, set price L £18/
D £28. ☺ H/wine £12
Times: 12.30-2pm/7-9pm.
Additional: Sunday L. Bar food L.
Children welcome
Seats: 85. Private dining room 65
Style: Classic, Formal
Smoking: No smoking in dining room;
Air conditioning
Accommodation: 27 rooms (27 en
suite) ★ ★ ★ ★

Expect classic dishes with clean flavours, served with reverential attention. A recent crème brûlée with raspberry coulis exceeded expectations with its silky texture. The set menu - seven courses at dinner - changes daily.

Victoria Hotel

A smart dining room in the imposing Victorian built hotel, one of Sidmouth's best. Try a starter of millefeuille of Parma ham with goats' cheese, onion confit and pesto or alternatively scampi and monkfish in puff pastry with white wine and dill sauce. Roasted saddle of lamb has a full-flavoured jus and medallions of local venison are served with caramelised walnuts.

Seats: 120. Private dining room 30. **Style:** Formal. **Smoking:** No smoking in dining room. **Accommodation:** 61 rooms (61 en suite) ★★★★. **Directions:** At the western end of The Esplanade

Directions: From M5 J30 take A3052 to Sidmouth. Situated in centre of The Esplanade

The Esplanade, EX10 8RY
Tel: 01395 512651
Fax: 01395 579154
e info@victoriahotel.co.uk
Chef(s): M Pyro & D Gardner
Owner(s): Brend Hotels
Cost: Alc £27.50, set price L £16/ D £27.50. H/wine £8.75
Times: 12.30-2.30pm/7-9pm.
Additional: Sunday L. Bar food. Children welcome

STAVERTON Map 3 SX76

Sea Trout Inn

This 15th-century inn is named after a previous landlord's catch in the nearby River Dart. A pretty, whitewashed building, it offers a friendly pub atmosphere and is decorated in a fitting style, with real fires, beamed ceilings and (of course) fish in showcases. Dine in the bar area or the bright conservatory, where the menu offers a mixture of the fairly classic (char-grilled venison with mash, game jus and apricots) and modern dishes - perhaps roasted chicken breast on egg noodles with wild mushrooms and vegetables. Service is relaxed, informal and efficient.

Accommodation: 11 rooms (11 en suite) ★★
Directions: From A38 take A384 to Staverton

TQ9 6PA
Tel: 01803 762274
Fax: 01803 762506
Chef(s): Kim Olsen
Owner(s): Nicholas Brookland
Cost: Set price L £12.95/D £20. ☺ ☺ H/wine £9.75
Times: Noon-3pm/7-11pm.
Closed L Mon-Sat, D Sun
Additional: Sunday L. Bar food. Children welcome
Seats: 32. **Style:** Classic, Bistro-Style
Smoking: No smoking in dining room; Air conditioning

TAVISTOCK Map 2 SX47

Bedford Hotel

In the centre of Tavistock, this imposing castellated hotel was built in the ruins of an ancient Benedictine abbey. A private dwelling for the Dukes of Bedford for over 100 years, the restaurant has been named Woburn after their family home. The decor is classically smart and sophisticated and good technical skills underlie the imaginative menu. The freshness and quality of the produce is evident in dishes such as seared tuna, scallops with red pepper and citrus beurre blanc, and chicken breast with fricassée of wild mushrooms. The attractive presentation certainly encourages the appetite.

e jane@bedford-hotel.co.uk
Cost: Alc £21.95/D £21.95. ☺ ☺ H/wine £10.45
Times: noon-2.30pm/7-9.30pm.
Additional: Sunday L. Bar food. Children welcome
Seats: 55. Private dining room 24
Style: Modern, Country-house
Smoking: No smoking in dining room
Accommodation: 29 rooms (29 en suite) ★★★
Directions: Leave M5 J31, take (Okehampton) A30. Take A386 (Tavistock). On entering Tavistock follow signs for town centre. Hotel opposite church

1 Plymouth Road, PL19 8BB
Tel: 01822 613221
Fax: 01822 618034

TAVISTOCK *Continued*   Map 2 SX47

Browns Hotel & Brasserie   NEW

80 West Street, PL19 8AQ
Tel: 01822 618686
Telephone for further details

Reputedly the oldest licensed premises in Tavistock, Browns is a pleasing blend of panache and understated style. Richard Hunt's food is thoroughly enjoyable, and perfectly pitched for the relaxed atmosphere of the restaurant: at lunchtime there's a brasserie menu, while the short fixed price evening *carte* attracts a more discerning crowd. Expect broccoli and blue cheese soup, cannon of English lamb on a lemon and thyme mash, roasted garlic and rosemary, and to finish a splendid example of the classic crème brûlée with vibrant fruit coulis and dustings of cocoa powder. Close with good cafetière coffee and petits fours.

THURLESTONE   Map 3 SX64

Thurlestone Hotel

TQ7 3NN
Tel: 01548 560382
Fax: 01548 561069
e enquiries@thurlestone.co.uk
Chef(s): David Bunn
Owner(s): Grose family
Cost: Set price L £30/D £30. ☺
H/wine £9.75
Times: 12.30-2pm/7.30-9pm.
Closed L Mon-Sat
Additional: Sunday L. Bar food L.
Children welcome
Seats: 150. Private dining room 18.
Jacket and tie preferred
Style: Classic, Traditional

This family run hotel has lovely views of the south Devon coast and equally impressive grounds. The restaurant is a traditionally elegant setting with a menu to match. A meal might begin with confit of duck with parsnip purée and red wine jus, followed by a main course of braised rump of lamb with puy lentils, fondant potatoes and lamb jus. Desserts range from homely (sticky toffee pudding with toffee sauce) to extravagant creations such as light blood orange bavarois wrapped in chocolate tuile. All courses are attractively presented and make good use of quality ingredients.

Smoking: No smoking in dining room; Air conditioning
Accommodation: 67 rooms (67 en suite) ★ ★ ★ ★
Directions: A381 (Kingsbridge), then A379 (Churchstow), turn onto B3197, then turn into lane signposted Thurlestone

TORQUAY   Map 3 SX96

Dunstone Hall   NEW

Lower Warberry Road, TQ1 1QS
Tel: 01803 293185
Telephone for further details

Simple canapés, lovely home-made breads and loin of lamb cooked to pink perfection, while the fresh vegetables 'were exceptional in freshness and flavour', and a delightfully cleansing lemon syllabub to finish. What more encouragement could you need to visit this Edwardian conservatory restaurant with stunning views?

Grand Hotel

Sea Front, TQ2 6NT
Tel: 01803 296677
Fax: 01803 213462
e grandhotel@netsite.co.uk
Chef(s): Wayne Maddern
Cost: *Alc* £30, set price L £15/D £25.
H/wine £12.50
Times: 12.30-2pm/7-9.30pm.
Additional: Sunday L. Bar food L.
Children welcome
Seats: 180. Private dining room 200

An elegant and formal hotel restaurant, but not too stiff and starchy. The menu includes zingy modern dishes such as mango soup with lemon grass, lobster and chives alongside favourites such as Tournedos Rossini or Dover sole with lemon and parsley butter. The well balanced wine list complements any choice.

Style: Traditional, Edwardian
Smoking: No smoking in dining room
Accommodation: 110 rooms (110 en suite) ★ ★ ★ ★
Directions: A380 to Torquay sea front, hotel immediately on right

England

The Grosvenor Hotel, Mima's Restaurant

Belgrave Road, TQ2 5HG
Tel: 01803 215515
Fax: 01803 215515
Telephone for further details

STOP PRESS
Change of Chef

All change as we went to press at this hotel just off the seafront, with Mima's Restaurant about to relaunch following the departure of Richard Hunt. The style is expected to stay broadly the same with the use of good quality produce and some imaginative lively combinations.

Imperial Hotel

Park Hill Road, TQ1 2DG
Tel: 01803 294301
Fax: 01803 298293
e imperialtorquay@paramount-hotels.co.uk

A variety of dining options all offer superb views over Torbay. The service is surprisingly relaxed and easy-going for a Five Star hotel, although none of the professionalism is sacrificed. Steamed sea bass with lime and ginger risotto and cardamom sauce is a dish packed with delicate flavours and textures.

Style: Modern
Smoking: No smoking in dining room; Air conditioning
Civil licence: 300
Accommodation: 153 rooms (153 en suite) ★ ★ ★ ★ ★
Directions: M5 to Exeter, A380 then A3022 to Torquay. Park Hill Rd is off Torwood Street/ Babbacombe Rd, just N or New Harbour

Chef(s): Richard Allsopp
Cost: Alc £32, set price D £25-£32
Times: 12.30-2pm/7-9.30pm.
Closed L Mon-Sat
Additional: Sunday L. Bar food. Children welcome
Seats: 200. Private dining room 350. Jacket and tie preferred

Mulberry House

1 Scarborough Road, TQ2 5UJ
Tel: 01803 213639
Chef(s): Lesley Cooper
Owner(s): Lesley Cooper
Cost: Alc £17.50. ☺ ☺ H/wine £10
Times: Noon-2pm/7.30-9.30pm.
Closed Mon-Tue (ex residents), L Wed-Thu
Additional: Sunday L. Children welcome
Seats: 24. Jacket and tie preferred

Set in a homely Victorian villa, this restaurant has a cosy cottage tearoom atmosphere and an equally comforting menu. The carefully prepared dishes might include home-made tagliatelli with prawn, cream and tomato sauce or ragout of Devon lamb fillet pieces with tomato, onion, fresh herbs and white wine sauce.

Style: Traditional, Country-House
Smoking: No smoking in dining room
Accommodation: 3 rooms (3 en suite) ♦♦♦♦
Directions: From the seafront turn up Belgrave Road, then 1st R into Scarborough Road

England

TORQUAY *Continued* **Map 3 SX96**

Orchid Restaurant

at Corbyn Head Hotel, Torquay Road,
Sea Front TQ2 6RH
Tel: 01803 296366
Fax: 01803 296152
info@corbynhead.com
Chef(s): Daniel Kay
Cost: *Alc* £34, set price L £24.95-
£34.95/D £24.95-£50. ☺
H/wine £12.50
Times: 12.30-2pm/7-10pm.
Closed Sun-Mon
Additional: Children 10yrs+
Seats: 24

Smart and formal with sweeping views across Torbay, the
Orchid lives up to its name with an orchid on each candlelit
table. A winter meal included starters of pigeon breast with a
leek and Parmesan risotto and a confit of duck with crouton
and pine nut dressed salad leaves. Best end of lamb had a
pleasing rosemary flavour while a fillet of salmon was served on
a purée of fennel with an orange sauce. Strawberry soufflé was
accompanied by an 'impressive' basil ice cream, and a tangy
lemon tart by cassis sorbet in a brandy snap.

Smoking: No smoking in dining room. Air conditioning

Orestone Manor   NEW

Wonderful small country house hotel set within tranquil
grounds, overlooking Lyme Bay. Elegant dining room has a
distinctly colonial look, an appropriate setting for some
accomplished cuisine. Seared scallops with a Japanese sauce,
roasted loin of venison with a juniper jus (a strong dish) and a
creditable lemon tart, typify the style.

Seats: 45. **Style:** Modern English
Smoking: No smoking in dining room
Accommodation: 12 rooms (12 en suite) ★★★

Rockhouse Lane,
Maidencombe, TQ1 4SX
Tel: 01803 328098
Fax: 01803 328336
enquiries@orestone.co.uk
Chef(s): Anthony Hetherington
Owner(s): Peter Morgan
Cost: *Alc* £30, set price D £30. ☺
H/wine £9.75
Times: Noon-2pm/7-9pm.
Additional: Sunday L. Children
welcome

Osborne Hotel

Hesketh Crescent, Meadfoot,
TQ1 2LL
Tel: 01803 213311
Fax: 01803 296788
rec@osborne-torquay.co.uk
Chef(s): Chris Billingsley
Cost: *Alc* £29, set price D £22. ☺
H/wine £12.50
Times: Dinner only, 7-9.30pm
Additional: Bar food. Children
welcome. Vegetarian by request only
Seats: 70. Private dining room 26
Smoking: No smoking in dining room
Accommodation: 29 rooms (29 en
suite) ★★★

England

With superb views over the beach and Torbay, the Osborne forms the centrepiece of an elegant Regency terrace. The restaurant looks over five acres of gardens towards the sea, and provides a traditional setting in which to enjoy the modern British based menu. A meal might include goats' cheese salad followed by fillet of salmon en croute with a saffron sauce.

Directions: Follow A3022 to seafront, turn L towards Harbour. At Clock Tower turn L; at next junction/traffic lights turn R. Over brow of hill and gates of Hesketh Crescent and hotel are opposite

Toorak Hotel

Excellent leisure facilities attract active types to this hotel, and there's a comfortable restaurant to relax in after the exertions. Traditional dishes like steaks, roasts and fresh fruit and cream desserts appear on the menu alongside field mushroom terrine with summer leaves, tarragon-scented sirloin of beef, and blackberry frangipane tart with cream.

Chestnut Avenue, TQ2 5JS
Tel: 01803 400400
Fax: 01803 400140
Telephone for further details

TOTNES   Map 3 SX86

Durant Arms Restaurant

Local artists' work decorates the dining room walls at this neat 18th-century inn. A blackboard shows daily-changing dishes like celery and coconut soup, and simple but effective fillet of lamb with herb crust. Finish with delicious treacle tart made, like everything else, from quality, fresh ingredients.

Ashprington TQ9 7UP
Tel: 01803 732240
Fax: 01803 732471
Chef(s): William Steer
Owner(s): Mr & Mrs G Ellis
Cost: *Alc* £20, set price L £12-£18/ D £18-£25. ☺ ☺ H/wine £8.95
Times: 11.30-2.30pm/7-10pm.
Closed 25-26 Dec
Additional: Sunday L. Bar food. Children welcome
Seats: 65. Private dining room 25
Style: Traditional, Country-house
Smoking: No smoking in dining room
Accommodation: 6 rooms (6 en suite)
♦♦♦♦
Directions: Telephone for directions

TWO BRIDGES   Map 2 SX67

Prince Hall Hotel

There's a cosy feel to the granite walled dining room of this 18th century country house. The open fire, warm lighting and huge wine rack all suit its Dartmoor location, as does the menu, which makes good use of local products including venison, lamb and wild salmon. A meal could start with canapés in the bar, followed by pan fried pigeon breast, fillet of local sea bass, and a sinful dessert such as banana fritters with toffee ice cream. You might, however, feel you have missed out unless you sample the local cheeses which beckon from the lovely pine dresser.

Smoking: No smoking in dining room
Accommodation: 9 rooms (9 en suite) ★ ★
Directions: From Two Bridges take B3357 Dartmeed Road; hotel is hidden 1 mile on R

PL20 6SA
Tel: 01822 890403
Fax: 01822 890676
e bookings@princehall.co.uk
Chef(s): Adam Southwell, Les Pratt
Owner(s): Adam & Carrie Southwell
Cost: Set price D £29.
H/wine £10.50
Times: Dinner only, 7-8.30pm.
Closed mid Dec-mid Feb
Additional: Children 12yrs+. Vegetarian by request only
Seats: 24
Style: Country-house

England

TWO BRIDGES *Continued*   Map 2 SX67

Two Bridges Hotel

PL20 6SW
Tel: 01822 890581
Fax: 01822 890575
 twobridges@warm-welcome-hotels.co.uk
Cost: *Alc* £23.50, set price L £21.95.
☺ ☺ H/wine £10.45
Times: Noon-2.30pm/7-9.30pm
Additional: Sunday L. Bar food.
Children welcome
Seats: 85
Style: Country-house
Smoking: No smoking in dining room
Accommodation: 29 rooms (29 en suite) ★ ★
Directions: From Tavistock take B3357, hotel at junct with B3312

Since the 18th-century, the Two Bridges Hotel has welcomed travellers on Dartmoor. Whether in summer when the gardens and the nearby river beckon or winter when the cosy interior is warmed by log fires, make an excuse to stop at the Tor restaurant. Justly celebrated for robust West Country cuisine created from the abundant local produce, the kitchen does not shy away from bold flavours. So, local pigeon may be set on a black pudding mash and finished with a raspberry vinaigrette, while a lighter touch is shown in poached chicken supreme filled with a truffle mousse served with a mange tout purée.

VIRGINSTOW   Map 2 SX38

Percy's Country Hotel

Coombeshead Estate,
Nr Okehampton, EX21 5EA
Tel: 01409 211236
Fax: 01409 211275
 info@percys.co.uk
Chef(s): Tina Bricknell-Webb
Owner(s): Tony & Tina Bricknell-Webb
Cost: *Alc* £32.50, set price L & D £32.50-£37.50. H/wine £12

Contemporary country cooking at this charming 16th-century Devon long-house is enhanced by use of organic ingredients with many herbs and vegetables grown in the hotel's own grounds. Seafood is direct from the daily fish auctions at Looe while game and local lamb come from the 130-acre Coombeshead Estate. Carefully seared scallops might be served with dill and honey dressing over fresh garden leaves and loin of home-reared Tamworth pork fanned around hot mash with

rosemary jus. A signature dish of lemon tart is accompanied by home made ice cream, perhaps also flavoured with fresh rosemary.

Directions: A388 from Launceston towards Holsworthy. R at St Giles-on-the-Heath. Percy's 2.2miles/A3079 from Okehampton, L at Metherell Cross. Percy's 6.5miles

Times: Noon-2pm/6.30-9pm.
Additional: Children 12yrs+
Seats: 50. Private dining room 24
Style: Country-house, Modern
Smoking: No smoking in dining room
Civil licence: 40
Accommodation: 8 rooms (8 en suite)
★★

WINKLEIGH   Map 3 SS60

Pophams

This long renowned destination opens for lunch only three days per week, so the tip for those who've not booked literally weeks ahead is to telephone in the morning in case of late cancellations. The kitchen and three dining tables occupy the same room; cash and cheques only are accepted; and diners must take their own wine. The sheer joy of it all is an afternoon's entertainment provided by Melvyn Popham and Dennis Hawkes that extends the "lunch hour" well into the afternoon and celebrates everything good about entertainment and classic cooking. The emphasis on freshness and quality is as consistent as ever and the food is a rare treat. On any day there might be starters of baked goats' cheese on a spicy chutney crouton, fresh salmon fishcake with creamy curry sauce and asparagus, prawns and Parma ham tossed in lemon and olive oil dressing. Alternatives that follow could be chicken breast filled with smoked ham, fresh basil and mozzarella and boned best end of local lamb encased in puff pastry with mushroom pâté and Madeira sauce; followed by fresh orange tart with Grand Marnier sauce or sticky toffee pudding topped with an irresistible blob of clotted cream.

Castle Street, EX19 8HQ
Tel: 01837 83767
Chef(s): Melvyn Popham
Owner(s): Melvyn Popham, Dennis Hawkes
Cost: Alc £29.50
Times: 11.30-2.30pm/Closed L Sat-Tue, D All week, Feb
Additional: Unlicenced - BYO. Children 14 yrs+. Vegetarian not available
Seats: 10
Style: Bistro-Style
Smoking: No smoking in dining room; Air conditioning
Credit cards: None accepted
Directions: In village centre, about 9 miles from Okehampton

WOOLACOMBE   Map 2 SS44

Watersmeet Hotel

This modern but traditionally styled restaurant really makes the most of its location: from almost every side, windows look over craggy rocks to sand and sea. The fixed price menu offers an imaginative and innovative selection of dishes, ranging from Scotch beef with a green peppercorn, brandy and cream sauce to poached lemon sole with prawns and a coconut and chilli sauce.

Mortehoe, EX34 7EB
Tel: 01271 870333
Fax: 01271 870890
e watersmeethotel@compuserve.com
Chef(s): John Prince
Owner(s): Mr & Mrs K Wickman
Cost: Alc £24.50/D £24.50-£28. ☺ ☺
H/wine £10.95
Times: D only, 7-8.30pm.
Closed Jan
Additional: Bar food L. Children 8yrs+. Vegetarian by request only
Seats: 50. Jacket and tie preferred
Style: Classic, Formal
Smoking: No smoking in dining room
Civil licence:
Accommodation: 22 rooms (22 en suite) ★★★
Directions: M5 J27. Follow A361 to Woolacombe, R at beach car park, 300yds on R

DORSET

England

BEAMINSTER
Map 3 ST40

Bridge House Hotel

Set-price menus at lunch and dinner on offer in the candlelit Georgian restaurant at this 13th-century clergy house. Canapés are served in the bar and home-made bread at the table. Dishes include chicken liver parfait with delicious toasted walnut bread, and roast rack of lamb simply presented with a rich redcurrant sauce. A separate vegetarian menu is available.

Additional: Sunday L. Children welcome
Seats: 36. Private dining room 20
Style: Country House
Smoking: No smoking in dining room
Accommodation: 14 rooms (14 en suite) ★★★
Directions: On A3066, 200mtrs down hill from town centre

3 Prout Bridge, DT8 3AY
Tel: 01308 862200
Fax: 01308 863700
e enquiries@bridge-house.co.uk
Chef(s): Linda Paget
Owner(s): Peter Pinkster
Cost: Set price L £10.25-£14.25/ D £25.50-£28.50. ☺ H/wine £11.75
Times: Noon-2pm/7-9pm.
Closed 31 Dec

BLANDFORD FORUM
Map 3 ST80

Castleman Hotel

This former dower house has plenty of atmosphere (Regency style drawing room, plasterwork ceilings and a galleried hall). It prides itself on its restaurant, where the British based menu makes good use of local produce including wild mushrooms, air dried ham and carrots freshly pulled from the garden. The wine list runs to 50 bins and has a modish, contemporary feel.

Additional: Sunday L. Children welcome
Seats: 40
Style: Country House
Smoking: No smoking in dining room
Accommodation: 8 rooms (8 en suite)
Directions: 1 mile from A354. Hotel is signposted in village

Chettle, DT11 8DB
Tel: 01258 830096
Fax: 01258 830051
e chettle@globalnet.co.uk
Chef(s): Barbara Garnsworthy, Richard Morris
Owner(s): Barbara Garnsworthy, Edward Bourke
Cost: A/c £22.50, set price L £15.
☺ ☺ H/wine £10
Times: Noon-2pm/7-9.30pm.
Closed L Mon-Sat, Feb

BOURNEMOUTH
Map 4 SZ09

Bistro on the Beach

The waterside setting of this informal bistro makes it a popular venue. The fixed price menu offers a short selection of starters and mains, which, for a small supplement, can be widened to include say, tiger prawns sautéed in Malibu and topped with coconut, or fillet of brill with a lobster and brandy sauce. Good selection of desserts and wines.

Times: Dinner only, 7-late. Closed Sun-Tue, 3 wks Nov, 2 wks March
Additional: Sunday L. Children welcome
Seats: 65
Style: Modern
Smoking: No smoking in dining room; Air conditioning
Directions: Telephone for directions

Solent Promenade,
Southbourne Coast Road,
Southbourne BH6 4BE
Tel: 01202 431473
Fax: 01202 470048
e bistro.bridge@virgin.net
Chef(s): David Ryan
Owner(s): Sheila & David Ryan
Cost: A/c £20/D £15.95-£19.70. ☺ ☺ H/wine £9.95

England

Bournemouth Highcliff Marriott

Well worth getting a window seat if you possibly can. Delicately prepared pan fried cutlets of English lamb with roasted peppers and a sweet garlic sauce and a warm sticky toffee pudding presented with a caramel and vanilla sauce have both been noted as successes.

Style: Classic
Smoking: No smoking in dining room; Air conditioning
Civil licence:
Accommodation: 152 rooms (152 en suite) ★ ★ ★ ★
Directions: Take A338 dual carriageway though Bournemouth, then follow signs for Bournemouth International Centre to West Cliff Rd, then 2nd right

St Michaels Road, West Cliff,
BH2 5DU
Tel: 01202 557702
Fax: 01202 293155
Chef(s): Mike Dobson
Cost: Alc £25, set price L £12.50-£16.50/D £25. H/wine £12.95
Times: 12.30-2pm/7-10pm.
Closed L Sat
Additional: Sunday L. Bar food.
Children welcome
Seats: 210. Private dining room 30

Chine Hotel

Set in three acres of lovely gardens, Chine Hotel boasts a large, well run restaurant with superb sea views. The dinner menu offers four or five fairly standard choices per course, including such dishes as ragout of seafood, spinach and ricotta tortellini and beef stroganoff. Dessert could be Bailey's cheesecake or possibly sticky toffee pudding.

Directions: From M27, A31 and A338 follow signs to Boscombe Pier, Boscombe Spa Road is off Christchurch Road near Boscombe Gardens.

Boscombe Spa Road, BH5 1AX
Tel: 01202 396234
Fax: 01202 391737
e reservations@chinehotel.co.uk
Chef(s): Kevin Drake
Owner(s): FJB Hotels
Cost: Set price L £15.50/D £19.75. ☺
☺ H/wine £11.50
Times: 12.30-2pm/7-8.30pm.
Closed L Sat
Additional: Sunday L. Bar food.
Children welcome
Seats: 160. Private dining room 130
Style: Traditional, Country-house
Smoking: No smoking in dining room
Civil licence: 130
Accommodation: 92 rooms (92 en suite) ★ ★ ★

Langtry Manor

Edward VII built the house in 1877 for the actress Lillie Langtry. She would certainly have approved of the restaurant's theatricality - Saturday night Edwardian banquets are a real crowd-pleaser. Further cabaret includes flambé demonstrations involving, perhaps, steak Diane and the option of similar treatment for Jamaican bananas with dark rum butter as an encore.

Style: Country House, Traditional
Smoking: No smoking in dining room
Civil licence: 120
Accommodation: 26 rooms (26 en suite) ★ ★ ★
Directions: On the East Cliff, at corner of Derby & Knyveton Roads

26 Derby Road, East Cliff, BH1 3QB
Tel: 01202 553887
Fax: 01202 290115
e lillie@langtrymanor.com
Chef(s): Stuart Glanville
Owner(s): Mrs P Hamilton-Howard
Cost: Alc £23.75/D £23.75. ☺
H/wine £12.50
Times: Dinner only, 7-11pm
Additional: Bar food L.
Seats: 60. Private dining room 16.
Jacket and tie preferred

BOURNEMOUTH *Continued*　　　　Map 4 SZ09

Menzies Carlton

Smart hotel serving a variety of British and European dishes, such as lobster and crab salad with salmon caviar or fillet of Scottish beef with parsley creamed potato. Desserts, such as hot chocolate ganache, are enjoyable and well presented. The restaurant is decorated in traditional style, with tall windows looking onto the pool and gardens.

Style: Classic, Traditional
Smoking: No smoking in dining room; Air conditioning
Civil licence: 180
Accommodation: 73 rooms (73 en suite) ★★★★
Directions: M3/M27, follow A338 (Bournemouth). Follow signs to town centre and East Overcliff. Hotel is on the seafront

East Overcliff, BH1 3DN
Tel: 01202 552011
Fax: 01202 299573
e carlton@menzies-hotel.co.uk
Chef(s): Robert Bird
Cost: *Alc* £30.50, set price L £13.50/D £27.50. ☺ H/wine £13.50
Times: 12.30-2.30pm/7-9.45pm.
Additional: Sunday L. Bar food. Children welcome
Seats: 120. Private dining room 180. Jacket and tie preferred

'Oscars' at the Royal Bath Hotel

Oscars restaurant refers to Mr Wilde who, when the room was the hotel library, did much writing there. It is now the venue for some punchy cooking with starters like scallops with butternut squash risotto and spring lamb with rosemary and baby root vegetables. Good wine list.

Style: Edwardian
Smoking: No smoking in dining room; Air conditioning
Civil licence: 200
Accommodation: 140 rooms (140 en suite) ★★★★
Directions: Follow signs for Bournemouth Pier and beaches

Bath Road, BH1 2EW
Tel: 01202 555555
Fax: 01202 554158
Chef(s): Jonathan Wood
Cost: *Alc* £40, set price D £32. ☺ H/wine £14.95
Times: 12.30-2pm/7.30-10pm.
Closed Mon, D Sun
Additional: Sunday L. Vegetarian by request only
Seats: 40. Jacket and tie preferred

Queens Hotel

This truly elegant hotel dining room is only yards from the bustle of the sea front. A light and airy atmosphere is ideal for full enjoyment of serious cuisine such as beef stroganoff garnished with julienne of gherkin and served with a tian of rice. A cold buffet is also available.

Additional: Sunday L. Bar food. Children welcome
Seats: 200. Private dining room 180. Jacket and tie preferred
Style: Modern, Minimalist
Smoking: No smoking in dining room; Air conditioning
Accommodation: 114 rooms (114 en suite) ★★★
Directions: Follow signs to East Cliff, hotel is one road back from seafront

Meyrick Road, East Cliff, BH1 3DL
Tel: 01202 554415
Fax: 01202 294810
e hotels@arthuryoung.co.uk
Chef(s): William Summerell
Cost: *Alc* £24.95, set price L £9.95/ D £19.95. ☺ ☺ H/wine £11.95
Times: 12.30-1.30pm/7-8.30pm

England

Saint Michel

Bournemouth Highcliff Marriott
Hotel, St Michaels Road, BH2 5DU
Tel: 01202 315716
Fax: 01202 315716
Chef(s): Claudio Notarbartolo
Owner(s): Mr Kralj &
Mr Notarbartolo
Cost: Alc £27, set price L £15.50.
☺ ☺ H/wine £11.50
Times: Noon-2pm/7-9.30pm.
Closed L Sat, D Sun
Additional: Sunday L. Bar food.
Children welcome
Seats: 70. Private dining room 22
Style: Classic, Bistro-Style
Smoking: No cigars

Simplicity works well in this busy brasserie with sparkling
glassware on marble tables. Clear, distinct flavours characterise
dishes such as smoked chicken and foie gras terrine. A more
adventurous spirit is in evidence in the successful, if somewhat
exuberant combination of a delicious fillet of sea bass with a
vanilla emulsion.

Directions: Follow signs for Bournemouth International Centre;
along Exeter Rd to mini-rdbt, up hill onto Priory Rd. 3rd L into
St Michaels Road. 50 metres on L

BRIDPORT   Map 3 SY49

Riverside Restaurant

West Bay, DT6 4EZ
Tel: 01308 422011
Chef(s): Paul Morey, Nic Larcombe
Owner(s): Mr & Mrs A Watson
Cost: Alc £25, set price L £15.95.
☺ ☺
Times: 11.30-2.30pm/6.30-9pm.
Closed Mon(ex BHs), D Sun,
1 Dec-mid Feb
Additional: Sunday L. Children
welcome
Seats: 80. Private dining room 20
Style: French
Smoking: No smoking in dining room
Directions: In the centre of West Bay
by the river

Peerless views of the village and river, a bustling and easygoing
atmosphere coupled with top-notch seafood all adds-up to a
special place. Seared scallops with mixed leaves, lardons and
croutons typifies the simple but effective style with roast cod
with spring onion mash, garlic oil and salsa also winning praise.
Impressive, cosmopolitan wine list that naturally favours the
whites.

England

CHARMOUTH   Map 3 SY39

Thatch Lodge Hotel

Formerly a monks' retreat for nearby Forde Abbey, the hotel graces the high street of this much-visited Dorset town. Following canapés in the antique lounge, dinner is taken at 8pm in a tiny dining room (reservations essential) that creates much of a dinner party atmosphere. Locally smoked salmon with orange dressing and herbed leaves, accompanied by freshly baked breads, is a likely precursor to perfectly pink rack of Dorset lamb with port and redcurrant jus on the nightly-changing menu. Options to follow include a "not to be missed" hot vanilla soufflé with raspberry and Cointreau filling and Westcountry cheeses served in season with home-grown grapes.

Accommodation: 6 rooms (6 en suite) ♦♦♦♦♦
Directions: From A35 follow signs for Charmouth. Hotel in halfway along High Street on R

The Street, DT6 6PQ
Tel: 01297 560407
Fax: 01297 560407
e thatchlodgehotel@cs.com
Chef(s): Andrea Ashton-Worsfold
Owner(s): Mr & Mrs Worsfield
Cost: Set price D £30 H/wine £11
Times: Dinner only, at 8pm.
Closed Sun-Mon, mid-Dec-mid- Mar
Additional: Children 18 years+.
Vegetarian by request only
Seats: 14. Jacket and tie preferred
Style: Country-house
Smoking: No smoking in dining room

CHIDEOCK   Map 3 SY49

Chideock House

It's the interesting range of freshly prepared dishes that really set this hotel restaurant apart. The surroundings help though - a part-thatched 15th-century building with an inglenook fireplace, beams and candlelit tables. Expect the likes of an accomplished cheese and spinach soufflé or a good piece of turbot wrapped in smoked salmon and served in a pastry case with cream and chive sauce.

Main Street, DT6 6JN
Tel: 01297 489242
Fax: 01297 489184
e enquiries@chideockhousehotel.com
Chef(s): Anna Dunn
Owner(s): Anna Dunn
Cost: Alc £23. ☺ ☺ H/wine £10.95
Times: Noon-2pm/7-9pm.
Closed Mon, L Tue-Sat, D Sun, Jan
Additional: Sunday L. Children welcome. Vegetarian by request only
Seats: 32. Jacket and tie preferred
Style: Country-house
Smoking: No-smoking area
Accommodation: 9 rooms (8 en suite) ★★
Directions: 3 miles W of Bridport, on A35 in centre of village

CHRISTCHURCH   Map 4 SZ19

Bistro on the Bridge   NEW

New big brother to David Ryan's fun Bistro on the Beach, the 'Bridge' proves every bit a rising South Coast star. Blonde-wood, harmonising deep blues and clean lines offer light, contemporary and stylish good looks. Front of house is well-directed by Mark Walters (ex-head sommelier at Chewton Glen), and smartly attired staff are friendly, efficient and knowledgeable. The evolving modern British menu displays fine credentials too via a good-value, fixed-priced jour and

3-5 Bridge Street,
BH23 1DY
Tel: 01202 482522
Fax: 01202 470048
e bistro.bridge@virgin.net
Chef(s): David Ryan, Phil Burt
Owner(s): David & Sheila Ryan
Cost: Alc £25, set price D £16.95.
☺ ☺ H/wine £9.95
Times: Noon-2.15pm/7-11pm.

supplemented specials that allow for mix-and-matching. Must tries include chef's dessert platter, double-baked stilton soufflé with grape chutney, foie gras terrine with apple jelly and veal cutlet with wild mushroom ragout.

Smoking: No smoking in dining room; Air conditioning
Directions: From town centre towards Christchurch Priory. At small rdbt turn L into Castle St. Bistro in 0.25 mile

Closed Mon, Tue, BHs
Additional: Sunday L.
Children welcome
Seats: 95
Style: Modern, Minimalist

Splinters

12 Church Street, BH23 1BW
Tel: 01202 483454
Fax: 01202 480180
e eating@splinters.uk.com
Chef(s): Jason Davenport
Owner(s): Tim Lloyd & Robert Wilson
Cost: Alc £35, set price L £21/
D £23.50. ☺ ☺ H/wine £12.95
Times: 11am-3.30pm/7-Midnight.
Closed Sun-Mon, 26 Dec, 31 Dec
Additional: Bar food L. Children
welcome
Seats: 42. Private dining room 22
Style: French, Bistro

Walking up the cobbled street leading to Christchurch Priory, you will see Splinters, a period building, which houses the three separate dining areas. An accomplished *carte* dinner could begin with roasted celeriac soup with smoked chicken ravioli and white truffle oil, or perhaps plum tomato tart with basil oil and rocket salad. Some Eastern influences apparent as in John Dory fillets with Bombay potato, steamed pak choi and coconut sauce and round off with one of four or five fruity desserts. These may include lemon or banana tart, passion fruit soufflé and hot chocolate fondant with white chocolate ice cream. A special place.

Smoking: No-smoking area; no pipes
Directions: Splinters is directly in front of Priory gates.

Waterford Lodge

Claiming a blend of classically influenced cuisine and exciting contemporary dishes, Manners Restaurant makes extensive use of local ingredients. Dishes have good flavour and texture and may include cassoulet of steamed lobster with a herb and shellfish cream, or supreme of guinea fowl wrapped in parma ham. Anticipate good service from the friendly staff at this mock-Tudor hotel.

Additional: Sunday L. Bar food. Children welcome
Seats: 40. Private dining room 70
Style: Modern
Smoking: No smoking in dining room
Accommodation: 18 rooms (18 en suite) ★ ★ ★
Directions: 2 miles E of Christchurch on A337 then S to Friars Cliff

87 Bure Lane, Friars Cliff,
Mudeford BH23 4DN
Tel: 01425 272948
Fax: 01425 279130
e Waterford@bestwestern.co.uk
Chef(s): James Penn
Owner(s): Mr N Badley
Cost: Set price L £14.95/D £25.50.
☺ H/wine £10.20
Times: Noon-1.30pm/7-9pm.
Closed 27 Dec-3 Jan

England

CORFE CASTLE
Map 3 SY98

Mortons House

A welcome emphasis on fresh ingredients in a wide selection of dishes on offer in the hotel's well-presented, comfortable and usually busy restaurant. Prawn and saffron risotto with Parmesan crisps and a pesto dressing has been noted as a highlight, and it is generally the simpler dishes that work best as in fillet steak with a decent hollandaise and oyster mushrooms.

East Street, BH20 5EE
Tel: 01929 480988
Fax: 01929 480820
e stay@mortonshouse.co.uk
Chef(s): Dan Giles
Owner(s): Mr & Mrs Hageman & Clayton
Cost: Alc £26, set price L £16/D £24.
☺ ☺ H/wine £13
Times: Noon-2pm/7-8.30pm.
Additional: Sunday L. Bar food L.
Children welcome

Seats: 60. Private dining room 22. Jacket and tie preferred
Style: Classical, Formal
Smoking: No smoking in dining room
Accommodation: 17 rooms (17 en suite) ★ ★ ★
Directions: In centre of village on A351

CORSCOMBE
Map 3 ST50

The Fox Inn   NEW

'No Microwaves and No Chips' states the sign outside this quintessential, rose-adorned, 17th-century thatched inn, set down winding lanes in deepest Dorset. Instead, look to the chalkboards in the classic beamed bars for quail stuffed with thyme risotto, rack of lamb with rosemary gravy and excellent, freshly prepared fish and seafood, perhaps Szechuan peppered squid with roast red pepper relish, mussels steamed with pesto and coconut milk, and roast cod with anchovies, garlic and olive oil.

DT2 0NS
Tel: 01935 891330
Fax: 01935 891330
e dine@fox-inn.co.uk
Chef(s): George Marsh, Dan Clarke
Owner(s): Martyn & Susie Lee
Cost: Alc £19.50. ☺ ☺ H/wine £9.95
Times: Noon-3pm/7-Midnight.
Closed 25 Dec
Additional: Sunday L.
Children welcome
Seats: Private dining room 30
Style: Traditional
Smoking: No-smoking area
Accommodation: 3 rooms (2 en suite)
♦ ♦ ♦ ♦
Directions: 5 miles off A37 (Yeovil to Dorchester road). 1 mile off A356 (Crewkerne to Maiden Newton road)

CRANBORNE
Map 4 SU01

La Fosse at Cranborne

London House, The Square, BH21 5PR
Tel: 01725 517604
Fax: 01725 517778
Chef(s): M J Lafosse
Owner(s): Mr & Mrs M J LaFosse
Cost: Alc £25, set price L £12.50/ D £18. ☺ ☺ H/wine £9.95
Times: Noon-2pm/7-10pm.
Closed Mon, L Sat, D Sun
Additional: Sunday L. Children welcome
Seats: 40
Style: Classic, Modern
Smoking: No smoking in dining room

A refreshingly unpretentious restaurant that makes a virtue of resisting the sometimes bland contemporary flow. Try fresh large Cornish sardines with garlic or supreme of salmon with an almond crust on a champagne sauce, scattered with fresh grapes, or perhaps a New Forest venison steak with a rich red wine sauce.

Accommodation: 5 rooms (4 en suite)
Directions: M27 - W onto A31 to Ringwood, then to Verwood, then Cranborne

DORCHESTER

Map 3 SY69

The Mock Turtle

A modern, earthy feel: red sofas and rustic fires set the scene for brasserie style food such as shoulder of lamb on mixed pulses or delice of cod on a tomato and olive ragoût. Side orders include a basket of chunky wholemeal bread and courgettes in garlic butter. Friendly staff conjure up a relaxed, informal atmosphere.

Seats: 65. **Style:** Traditional
Smoking: No smoking in dining room; Air conditioning
Directions: Town centre, top of High Street West

34 High West Street, DT1 1UP
Tel: 01305 264011
e tim@themockturtle.com
Chef(s): Timothy Emberley
Owner(s): Timothy Emberley
Cost: Alc £21, set price L £10/ D £14.95-£27.50. ☺ ☺ H/wine £9.75
Times: noon-2.30pm/6.30pm-9.30pm. Closed Sun, L Mon & Sat

Yalbury Cottage

Oak-beams, inglenook fireplaces, stone walls and a thatched roof, some of the ingredients in the recipe that is three-hundred-year-old Yalbury Cottage. The cuisine, though, is up to the minute, spanning modern European to more robust traditional dishes. A starter of pheasant consommé with truffles and trompettes, or roasted quail with wilted spinach, wild mushrooms and a red wine jus might appeal to game lovers. For mains, tomato, fennel and aubergine pithivier with olive oil mash and red wine sauce and tournedos of braised ox-tail with seared foie gras are notable successes.

Accommodation: 8 rooms (8 en suite) ♦♦♦♦
Directions: Two miles east of Dorchester, off A35

Lower Bockhampton, DT2 8PZ
Tel: 01305 262382
Fax: 01305 266412
e yalbury.cottage@virgin.net
Chef(s): Russell Brown, Darren Erransbury
Owner(s): Mr & Mrs D Furminger
Cost: Set price D £26 H/wine £11
Times: Dinner only, 7-11pm. Closed Jan & New Year
Additional: Children welcome
Seats: 30
Style: Traditional, cottage style
Smoking: No smoking in dining room

EVERSHOT

Map 3 ST50

The Acorn Inn

NEW

DT2 0JW
Tel: 01935 83228
Fax: 01935 83707
e stay@acorn-inn.co.uk
Chef(s): Howard Mosley
Owner(s): Martyn & Susie Lee
Cost: Alc £19.50. ☺ ☺ H/wine £9.95
Times: Noon-2pm/7-9pm.
Additional: Sunday L. Bar food. Children welcome
Seats: 45. Private dining room 30
Style: Rustic, Traditional
Smoking: No-smoking area
Accommodation: 9 rooms (9 en suite) ♦♦♦♦
Directions: 1 mile off A37 midway between Yeovil & Dorchester

Immortalised as the 'Sow and Acorn' in Hardy's Tess of d'Ubervilles, The Acorn Inn oozes olde worlde charm with open fires, flagstone floors and exposed beams. Menus really

England

shine with an impressive repertoire of fish dishes, simple ideas and sunny flavours. Try, for example, roasted cherry tomato and goats' cheese filo tartlet or oven-baked black bream with sea salt, lemon and thyme.

Summer Lodge

Blessed with a picture book setting, this comfortable country house hotel makes the most of the deepest Dorset countryside surrounding it. Full-length windows grace the dining room, where formal service and table settings suggest a serious

DT2 0JR
Tel: 01935 83424
Fax: 01935 83005
e enquiries@summerlodgehotel.com
Chef(s): David Richard
Owner(s): Nigel and Margaret Corbett
Cost: *Alc* £39.50, set price L £15.50/
D £39.50 ☺ H/wine £7.75
Times: 12.30pm-4pm/7-Midnight.
Additional: Sunday L. Bar food L.
Children 8yrs+ at D. Vegetarian by
request only
Seats: 50. Private dining room 20
Style: Traditional, Country-style
Smoking: No smoking in dining room
Civil licence:
Accommodation: 18 rooms (18 en
suite) ★ ★ ★
Directions: 1 mile W off A37
between Dorchester & Yeovil.
Entrance in Summer Lane

attitude towards food. There's plenty of scope on the menus: light dishes like Dover sole (pan-fried or grilled), West Bay lobster or crab, and char-grilled chicken breast salad are complemented by the more substantial roast sirloin of beef with Yorkshire pudding perhaps, or loin of pork with crackling and baked apple. For more adventurous choices consider scallop mousse with crab and lemon butter sauce (tremblingly light and perfectly executed), and venison with sticky cabbage and spicy sauce, or rack of lamb with a parsley and garlic crust, celeriac fondant and watercress sauce. Desserts include the familiar (chocolate fondant) and the truly desirable (peaches poached with raspberry and mint sauce), and some yummy petits fours.

The Dormy

New Road, BH22 8ES
Tel: 01202 872121
Fax: 01202 895388
e devere.dormy@airtime.co.uk
Chef(s): Gareth Bowen
Cost: *Alc* £40, set price L £15-£20/
D £22.50-£36.50. ☺ ☺ H/wine £14
Times: 12.30-2pm/7-9.30pm.
Closed Sun, L Sat & Mon
Additional: Children 1 yr+
Seats: 40. Private dining room 20.
Jacket and tie preferred
Style: Rustic, Country-house
Smoking: No smoking in dining room;
Air conditioning

Named after (and now home to) the golf trophy, this purpose built restaurant has a formal appearance, with well spaced tables, white linen and Bristol blue water goblets. The food is pretty much as classy as the surroundings: begin with an excellent selection of canapés in the bar before dining from the modern, European based menu. Care and attention are evident throughout, from the complimentary appetiser to the accomplished main courses. These might include crab and five spice beignet followed by seared loin of bluefin tuna with herb risotto and red wine jus. Service is professional yet friendly.

Accommodation: 115 rooms (115 en suite) ★ ★ ★ ★
Directions: From Bournemouth take A338. At junction signed Bournemouth International Airport turn R at lights onto B3073. L onto A347, Dormy 1 mile on R

HIGHCLIFFE Map 4 SZ29

The Lord Bute Restaurant

A recently constructed orangery lounge successfully capitalises on very attractive formal gardens. Although sometimes lacking somewhat in ambition, the cuisine is well prepared using good, sound ingredients in dishes such as roasted pork fillet wrapped in Parma ham and spinach, set on a pool of sun dried tomato and roasted pepper sauce.

Lymington Road, BH23 4JS
Tel: 01425 278884
Fax: 01425 279258
e mail@lordbute.co.uk
Chef(s): Christopher Denley, Kevin Brown
Owner(s): S & C Denley, S Caunter
Cost: *Alc* £28, set price L £13.95-£16.95/D £24.95. ☺ ☺
H/wine £11.95
Times: noon-2pm/7-9.45pm. Closed Mon, L Sat, D Sun
Additional: Sunday L. Children 10yrs+
Seats: 80. Jacket and tie preferred
Style: Traditional
Smoking: No smoking in dining room; Air conditioning
Accommodation: 10 rooms (10 en suite)
Directions: A337 to Lymington. Opposite St Mark's Churchyard

MAIDEN NEWTON Map 3 SY59

Le Petit Canard

Friendly service, classical music and candlelight create a relaxed atmosphere in this former coaching inn. The English based menu

Dorchester Road, DT2 0BE
Tel: 01300 320536
Fax: 01300 321286
e craigs@le-petit-canard. freeserve.co.uk
Chef(s): Gerry Craig
Owner(s): Mr & Mrs G Craig
Cost: Set price D £26. H/wine £12.50
Times: Dinner only, 7-9pm. Closed Sun-Mon (ex 3rd Sun in month for L)
Additional: Sunday L. Children 12yrs+
Seats: 28
Style: Classic/ Simple Traditional
Smoking: No smoking in dining room
Directions: In the centre of Maiden Newton, 8 miles west of Dorchester

MAIDEN NEWTON *Continued* Map 3 SY59

makes good use of local products, and might include salmon on char grilled peppers or rump of lamb on rosemary mash. The simpler dishes, such as pan-fried scallops, are the most effective.

POOLE Map 4 SZ09

Haven Hotel

Banks Road, Sandbanks, BH13 7QL
Tel: 01202 707333
Fax: 01202 708796
🅴 reservations@havenhotel.co.uk
Chef(s): Karl Heinz Nagler
Owner(s): Mr. J Butterworth
Cost: *Alc* £37, set price D £25.
H/wine £5.50
Times: Dinner only, 7-11pm.
Closed Sun, Mon, Xmas
Additional: Bar food L. Children welcome
Seats: 59. Private dining room 160.
Jacket and tie preferred
Style: Modern, Minimalist
Smoking: No smoking in dining room; Air conditioning

On the southernmost point of the Sandbanks peninsula, La Roche restaurant enjoys stunning views across Poole Bay. Part of a covered terrace running the full length of the building, its high ceilings and huge windows make for an airy, sometimes 'echoing' environment. Specialising in fish, the bigger proportion of the menu is devoted to fruits of the sea. Baked scallops glazed with lime butter might precede seafood ragout, or steamed sea bass and scallop mousseline. The dessert menu features some off-beat ice creams such as Guinness, or ginger and chilli.

Civil licence: 180
Accommodation: 94 rooms (94 en suite) ★ ★ ★ ★
Directions: Follow signs to Sandbanks Peninsula; hotel next to Swanage ferry departure point.

Mansion House

Thames Street, BH15 1JN
Tel: 01202 685666
Fax: 01202 665709
🅴 enquiries@themansionhouse.co.uk
Chef(s): Gerry Godden,
Daren Rockett
Owner(s): Robert Leonand, Julie & Gerry Godden
Cost: *Alc* L £18.50, set price L £15.95/D £23-£25.50.
☺ ☺ H/wine £12.95
Times: noon-2pm/7-9.30pm.
Closed L Sat, D Sun
Additional: Sunday L. Bar food. Children 5yrs+ at D
Seats: 85. Private dining room 30
Style: Classic
Smoking: No-smoking area; Air conditioning

Tucked away off the old quay, a sophisticated hotel with a serious attitude towards food. The Regency dining room exudes

Georgian charm, while a contemporary style of cooking which owes more to modern Britain than the 18th-century continues to impress. As you would expect, the sea plays a prominent role, with dishes like fillet of monkfish with celeriac mash and cep jus, pan-fried scallops with parsnips and a caper raisin jus, and steamed sea bass with pak choi and a lemongrass and coconut milk sauce. Also present are well-handled rack of lamb, roast guinea fowl, and fillet of beef.

Civil licence: 35
Accommodation: 32 rooms (32 en suite) ★ ★ ★
Directions: Follow signs to Channel Ferry/Poole Quay, L at bridge, 1st L is Thames St

Salterns Hotel

38 Salterns Way, Lilliput, BH14 8JR
Tel: 01202 707321
Fax: 01202 707488
e reception@salterns.co.uk
Chef(s): Nigel Popperwell
Owner(s): John Smith
Cost: Alc £30, set price L £20-£30/ D £25-£35. ☺ ☺ H/wine £13.50
Times: Noon-2pm/7-9.30pm
Additional: Sunday L. Bar food. Children welcome
Seats: 50. Private dining room 120
Style: Formal
Smoking: No-smoking area; Air conditioning
Civil licence: 120

Expect stunning views of Poole harbour from this waterside restaurant in Lilliput. Appropriately, the menu keeps things on a small scale and is all the better for it: you can rely on the kitchen to deliver quality ingredients (local wherever possible) and satisfying flavour combinations. The modern, French style of the cooking is illustrated by dishes such as calf's liver and bacon with a Puy lentil jus or duck confit with a bacon and cabbage parcel. Most tastes are catered for, with interesting salads, vegetarian options and (of course) fish dishes offered alongside a thoughtful selection of side orders.

Accommodation: 20 rooms (20 en suite) ★ ★ ★
Directions: From Poole take B3369 for Sandbanks; after 1.5 miles in Lilliput turn R (Salterns Way). Hotel on R at end

Sandbanks Hotel

15 Banks Road, Sandbanks, BH13 7PS
Tel: 01202 707377
Fax: 01202 708885
e reservations@sandbankshotel.co.uk
Chef(s): Nick Alcock
Owner(s): Mr J Butterworth
Cost: Alc £22.95, set price L £18/ D £28.50. H/wine £12.25
Times: Noon-3pm/6-10pm. Closed D Sun-Tue
Additional: Sunday L. Bar food L. Children welcome
Seats: 55. Private dining room 40. Jacket and tie preferred
Style: Traditional, Bistro-Style
Smoking: No smoking in dining room; Air conditioning

Panoramic views of the beach from this recently constructed waterside restaurant do much to attract its clientele. Not

POOLE Continued

Map 4 SZ09

surprisingly, the menu features several fish options. You could, for instance, begin with cocktail of Poole crab bound in a dill rouille, moving on to pan fried scallops or Thai green seafood curry, though meat devotees and veggies are catered for too.

Accommodation: 116 rooms (116 en suite) ★ ★ ★
Directions: From Poole or Bournemouth, follow signs to Sandbanks Peninsula. Hotel on L.

SHAFTESBURY

Map 3 ST82

La Fleur de Lys

⊜⊜
25 Salisbury Street, SP7 8EL
Tel: 01747 853717
🄴 lafleurdelys@fsbdial.co.uk
Chef(s): D Shepherd, M Preston
Owner(s): D Shepherd, D Griffin, M Preston
Cost: Alc £33, set price D £25.50. ☺ H/wine £12
Times: noon-2.30pm/7-10pm. Closed L Mon, D Sun, 2 wks Jan
Additional: Sunday L. Children welcome
Seats: 40
Style: Modern French
Smoking: No cigars
Directions: Town centre, near the Post Office, on the main road

The restaurant lies on the edge of the historic hill top town of Shaftesbury. First floor dining with wonderful views over Blackmore Vale. The kitchen offers a mainly French-inspired menu that makes good use of carefully sourced local produce. Restrained garnishing and careful marrying of complimentary flavours are a real virtue. Menus make much effort to meet varying audiences with differing lunch, set and à la *carte* menus. Roasted saddle of local venison with glazed peppered pear and figs in a rich port-wine sauce, from the à la *carte* menu has won plaudits. Classic flavours continue at pudding with pecan and coffee beignets, soufflé served with Tia Maria ice cream and white chocolate sauce - the latter being described as "tremendous".

Royal Chase Hotel

⊜
Royal Chase Roundabout, SP7 8DB
Tel: 01747 853358
Fax: 01747 851969
🄴 royalchasehotel@btinternet.com
Chef(s): Andrew Wheatcroft
Cost: Alc £23.50, set price L £21-£23.50/D £21-£23.50. ☺ H/wine £12
Times: Noon-2.30pm/6.30-9.30pm. Closed L Wed
Additional: Sunday L. Bar food. Children welcome
Seats: 65. Private dining room 120
Style: Classic
Smoking: No smoking in dining room
Civil licence: 78
Accommodation: 33 rooms (33 en suite) ★ ★ ★

Former monastery located on the fringe of the town close to the famous Gold Hill. Some dishes are quite intricate (filo

basket with a wild mushroom fondue) but the flavours tend to
be sturdy and well defined. There's always a good variety of
fish, as well as a selection of grills featuring well-sourced meats.
In good weather it's possible to eat on the terrace and enjoy the
attractive grounds.

Directions: On roundabout at junction of A350 & A30 (avoid
town centre)

Wayfarers Restaurant

Sherborne Causeway, SP7 9PX
Tel: 01747 852821
Fax: 01747 852821
Chef(s): Mark Newton
Owner(s): Mark & Clare Newton
Cost: Alc £32, set price L & D
£15.95-£18.15. ☺ ☺ H/wine £9.75
Times: Noon-1.30pm/7-9.15pm.
Closed Mon, L Sat (all lunches
bookings only), D Sun, 2 wks after
25 Dec
Additional: Sunday L. Children 8yrs+
Seats: 35. Jacket and tie preferred
Style: Country-house
Smoking: No-smoking area
Accommodation: 1 room (1 en suite)
Directions: 2 miles W of Shaftesbury
on A30 (towards Sherborne and
Yeovil)

Another successful husband and wife team. Chef Mark works
on his own most of the time, while Clare runs the front of
house, seating and waiting at this 18th-century cottage near to
the busy Sherbourne causeway. The kitchen however, takes a
modern, continental approach to its work, producing the likes
of a warm terrine of salmon and lobster, on new-potatoes with
a sauce americaine and basil purée. Dishes tend to be rich,
including starters such as brioche filled with sautéed herring
roes, or truffle scented boudin of foie gras wrapped in Parma
ham. Interesting dishes from the à la *carte*, (they also have a
weekday bistro menu available which is especially good value)
include steamed tranche of brill served on puff-pastry with
leek and mushroom fondue and Ricard-scented velouté with
caviar.

SHERBORNE   Map 3 ST61

Eastbury Hotel

It's worth finding the rear car park and walking through pretty
gardens to this predominantly Georgian town house hotel. The
conservatory style restaurant offers a friendly environment with
well paced, attentive service. Modern, European style dishes
range from fillet of Angus beef with potato rösti to saffron
risotto.

Style: Classic, Modern
Smoking: No smoking in dining room
Civil licence: 120
Accommodation: 15 rooms (15 en suite) ★ ★ ★
Directions: At bottom of Cheap Street turn R. Hotel 800yds on R

Long Street, DT9 3BY
Tel: 01935 813131
Fax: 01935 817296
Chef(s): Justin White
Owner(s): Mr & Mrs P King
Cost: Alc £27.50, set price L £10.95/
D £18.95. ☺ ☺ H/wine £8.95
Times: Noon-2.30pm/7-9.30pm.
Additional: Sunday L. Bar food.
Children welcome
Seats: 40. Private dining room 12

SHERBORNE *Continued*   **Map 3 ST61**

Grange Hotel

Victorian residence with open fires and comfortable sitting
areas, open plan with the bar and restaurant offering views of
impressive formal gardens. The menus are traditional in style,
with options such as tournedos Rossini and roast monkfish
wrapped in Parma ham served in generous portions. In trad
fashion, a choice of desserts is offered from the trolley.

Style: Classic, Traditional
Smoking: No smoking in dining room
Accommodation: 10 rooms (10 en suite) ♦♦♦♦♦
Directions: Situated just off A30, 1m E of Sherboune, Clearly
signposted

Oborne, DT9 4LA
Tel: 01935 813463
Fax: 01935 817464
Chef(s): Martin Barrett, Julian Batten
Owner(s): Karen & Jonathan Arthur
Cost: *Alc* £27, set price D £24.50. ☺
H/wine £11.90
Times: Dinner only, 7-9pm.
Closed D Sun, L Mon-Sat (ex
bookings), 26 Dec-12 Jan
Additional: Sunday L. Children 3 yrs+
Seats: 60. Private dining room 22

Pheasants Restaurant

With its antique furniture exuding an air of elegance this is an
attractive dining room with an appealing menu. Offering as it
does an eclectic range of tempting dishes, selecting may prove
tricky. The asparagus and vegetable feuilleté (inclining to the
Mediterranean) sits alongside devilled Cornish crab and a
charcuterie salad. Main courses include plaice fillets with a
scampi and mussel ragout or grilled aubergine with halloumi
and wild mushrooms. Some desirable desserts may perplex the
indecisive: ginger and ricotta cheesecake with cherries,
blueberry and lemon bavarois or blackberry and apple crumble
with clotted cream and a walnut and amaretti topping, can all
be expected to impress.

Accommodation: 6 rooms (6 en suite) ♦♦♦♦
Directions: At the top of the High Street, A30 (Salisbury/Yeovil)

24 Greenhill, DT9 4EW
Tel: 01935 815252
Fax: 01935 815252
Chef(s): Neil Cadle, Will Blackburn
Owner(s): Mr A Overhill
Cost: *Alc* £27.50, set price L £17.50/
D £25-£30. ☺ H/wine £11
Times: Noon-2pm/6.30-10pm. Closed
Mon, L Tue-Fri, D Sun, 2wks mid Jan
Additional: Sunday L. Children
welcome
Seats: 40. Private dining room 10
Style: Traditional, Country-house
Smoking: No cigars

STURMINSTER NEWTON   **Map 3 ST71**

Plumber Manor

This beautiful Jacobean manor set in lovingly tended grounds is
a family home of some character. The restaurant has a
reputation for good, traditional cooking prepared from quality,
fresh ingredients and the hosts certainly know their trade.
Fixed price menus of two, three or four courses are available,

Hazelbury Bryan Road, DT10 2AF
Tel: 01258 472507
Fax: 01258 473370
🄴 book@plumbermanor.com
Chef(s): Brian Prideaux Brune
Owner(s): R Prideaux-Brune
Cost: *Alc* £24.50, set price L
£17.50/D £22-£30. ☺ H/wine £10
Times: Noon-2pm/7.30-9.30pm.
Closed L Mon-Sat, Feb
Additional: Sunday L. Children
welcome. Vegetarian by request only
Seats: 65. Private dining room 24
Style: Country-house
Smoking: No smoking in dining room
Accommodation: 16 rooms (16 en
suite) ★★★
Directions: In Sturminster Newton
cross the packhorse bridge, R to
Stalbridge (A537). 1st L to Hazelbury
Bryan. 2 miles on L opposite Red Lion

this latter billed a 'gourmet dinner'. Typical starters might include smoked salmon paupiettes with cream cheese and chives or courgette and rosemary soup. Signs of recent innovation are in evidence in main courses such as supreme of chicken with a Thai curry sauce, but essentially adherence to the familiar is the order of the day.

SWANAGE
Map 4 SZ07

Grand Hotel

Refurbished dining room, a new chef and a new menu all arrived in the middle of last year, but the wonderful views across Swanage Bay are unchanged. Wild mushrooms and asparagus in a filo basket with a cream sauce comes recommended amongst the starters, while main courses include some good fish and a very popular braised shank of lamb.

Burlington Road, BH19 1LU
Tel: 01929 423353
Fax: 01929 427068
Telephone for further details

WAREHAM
Map 3 SY98

Kemps Country House

A restaurant especially popular with local dining clubs offering an extensive menu based on local produce. From the freshly baked bread at the start of the meal to the home-made fudge served with coffee, there is a consistently good standard, although a simple starter of grilled goats' cheese with mixed leaves, bacon pieces and pesto sauce stood out.

Additional: Sunday L. Bar food L. Children welcome
Seats: 60. Private dining room 32
Style: Country House
Smoking: No smoking in dining room
Accommodation: 14 rooms (14 en suite) ★ ★
Directions: On A352 midway between Wareham and Wool

East Stoke, BH20 6AL
Tel: 01929 462563
Fax: 01929 405287
Chef(s): Jon Newing
Owner(s): Mr & Mrs Warren
Cost: Alc £23, set price L £10.95-£13.45/D £21.95. ☺ ☺ H/wine £9.95
Times: Noon-1.30pm/7-9.30pm. Closed L Sat

Priory Hotel

Once a priory, the gently lit vaulted stone cellar is now a restaurant. Nothing monastic about the menu though, packed as it is, with the likes of caviar, terrine of foie gras, Champagne sorbet and fillet of beef Wellington on truffled Madeira sauce. The comprehensive wine list (majoring on heavyweight French) is serious and not cheap. During the week, lunches are served in the attractive Garden Room (the grounds lead down to the River Frome).

Additional: Sunday L. Bar food L. Children 8yrs+
Seats: 45. Private dining room 25. Jacket and tie preferred
Smoking: No smoking in dining room
Accommodation: 19 rooms (19 en suite) ★ ★ ★
Directions: Town centre between church and River Frome

Church Green, BH20 4ND
Tel: 01929 551666
Fax: 01929 554519
e reception@theprioryhotel.co.uk
Chef(s): Stephen Astley
Owner(s): Stuart & John Turner
Cost: Alc £40.79, set price D £27.50-£32.50. ☺ H/wine £14.95
Times: 12.30-2pm/7.30-10pm

England

WEYMOUTH

Map 3 SY67

Moonfleet Manor

Fleet, DT3 4ED
Tel: 01305 786948
Fax: 01305 774395
Chef(s): Tony Smith
Owner(s): Mr N Dickson
Cost: Alc £24, set price L £16. ☺
H/wine £12
Times: 12.30-2.15pm/7-9.30pm.
Closed L Mon-Sat
Additional: Sunday L. Bar food L.
Children welcome
Style: Classic, Modern
Smoking: No smoking in dining room
Accommodation: 39 rooms (39 en
suite) ★ ★ ★

This is not your typical hotel restaurant. Situated in the 'enchanting' Moonfleet Manor, its light, Mediterranean-style décor complements lovely sea views. The menu is British-based but doesn't ignore the rest of Europe: you might find chicken served on buttered spinach with goats' cheese and tortellinis or home smoked salmon accompanied by salad, new potatoes and gazpacho dressing. Dishes such as Maryland crab cake with orange and saffron cream sauce reveal flair for even the most delicate flavours. Home-made bread, tasty desserts and an interesting (largely New World) wine list complete the picture. Good use of fresh and seasonal produce.

Directions: A354 from Dorchester, R into Weymouth at Manor rdbt. R at next rdbt, L at next rdbt, up hill (B3157) then L, 2 miles towards sea

Perry's Restaurant

4 Trinity Road, The Old Harbour,
DT4 8TJ
Tel: 01305 785799
Fax: 01305 787002
Chef(s): Andy Pike
Owner(s): R, A & V Hodder
Cost: Alc £23, set price L £16. ☺ ☺
H/wine £9.75
Times: noon-2pm/7-9.30pm.
Closed L Mon & Sat, D Sun Sep-
Easter, 25-26 Dec,1 Jan
Additional: Sunday L. Children 5yrs+
Seats: 60. Private dining room 30
Style: Bistro-Style
Smoking: No-smoking area; no cigars
Directions: On western side of old
harbour – follow for Brewers Quay

Fish and seafood specials are the main draw at this attractive Georgian restaurant overlooking the harbour, with dishes like scallops cooked in their shells with lemon and garlic, and gratin

of Portland crab with a Chablis sauce bursting with fresh sea flavours. Otherwise the British menu concentrates on the likes of roast medallions of English lamb with a thyme sauce, and pan-fried fillet of beef with glazed shallots, garlic and red wine sauce. Starters include Perry's home-made soup, and perhaps

England

Loch Fyne kiln-roast salmon on marinated leeks with mustard seed dressing. Find space for hot chocolate pudding with crème anglaise to finish.

WIMBORNE MINSTER
Map 4 SZ09

Beechleas Restaurant

An elegant Georgian town house, Beechleas has an airy conservatory restaurant. A typical dinner menu offers a choice of, honest fare, with many ingredients sourced from a nearby organic farm. Start with local mussels in garlic, wine and cream sauce, then ratatouille crêpes with a light cheese sauce to follow, leaving room for hot chocolate sponge and home-made ice cream.

17 Poole Road, BH21 1QA
Tel: 01202 841684
Fax: 01202 849344
e beechleas@hotmail.com
Chef(s): Roger Northey, Simon Hallam
Owner(s): Mrs J McQuillan
Cost:, set price L £18.75/D £23.75.
☺ ☺ H/wine £11.75
Times: Dinner only, 7-11pm.
Closed L ex Dec, Xmas-mid Jan
Additional: Sunday L. Bar food.
Children welcome
Seats: 40. Private dining room 12
Style: Country-house
Smoking: No smoking in dining room
Accommodation: 9 rooms (9 en suite)
★★
Directions: On A349 at Wimborne, 5 miles from Bournemouth, access via A31

Les Bouviers

The personal touch is very much a hallmark of the Cowards' well-run restaurant: their passion for good food is clear from the use of prime, fresh local ingredients. For lunch, choices might be as simple as winter salad with grilled vegetables and chicken chasseur with mushrooms and tarragon. From the Menu Gourmand select perhaps lobster rillettes with beetroot dressing, seared cod steak with caper meunière and chocolate fondant with pistachio ice cream and blackberry compôte, cooked and presented with diligence and enthusiasm. A new bar, lounge and kitchen are part of recent refurbishment that has enhanced its feeling of comfort and well-being.

Smoking: No-smoking area; no cigars; Air conditioning
Directions: 0.5 mile S of A31 Wimborne by-pass on A349

Oakley Hill, Merley, BH21 1RJ
Tel: 01202 889555
Fax: 01202 889555
e info@lesbouviers.co.uk
Chef(s): James Coward
Owner(s): James & Kate Coward
Cost: Alc £28.95, set price L £13.95/D £19.95-£24.95. ☺ ☺
H/wine £10.25
Times: Noon-2.15pm/7-10pm. Closed Mon, L Sat, D Sun, 26 Dec, 1st wk Jan
Additional: Sunday L. Children welcome
Seats: 50. Private dining room 32
Style: French

DURHAM, COUNTY

BEAMISH
Map 12 NZ25

Beamish Park Hotel

Conservatory style bistro offering modern, light and even cutting-edge cooking. Daily changing specials include a smattering of fusion-style dishes. Starters might include Chinese style duck salad with Asian coleslaw or warm Mediterranean squid salad with pesto dressing. Winter main courses might include pot roast breast of guinea fowl with boulanger of root vegetables and a red wine jus or plump breast of chicken on creamed cabbage with butter beans and lardons of pancetta. Amongst the desserts, white chocolate and raspberry brûlée with lemon meringue ice cream and nut brittle has been described as "superb".

Accommodation: 47 rooms (47 en suite) ★ ★ ★
Directions: Just off A6076 Newcastle to Stanley Road

Beamish Burn Road, Marley Hill, NE16 5EG
Tel: 01207 230666
Fax: 01207 281260
🇪 reception@beamish-park-hotel. co.uk
Chef(s): Martin Charlton
Owner(s): William Walker
Cost: *Alc* £20. ☺ ☺ H/wine £10.95
Times: Noon-2pm/7-10.15pm
Additional: Sunday L. Bar food. Children welcome
Seats: 70. Private dining room 80
Style: Bistro-Style

CHESTER-LE-STREET
Map 12 NZ25

Austins Bar & Bistro

A dinner menu offering sole fillets with smoked salmon mousselline in a lobster and saffron scented fricassée is entirely in keeping with the sophisticated, modern surroundings of this popular bar and bistro. A lighter, more simple lunch menu is also available.

Durham County Cricket Club, County Ground, Riverside DH3 3QR
Tel: 0191 388 3335
Fax: 0191 387 4697
🇪 confbanq.durham@ecb.co.uk
Chef(s): Chris Clark
Owner(s): Durham County Cricket Club
Cost: *Alc* £25. ☺ ☺ H/wine £12.50
Times: Closed D Sun, 25-26 Dec, 1 Jan
Additional: Sunday L. Children welcome
Seats: 85
Smoking: No-smoking area
Directions: From A1M J63 follow Riverside sign, on outskirts of Chester-le-Street

DARLINGTON
Map 8 NZ21

Hall Garth Hotel

Standing amidst its own gardens and golf course, the extended 16th-century Georgian country house is a successful blend of traditional and modern, conveniently close to the A1M. Fronted by a long-standing team, the restaurant has agreeable ambience and a wide choice of daily lunch and dinner menus, based on sensible choices of ingredients. Traditional, well-flavoured combinations result in starters of crab ravioli with leek purée, followed by cannon of lamb with

Coatham Mundeville, DL1 3LU
Tel: 01325 300400
Fax: 01325 310083
Chef(s): Kirk Alderson
Owner(s): Corus & Regal Hotels
Cost: *Alc* £28, set price D £21-£22.95. ☺ ☺ H/wine £11.75
Times: 12.30-2pm/7-10pm. Closed L Mon-Sat

spinach and a mushroom duxelle encased in puff pastry, full of natural flavours.

Smoking: No smoking in dining room
Civil licence: 160
Accommodation: 41 rooms (41 en suite) ★ ★ ★
Directions: A1(M) J59 (A167) (Darlington), top of hill turn L signed Brafferton, hotel 200yds on R

Additional: Sunday L. Bar food. Children welcome
Seats: 50. Private dining room 16
Style: Country-house

Headlam Hall

Set in an impressive Jacobean mansion, this restaurant occupies a conservatory and two stately rooms, one panelled and one Victorian-style with deep green walls and a chandelier. This time-honoured style is echoed in the menu, which includes classics such as ribeye steak with mustard sauce or roast lamb on parsnip mash.

Smoking: No smoking in dining room
Civil licence: 150
Accommodation: 36 rooms (36 en suite) ★ ★ ★
Directions: From Darlington take A67 W towards Barnard Castle, after 5 miles R signed Headlam Hall. 3 miles to hotel

Headlam, Gainford, DL2 3HA
Tel: 01325 730238
Fax: 01325 730790
e admin@headlamhall.co.uk
Chef(s): Alex McMurray
Owner(s): J H Robinson
Cost: *Alc* £24, set price L £12.50/ D £21. ☺ ☺ H/wine £9.95
Times: noon-2pm/7-9.30pm
Additional: Sunday L. Children welcome
Seats: 70. Private dining room 30
Style: Traditional, Country-house

DURHAM   Map 12 NZ24

Bistro 21

This restored farmhouse has proved to be a very popular informal dining place despite not being in the centre of the City. Clever architecture of cloisters around the entrance provides an intimate atmosphere enhanced by simple, attractive décor. Fresh flavours abound in simple combinations such as warm duck salad with plum sauce.

Aykley Heads House, Aykley Heads, DH1 5TS
Tel: 0191 384 4354
Fax: 0191 384 1149
Chef(s): Terence Laybourne
Owner(s): Terence Laybourne
Cost: *Alc* £25, set price L £14.50. ☺ ☺ H/wine £10.50
Times: noon-2pm/7-10.30pm. Closed Sun, 25 Dec,New Year, BHs
Additional: Children welcome
Seats: 55. Private dining room 20
Style: Classic, Bistro-Style
Smoking: No smoking in dining room
Directions: Off B6532 from Durham centre, pass County Hall on R and Dryburn Hospital on L; turn R at double rdbt into Aykley Heads

Durham Marriott, Royal County

The County restaurant offers elegant fine dining with interesting dishes on both the set price and *carte* menus. Friendly and efficient service from smartly uniformed staff adds to the experience. Simple yet effective use of ingredients is the key here. Dishes include a fine example of a double-baked soufflé of cheddar cheese with grain mustard cream. Main

Old Elvet, DH1 3JN
Tel: 0191 386 6821
Fax: 0191 386 0704
e durhamroyal.marriott@whitbread. com
Chef(s): Ken Thompson

DURHAM *Continued*   Map 12 NZ24

courses such as a generous fillet of roast salmon might be accompanied by squares of mediterranean-style aubergine and peppers, with crushed potatoes. A classic tarte Tatin served with almond ice cream rounds off a delightful experience.

Durham Marriott, Royal County

Cost: *Alc* £35, set price L £16.50/ D £25.50 ☺ H/wine £13.75
Times: 12.30-2pm/7.15-10.15pm.
Additional: Sunday L.
Children welcome
Seats: 90. Private dining room 120.
Jacket and tie preferred
Style: Classic
Smoking: No smoking in dining room;
Air conditioning
Civil licence: 60
Accommodation: 138 rooms (138 en suite) ★ ★ ★ ★
Directions: From A1(M) onto A690. Follow City Centre signs, straight ahead at 1st rdbt, L at 2nd, over bridge, L at lights, hotel on L

Kings Lodge Hotel   NEW

Fine art, chic décor, lighting that changes subtly throughout the meal and live jazz piano. A pretty cool venue and a recipe that seems to be working judging by the buzz on a weekday evening. The cooking is bold and modish ranging from tempura of king prawns with Thai dressing, through smoked trout with black pudding (it worked apparently) and pan fried loin of milk fed veal with blue cheese polenta, braised button mushrooms and crisp panchetta. A range of side orders (including delicious chips) are on offer. Puds have included bread and butter pudding with honey ice cream.

Smoking: No smoking in dining room; Air conditioning
Accommodation: 21 rooms (21 en suite) ★ ★ ★
Directions: A1 J62, ahead at 1st 3 rdbts, turn R at 4th. 1st L, 1st R, hotel at end of road

Flass Vale, DH1 4BG
Tel: 01913 709977
Fax: 01913 709988
🅴 tinahamelton@msnmail.co.uk
Chef(s): Mark Stonley
Cost: *Alc* £25/D £19.95. ☺ ☺
H/wine £9.25
Times: 12.30-2pm/6.30-9.45pm.
Additional: Sunday L. Bar food.
Children 1yrs+
Seats: 75. Private dining room 20

REDWORTH   Map 8 NZ22

Redworth Hall

Due to a major refurbishment, the restaurants are closed at the time of going to press. However, the committed kitchen team plans to re-open still maintaining a good Two-Rosette standard. See the AA web site for current details. (www.theAA.com/restaurants)

Accommodation: 100 rooms (100 en suite) ★ ★ ★ ★
Directions: From A1(M) J58 take A68 to rdbt. Hotel on A6072 on L
Telephone for further details

DL5 6NL
Tel: 01388 770600
Fax: 01388 770654
🅴 redworthhall@paramount-hotels.co.uk

ROMALDKIRK
Map 12 NY92

Rose & Crown

DL12 9EB
Tel: 01833 650213
Fax: 01833 650828
📧 hotel@rose-and-crown.co.uk
Chef(s): C Davy, D Stephenson
Owner(s): Mr & Mrs C Davy
Cost:, set price L £13.95/D £25. ☺ ☺
H/wine £9.95
Times: noon-1.30pm/7.30-9pm.
Closed L Mon-Sat, D Sun, Xmas
Additional: Sunday L. Bar food
Seats: 24
Style: Traditional
Smoking: No-smoking area; no cigars

Originally, in 1773, travellers came to visit by coach and horses and still today there's a real old country inn feel about the place. The oak panelled restaurant, displaying its collection of blue and white china, maintains the charm that attracts regular visitors - this and, of course, the good food. The choice is not extensive, but the four course dinner menu concentrates on quality. You could try duck liver parfait with sloe jelly and toasted brioche for an interesting opening combination, followed by pan fried breasts of woodpigeon with root rösti, confit of onions and juniper berry sauce.

Accommodation: 12 rooms (12 en suite) ★ ★
Directions: 6 miles NW of Barnard Castle on B6277

RUSHYFORD
Map 8 NZ22

Swallow Eden Arms

DL17 0LL
Tel: 01388 720541
Fax: 01388 721871
📧 edenarms.swallow@whitbread.com
Chef(s): Chris Nicholson
Cost: Alc £18.95/D £18.95-£22. ☺ ☺
H/wine £12.50
Times: Dinner only, 7-9.30pm.
Closed L Mon-Sat
Additional: Sunday L. Bar food.
Children welcome
Seats: 90. Private dining room
Style: Traditional, Classic
Smoking: No smoking in dining room; no cigars
Civil licence: 100
Accommodation: 45 rooms (45 en suite) ★ ★ ★
Directions: From A1/M J60, follow A689 for 2 miles to Rushyford rdbt. Hotel opposite

17th-century coaching inn that is a prominent local landmark. A fairly lengthy menu offers a broad variety of dishes with influences from across the globe. Amongst the starters try tartlet of sun-blushed tomatoes with a grain mustard sabayon and a watercress and walnut salad or melon marinated in sweetened vodka with pineapple and lemon scented crème fraîche. Mains might include seared lamb rosettes with black pudding and a casserole of field mushrooms.

England

SEAHAM

Map 12 NZ44

Seaham Hall

NEW

No expense spared in the transformation of this stately home into a stylish new hotel. It looks great (imagine the home of an impeccably cool, globetrotting aristocrat) but despite the modern artwork, it retains an air of grandeur appropriate for the building in which Lord Byron married Anabella Milbank 168 years ago. The restaurant menu is gloriously free from pretension, offering dishes such as braised escalope of turbot with chive scented jus or fillet of Angus beef with a mushroom and mustard crust, alongside a wine list the size of a small book.

Civil licence: 100
Accommodation: 19 rooms (19 en suite) ★ ★ ★ ★
Directions: Leave A19 at 1st exit signed B1404 Seaham, at junct turn L into Seaham. At lights straight ahead over level crossing. Hotel 0.25 mile on R

Lord Byron's Walk, SR7 7AG
Tel: 0191 516 1400
Fax: 0191 516 1410
e reservations@seaham-hall.com
Chef(s): Simon Haigh
Owner(s): Tom & Jocelyn Maxfield
Cost: Alc £40, set price L £25/D £34. H/wine £14.50
Times: Noon-2pm/7-9.30pm
Additional: Sunday L.
Children welcome
Seats: 55. Private dining room 20
Style: Modern, Chic
Smoking: No smoking in dining room; Air conditioning

STOCKTON-ON-TEES

Map 8 NZ41

Parkmore Hotel

At the heart of this modern hotel stands a Victorian house, home to Reeds at Six Three Six restaurant. The décor is light and modern, with well-spaced tables - a real advantage in a place this popular. Dishes include old favourites (lasagne, steak and kidney pie) and interesting vegetarian options such as char-grilled aubergine, courgette and mozzarella stack.

Seats: 60. Private dining room 30
Style: Traditional
Smoking: No smoking in dining room
Civil licence: 100
Accommodation: 56 rooms (56 en suite) ★ ★ ★
Directions: On A135 between Yarm & Stockton-on-Tees, almost opposite Eaglescliffe Golf Course

636 Yarm Road, Eaglescliffe, TS16 0DH
Tel: 01642 786815
Fax: 01642 790485
e enquiriesl@parkmorehotel.co.uk
Chef(s): Fergus Robertson
Owner(s): Brian Reed
Cost: Alc £20, set price L £12.95/ D £17.95. ☺ ☺
Times: Noon-2pm/6.45-9.30pm.
Closed L Sat
Additional: Sunday L. Bar food L.
Children welcome

WEST AUCKLAND

Map 12 NZ12

Manor House

Good presentation is a byword at the 14th-century Manor House. The restaurant offers good, eye-appealing modern cooking. The seasonally-changing menu has plenty of fresh fish such as pan-fried swordfish or monkfish. Try seared fillet of lamb with parsnip purée and Madeira sauce or if you are looking for something different, how about ostrich?

Style: Country-House, Formal
Smoking: No-smoking area
Civil licence: 120
Accommodation: 35 rooms (35 en suite) ★ ★ ★
Directions: On A68 in West Auckland. 8 miles from A1(M) J58

The Green, DL14 9HW
Tel: 01388 834834
Fax: 01388 833566
e enquiries@manorhousehotel.net
Chef(s): Tarek Thoma
Cost: Alc £20. H/wine £10.30
Times: Noon-2pm/7-9.30pm.
Closed D Sun
Additional: Sunday L. Bar food.
Children welcome

ESSEX

BRENTWOOD
Map 5 TQ59

Marygreen Manor

Impressive 16th-century manor house a few minutes from the M25 but worlds away in atmosphere. Dine in the lofty, beamed baronial hall, from a modern international menu that might offer seared Cajun squid with sliced chorizo, tomato salsa and ruby chard dressed with lemon oil, and roast whole chump of lamb with a rosemary gravy, caramelised carrots, shallots and champ potatoes.

Directions: 1 mile from Brentwood town centre, 0.5 mile from M25 J28

London Road, CM14 4NR
Tel: 01277 225252
Fax: 01277 262809
Chef(s): Theresa Valentine, Tony Valentine
Cost: Alc £36, set price L £18.50/ D £29. ☺ H/wine £16
Times: 12.30-2.30pm/7.15-10.15pm. Closed 25 Dec
Additional: Sunday L. Bar food. Children welcome
Seats: 80. Private dining room. Jacket and tie preferred
Style: Traditinal, Formal
Smoking: No smoking in dining room
Civil licence: 60
Accommodation: 43 rooms (43 en suite) ★ ★ ★ ★

COGGESHALL
Map 5 TL82

Baumann's Brasserie

Value for money brasserie, typically packed to the gunwhales. The décor is simple, smart but informal, with pine set against whitewashed walls, and mismatched chairs at tables dressed in crisp white linen. Dishes along the lines of honey-coated roast saddle of lamb served with vibrant, fresh vegetables.

4-6 Stoneham Street, CO6 1TT
Tel: 01376 561453
Fax: 01376 563762
e food@baumanns.fsbusiness.co.uk
Chef(s): Mark Baumann, Jason Shaw
Owner(s): Mark Baumann
Cost: Alc £26, set price L £14/ D £16.50. ☺ ☺ H/wine £10.25
Times: 12.30-2pm/7-10pm. Closed Mon & Tue, 1st 2 wks Jan
Additional: Sunday L. Children welcome
Seats: 80
Style: Chic, French
Smoking: No-smoking area
Directions: Near Colchester. In centre of Coggeshall opposite the clock tower

England

DEDHAM   Map 5 TM03
Le Talbooth Restaurant

CO7 6HP
Tel: 01206 323150
Fax: 01206 322309
📧 ltreception@talbooth.co.uk
Chef(s): Terry Barber, Daniel Clarke
Owner(s): Gerald Milsom,
Paul Milsom
Cost: Alc £35, set price L £19.50/
D £27. H/wine £13.50
Times: noon-2pm/7-9.30pm.
Closed D Sun in winter
Additional: Sunday L. Children
welcome
Seats: 75. Private dining room 34.
Jacket and tie preferred
Style: Classic, Country-house

It is hard to imagine a prettier scene, a heavily beamed Tudor building in a lovely village by the river, captured by Constable himself in his painting of Dedham Vale (now in the National Gallery of Scotland). You can eat in the traditionally styled restaurant or out on the riverside terrace, alongside well-to-do locals or residents from Maison Talbooth. Service is provided by a well-drilled young team offering a fixed-price menu of favourites and a more imaginative *carte*, with dishes like saddle of venison wrapped in pancetta, with spiced poached pear, broccoli and hazelnut purée, and Cognac sauce.

Smoking: No cigars
Civil licence: 50
Accommodation: 10 rooms (10 en suite) ★ ★ ★
Directions: 6 miles from Colchester: follow signs from A12 to Stratford St Mary, restaurant on L before village

Milsom's   **NEW**

Contemporary setting for this outpost of the nearby Le Talbooth (see above). Two dining areas of which one is less formal with scrubbed wooden tables and another raised area with more sumptuous leather seating. Smart casual staff offer a pleasingly straightforward menu with the likes of Cypriot salad with toasted halloumi, char grilled rib-eye with delicious fat chips and a really good mixed leaf salad. Good wine list too.

Stratford Road, CO7 6HN
Tel: 01206 322795
Fax: 01206 323689
📧 milsoms@talbooth.co.uk
Chef(s): Stas Anastasiades
Owner(s): Paul & Gerald Milsom
Cost: Alc £17. ☺ ☺ H/wine £9.75
Times: Noon-2.30pm/6-9.30pm
Additional: Bar food. Children
welcome
Seats: 80. Private dining room 14

Style: Country-House
Smoking: No-smoking area; Air conditioning
Accommodation: 15 rooms (15 en suite) ★ ★ ★
Directions: 7 miles N of Colchester, just off A12

FELSTED   Map 5 TL62
Reeves Restaurant   **NEW**

Genuine 16th-century beamed interior is the setting
for a traditionally furnished restaurant serving a mixture of
modern and traditional English and international cuisine.

Rumbles Cottage, Braintree Road,
CM6 3DJ
Tel: 01371 820996
Fax: 01371 820100

The impressively knowledgeable staff are happy to clarify the finer points of the dishes which might include grilled Stilton and pesto-stuffed mushroom, and baked salmon on creamy leeks.

 reeves-restaurant.co.uk
Chef(s): Darren Reeve
Owner(s): Darren Reeve
Cost: Alc £25, set price L £10. ☺ ☺ H/wine £9.75
Times: noon-2.30pm/6.30-10pm. Closed Mon, D Sun
Additional: Sunday L. Children welcome
Seats: 50. Private dining room 12
Style: Traditional, Country-house
Smoking: No-smoking area
Directions: Between Chelmsford & Dunmow off A130. Turn R at The Boote House, Restaurant 4th on R. Parking on road

GREAT DUNMOW　　　　Map 4 TL62

Starr Restaurant

Market Place, CM6 1AX
Tel: 01371 874321
Fax: 01371 876337
 terry@starrdunmow.demon.co.uk
Chef(s): Mark Fisher
Owner(s): Mr B G Jones
Cost: Set price L £17.50-£24.50/ D £25-£32.50. ☺ ☺ H/wine £12.50
Times: noon-1.45pm/7-9.30pm. Closed D Sun
Additional: Sunday L. Children welcome
Seats: 70. Private dining room 36
Style: Classic

With some 15th-century origins concealed behind its Georgian façade, a popular restaurant-with-rooms whose diners will be encouraged by its short hand-written menus and the helpful attitude of predominately youthful staff. The wine list is worth more than a casual glance while contemplating the virtues of caramelised scallops on a creamy risotto, followed by roast rack of lamb with spinach and potato rösti, sea-fish medley with basil butter and squid-ink noodles or roast partridge with bubble-and-squeak and truffle-and-chestnut jus. Home-made puddings are "of the moment" and super petits fours accompany the coffee.

Smoking: No smoking in dining room
Accommodation: 8 rooms (8 en suite) ♦♦♦♦
Directions: M11 J8, A120 7 miles E towards Colchester. In town centre

GREAT YELDHAM   Map 5 TL73

White Hart

CO9 4HJ
Tel: 01787 237250
Fax: 01787 238044
Telephone for further details

Real ale lovers and fine wine connoisseurs are equally well catered for at this popular country pub. An inglenook fireplace divides the bar from the formal restaurant, where enjoyable food makes a consistently good impression. Seared scallops with wilted rocket leaves, and confit of duck leg might precede lemon tart with crème anglaise.

HARLOW   Map 5 TL73

Swallow Churchgate Hotel

Jacobean house in a quiet village location. Elegance and comfort inform the décor of the Manor restaurant with quality and clarity guiding the approach to cuisine. A starter of tuna niçoise with grain mustard and garlic might be followed by cannon of lamb with stir fry vegetables.

Seats: 70. Private dining room 60. Jacket and tie preferred
Style: Traditional, Country-House
Smoking: No smoking in dining room; no cigars
Civil licence: 80
Accommodation: 85 rooms (85 en suite) ★ ★ ★
Directions: From M11 J7 take A414 towards Harlow. Take B183 at 4th rdbt, then L into village street; hotel past church, at bottom of hill

Churchgate Street Village,
Old Harlow, CM17 0JT
Tel: 01279 420246
Fax: 01279 437720
🄴 oldharlow.swallow@whitbread.com
Chef(s): Lee Acreman
Owner(s): Swallow Hotels
Cost: Set price L £15/D £22. ☺ ☺
H/wine £12.75
Times: 12.30-2pm/7-10pm.
Closed L Sat, 25 Dec
Additional: Sunday L. Bar food.
Children welcome

HARWICH   Map 5 TM23

The Pier at Harwich

Overlooking the harbour, why not arrive by boat at the local marina? In any event, it's no bad place to lay anchor. The chef has the pick of the choicest seafood landed on the quayside while salt water tanks keep lobsters, a house speciality, in tip-top condition. Many dishes appear with two prices, according to portion size. This way you can effectively have two starters or just a small main and a glass of wine. It's a flexible approach and popular with the clientèle. Typical dishes include, moules marinières, fillet of salmon with a basil and pesto crust, and chef's fish pie.

The Quay, CO12 3HH
Tel: 01255 241212
Fax: 01255 551922
🄴 leslie@thepieratharwich.co.uk
Chef(s): Chris Oakley
Owner(s): Mr G M W Milsom
Cost: A/c £25, set price L £17.50/
D £19.50. ☺ ☺ H/wine £11.95
Times: noon-2pm/6-9.30pm
Additional: Sunday L. Children welcome

Civil licence: 50
Accommodation: 14 rooms (14 en suite) ★★★
Directions: A12 to Colchester then A120 to Harwich harbour

Seats: 90. Private dining room 40.
Jacket and tie preferred
Style: Classic, Formal
Smoking: No smoking in dining room

MALDON
Map 5 TL80

Francine's Restaurant NEW ⊛

Speciality Greek nights are popular at Rose Clayton and Greek Cypriot Andreas Andreou's intimate restaurant, but the *carte* also has a strong following: fresh foie gras, or porcini mushroom risotto, perhaps, and pan-fried guinea fowl or salmon escalope stuffed with langoustine mousse to choose from, with chocolate mousse terrine a rich dessert.

Additional: Sunday L. Children welcome
Seats: 24
Style: Classic, Country-house
Smoking: No pipes
Directions: 10 miles from Chelsmford in High Street next to police station

1A High Street CM9 7PB
Tel: 01621 856605
Fax: 01621 856605
e francines_restaurant@hotmail.com
Chef(s): Andreas Andreou
Owner(s): Andreas Andreou & Rose Clayton
Cost: *Alc* £25. ☺ ☺ H/wine £9.75
Times: Noon-2pm/7-11pm.
Closed Sun, Mon, L Sat

MANNINGTREE
Map 5 TM13

Stour Bay Café ⊛

Striking bright orange décor and walls hung with the work of local artists are set against 15th-century beams and an inglenook fireplace at this distinctive eaterie. A good value lunch might include rich seafood bisque, duo of fish (fresh fillet of mackerel and salmon) grilled and served on a bed of noodles with stir-fried vegetables, and a full flavoured chocolate pannacotta.

Additional: Sunday L. Children welcome
Seats: 50
Style: Modern, Bistro-Style
Smoking: No smoking in dining room
Directions: Town centre (A317 from Colchester to Ipswich) – large green building in High Street

39-43 High Street, CO11 1AH
Tel: 01206 396687
Fax: 01206 395462
e jaynewarner@ukonline.co.uk
Chef(s): Andrew Warner
Owner(s): Mr & Mrs A Warner
Cost: *Alc* £24, set price L £10/D £15.
☺ ☺
Times: noon-2pm/7-9.30pm.
Closed Sun & Mon, L Sat, early Jan

England

ROCHFORD

Map 5 TQ89

Hotel Renouf

Bradley Way, SS4 1BU

Modern hotel offering a trad menu with French leanings. Expect the likes of lobster bisque, duck and orange terrine, Oriental marinated salmon, and roast rack of lamb. Desserts (presented in a cabinet) have included a zesty lemon tart.

Tel: 01702 541334
Fax: 01702 549563
e reception@hotelrenouf.fsnet.co.uk
Chef(s): Melvin Renouf
Owner(s): Mr D Renouf
Cost: *Alc* £27, set price L £17.50/D £17.50.
☺ H/wine £11
Times: Noon-1.30pm/7-9.30pm. Closed L Sat, D Sun (ex residents), 26-Dec, 1 Jan
Additional: Sunday L. Children welcome
Seats: 40. Private dining room
Smoking: No smoking in dining room; Air conditioning
Accommodation: 23 rooms (23 en suite) ★★★
Directions: M25 J29/A127 into Rochford, then onto B1013

STANSTED

Map 5 TL52

Whitehall Hotel

Amiable, family-run hotel dating back to Elizabethan times, with an impressive timber-vaulted restaurant to boot. Get past the canapés, amuse-bouche and sorbets to a meaningful menu. Sound preparation reveals itself in food such as well-timed chicken livers on a potato scone or pan-fried lemon sole on pea purée.

Church End, CM6 2BZ
Tel: 01279 850603
Fax: 01279 850385
e sales@whitehallhotel.co.uk
Chef(s): Paula Keane
Owner(s): Mr R Bartella
Cost: *Alc* £30, set price L £25.
H/wine £16
Times: 12.30-1.30pm/7.30-9.30pm.
Closed 27-30 Dec
Additional: Sunday L.
Children welcome
Seats: 50. Private dining room 12
Style: Elizabethan
Smoking: No cigars
Civil licence: 120
Accommodation: 26 rooms (26 en suite) ★★★
Directions: From M11 J8 follow signs for Stansted Airport and then for Broxted

---

  Indicates a restaurant that has told us they offer a two-course lunch for less than £15

  Indicates a restaurant that has told us they offer a three-course dinner for less than £25

THORPE-LE-SOKEN
Map 5 TL12

The Olive Branch Brasserie NEW

High Street, CO16 0EA

There's a bustling atmosphere at this popular split-level restaurant, with immaculate staff keeping up the pace. A small *carte* guarantees consistency in imaginative dishes like chicken liver pâté with rich orange marmalade, ham and Gruyere soufflé, and medallions of beef with wild mushroom and pepper sauce. Good espresso and wine list.

Style: Modern
Smoking: No smoking in dining room; Air conditioning
Accommodation: 4 rooms (4 en suite) ♦♦♦♦
Directions: From Colchester take A120, then A135 to Weeley. Take B1033 to Thorpe-le-Soken (approx 10 miles from Colchester)

Tel: 01255 861199
Fax: 01255 860758
Chef(s): Paul Wharrier
Owner(s): Paul & Andrea Wharrier
Cost: Alc £22, set price L £12/D £15. ☺ ☺ H/wine £10.95
Times: noon-2.30pm/7-10pm
Additional: Sunday L. Bar food. Children welcome
Seats: 60

TOLLESHUNT KNIGHTS
Map 5 TL91

Five Lakes Hotel

Colchester Road, CM9 8HX

The Camelot Restaurant, with its floor-standing candelabra, red and gold tapestry hangings, and its mahogany seating, brings a medieval flavour to a contemporary setting. Try pressed potato, duck and chicken liver terrine with home-made bread and piccalilli to begin, with maybe poached salmon, sun-dried tomato mash and champagne basil sauce to follow.

Style: Modern. **Civil Licence:** 200
Smoking: No smoking in dining room; Air conditioning
Accommodation: 114 rooms (114 en suite) ★★★★
Directions: M25 J28, then N on A12. At Kelvedon take B1024 then B1023 to Tolleshunt Knights

Tel: 01621 868888
Fax: 01621 869696
e enquiries@fivelakes.co.uk
Chef(s): Andrew South
Owner(s): Mr A Berjerano
Cost: Alc £35, set price D £24.50. ☺ H/wine £15.75
Times: Dinner only, 7-10pm. Closed Mon, Sun
Additional: Children welcome
Seats: 80. Jacket and tie preferred

WETHERSFIELD
Map 5 TL73

Dicken's Restaurant

The Green, CM7 4BS

Wood flooring and scrubbed tables in the front section of the restaurant nicely contrasts with the tiled floors of the main dining area. Bright coloured prints on the wall enliven the décor whilst a personable touch to the service complements the otherwise smart and efficient approach. A starter of full-flavoured plum tomatoes carefully roasted with goats' cheese melted over the top was very simple but very enjoyable. Similarly a main of succulent chicken breast served on a large baked mushroom with lemon and garlic butter and some very good wilted spinach.

Directions: From M11/Stansted Airport take A120, bypass Great Dunmow towards Braintree. Turn L to Great Saling, then R towards Shalford. Wethersfield next village

Tel: 01371 850723
Fax: 01371 850723
Chef(s): John Dicken
Owner(s): John Dicken
Cost: Alc £23. ☺ ☺ H/wine £9.95
Times: Noon-2pm/6.30-9.30pm. Xmas opening times may vary
Additional: Sunday L. Children welcome
Seats: 40. Private dining room 16
Style: Modern, European
Smoking: No smoking in dining room

England

GLOUCESTERSHIRE

BARNSLEY   Map 4 SP00

The Village Pub   NEW

GL7 5EF

Preserving its unusual name, this 'village pub' is not your average local. Mellow-stoned and beautifully refurbished, it has been transformed into one of the successful new breed of pub-restaurants, where innovative, modern British food is served in an informal pub atmosphere. Order a pint and a sandwich at the bar or go the whole hog and linger over four courses by the fire. Short daily menus list robust, often ambitious dishes cooked with flair and imagination using organic or traceable meats and quality local produce. Begin with grilled red mullet with sweet chilli and carrot or rare roast pigeon with beetroot and horseradish, moving on to navarin of lamb with braised beans and pasta or baked haddock with lettuce, clams and chorizo. Finish with a memorable milk chocolate pannacotta with red wine, figs, and decent coffee.

Tel: 01285 740421
Fax: 01285 740142
e info@thevillagepub.co.uk
Chef(s): Dominic Blake
Owner(s): Tim Haigh, Rupert Pendered
Cost: Alc £22. ☺ ☺ H/wine £10.95
Times: 11am-4pm/6-11pm
Additional: Sunday L. Bar food. Children welcome. Vegetarian by request only
Seats: 100
Style: Traditional
Smoking: No smoking area
Accommodation: 6 rooms (6 en suite)

BIBURY   Map 4 SP10

Bibury Court

GL7 5NT
Tel: 01285 740337
Fax: 01285 740660
e information@biburycourt.co.uk
Chef(s): Tom Bridgeman
Owner(s): Mr & Mrs Johnston, Miss Collier
Cost: Set price D £32. ☺ H/wine £12.50
Times: noon-2pm/7-9pm.
Additional: Sunday L. Bar food. Children welcome
Seats: 50. Private dining room 30
Style: Traditional, Country-house
Smoking: No smoking in dining room
Accommodation: 18 rooms (16 en suite) ★ ★ ★
Directions: On B4425 between Cirencester & Burford; hotel behind church

Choose from the bright and airy conservatory or the high-ceilinged, salmon pink dining room at this historic and somewhat hidden country house. The cooking offers a varied selection of broadly modern British dishes. Expect quality and seasonal produce to be evident in the likes of saddle of venison with parsnip and sweet potato galette, poached pear and juniper berries for example. Weather permitting there is the opportunity to admire the nearby river and extensive grounds that surround the elegant Tudor manor.

Swan Hotel

GL7 5NW

The creeper-clad stone frontage of this riverside hotel makes it an attractive venue. Venture into the richly draped Signet Dining Room and you will find an elegant, unpretentious place where the service is unobtrusive and friendly. The kitchen uses local produce where possible and so you may find on the menu, for instance, seared Bibury trout fillets from the village stream. Some imaginative dishes might take your fancy such as salad of

Tel: 01285 740695
Fax: 01285 740473
e swanhot1@swanhotel-cotswold.co.uk
Chef(s): Shaun Naen
Owner(s): Miss E Rose

roasted pigeon breast with poached egg and raspberry vinaigrette to start, or to finish, caramelised peppered pineapple. An extensive selection of international wines is available.

Cost: *Alc* £42.50, set price D £35. H/wine £13.50
Times: Noon-2.30pm/7-9.30pm. Closed L Mon-Sat
Additional: Sunday L. Bar food. Children welcome
Seats: 60. Private dining room 30. Jacket and tie preferred
Style: Modern, Formal

Smoking: No smoking in dining room
Civil licence: 90
Accommodation: 20 rooms (20 en suite) ★ ★ ★
Directions: On B4425 between Cirencester (7miles) and Burford (9 miles). Beside bridge in centre of Bibury

BLOCKLEY   Map 4 SP13

Lower Brook House NEW

Lower Street, GL56 9DS
Tel: 01386 700286
Fax: 01386 700286
Telephone for further details

Be sure to book at this popular restaurant where warm red walls, old beams and white linen create a welcoming atmosphere. The cuisine is simple and unaffected, focusing on the ingredients' inherent flavour. Parsnip and spinach soup followed by a tasty fillet of salmon wrapped in bacon and served with a piquant red pepper coulis prove an excellent combination.

BOURTON-ON-THE-WATER Map 4 SP12

Dial House Hotel

The Chestnuts, High Street, GL54 2AN
Tel: 01451 822244
Fax: 01451 810126

A charming, mellow Cotswold stone hotel which dates from 1698, and attracts guests who appreciate the high standards of

BOURTON-ON-THE-WATER *Continued* Map 4 SP12

cooking. Dinner is a particular strength, with a good choice of menus offering imaginative dishes. Creative energy goes into the likes of chicken liver and foie gras parfait with a smoked bacon and thyme crouton, and monkfish and smoked bacon in a creamy saffron sauce (beautifully cooked). Desserts such as bitter chocolate pavé with kirsch cherries and Amaretto biscuits exceed expectations. The two small dining rooms are tastefully decorated, and a focal point of the hotel.

Smoking: No smoking in dining room
Accommodation: 14 rooms (13 en suite) ★ ★
Directions: In village centre; A436 from Cheltenham, A40-A424 from Oxford.

e info@dialhousehotel.com
Chef(s): Calum Williamson
Owner(s): Jane & Adrian Campbell-Howard
Cost: *Alc* £25, set price L £13.75/ D £14.95. ☺ ☺ H/wine £10.50
Times: noon-2.15pm/7-9.30pm
Additional: Sunday L. Bar food L. Children welcome at L
Seats: 28
Style: Traditional, Country-house

BUCKLAND   Map 4 SP03

Buckland Manor

An impressive example of the quintessentially British Country House Hotel whose focus is on comfort rather than grandeur: conducive to total relaxation, there are fine grounds to wander in and large open fires in front of which to relax at leisure. This understated brand of hospitality shows at its best in the dining-room, hung with classic oils and exuding comfort at its well-spaced polished wooden tables. Cuisine is very composed and technically correct, featuring modern interpretations of well-worked classics aided by flawless produce from the hotel gardens, the nearby Vale of Evesham and specialist fine food suppliers. Sea scallop and truffle baked in brioche served on a scallop and cabbage rosette with light herb froth highlights a number of strengths, not least in its restraint. The same assurance of touch may be found in the sautéed loin of venison that follows, served with braised red cabbage, cauliflower purée and blueberry and pepper sauce. Attentive staff help engender an almost house-party feel at times, and offer helpful advice on wine choices from the massive list.

WR12 7LY
Tel: 01386 852626
Fax: 01386 853557
e buckland-manor-uk@msn.com
Chef(s): Ken Wilson
Owner(s): Mr R Vaughan
Cost: *Alc* £55, set price L £29.50/ D £55 ☺ H/wine £15.50
Times: 12.30-1.45pm/7.30-9pm
Additional: Sunday L. Bar food L. Children 8 yrs+
Seats: 40. Jacket and tie preferred
Style: Formal Country-house
Smoking: No smoking in dining room
Accommodation: 13 rooms (13 en suite) ★ ★ ★
Directions: 2miles SW of Broadway. Take B4632 signposted Cheltenham, then take turn for Buckland. Hotel is through village on R

CHARINGWORTH   Map 4 SP13

Charingworth Manor

This 14th-century manor in a lovely setting has wonderful views across open countryside. The four-course menu lists a good

GL55 6NS
Tel: 01386 593555
Fax: 01386 593353

choice of dishes. A more adventurous opener than the half avocado with prawns and mayonnaise might be home-made crabcakes, whilst main courses, which include a vegetarian choice, take in amongst others, calves' liver, salmon, and duck.

 charingworthmanor@
englishrosehotels.co.uk
Chef(s): John McIntyre
Owner(s): English Rose Hotels
Cost: Alc £40, set price L £17.95-£20/
D £39.50 ☺
Times: 12.30-2pm/7-9.30pm
Additional: Sunday L. Bar food L.
Children welcome. Vegetarian by
request only
Seats: 48. Private dining room 40.
Jacket and tie preferred
Style: Traditional
Smoking: No smoking in dining room
Civil licence: 50
Accommodation: 26 rooms (26 en
suite) ★ ★ ★
Directions: From A429 Fosse Way,
take B4035 towards Chipping
Campden. Hotel 3 miles on R

CHELTENHAM Map 3 SO92

Beaujolais Restaurant

Offering essentially modern European cuisune, there's a distinctly French flavour to this pretty little restaurant. Bright yellow tablecloths create a warm and sunny feel inclining you, perhaps, toward Tuscany soup or a filo pastry basket filled with stir-fried duck, before going on to sample stuffed peppers or pork tenderloin medallions with an apple and brandy jus.

Style: French
Smoking: No pipes
Directions: Telephone for directions

15 Rotunda Terrace, Montpellier,
GL50 1SW
Tel: 01242 525230
Chef(s): Mark Lord
Owner(s): Miss G Shaw
Cost: Alc £20.95, set price L
£10.95/D £14.95. ☺ ☺ H/wine £9.95
Times: 12.30-2pm/7-9.30pm.
Closed Sun-Mon, Xmas
Additional: Children welcome
Seats: 40

Le Champignon Sauvage

David Everitt-Matthias continues to amaze all-comers at his exemplary edge of town restaurant. For the first timer, the location (in a terrace of shops on a busy street) can itself be a surprise - "The last place you'd expect to find a restaurant of this calibre" commented one correspondent - but it would be nice to dream that this is the start of a trend for suburban locations throughout the land. Wishful thinking indeed, for this

◉◉◉◉
24 Suffolk Road, GL50 2AQ
Tel: 01242 573449
Fax: 01242 254365
Chef(s): David Everitt-Matthias
Owner(s): Mr & Mrs D Everitt-
Matthias
Cost: Alc £37.50, set price L
£19.95/D £39-£46. ☺ ☺
H/wine £10.50
Times: 12.30-1.30pm/7.30-9pm.
Closed Sun-Mon, 10 days Xmas,
1 Jan, Easter, 2 wks summer
Additional: Children welcome.
Vegetarian by request only
Seats: 28
Style: Modern, Chic
Smoking: No cigars
Directions: South of the town centre,
near Boys' College on A40 (Oxford).
Please phone for exact details

CHELTENHAM *Continued*   Map 3 SO92   *Le Champignon Sauvage*

is a very special restaurant. Relatively small (about 10 tables) and warmly decorated in sunny yellow with displays of bold artwork there is a refreshing lack of pretension and a genuine focus to the operation that is enhanced by the fact that David and wife Helen play the major roles both front of house and behind the stove. The cooking is in similar vein with the concentration on allowing the full flavour of top quality ingredients to express themselves. There is no shortage of flair and innovation but there is a welcome absence too, of showing off for the sake of it. There is an earthy feel to many of the dishes with, for instance croquettes of pig trotter and guinea fowl with wild rocket and wild mushrooms that although delicate in execution packs a robust, peppery punch or seared foie gras with roasted quince, walnuts and a Banyuls syrup (an exquisite combination of textures and flavours). A fillet of Whitby cod with spiced bread crust and split pea purée has been cited as typical of the pinpoint accuracy and respect for the main ingredient. In this case a "perfectly" cooked piece of the freshest fish with a garnish of saffron potatoes with blushed tomatoes and asparagus. Desserts are a strength amongst strengths with lemon panacotta with yoghurt ice cream and muscovado or hot fig tart with a honey spiced bread ice cream standing out. The lunch menu is an absolute bargain for food of this quality.

The Daffodil

18-20 Suffolk Parade, Montpellier, GL50 2AE
Tel: 01242 700055
Fax: 01242 700088
daffodilrest@cs.com
Owner(s): Marcel Frichot
Cost: *Alc* D £25,
set price L £13.75.
☺ ☺ H/wine £12.50
Times: noon-2.30pm/6.30-10.30pm. Closed Sun, Xmas
Additional: Children welcome
Seats: 150
Style: Classic, Modern
Smoking: No-smoking area

STOP PRESS Change of Chef

Worth a visit to see the bizarre concept of an art deco cinema, successfully converted to a stylish brasserie. In between times a bingo hall, it could now be dubbed a full house! Cutting to the food action, the two-choice set menu offers good value and has options, such as Malaysian squid curry, for the more adventurous. The *carte* selection cuts from crispy aromatic duck pancake, or mini beef Wellington for example, through a cast of Thai fishcake, chargrilled calves' liver, and Mediterranean vegetable tartlet, to such stars as glazed lemon tart, steamed ginger pudding or chocolate and almond torte. Happily, in this context, no double bills.

Directions: S of town centre, just off Suffolk Rd, nr Cheltenham Boys' College

England

The Greenway

Shurdington, GL51 4UG
Tel: 01242 862352
Fax: 01242 862780
e greenway@btconnect.com
Chef(s): Dean Selby
Cost: *Alc* £35, set price L £18.50/
D £35. H/wine £14
Times: Noon-2pm/7-9.30pm.
Closed L Sat, BHs
Additional: Sunday L. Children 7yrs+
Seats: 50. Private dining room 20.
Jacket and tie preferred
Style: Classic, Country-House
Smoking: No smoking in dining room
Civil licence: 64
Accommodation: 19 rooms (19 en
suite) ★ ★ ★

An Elizabethan manor house dating back to 1587, the Greenway enjoys a tranquil South Cotswold setting whilst handily placed at the edge of suburban Cheltenham. It offers a relaxed and gentle restaurant environment, recently smartened up in gold, cream and crimson décor, with large French windows affording views across a sunken garden and lily pond to the hills beyond. The fixed-price à la *carte* menu provides luxury at a premium, taking full advantage of fresh local produce on a seasonal basis. Expect to find crab, tarragon and tomato risotto with baby leeks and gingered sea-food froth, followed by breast of guinea fowl with foie gras and sage, or pavé of Scottish beef with parsnip dauphinoise, glazed shallot and haricot beans, exhibiting touches of accomplishment and ambition in equal measure. Greenway honey forms the base of a praline iced parfait with caramelised banana, while alternative selections of British and French cheeses are accompanied by classic vintage ports from a comprehensive list.

Directions: 2.5m S of Cheltenham on A46 (Stroud)

Hotel Kandinsky, Café Paradiso

Bayshill Road, Montpellier,
GL50 3AS
Tel: 01242 527788
Fax: 01242 226412
e info@hotelkandinsky.com
Chef(s): Sarah Payton
Owner(s): Nigel Chapman &
Nicholas Dickinson
Cost: *Alc* £25, set price L £9.75. ☺ ☺
H/wine £11.95
Times: Noon-2pm/7-10pm.
Closed D Sun (ex residents)
Additional: Sunday L. Bar food.
Children welcome
Seats: 40. Private dining room 16
Style: Classic, Modern
Smoking: No smoking in dining room
Accommodation: 48 rooms (48 en
suite) ★ ★ ★ ★
Directions: From M5 J11 follow A40
towards town centre. R at 2nd rdbt,
2nd exit at next rdbt into Bayshill Rd

The hotel's Café Paradiso is bright and buzzy - a splash of colour, you might even say. It offers a simple brasserie menu and houses an impressive pizza oven from which will emerge 'your personal pizza'. Other main course options include roasted bass, spiced fillet of pork and braised lamb kleftico.

CHELTENHAM *Continued*　　　　　Map 3 SO92

Le Petit Blanc

The Promenade, GL50 1NN
Tel: 01242 266800
Fax: 01242 266801
Chef(s): Tim Cook
Owner(s): Raymond Blanc
Cost: A/c £15, set price L £12.50-£15/D £12.50-£15. ☺ ☺
H/wine £10.65
Times: 12-3pm/6-10.30pm.
Closed 25 Dec
Additional: Sunday L. Bar food.
Children welcome
Seats: 150. Private dining room 80
Style: Modern, Chic

The second 'Le Petit Blanc' in Raymond Blanc's empire. It's an easygoing atmosphere in which to choose from a traditional style brasserie menu comprising both classical French dishes and contemporary selections, all from a fixed price menu, a fast food menu, or a children's menu. Confit of guinea fowl, wild mushrooms and a Madeira jus or caramelised skate with fresh noodles, grey shrimps and jus Parisienne typify the style. Execution is generally consistent and although there can be some delays, staff are bright and accommodating.

Smoking: No smoking in dining room; Air conditioning
Directions: Situated in the Queens Hotel, town centre

The Bacchanalian

at The Hotel on the Park,
38 Evesham Road, GL52 2AH
Tel: 01242 227713
Fax: 01242 511526
e stay@hotelonthepark.co.uk
Chef(s): Simon Hulstone
Owner(s): Peter Dann
Cost: A/c £35, set price L £17.95/D £21.50. ☺ ☺ H/wine £12.35
Times: Noon-2pm/7-9pm.
Additional: Sunday L. Bar food.
Children welcome at L
Seats: 35. Private dining room 18
Style: Modern, Country-house
Smoking: No smoking in dining room
Accommodation: 12 rooms (12 en suite) ★ ★ ★

Housed in the classy Hotel on the Park in the centre of town, the restaurant here nonetheless lays claim to the best traditions of modern country house dining unconcerned by its urban setting. An elegant bar and drawing room are unashamedly Regency in style whilst the dark striped, grey-and-black décor, combined with a mural of the nearby Pitville Pump Room, add an individual touch to the dining-room. Menus display a clear focus on quality ingredients and simple combinations on both set-price lunch and à la *carte* menus. "Concepts of the Kitchen" gives the chef a chance to shine in a starter of roast pigeon, timed to perfection, with wild mushroom ravioli and well-balanced truffle foam, followed by roast turbot with foie gras, caramelised mango and pea sauce - a busy yet vibrant dish that successfully delivers the promised balance of flavours. An excellent dessert of banana brûlée with bitter chocolate sorbet impresses for its top-class intensity, flavour and presentation. Fine table appointments, attentive service and sound wine choices all pass muster.

Directions: A435 (Evesham) from Cheltenham centre. Hotel at 3rd lights opposite Pittville Park

England

CHIPPING CAMPDEN   Map 4 SP13
Cotswold House

This Regency hotel was originally the family home of a prosperous wool merchant. Nowadays its air of refinement and luxury is enhanced by an efficient, welcoming team. The restaurant is a good example of this: friendly, unfussy service, well spaced tables and views of the rear garden create a genuinely relaxed atmosphere. The cooking is notable for its well-judged flavours and textures - as in a simple but impressive main course of roast saddle of venison with fondant potatoes, full flavoured wild mushrooms and a truffle sauce. Ingredients are high quality, right down to the coffee and petits fours.

The Square, GL55 6AN
Tel: 01386 840330
Fax: 01386 840310
e reception@cotswoldhouse.com
Chef(s): Alan Dann
Owner(s): Christa & Ian Taylor
Cost: *Alc* £38, set price L £25-£32/ D £38-£55. ☺ H/wine £12.50
Times: Noon-2.30pm/7-9.30pm.
Closed L Mon-Sat
Additional: Sunday L. Children welcome. Vegetarian by request only
Seats: 39. Private dining room 20
Style: Modern, Chic

Smoking: No smoking in dining room
Civil licence: 40
Accommodation: 15 rooms (15 en suite) ★ ★ ★
Directions: 1 mile N of A44 between Moreton-in-Marsh and Broadway on B4081

The Malt House

This restaurant, with its leaded windows, panelled walls and oak beams, nestles in a classic Cotswolds cottage. Dating back to the 15th-century, the room has character and style. Just as we went to press, new chef Janice Rodgers took the helm and will continue to offer a contemporary menu based on the best of local produce (organic where possible). Under the previous regime smoked Scottish salmon with aubergine Provençal and chive crème fraîche or butternut squash risotto with Parma ham typified the style. Main courses included the likes of seared chump of lamb with sautéed mushrooms, red onion and mashed potatoes.

Broad Campden, GL55 6UU
Tel: 01386 840295
Fax: 01386 841334
e nick@the-malt-house.
freeserve.co.uk
Chef(s): Janice Rodgers
Owner(s): Nick Brown
Cost: *Alc* £28.50, set price D £28.50.
☺ H/wine £16.50
Times: Dinner only, 7.30-10.30pm.
Closed D Tue-Wed, Xmas
Additional: Children welcome
Seats: 22
Style: Modern

Smoking: No smoking in dining room
Accommodation: 8 rooms (8 en suite) ♦♦♦♦♦
Directions: Entering Chipping Campden on A44, turn R for Broad Campden, follow four sharp turns to Malt House

Noel Arms Hotel

High Street, GL55 6AT
Tel: 01386 840317
Fax: 01386 841136
Telephone for further details

The balance between past and present is well judged at this 14th-century hotel: the original character remains intact with

England

exposed stone walls, beams and tapestries, while in the restaurant an exciting twist is added to European classics, with some interesting contrasts of flavour. Duck confit with butternut squash and tomato sauce might feature on the short menu, each part of the dish complementing the next, while sea bass with a black olive crust and basil mash is a simple but effective main course which packs a punch. The deceptively plain looking chocolate fondant with white chocolate ice cream is a knock-out. Good strong coffee.

Seymour House Hotel

Occupying a conservatory-style room, where an impressive vine creates a verdant canopy, the restaurant in this charming old building offers an Italian influenced menu. The chef's sometimes unusual food combinations don't always work harmoniously, but there is plenty to choose from, including pot roasted rabbit and a fresh fish of the day option.

Seats: 60. Private dining room 28
Style: Italian
Smoking: No smoking in dining room
Civil licence: 65
Accommodation: 15 rooms (15 en suite) ★ ★ ★
Directions: In village centre

High Street, GL55 6AH
Tel: 01386 840429
Fax: 01386 840369
e enquiry@seymourhousehotel.com
Chef(s): Tocchini Felice
Owner(s): Mr V P Mellini
Cost: *Alc* £26, set price L £15.95. ☺
☺ H/wine £12
Times: noon-2pm/7-10pm
Additional: Sunday L. Bar food.
Children welcome

Three Ways House

Built in 1870, this classical Cotswold building, overlooks the village square. There's an informal, relaxed feel in the stylish, air-conditioned dining room, though no compromise in efficiency. Food is prepared and served simply. Try ricotta cheese, walnut and spinach pancake, but save yourself for dessert: home, of the renowned Pudding Club, you'll have a host of puds to choose from.

Mickleton, GL55 6SB
Tel: 01386 438429
Fax: 01386 438118
e threeways@puddingclub.com
Chef(s): Mark Rowlandson
Owner(s): Simon Coombe & Peter Henderson
Cost: *Alc* £25, set price L £16.50/ D £24.50. ☺ ☺ H/wine £10.95
Times: noon-2.30pm/7-9.30pm.
Additional: Sunday L. Bar food. Children welcome
Seats: 80. Private dining room 70
Style: Classic, Modern
Smoking: No smoking in dining room; Air conditioning
Civil licence: 60
Accommodation: 41 rooms (41 en suite) ★ ★ ★
Directions: On B4632, in village centre

Crown of Crucis

A delightful hotel occupying a 16th-century coaching inn which houses the restaurant, and a modern block surrounding a

Ampney Crucis, GL7 5RS
Tel: 01285 851806
Fax: 01285 851735

courtyard. Imaginative cooking of a high standard is served here, and staff are efficient and friendly.

Telephone for further details
Directions: 2.5m E of Cirencester on A417

CLEARWELL
Map 3 SO50

Tudor Farmhouse Hotel

Ancient wooden beams, exposed stone and open fireplaces give this converted 13th-century cottage a delightful ambience. Adjacent to the main hotel, the restaurant has an extensive grill menu but also offers local duck cooked pink with a plum sauce as well as monkfish, prawn and scallops in a filo basket with cream sauce.

Accommodation: 21 rooms (21 en suite) ★ ★
Directions: Leave Monmouth to Chepstow road at Redbrook, follow signs Clearwell, turn L at village cross, Hotel on the L

GL16 8JS
Tel: 01594 833046
Fax: 01594 837093
Cost: Alc £25/D £19.95-£21.95. ☺
H/wine £9.95
Times: Dinner only, 7-9pm.
Closed Sun, 23-27 Dec
Additional: Children welcome
Smoking: No smoking in dining room

COLN ST-ALDWYNS
Map 4 SP10

New Inn at Coln

GL7 5AN
Tel: 01285 750651
Fax: 01285 750657
✉ stay@new-inn.co.uk
Chef(s): Alastair Ward
Owner(s): Mr & Mrs B A Evans
Cost: Set price L £16.75-£23.50/
D £27.50. H/wine £10.75
Times: noon-2pm/7-9pm

A delightful village coaching inn, the New Inn is, in fact, a very old inn. Combining the best of both worlds, the restaurant brings a modern slant to traditional recipes, but new tastes and combinations feature too. Delicious home-baked bread is worth a mention, before moving on to, say, marinated sea bass with roasted red pepper sauce. Tender pork fillet wrapped in bacon with a thyme and apple rösti is a flavoursome main course and several agreeable desserts tempt the tastebuds. Notably friendly

England

COLN ST-ALDWYNS *Continued*   Map 4 SP10

staff and a hospitable atmosphere make this a popular venue, and as the cosy dining room only seats about twenty, be prepared to book.

Accommodation: 14 rooms (14 en suite) ★★
Directions: 8m E of Cirencester, between Bibury and Fairford

Additional: Sunday L. Bar food.
Children 10yrs+
Seats: 32. Private dining room 20
Style: Rustic, Chic
Smoking: No smoking in dining room

CORSE LAWN   Map 3 SO83

Corse Lawn House

Cleaning your car will seem a breeze once you've seen the large pond, built to wash a stage coach complete with horses, at the front of this attractive country house. Inside, choose from the relaxed bistro (British, French and Mediterranean food) or the formal restaurant, full of sparkling cutlery on crisp linen. Here, a more ambitious menu focuses on Britain and France: amongst the starters, baked goats' cheese, pumpkin soup and moules mariniere, whilst main courses might include roast duckling breast, monkfish or ribeye beef with bourguinon sauce. The service is attentive and efficient.

Smoking: No smoking in dining room. **Civil licence:** 80
Accommodation: 19 rooms (19 en suite) ★★★
Directions: 5m SW of Tewkesbury on B4211, in village centre

GL19 4LZ
Tel: 01452 780771
Fax: 01452 780840
📧 hotel@corselawnhouse.u-net.com
Chef(s): Baba Hine, Andrew Poole
Owner(s): Mr & Mrs Hin, Giles Hine
Cost: *Alc* £35, set price L £18.50/D £27.50. H/wine £10.50
Times: noon-2pm/7-9.30pm.
Closed 24-26 Dec
Additional: Sunday L. Bar food.
Children welcome
Seats: 50. Private dining room 28
Style: Country-house

EWEN   Map 3 SU09

Wild Duck Inn

Drakes Island, GL7 6BY
Tel: 01285 770310
Fax: 01285 770924
📧 wduckinn@aol.com
Chef(s): Richard Mann, Mark Thomas
Owner(s): Mr D & Mrs T B Mussell
Cost: *Alc* £25. ☺ ☺ H/wine £9.50
Times: noon-2pm/6.45-10pm.
Closed 25 Dec
Additional: Sunday L. Bar food.
Children welcome
Seats: 50. Private dining rooms
Style: Traditional, Bistro-Style
Accommodation: 12 rooms (12 en suite) ★★
Directions: Telephone for directions

This charming Elizabethan inn is bursting with character, from the mismatched wooden furniture to the deep red walls and candlelight. The table menu and a blackboard of specials offer old favourites such as fish and chips alongside rustic, international style meals - perhaps crispy duck breast with chilli and ginger salsa or roast lamb with chorizo, thyme and garlic.

FOSSEBRIDGE   Map 4 SP01

Fossebridge Inn

GL54 3JS
Tel: 01285 720721
Fax: 01285 720793

Traditional stone-built coaching inn set in the beautiful Coln Valley, where oak beams and open fires are all part of the experience. The menu goes global with tempura fried tiger prawns, confit of belly pork, and beer battered cod with chips and mushy peas. For local flavour, check out the roast rack of Cotswold lamb.

Style: Traditional
Smoking: No smoking in dining room
Civil licence: 75
Accommodation: 11 rooms (11 en suite) ★ ★
Directions: On A429 between Cirencester and Northleach

e fossebridgeinn@compuserve.com
Chef(s): Iain Rosbotham
Owner(s): Tim & Caroline Bevan
Cost: *Alc* £18.50. ☺ ☺ H/wine £9.95
Times: 11am-3pm/6-11pm.
Additional: Sunday L. Bar food L. Children welcome
Seats: 50. Private dining room 60

FRAMPTON ON SEVERN   Map 3 SO70

Restaurant on the Green

Beside what is claimed to be the longest village green in England is an intimate country house restaurant. Only open for part of the week, the candlelit restaurant offers friendly service and a menu that is a combination of French and English cuisine. Typical menu offerings might be spinach and goats' cheese tartlet, fillet of beef with porcini and red wine and caramelised shallots, pistachio parfait or Normandy apple and frangipane tart. The monthly-changing menu uses fresh, seasonal local produce only, with the exception of fish - one of the restaurant's strengths - which comes daily from Cornwall.

Directions: M5 J13, A38 towards Bristol. R at Frampton/Saul sign. 1 mile, L across village green

The Green, GL2 7DY
Tel: 01452 740077
Chef(s): Tamzin Aronovitz, Louise Palmer
Cost: *Alc* £25. H/wine £8.50
Times: 12.30-2.30pm/7.30-Midnight. Closed Mon-Tue, L Wed-Sat (ex Sat in Summer), D Sun
Additional: Sunday L. Children welcome. Vegetarian not available
Seats: 26
Style: Informal
Smoking: No-smoking area

LOWER SLAUGHTER   Map 4 SP12

Lower Slaughter Manor

This traditional Cotswold manor house with an history dating back to 1658 stands in landscaped gardens at the edge of an historic conservation village. Its interior remains traditional, with heavy drapes, starched linen, cut glass and polished silver prominent in the restaurant. Service is far from starchy without compromising required professional standards, although dinner menus reflect long-standing country house tradition. Some unevenness has been noted following changes of chef and management. Starters such as foie gras with mushy peas and black pudding, followed by roast Goosnargh duck breast with confit leg, buttered Savoy cabbage and mousseline of forest mushrooms are firmly rooted in modern English cooking, indicating that as the new brigade is strengthened some good results will be in prospect.

Directions: Off A429, signposted `The Slaughters'. 0.5 mile into village on R

GL54 2HP
Tel: 01451 820456
Fax: 01451 822150
Chef(s): Jonathan Baron
Owner(s): Mr & Mrs R Vaughan
Cost: *Alc* £45 ☺
Times: 12.30-2pm/7-9.30pm
Additional: Sunday L. Bar food L. Children 12yrs+
Seats: 34. Private dining room 20. Jacket and tie preferred
Style: Traditional, Country-house
Smoking: No smoking in dining room
Accommodation: 16 rooms (16 en suite) ★ ★ ★

Washbourne Court

Set on the banks of the river Eye in picturesque Lower Slaughter, this 17th-century hotel boasts beamed ceilings, log fires and splendid displays of fresh flowers. In the elegant restaurant, polished tables and oil paintings create the feel of a private house. The menu gives more than a passing nod to the traditional English setting, but includes many modern European touches. Dishes might include roast Cotswold lamb

GL54 2HS
Tel: 01451 822143
Fax: 01451 821045
e washbourne@msn.com
Chef(s): Sean Ballington
Owner(s): Mr & Mrs R Vaughan
Cost: *Alc* £40, set price L £21.95/ D £40. H/wine £15.50

England

LOWER SLAUGHTER *Continued*　　　Map 4 SP12

in a brioche and herb crust or seared tuna steak on a warm niçoise salad topped with a lightly poached egg and a balsamic vinegar reduction. An interesting wine list and friendly staff complete the picture.

Smoking: No smoking in dining room
Accommodation: 28 rooms (28 en suite) ★ ★ ★
Directions: Off A429 village centre by the river

Times: 12.30-2pm/7.30-9.30pm
Additional: Sunday L. Bar food.
Children 12yrs+
Seats: 60. Private dining room 16.
Jacket and tie preferred
Style: Modern, British

MORETON-IN-MARSH　　　Map 4 SP23

Manor House Hotel

This honey coloured 16th-century coaching inn houses a pretty restaurant with Van Gogh chairs and yellow walls. The modern British menu is a melting pot in which Thai noodles, pavé of beef and risotto might all appear. Desserts such as blackberry and mango brûlée or chocolate fondant with coconut and vanilla cream complete an imaginative array. Quality ingredients throughout.

Style: Traditional, Country-House
Smoking: No smoking in dining room
Civil licence: 100
Accommodation: 28 rooms (28 en suite) ★ ★ ★
Directions: Off A429 at S end of town

High Street, GL56 0LJ
Tel: 01608 650501
Fax: 01608 651481
e bookings@cotswold-inns-hotels. co.uk
Chef(s): Jonathan Harvey Barnes
Owner(s): Cotswold Inns & Hotels
Cost: Set price L £12.95/D £30. ☺ H/wine £12.50
Times: Noon-3pm/7-11pm.
Additional: Sunday L. Bar food L.
Children welcome
Seats: 52. Private dining room 36

Marsh Goose Restaurant

Local Cotswold stone provided the building materials, a local gallery provides the artwork and the talented kitchen staff provide some really good cooking. Rustic, relaxed dining in a warren of seating areas with crisp table arrangements. The food too combines a sophisticated, European approach to flavour (sautéed chicken and foie gras sausage with lemon and cumin sauce and a tomato concasse) with simplicity (a superb apricot parfait decorated only by a luxuriant white chocolate sauce.) The establishment is in the centre of the town and comprises café, restaurant and delicatessen - so well worth a visit at all times of the day.

Smoking: No smoking in dining room
Directions: In High Street, opposite War Memorial

High Street, GL56 0AX
Tel: 01608 653500
Fax: 01608 653510
Chef(s): Sonya Kidney
Owner(s): Leo Brooke-Little, Sonya Kidney
Cost: Set price L £17 ☺ H/wine £12.50
Times: 12.30-2.30pm/7.30-9.30pm.
Closed Mon, L Tue, D Sun, 25 Dec
Additional: Sunday L. Children welcome
Seats: 45. Jacket and tie preferred
Style: Modern

NAILSWORTH　　　Map 3 ST89

Egypt Mill Hotel

A converted 16th-century corn mill with many original features, its pleasant riverside setting makes this an attractive venue. The restaurant menu caters for a variety of tastes, from the vegetarian brie and broccoli pithivier, or roast root vegetable crumble, to tournedos Rossini fillet steak. A fairly familiar choice of desserts again offers a good range.

Smoking: No smoking in dining room
Accommodation: 17 rooms (17 en suite) ★ ★
Directions: Centre of Nailsworth, on A46

GL6 0AE
Tel: 01453 833449
Fax: 01453 836098
Chef(s): Michael Brook
Owner(s): S R Webb
Cost: *A*/c £20. ☺ H/wine £9.90
Times: Dinner only, 7-10pm. Closed Mon, Tue, Wed, L Mon-Sat
Additional: Sunday L. Bar food.
Children welcome
Seats: 60. Private dining room 80

Waterman's

Old Market, GL6 0BX
Tel: 01453 832808
Chef(s): Sarah Waterman
Owner(s): Mr & Mrs J Waterman
Cost: *Alc* £23.50. ☺ ☺ H/wine £9.95
Times: 10-2pm/6-11pm.
Closed Sun-Mon, L Sun-Fri, 2 wks Jan
Additional: Bar food L. Children
welcome
Seats: 28. Private dining room 12
Style: Traditional
Smoking: No-smoking area; no pipes
Directions: Signposted off A46, in
centre of Nailsworth

The restaurant occupies a 16th-century cottage of Cotswold stone in the centre of the village. It is a husband and wife operation with Sarah Waterman cooking and husband John front of house. John's skills also run to gardening, and he happily produces strawberries, red and yellow raspberries, rainbows of salad stuff, garlic and potatoes from his organic allotment. A menu of good home-cooked dishes based on quality ingredients is offered alongside a straight to the point wine list. Roast tomato tart with basil crème fraîche, fish of the day, and white chocolate mousse have been reported as carefully assembled and accurate.

PAINSWICK   Map 3 SO80

Painswick Hotel

Kemps Lane, GL6 6YB
Tel: 01452 812160
Fax: 01452 814059
e reservations@painswickhotel.com
Chef(s): Kevin Barron
Owner(s): Mr & Mrs Pugh
Cost: Set price L £16/D £26.
☺ H/wine £12.75
Times: noon-2pm/7-9.30pm.
Additional: Sunday L. Bar food L.
Children welcome
Seats: 32. Private dining room 18
Style: Country-house
Smoking: No smoking in dining room
Civil licence: 100

This unusual, oval shaped restaurant, part pine panelled, is simply decorated with terracotta walls and white linen, combining to lend an air of elegance and simplicity. A fixed price lunch menu and evening *carte* offer an eclectic choice. For flavour and balance, choose roast monkfish salad with confit tomatoes and aubergine purée to begin. Gressingham duck, Cornish turbot and Cotswold lamb are typical main course stalwarts, whilst depending on the degree of sophistication sought, you might select acacia honey parfait, warm vanilla rice pudding and poached apricots, or hot chocolate fondant with malteser ice-cream.

Accommodation: 19 rooms (19 en suite) ★ ★ ★
Directions: From A46 turn by church in Painswick, R at The March Hare. Hotel 200yds on R

England

PAXFORD

Map 4 SP13

Churchill Arms

GL55 6XH
Tel: 01386 594000
Fax: 01386 594005
e the-churchill-arms@hotmail.com
Chef(s): Ivan Reid
Owner(s): Sonya & Leo Brooke-Little
Cost: *Alc* £20. ☺ ☺ H/wine £9.50
Times: noon-2.15pm/7-9.15pm
Additional: Sunday L. Bar food.
Children welcome
Seats: 60
Style: Rustic, Country-house
Smoking: Air conditioning

Pub restaurant food at its best. The blackboard menu is constantly changing but a starter of superb fresh squid with harrisa and a sprightly apricot couscous illustrate the style. Look forward also to mains such as a memorable calves' liver with a sultana, lime and ginger reduction, and perfect chocolate torte for dessert. Despite such high culinary standards the establishment still manages to maintain an appealing traditional Cotswold pub atmosphere in its décor, cheerful service and in the good variety of ales, beers, ciders and wines (available by the glass) on offer.

Accommodation: 4 rooms (4 en suite)
Directions: Situated 2miles E of Chipping Campden

STONEHOUSE

Map 3 SO80

Stonehouse Court

Bristol Road, GL10 3RA
Tel: 01453 825155
Fax: 01453 824611
e stonehouse.court@pageant.co.uk
Chef(s): Ali Hussain
Owner(s): Pageant Hotels Ltd
Cost: *Alc* £30, set price D £25-£30.
☺ H/wine £12.95
Times: noon-2pm/7-10pm.
Closed L Sat
Additional: Sunday L. Bar food.
Children welcome
Seats: 60. Private dining room 20
Style: Traditional, Country-house
Smoking: No smoking in dining room

Built in 1601, this attractive manor house is set in six acres of gardens. An extensive wine list complements the fixed-price and *carte* menus. There's a touch of the exotic in the option of chargrilled noisette of crocodile, but the less snappy dishes are more effective. Cajun grilled loin of lamb with roasted vegetables, creamed nutmeg spinach and port sauce, or roasted monkfish wrapped in Parma ham with honey pea purée and ratatouille sauce might prove to be good choices. Desserts could include lemon and Malibu soufflé with coconut shortbread, and the British cheese menu is certainly tempting.

Civil licence: 100
Accommodation: 36 rooms (36 en suite) ★ ★ ★
Directions: M5 J13/A419 (Stroud). Straight on at 2 rdbts, under rail bridge. Hotel 100yds on R

STOW-ON-THE-WOLD

Map 4 SP12

Grapevine Hotel

Sheep Street,
GL54 1AU
Tel: 01451 830344
Fax: 01451 832278
e enquires@vines.co.uk
Chef(s): Mark Jenkins
Owner(s): Mrs S Elliott
Cost: *Alc* £28, set price L £14.50-£19.50/D £28-£33. ☺ H/wine £14.75
Times: noon-2pm/7-9.30pm
Additional: Sunday L. Bar food.
Children welcome
Seats: 50. Private dining room 25.
Jacket and tie preferred
Style: Rustic
Smoking: No smoking in dining room
Civil licence: 60
Accommodation: 22 rooms (22 en suite) ★ ★ ★

This delightful 17th-century hotel takes its name from the one hundred year old vine which forms a leafy canopy to the conservatory restaurant, lending an airy, al fresco feel to the dining experience. A short *carte* menu dishes up accomplished cuisine with a less formal brasserie-style menu available at lunch.

Directions: Take A436 towards Chipping Norton; 150yds on R facing green.

Hamilton's Restaurant   NEW

Decorated along crisp, functional lines with limestone flooring, cherry and walnut wood and bare white walls adorned with modern art. Hamilton's stands out with its cool interior and modern frontage, adding a touch of metropolitan chic to the Cotswolds. The place has an informal feel, but service is still happily efficient. As for the food - it's modern British without ignoring traditional favourites like sticky toffee or crumble. Amongst the dishes, you may find an 'out of this world' spring onion and Cheddar mash accompanying a well-judged roast chump of lamb on garlic, white bean and mint cassoulet.

Smoking: No cigars; Air conditioning
Directions: Telephone for directions

GL54 1AQ
Tel: 01454 831700
Fax: 01454 831388
e goodfood@hamiltons.br.com
Chef(s): Chris Short
Cost: *Alc* £21.75. ☺ ☺ H/wine £11
Times: Noon-2.30pm/6-11pm.
Closed D Sun
Additional: Sunday L.
Children welcome
Seats: 55
Style: Modern, Chic

947AD at The Royalist   NEW

It's a fair way from the Fulham Road both in terms of sheer geography and as a cultural shift, but Alan and Georgina Thompson have already put their stamp on what is reputedly the oldest inn in England. London's loss is Gloucestershire's gain. The assured touch apparent in their previous incarnation has not been lost and the polish apparent in, for instance, a starter of roast quail with foie gras cassoulet and pancetta has been summed up as simply "fabulous". Venison with juniper berry tarte tatin, pear and savoy cabbage has also won plaudits for "melt in the mouth" meat and well-seasoned cabbage together with an excellent caramelised pear in a robust and "deeply satisfying combination". Peripherals are taken seriously - an amuse of baked goats cheese with cherry tomatoes and balsamic vinegar or a pre-dessert of caramelised lemon curd in a ramekin - and bread is top-notch. Desserts have included a signature banana and passion fruit parfait with banana crisps "beautifully presented" and petits fours are accomplished.

Digbeth Street, GL54 1BN
Tel: 01451 830670
Fax: 01451 870048
e info@theroyalisthotel.co.uk
Chef(s): Alan Thompson
Owner(s): Alan Thompson
Cost: *Alc* £25, set price L £9.50-£12.50. ☺ ☺ H/wine £12.50
Times: Noon-2.30pm/7-9.30pm.
Closed Mon, D Sun
Additional: Sunday L. Bar food.
Children welcome
Seats: 35. Private dining room 16
Style: Country-house, Chic
Smoking: No smoking in dining room
Accommodation: 8 rooms (8 en suite)
★ ★ ★
Directions: Telephone for directions

Wyck Hill House

Locally-sourced ingredients of commendable quality continue to have an impact on country house style menus that are nonetheless dotted with lighter options for lunch. The restaurant and adjacent conservatory revel in fine views of the Cotswolds and Windrush valley, an eclectic wine list and attentive service adding to the overall sense of well-being. Successes from the fixed-price dinner menu have included ballotine of foie gras and rabbit confit, duck with juniper-flavoured redcurrant sauce and an assiette of lemon brûlée, pannacotta and ice cream of subtle resonance. Filter coffee and petits fours have been less inspiring.

Accommodation: 32 rooms (32 en suite) ★ ★ ★ ★
Directions: 3 miles S of Stow on A424 towards Burford

Burford Road, GL54 1HY
Tel: 01451 831936
Fax: 01451 832243
e wyckhill@wrensgroup.com
Chef(s): David Bates
Owner(s): The Wrens Hotel Group
Cost:, set price L £14/D £36.50. ☺ ☺ H/wine £14.95
Additional: Sunday L. Bar food L.
Children welcome
Seats: 60. Private dining room 40
Style: Traditional, Country-house
Smoking: No smoking in dining room; Air conditioning
Civil licence: 80

England

STROUD

Map 3 SO80

The Halfway Inn   NEW

Box, GL6 9AE
Tel: 01453 832631
Chef(s): Dominic Brockbank
Owner(s): Mr R Smith
Cost: *Alc* £21.50, set price L £13.95.
☺ ☺ H/wine £10.75
Times: 11-2pm/7-9.30pm
Additional: Sunday L. Bar food.
Children welcome
Seats: 80. Private dining room 40
Style: Modern
Smoking: No-smoking area; no pipes
Directions: From A419 (Stroud-Cirencester) follow signs to Minchinhampton Common then to Box. From A46 (Stroud-Nailsworth) in Nailsworth follow signs to Box

This former inn on the edge of Minchinhampton Common has been refurbished to provide a spacious restaurant with waxed furniture, pastel décor and subtle lighting. Daily specials have included cod fishcake and french onion soup. Pan-fried beef fillet might be taken from the seasonal *carte*. A delicately scented lavender brûlée might make a refreshing change from the fruity variety.

TETBURY

Map 3 ST89

Calcot Manor

Calcot, GL8 8YJ
Tel: 01666 890391
Fax: 01666 890394
🅔 reception@calcotmanor.co.uk
Chef(s): Michael Croft
Cost: *Alc* £30. ☺ H/wine £14
Times: noon-2pm/7-9.30pm.
Additional: Sunday L.
Children welcome
Seats: 90. Private dining room 90
Style: Modern English
Smoking: No smoking in dining room
Civil licence: 90
Accommodation: 28 rooms (28 en suite) ★★★

In an attractive courtyard of ancient barns and stables, built by 14th-century Cistercian monks, this elegantly converted country house retains considerable charm. The stylish conservatory restaurant, with its flagstone floor and airy atmosphere, serves imaginative food, full of flavour and with a Mediterranean bias. Tasty home-made bread begins your meal, followed by a choice of a dozen or so starters: light curried mussels, beef bresaola, tomato tarte Tatin etc. For a main course try grilled marinated fillet mignon of yellowfin tuna, complemented by Moroccan vegetables and couscous, while the dessert menu and wine list both provide plenty of options.

Directions: 3 miles W of Tetbury on A4135 close to intersection with A45

England

Close Hotel

8 Long Street, GL8 8AQ
Tel: 01666 502272
Fax: 01666 504401
e reception@theclosehotel.co.uk
Chef(s): Daren Bale
Owner(s): Mr & Mrs D Bale
Cost: *Alc* £40, set price L £16.50/
D £29.50. ☺ H/wine £14.50
Times: Noon-2pm/7-9.30pm.
Additional: Sunday L. Bar food.
Children 12yrs+ at D
Seats: 32. Private dining room 22.
Jacket and tie preferred
Style: Classic, Country-house
Smoking: No smoking in dining room
Civil licence: 70
Accommodation: 15 rooms (15 en
suite) ★ ★ ★

London comes to the country here in Tetbury in one of the finest townhouses in the Cotswolds. Chamber music, French waiting staff, log burning fires and squishy sofas set the scene in the lounge areas. High levels of both comfort and quality in the restaurant too, where chef Darren Bale offers some impressive modern British cooking. This is technically accomplished cuisine with clean, clear flavours and contrasts well handled. Guests are treated to the best of Cotswold produce with quality ingredients providing a strong foundation. Luxury items (foie gras, truffles, scallops) are much in evidence accompanying, for instance, veal, salmon and chicken main courses. Fish has been noted as a strength, in the likes of roast monkfish tail with cucumber and vanilla risotto and cappuccino of red wine and thyme. Desserts are a real star, as in a "sublime" caramelised tarte Tatin and service is confident yet relaxed with a strong management team much in evidence.

Directions: From M4 J17 onto A429 to Malmesbury. From M5 J14 onto B4509

Snooty Fox

Market Place, GL8 8DD
Tel: 01666 502436
Fax: 01666 503479
Telephone for further details

An historic 16th-century coaching inn combining atmosphere with high levels of comfort and quality, and popular as a weekend retreat. The bright menu offers seasonal dishes in the charming dining room, with its window seats and moody lighting: chicken with asparagus and lemon mousse was a recent highlight, and game also features strongly.

England

Map 3 ST89

The Trouble House NEW

From heading a brigade of fifteen at City Rhodes, talented chef Michael Bedford has turned his back on London and is now solo in the kitchen at this spruced up pub in the heart of Gloucestershire. Humble scrubbed tables fronting blazing log fires within simply adorned bars is now the setting for enjoying Bedford's inspired cooking. Tip-top fresh ingredients and general attention to detail are clearly evident in such honest and full-flavoured main dishes as crispy duck confit with white beans and lentils or pan-fried cod on olive oil mash with capers and parsley, and braised oxtails with roast parsnips. Short, simply described, daily blackboard menus may also offer chicken liver and foie gras pâté to start and vanilla cream parfait with marinated pineapple for pudding.

Cirencester Road, GL8 8SG
Tel: 01666 502206
Fax: 01666 504508
Chef(s): Michael Bedford
Owner(s): Michael & Sarah Bedford
Cost: Alc £25. ☺ ☺ H/wine £10
Times: Noon-2pm/7-9.30pm.
Closed Mon (ex BHs)
Additional: Bar food. Children welcome
Seats: 50
Style: Traditional, country pub
Directions: Telephone for directions.

Map 3 ST69

Thornbury Castle

Henry VIII, Anne Boleyn and Mary Tudor have walked these corridors, and it's easy to imagine the decadent medieval banquets which must have taken place here. The dining rooms are filled with stern portraits, real fires and heraldic shields - as well as a fair number of Americans lured by the beautiful, historic setting. The cooking is another good reason to visit, for it allows the guests to sample traditional ingredients in a variety of exciting, original dishes: haggis, for example, appears in a rösti, topped with local Tortworth pheasant, whilst Welsh black beef might be served on a vegetable pavé with chestnuts..

Castle Street, BS35 1HH
Tel: 01454 281182
Fax: 01454 416188
e thornburycastle@compuserve.com
Chef(s): Colin Woodward
Owner(s): Von Essen Hotels
Cost: Set price L £25-£29.50/
D £42.50-£47. H/wine £12
Times: Noon-2pm/7-10pm.
Closed 4 days Jan
Additional: Sunday L.
Children welcome
Seats: 60. Private dining room 30.
Jacket and tie preferred
Style: Classic, Country-house
Smoking: No smoking in dining room
Civil licence: 50
Accommodation: 24 rooms (24 en suite) ★ ★ ★
Directions: From High St into Castle St. Opp church. Follow brown Historic Castle signs.

Map 4 SP12

Lords of the Manor

In an area not short of up-market country house hotels with very good restaurants what's so different about Lords of the Manor? Look to the kitchen. This is an up-market country house hotel with an *exceptional* restaurant and at the root of that happy equation is the singular talent and dedication of John Campbell. Recent success hasn't come about by accident, few chefs can have put as much thought and intellectual rigour

GL54 2JD
Tel: 01451 820243
Fax: 01451 820696
e lordsofthemanor@btinternet.com
Chef(s): John Campbell
Cost: Alc £45, set price L £17.95/
D £79 (7 courses). ☺ H/wine £15.95
Times: 12.30-2pm/7.30-9.30pm

into their development and it shows in cooking that is technically skilled, sometimes innovative and occasionally inspired. The menu reads like a bit of an adventure and it's probably not surprising that the all encompassing sweep of the 7-course tasting menu has many takers. There is a welcome understatement to menu descriptions that reflects the clarity of purpose evident in the dishes. Roast scallop, for instance, comes with foie gras and sauce epicée in a combination notable for its harmony and judicious spicing. Slow cooking at low temperatures is a favoured, and dramatically successful technique, as evidenced by a marinated fillet of beef with onion ice cream that received hyperbolic praise. There is much in the way of extras too, with amuse such as risotto of smoked haddock with mustard sherbet and pre-desserts like coffee and orange ice cream. More ice cream accompanying a pinpoint dessert of tarte Tatin of peach - this time a brilliantly conceived and equally well-executed pepper version. "Some of the most exciting cooking in the country" is a recent comment that seems to sum it up. A weighty and well sourced wine list with a special selection by the glass to accompany the tasting menu completes the impressive picture.

Additional: Sunday L. Bar food. Children 12yrs+
Seats: 50. Private dining room 30
Style: Traditional, Country-house
Smoking: No smoking in dining room
Civil licence: 50
Accommodation: 27 rooms (27 en suite) ★ ★ ★
Directions: Follow signs towards The Slaughters off A429. The restaurant is in centre of Upper Slaughter

WINCHCOMBE

Map 4 SP02

Wesley House

High Street, GL54 5LT
Tel: 01242 602366
Fax: 01242 604046
 reservations@wesleyhouse.co.uk
Chef(s): Alex Breach
Owner(s): Matthew Brown
Cost: Alc £31, set price L £14.50/ D £18.50-£31. ☺ ☺ H/wine £11.50
Times: Noon-5pm/6.45-Midnight. Closed D Sun
Additional: Sunday L. Bar food L. Children welcome
Seats: 50
Style: Rustic, Traditional
Smoking: No-smoking area
Accommodation: 6 rooms (6 en suite) ♦♦♦♦
Directions: In the centre of Winchcombe on the main road

A gorgeous half-timbered building dating back to 1435, close to Sudeley Castle and in the midst of the idyllic Cotswolds. As one would expect, warm log fires and plump sofas ensure that all augurs well for visiting guests and diners who aim to get away from it all. Wesley House is well known for its food, with a French-style menu that also incorporates other Mediterranean and occasional Oriental flavours. Seared loin of tuna with Thai dressing and black beans sits cosily alongside terrine of smoked duck and foie gras with beetroot and chilli jam and toasted herb brioche. South Africa is a speciality of the wine list, which kicks off with eight recommendations of the house.

GREATER MANCHESTER

GREATER MANCHESTER

ALTRINCHAM   Map 7 SJ78

Juniper

Paul Kitching, having in the last year taken over as co-owner, has not been slow in undertaking a programme of refurbishment that has resulted in extensions to both restaurant and kitchen. If ambition alone is worthy of reward, then he and his partner, Jane, both have continued success and growth firmly in their hands. Simple, clean and clear flavours are highlights of a menu that might include scallop, rabbit and coriander ragout, or sautéed foie gras with red cabbage juice as precursors to grilled brill with artichokes and an Earl Grey infusion or truffled wood-pigeon with sweet chestnut and mango beignets. At heart the cooking is classically French, carefully balanced and tempered with individualistic ideas that generally work well. Matched by interior design that looks towards Tuscany - with a touch of art deco - Juniper remains one of the region's foremost destination restaurants. Classic, fine wines - full of surprises - complement service that is slick yet unintrusive.

21 The Downs, WA14 2QD
Tel: 0161 929 4008
Fax: 0161 929 4009
e reservations@juniper-restaurant.co.uk
Chef(s): Paul Kitching
Owner(s): P & D Keeling, P Kitching, K O'Brien
Cost: Alc £33, set price L £18. ☺
H/wine £16
Times: Noon-2.15pm/7-9.30pm. Closed Sun & Mon, L Sat, 2 wks Summer, 1 wk Jan
Additional: Children welcome. Vegetarian by request only
Seats: 34
Style: Classic, Bistro-Style
Smoking: No smoking in dining room; Air conditioning
Directions: A556 Chester-Manchester road

Woodland Park Hotel

There's an away-from-it-all feel at this secluded hotel, located in a residential area four miles from Manchester. The elegant restaurant has a conservatory bar attached and offers a brasserie-style menu. Medley of seafood, lightly poached in vermouth with dill and cream, and pan-fried calves' liver with glazed shallots and light Madeira jus are two options from a good selection.

Seats: 80. Private dining room 40
Style: Classic, Traditional
Smoking: No smoking in dining room; Air conditioning
Civil licence: 60
Accommodation: 46 rooms (46 en suite) ★ ★ ★
Directions: 4 miles from Manchester Airport. 300 yards from Metrolink to city centre

Wellington Road, Timperley, WA15 7RG
Tel: 0161 928 8631
Fax: 0161 941 2821
e info@woodlandpark.co.uk
Chef(s): Jeff Spencer
Owner(s): Mr & Mrs Walker
Cost: Alc £22, set price L £12.95/ D £14.95-£20.45. ☺ ☺
H/wine £10.95
Times: Noon-2pm/7-10pm. Closed Sun, L Sat, Xmas, New Year, BHs
Additional: Bar food L. Children welcome

England

MANCHESTER Map 7 SJ89

Crowne Plaza Manchester-The Midland

Peter Street, M60 2DS
Tel: 0161 236 3333
Fax: 0161 932 4100
e sales@basshotels-uknorth.co.uk

There's a touch of Edwardian elegance about this city-centre hotel, and its fine French cooking based on many luxury foods is by no means out of place. Bruno Lucchi leads the waiting team with a star-quality performance. Classic influences seep into slow-roasted cod fillet with Burgundy and trompette mushroom risotto (available also as a main course), and duck liver parfait with red onion marmalade and toasted brioche. Tournedos of Scottish beef fillet, pommery gratin potato, artichoke crumble and a rich red wine jus shows the unstinting use of quality produce, and desserts are spread across the sumptuous and the irresistible: rum-flavoured rich chocolate bread and butter pudding with ginger biscuits and clotted cream is a prime example. There's a traditional wine list marked by drinking styles and the set menu offers a good value option.

Chef(s): Simon Holling
Owner(s): Bass Hotels & Resorts
Cost: Alc £45.50, set price D £29-£38. H/wine £13.50
Times: Dinner only, 7-10.30/11pm. Closed D Sun Bhs
Additional: Children welcome
Seats: 40. Jacket and tie preferred. **Style:** French
Smoking: No cigars; Air conditioning
Civil licence: 450
Accommodation: 303 rooms (303 en suite) ★★★★
Directions: M62 J 12 towards Liverpool, M602 city centre

Little Yang Sing

17 George Street, M1 4HE
Tel: 0161 228 7722
Fax: 0161 237 9257
Chef(s): Thuc Bac Phyong
Owner(s): LYS Ltd
Cost: Alc £18, set price L £9.95/ D £16-£25. ☺ ☺ H/wine £9.95
Times: Noon-11.30pm. Closed 25 Dec
Additional: Sunday L. Children welcome

Bustling, non-standard Cantonese basement restaurant with mirror-clad blue décor and smart, friendly Chinese staff. Prawn and meat steamed dumplings, chicken in rice paper and bean curd flapjack all succeed through quality of ingredients and some crisp cooking.

Seats: 87. **Style:** Traditional
Smoking: Air conditioning
Directions: Centre of Manchester's China Town. Behind Piccadilly Plaza. On Metrolink route

Lowry Hotel, River Room Marco Pierre White NEW

50 Dearmans Place, Chapel Wharf, M3 5LH
Tel: 0161 827 4000
Telephone for further details

Marco Pierre White has brought his magic touch to the North with the opening of the River Room. This is 'quite clearly the best food in Manchester's city centre' served in a modern, minimalist environment with acres of white walls, frosted glass and polished wooden floors. Unfortunately at the time or our visit, the poor service detracted somewhat from the superb meal. Opening with a terrine of foie gras, the perfectly cooked Aberdeen Angus fillet en daube that followed was supported by celeriac purée, Bourgogne garnish plus a fresh and fragrant mash. The marquis au chocolat was as clever as anticipated. Definitely one to watch.

MANCHESTER *Continued*   Map 7 SJ89

Marriott Worsley Park

Enchanting combination of new and old, including remnants from the restaurant's former stable days. The satisfying food matches the décor with a modern take on traditional favourites. You could make a meal of the chunky French bread or cheese loaves, but would miss surprising combinations which work really well like salmon on woodland mushroom risotto - with perfectly timed fish, and truffle oil to heighten the flavours.

Worsley Park, Worsley, M28 2QT
Tel: 0161 975 2000
Fax: 0161 799 6341
e sales@worsleypark.com
Chef(s): Gary Jenkins
Cost: *Alc* £30, set price L £17-£25/ D £25-£37. ☺ ☺ H/wine £13.50
Times: noon-2pm/7-10pm. Closed L Sat
Additional: Sunday L. Bar food. Children welcome. Vegetarian by request only
Seats: 150. Private dining room 200
Style: Classic, Country-house
Smoking: No-smoking area; Air conditioning
Civil licence: 200
Accommodation: 158 rooms (158 en suite) ★ ★ ★ ★
Directions: Located just off J13 of M60, take A575. Hotel on L

Moss Nook

A meal here is a major agenda item for business people flying into Manchester - the restaurant is located just outside the perimeter of the airport. As for the locals, they are more devotees than regulars, so it pays to book. The setting is intimate with red suede walls, crystal candle lamps and lace table covers inside, and a flower garden and terrace outside. The food has a traditional French base with anglicised interpretation. English lamb, served sliced around a chicken and tarragon mousse, with a Madeira sauce and fried broccoli, are both interesting and good to eat.

Ringway Road, Moss Nook, M22 5WD
Tel: 0161 437 4778
Fax: 0161 498 8089
Chef(s): Kevin Lofthouse
Owner(s): P & D Harrison
Cost: *Alc* £40, set price £18.50/ D £31.50. H/wine £9.95
Times: Noon-2pm/7-9.30pm. Closed Sun & Mon, L Sat, 2 wks Xmas
Additional: Children 12yrs+
Seats: 65. Jacket and tie preferred
Style: Modern
Smoking: No pipes
Directions: 1mile from airport – at junction of Ringway with B5166

The New Emperor

52-56 George Street, M1 4HF
Tel: 0161 228 2883
Fax: 0161 228 6620
📧 reservations@newemperor.co.uk
Chef(s): Tommy Chan
Owner(s): Johnny Lee
Cost: Alc £16. ☺ ☺ H/wine £10.50
Times: Noon-2pm/D until Midnight.
Additional: Children welcome
Seats: 250. Private dining room 20.
Jacket and tie preferred
Style: Modern
Smoking: Air conditioning
Directions: Heart of Chinatown, near
Manchester Piccadilly

Busy restaurant in the heart of Chinatown, popular with
business people, Chinese regulars and locals. Prawn and meat
dumplings and light crisp spring rolls are full of flavour, and
dishes based on quality ingredients and interesting
combinations are enhanced by individual saucing. In addition to
a comprehensive menu there is an attractively priced set meal
and a range of banquets.

Nico Central

High ceilings, pale yellow décor and Art Deco detailing gives
the restaurant a light and spacious feel. Service is professional
and friendly with gratifying attention to detail - single diners
are offered a newspaper for example. Mains such as scallops
with peppered spinach, pancetta and saffron butter sauce show
balance, skill and care.

Seats: 90. **Style:** Modern
Smoking: No-smoking area; no pipes; Air conditioning
Directions: Located to side of Crowne Plaza Manchester – The
Midland Hotel

Mount Street, M60 2DS
Tel: 0161 236 6488
Fax: 0161 236 8897
Chef(s): Ryan Jackson
Owner(s): The Restaurant Partnership
Cost: Alc £23, set price L £14.95/
D £14.95 (pre-theatre only). ☺ ☺
H/wine £13.30
Times: Noon-2.30pm/6-10.30pm.
Closed L Sat
Additional: Sunday L. Bar food.
Children welcome

Le Petit Blanc   NEW

55 Kings Street, M5 4LQ
Tel: 0161 832 1000
Telephone for further details

The latest of the Blanc offspring. Brasserie style dishes
competently handled in a large stylish dining room of 130
covers with four private dining areas also available. Expect
punchy cooking of, for instance, fricassée of wild mushrooms
with herb and garlic croutons or pan-fried sea bream fillet with
ratatouille and raw tomato coulis. Amongst the dessert there is
to be found, of course, floating island 'Maman Blanc'.

England

MANCHESTER *Continued*   Map 7 SJ89

Rhodes & Co

Rhodes & Co in Manchester is part of the Quays development, attached to the Quality Inn. Window tables look out over Manchester United football ground, while at the centre of the room the core of tables and high backed chairs resemble little booths. Elsewhere, comfortable leather seats encourage diners to linger. There is a fair-sized bar, used purely for dining on match days, where bar-snacks are served. The brasserie menu is similar in style to Rhodes & Co in Edinburgh, with a good choice incorporating steak and kidney sausages with mash and onion gravy, and roast cod with garlic-baked beans.

Waters Reach, Trafford Park,
M17 1WS
Tel: 0161 868 1900
Fax: 0161 868 1901
e rhodesmanchester@sodexho-uk.com
Chef(s): Ian Morgan
Owner(s): Gary Rhodes/Sodexho
Cost: *Alc* £26.50. ☺ ☺
H/wine £12.50
Times: Noon-2.30pm/6.30-9.45pm.
Closed L Sat-Sun
Additional: Bar food. Children welcome
Seats: 85. Private dining room 80
Style: Modern, Minimalist
Smoking: Air conditioning
Directions: Opposite Old Trafford Football Ground, off A5081

Simply Heathcotes

A feeling of space and comfort is achieved in this modern restaurant by the use of minimalist styling and bold colours. The menu is extensive and flexible (starters, for example, are available as main course portions) and whilst the feel of the cooking is traditional — witness sea bass with herb risotto or a 'lovely' Goosnargh duck confit with mixed bean cassoulet. Tastes and textures are skillfully balanced throughout, and the vegetarian options might even tempt the meat eaters. A wide choice of desserts could include baked cherry pie with chestnut ice cream or Heathcotes' egg custard scented with rosewater.

Civil licence: 60
Directions: M62 J17. Restaurant at top end of Deansgate

Jacksons Row, Deansgate,
M2 5WD
Tel: 0161 835 3536
Fax: 0161 835 3534
e manchester@simplyheathcotes.co.uk
Chef(s): David Aspin
Owner(s): Mr P Heathcote
Cost: *Alc* £25, set price L £15.50/
D £15.50. ☺ ☺ H/wine £11.50
Times: 11.45-2.30pm/5.30-10pm.
Closed 25-26 Dec, 1 Jan, BHs
Additional: Sunday L.
Children welcome
Seats: 170. Private dining room 60
Style: Modern
Smoking: No cigars; Air conditioning

Stock

The Stock Exchange, 4 Norfolk Street,
M2 1DW
Tel: 0161 839 6644
Fax: 0161 839 6655
Chef(s): Vincenzo Mauro
Owner(s): Mr E Mauro
Cost: *Alc* £25, set price L £13.50.
☺ ☺ H/wine £12.95
Times: Noon-10pm. Closed Sun,
25-26 Dec
Additional: Children welcome
Seats: 100. Private dining room 34
Style: Classic, Italian-Style
Smoking: No pipes; Air conditioning
Directions: Telephone for directions

The former stock exchange building in the centre of
Manchester makes an impressive setting for this acclaimed
Italian restaurant, with its stained glass windows, domed ceiling
and marble columns. The *carte* changes fortnightly, and presents
a good choice including a daily home-made ravioli, market
fresh fish and classics like veal Milanese. Pasta dishes can also
be served as a main course.

Tai Pan   NEW

81-97 Upper Brook Street, M13 9TX
Tel: 0161 273 2798
Fax: 0161 273 1578
Chef(s): Hon Sun Woo
Cost: ☺ ☺
Times: Noon-3pm/3-11.30pm
Additional: Children welcome
Seats: 350. Private dining room 100

A bustling Chinese with as many Far Eastern customers as
locals. There is a business lunch menu, and some ubiquitous
choices, but for the genuine article try the *carte*. A delicate
shark fin soup with fresh crab, and refined shredded beef fillet
with chilli and garlic show how Chinese cooking should be.

Style: Chinese
Smoking: No smoking in dining room; Air conditioning
Directions: 2 miles from city centre

MANCHESTER AIRPORT   Map 7 SJ88

Etrop Grange

Thorley Lane, M90 4EG
Tel: 0161 499 0500
Fax: 0161 499 0790
e etropgrange@corushotels.com
Chef(s): Hamish Deas
Owner(s): Corus & Regal Hotels
Cost: Set price D £29.50-£36.50. ☺
H/wine £13.95
Times: noon-2pm/7-10pm.
Closed L Sat
Additional: Sunday L. Bar food.
Children welcome
Seats: 50. Private dining room 90

Located near the airport, this is a good stopping off point for
that last meal before surrendering to airline food. The
restaurant of this Grade II listed country house is suitably
decked out in ostentatious rich gold and burgundy. Presentation
is clearly a spur on the plate too, with skilful cooking apparent
in a main course of chicken breast with spinach mousseline and
baby vegetables on a Champagne sauce. Romantics take note;
lighting is subdued and there are plenty of tables for two away
from the centre of the room.

Style: Traditional, Country-house
Smoking: No smoking in dining room
Civil licence: 80
Accommodation: 64 rooms (64 en suite) ★ ★ ★
Directions: Off M56 J5. At main airport roundabout, take 1st L
(to Terminal 2), then 1st R (Thornley Lane), 200yds on R

England

Radisson SAS Hotel
Manchester Airport

Chicago Avenue, M90 3RA
Tel: 0161 490 5000
Fax: 0161 490 5100
e sales@manzq.rdsas.com
Chef(s): Richard Williamson
Owner(s): Mr T Hellebust
Cost: *Alc* £28, set price L £18/
D £26-£32. H/wine £17
Times: 12-2.30pm/6-10.30pm.
Additional: Sunday L. Bar food.
Children welcome
Seats: 140. Private dining room 280
Style: Modern, Chic
Smoking: No-smoking area; no pipes;
Air conditioning
Civil licence: 80

Rather than modern jumbos, one can almost envisage colourful hot-air balloons floating by the floor-to-ceiling windows of the Phileas Fogg restaurant at this ultra-modern airport hotel. Lancashire parsnip soup, calves' liver with bubble-and-squeak and apple pie with a Stilton crumble, echoing such days past, are balanced by Thai-spiced chicken and oyster mushrooms on an open ravioli and confit duck leg with hot-and-sour cabbage. There is considerable style to the service and the impressive crockery in an atmosphere that copes manfully with a mixed-age, polyglottic clientele.

Accommodation: 360 rooms (360 en suite) ★ ★ ★ ★
Directions: Exit M56 J5, follow signs for Terminal 2, take 1st exit at roundabout for railway station, hotel is opposite the station

OLDHAM   Map 7 SD90

Hotel Smokies Park

With a name like Cosi Fan Tutti, the restaurant at this modern hotel has to be Italian. The setting is attractive - polished floors and sweeping ceiling fans - and service is friendly. As well as the usual Italian favourites, more technically daring dishes are offered from the blackboard specials and set price daily menu.

Seats: 80. Private dining room 100
Style: Modern, Italian
Smoking: Air conditioning
Accommodation: 73 rooms (73 en suite) ★ ★ ★
Directions: On A627 between Oldham and Ashton-under-Lyme

Ashton Road, Bardsley, OL8 3HX
Tel: 0161 785 5050
Fax: 0161 785 5010
e cosifantutti@smokies.co.uk
Chef(s): Kevin Amesbury
Cost: *Alc* £20, set price L £6.95-
£17.95. ☺ ☺ H/wine £10
Times: Noon-2pm/7-10pm. Closed L
Sat, L BHs, D 25 Dec & 1 Jan
Additional: Sunday L. Bar food.
Children welcome

Menzies Avant Hotel

This bright, comfortable restaurant serves up an imaginative menu: how common are roast ostrich steaks in Oldham? However, it is the grilled fillets of John Dory served with beetroot tagliatelle, baby fennel and a saffron cream which steal

Windsor Road, Manchester Street,
OL8 4AS
Tel: 0161 627 5500
Fax: 0161 627 5896
e info@menzies-hotels.co.uk

the show, followed a close second by the hospitality of the friendly staff.

Smoking: No smoking in dining room
Air conditioning
Civil licence: 200
Accommodation: 103 rooms (103 en suite) ★ ★ ★ ★
Directions: From M62 J20 take A627(M) towards Oldham, then A62 Manchester Street. Hotel on L

Chef(s): Gary Davey
Cost: *Alc* £28, set price L £8.50/ D £17.50. ☺ ☺ H/wine £9.95
Times: Noon-2.30pm/7-10pm.
Additional: Sunday L. Bar food. Children welcome
Seats: 104. Private dining room 150
Style: Classic, Traditional

White Hart Inn

Overlooking The Pennines, this 18th-century stone-built inn offers both a brasserie and restaurant menu, with some overlap of dishes. Deferring to the modern trend for healthy eating, the kitchen makes a point of volunteering dishes with less fat and oil content. What a pity to shun the British cheese platter, or the home-made sausage selection, encompassing chicken and black pudding, or venison and juniper options. There's a contemporary Mediterranean leaning in dishes such as toasted goats' cheese rolled in poppy seeds with wild mushroom tagliatelle and aubergine caviar, or smoked haddock and pesto fishcake with a caper beurre blanc.

Accommodation: 12 rooms (12 en suite)
Directions: From Oldham take A669 Lees road, through Lees & Grotton. At brow of steep hill turn L, Inn 50yds on L

☺☺
51 Stockport Road, Lydgate, OL4 4JJ
Tel: 01457 872566
Fax: 01457 875190
Chef(s): John Rudden
Owner(s): Mr C Brierley & J Rudden
Cost: *Alc* £25, set price L £16. ☺ H/wine £11
Times: 1-3.30pm/6.30-9.30pm.
Closed Mon, L Tue-Sat, D Sun
Additional: Sunday L. Bar food. Children welcome. Vegetarian by request only
Seats: 40. Private dining room 18
Style: Modern
Smoking: No smoking in dining room; Air conditioning
Civil licence: 70

ROCHDALE   Map 7 SD81

Nutter's

The whackiness is all on the surface and once you dig beneath the name and the television image, you quickly hit solid foundations of intelligent cooking based on quality produce. Particular successes have included cherry tomato and smoked garlic soup with truffle ice cream as well as crispy duck confit with stir-fried pak choy. Just occasionally it slightly misses the mark (disappointing smoked salmon bagels as appetisers and a heavy-handed diced apple and raisin brûlée for dessert). "Nutters' Masterclass" is a regular feature - cookery demos after which everyone stays for lunch.

Directions: On A680 between Rochdale & Edenfield

☺☺
Edenfield Road (A680), Cheesden, Norden OL12 7TY
Tel: 01706 650167
Fax: 01706 650167
Chef(s): Andrew Nutter
Owner(s): Mr A Nutter, Mr & Mrs R Nutter
Cost: *Alc* £29, set price D £29.95. H/wine £10.95
Times: Noon-2pm/6.45-9.30pm.
Closed Tue, 1st 2 wks Aug
Additional: Children welcome
Seats: 52. Private dining room 40
Smoking: No smoking in dining room

SALE

Map 7 SJ79

Belmore Hotel

Built in 1875, The Victorian restaurant within the Belmore Hotel overlooks a balustraded stone terrace and mature gardens. Cada's is a recent addition, and offers a simpler dining option, but is noteworthy for its excellent bottled beer collection. The main restaurant serves a good range of canapés, bread rolls and appealing starters like nicely seared and still juicy scallops unusually served with a bubble and squeak pattie and artichoke cream sauce. Venison may be a good option for mains, coming as it does, tender and pink perhaps with a stew of bacon, shallots, lentils and pearls of turnip. Desserts are also classic country house in style with around six options. Impressive wine list of immense proportions.

Accommodation: 23 rooms (23 en suite) ★ ★ ★ ★
Directions: From M6 J19/M60 J7 or M56 take A56 then A6144, turn R at lights (by Brooklands Stn) into Brooklands Rd, 0.5m turn L into Norris Rd for main entrance

143 Brooklands Road,
M33 3QN
Tel: 0161 973 2538
Fax: 0161 973 2665
e belmore_hotel@hotmail.com
Chef(s): Wayne Hatenboer
Owner(s): Carol Deaville
Cost: Alc £38, set price L £16.95 ☺
Times: Noon-2pm/7-9.30pm.
Closed L Sat, D Sun
Additional: Sunday L. Children welcome
Seats: 36. Private dining room 12
Style: Classic, Country-house
Smoking: No smoking in dining room
Civil licence: 60

WIGAN

Map 7 SD51

Wrightington Hotel

Smart hotel restaurant decorated in creams and blues. The menu draws inspiration from Britain and Europe, and though there are some great ideas here, the execution can occasionally be shaky. A meal might begin with imaginative canapés, before progressing to ravioli of goats' cheese followed by turbot on a pea purée with morels.

Smoking: No-smoking area
Civil licence: 100
Accommodation: 47 rooms (47 en suite) ★ ★ ★
Directions: From M6 J27, 0.25 mile W towards Parbold. 200yds past church, fork R. Hotel is 100yds on R

Moss Lane, Wrightington WN6 9PB
Tel: 01257 425803
Fax: 01257 425830
e info@wrightingtonhotel.co.uk
Cost: Alc £19.95, set price L £11.95-£14.95/D £19.95-£22. ☺ ☺
H/wine £9.95
Times: noon-2pm/7-9.30pm.
Closed D Sun
Additional: Sunday L. Bar food L. Children welcome
Seats: 95. Private dining room 50
Style: Modern

HAMPSHIRE

ALTON

Map 4 SU73

Alton Grange

Truffles is the restaurant at Alton Grange, an intimate venue with Tiffany lights and an Oriental atmosphere. Influences from around the world are evident in charred fillet of turbot with roast kumara, nam jim marinated pimentos and mint hollandaise, and aromatic braised belly of pork with enoki mushrooms, noodles and coriander broth.

Style: Country-house
Smoking: No smoking in dining room
Civil licence: 100
Accommodation: 30 rooms (30 en suite) ★ ★ ★
Directions: M3 J4 onto A331 towards Farnham. Then A31 to rdbt signed B3004. R, Hotel 350yds on L

London Road, GU34 4EG
Tel: 01420 86565
Fax: 01420 541346
e info@altongrange.co.uk
Chef(s): William Jack
Owner(s): Mr & Mrs Levene
Cost: Alc £30. ☺ H/wine £10.95
Times: noon-2.30pm/7-9.30pm.
Closed L Sat
Additional: Sunday L. Bar food. Children 5yrs+
Seats: 45. Private dining room 18

England

ANDOVER
Map 4 SU34

Esseborne Manor

A 100-year-old manor house in the North Wessex Downs, with a fabric-lined dining room overlooking gardens and farmland. Dishes are created from natural combinations of locally produced ingredients, including home-grown herbs - typically ceviche of brill and smoked salmon with hot and sour fennel, or roast chump of lamb with fondant potatoes and rosemary jus. Fixed-price menus are offered at lunch and dinner, and in the evening a choice of pudding wines and ports by the glass. Puddings are a strength, with the likes of hot chocolate fondant, and French apple tart with apple and Calvados parfait. Delightful staff add much to the experience.

Accommodation: 15 rooms (15 en suite) ★★★
Directions: Between Andover & Newbury on A343, just N of Hurstbourne Tarrant

Hurstbourne Tarrant,
Hurstbourne Tarrant SP11 0ER
Tel: 01264 736444
Fax: 01264 736725
e esseborne@cs.com
Chef(s): Neil Patterson
Owner(s): Ian Hamilton
Cost: *Alc* £30, set price L £17-£22/ D £22-£30. ☺ H/wine £14
Times: Noon-2pm/7-9.30pm.
Additional: Sunday L. Bar food. Children welcome
Seats: 35. Private dining room 40. Jacket and tie preferred (weekends only)
Style: Traditional, Country-house
Smoking: No smoking in dining room
Civil licence: 100

BASINGSTOKE
Map 4 SU65

Audleys Wood

The vaulted ceiling is a striking feature of the restaurant in this Edwardian Gothic-style hotel. The *carte* offers modern cuisine around a French theme as in daube de boeuf bourguignon garnished with pommes mousseline and fumée of red wine or ballotine of guinea fowl with morelles and pommes parmentier. Starters might include gravadlax and oysters in a lemon vinaigrette.

Alton Road, RG25 2JT
Tel: 01256 817555
Fax: 01256 817500
e audleys.wood@thistle.co.uk
Chef(s): Phil Lie
Owner(s): Thistle Hotels Plc.
Cost: *Alc* £37.50, set price L £22.50/D £31.95. H/wine £15
Times: Noon-1.45pm/7-9.45pm. Closed L Sat
Additional: Sunday L. Bar food. Children welcome
Seats: 48. Private dining room 14. Jacket and tie preferred
Style: Modern, Country-house
Smoking: No smoking in dining room; Air conditioning
Civil licence: 50
Accommodation: 72 rooms (72 en suite) ★★★★
Directions: M3 J6, then A339 (Alton). Hotel 1.5 m S of Basingstoke

BASINGSTOKE *Continued* Map 4 SU65

Hanover International Hotel NEW

Extensive hotel popular with the business community who appreciate the well designed accommodation, public areas and conference facilities. The Winchester Restaurant provides a comfortable setting for a modern menu, including steaks and fish from the chargrill and dishes like seared sea scallops with Singapore chow mein noodles, and slow braised shank of lamb with garlic mash and rich gravy.

Style: Traditional
Smoking: No smoking in dining room; Air conditioning
Civil licence: 80
Accommodation: 100 rooms (100 en suite) ★ ★ ★
Directions: On A30 between Nateley Scures and Hook

Scures Hill, Nately Scures, Hook RG27 9JS
Tel: 01256 764161
Fax: 01256 768341
Chef(s): Jon Powell
Cost: *Alc* £35.75, set price L £14.50/ D £19.95-£22.15. ☺ ☺
H/wine £12.75
Times: 12.30-2pm/7-10pm.
Closed L Sat, D Sun, 24 Dec-2 Jan
Additional: Sunday L. Bar food.
Children 1yrs+. Jacket and tie preferred

BEAULIEU Map 4 SU30

Beaulieu Hotel

Away-from-it-all hotel in the heart of the New Forest with great views from the restaurant. The menu leans towards the contemporary with good use of fish and game. Home-made breads are a highlight, and dishes encompass steaks, fillet of sea bass with creamed leeks, and venison medallions with braised red cabbage, globe artichokes and port.

Style: Modern, Country-house
Smoking: No smoking in dining room
Civil licence: 60
Accommodation: 18 rooms (18 en suite) ★ ★ ★
Directions: On B3056 between Lyndhurst and Beaulieu. Near Beaulieu Rd railway station

Beaulieu Road, SO42 7YQ
Tel: 02350 293344
Fax: 02350 292729
🖂 information@carehotels.co.uk
Chef(s): Dave Witlea
Owner(s): Care Hotels
Cost: Set price L £12.95/D £21.50.
☺ ☺ H/wine £10.95
Times: Dinner only, 7-9pm
Additional: Children welcome
Seats: 40. Private dining room 60

Montagu Arms NEW

Charming creeper clad hotel. Good quality, often local ingredients are offered in largely classic French combinations but with one or two interesting twists. Some robust starters (boudin blanc with apple galette and basil oil or salad of crispy duck with a poached pear and mustard sabayon) and mains that have included ragout of chicken with puy lentils and braised shallots. Intricate desserts such as a trio of delicate lemon offerings.

Palace Lane, SO42 7ZL
Tel: 01590 612324
Telephone for further details

BISHOP'S WALTHAM Map 4 SU51

Banks Bistro

A popular restaurant with a good local following, Banks is a classic, white painted bistro full of bare wooden beams. Begin a relaxed meal in the bar before ordering from the daily changing, international menu. A wide range of dishes, from

Bank Street, SO32 1AE
Tel: 01489 896352
Fax: 01489 896288
Chef(s): Peter Hayes, Giles Hester
Owner(s): Peter Hayes, Giles Hester

roast lamb shank to salmon with curry spices, is complemented by a well balanced wine list.

Seats: 120. Private dining room
Style: Modern, Bistro-Style
Smoking: No-smoking area; no pipes; Air conditioning
Directions: M27 J7 through Hedge End and follow signs for Bishop's Waltham

Peppers Bar & Bistro NEW

The Ruthven-Stuart's are in town to stamp their pedigree on the ex-Cobblers restaurant. Previously at the Old Chesil Rectory, Winchester and Old House Hotel, Wickham, their eclectic repertoire at Peppers sings in tune with today's bistro scene, while displaying style, confidence and skill. A twice-cooked cheese soufflé signature or tartlet of caramelized onion and grilled goats' cheese are typical starters. Baked Cornish cod wrapped in Parma ham on a bed of spinach with saffron mash has been singled out as an admirable main, and what better than a perfect classic crème brûlée heading up desserts. Bold colours, split-level dining, floorboards and wrought-iron chandelier add real character to friendly, confident service.

BROCKENHURST Map 4 SU30

Balmer Lawn Hotel

Historic house in the heart of the New Forest. The kitchen demonstrates an inventive spirit which results in the occasional house classic such as tea-smoked monkfish wrapped in Parma ham served on mixed leaves. Dishes show imagination as in rum-soaked savarin with blood orange ice-cream and caramelised kumquats.

Seats: 90. Private dining room 120
Style: Traditional, Country-house
Smoking: No smoking in dining room
Civil licence: 120
Accommodation: 55 rooms (55 en suite) ★ ★ ★
Directions: Take A337 towards Lymington, hotel on L behind village cricket green

Carey's Manor

Careys - a manor house re-built in 1888 - is one of the first buildings you come across in this New Forest village. It has two dining options, with Blaireau's bar and bistro providing an informal French alternative to the main hotel restaurant. The latter offers a fixed-price menu featuring fish, game and free-range meats in line with the hotel's ethical food policy.

Style: Classic, Traditional
Smoking: No smoking in dining room
Civil licence: 100
Accommodation: 79 rooms (79 en suite) ★ ★ ★
Directions: M27 J1, follow signs for Lyndhurst and Lymington A337. Railway station 5 minutes from hotel

Cost: Alc £20, set price (Mon-Tue) L £9.95/D £11.95. ☺ ☺ H/wine £8.95
Times: Noon-2pm/7-9.30pm.
Closed Sun, Xmas, New Year, BHs
Additional: Bar food L.
Children welcome

The Square, SO32 1AR
Tel: 01489 891515
Fax: 01489 891577
Telephone for further details

Lyndhurst Road, SO42 7ZB
Tel: 01590 623116
Fax: 01590 623864
e blh@btinternet.com
Chef(s): Mr. K Newton
Owner(s): Mr. C Wilson
Cost: Alc £30, set price L £12/D £24.95. ☺ ☺ H/wine £14.95
Times: Noon-2.30pm/6.30-9.45pm.
Closed L Sat
Additional: Sunday L. Bar food. Children welcome. Vegetarian by request only

SO42 7RH
Tel: 01590 623551
Fax: 01590 622799
e info@careysmanor.com
Chef(s): Gary Damien Morton-Jones
Owner(s): Mr J Leach
Cost: Alc £39, set price L £13.75/D £24.75. ☺ ☺ H/wine £12.95
Times: 12.15-2pm/7-10pm.
Closed D 26,30 Dec
Additional: Sunday L. Children 7yrs+
Seats: 80. Private dining room 100

England

New Park Manor

Lyndhurst Road, SO42 7QH
Tel: 01590 623467
Fax: 01590 622268
Telephone for further details

The Stag Restaurant is a wood panelled, intimate and candlelit dining room in this historic former hunting lodge. A log fire adds to the charm of a venue that offers a contemporary selection of dishes with a welcome absence of over elaboration and an emphasis on good quality ingredients. Starters might include a risotto of red onion, thyme, lemon & courgette or foie gras with red onion purée balsamic vinegar and sweet cassis jus. Main courses are similarly punchy with the likes of scallops, salsafi purée, braised courgette and sun dried tomato vinaigrette or a robust sounding dish of braised lamb, boulangère potato and baby vegetables.

Rhinefield House

Rhinefield Road, SO42 7QB
Tel: 01590 622922
Fax: 01590 622800
e rhinefield-house@arcadianhotels.co.uk
Chef(s): Simon Barlow
Owner(s): Hand Picked Hotels Ltd (Arcadian Hotels)
Cost: *Alc* £40, set price L £17.95/ D £27.50. ☺ H/wine £14.50
Times: 12.30-2pm/7-10pm
Additional: Sunday L. Bar food. Children welcome
Seats: 58. Private dining room 110
Style: Modern
Smoking: No-smoking area
Civil licence: 125
Accommodation: 34 rooms (34 en suite) ★ ★ ★

The oak-panelled Armada Restaurant is named after the carving above the fireplace depicting the naval battle. The house itself provides an impressive setting with magnificent forest views. Both set price and *carte* menus are available offering interesting choices such as whole boneless baby chicken filled with barley and mixed fruits.

Directions: From M27 J1 take A337 to Lyndhurst, follow A35 W towards Christchurch. 3.5 miles from Lyndhurst, turn L into The Forest at the sign for Rhinefield House. Hotel is 1.5 miles on R

Simply Poussin

The Courtyard,
Brookley Road, SO42 7RB
Tel: 01590 623063
Fax: 01590 623144
e sales@simplypoussin.co.uk
Chef(s): Marc Lashley
Owner(s): Le Poussin Ltd
Cost: *Alc* £27.50, set price L
£12.50/D £27.50. ☺ ☺
H/wine £12.50
Times: Noon-2pm/7-10pm.
Closed Sun & Mon, 25-26 Dec
Additional: Children 7yrs+.
Vegetarian by request only
Seats: 30
Style: Modern
Smoking: No smoking in dining room
Directions: Village centre through an
archway between two shops

Pass through an archway in the village centre and you find
yourself in a courtyard where what was once a stable is now an
excellent restaurant. The setting is intimate with heaps of
cottage charm. A weekday fixed price lunch and dinner menu
offers no choice, but good value. Typical fare is a split pea
velouté, followed by farm-reared breast of lemon chicken, then
sticky toffee pudding. Choices from the *carte* include braised
ham hock with mustard mash and spring vegetables and for
dessert, blueberry frangipane or vanilla and strawberry
pannacotta with summer fruits.

Thatched Cottage Hotel

16 Brookley Road,
SO42 7RR
Tel: 01590 623090
Fax: 01590 623479
e thatchedcottagehotel@email.
msn.com
Chef(s): Martin Matysik
Owner(s): Family Matysik
Cost: *Alc* £38, set price L £24/
D £35-£45. ☺ H/wine £12.50
Times: 12.30-2.30pm/7.30-9.30pm.
Closed Mon, D Sun, Jan
Additional: Bar food. Children
welcome at L. Vegetarian by request
only

Built in 1627, the décor of this quaint country cottage
restaurant helps lend a romantic air to the place, yet there's
also a rather serious formality to the proceedings. Food here is
of consistently good quality and is likely to include local, New
Forest inspired choices as well as dishes with eastern influences.
Fillet of wild sea bass with Oriental red wine sauce and salted
cucumber salad, along with roasted medallion of New Forest
Venison in baby spinach with burgundy glazed carrots, chestnut
crêpes and elderberry sauce demonstrate the range. There is an
appealing short selection of desserts to round off.

Seats: 20. Private dining room 8
Style: Country-house
Smoking: No smoking in dining room
Accommodation: 5 rooms (5 en suite) ◆◆◆◆◆
Directions: Off A337 in Brockenhurst.

Whitley Ridge Hotel

Beaulieu Road,
SO42 7QL
Tel: 01590 622354
Fax: 01590 622856
e whitleyridge@brockenhurst.co.uk
Chef(s): Gary Moore
Owner(s): Mr & Mrs R Law
Cost: *Alc* £25, set price L £14/
D £24.50. ☺ ☺ H/wine £10.50

This charming hotel enjoys a picturesque setting in the heart of
the New Forest. Built in the late 18th-century in Georgian style
then extended in Victorian times, its varied history includes
many years as a royal hunting lodge and it was requisitioned in
the war years by the War Ministry. Nowadays it's a relaxing
place, decorated in country house style. The dining room offers
lovely forest views and a rather eclectic menu. Influences range
from Oriental (hot and sour tiger prawns) to traditional (roast

BROCKENHURST *Continued*   Map 4 SU30

fillet of Dorset lamb) whilst the good range of vegetarian options might include mushroom risotto or (believe it or not) nut roast.

Smoking: No smoking in dining room
Accommodation: 14 rooms (14 en suite) ★★★
Directions: A337 (from Lyndhurst) turn L towards Beaulieu on B3055, approx 1 mile

Times: Noon-2pm/6.30-9pm.
Closed L Mon-Sat
Additional: Sunday L. Bar food L.
Children welcome
Seats: 36. Private dining room 20.
Jacket and tie preferred
Style: Classic

BROOK   Map 4 SU21

Bell Inn

In the heart of the New Forest, a golfing hotel effortlessly blending 18th-century elegance with modern-day comforts. The menu is Anglo-French, covering dishes like terrine of chicken and leek, and warm roasted tomato tart, then perhaps grilled tuna steak, and fillet of black bream. Traditional puds like steamed syrup sponge with vanilla custard, or crêpes Suzette prepared at your table.

Style: Classic, Traditional
Smoking: No smoking in dining room
Accommodation: 25 rooms (25 en suite) ★★★
Directions: M27 J1 (Cadnam) 3rd exit onto B3078, signed Brook, 0.5mile

SO43 7HE
Tel: 023 8081 2214
Fax: 023 8081 3958
e bell@bramshaw.co.uk
Chef(s): Malcolm Lugg
Owner(s): Crosthwaite-Eyre family
Cost: *Alc* £35, set price L £15.50/
D £27.50. ☺ ☺ H/wine £12.50
Times: noon-2.30pm/7-9.30pm
Additional: Sunday L. Bar food.
Children welcome
Seats: 50. Private dining room 40.
Jacket and tie preferred

BUCKLERS HARD   Map 4 SU40

Master Builder's House

Located beside the Marina and overlooking Beaulieu River, this 18th-century house is a lovely setting in which to enjoy The Riverview Restaurant's varied, imaginative fare. Starters feature crab soup flavoured with coconut milk and lemon grass or, maintaining the seafood theme, pan-fried scallops with white bean purée and tomato confit. Comfort yourself with a sophisticated version of corned beef hash for an unusual main course, or think French and order sea bass en papilotte. An intriguing blueberry and liquorice jelly comes with a white chocolate mousse. Imaginative cuisine in an idyllic setting.

Accommodation: 25 rooms (25 en suite) ★★★
Directions: From M27 J2 follow signs to Beaulieu. Turn L onto B3056. 1st L. Hotel in 2 miles

SO42 7XB
Tel: 01590 616253
Fax: 01590 616297
e res@themasterbuilders.co.uk
Chef(s): Denis Rhoden
Owner(s): Jeremy Willcock,
John Illsley
Cost: *Alc* £29.50, set price L £17.95-
£20.95/D £29.50. H/wine £13.50
Times: Noon-3pm/7-10pm.
Additional: Sunday L. Children welcome
Seats: 80. Private dining room 40
Style: Modern
Smoking: No cigars
Civil licence: 60

CADNAM   Map 4 SU31

Bartley Lodge

The warmth and friendliness of staff puts guests immediately at ease in the rather formal Crystal Restaurant, with its high ceilings and imposing pillars. Views towards the forest are also a delight, and the setting is very peaceful, at the end of a long driveway. The chefs' commitment to the freshest of quality produce is evident. Witness a starter of seared Dorset scallops, served with a pesto and pine nut salad and a trio of dressings. Honey roast duck worked well with a neatly balanced Thai

Lyndhurst Road, SO40 2NR
Tel: 023 80812248
e info@carehotels.co.uk
Chef(s): Richard Turner
Owner(s): Mrs C Turner
Cost: *Alc* £27, set price L £11.95/D
£21.50-£24.45. ☺ ☺ H/wine £10.95
Times: 12.30-2pm/7-9pm.
Closed L Mon-Sat

sauce. The excellent cheeseboard comes complete with written descriptions and a choice of three ports by the glass.

Civil licence: 80
Accommodation: 31 rooms (31 en suite) ★ ★ ★
Directions: M27 J1, A337 and follow signs for Lyndhurst. Hotel on L

Additional: Sunday L. Bar food.
Children welcome
Seats: 60
Style: Country-house
Smoking: No smoking in dining room

DENMEAD
Map 4 SU61

Barnard's Restaurant

Floral prints, linen cloths and candlelit tables lend a cottagey feel to this village restaurant. The proprietors provide informal, friendly service and a well-rounded menu that travels through most of Europe, occasionally venturing further east. Dishes might include chicken liver parfait followed by sea bream with spring onion mash and lemon grass sauce.

Additional: Children welcome. Vegetarian by request only
Seats: 40. Private dining room 34
Style: French
Smoking: No-smoking area
Directions: A3M J3, follow B1250 into Denmead. Opposite church

Hambledon Road, PO7 6NU
Tel: 023 9225 7788
Fax: 023 9225 7788
Chef(s): David Barnard, Brian Wright
Owner(s): Mr & Mrs D Barnard, Mrs S Barnard
Cost: Alc £23.50, set price L £15.30.
☺ ☺ H/wine £10
Times: Noon-1.30pm/7-9.30pm.
Closed Sun & Mon, L Sat, 25-26 Dec, New Year

EAST TYTHERLEY
Map 4 SU22

Star Inn

SO51 0LW

This pub is simply packed with good things, not least simple charm, from the open fires to the bare beamed ceilings. The food is pretty impressive, with an extensive blackboard menu making it difficult to decide between old favourites (rib eye steak with chips; lambs' liver with mash) or contemporary dishes such as tuna fish and smoked duck with aubergine caviar and sweet and sour vegetables.

Smoking: No smoking in dining room
Accommodation: 3 rooms (3 en suite) ♦ ♦ ♦
Directions: 5 miles north of Romsey off A3057, take left turn to Dunbridge on B3084, take left turn for Awbridge & Lockerley follow road through Lockerley for 1 mile

Tel: 01794 340225
Fax: 01264 810954
info@starinn-uk.com
Chef(s): Paul Bingham
Owner(s): P & S Bingham, R Wilson
Cost: Alc £25. ☺ ☺ H/wine £10
Times: Noon-2.30pm/7-9.30pm.
Closed 26 Dec, D 25 Dec
Additional: Sunday L. Bar food.
Children welcome
Seats: 50. Private dining room 30
Style: Traditional, Rustic

EMSWORTH
Map 4 SU70

Fat Olives
NEW

30 South Street, PO10 7EH
Tel: 01243 377914
fatolives@lcmjm.fsnet.co.uk

A zesty brasserie style restaurant in a converted fisherman's terraced cottage. Lawrence Murphy cooks a short individually priced menu, featuring modern dishes with varied influences: scallops with gazpacho, duck confit, chicken with lemon grass and coconut. Puds are good, wines have been selected with care, and service is attentive and helpful.

Seats: 28
Smoking: No smoking in dining room
Directions: In town centre, 1st R after Emsworth Square, 100yds towards the Quay, Restaurant on L with public car park opposite

Chef(s): Lawrence Murphy
Owner(s): Lawrence & Julia Murphy
Cost: Alc £26, set price L £14.50. ☺
☺ H/wine £10.95
Times: Noon-2pm/7-10pm.
Closed Sun-Mon, 2 wks at Xmas-Jan, Tue after BH
Additional: Children 8yrs+

EMSWORTH *Continued*   Map 4 SU70

Spencers

36 North Street, PO10 7DG
Tel: 01243 372744
Fax: 01243 372744
Chef(s): Denis Spencer
Owner(s): Denis & Lesley Spencer
Cost: *Alc* £22. ☺ H/wine £10.50
Times: Dinner only, 7-10.30pm.
Closed Sun-Mon, 25-26 Dec
Additional: Children welcome
Seats: 34
Style: Chic
Smoking: No-smoking area; no cigars;
Air conditioning
Directions: Follow A259 to Emsworth
roundabout, turn L into North Street,
restaurant is 0.5 mile on L

Bustling restaurant and brasserie with an extensive fish menu,
ranging from the traditional (grilled dover sole, seared scallops)
to more inventive dishes such as salmon stuffed with crab and
asparagus, baked in filo pastry and served on a crab and brandy
sauce. Other options include lamb shank, pheasant and
venison. Friendly and attentive service.

36 On The Quay

47 South Street, PO10 7EG
Tel: 01243 375592/372257
Fax: 01243 375593
Chef(s): Ramon Farthing
Owner(s): Ramon & Karen Farthing
Cost: *Alc* £37.90, set price L £19.95-
£25.50/D £34.95-£42.50 (7 courses).
H/wine £13.50
Times: Noon-2pm/7-10pm.
Closed Sun, L Mon & Sat, 1-22 Jan,
23-30 Oct
Additional: Children welcome
Seats: 38. Private dining room 11
Style: Classic, Country-house
Smoking: No smoking in dining room
Directions: Last building on R in
South Street, which runs from the
Square in the centre of Emsworth

In what started life as a smugglers' inn three hundred years ago,
Karen and Ramon Farthing's exemplary husband-and-wife
operation offers a bright and friendly ambience complemented
by pastel shaded décor and soft furnishings, luxury seating and
immaculate tableware. A restricted lunch selection might offer
tomato and shallot risotto with a light fresh cod casserole,
followed by fresh farm chicken on creamed chicory and braised
lentils and apple and frangipane tart with melting Calvados
cream. Dinner choices are wider and more extravagantly
executed, displaying to best advantage Ramon's well-honed
skills. Seriously satisfying results include warm salad of skate
with slivers of smoked salmon, balsamic and light cream
dressing topped with plump tempura prawns. Typically to
follow there might be boned and roast partridge with bubble
and squeak and grilled figs or brill fillets layered with fresh crab
and leeks on spinach and saffron potatoes. A photogenic
rhubarb pannacotta with warm red fruit compôte set in a green
glass dish offers both artistry and technical accomplishment. A
special seven-course surprise menu is offered to any entire table
wishing to explore the full range of the repertoire.

EVERSLEY
Map 4 SU76

New Mill

New Mill Road, RG27 0RA
Tel: 0118 9732277
Fax: 0118 9328780
✉ mark@thenewmill.co.uk
Cost: ☺ ☺ H/wine £10.50
Times: noon-2pm/7-10pm.
Closed L Sat
Additional: Sunday L.
Children welcome
Seats: 80. Private dining room 40
Style: Traditional, Formal
Smoking: No cigars; Air conditioning
Civil licence: 180
Directions: From Eversley take A327
(Reading) cross river, turn L at cross
roads into New Mill Road

Four-hundred years of history has not passed without
depositing bags of charm - not least the still-operational mill
wheel and workings. A grill option offers an informal classicism
whilst the *à la carte* and fixed price menus hold to a modern
British style in dishes such as wild venison with celeriac purée.
Outstanding wine list.

FAREHAM
Map 4 SU50

Lysses House Hotel

Set in a Georgian building in the centre of town. The Richmond
restaurant is traditional in style, in pastel shades with delicate
table arrangements, and has a separate lounge area for drinks
or coffee. A decent selection of dishes is offered from the *carte*
and set-price menus, including steak, chicken and salmon from
the chargrill.

Style: Classic
Smoking: No smoking in dining room; Air conditioning
Civil licence: 90
Accommodation: 21 rooms (21 en suite) ★ ★ ★
Directions: M27 J11, follow signs for Fareham. Stay in left lane
to rdbt, 3rd exit into East St. Hotel on L opposite junction with
Civic Way

51 High Street, PO16 7BQ
Tel: 01329 822622
Fax: 01329 822762
✉ lysses@lysses.co.uk
Chef(s): Clive Wright
Owner(s): Prosig Ltd
Cost: *Alc* £25, set price L £13.95/
D £19.25. ☺ ☺ H/wine £9.95
Times: noon-1.45pm/7.30pm-9.45pm.
Closed Sun, L Sat, 24 Dec-2 Jan, BHs
Additional: Bar food. Children
welcome
Seats: 60. Private dining room 10

Solent Hotel

This friendly restaurant is set in a comfortable 16th-century
coaching inn. The menu reveals influences from France, Britain
and further afield: dishes might include saffron roasted cod with
garlic mash, mussels and chive cream or confit of duck with
ginger apple sauce and bok choi. Quality ingredients and
intelligent combinations of flavours make this a popular venue.

Seats: 130. Private dining room 50
Style: Classic, Traditional, Rustic
Smoking: No smoking in dining room; Air conditioning
Civil licence: 160
Accommodation: 111 rooms (111 en suite) ★ ★ ★ ★
Directions: From M27 J9 follow signs to Solent Business Park &
Whiteley. At roundabout 1st L, then R at mini roundabout

Rookery Avenue, Whiteley, PO15 7AJ
Tel: 01489 880000
Fax: 01489 880007
✉ solent@shireinns.co.uk
Chef(s): Peter Williams
Owner(s): Shire Inns Ltd
Cost: *Alc* £32.50, set price L
£18.50/D £28.50. ☺ ☺
H/wine £12.95
Times: 12.15-2pm/7.15-10pm.
Closed L Mon-Sat (ex by
arrangement)
Additional: Bar food. Children
welcome

England

FLEET
Map 4 SU85

The Gurkha Square

327 Fleet Road, GU13 8BU
Tel: 01252 810286
Fax: 01252 810101
📧 namastenepaal30@aol.com
Chef(s): Indra Gurung,
Pradeep Basnet
Owner(s): D. Gurung
Cost: Set price L £17-£25/D £16.99.
☺ ☺ H/wine £10
Times: Noon-2.30pm/6-11pm.
Closed Xmas, New Year
Additional: Sunday L. Bar food.
Children 12yrs+. Vegetarian by
request only
Seats: 44
Style: Traditional
Smoking: No cigars; Air conditioning
Directions: Telephone for directions

A great chance to imbibe Himalayan culture and cuisine in these comfortable, relaxed Nepalese-style surroundings. Try the chef's special chaure khasi or thulo jhingey - authentic Nepalese lamb and prawn dishes respectively. The food is characterised by blended herbs and spices and the menu helpfully indicates the degree of 'heat' to expect from each dish.

FORDINGBRIDGE
Map 4 SU11

Ashburn Hotel

The butcher and fishmonger call every day at this hotel, maintaining a steady supply of fresh, quality ingredients. The traditional dining room overlooks landscaped gardens and offers a variety of dishes, from classics (seared calves' liver with caramelised shallots) to international twists such as ragout of tiger prawns and scallops with a sweet chilli sauce.

Style: Country-house
Smoking: No smoking in dining room
Civil licence: 180
Accommodation: 20 rooms (20 en suite) ★★
Directions: From M27 J1 take B3078 to Fordingbridge. In town turn L at mini-rdbt and follow road towards Sandleheath/Damerham for 0.3 mile

Station Road, SP6 1JP
Tel: 01425 652060
Fax: 01425 652150
📧 ashburn@mistral.co.uk
Chef(s): Simon Reed, Richard Deeley,
James Noyce
Owner(s): Mr & Mrs Robson
Cost: Alc £23.50, set price D £17.50-
£21. ☺ ☺ H/wine £9.50
Times: Noon-3pm/7-11pm.
Closed L Mon-Sat
Additional: Sunday L. Bar food.
Children welcome
Seats: 50. Private dining room 120

Hour Glass
NEW

A thatched cottage with all the trimmings - oak beams, inglenook fireplace - but given a touch of contemporary chic with the new décor. Menus might include moist salmon ravioli with a delicious leek cappuccino, and roast monkfish tail simply presented on a good chive mash with wilted spinach and a subtly-flavoured curry sauce. Well balanced cooking.

Seats: 45. Private dining room 20
Style: Modern, Traditional
Smoking: No-smoking area; no cigars
Directions: 1 mile outside Fordingbridge on A338 heading towards Salisbury

Burgate, SP6 1LX
Tel: 01425 652348
Fax: 01425 656022
Chef(s): Greg Dawson
Owner(s): Yvonne & Charlotte
Wiggins
Cost: Alc £30, set price L £14.90.
☺ ☺ H/wine £10.50
Times: Noon-2pm/7-10pm.
Closed Mon, D Sat, 1st 2 wks Jan,
BH Mon
Additional: Sunday L. Bar food L.
Children welcome

The Three Lions

You might be forgiven for thinking you've wandered into a country pub, but any plans to enjoy a pork pie or chicken in the basket with your pint will be quickly dashed. Real ale they do serve, but it's the comprehensive wine list with its many half bottles that will delight the connoisseur. The food itself is a

triumph of understatement; drawing from an international repertoire to produce a balanced menu featuring the likes of sautéed langoustine and crispy noodles, or game pastry, creamed chicory and sultanas amongst the starters. Wild boar with lemon and apple sauce, and grilled sea bass, red wine and star anise are typical of the fairly direct style. Amongst the successes have been seared scallops on a bed of seaweed with citrus sauce, and confit of pork with orange and mint (both recommended). Desserts have been described as unmissable with lemon posset and crème caramel singled out for praise. Service in the cosy restaurant is relaxed but efficient, even when it's hectic.

Stuckton, SP6 2HF
Tel: 01425 652489
Fax: 01425 656144
e the3lions@btinternet.com
Chef(s): M Womersley
Owner(s): Mr & Mrs Womersley
Cost: A/c £27.50, set price L £14.50.
☺ ☺ H/wine £13.50
Times: noon-2pm/7-11pm. Closed Mon, D Sun, mid Jan to mid Feb
Additional: Sunday L. Children welcome
Seats: 60. Private dining room 30
Style: Farmhouse, Rustic
Smoking: No smoking in dining room
Accommodation: 3 rooms (3 en suite)
♦♦♦♦♦
Directions: 1m E of Fordingbridge, from either A338 or B3078. From Q8 Garage follow brown tourist signs

---

LIPHOOK   Map 4 SU83

Nippon Kan

Laquered wood tables and simple oriental décor announce that this is not a traditional hotel restaurant. Nippon-Kan serves an extensive Japanese menu, but teppanyaki is the speciality: opt for this and your meal will be prepared before your eyes then cooked on the teppan (a stainless steel plate on the table). Not only is it a great spectacle; presentation, clarity of flavour and

at Old Thorns Hotel, Griggs Green
GU30 7PE
Tel: 01428 724555
Fax: 01428 725036
e info@oldthorns.com
Chef(s): Takeo Suzuki
Owner(s): Kosaido Europe Resorts
Cost: A/c £33.50, set price L £16-£20.50/D £22-£30. ☺ ☺ H/wine £12
Times: Noon-3.30pm/6.30-Midnight. Closed Mon
Additional: Sunday L. Children welcome
Seats: 40. Private dining room 16
Style: Japanese Teppan Yaki
Smoking: No cigars
Civil licence: 80
Accommodation: 32 rooms (32 en suite) ★ ★ ★
Directions: Approx 500yds from Griggs Green exit off A3, south of Liphook

LIPHOOK *Continued*   Map 4 SU83

quality of products are all 'stunning'. A set teppanyaki dinner
includes (among other things) an appetiser, soup, salad, rice,
meat or fish dishes, vegetables and dessert. Look out for the
full but delicately flavoured lychee ice cream.

Thorns Restaurant

Thorns Restaurant is the more conservative option at this lively
hotel complex offering country house-style surroundings and
serving quality modern European cuisine. A bowl of strongly
flavoured linguine proves a lively starter with breast of chicken
on Mediterranean vegetables providing a main course well-
balanced in textures and flavours.

Directions: Approx 500yds from Griggs Green exit off A3, south
of Liphook

at Old Thorns Hotel, Longmoor Road,
Griggs Green, GU30 7PE
Tel: 01428 724555
Fax: 01428 725036
✉ reservations@oldthorn.freeserve.
co.uk
Chef(s): Charles Rushworth
Owner(s): Old Thorns Hotel
Cost: *Alc* £28, set price L £15/D £22.
☺ ☺ H/wine £12
Times: Noon-2pm/7-9.30pm.
Additional: Sunday L. Bar food.
Children welcome
Seats: 40. Private dining room 90.
Jacket and tie preferred
Style: Traditional, Formal
Smoking: No smoking in dining room
Civil licence: 100
Accommodation: 32 rooms (32 en
suite) ★ ★ ★

LYMINGTON   Map 4 SZ39

Stanwell House

If it's possible to have a contemporary take on a medieval
theme, this is it. The restaurant at this modern hotel works from
a rich palette of fuchsia, burgundy, amethyst, rose and violet
velvets set against burnt gold walls, with candles providing

High Street, SO41 9AA
Tel: 01590 677123
Fax: 01590 677756
✉ sales@stanwellhousehotel.com
Chef(s): Ian McLelland
Owner(s): Mrs J McIntyre
Cost: Set price L £24.95/D £24.95. ☺
H/wine £13.50
Times: Noon-2pm/7-9.30pm.
Additional: Sunday L. Bar food.
Children welcome
Seats: 60. Private dining room 40
Style: Modern, Bistro-Style
Smoking: No smoking in dining room
Civil licence: 60
Accommodation: 30 rooms (30 en
suite)
Directions: 2 miles from M27 J1-
A337 through New Forest towards the
coast

atmospheric lighting. Wrought iron chairs are set on stone floors, and large glass doors lead out into the gardens. The wine list is impressive, and the brasserie-style menus are written in an economic style with few adjectives. The food is to match, simply prepared from quality produce - tian of Solent brown crab, Isle of Wight seabass with Scottish girolles, and marinated saddle of sika deer.

LYNDHURST   Map 4 SU30

Le Poussin at Parkhill

Re-located in 1999 from hidden-away premises nearby, Alex Aitken's long established Poussin benefits greatly from its new home in an elegant country house hotel set amidst unspoilt park and woodland at the heart of the New Forest. His passion for local, seasonal ingredients remains undimmed as he continues to scour the forest for wild herbs and mushrooms and sources the finest game for renowned specialities such as roast whole woodcock, off the bone, with cranberries and plump fresh partridge breast stuffed with foie gras and truffle in rich game sauce. There remains nonetheless an assured lightness of touch in his signature poussin terrine that incorporates prunes soaked in Earl Grey and perhaps pan-fried fillet of brill topped with oyster mushrooms, laid on steamed leaf spinach and creamed leeks. Further indication of versatility can be found in the hot passion fruit soufflé accompanied by delicate fruit sorbet in a tuile cone. Formal, precise and very French service echoes a passion for Bordeaux that shines through the wine list.

Additional: Sunday L. Children welcome
Seats: 50. Private dining room 35
Style: Modern
Smoking: No smoking in dining room
Civil licence: 70
Accommodation: 20 rooms (20 en suite) ★★★
Directions: On entering Lyndhurst from M27, take A35 towards Southampton. Immediately after turning for Lyndhurst Park Hotel, take next R towards Beaulieu, B3056. Hotel 1 mile

❀❀❀
Beaulieu Road, SO43 7FZ
Tel: 023 8028 2944
Fax: 023 8028 3268
e sales@lepoussinatparkhill.co.uk
Chef(s): Alexander Aitken
Owner(s): Alexander Aitken
Cost: Alc £37, set price L £20-£25/ D £37-£45. ☺ H/wine £12.50
Times: Noon-2pm/7-9.30pm

MIDDLE WALLOP   Map 4 SU23

Fifehead Manor

Mullioned windows, dark red walls and candlelight make for a suitably atmospheric setting at this old manor house restaurant. Grilled goats' cheese with smoked salmon served with mixed leaves and sweet chilli-style marmalade sauce offers some vibrant flavours.

Style: Country-house
Smoking: No smoking in dining room
Civil licence: 65
Accommodation: 17 rooms (17 en suite) ★★★
Directions: From M3 J8 take A343 to Andover, then take A303 S 6 miles to Middle Wallop

❀
SO20 8EG
Tel: 01264 781565
Fax: 01264 781400
e fifeheadmanorhotel@ukonline. co.uk
Chef(s): Paul Quinn
Owner(s): Chris Paul & Colin Dabin
Cost: Alc £28, set price L £18.95/D £18.95. ☺ ☺ H/wine £10.25
Times: noon-3pm/7-11pm
Additional: Sunday L. Bar food. Children welcome
Seats: 40. Private dining room 20

England

MILFORD ON SEA

Map 4 SZ29

The Rouille Restaurant

Locals of this New Forest seaside village will know what a little gem they have on their doorstep. Great-value menu du jour, inspired *carte* offerings, and a friendly, informal atmosphere. Chef patron Lui Hollomby's innovative repertoire is rooted in contemporary French cuisine. Quality ingredients draw on sea and forest; ballotine of truffled quail with Moscatel and sultana sauce, grilled John Dory with baby fennel risotto and crab bisque. Warm apple tart with vanilla sauce has been a success too, with good gingerbread ice cream. Saucing, balance and presentation are high points, while breads, canapés and petits fours come home-made. At front of house, wife Nicky is efficient, personable and well-informed.

Smoking: No-smoking area; no pipes; Air conditioning
Directions: From A337 take B3058 to Milford, 150yds on L in village centre

69-71 High Street, SO41 0QG
Tel: 01590 642340
Fax: 01590 642340
e Rouille@ukonline.co.uk
Chef(s): Lui Hollomby
Owner(s): Mr & Mrs Hollomby
Cost: *Alc* £27.50, set price L & D
£12.95-£24.95. ☺ ☺ H/wine £13.50
Times: Noon-2pm/7-9.30pm. Closed
Sun, Mon, L Tue (Wed-Sat by
arrangement), 2wks Nov
Additional: Children welcome
Seats: 30
Style: Modern, French

South Lawn Hotel

In the capable hands of the Barten family for over thirty years now, this mock-Tudor country house restaurant serves a good range of honest home-cooking, making generous use of fresh local produce, such as Dover sole and New Forest venison. Look out on the dessert trolley for the proprietor's own recipe sherry trifle.

Seats: 80. Jacket and tie preferred
Style: Country-house
Smoking: No smoking in dining room
Accommodation: 24 rooms (24 en suite) ★ ★ ★
Directions: A337 from Lymington, turn left onto B3058. Hotel 1 mile on R

Lymington Road, SO41 0RF
Tel: 01590 643911
Fax: 01590 644820
e enquiries@southlawn.co.uk
Chef(s): Ernst Barten, David Gates
Owner(s): Ernst & Jennifer Barten
Cost: *Alc* £27.50, set price L
£12.50/D £22-£35. ☺ ☺ H/wine £12
Times: Noon-1.45pm/7-9pm.
Closed L Mon, 20 Dec-19 Jan
Additional: Sunday L. Bar food L.
Children 7yrs+

Westover Hall

Park Lane,
SO41 0PT
Tel: 01590 643044
Fax: 01590 644490
e westoverhallhotel@barclays.net
Chef(s): Neil Johnson
Owner(s): N Musetti & S Mechem

This impressive Victorian mansion on the edge of The New Forest enjoys spectacular views across Christchurch Bay. Inside, lavish oak panelling, ornate ceiling moulds and stunning stained glass windows make for a special venue. Good quality ingredients lie at the heart of the cuisine here and dishes are

England

carefully constructed with attention to flavour. Parfait of chicken livers with red onion marmalade, or risotto of wild mushrooms with Parmesan shavings make pleasant starters, while a typical main course selection will take in a range of pan-fried or chargrilled dishes. Rhubarb and cardamom soup with roasted almond ice cream is a winning dessert.

Accommodation: 14 rooms (14 en suite) ★ ★ ★
Directions: From M27 J1 take A337 then B3058. Hotel is situated just out of Milford centre, towards clifftop

Cost: *Alc* £29.50, set price L £21.50/D £27.50 ☺ H/wine £12.95
Times: Noon-2pm/7-9pm.
Additional: Sunday L. Bar food L. Children 7yrs+
Seats: 40. Private dining room 10
Style: Modern, Country-House
Smoking: No smoking in dining room
Civil licence: 50

NEW MILTON
Map 4 SZ29

Chewton Glen

Christchurch Road, BH25 6QS
Tel: 01425 275341
Fax: 01425 272310
e reservations@chewtonglen.com
Chef(s): Pierre Chevillard
Owner(s): Mr & Mrs Skan
Cost: *Alc* £55. ☺ H/wine £16.25
Times: 12.30-7.30-
Additional: Sunday L. Children 7yrs+. Vegetarian by request only
Seats: 120. Private dining room 120. Jacket and tie preferred
Style: Classic, Country-house
Smoking: No smoking in dining room; Air conditioning
Civil licence: 60
Accommodation: 62 rooms (62 en suite) ★ ★ ★ ★ ★

Martin and Brigitte Skan's fine country hotel has lived in a land of superlatives for the last thirty years and shows few signs that it shall not ever be this way. Spa and leisure facilities are unsurpassed; the lounges overlook gardens that lead to a path down to the sea, and dining remains a treat in the canopied conservatory restaurant. Service and hospitality are discreet and professional. Produce, obtained locally or from small specialist suppliers nationally, is of the highest provenance and used to good effect on seasonal menus that lean slightly towards a certain conservatism that is arguably customer-led. Typically, timbale of crab and avocado or pigeon and foie gras salad are curtain-raisers to lobster and pork cheeks with ginger and coriander broth or pan-fried venison loin with winter fruits, black pepper and game sauce. Special celebrations are marked by Sevruga caviar, crème fraîche and Melba toast, accompanied by fine wines from one of this country's classic lists.

Directions: Off A35 (Lyndhurst) turn R through Walkford, 2nd L into Chewton Farm Road

OLD BURGHCLERE
Map 4 SU45

Dew Pond

Once a pair of 16th-century drovers' cottages, this is a lovely building offering peaceful rural views to the Hampshire Downs. Weather permitting, enjoy a pre-dinner drink on the terrace. Punchy cooking with bright flavours based on good quality produce in combinations such as plump crevettes marinated in

RG20 9LH
Tel: 01635 278408
Fax: 01635 278408
Telephone for further details

England

OLD BURGHCLERE *Continued*   Map 4 SU45

coriander, chilli and lime, served with garlic and ginger mayonnaise. Crispy confit of duck might come with a rich shallot and cassis glaze and a creamy mash. Amongst the desserts, a trio of chocolate desserts (warm tart, white parfait and Bailey's mousse) received an enthusiastic review. Global list of wines arranged by taste.

PETERSFIELD   Map 4 SU72

JSW   **NEW**
@@@

1 Heath Road, GU31 4JE
Tel: 01730 262030
Chef(s): Jake Watkins
Owner(s): Jake Watkins
Cost: *Alc* £27.50, set price L £15.50/D £25.50. H/wine £13.50
Times: Noon-2pm/7-10pm.
Closed Sun, Mon, 2 wks Jan
Additional: Children welcome
Seats: 22
Style: Chic
Smoking: No cigars

The kind of little neighbourhood restaurant that, in a perfect world, would be found in small towns throughout the land. The food, like the décor (pale walls with bold line drawings) is admirably understated and to the point. Fish dishes can be particularly successful with a deft touch evident in the likes of an open ravioli of scallops and leeks or a main course of sea bass with sauce vierge. Heftier meat dishes also boast some dexterity with, for instance an intelligently conceived dish of veal loin with broad beans and truffles. Lunch, in particular is something of a bargain, although the restrained pricing applies to dinner and a well-chosen wine list too.

Directions: In Peterfields, follow signs to Festival Hall. Restaurant, 80yds from Festival Hall

Langrish House
@

Langrish, GU32 1RN
Tel: 01730 266941
Fax: 01730 260543
e frontdesk@langrishhouse.co.uk
Chef(s): Philip Bearden
Owner(s): Mr & Mrs Talbot - Ponsonby
Cost: *Alc* £20/D £24.95-£30. ☺ ☺ H/wine £9.75
Times: Dinner only, 7-9pm.
Closed D Sun (L by arrangement only)
Additional: Sunday L. Bar food. Children 8yrs+ at D
Seats: 24. Private dining room 20

This traditional country house stands in lovely countryside just outside Petersfield. The restaurant, a small cosy lounge with a feature fireplace, serves a satisfying selection of modern and traditional British cooking. A meal might include duck liver parfait followed by supreme of salmon with parsley mash and sweet and sour tomatoes.

Style: Traditional, Country House
Smoking: No smoking in dining room
Civil licence: 60
Accommodation: 14 rooms (14 en suite) ★ ★
Directions: From Petersfield A272 towards Winchester and turn L into Langrish and follow Hotel signs

RINGWOOD   Map 4 SU10

Moortown Lodge
@

244 Christchurch Road, BH24 3AS
Tel: 01425 471404
Fax: 01425 476052
e restaurant@moortownlodge.co.uk
Chef(s): Jilly Burrows-Jones
Owner(s): Mr & Mrs Burrow-Jones
Cost: *Alc* £22.75, set price D £20.95-£23.95. ☺ H/wine £9.95
Times: Dinner only, from 7.
Closed D Sun (ex residents), 24 Dec-mid Jan, 1 wk in Jul

Comfortably furnished, the restaurant in this small, friendly Georgian hotel offers a very good fixed price menu, with locally sourced food, capably prepared by the proprietor. Home-made soup of the day or warm goats' cheese salad might lead nicely into a casserole of venison in red wine with a puff pastry topping.

Additional: Children welcome. Vegetarian by request only
Seats: 24. Jacket and tie preferred
Style: French. **Smoking:** No smoking in dining room
Accommodation: 6 rooms (5 en suite) ★ ★
Directions: On B3347 1.5 miles south from Ringwood

England

ROMSEY

Map 4 SU32

Bertie's

The setting is simple - polished wooden tables behind a shop front overlooking the bustle of Romsey - but the food is delightfully vivacious and the atmosphere convivial. There's plenty of choice, with a set menu offering two or three competitively priced courses at lunch and dinner, plus lunchtime snacks and special sandwiches, and an evening *carte*. The international cooking defies cliché with utterly modern dishes like pan-seared john dory with tomato and chive couscous and spinach, while Bertie's 'famous' fishcakes are bursting with flavour and freshness. Popularity has forced an extension next door, providing much needed extra tables and a courtyard.

Chef(s): Michael Weir
Owner(s): David Birmingham
Cost: *Alc* £27.50, set price L £14.95/D £14.95
Times: Noon-2pm/6.30-10pm. Closed Sun, 26-31 Dec
Additional: Bar food L. Children welcome
Seats: 34. Private dining room 36
Style: Bistro-Style
Smoking: No-smoking area; no pipes
Accommodation: 7 rooms (7 en suite)
Directions: 200 metres from Broadlands' gate in the centre of town

80 The Hundred, SO51 8BX
Tel: 01794 830708
Fax: 01794 507507
e sales@berties.co.uk

Old Manor House Restaurant

21 Palmerston Street,
SO51 8GF
Tel: 01794 517353
Chef(s): Mauro Bregoli
Owner(s): Mauro & Esther Bregoli
Cost: *Alc* £30, set price L £19.50.
H/wine £11.50
Times: noon-2pm/7-9.30pm.
Closed Mon, D Sun
Additional: Sunday L.
Children welcome
Seats: 26
Style: Traditional
Smoking: No cigars
Directions: Opposite the entrance to Broadlands Estate

Wild boar tusks and deer antlers are not out of place on the walls of this Elizabethan restaurant, and nor is the beef smoking over a roaring log fire in the huge inglenook fireplace. Mauro Bregoli hunts his own game, but in the kitchen he shows all the delicacy and sensitivity of the artist. Combinations such as pork and salsa are almost shockingly appropriate, and his refreshingly home-made pasta bears no resemblance to supermarket counterparts. A short *carte* and set menus with several specials might include an outstanding tortellini filled with smoked Italian cheese in a cream sauce, and porchetta - roasted piglet, rolled and stuffed with fennel and thyme, served with a vibrant salsa verde. Flavours are lively and genuine, and the quality extends to canapés and petit fours. Good choice of house wines, and a wide range from old and new worlds, with some very expensive Italians and château-bottled French.

ROTHERWICK

Map 4 SU75

Tylney Hall

RG27 9AZ
Tel: 01256 764881
Fax: 01256 768141
e sales@tylneyhall.com
Chef(s): Stephen Hine
Cost: *Alc* £45, set price L £23/D £35.
H/wine £16.50
Times: 12.30-2pm/7.30-9.30pm.
Additional: Sunday L. Bar food L.
Children welcome
Seats: 80. Private dining room 100.
Jacket and tie preferred
Style: Formal, Country-house
Smoking: No smoking in dining room

Listed country house set in 66 acres of rolling Hampshire countryside, including woodlands, lakes and beautifully kept gardens designed by Gertrude Jekyll. Oak panelling, chandeliers and a baby grand piano set the tone of the traditionally styled restaurant, with formal service provided by dicky-bowed waiters armed with cloches. Dishes likely to impress from the fixed-price menu include twice-baked Roquefort soufflé, a well-timed dish of sea bass pan-fried with baby fennel, asparagus and artichoke in a light nage, and a decent breast of duck with foie gras. A popular option is the daily dish from the carving trolley.

Civil licence: 100
Accommodation: 110 rooms (110 en suite) ★ ★ ★ ★
Directions: M3 J5 take A287 (Newnham). From M4 J11 take B3349 (Hook), at sharp bend L (Rotherwick), L again and L in village (Newnham), 1 mile on R

SHEDFIELD

Map 4 SU51

Marriott Meon Valley   NEW

Sandy Lane, SO32 2HQ
Tel: 01329 833455
Telephone for further details

A bright and friendly restaurant in this large country club hotel which nestles in the countryside. Interesting contrasts work well in dishes like duck liver parfait with toasted sultana bread and apricot chutney, grilled salmon with creamed fennel sauce on lobster mash, and pannacotta with passion fruit sauce and fruit salad.

SILCHESTER

Map 4 SU66

Romans Hotel

Little London Road,
RG7 2PN
Tel: 01189 700421
Fax: 01189 700691
e romanhotel@hotmail.com
Chef(s): Andrew Farmer
Owner(s): Mr Tuthill

A Lutyens style manor house standing in three acres of grounds. The dining room is full of character, with an open fireplace, wood panelled walls, and antique rugs covering bare floors. The menu is traditional but occasionally imports ideas from abroad: dishes range from roast lamb with mashed potato to tuna steak on a bok choi stir fry.

Cost: *Alc* £25, set price L £20/D £20.
☺ ☺ H/wine £13
Times: Noon-2pm/7-9.30pm.
Closed L Sat, 1st wk Jan
Additional: Sunday L. Bar food.
Children welcome
Seats: 25. Private dining room 20
Style: Country-house
Smoking: No smoking in dining room
Civil licence: 65
Accommodation: 25 rooms (25 en suite) ★ ★ ★

Directions: Singposted from A340 between Basingstoke and Tadley

SOUTHAMPTON　　　　　Map 4 SU41

Botleigh Grange

Hedge End, SO30 2GA
Tel: 01489 787700
Fax: 01489 788535
e enquiries@botleighgrangehotel.co.uk
Chef(s): Darren Brown
Owner(s): David K Plumpton
Cost: *Alc* £24, set price L £24/D £24.
☺ ☺ H/wine £13
Times: 12.30-2.30pm/6.30pm-10pm.
Closed L Sat
Additional: Sunday L. Bar food.
Children welcome
Seats: 150. Private dining room 150
Style: Country-house
Smoking: No smoking in dining room

In family ownership since the 1940s, a much-extended mansion set in extensive grounds that makes a particular feature of weddings and mid-week conferences. Despite this emphasis the dining-room's set monthly menus exhibit welcome consistency in a serene glass-domed setting that overlooks the gardens. On the set menu are choices such as smoked bacon salad with poached egg, roast duck breast with cumin lentils and banana bread-and-butter pudding with custard. Alternatives *à la carte* include ravioli of New Forest game with roasted vegetables, char-grilled beef fillet with sweetbread tortellini and a selection of British cheeses with fruit bread and chutney.

Civil licence: 200
Accommodation: 59 rooms (59 en suite) ★ ★ ★ ★
Directions: On A334, 1mile from M27 J7

Woodlands Lodge

Beautiful restored hunting lodge in four acres of attractive grounds on the edge of the New Forest. The Wedgewood restaurant is so named for its ornate cornice and plasterwork and hosts a sophisticated modern/classical cuisine. Plenty of technical ability is evident in the execution of a largely French

Bartley Road, Woodlands, SO40 7GN
Tel: 023 8029 2257
Fax: 023 8029 3090
e woodlands@nortels.ltd.uk
Chef(s): M Harris, R Di Maiolo

England

SOUTHAMPTON *Continued*   Map 4 SU41

inspired menu. Quality locally sourced ingredients and pronounced flavours are to the fore. Mosaic terrine of guinea fowl, celeriac, apple and potato wrapped in bacon with a fig chutney, creamed truffle dressing and toasted brioche is fairly typical of the intricate style. Delicate and complementary handling of some complex combinations. Desserts have been described as "sublime".

Style: Classic, Country-house
Smoking: No smoking in dining room
Civil licence: 60
Accommodation: 16 rooms ★ ★ ★
Directions: Telephone for directions

Owner(s): David & Jenny Norbury
Cost: *Alc* £26.50, set price L £11.95/D £26.50-£29.50. ☺
H/wine £11.95
Times: noon-2pm/7-9pm.
Closed L Mon-Sat
Additional: Sunday L. Bar food. Children welcome. Vegetarian by request only
Seats: 30. Private dining room 20.
Jacket and tie preferred

SWAY   Map 4 SZ29

String of Horses
Country House Hotel   NEW

Mead End Road, SO41 6EH
Tel: 01590 682631
Fax: 01590 682911
🄴 relax@stringofhorses.co.uk
Chef(s): Christopher Proctor
Owner(s): Mr & Mrs Proctor
Cost: *Alc* £24, set price L £16. ☺
Times: Noon-1.30pm/7-9.30pm.
Closed L Mon-Sat, D Sun
Additional: Sunday L. Bar food. Children welcome
Seats: 36. Private dining room 36.
Jacket and tie preferred
Style: Romantic
Smoking: No smoking in dining room
Accommodation: 8 rooms (8 en suite)
★ ★ ★
Directions: Telephone for directions

Candlelit dining in the oak beamed Carriages Restaurant. An interesting menu offers a contemporary sounding selection with some obvious Southern European influences. Starters might include a medley of wild mushrooms sautéed & served with mixed leaves & pine kernels and a balsamic vinegar dressing and mains have featured grilled fillet of local sea bass with fresh asparagus & shallot butter.

WICKHAM   Map 4 SU51

Old House Hotel

The Georgian village of Wickham has a special charm and this 18th-century building offers a similarly appealing setting in which to enjoy accomplished cuisine with a modern European feel. The weekly changing menu offers plenty of punchy classics like seafood bisque with aïoli and Gruyère or confit duck leg with chorizo, thyme scented potato blini and balsamic dressing. Main courses have a similar style with Cornish cod coming in the company of Parma ham and smoked garlic mash with a vanilla basil reduction and braised shank of lamb partnered by a baby vegetable hot pot and celeriac rösti.

The Square, PO17 5JG
Tel: 01329 833049
Fax: 01329 833672
🄴 enq@theoldhousehotel.co.uk
Chef(s): Peter Howard
Owner(s): John & Gloria Goodacre
Cost: *Alc* £30, set price L £20/D £20.
☺ ☺ H/wine £10.95
Times: noon-3pm/7-12pm. Closed L Mon, D Sun, Xmas 10 days

Additional: Sunday L. Bar food L. Children 12yrs+
Seats: 36. Private dining room 14
Style: Formal
Smoking: No smoking in dining room
Accommodation: 9 rooms (8 en suite)
★★
Directions: In the centre of Wickham, 3 miles N of Fareham at junction of A32/B2177

WINCHESTER

Map 4 SU42

Bertie's

(Formerly Hunters)

5 Jewry Street, SO23 8RZ
Tel: 01962 860006

Business lunches and romantic evening meals in a relaxed atmosphere highlighted by Jenny Muncaster's wall paintings. A high proportion of seafood and game features on the new chef's predominantly fixed-price menus: lime-seared scallops and pressed game and vegetable terrine, followed by salmon fillets with a sweet and sour glaze and juniper infused venison with swede purée. Finish with a chocolate brownie to die for.

Chef(s): Simon Lakey
Owner(s): David Birmingham
Cost: *Alc* £26, set price L £12.95/D £14.95. ☺ ☺ H/wine £11.50
Times: noon-2pm/6.30-10pm. Closed Sun, BHs, Xmas, New Year
Seats: 40. Private dining room 26
Style: Bistro-Style
Smoking: No-smoking area
Directions: Towards the top of the City just off High Street, 200 yards from Theatre Royal and Library car park

The Chesil Rectory

The Chesil Rectory may be the oldest house in Winchester, but the menu is bang up to date, and the young chef/owner Philip Storey's approach is both contemporary and original. The building dates from 1450 and retains its original charm with black beams and simple whitewashed walls. Menus are based on seasonal local produce - and mains might include roasted salmon with rhubarb, smoked salmon mash and ginger sauce, or pork and black pudding with mustard mash, spinach and apple butter sauce. A twice-baked soufflé, well risen and full of delicious Roquefort cheese came in for particular praise. Service is attentive but not intrusive and a creditable wine list offers a good selection of house bottles.

Directions: From King Alfred's statue at the bottom of The Broadway, cross the small bridge and turn R; the restaurant is to the left, just off mini roundabout

1 Chesil Street, SO23 0HU
Tel: 01962 851555
Fax: 01962 869704
Chef(s): Philip Storey
Owner(s): Mr P Storey
Cost: *Alc* £37, set price L £20-£24/D £34-£40
Times: noon-2.30pm/7-9.15pm. Closed Sun & Mon, 1 wk Xmas, 1 wk Aug
Additional: Children welcome
Seats: 40. Private dining room 30
Style: Traditional, Classic
Smoking: No-smoking area

WINCHESTER *Continued*   Map 4 SU42

Hotel du Vin & Bistro

Centrally located, this popular town house bistro has a charming, unpretentious feel. The mood is relaxed and the food is both imaginative and enjoyable. Smoked duck and fig salad with truffle vinaigrette, or beetroot tarte Tatin with goats' cheese make interesting possible starters. A good range of main courses might include roasted cod wrapped in pancetta with creamed leeks, or tomato and artichoke risotto. A typical winter dessert menu will have you spoilt for choice, though the toasted brioche with rice pudding ice cream is extremely tempting. The impressive wine list, which has been expertly selected, is truly international.

14 Southgate Street, SO23 9EF
Tel: 01962 841414
Fax: 01962 842458
e info@winchester.hotelduvin.co.uk
Chef(s): Gareth Longhurst
Cost: *Alc* £35. H/wine £11.95
Times: Noon-1.45pm/7-9.45pm.
Additional: Sunday L. Children welcome. Vegetarian by request only
Seats: 65. Private dining room 48
Style: Bistro-Style
Smoking: No cigars

Accommodation: 23 rooms (23 en suite) ★ ★ ★ ★
Directions: M3 J11, follow signs to Winchester town centre

Lainston House

Sparsholt, SO21 2LT
Tel: 01962 863588
Fax: 01962 776672
e enquiries@lainstonhouse.com
Chef(s): Friedrich Litty
Cost: *Alc* £40, set price L £12.50/ D £29.50-£37.50. H/wine £19
Times: 12.30-2pm/7-10pm.
Additional: Children welcome
Seats: 55
Style: Classic, Country-house
Smoking: No smoking in dining room
Accommodation: 38 rooms (38 en suite) ★ ★ ★ ★
Directions: Off A272, road to Stockbridge, signposted

A stunning avenue of protected lime trees sweeps up to the façade of this grand mansion. Styled in the tradition of great houses, the restaurant, overlooking the beautiful grounds, is oak panelled and hung with old masters. The kitchen's distinctive style produces many skilfully executed traditional dishes with a modern slant such as roast saddle of venison with Savoy cabbage, farcie lentils du Puy, creamed parsnip and sauce grand veneur. A starter of pan-fried langoustine is served on a courgette, carrot and mango salad with black pepper and vanilla bean dressing and a dessert of cherry and white chocolate parfait is served with Griottines coulis.

Nine the Square

An enviable address overlooking the towering Norman cathedral is home to this buzzy ground-floor bistro and more formal first-floor restaurant - open evenings only. The repertoire has a strong Mediterranean flavour; coriander salsa, chilli pesto, sun-blushed tomatoes, pistou, feta and pancetta all conspire with quality main ingredients to capture a robust, no-nonsense Latin style. Chef David Bennett's time with Franco Taruschio in the past has obviously proved an enduring influence, and the compact menu's fish and pasta dishes are

9 Great Minster Street, SO23 9HA
Tel: 01962 864004
Fax: 01962 879586
Chef(s): David Bennett
Owner(s): David & Debra Bennett
Cost: *Alc* £15, set price D £24.95.
☺ ☺ H/wine £12.25
Times: noon-2pm/7-10pm.
Closed Sun, 25-26 Dec, some BHs

enticing. Desserts have a familiar ring; sticky toffee pudding or chocolate brownies for instance. Yellow walls, blond floorboards, soft lighting and friendly service set the restaurant's mood.

Directions: In the main square, just outside the cathedral grounds and opposite the museum

The Winchester Royal

Though it's been a hotel for the past 150 years, this 16th-century building has also served as a private house, bishop's residence and convent. The restaurant's exposed brickwork, hanging baskets and garden views create a courtyard atmosphere in which to enjoy traditional dishes such as herb roasted rack of lamb or Scotch salmon with Puy lentils and red wine sauce.

Directions: Take one-way system through Winchester, turn R off St. George's Street into St. Peter Street. Hotel on R

Wykeham Arms

The Wykeham Arms is tucked away between the cathedral and the college in a narrow street in the oldest part of the city. It has all the atmosphere of a thriving local, but food and wine are taken very seriously. Options range from roast chicken sandwich to rack of lamb on Puy lentils with red wine and wild mushroom sauce.

Additional: Bar food L. Children welcome
Seats: 42. Private dining room 25
Style: Italian, Bistro-Style
Smoking: No cigars; Air conditioning

St Peter Street, SO23 8BS
Tel: 01962 840840
Fax: 01962 841582
e royal@marstonhotels.com
Chef(s): Gerd Jacobmeyor
Owner(s): Marston Hotels
Cost: *Alc* £28, set price L £16.50/ D £19.50. ☺ ☺ H/wine £12.60
Times: Noon-2pm/7-10pm
Additional: Sunday L. Bar food. Children welcome
Seats: 95. Private dining room 30. Jacket and tie preferred
Style: Traditional, British
Smoking: No smoking in dining room; Air conditioning
Civil licence: 120
Accommodation: 75 rooms (75 en suite) ★ ★ ★

75 Kingsgate Street, SO23 9PE
Tel: 01962 853834
Fax: 01962 854411
Chef(s): Nicola Saunders, Gary Stickland
Cost: *Alc* £25. ☺ ☺ H/wine £10.95
Times: Noon-2.30pm/6.30-8.45pm. Closed Sun, 25 Dec
Additional: Bar food L. Children 14yrs+
Seats: 90
Style: Traditional
Smoking: No-smoking area
Accommodation: 14 rooms (14 en suite) ♦♦♦♦
Directions: S out of city along Southgate St. Take 3rd turning L into Cannon St, inn on R at end

England

HEREFORDSHIRE

HEREFORD

Map 3 SO53

Ancient Camp Inn

All change at this charming country inn with a change of ownership as we went to press. Perched high above the River Wye, with peerless views from the restaurant and bar, the former cider house has been home to some notable cooking over recent years. For the latest information check our website (www.theAA.com/restaurants).

Ruckhall, HR2 9QX
Tel: 01981 250449
Telephone for further details

Castle House

Castle Street, HR1 2NW
Tel: 01432 356321
Fax: 01432 365909
e info@castlehse.co.uk
Chef(s): Stuart McLeod
Owner(s): Dr A Heijn
Cost: Set price L £18.95/D £29.95. ☺ H/wine £14
Times: 12.30-2pm/7-10pm
Additional: Sunday L. Bar food. Children welcome
Seats: 32. Jacket and tie preferred
Style: Classic, Chic
Smoking: No cigars; Air conditioning
Accommodation: 15 rooms (15 en suite) ★ ★ ★
Directions: City centre, near cathedral

This extraordinary and unashamedly plush hotel is the setting for the older of Stuart McLeod's two fine dining charges (see La Rive) although it is still an infant itself. Not that you would know it from the assured and confident cooking that emerged from a kitchen which, in size terms is very much the poor relation of its neighbour, but nevertheless produces food of equally outstanding quality. The style is along French classic lines and there is the expected degree of intricacy. It's an approach that requires both technical proficiency and an acute judgement of flavours. Happily both are abundantly evident in the likes of a butternut squash and lemon cappuccino with a galette of foie gras or an "exquisite" dish of caramelised sea scallops with tomato and balsamic relish. There is no stinting on the quality of ingredients with fillet of Hereford beef a consistent feature in the company of cep purée, crushed root vegetables and a daube. A "mightily intense" combination beautifully crafted. Fish is deftly handled in, for instance, seared Cornish halibut with lemon and watercress mash, lobster and coriander won tons and a shellfish emulsion, with balance and dexterity, once again being the important factors. Desserts are in the same vein with an abundance of layers of flavour and texture whether in an assiette of Valrhona chocolate or a study in banana puddings. The seven course tasting menu offers the opportunity to take a broad sweep through the repertoire and, like the *carte*, is terrific value for cooking of this quality.

England

La Rive NEW

◎◎◎◎
Bridge Street, HR4 9RG
Tel: 01432 349008
Fax: 01432 349012
e info@leftbank.co.uk
Chef(s): Stuart McLeod
Owner(s): Dr & Mrs Heijn
Cost: *Alc* £32.50. Set price L
£18.95/D £29.95-£42.95 (7 courses).
☺ H/wine £16
Times: 12.30-2pm/7-9.30pm.
Closed L Sat, D Sun
Additional: Sunday L. Children
welcome
Seats: 40. Private dining room 25
Style: Modern, Chic
Smoking: No-smoking area, no pipes.
Air conditioning
Civil licence: 50
Directions: City centre

What is it about the Welsh/English border? The rich vein of good places to eat out in this area now extends to this quite remarkable effort from the team that brought us Castle House (see entry above) last year. La Rive is part of a modern riverside complex that includes a brasserie (Floodgates), a cocktail bar and a florist together with a nearby terrace including a delicatessen, bakery and a coffee shop. The philanthropic figure behind all this vibrancy is a Dutch businessman by the name of Dr A Heijn but at the culinary helm is Stuart McLeod overseeing the vast brigade that service the three restaurants. The McLeod style will be familiar to those that have frequented Castle House - expansive, precise cooking with a classical bent, but shot through with unexpected twists and the occasional explosion of flavour. With the standard three course menu embellished with beautifully honed canapés, an amuse-bouche and a stunning pre-dessert of strawberry champagne jelly, this has got to be some of the best value in the country. Intricate cooking it is, but crucially, they can carry it off. Typical of the style are an astonishingly light starter of mussel, crab and saffron nage with spring vegetables and cannelloni of lobster or a more forceful alternative of seared scallops with a mightily intense tarte Tatin of vine tomatoes and tapenade. An uncompromising approach to quality is especially evident in the meats where Trelough duck (pepper glazed with spiced lentils and a ravioli of the leg) and smoked Hereford beef (with braised celeriac, truffle mash, faggot of oxtail and foie gras) have both been lauded for that extra concentration of flavour. Amongst the desserts a sweet chilli and lemongrass parfait proved an "inspired" combination for a tangerine ice with lemon syrup and an assiette of Valrhona chocolate "flawlessly executed". Formal, intelligent service and reasonably priced, extensive wine list. Take me to the river.

KINGTON

Map 3 SO25

The Stagg Inn and Restaurant NEW

@@

Titley, HR5 3RL
Tel: 01544 230221
e reservations@thestagg.co.uk
Chef(s): Steve Reynolds,
Adam Davidson, Andrew Lynch,
Elaine Smith
Owner(s): Steve Reynolds &
Nicola Holland
Cost: Alc £21.50, set price L £24.
☺ ☺ H/wine £9.50
Times: Noon-3.30pm/6.30-11.30pm.
Closed Mon, 1st 2 wks Nov
Additional: Sunday L. Bar food.
Children welcome
Seats: 50. Private dining room 30

Quite difficult to find tucked away amidst beautiful rolling countryside close to the Welsh Border, Titley's rustic local is fast becoming one of the finds of modern British cooking. The key to this success lies in the Marches, which are a treasure-trove of fine produce and put to best use by the Roux-trained chef Steve Reynolds. Seasonal menus served throughout the homely bar and informal dining room reflect his pedigree with main courses of Hereford duck breast with sweet and sour rhubarb sauce, perfectly cooked rack of Herefordshire lamb with fennel and garlic purée, and fresh brill with spinach and saffron sauce. Precede with local goats' cheese and fennel tart or simply seared scallops with Swiss chard and black pepper oil, and finish with caramelised lemon tart or some impressive cheeses from independent lcoal producers. Business is very brisk - best to book well ahead if you're coming from afar.

Style: Traditional
Smoking: No smoking in dining room
Accommodation: 2 rooms (2 en suite)
Directions: Between Kington and Presteigne on B4335

LEDBURY

Map 3 SO73

Feathers Hotel

@

High Street, HR8 1DS
Tel: 01531 635266
Fax: 01531 638955
e mary@feathers-ledbury.co.uk
Chef(s): John Capaldi
Owner(s): David Elliston
Cost: Alc £28. ☺ ☺ H/wine £10.95
Times: Noon-2pm/7-9.30pm.
Additional: Sunday L. Bar food L.
Children welcome
Seats: 55. Private dining room 60
Style: Traditional
Smoking: No-smoking area; no cigars;
Air conditioning
Civil licence: 100
Accommodation: 19 rooms (19 en
suite) ★ ★ ★
Directions: Ledbury is on
A449/A438/A417, and the hotel is
prominent on the main street

Timbered-framed town centre coaching inn, where the hop-bedecked Fuggles brasserie is named after Hereford's renowned hop variety. A wide choice of dishes includes plenty of fresh fish, vegetarian and lighter options. These are further supplemented by blackboard specials - maybe sautéed supreme of chicken with sun-dried tomato and pancetta.

ROSS-ON-WYE

Map 3 SO52

Chase Hotel

Gloucester Road, HR9 5LH
Tel: 01989 763161
Fax: 01989 768330
e info@chasehotel.co.uk
Chef(s): Richard Birchall

Regency decadence awaits just a short walk from the town centre. Expect guinea fowl strewn with smoked bacon, button onions and mushrooms. The wine list includes old favourites as well as New World rising stars.

Owner(s): The Porter family
Cost: *Alc* £30, set price L £14.50/
D £22.50. ☺ ☺ H/wine £9.95
Times: noon-2pm/7-10pm.
Closed L Sat, 26-29 Dec
Additional: Sunday L. Bar food.
Children welcome
Seats: 50. Private dining room 60
Style: Traditional
Smoking: No smoking in dining room
Civil licence: 300
Accommodation: 36 rooms (36 en
suite) ★ ★ ★

Directions: M50 J4, A449, A440 towards Ross-on-Wye

Glewstone Court

This is a relaxed restaurant with antiques, interesting paintings and apricot ragged walls. Service is friendly and, as you might expect, the cooking is both thoughtful and unpretentious. Traditional favourites (pheasant, smoked salmon, rack of lamb) feature alongside more contemporary items such as Thai style prawns. All are confidently done with clear flavours.

Seats: 36. Private dining room 36
Style: Traditional, Country-House
Smoking: No cigars
Accommodation: 8 rooms (8 en suite) ★ ★
Directions: From Ross Market Place take A40/A49 (Monmouth/Hereford) over Wilton Bridge. At rdbt L onto A40 (Monmouth/S Wales), after 1m turn R for Glewstone

Glewstone,
HR9 6AW
Tel: 01989 770367
Fax: 01989 770282
e glewstone@aol.com
Chef(s): Christine Reeve-Tucker,
Phillip Meek
Owner(s): C & W Reeve-Tucker
Cost: Set price D £26. ☺ ☺
H/wine £10
Times: noon-2pm/7-9.30pm.
Closed 25-27 Dec
Additional: Sunday L. Bar food.
Children welcome

Hunsdon Manor

Dating back to Elizabethan times, this mellow sandstone manor house offers a pleasant hotel dining experience. Plenty to choose from on a set-price menu that makes good use of local products: home-made spiced sausages comes with creamy mashed potatoes and red wine gravy, with perhaps lemon tart, decent coffee and fudge to finish.

Gloucester Road,
Weston under Penyard,
HR9 7PE
Tel: 01989 563376
Telephone for further details

Pencraig Court

Gaze at the River Wye from this large Georgian house with impressive views. The food is pretty appealing, too, with old favourites like coquille St Jacques, pork tenderloin with apple and Calvados sauce, vivid veggies, and Bramley apple pie and rich custard. Light crusty breads are a highlight.

Pencraig, HR9 6HR
Tel: 01989 770306
Telephone for further details

England

England

ROSS-ON-WYE *Continued*   Map 3 SO52

Pengethley Manor

Peacefully-situated, this Georgian manor house has all the ingredients for a relaxing visit. On offer is a fine range of British and international food served in the bright, elegant dining room that overlooks the Herefordshire countryside. A meal here might open with seafood pillow - puff pastry filled with smoked haddock, sweetcorn and braised leek on a Veronique sauce, or possibly game and cognac terrine served with a Cumberland and diced apple dressing; to follow perhaps poached darne of salmon with a champagne cream sauce, or chicken supreme, served with a mornay chive cream sauce.

Pengethley Park, HR9 6LL
Tel: 01989 730211
Fax: 01989 730238
e reservations@pengethleymanor.co.uk
Chef(s): Fred van der Knaap
Owner(s): Mr & Mrs P Wisker
Cost: *Alc* £25, set price L £15/D £15-£26.50. ☺ H/wine £12.90
Times: noon-2.30pm/7-9.30pm.
Additional: Sunday L. Bar food. Children welcome
Seats: 50. Private dining room 80. Jacket and tie preferred
Style: Country-house
Smoking: No smoking in dining room
Civil licence: 80
Accommodation: 25 rooms (25 en suite) ★ ★ ★
Directions: 4 miles N on A49 Hereford Rd

WEOBLEY   Map 3 SO45

The Salutation Inn

A country inn dating back to the 16th-century, with a heavily beamed oak frame and inglenook fireplaces in the bars and restaurant. Menus encompass lunchtime snacks (smoked bacon tagliatelli and seafood gratin) and numerous vegetarian options. Served rather more formally in the restaurant, starters might be pheasant timbale with ceps and cream or croustade of duck liver, followed by a daily fish dish or perhaps braised lamb shank with winter vegetables.

Market Pitch, HR4 8SJ
Tel: 01544 318443
e salutationinn@btinternet.com
Chef(s): Graham Leavsley
Owner(s): Dr M Tai
Cost: *Alc* £26. ☺ ☺ H/wine £9.50
Times: Closed L Mon, D Sun, 25 Dec
Additional: Sunday L. Bar food.
Seats: 38. Jacket and tie preferred
Style: Traditional
Smoking: No smoking in dining room
Accommodation: 3 rooms (3 en suite) ♦♦♦♦
Directions: On A4112, just off Leominster-Hereford road

HERTFORDSHIRE

BISHOP'S STORTFORD

Map 5 TL42

Ibbetson's

NEW

Palatial establishment with a long history, which came into the hands of Sir Henry Selwin-Ibbetson in the late 19th-century - hence the restaurant's name. For a little gracious living, sample the likes of pan-roasted turbot with leek and oyster flan, or medallions of beef layered with foie gras on chargrilled potatoes.

at Down Hall, Hatfield Heath,
CM22 7AS
Tel: 01279 731441
Fax: 01279 730416
e Ibbetsons@downhall.co.uk
Chef(s): Chris Wheeldon
Owner(s): Down Hall
Cost: Alc £55, set price L £22.50.
H/wine £15.50
Times: 12.30-2pm/7-10pm.
Closed Sun & Mon, L Sat, Xmas, New
Year, BHs
Additional: Children 12 yrs+
Seats: 36. Jacket and tie preferred
Style: Traditional, Formal
Smoking: No smoking in dining room;
Air conditioning
Civil licence: 100
Accommodation: 99 rooms (99 en
suite) ★★★★
Directions: From Bishop's Stortford
follow A1060, at Hatfield Heath, keep
left, turn R into lane opposite Hunters
Meet restaurant, then L at the end and
follow signs for Down Hall

ELSTREE

Map 4 TQ19

Edgwarebury Hotel

NEW

A Tudor revivalist mansion set in manicured grounds not far from Elstree Studios, with lovely views out over London, especially at night. Timbered beams and wood panelling feature throughout, and the elegant restaurant avoids being 'stuffy'. Subtle influences from the East and Italy have infiltrated the British cooking to produce an eclectic menu with variety, and something to please most tastes. Grilled smoked Welsh sausage, or pan-seared scallop in Thai broth and pesto risotto, might be followed by roast breast of duck with pot-roast beetroot, shitake mushrooms, fondant potatoes and tagliatelle of wild mushrooms. Service is exceptionally attentive and good natured.

Barnet Lane, WD6 3RE
Tel: 0208 953 8227
Fax: 0208 207 3668
e edgwarebury@corushotels.com
Chef(s): Jack Brabham
Owner(s): Corus Hotels
Cost: Alc £32.50. ☺ ☺
H/wine £13.50
Times: 12.30-2.15pm/7-9.30pm.
Closed L Sat
Additional: Sunday L. Bar food.
Children welcome
Seats: 60. Private dining room 40
Style: Classic, Traditional
Smoking: No smoking in dining room
Civil licence: 100
Accommodation: 47 rooms (47 en
suite) ★★★
Directions: Access from M1 J4 & 5,
M25 J19 & 23, Barnet Lane is signed
Elstree & Aldenham

England

HATFIELD

Map 4 TL20

Bush Hall

NEW

Mill Green, AL9 5NT
Tel: 01707 271251
Fax: 01707 272289
📧 enquiries@bush-hall.com
Chef(s): Peter Allmark,
Scott McKenzie
Cost: *Alc* £35. ☺ ☺ H/wine £12.50
Times: Noon-3pm/7-10.30pm.
Closed Sun, L Sat, after L 25 Dec-
early Jan
Additional: Bar food L.
Children 8 yrs+
Seats: 38. Private dining room 22.
Jacket and tie preferred
Style: Classic, Traditional
Smoking: No cigars; Air conditioning

Bush Hall stands in attractive grounds (part of the Hatfield estate) which include ponds, a river and ornamental gardens. Kipling's restaurant overlooks these and offers an intimate ('almost cave like') setting with traditional décor and twists of modern colour. Dishes range from 'Thai inspired' sea bass to pheasant with chestnut purée and red wine jus. Don't miss the cheese menu, on which a well-balanced English selection is described in the sort of mouthwatering detail usually reserved for wine lists. Service from the French staff is so slick it's almost imperceptible.

Civil licence: 150
Accommodation: 25 rooms (25 en suite) ★ ★ ★
Directions: From A1 (M) follow signs for A414 (Hereford/Welwyn Garden City). Take slip road onto A1000 (signs for Hatfield House). L at lights, immediately L into Hotel drive

ST ALBANS

Map 4 TL10

St Michael's Manor

Fishpool Street, AL3 4RY
Tel: 01727 864444
Fax: 01727 848909
📧 smmanor@blobalnet.co.uk
Chef(s): Steve Juett
Owner(s): David & Sheila
Newling-Ward

The large conservatory restaurant at St Michael's Manor overlooks the award-winning gardens and lake. Menus offer plenty of choice and reflect the changing seasons in the quality and range of produce offered. Mediterranean influences are apparent with dishes such as supreme of chicken stuffed with oregano, Mozzarella and garlic, wrapped in Parma ham and served with a shitake mushroom sauce, or fillet of venison with chasseur sauce and Bordelaise potatoes. There is also a serious approach to vegetarian options - perhaps marinated Halloumi cheese brochettes with thyme, oregano and rosemary, served with wild rice and roast cherry tomatoes.

Accommodation: 23 rooms (23 en suite) ★ ★ ★
Directions: At the Tudor Tavern in High St turn into George St. After Abbey & Boys' school on L, road continues into Fishpool St. Hotel is 1 mile on L

Cost: Alc £28-£45, set price L £22.50/D £35. H/wine £12.50
Times: 12.30-2pm/7-9.30pm
Additional: Sunday L. Bar food L. Children welcome
Seats: 90. Private dining room 20. Jacket and tie preferred
Style: Traditional, Country-house
Smoking: Air conditioning
Civil licence: 70

Sopwell House

The name 'Magnolia Restaurant' doesn't imply a few bits of blossom or some botanical pictures: this conservatory style restaurant is actually built around a magnolia tree The stunning centrepiece is complemented by plenty of foliage and bamboo style chairs. 'Superb' home-made breads begin the meal - expect to be spoilt for choice - and the well-balanced menu offers a similar scope. Dishes range from traditional (braised shank of lamb with caramelised root vegetables) to Indian (tandoori marinated chicken breast with cumin rice pilaf and cucumber mint raita). Service is professional yet informal.

Cottonmill Lane, Sopwell, AL1 2HQ
Tel: 01727 864477
Fax: 01727 844741/845636
e enquiries@sopwellhouse.co.uk
Chef(s): Sam Walker
Owner(s): Abraham Bejerano
Cost: Alc £35, set price L £17.95/ D £24.95. ☺ H/wine £17.95
Times: 12.30-2pm/7.30-9.30pm. Closed L Sat, 3 days after Xmas
Additional: Sunday L. Bar food L. Children welcome
Seats: 120. Jacket and tie preferred
Style: Traditional, Formal
Smoking: No smoking in dining room; Air conditioning
Civil licence: 150
Accommodation: 128 rooms (128 en suite) ★ ★ ★ ★
Directions: On London Road from St Albans follow signs to Sopwell, over mini-rdbt, hotel on L.

SAWBRIDGEWORTH Map 4 TL41

Goose Fat & Garlic

A laid-back bistro-style eatery with polished wooden floors and modern lighting. The menu takes a central European sweep, from seared scallops on chorizo sausage with cucumber spaghetti and rocket leaves (recommended), to confit of duck leg with roasted vegetables and a Jack Daniel's sauce. Desserts like iced caramel and brandy parfait with orange compôte, and great cappuccino.

Style: Modern, Bistro-Style
Smoking: No-smoking area; Air conditioning
Directions: From M11 J7 take A414 (Harlow); continue as road becomes A1186 (Bishop's Stortford). Sawbridgeworth is midway between Harlow and Bishop's Stortford

52 Bell Street, CM21 9AN
Tel: 01279 722554
Fax: 01279 600766
e lwootan@btconnect.com
Chef(s): Toby Didier'Serre
Owner(s): Mr L Wooton, Mr & Mrs Gowan
Cost: Alc £25.25. ☺ ☺ H/wine £12.50
Times: Noon-2pm. Closed L Sat, D Sun, 2 wks after Xmas
Additional: Sunday L. Children welcome
Seats: 60. Private dining room 40

England

TRING
Map 4 SP91
Pendley Manor

Cow Lane, HP23 5QY
Tel: 01442 891891
Fax: 01442 890687
✉ info@pendley-manor.co.uk
Chef(s): Paul Haverson
Cost: *Alc* £28, set price L £28/
D £28-£37. H/wine £13.95
Times: 12.30-2.30pm/7-9.30pm
Additional: Sunday L. Bar food.
Children welcome
Seats: 60. Private dining room 200.
Jacket and tie preferred
Style: Traditional, Country-house
Smoking: No smoking in dining room
Civil licence: 225
Accommodation: 74 rooms (74 en
suite) ★ ★ ★ ★

A Victorian mansion set in impressive, landscaped grounds.
Meals begin with an aperitif in the conservatory or library,
before progressing to the grand Oak Restaurant. Dishes on the
international style menu range from pan-fried calves' liver with
sage and onion mash to vegetable curry in a poppadom basket.

Directions: M25 J20. Take A41. Take Tring exit and follow signs
for Berkhamsted. 1st L, R after rugby club

WARE
Map 5 TL31
Marriott Hanbury Manor

Ware, Hertfordshire, SG12 0SD
Tel: 01920 487722
Telephone for further details

Nearby Hatfield House reputedly inspired this stunning
Jacobean-style mansion. Surprising, in such a grand-looking
hotel, to find a small and intimate restaurant with unstuffy
service. The menu looks towards France for inspiration, with
imaginative dips in cosmopolitan directions producing seared
scallops (fantastic quality) with celeriac purée and champagne
beurre blanc, and the signature fillet of lamb with barley risotto.
Canapés, amuse-bouche and breads all show good attention to
detail, and lemon tart with crème fraiche ice cream and autumn
berry compôte was a culinary extravaganza. Be prepared to
linger over your meal, with a heavyweight wine list to help.

England

WELWYN

Map 4 TL21

Auberge du Lac

This is somewhere you'll really want to take some time - a wonderfully comfortable restaurant, on a lake amid a beautiful estate, where the pace is really relaxed. The food is contemporary with some Asian influence, offered from a *carte* at lunch and dinner, plus daily specials in the evening. A lunchtime table d'hôte (Tuesday to Saturday) offers phenomenal value at £25 including a half bottle of wine - don't worry, the quality of the food is every bit as good as the *carte*. Expect baked seven hours leg of lamb in Cabernet Sauvignon, or pan-seared Cornish sea bass with caramelised endives and girolles.

Civil licence: 70
Accommodation: 16 rooms (16 en suite)
Directions: Telephone for directions

Brocket Hall, AL8 7XG
Tel: 01707 368888
Fax: 01707 368898
Chef(s): Pascal Breant
Owner(s): CCA International
Cost: Alc £41, set price L £25/
D £38-£45. H/wine £16
Times: Noon-2pm/7-10pm. Closed
Mon, D Sun
Additional: Sunday L. Children
welcome. Vegetarian by request only
Seats: 70. Private dining room 16
Style: Formal, Country-house
Smoking: No cigars; Air conditioning

KENT

ASHFORD

Map 5 TR04

Eastwell Manor

Eastwell Park, Boughton Lees,
TN25 4HR
Tel: 01233 213000
Fax: 01233 635530
🆎 eastwell@btinternet.com
Chef(s): Aidan McCormack
Owner(s): Turloo Parrett
Cost: Alc £37.50, set price L
£18.50/D £32. ☺ H/wine £13
Times: noon-2.30pm/7-10pm
Additional: Sunday L. Bar food.
Children welcome
Seats: 80. Private dining room 80.
Jacket and tie preferred
Style: Traditional
Smoking: No smoking in dining room
Civil licence: 250
Accommodation: 62 rooms (62 en
suite) ★ ★ ★ ★

A modern addition houses the superb leisure club, but the 16th-century manor house is a shrine to the traditional: stone fireplaces, oak-panelling and brass chandeliers abound, with plenty of fresh flowers, and luxurious deep red fabrics. The menu is short, but it generally packs a powerful punch, and on recent occasions the main course and dessert have been strongest. Turbot with dauphinoise potatoes, sautéed salsify, mushrooms and grain mustard froth show exemplary kitchen skills and coconut tart with lime caramel syrup is a dextrous balancing act. A well-priced lunch menu offers good value: goats' cheese mousse with figs and confit walnuts, followed perhaps by grilled fillet of mackerel with warm potato salad and grain mustard velouté, with glazed lemon tart and crème fraiche, or blackcurrant mousse with mango sauce going down well as a finale.

Directions: M20 J9 follow A251 to Faversham, hotel on L after Kennington. From Canterbury, A28 to Ashford, L turn to Boughton Lees

England

BEARSTED

Map 5 TQ85

Soufflé Restaurant

A beautiful 16th-century Grade II listed building stocked with classic furnishings that add much to the restaurant's character. The clearly presented menu, full of imaginative ideas is modern yet not a slave to trends and service comes at a nice pace. Start perhaps with spring onion and Gruyère tart dressed with wild rocket and balsamic dressing or terrine of crab, chicken and veal sweetbreads with a shellfish vinaigrette; then proceed to the likes of roast monkfish with turmeric, coriander and ginger sauce and braised pig's trotter stuffed with morels and mashed potato. A duo of quail baked in puff pastry with foie gras and chicken mousse drew warm praise, as did a lightly caramelised rhubarb tarte Tatin.

Directions: Telephone for directions

31 The Green, ME14 4DN
Tel: 01622 737065
Fax: 01622 737065
Chef(s): Nick Evenden
Owner(s): Nick & Karen Evenden
Cost: *Alc* £30, set price L £16.50/ D £22.50. ☺ ☺ H/wine £12.50
Times: Noon-2pm/7-9.30pm. Closed Mon, L Sat, D Sun
Additional: Sunday L. Children welcome
Seats: 40. Private dining room 23
Style: Classic, French
Smoking: No cigars

BIDDENDEN

Map 5 TQ83

West House Restaurant

A labour of love for the owners and it shows in the devoted approach to preparation and uncompromising approach to service. Uncompromising in the sense that bookings are staggered as much as possible to ensure the quality of the food, and service is often necessarily slow placed. But if you're going to wait for food it might as well be in a room as lovely as this one - beamed ceiling, bare floorboards and a centrepiece stove in the period inglenook. When the food arrives it fairly glows with the devotion, enthusiasm and respect for ingredients of chef Susan Cunningham. A typical meal might include a starter of crab sausage with julienne of vegetables and a fish sauce, a main course of roast quail, barley risotto with bacon and sage and a dessert of warm chocolate mousse cake with a white chocolate sauce.

Directions: Junction of A2862 and A274. 14 miles S of Maidstone

28 High Street, TN27 8AH
Tel: 01580 291341
Fax: 01580 291341
e westhouse.restaurant@virginnet. co.uk
Chef(s): Susan Cunningham
Owner(s): David & Susan Cunningham
Cost: Set price D £27.50 H/wine £10.50
Times: Dinner only, 7-9pm. Closed Sun-Tue, 1 wk Sep, 25-26 Dec, 31 Dec, 2 wks Jan
Additional: Children welcome. Vegetarian by request only
Seats: 20
Style: Traditional
Smoking: No cigars

CANTERBURY

Map 5 TR15

Augustine's Restaurant

Neighbourhood restaurant, well situated for tourists, and growing in popularity with locals. There are two rooms, one with a small bar and sofas and both with open fires, all contained in a fine Georgian house looking up the wide street to the 8th-century monastery founded by St Augustine. Accomplished cooking of broadly modern European dishes such as sea bass with cucumber spaghetti and citrus vinaigrette.

Seats: 30
Style: Modern
Smoking: No smoking in dining room
Directions: Follow signs to St Augustine's Abbey

1 & 2 Longport, CT1 1PE
Tel: 01227 453063
Chef(s): Robert Grimer
Owner(s): Mr R & Mr T Grimer
Cost: *Alc* £25, set price L £8.95. ☺ ☺ H/wine £9.95
Times: Noon-1.45pm/6-10pm. Closed Mon, D Sun, Jan
Additional: Sunday L. Children welcome

England

Canterbury Hotel

71 New Dover Road, CT1 3DZ
Tel: 01227 450551
Fax: 01227 780145
e canterbury.hotel@btinternet.com
Chef(s): Michel Supparo
Owner(s): Mr & Mrs F Bevan
Cost: Alc £23.50/D £20.50. ☺
H/wine £9.90
Times: Dinner only, 7-10pm
Additional: Bar food. Children 6yrs+
Seats: 30. Private dining room 20
Style: Traditional
Smoking: No-smoking area; no cigars
Accommodation: 23 rooms (23 en suite) ★ ★
Directions: On A2, Dover Road, near city centre

The restaurant goes by the name of La Bonne Cuisine, signalling French staff, a French menu and a pretty authentic gallic ambience. The kitchen's strengths lie in the classical repertoire, including a silky foie gras parfait prepared with Muscat, and biscuit chocolat with an orange confit mousse.

The Dove

Any place with an address as evocative as Plumpudding Lane should be worth a visit, and you won't be disappointed at the Dove. It is an ivy-clad, rural, red brick pub where stripped floorboards, wooden tables and chairs provide a rustic setting for good food with French/Mediterranean flavours. Kick off with an intensely flavoured terrine of foie gras with spicy chutney and a garnish of rocket and Parmesan. Local plaice - a delicious piece of fish, plump, fresh and beautifully cooked - has made for a delicately balanced main course with a shallot, caper and herb butter and simply prepared vegetables.

Directions: Telephone for Directions

Plumpudding Lane, Dargate,
ME13 9HB
Tel: 01227 751360
e thedovechef@netscapeonline.co.uk
Chef(s): Nigel Morris
Owner(s): Nigel Morris
Cost: Alc £25. ☺ ☺ H/wine £11
Times: Noon-2pm/7-9pm.
Closed Mon, D Sun & Tues
Additional: Sunday L. Bar food L.
Children welcome. Vegetarian by request only
Seats: 26. **Style:** Rustic

CHATHAM   Map 5 TQ76

Bridgewood Manor

Access to the Channel Tunnel road link and local motorways are decided bonuses for guests at this modern hotel with a classic Gothic flavour, close to Rochester. Squires restaurant is more formal than the alternative Terrace bistro; in both, modern European styles predominate though more attention to seasonality would be welcome. A prosaic tian of cold Mediterranean vegetables proved less impressive as a starter than an unusual chicken roulade with vanilla and banana as a main-course. Impressive wine list organised by style.

Style: Classical, French
Smoking: No-smoking area; no cigars; Air conditioning
Civil licence: 150
Accommodation: 100 rooms (100 en suite) ★ ★ ★ ★
Directions: From M2 J3 or M20 J6 follow A229 towards Chatham. At Bridgewood rdbt take 3rd exit (Walderslade). Hotel 50yds on L

Bridgewood Roundabout,
Walderslade Woods, ME5 9AX
Tel: 01634 201333
Fax: 01634 201330
e bridgewoodmanor@
marstonhotels/co.uk
Chef(s): Jean-Claude MacFarlane
Owner(s): Marston Hotels
Cost: Alc £26, set price L £17.50.
☺ ☺ H/wine £12.60
Times: 12.30-2pm/7-10pm.
Closed L Sat, 24-27 Dec (ex residents)
Additional: Sunday L. Bar food L.
Children welcome
Seats: 80. Private dining room 30

England

CRANBROOK
Map 5 TQ73

Kennel Holt Hotel

A lovely Elizabethan and Edwardian manor house, built in the warm red brick so common in the Weald. The pretty gardens set visitors on the path to relaxation, aided by friendly, caring staff. The dining room is just as the setting would suggest - bare beams, open walls and log fires. Whilst the menu makes impressive use of local produce, it does not restrict itself to British ideas: a meal might include a freshly made shallot tart Tatin followed by griddled pork with a light Gorgonzola sauce and fried potatoes. Interesting, French based wine list.

Goudhurst Road, TN17 2PT
Tel: 01580 712032
Fax: 01580 715495
e hotel@kennelholt.demon.co.uk
Chef(s): Neil Chalmers,
Audrey Ratcliff
Owner(s): Neil & Sally Chalmers
Cost: Set price L & D £27.50-£32.50.
☺ H/wine £12.50
Times: 12.30-3pm/7.30-11pm.
Closed Mon & Sun (ex residents),
L Sat, 2 wks Jan
Additional: Sunday L. Children
10yrs+
Seats: 25. Private dining room 16
Style: French, Country-house
Smoking: No smoking in dining room
Accommodation: 10 rooms (10 en
suite) ★ ★
Directions: On A262, 1 mile from
A229 crossroads, 3 miles from
Goudhurst towards Cranbrook

Soho South

23 Stone Street, TN17 3HF
Tel: 01580 714666
Fax: 01580 715653
Chef(s): Nigel Tarr
Owner(s): Nigel & Linnea Tarr
Cost: Alc £13-£28. ☺ ☺
H/wine £9.50
Times: 11am-2.30pm/6.30pm-late.
Closed Sun-Tue, 2 wks Xmas, 2 wks
Aug
Additional: Children 8yrs+ at D
Seats: 33
Style: Rustic, Bistro-Style
Smoking: No cigars

This timber clad building dates back to 1530 and was originally part of a Flemish weaving factory. Nowadays it houses a welcoming, bistro style restaurant. A wooden floor and bottled herbs set the scene for a rustic style of cooking, European in scope but rooted in France. A meal might include gravadlax with a light smoked salmon mousse followed by sautéed lambs' liver with Provençal sauce, celeriac and potato dauphinoise. Cooking is simple, high quality and offers 'the best of flavours'. A French bias is also evident in the impressive wine list.

Directions: In town centre, opposite Barclays Bank, 50 metres from tourist information centre & church

England

DARTFORD
Map 5 TQ57

Rowhill Grange

Magnificent thatched country house, whose Garden Restaurant overlooks the pretty terrace and grounds. An eclectic menu with some bold combinations (crab and avocado with tomato confit and guacamole), well executed dishes (spit-roasted chicken with a lemon and thyme risotto), and freshly-cooked desserts (squidgy chocolate fondant). Very good coffee.

Style: Modern, Formal
Smoking: No smoking in dining room
Civil licence: 120
Accommodation: 38 rooms (38 en suite) ★★★★
Directions: M5 J3, take B2173 towards Swanley, then B258 towards Hextable. Straight on at 3 rdbts. Hotel 1.5m on L

DA2 7QH
Tel: 01322 615136
Fax: 01322 615137
e admin@rowhillgrange.com
Chef(s): Richard Cameron
Owner(s): Utopia Leisure
Cost: Alc £35, set price L £19.95/ D £29.95. H/wine £14.95
Times: 12.30-2.30pm/7-9.30pm. Closed L Sat
Additional: Sunday L. Bar food. Children welcome
Seats: 100. Private dining room 170. Jacket and tie preferred

DEAL
Map 5 TR35

Dunkerleys Hotel

Sitting almost opposite the pier, it's hardly surprising that Dunkerleys focuses intently on fresh local seafood, simply cooked. It's not all fish, though, and duck liver parfait with brioche and salad leaves might start a meal, but most people opt for main courses like red mullet fillet on a sun-dried tomato and basil rösti with shellfish butter. A recent high spot was strawberry tarte Tatin, an interesting dessert served with excellent vanilla ice cream. The hotel stands out for its bright array of window boxes in summer, whilst views of the Channel can be admired from the popular restaurant all year round.

19 Beach Street, CT14 7AH
Tel: 01304 375016
Fax: 01304 380187
e dunkerleysofdeal@btinternet.com
Chef(s): Ian Dunkerley
Owner(s): Ian Dunkerley
Cost: Alc £30, set price L £10.50. ☺ ☺ H/wine £9.50
Times: Noon-2.30pm/6-9.30pm. Closed Mon
Additional: Sunday L. Bar food. Children welcome
Seats: 40
Style: Modern, English
Smoking: No smoking in dining room; Air conditioning
Accommodation: 16 rooms (16 en suite) ★★★
Directions: Turn off A2 onto A258 to Deal – situated 100yds before Deal Pier

DOVER
Map 5 TR34

Wallet's Court

The hotel is formed from a cluster of medieval buildings and the main house and its dining room have the best of the period features - open fires and carved oak beams and pillars. The décor is typical country house with white linen and old silver, and the staff are young, friendly and well-managed. Seasonal fixed-price menus are presented for lunch and dinner, plus a chef's set speciality menu - five courses for £40. Country house fare includes roasted breast of wood pigeon on Clonakilty

West Cliffe, St Margarets-at-Cliffe, CT15 6EW
Tel: 01304 852424
Fax: 01304 853430
e wc@wallettscourt.com
Chef(s): Stephen Harvey
Owner(s): Chris & Lea Oakley
Cost: Alc £37.50, set price L £17.50/D £27.50-£35. ☺ H/wine £14

England

DOVER Continued

Map 5 TR34   ***Wallet's Court***

pudding and clapshot, and rack of Romney Marsh lamb with its own sweetbreads and casserole of beans.

Times: Noon-2pm/7-9pm.
Additional: Sunday L. Children welcome
Seats: 60. Private dining room 40
Style: Country-house
Smoking: No smoking in dining room

Accommodation: 16 rooms (16 en suite) ★ ★ ★
Directions: Telephone for directions

EDENBRIDGE

Map 5 TQ44

Haxted Mill & Riverside Brasserie

Popular riverside restaurant adjoining the watermill. The menu is simple but interesting: a focus on seafood ensures quality fish and exact timing, as in poached salmon on a bed of samphire or pan-fried monkfish on herb mash. Game dishes - such as casserole of rabbit or pan-fried pigeon breast - are a speciality.

Haxted Road, TN8 6PU
Tel: 01732 862914
Fax: 01732 865705
e davinahaxtedmill.co.uk
Chef(s): Christopher Friar, David Peek
Owner(s): David & Linda Peek
Cost: *Alc* £37.50, set price L £20/D £35. ☺ H/wine £11.95
Times: Noon-2pm/7-9.30pm. Closed Mon, D Sun, 23 Dec-6 Jan, 2wks in Sep
Additional: Sunday L. Bar food L. Children welcome. Vegetarian by request only
Seats: 100
Style: Rustic
Smoking: No smoking in dining room
Directions: Telephone for directions

Honours Mill Restaurant

An 18th-century watermill, where in summer a balcony overlooking the millpond comes into its own. Modern Anglo-French cooking in a choice of fixed-price menus offering the likes of a sturdy cassoulet Toulousaine or grilled rib of beef in pancetta with foie gras and Madeira.

Seats: 36. **Style:** French. **Smoking:** No cigars
Directions: Town centre, southern end of High Street, just N of the bridge

87 High Street, TN8 5AU
Tel: 01732 866757
Chef(s): Martin Radmall
Owner(s): D N & N Goodhew
Cost: *Alc* £32.75, set price L £15.50/D £19.95. ☺ ☺ H/wine £10.15
Times: 12.15-2.00pm/7.15-9.30pm. Closed Mon, L Sat, D Sun, 2 wk Xmas
Additional: Sunday L. Children welcome. Vegetarian by request only

FAVERSHAM

Map 5 TR06

Read's Restaurant

As we went to press, Read's was in transit, departing its Painters Forstal venue of some 24 years and taking up residence just a couple of miles away. David and Rona Pitchford have finally realised an ambition to offer some bedrooms and if their approach to hotel keeping is similar to the way they run their restaurant, it has to be good news for visitors to this part of Kent. Whatever the surroundings we can expect the same direct style of cooking with a broadly French bias and a strong foundation of high quality, often local produce. David Pitchford's menus are liberally sprinkled with gastronomic quotes ranging from Abraham Lincoln to Miss Piggy but it's the dishes that catch the eye. From Hythe sea scallops with a sesame crust on a ginger butter sauce, through Whitstable oak smoked haddock served three different ways, to "old fashioned" jugged hare or loin of Kentish lamb with wild mushrooms and pea purée, there is much to entice. Puds tend to be classic (rice pudding crème brûlée with prune and Armagnac ice cream for example and cheeses are taken seriously.

Macknade Manor,
Canterbury Road,
ME13 8XE
Tel: 01795 535344
Fax: 01795 591200
e enquiries@reads.com
Chef(s): David Pitchford
Owner(s): David & Rona Pitchford
Cost: *Alc* £38, set price L £18.50/
D £36-£38. H/wine £15
Times: Noon-2pm/7-9.30pm.
Closed Sun, Mon
Additional: Children welcome.
Vegetarian by request only
Seats: 40. Private dining room 30
Style: Traditional, Country-house
Smoking: No cigars
Civil licence: 60
Accommodation: 6 rooms (6 en suite)
Directions: Telephone for directions

FOLKESTONE

Map 5 TR23

Sandgate Hotel
Restaurant La Terrasse

The scents and flavours of France have miraculously survived the Channel crossing to Kent, and can be savoured in their full intensity in this English seaside village. An elegant mid 19th-century residence has been tenderly converted into a French country house hotel where smart Gallic staff pay close attention to their guests' needs. Nowhere is the French connection more potently experienced than in La Terrasse restaurant, where cast iron fire places and paintings of the Loire Valley indicate the influences. With an apprenticeship at Raymond Blanc's Le Manoir comfortably behind him, chef Samuel Gicqueau combines innovation with experience to create some marvellously memorable dishes. Typical of his light style is pan-fried scallops with black truffles and their own jus, a deeply satisfying starter, and Aberdeen Angus beef with ceps, foie gras, button onions, whole green beans, pommes anna and Madeira sauce. Canapés and desserts also worthy of note. Decent wine list too.

Directions: On A259 coastal road in Sandgate, between Hythe and Folkstone

The Esplanade, Sandgate,
CT20 3DY
Tel: 01303 220444
Fax: 01303 220496
Chef(s): Samuel Gicqueau
Owner(s): Samuel & Zara Gicqueau
Cost: *Alc* £43, set price L £22-£31/
D £22-£31. ☺
Times: 12.15-1.30pm/7.15-9.30pm.
Closed Mon, L Sun, D Tue, 4 wks Jan,
1wk Oct
Additional: Sunday L.
Children welcome
Seats: 22
Style: Classic, French
Smoking: No smoking in dining room
Accommodation: 14 rooms (14 en suite) ★★

HYTHE

Map 5 TR13

The Hythe Imperial

Grande dame of seafront hotels, with discreet pastels, heavy chintz drapes and patterned wallpaper, all beautifully done within the context of the genre. There is a set-price three-course menu with a speciality selection available at a supplement, such

Princes Parade, CT21 6AE
Tel: 01303 267441
Fax: 01303 264610
e hytheimperial@marstonhotels.
co.uk

England

HYTHE *Continued*

Map 5 TR13

as home cured gravadlax, and cannon of lamb with spinach, fondant potato, and redcurrant and mint jus.

Seats: 200. Private dining room 60. Jacket and tie preferred
Style: Classical, Traditional
Smoking: No smoking in dining room; Air conditioning
Civil licence: 100
Accommodation: 100 rooms (100 en suite) ★★★★
Directions: M20 J11 A261 to Hythe signs to Folkestone, R into the Twiss Road opposite Bell Inn towards seafront.

Chef(s): Michael Rieder
Cost: *Alc* £39, set price L £19.50-£27. H/wine £13.50
Times: 12.30-2pm/7-9.30pm.
Closed L Sat (ex Bistro)
Additional: Sunday L. Bar food L. Children welcome

Stade Court

Mock Tudor hotel just a few steps away from the shingle strand. Some imaginative bar food provides an interesting supplement to the restaurant menu, the latter being a fixed-price affair with five options per course - maybe smooth chicken liver parfait with salad leaves, and roast top side of beef traditionally served with Yorkshire pudding.

Seats: 65. Private dining room 25
Smoking: No smoking in dining room
Accommodation: 42 rooms (42 en suite) ★★★
Directions: M20 J11 then A261 to Hythe

West Parade, CT21 6DT
Tel: 01303 268263
Fax: 01303 261803
e stadecourt@marstonhotels.com
Chef(s): Jeff Lewis
Cost: *Alc* £26, set price L £13.95/ D £22. ☺ ☺ H/wine £11.95
Times: 12.30-2pm/6.30-9pm.
Closed L Mon-Sat
Additional: Sunday L. Bar food. Children welcome

LENHAM

Map 5 TQ85

Chilston Park

Sandway, ME17 2BE
Tel: 01622 859803
Fax: 01622 858588
e chilstonpark@arcadianhotels.co.uk
Chef(s): Peter Malcher
Owner(s): Arcadian Hotels
Cost: *Alc* £48, set price L £19.50/ D £32. H/wine £16
Times: 12.30-2.30pm/7-10pm.
Closed L Sat
Additional: Sunday L. Bar food. Children welcome
Seats: 35. Private dining room 20
Style: Classic, Country-house
Smoking: No smoking in dining room

Hundreds of candles set in forbidding wrought iron candlesticks makes for a dramatic setting in the Marble Hall dining room at Chilston Park, giving an eerie cast to the room with its tapestries, numerous gilt-framed oil paintings and wooden floors. The food however is safely modern European with the odd fusion twist. There's a choice of *carte* or fixed-price menus taking in a robust cannon of saltmarsh lamb with kidney beignets, black pudding and English mustard sauce, and a more quixotic tronçon of turbot with saffron noodles, trompette de la mort, baby leeks and sun-dried tomatoes.

Civil licence: 90
Accommodation: 53 rooms (53 en suite) ★★★★
Directions: Telephone for directions

England

The Lime Tree

Exposed beams, a huge fireplace and lots of wine bottles add character to this traditional hotel restaurant. Set in a 14th-century building in the square of the village, its menu is heavily influenced by its proximity to France: dishes include Tournedos Rossini, carré d'agneau and steak de sanglier.

Additional: Sunday L. Bar food L. Children welcome
Seats: 65. Private dining room 20
Style: Classic, French
Smoking: No smoking in dining room
Accommodation: 10 rooms (10 en suite)
Directions: Off A20. 8 miles from M20 J8

8-10 The Limes,
The Square, ME17 2PL
Tel: 01622 859509
Fax: 01622 850096
Chef(s): Colum Cluskey
Owner(s): Musa & Anita Kivrak
Cost: Alc £27, set price L £27-£35/ D £27. H/wine £14
Times: Noon-2.30pm/6.30-10pm.
Closed L Sat & Mon, D Sun

SANDWICH

Fishermans Wharf   NEW

The Quay, CT13 9RU
Tel: 01304 613636
Fax: 01304 620707
e fishwharf@aol.com
Chef(s): Nigel Bull
Owner(s): The Ash Family
Cost: Alc £25, set price D £14.95.
☺ ☺ H/wine £9.50
Times: Noon-2.30pm/6.30-9.30pm.
Additional: Sunday L. Bar food.
Children welcome
Seats: 50
Style: Rustic, Formal
Smoking: No-smoking area; no cigars
Directions: On river's edge, next to toll bridge. Parking is adjacent to quay

An old wharfside building overlooking the River Stour offering a choice of dining venues. Informal downstairs brasserie and terrace and a first floor restaurant featuring a short, imaginative *carte* favouring fresh fish and seafood. From seafood chowder with pesto and grilled scallops with soy and ginger, main dishes may include hot fish and seafood platter for two, sea bass with potato confit and sweet onion marmalade, and roast lamb fillet with Puy lentils on carrot and parsnip mash.

SEVENOAKS   Map 5 TQ55

Royal Oak Hotel

Flint-fronted hotel with a refurbished bar and bistro (No 5) decorated in butterscotch yellow and furnished with sturdy wicker chairs. Specialities include robust offerings such as eggs Benedict, sausage and mash with onion rings, and Caesar salad with grilled chicken. Salmon fishcakes on wilted leaves with roast pepper dressing won special praise.

Style: Modern, Minimalist
Smoking: No cigars; Air conditioning
Accommodation: 37 rooms (37 en suite) ★ ★ ★
Directions: M25 J5; at far end of High Street, opposite Sevenoaks school, walking distance from the town centre

Upper High Street, TN13 1HY
Tel: 01732 451109
Fax: 01732 740187
e info@royaloak.demon.co.uk
Chef(s): Mark Belsey
Owner(s): Brock Hotels Plc
Cost: Alc £24, set price L £14.95/ D £21.95. ☺ ☺ H/wine £11.95
Times: Noon-2.30pm/6-10pm.
Additional: Sunday L. Bar food.
Children welcome
Seats: 100. Private dining room 20

England

SISSINGHURST

Map 5 TQ73

Rankins

A husband and wife operation with a relaxed ambience. In a rustic and cosy atmosphere (Kent weather-board and slate roof) weekly menus and Sunday lunch follow a sensible fixed-price policy without supplements except for the coffee selection. To start, Rankins Smokie features haddock in creamy lemon sauce glazed with Cheddar. To follow choose from lamb loin noisettes with roast garlic and tarragon gravy or Loch Fyne salmon with mussel choucroute and parsley cream sauce. Desserts include coffee fudge pudding and prune-and-Armagnac fool.

Directions: Village centre, on A262 (Ashford)

The Street, TN17 2JH
Tel: 01580 713964
Chef(s): Hugh Rankin
Owner(s): Hugh & Leonora Rankin
Cost: Alc £30, set price L £23/D £28. H/wine £10
Times: 12.30-1.30pm/7.30-9.00pm. Closed Mon, Tue, L Wed-Sat, D Sun, BHs
Additional: Children welcome. Vegetarian by request only
Seats: 25
Style: French, Rustic
Smoking: No smoking in dining room

SITTINGBOURNE

Map 5 TQ96

Hempstead House

Large conservatory restaurant, appointed in a formal style with crystal chandeliers and housed within a Victorian country house. Dishes include locally smoked trout mousse wrapped in smoked salmon and served with a salad of cucumber or hot smoked duck breast carved over a parsnip purée with sherry sultana jus.

London Road, Bapchild, ME9 9PP
Tel: 01795 428020
Fax: 01795 436362
🄴 info@hempsteadhouse.co.uk
Chef(s): Stuart George
Owner(s): Mr & Mrs A J Holdstock
Cost: Alc £23.50, set price L £15.50/D £19.50. ☺ ☺ H/wine £10.95
Times: Noon-2pm/7-10pm. Closed Sun
Additional: Children welcome
Seats: 70. Private dining room 20
Style: Classic, Country House
Smoking: No smoking in dining room
Civil licence: 70
Accommodation: 14 rooms (14 en suite)
Directions: 1.5m E of Sittingbourne on A2

(ROYAL) TUNBRIDGE WELLS

Map 5 TQ53

Hotel du Vin & Bistro

As a private residence this impressive sandstone building was favoured by the young Queen Victoria. Maybe she'd have been amused by the more recent combination of such fine surroundings with the seriously good cooking now on offer in the bistro style restaurant. Wine ephemera is ubiquitous to the extent of wine-crate bread boards but such novelties do not detract from the serious approach to food demonstrated, for example, by full-flavoured corn fed chicken with wild mushrooms and fondant potato. An exemplary chocolate fondant dessert yielded a rich, velvet chocolate centre and came with a rich pistachio ice cream.

Accommodation: 32 rooms (32 en suite) ★ ★ ★ ★
Directions: Telephone for directions

Crescent Road, TN1 2LY
Tel: 01892 526455
Fax: 01892 512044
🄴 reception@tunbridgewells. hotelduvin.co.uk
Chef(s): Graham Ball
Owner(s): Mr P Chittick
Cost: Alc £25. ☺ ☺ H/wine £11
Times: Noon-1.45pm/7-9.30pm
Additional: Sunday L. Children welcome
Seats: 80. Private dining room 70
Style: Bistro
Smoking: No cigars

England

Right on the Green

15 Church Road, Southborough,
TN4 0RX
Tel: 01892 513161
Fax: 01892 513161
Chef(s): Peter Bruschi
Owner(s): Paula Black, Peter Bruschi
Cost: Set price L £13.95-£16.95/
D £21.95-£27.50. ☺ ☺
H/wine £12.95
Times: Noon-2pm/7-9.30pm.
Closed Sun-Mon, L Tue, Fri, Sat
Additional: Children welcome
Seats: 32. Private dining room 16
Style: French
Smoking: No-smoking area; no cigars

Light, airy restaurant with an air of style and refinement appropriate to its Tunbridge Wells location. The menu is classically French, with some contemporary interpretations. New chef, Peter Bruschi, was Roux apprenticed and demonstrates his fluency in dishes such as chicken boudrain, halibut in mustard grain sauce and navarin of lamb. Flavours have real depth and balance, and meals are presented with impressive technical skill. Desserts such as a 'superb' chocolate tart or stuffed baked apples in caramel sauce round off a satisfying dining experience, enhanced by attentive and relaxed service

Directions: From A21 take A265. Restaurant 2 miles on R, next to antiques shop

Royal Wells Inn

Mount Ephraim, TN4 8BE
Tel: 01892 511188
Fax: 01892 511908
e info@royalwells.co.uk
Chef(s): Robert Sloan
Owner(s): R & D Sloan
Cost: Alc £23.25, set price L £12/
D £23.25. ☺ ☺ H/wine £10.20
Times: 12.30-2.15pm/7.30-10pm.
Closed Sun-Mon, 25-26 Dec,1 Jan
Additional: Sunday L. Bar food.
Children welcome
Seats: 30. Private dining room
Style: Classic, Victorian Conservatory
Civil licence: 50

Frequented in the 19th-century by a young princess Victoria, this family-run hotel includes a first floor conservatory restaurant with stunning views of Tunbridge Wells common. The menu draws ideas from places as diverse as Britain, Thailand, France and the Mediterranean: a meal might include warm crispy duck salad with aromatic dressing, followed by slow cooked daube of beef in red wine with shallots, mushrooms and pancetta. Desserts range from American cheesecake to creme brûlée. A well priced, interesting wine list and cheerful service complete a happy picture.

Accommodation: 18 rooms (18 en suite) ★ ★ ★
Directions: 75yds from Jct of A21 & A264

England

(ROYAL) TUNBRIDGE WELLS *Continued*
Map 5 TQ53

Signor Franco

Tucked away on the first floor and accessed by a stairway lined with celebrity photos, this is a surprisingly stylish, airy restaurant (the curved front wall of windows came from a conservatory in Hever castle). The Mediterranean cuisine might include fresh gnocchi in rich tomato sauce with melted mozzarella or fresh sardines baked in white wine, parsley and garlic.

Style: Classic, Italian
Smoking: No pipes; Air conditioning
Directions: Opposite Tunbridge Wells railway station

5a High Street, TN1 1UL
Tel: 01892 549199
Fax: 01892 541378
Chef(s): Giuseppe Miranda
Owner(s): Franco de Tommaso
Cost: Alc £25. ☺ ☺ H/wine £12.50
Times: 12.30-3pm/6.45-11pm.
Closed Sun, BHs
Additional: Children welcome
Seats: 70. Jacket and tie preferred

The Spa Hotel

This restaurant could never feel overcrowded: it is a huge, tall-windowed room with chandeliers sparkling from a distant ceiling. The menu favours classic British and French cooking, but also includes surprises such as artichoke soup with aubergine fritters or sea bass with crab, couscous and sweet and sour sauce. Lovely country house setting overlooking Tunbridge Wells.

Mount Ephraim, TN4 8XJ
Tel: 01892 520331
Fax: 01892 510575
🅔 info@spahotel.co.uk
Chef(s): Edward Heasman
Owner(s): Goring Family
Cost: Set price L £24/D £24. ☺ ☺ H/wine £10.75
Times: 12.30-2pm/7-9.30pm.
Closed L Sat
Additional: Sunday L. Bar food. Children welcome. Vegetarian by request only
Seats: 80. Private dining room 250
Style: Classic French
Smoking: No-smoking area; no pipes
Civil licence: 200
Accommodation: 71 rooms (71 en suite) ★ ★ ★
Directions: On A264 leaving Tunbridge Wells towards East Grinstead

The Tagore

Producing Pakhtoon cuisine in the Pantiles, the Tagore is the first restaurant of its kind in England and a cut above the general run of Indian eateries. It's an attractive venue in a Grade II listed building with a tented fabric ceiling on the ground floor and wooden beams on the first. Specialities of the house include koh-e-avadh, knuckles of lamb 'dum', cooked in their own juices with cardamon and saffron flavoured marrows; a mild murg keshari nazaqut of chicken cooked in a rich cashew sauce with saffron and cream, and a mouth tingling dakshin chammeen - prawns in fresh coconut milk with kerala.

Smoking: No smoking in dining room; Air conditioning
Directions: Telephone for directions

4 Neville Street, TN2 5SA
Tel: 01892 615100
Fax: 01892 549877
🅔 thetagore_i@hotmail.com
Chef(s): M. Rahman & N. Monie
Owner(s): Nur Monie
Cost: Alc £18, set price L £14.95/D £14.95. ☺ ☺ H/wine £10.95
Times: Noon-2.30pm/6-11pm.
Closed 25-26 Dec, 1 Jan
Additional: Sunday L. Children 6yrs+. Vegetarian by request only
Seats: 85. Private dining room 45
Style: Modern

Thackeray's House Restaurant

TN1 1EA
Tel: 01892 511921
Fax: 01892 511921
Telephone for further details

An elegant dining experience is all part of the service at this restaurant, and the best advice is to sit back and enjoy it. Game features heavily on the set menu in season, and a pâté of pheasant, venison and duck is a fine example of terrific kitchen skills. Roe deer haunch with port sauce, red cabbage and honey parsnips, pheasant breast with squash risotto and wild mushrooms, and best end of lamb with mustard and herb crust offer inviting alternatives and sharp apple tart with a superb crust should prove irresistible. Very attentive service.

WEST MALLING   Map 5 TQ65

The Swan   **NEW**

35 Swan Street, ME19 6JU
Tel: 01732 521910
Telephone for further details

Pub-like on the outside, it's a different story inside: a smart bar and separate restaurant in light wood and cream. Light lunch dishes with blackboard specials include crab tart, ceviche of salmon, and chicken with bubble and squeak. For dinner roast smoked haddock on potato hash with spinach and poached eggs is amongst the offerings.

WYE   Map 5 TR04

Wife of Bath Restaurant

4 Upper Bridge Street, TN25 5AF
Tel: 01233 812540
Fax: 01233 813630
e reservations@wifeofbath.com
Chef(s): Robert Hymers
Owner(s): John Morgan
Cost: Alc £27.35, set price L £15.25/D £25.75. ☺ H/wine £14.50
Times: Noon-2pm/7-10.30pm. Closed Sun & Mon, 1wk after Xmas
Additional: Children welcome. Vegetarian by request only
Seats: 50
Style: Country-house, Traditional
Smoking: No cigars
Accommodation: 6 rooms (5 en suite)
Directions: Just off A28 Ashford to Canterbury Road

Traditional but fresh décor - flagstones, yellow walls and cast iron candleholders - hint at the style of the menu, which includes many classics but also delights in adding modern, international touches: sea bass might come on a bed of ratatouille; duck with a green peppercorn and tomato salsa. Imaginative, good quality food.

England

LANCASHIRE

ACCRINGTON
Map 7 SD72

Dunkenhalgh Hotel

A historic country house set back from the road in attractive grounds. Imaginative menus blend classical technique with modern ideas to produce skilfully-crafted dishes. Goats' cheese with toasted brioche, roasted lamb shank with Puy lentils, and chocolate and orange brûlée constitute a typical meal. Imaginative vegetarian choices on the balanced menu.

Blackburn Road, Clayton-le-Moors, BB5 5JP
Tel: 01254 398021
Fax: 01254 872230
Telephone for further details

BLACKBURN
Map 7 SD62

Millstone Hotel

Church Lane, Mellor, BB2 7JR
Tel: 01254 813333
Fax: 01254 812628
Telephone for further details

An inviting stone-built former coaching inn in a peaceful village offering a variety of meal options. Relax in the informal, cosy restaurant, where the small menu might include tempura king prawns, and roast monkfish and ham with pea purée, olive mash and balsamic dressing. Lemon tart with raspberry sauce is a typical dessert.

BLACKPOOL
Map 7 SD33

Kwizeen

47-49 Kings Street, FY1 3EJ
Tel: 01253 290045
Chef(s): Marco Calle Calatayud
Owner(s): Marco Calle-Calatayud, Antony Boswick
Cost: *Alc* £19.50, set price L £9.25/ D £12.50. ☺ ☺ H/wine £9.50
Times: Noon-2pm/6-10.30pm. Closed Sun, Last 2 wks of Feb
Additional: Children welcome
Seats: 40
Style: Bistro-Style
Smoking: No cigars
Directions: Telephone for directions

Not surprisingly, this cheerful restaurant on a rather ordinary street has a great reputation locally. Inside it is beautiful in blue, and a modern menu plus daily specials offers black pudding with bubble and squeak, roasted sea bass with juniper and lemon glaze, and parsnip nut loaf with sweet chilli sauce. The restaurant also caters for functions.

CHIPPING
Map 7 SD64

Gibbon Bridge Hotel

Attractive traditionally styled restaurant with an adjoining conservatory affording views of the hotel's award-winning gardens that keep the kitchen supplied with fresh vegetables. A broad range of menus offer variety in some interesting combinations of flavours and old favourites like fillet of beef with a port sauce.

Style: Traditional, Country-House
Smoking: No smoking in dining room; Air conditioning
Civil licence: 180. **Accommodation:** 29 rooms (29 en suite)
Directions: In Chipping, R for Clitheroe, hotel 0.75m

Forest of Bowland, PR3 2TQ
Tel: 01995 61456
Fax: 01995 61277
e reception@gibbon-bridge.co.uk
Chef(s): Gary Buxton
Owner(s): Janet Simpson
Cost: Alc £27.50, set price L £11.75-£14/D £23.50. ☺ ☺ H/wine £12.50
Times: Noon-1.30pm/7-9pm
Additional: Sunday L.
Children welcome
Seats: 48. Private dining room 35

CHORLEY
Map 7 SD51

Shaw Hill Hotel

Expect all the trimmings at this grand Georgian mansion: canapés, home-made bread, 'great' petits fours and efficient, hospitable service. The menus are thorough, too: a wide choice of dishes, often French and British in style, cater for most tastes, ranging from sirloin steak to king prawn ravioli broth. If you like golf, you'll love the view.

Seats: 100. Private dining room 32
Style: Traditional, Country-house
Smoking: No smoking in dining room. **Civil licence:** 200
Accommodation: 30 rooms (30 en suite) ★ ★ ★
Directions: From Chorley on A6, then A49. At lights turn L past golf course, L to Dawson Lane. R at T-junction. Hotel 50yds on R

Preston Road, Whittle-le-Woods, PR6 7PP
Tel: 01257 269221
Fax: 01257 261223
e info@shaw-hill.co.uk
Chef(s): Paul Robinson
Owner(s): Mrs Tyrer
Cost: Alc £28, set price L £14.50-£16.50/D £18.50-£23.50. ☺ ☺
H/wine £10.50
Times: Noon-1.45pm/7-9.45pm.
Closed L Sat, 26 Dec & 1 Jan
Additional: Sunday L. Bar food.
Children welcome

LANGHO
Map 7 SD73

Northcote Manor

Northcote Road, Nr Blackburn, BB6 8BE
Tel: 01254 240555
Fax: 01254 246568
e admin@northcotemanor.com
Chef(s): Nigel Haworth, Warrick Dodds
Owner(s): Nigel Haworth & Craig Bancroft
Cost: Alc £42, set price L £16/D £25-£40. ☺ H/wine £14.50
Times: Noon-1.30pm/7-9.30pm.
Closed L Sat, 25 Dec, 1 Jan
Additional: Sunday L.
Children welcome
Seats: 80. Private dining room 40.
Jacket and tie preferred
Style: Modern, Chic
Smoking: No smoking in dining room

Rapidly approaching their twentieth year in dedication to excellence, the Nigel Haworth/Craig Bancroft partnership

England

LANGHO *Continued* Map 7 SD73 *Northcote Manor*

continues to put good food, fine wines and exceptional service at the top of its agenda. Yet beside its gastronomic achievements, the Manor remains equally praiseworthy for the quality and comfort of accommodation that is filled with the very best of warmth and hospitality. Nigel's cooking has gained a new lease of life in the vibrantly restyled restaurant, while Craig's passion is for food with matching wine combinations sourced from his remarkable cellar. Kitchen production is a regional joy: Morecambe Bay shrimps, Pendle lamb, Goosnargh duck and Mrs Kirkham's cheese soufflé sharing the limelight with pan-roast Scottish salmon with caramel sauce, breast of Radholme mallard with roast beetroot and celeriac samosas and roast banana tarte Tatin with black cardamom cream. An airy, high-ceilinged dining-room with sliding doors leading onto the gardens - with views to Pendle Hill and beyond - which echo the successful marriage of simplicity and style that continues to blossom.

Directions: From M6 J31 take A59, following signs for Clitheroe. L at first traffic light, onto Skipton/Clitheroe Rd for 9 miles. L into Northcote Rd, Hotel on R

Civil licence: 40
Accommodation: 14 rooms (14 en suite) ★ ★ ★

LONGRIDGE Map 7 SD63

Paul Heathcote's Restaurant

The only ingredient sometimes missing from this charming restaurant is Paul Heathcote himself, and nowadays he's just as likely to be found in a business suit as chef's whites. Otherwise the signature dishes which have gone on to be successful in the other Heathcote outlets are all here, along with local specialities like Goosnargh chicken, black pudding and Mrs Kirkham's Lancashire cheeses. A move back to basics results in quality fresh ingredients and ever clearer flavours, as in deep-fried stilton fritters with walnut dressing, braised shoulder of lamb with rosemary potatoes and green beans, and pan-fried fillet of red mullet on chive-crushed potatoes with sea asparagus. Don't miss Heathcote's bread and butter pudding with apricot compôte and clotted cream, or white and dark chocolate layered terrine with rum and muscovado ice cream. The converted cottage offers a high degree of elegance and comfort without losing the building's character, and service is polished.

⊛⊛⊛
104-106 Higher Road,
PR3 3SY
Tel: 01772 784969
Fax: 01772 785713
📧 longridge@heathcotes.co.uk
Chef(s): Paul Heathcote
Owner(s): Paul Heathcote
Cost: *Alc* £45, set price L £16.50/ D £38. ☺ H/wine £13.50
Times: noon-2pm/7-9.30pm. Closed Mon-Tue, L Sat, 1 Jan
Additional: Sunday L. Children welcome
Seats: 60. Private dining room 18
Style: Modern
Smoking: No-smoking area; no pipes
Directions: Follow signs for Golf Club & Jeffrey Hill. Higher Rd is beside White Bull Pub in Longridge

LYTHAM ST ANNES

Map 7 SD32

Greens Bistro

NEW

3/9 St Andrews Road,
St Annes On Sea, FY8 1SX

Lurking in this cellar is a rustic, stone floored restaurant full of cosy alcoves in which to enjoy the bistro style food. It's a relaxing setting, with 'excellent' service. The weekly changing menu lends a modern touch to many old favourites: dishes might include Scottish rib eye steak with basil ratatouille and French fries or noisettes of lamb with roasted vegetable tart and basil mash. Desserts such as banana crème brûlée with home-made cookies reveal the same ability to combine originality with accessibility. Ingredients are seasonal, fresh and bought locally wherever possible.

Tel: 01253 789990
Fax: 01253 789908
e info@greensbistro.co.uk
Chef(s): Paul Webster
Owner(s): Paul Webster
Cost: *Alc* £19, set price L £7.50/D £12.50. ☺ ☺ H/wine £9.95
Times: Noon-2.30pm/6-10pm. Closed Sun, Mon, L Sat, BHs, 24 Dec
Additional: Children welcome. **Seats:** 38
Style: Modern, Bistro-Style
Directions: Telephone for directions

Q brasserie

5 Henry Street, FY8 5LE
Tel: 01253 733124
Fax: 01253 733326
e info@qbrasserie.co.uk
Chef(s): Giles Heywood
Cost: *Alc* £30, set price L £10/D £10. ☺ ☺ H/wine £10
Times: noon-3pm/6-11.30pm. Closed Mon, D Sun, Dec 25 & Jan 1

Modish and Mediterranean offering simple food with clean flavours. Marble topped tables and light wood chairs sit happily in the building's Victorian structure. Main courses include braised lamb leg shank, creamed potato, with rosemary gravy, and a daily selection of fresh fish and seafood (delivered each morning).

Additional: Sunday L. Children welcome
Seats: 74. Private dining room 20. **Style:** Modern, Minimalist
Smoking: No-smoking area; no cigars; Air conditioning
Directions: Town centre

PRESTON

Map 7 SD52

Simply Heathcotes

23 Winckley Square, PR1 3JJ
Tel: 01772 252732
Fax: 01772 203433
e preston@simplyheathcotes.co.uk

Light and contemporary restaurant with a correspondingly fresh and direct approach to food. The à la *carte* menu offers

PRESTON *Continued*   Map 7 SD52

starters along the lines of cream of wild mushroom soup, butternut squash risotto with Gorgonzola and walnuts and spiced tartar of salmon with crème fraîche and avocado. Main courses present good fresh ingredients in simple but well thought out combinations - pan fried fillet of seabass with pumpkin and spring onion, breast of Goosnarch duckling with celeriac, potato and chorizo for example. Desserts might include dark chocolate and mint marquise with almond wafers and blackberry sorbet, chilled chestnut creams with poached mulled plums.

Directions: Town centre

Chef(s): Matt Nugent
Owner(s): Paul Heathcote
Cost: Alc £25, set price L £11.50-£13.50/D £11.50-£13.50. ☺ ☺
H/wine £11.50
Times: noon-2.30pm/7-10pm.
Closed L Sat, Xmas
Additional: Bar food L.
Children welcome
Seats: 140
Style: Modern, Minimalist
Smoking: Air conditioning

WRIGHTINGTON   Map 7 SD51

High Moor Inn

A smart restaurant in a 17th-century moorland inn. The oak-beamed restaurant has a cosy atmosphere. There is plenty of choice on the menu and roast loin of lamb in a herb crust on buttered spinach, with a paprika and lemon sauce and boulangère potato, or marinated salmon with spiced couscous and sour cream, are among the favourites.

Directions: M6 J27, follow sign to Parbold, after hospital turn R into Robin Hood Lane, 1st L into High Moor Lane

🏵
Highmoor Lane, WN6 9QA
Tel: 01257 252364
Fax: 01257 255120
Chef(s): Thomas Lowe
Cost:, set price L £11.50/D £14. ☺ ☺
Times: Noon-2pm/5.30-10pm.
Closed Mon, L Sat, 26 Dec, 1 Jan
Additional: Bar food L. Children welcome
Style: Rustic, Traditional

Wrightington Hotel

See WIGAN, Greater Manchester

The Mulberry Tree   NEW

Up in the Lancashire hills, this pub is one of the best kept secrets in the area. The restaurant is spacious and airy with framed menus on the cream walls, and serves up some excellent gastropub style food. Saffron risotto with chargrilled vegetables and Parmesan shavings is singled out for particular praise. Sturdy mains along the lines of confit of rabbit with slow roast pork belly with apple sauce are matched by similarly robust puds (bread and butter pud with apricot sauce for example).

Directions: Situated 4 miles from Wigan. From M6 J27 towards Parbold, take immediate R after motorway exit, by BP garage into Mossy Lea Rd. On R after 2 miles

🏵
Wrightington Bar, WN6 9SE
Tel: 01257 451400
Fax: 01257 451400
Chef(s): Mark Prescott
Owner(s): Mr M Prescott & Mr J Moore
Cost: Alc £24. ☺ ☺ H/wine £9.50
Times: noon-2pm/6-10pm.
Closed Mon, 26 Dec-1 Jan
Additional: Sunday L. Bar food.
Children welcome
Seats: 60
Style: Classic, Modern
Smoking: No smoking in dining room

LEICESTERSHIRE

England

CASTLE DONINGTON
Map 8 SK42

The Priest House on the River

Kings Mills, DE74 2RR
Tel: 01332 810649
Telephone for further details

An historic hotel nestling in a picturesque riverside setting. There's a modern British flair to dishes like haddock terrine, and guinea fowl and wild mushroom casserole. The menu offers a good range of imaginative choices, with an emphasis on presentation, though desserts may be limited to sorbets and terrines. An interesting wine list.

HINCKLEY
Map 4 SP49

Sketchley Grange

Sketchley Lane, Burbage, LE10 3HU
Tel: 01455 251133
Fax: 01455 631384
e sketchleygrange@btinternet.com
Chef(s): David Grindrod
Owner(s): N. Downes
Cost: Alc £30, set price L £13.95/ D £23.95. ☺ ☺ H/wine £11.95
Times: 12.30-2.30pm/7-10pm. Closed Mon, L Sat, D Sun
Additional: Sunday L. Children welcome
Seats: 80. Private dining room 40. Jacket and tie preferred
Style: Modern
Smoking: No smoking in dining room; Air conditioning
Civil licence: 200
Accommodation: 55 rooms (55 en suite) ★ ★ ★
Directions: From M69 J1 take B4109. Straight on 1st rdbt, L at mini-rdbt & immediately R into Sketchley Lane. Hotel at end of lane

There are panoramic views of the landscaped gardens from this country house hotel restaurant, while candle lamps and soothing colours offer a peaceful dining experience. Anglo-French in style, the menu might offer crispy confit of duck with Parmesan crackers, mizuna leaves and plum syrup, and roast saddle of rabbit with pommery mustard tagliatelle and buttered leeks.

KEGWORTH
Map 8 SK42

Best Western Yew Lodge

Packington Hill, DE74 2DF
Tel: 01509 672518
Fax: 01509 674730
e info@yewlodgehotel.co.uk
Chef(s): Roger Webb
Owner(s): Jeremy Pick
Cost: Alc £25, set price L £14-£20/ D £20-£30. ☺ ☺ H/wine £11.75
Times: Noon-2pm/6.30-9.30pm
Additional: Sunday L. Bar food. Children welcome
Seats: 80. Private dining room 150
Style: Traditional, Country-house

Interesting dishes from a choice of menus at this smart modern restaurant - an L-shaped room with superb views over the surrounding countryside, and well-spaced tables attractively set with colourful plates and blue glass. Menus encompass chargrilled Tay salmon with lemongrass butter, and Dales lamb with wild mushrooms, potato rösti and redcurrant jus.

Smoking: No smoking in dining room; Air conditioning
Civil licence: 130
Accommodation: 63 rooms (63 en suite) ★ ★ ★
Directions: Exit M1 J24, follow signs Loughborough & Kegworth on A6. At bottom of hill take 1st R into Packington Hill. Hotel 400yds on R

England

LEICESTER

Map 4 SK50

Belmont Hotel

De Montfort Street, LE1 7GR
Tel: 0116 254 4773
Fax: 0116 247 0804

Two eating venues are offered at this town-centre hotel, the bistro and Cherry's Restaurant, named after the daughter of the house. The latter - recently refurbished and very smart - is accessed by an attractive conservatory walkway. Expect the likes of a huge tuna steak (perfectly cooked and accurately seasoned) and an assiette of chocolate with a tart fondant and a creditable mousse.

e info@belmonthotel.co.uk
Chef(s): Stephan Fitzpatrick
Owner(s): The Bowie Family
Cost: Alc £25. ☺ ☺ H/wine £11.95
Times: 12.30-2pm/7-10pm. Closed L Sat, D Sun, BHs Mondays
Additional: Sunday L. Bar food L. Children welcome
Seats: 65. Private dining room 30
Style: Classic, Town-House
Smoking: No smoking in dining room; Air conditioning
Civil licence: 120
Accommodation: 78 rooms (78 en suite) ★★★
Directions: M1 J21/A6. From Railway station, 1st R off A6 Southbound

The Tiffin

The formal layout of The Tiffin is more like a brasserie than a traditional Asian restaurant. Well known dishes are given uncommon care and attention. Tandoori chicken comes thoroughly marinated to produce a 'superb' flavour and the quality of meat in a lamb Madras is excellent.

1 De Montfort Street,
LE1 7GE
Tel: 0116 247 0420
Fax: 0116 255 3737
Chef(s): Mohammed Ali
Owner(s): Previn Parmar
Cost: Alc £18/D £18. ☺ ☺
H/wine £8
Times: Noon-2pm/6-11pm.
Closed Sun, L Sat, Xmas, New Year,
L BHs
Additional: Children welcome
Seats: 60. Private dining room 50.
Jacket and tie preferred
Style: Classical, Chic
Smoking: No smoking in dining room;
Air conditioning
Directions: Near railway station on the corner of De Mountfort Street and Londond Road (A6)

Watsons Restaurant & Bar   NEW

More London than Leicester, this swish modern restaurant has airy wooden-floored rooms, modern paintings and cacti on the tables. Service is anything but prickly. The menu offers an interesting selection of salads, grills and side dishes as well as

5-9 Upper Brown Street, LE1 5TE
Tel: 0116 222 7770
Fax: 0116 222 7771
Chef(s): John Molnar
Owner(s): Graeme Watson

main courses such as roast monkfish with sag aloo or chicken breast with oriental greens and soy butter sauce.

Cost: *Alc* £25, set price L £11. ☺ ☺
H/wine £9
Times: noon-2.30pm/7-10.30pm.
Closed Sun, BHs, 10 days at Xmas
Additional: Children welcome
Seats: 80
Style: Modern, Chic
Smoking: No cigars; Air conditioning
Directions: City centre of Leicester, next to Phoenix Arts Theatre

---

MARKET HARBOROUGH · Map 4 SP78

Three Swans Hotel

Extended former coaching inn located in the town centre with a formal restaurant providing attentive and professional service. The *carte* is strong on classical dishes, while the fixed-price dinner menu offers more innovative choices, perhaps sautéed fillets of chicken on a nest of Puy lentils, topped with a sauce of mango and mushrooms, spiced with a hint of curry.

Style: Traditional, International
Smoking: No smoking in dining room; Air conditioning
Civil licence: 150
Accommodation: 61 rooms (61 en suite) ★ ★ ★
Directions: Follow High Street S through town centre; hotel is on R at traffic lights

21 High Street, LE16 7NJ
Tel: 01858 466644
Fax: 01858 433101
e sales@threeswans.co.uk
Chef(s): Richard Payne
Cost: *Alc* £35, set price L £13.95/
D £19.95-£22.15. ☺ ☺
H/wine £10.95
Times: Noon-2.15pm/7-10pm.
Closed D Sun
Additional: Sunday L. Bar food.
Children welcome
Seats: 76. Private dining room 50.
Jacket and tie preferred

MELTON MOWBRAY · Map 8 SK71

Stapleford Park

A truly grand setting for a meal. This magnificent stately home stands in 500 acres of parkland originally designed by Capability Brown. Its restaurant is sumptously decorated with sparkling chandeliers, gold walls and 17th-century carved borders by Grinling Gibbons. A meal might begin with canapés offered on a tray in the bar, followed by an amuse bouche such as gravadlax of salmon. The menu changes daily and provides an interesting mix of classic and modern British cooking - perhaps dressed crab with scallop tempura and mango salsa followed by peppered Gressingham duck with truffle oil mash and foie gras.

Civil licence: 200
Accommodation: 51 rooms (51 en suite) ★ ★ ★ ★
Directions: Follow Melton ring road A607 (Grantham) onto B676, 4 miles turn R signposted Stapleford

Stapleford, LE14 2EF
Tel: 01572 787522
Fax: 01572 787651
e reservations@stapleford.co.uk
Chef(s): Geoff Balharrie
Owner(s): Peter de Savary,
Carnegie Clubs
Cost: *Alc* £46/D £46-£50.
H/wine £18
Times: Noon-2.30pm/7.30-9.30pm
(Booking essential)
Additional: Sunday L. Bar food
(Booking essential). Children 12yrs+
Seats: 60. Private dining room 190.
Jacket and tie preferred
Style: Classic, Country-house
Smoking: No smoking in dining room

England

QUORN
Map 8 SK51

Quorn Country Hotel

Four acres of landscaped grounds welcome diners to this pleasant hotel with two restaurant areas: the intimate Shires and the conservatory style Orangery. The set priced and à la *carte* menus offer a good range of high quality dishes ranging from the fairly traditional (noisettes of lamb cooked on a skillet and served with pea and mint puree and a redcurrant and rosemary sauce) to the more exotic (medallions of ostrich served with roast beetroot in balsamic and red onion compôte finished with red wine sauce).

Charnwood House, 66 Leicester Road, LE12 8BB
Tel: 01509 415050
Fax: 01509 415557
📧 quorncountryhotel@virgin.net
Chef(s): David Wilkinson
Owner(s): Mr Walshe
Cost: *Alc* £32.50, set price L £18.50/D £22.50-£25. ☺ ☺ H/wine £12.95
Times: Noon-2.30pm/7-9.30pm. Closed L Sat
Additional: Sunday L. Bar food. Children welcome
Seats: 112. Private dining room 120
Style: Country House, Modern
Civil licence: 120
Accommodation: 23 rooms (23 en suite) ★★★★
Directions: M1 J23/A6 towards Leicester, follow signs for Quorn

LINCOLNSHIRE

BELTON
Map 8 SK93

Belton Woods Hotel

The Manor Restaurant is the fine dining option at this smart establishment and overlooks the hotel's own golf courses. Dishes are well executed and service attentive. Expect the likes of king scallops with tomato, chilli and streaky bacon; turbot in a chervil and tomato nage, and brioche bread and butter pudding with vanilla sauce.

Style: Country-house, Traditional
Smoking: No smoking in dining room. **Civil licence:** 60
Accommodation: 136 rooms (136 en suite) ★★★★
Directions: 2 miles on A1 to Grantham, then A607 to Belton

NG32 2LN
Tel: 01476 593200
Fax: 01476 574547
📧 devere.belton@airtime.co.uk
Chef(s): Paul Moore
Cost: Set price L £16.50/D £18.50. ☺ ☺ H/wine £12.50
Times: 12.30-2pm/7-10pm. Closed Sun, L Mon-Sat
Additional: Sunday L. Children welcome
Seats: 160. Private dining room 20

BOURNE
Map 8 TF02

Black Horse Inn

Originally a coaching inn, the Black Horse is more of a dining pub these days, set around three sides of a courtyard in a small village on the Lincolnshire-Rutland border. It comprises a beamed bar, cosy lounge and buttery restaurant with exposed stone walls and tapestry hangings. An essentially English menu ranges through roast lamb shank with Stilton dauphinoise and rosemary jus, pan-fried liver with red onion marmalade and sage beurre blanc, and roast monkfish with mussels and a light cream curried sauce.

Grimsthorpe,
PE10 0LY
Tel: 01778 591247
Fax: 01778 591373
📧 dme@blackhorseinn.co.uk
Chef(s): Brian Rey
Owner(s): Brian & Elaine Rey
Cost: *Alc* £23. ☺ ☺ H/wine £9.95
Times: Noon-2pm/7-9pm. Closed Mon (ex Bar food), D Sun

England

Smoking: No smoking in dining room
Accommodation: 6 rooms (5 en suite)
Directions: Follow A151 for 4 miles, west towards Grantham

Additional: Sunday L. Bar food.
Children 7 yrs+
Seats: 48. Private dining room 12
Style: Modern, Classic

BRANSTON   Map 8 TF06

Branston Hall   **NEW**

An imposing house with a suitably ambitious menu served in the lakeside restaurant. Imaginative handling of seared scallops with oriental vegetables and noodle broth, and fillet of lamb on Parmesan potatoes, with desserts like lime brûlée tart with caramelised limes, or chocolate and chestnut pudding, plus delicious filter coffee.

Seats: 75. Private dining room 28. **Style:** Formal, Country-house
Smoking: No smoking in dining room. **Civil licence:** 35
Accommodation: 45 rooms (45 en suite) ★ ★ ★

Branston Park, LN4 1PD
Tel: 01522 793305
Fax: 01522 790549
e brahal@enterprise.net
Chef(s): Miles Collins
Cost: Alc £22.50, set price L £13.95-£15.50/D £17.95-£35. ☺ ☺
H/wine £10.95
Times: Noon-2pm/7-9.30pm
Additional: Sunday L. Bar food.
Children 5yrs+ at D

CLEETHORPES   Map 8 TA30

Kingsway Hotel

Traditional and friendly establishment, with the added bonus of excellent views over the Humber Estuary. Pleasant surroundings coupled with professional service make for a thoroughly enjoyable experience. A pan-seared salmon fillet on a niçoise salad, served with a mustard dressing has been singled out for praise.

Seats: 85. Private dining room 24
Style: Traditional
Accommodation: 50 rooms (50 en suite) ★ ★ ★
Directions: At junction of A1098 and seafront

Kingsway, DN35 0AE
Tel: 01472 601122
Fax: 01472 601381
Chef(s): Guy Stevens
Owner(s): Mr J Harris
Cost: Alc £28, set price L £14.75/D £18.95. ☺ ☺ H/wine £10.75
Times: 12.30-1.45pm/7-9pm.
Closed 25-26 Dec
Additional: Sunday L. Bar food L.
Children 5yrs+. Vegetarian by request only

GRANTHAM   Map 8 SK93

Harry's Place

The front room of a private house is the extraordinary setting for this tiny restaurant, with only three tables seating up to ten people. The intimate dining room in a beautiful Georgian residence is a scene of great pride, as Caroline Hallam welcomes and attends to guests while husband Harry creates his memorable dishes offstage. An equally tiny hand-written menu oozes quality and ingenuity, opening with bread straight from the oven, and delicate canapés to set the taste buds

17 High Street,
Great Gonerby, NG31 8JS
Tel: 01476 561780
Chef(s): Harry Hallam
Owner(s): Harry & Caroline Hallam
Cost: Alc £47.50. H/wine £20
Times: 12.30pm-2pm/7pm-9.30pm.
Closed Sun & Mon, 25-26 Dec
& BHs

England

GRANTHAM *Continued*

Map 8 SK93

popping. Lightly seared Orkney scallops with chilled spicy marinade and julienne of red pepper and orange was a recent knock-out starter, while fillet of turbot with a sauce of white wine, lentils, basil and coriander hits all the right spots. The culinary magic continues with Sao Tome chocolate mousse, with an added scoop of prune and Armagnac ice cream as a special treat. Unsurprisingly perhaps, the coffee is rich and smooth.

Additional: Children 5yrs+. Vegetarian by request only
Seats: 10
Style: Country-house
Smoking: No smoking in dining room
Directions: 2m N W of Grantham on B1174

GRIMSBY

Map 8 TA21

Harvey's Restaurant   NEW   ◎◎

On Thursday and Saturday evenings this popular coffee house and lunch venue transforms into a fine dining experience. The setting is warm and inviting, with pastel shades, soft lighting and a caring hostess. Weekly changing menus reveal a chef well versed in the classics but happy to add the odd modern twist: dishes might include an 'excellent' duck breast with honey and strawberry sauce, or beef fillet with garlic mash, crispy parsnips and port glaze. Vegetables are done just so, and the pace doesn't falter at dessert, where treats such as a 'superb' rich chocolate tart round off the meal in style. The wine list is good, too.

2 Louth Road, Scartho,
DN33 2EN
Tel: 01472 750560
Chef(s): Paul & Sarah Harvey
Owner(s): Mr & Mrs P Harvey
Cost: *Alc* £30, set price L £11.50-£20.50/D £24.50-£35.50. ☺ ☺
H/wine £9.35
Times: 10am-4pm/7-9pm.
Closed Sun, Mon, D Tues-Wed,
1 wk in Xmas
Additional: Bar food L. Children welcome
Seats: 24. Jacket and tie preferred
Style: Modern, Classic

Smoking: No smoking in dining room
Directions: A16. 1.5 miles S of Grimsby, in centre of Scartho

HORNCASTLE

Map 8 TF26

Magpies Restaurant   ◎◎

Inside this little row of black and white cottages is a collection of low-ceilinged rooms with modern décor and well spaced tables. It's a friendly, informal place to dine, popular with locals and drawing customers from a wide area. The no frills menu delivers classical British and French cooking of a consistently high standard: a starter of scallops with caviar velouté might be followed by lamb shank with creamy celeriac purée and a Madeira jus. Ingredients are good quality and local where possible. The staff comprise two brothers in the kitchen and relaxed, attentive waitresses.

71-75 East Street,
LN9 6AA
Tel: 01507 527004
Fax: 01507 524064
e magpies@fsbdial.co.uk
Chef(s): Matthew & Simon Lee
Owner(s): The Lee family
Cost: Set price L £12/D £22. ☺ ☺
H/wine £12
Times: 12.30-2.30pm/7-10pm.
Closed Mon-Tue, L Wed-Sat, D Sun,
3 wks Aug
Additional: Sunday L. Children welcome. Vegetarian by request only

Seats: 40. Private dining room 8
Style: Traditional. **Smoking:** No smoking in dining room
Directions: 0.5m from town centre on A158 toward Skegness

LINCOLN

Map 8 SK97

Castle Hotel   ◎

Medieval themed restaurant but, fortunately, without the wassailing. Dishes such as pigeon breast with a light pastry case and wild mushrooms have won praise on a menu that offers some good seafood options as well as local game.

Additional: Bar food. Children 7yrs+. Vegetarian not available
Seats: 40. Private dining room 4. **Style:** Traditional
Smoking: No smoking in dining room
Accommodation: 20 rooms (20 en suite) ★ ★
Directions: Follow signs for 'Historic Lincoln'. Hotel is at NE corner of castle

Westgate, LN1 3AS
Tel: 01522 538801
Fax: 01522 575457
e knights@castlehotel.net
Chef(s): Sherry Brown,
Bob Parkinson, Allison Burge
Owner(s): Sherry &
Malcolm Brown
Cost: *Alc* £22. ☺ H/wine £9.50
Times: Dinner only, 7-midnight

England

Jew's House

Snug restaurant within the historic stone walls of the Jew's House, completed in 1160. The menus offer various options on price, and diners can choose from the *carte* or a fixed-priced menu of two, three or four courses. Good home-made bread and very fresh fish are strong points (monkfish, served with a tangy saffron sauce for example).

Seats: 26. Private dining room 12
Style: Classic, Traditional
Smoking: No smoking in dining room
Directions: Town centre, At bottom of steep hill from the Cathedral

15 The Strait, LN2 1JD
Tel: 01522 524851
Fax: 01522 520084
Chef(s): Richard Gibbs
Owner(s): Mr & Mrs Gibbs
Cost: *Alc* £25, set price L £12.50-£15/D £22.50-£29.50. ☺ ☺
H/wine £11.50
Times: Noon-1.30pm/7-9pm.
Closed Sun, Mon, Xmas, New Year, BHs
Additional: Children welcome

Wig & Mitre

Well established in its new premises, the Wig & Mitre is an intriguing mixture of 14th-century, 16th-century and new build. The cosy main restaurant has skylight ventilation and striking views of the cathedral towers and castle walls. Spicy crab cakes, full flavoured confit of duck and a creamy rice pudding with stewed apricots have won praise.

30-32 Steep Hill,
LN2 1TL
Tel: 01522 535190
Fax: 01522 532402
e reservations@wigandmitre.co.uk
Chef(s): P Vidic, P Dodd
Owner(s): Mr M & Mrs V Hope,
Paul Vidic
Cost: *Alc* £22.50, set price L £9-£12.
☺ ☺ H/wine £10.45
Times: 8am-Midnight
Additional: Sunday L. Bar food.
Children welcome
Seats: 65. Private dining room 20
Style: Bistro Style, Traditional
Smoking: No smoking in dining room
Directions: Adjacent to Lincoln Catherdral, and Lincoln castle car park, at the top of Steep Hill

LOUTH   Map 8 TF38

Kenwick Park

Superb health and leisure facilities have turned this Georgian hotel into the ideal 'getaway' location. Tennis, golf, and swimming in the indoor pool are just some of the attractions, but the key to an agreeable stay here is in the restaurant, where some very capable cooking is created from quality ingredients. Choose from the *carte*, or a brief set menu where smoked salmon and brie bruschetta might be followed by seared noisettes of English lamb with an acacia honey and thyme jus. Finish with the likes of brandy snap basket with caramel ice cream and bitter chocolate sauce, while watching the golf outside.

Smoking: No smoking in dining room
Civil licence: 70
Accommodation: 34 rooms (34 en suite) ★ ★ ★
Directions: From A157 follow signs for Mablethorpe & Manby, 2 miles from Louth

Kenwick Park, LN11 8NR
Tel: 01507 608806
Fax: 01507 608027
e enquiries@kenwick-park.co.uk
Chef(s): Mark Vines
Owner(s): Mr S Flynn
Cost: *Alc* £38, set price L £18.50-£26.95/D £18.50-£26.95. ☺ ☺
H/wine £10.95
Times: Noon-2pm/7-9.30pm
Additional: Sunday L. Bar food.
Children welcome
Seats: 36. Private dining room 25.
Jacket and tie preferred
Style: Modern, Formal

England

SCUNTHORPE
Map 8 SE81

Forest Pines Hotel

As you might expect, pine trees are a major feature in the well tended grounds of this large, quality hotel with rockeries and ponds adding further interest to the view from the very elegant restaurant. Lovely presentation is coupled with good, strong flavours in dishes such as veal served on impressively light pasta.

Ermine Street, Broughton, DN20 0AQ
Tel: 01652 650770
Fax: 01652 650495
e enquiries@forestpines.co.uk
Chef(s): Graham Malia
Owner(s): Mr D & Mr A Middleton
Cost: Alc £29, set price L £17.25/ D £21.50. ☺ ☺ H/wine £8.65
Times: Noon-2pm/7-10pm
Additional: Sunday L. Bar food. Children welcome
Seats: 80. Private dining room 60. Jacket and tie preferred
Style: Traditional
Smoking: No smoking in dining room; Air conditioning
Civil licence: 300
Accommodation: 86 rooms (86 en suite) ★ ★ ★ ★
Directions: From M180 J4, at rdbt take 1st exit towards Scunthorpe. Take 2nd exit at next rdbt. Hotel on L

SPALDING
Map 8 TF22

Cley Hall

A fine Georgian manor house with a smart restaurant overlooking the gardens. 'Fine dining' menus are supplemented by daily fish specials, all with a traditional international flavour. Amongst the starters could be oak-smoked breast of chicken on Thai noodles with sesame and sweet chilli sauce, followed by pan-fried salmon fillet on crab potato cake with saffron butter sauce.

Style: Country-house
Smoking: No smoking in dining room
Civil licence: 30
Accommodation: 12 rooms (12 en suite) ★ ★
Directions: At junction off A151 & A16 (Macdonald's rdbt) take turn for Spalding. Hotel is further 1.5miles

22 High Street, PE11 1TX
Tel: 01775 725157
Fax: 01775 710785
e cleyhall@enterprise.net
Chef(s): Roy Macfarlane
Owner(s): Mr & Mrs Mowat
Cost: Alc £24.50/D £22.50. ☺ ☺ H/wine £8.95
Times: Noon-2.30pm/6.45-9.30pm
Additional: Sunday L. Bar food. Children welcome. Vegetarian by request only
Seats: 60. Private dining room 10.

STAMFORD
Map 8 TF00

George of Stamford

Vigorous cooking served in the well-dressed restaurant of a very British hotel, with summer dining in the courtyard. Good use is made of local produce, and main courses might comprise 'excellent' beef with leeks, a smoked bacon rösti and a shallot jus. Puddings arrive on the trolley in the traditional way.

Seats: 90. Private dining room 40. Jacket and tie preferred
Style: Traditional, Formal.
Smoking: No cigars.
Civil licence: 50
Accommodation: 47 rooms (47 en suite) ★ ★ ★
Directions: From A1 take roundabout signposted B1081. Follow road to 1st set of traffic lights, the hotel is on L

71 St Martins, PE9 2LB
Tel: 01780 750750
Fax: 01780 750701
e reservations@ georgehotelofstamford.com
Chef(s): Chris Pitman
Owner(s): Lawrence Hoskins
Cost: Alc £34, set price L £16.50-£17.50 H/wine £10.99
Times: Noon-2.30pm/7-10.30pm.
Additional: Sunday L. Children 10yrs+

WINTERINGHAM

Map 8 SE92

Winteringham Fields

🅰🅰🅰🅰
DN15 9PF
Tel: 01724 733096
Fax: 01724 733898
🅴 wintfields@aol.com
Chef(s): Germain Schwab
Owner(s): Mr & Mrs Schab
Cost: A/c £62, set price L £26-£32/D £32-£65. H/wine £17.50
Times: Noon-1.30pm/7-9.30pm. Closed Sun & Mon, 2 wks Xmas, 1st week Aug, last week Mar
Additional: Children welcome
Seats: 42. Private dining room 10
Style: French
Smoking: No smoking in dining room
Accommodation: 10 rooms (10 en suite) ★ ★
Directions: Village centre, off A1077, 4 miles S of Humber Bridge

The opulent dining room does tend to excite the adjectives but as has been commented, cooking this good tends to mean that your gaze is concentrated firmly on the plate. Germain Schwab is an artist and perfectionist who steers clear of the hype and devotes his energies to refining his considerable talent and offering up some of the most exciting food in the country. It's a happy ship and staff tend to stay here for, by modern standards, an age. That's important, the service (it has been described as "the best there is") is of a type seldom seen these days, and it relies upon skilled individuals who understand what makes Winteringham Fields tick.

The menu construction itself offers something of a challenge for the kitchen with a selection of fish courses, some of which can be taken as starters or mains as well. A couple of amuses (perhaps wood pigeon and wild mushroom consommé and a salted veal samosa with plum sauce) are the prelude to a meal that can set the heart racing. Freshness and flavours leap out and the precision is something to behold. Take for instance a starter of langoustine aspic with mousse of avocado and a basil fritter, which arrived as a crystal clear jelly in which was set the most pristine of langoustine outshone only by the deep fried leaf, dusted with lemon powder and fine sugar. "As near perfection as I've tasted" was the verdict on that one and a similar dexterity is evident in a more familiar duo of foie gras (terrine and pan-fried) with quince and fig chutney alongside a balsamic and vanilla reduction. Pan-fried cutlet of veal comes with poached oysters and a curried sabayon, leg of duck with fondant potato and creamed wild mushrooms. Cheeses are marvellous and served with authority whilst desserts (say dark chocolate and Glayva coulant in white chocolate crème patissière tuile with whisky glazed dried apricots) are inspired. Couple all this with an admirable wine list and you have a very special venue.

LONDON, CENTRAL

LONDON E1

Les Trois Garçons   NEW   Map G5

Promising to bring the glamour back to Shoreditch, this glitzy French restaurant verges on the surreal. A playful background of bejeweled stuffed animals, exotic glass and fascinating bric-a-brac is the backdrop to the classic *carte*, with its carre d'agneau, sautéed sweetbread, and roasted veal chop. Crème brûlée and tarte Tatin to finish.

Seats: 80. Private dining room 10
Style: Classic, Chic
Smoking: Air conditioning
Directions: Nearest Tube: Liverpool Street, 10 minutes walk from station, at the end of Brick Lane

1 Club Row, E1 6JX
Tel: 020 7613 1924
Fax: 020 7613 5960
e info@lestroisgarcons.com
Chef(s): Eric Vernice, Vincent Pascal
Owner(s): Stefan Karlson, Hussan Abdullah, Michel Lasserre
Cost: *Alc* £45. H/wine £16
Times: Noon-3pm/7-Midnight. Closed Sun, L Sat
Additional: Children 12 yrs+

Wapping Food   NEW   Map GtL D3

There's a distinct buzz at this converted power station, with its mixture of steel girders and concrete floors, yellow seating and black tables. The light-hearted, unpretentious menu reaches around the globe for grilled sardines goam masala, cep and cipolini risotto, and seafood fritto misto, served by friendly staff. Decent espresso too.

Additional: Sunday L. Children welcome
Seats: 100
Style: Modern, Minimalist
Smoking: No pipes; no cigars
Directions: Nearest tube: Wapping. Turn R from tube, walk east & parallel to the river, (approx 4 mins)

Wapping Power Station, Wapping Wall, E1W 3ST
Tel: 020 7680 2080
Fax: 020 7680 2081
e info@wapping-wpt.com
Chef(s): Justin Aubrey
Owner(s): Ian James & Jules Wright
Cost: *Alc* £35. ☺ H/wine £15
Times: Noon-3pm/7-Midnight. Closed D Sun

LONDON E2

The Thai Garden   Map GtL D3

Modest, family-run Thai restaurant in the East End with a loyal following. Going strong for ten years, the Thai Garden offers dependable Thai food, homing in on both seafood and vegetarian dishes. Examples include Thai aubergines and mixed vegetable curry with coconut cream or crispy tuna fish marinated in hot and sour sauce with red onion, chillies, spring onions and coriander.

Seats: 32. Private dining room 12
Style: Minimalist
Smoking: No-smoking area
Directions: Nearest tube: Bethnal Green. 2nd L off Roman Road (one way street), Nr London Buddhist Centre

249 Globe Road, E2 0JD
Tel: 020 8981 5748
e thaigarden@hotmail.com
Chef(s): Mrs N Duff
Owner(s): S & J Hufton
Cost: *Alc* £17, set price L £9.50/ D £16-£20. ☺ ☺ H/wine £7.50
Times: Noon-3pm/6-11pm. Closed L Sat & Sun, BHs
Additional: Children welcome

Viet-Hoa   Map GtL D4

Over 100 dishes available at this low-key Vietnamese restaurant, with fresh ingredients producing lovely clean flavours. Try fried Tilapia fish served with hot and sour sauce and grated mango, Chao-Tom prawns minced, pasted onto

70-72 Kingsland Road, E2 8DP
Tel: 020 7729 8293
Chef(s): Quyen Ly
Owner(s): Quyen Ly

sugar cane and fried, and Shaking beef - tasty crispy cubes of meat. The influences are Chinese and Thai, but lighter in style.

Seats: 150
Smoking: Air conditioning
Directions: Nearest tube: Old Street or Liverpool St

Cost: *Alc* £15, set price D £10-£20.
☺ ☺ H/wine £7.99
Times: Noon-3.30pm/5.30-11.30pm.
Closed Xmas, New Year
Additional: Sunday L.
Children welcome

LONDON E14

Four Seasons Hotel
Canary Wharf
Map GtL E3

Westferry Circus,
Canary Wharf, E14 8RS
Tel: 0207 510 1999
Fax: 0207 510 1998
Chef(s): Marco Bax
Cost: Set price L £25/D £28.
H/wine £18
Times: Noon-3pm/6-10.30pm.
Additional: Sunday brunch. Bar food.
Children welcome. Vegetarian by request only
Seats: 90 (terrace 35)
Style: Modern, Chic

A chic Thames-side eaterie where chefs strut their stuff behind a glass façade. There's a versatile range of modern Italian dishes to choose from, with starters like organic vegetable terrine with goats cheese salad making a strong impression. Pastas can be taken as a starter or a main choice, and the refined wine list is largely Italian.

Smoking: No-smoking area; no pipes; no cigars; Air conditioning
Civil licence: 220
Accommodation: 142 rooms (142 en suite) ★ ★ ★ ★ ★
Directions: Canary Wharf - Jubilee Line. Just off Westferry Circus rdbt

Ubon by Nobu
NEW Map GtL E3

34 Westferry Wharf,
London, E14 8RR
Tel: 0207 719 7800
Fax: 0207 719 7801
Owner(s): Nobu Matsuhisa
Times: Noon-2.30pm/6-10.15pm.
Closed Sun, L Sat, All BHs
Additional: Bar food (sushi)
Children welcome
Seats: 120
Style: Japanese
Smoking: No-smoking area; no pipes; no cigars; Air conditioning

Glass windows stretching from floor to ceiling make for spectacular views of Canary Wharf and the Thames. This is a sanctuary of light, airy simplicity high above the aggravations of London life with an open plan kitchen (cleverly revealed by well positioned mirrors) adding an element of theatre to proceedings. The food is funky Japanese with professional, well informed staff serving up the likes of lightly seared slices of tuna positioned around a generous mound of mixed leaves with an intense and memorable dressing. This might be accompanied by a more substantial dish of rock shrimp tempura with a creamy, spicy sauce.

Directions: Nearest tube: Westferry, Canary Wharf. Restaurant behind Four Seasons Hotel

LONDON EC1

Alba Restaurant
Map F4

107 Whitecross Street,
EC1Y 8JD
Tel: 020 7588 1798
Fax: 020 7638 5793
Chef(s): Marco Carta
Owner(s): R Venerandi
Cost: *Alc* £25/D £15. ☺ ☺
H/wine £11.50
Times: Noon-3pm/6-11pm.
Closed Sat & Sun, BHs
Additional: Bar food L.
Children welcome
Seats: 60. Private dining room 30

A congenial Italian eatery just a stone's throw from the Barbican. Menus are short and sensible, changing every six weeks and majoring on Piedmontese food. Home-made pastas are a strong point, from pappardelle with speck, sun-dried tomatoes and zucchini to squid ink tagliolini with seafood. Ample fish and meat dishes are available too.

Style: Italian
Smoking: No-smoking area; no pipes; no cigars; Air conditioning
Directions: Nearest tube: Barbican, 100yds from the Barbican Arts Centre

LONDON EC1 *Continued*

Le Café du Marché

Map E5

Tucked away in a quiet mews, this unpretentious French restaurant is not the easiest place to find but it is obviously no secret as the place is packed at lunchtime. The interior is rustic, with exposed ceiling rafters, wooden floors and red brick walls, and the menu is all in French but don't despair, the waiting staff have translations

Seats: 120. Private dining room 65
Style: Rustic, French. **Smoking:** Air conditioning
Directions: Nearest tube: Barbican

Charterhouse Mews, Charterhouse Square, EC1M 6AH
Tel: 020 7608 1609
Fax: 020 7336 7459
Chef(s): Simon Cottard
Owner(s): Anna Graham-Wood
Cost: Alc £35, set price L £24.95/D £24.95. H/wine £9
Times: Noon-2.30pm/6-10pm. Closed Sun, L Sat, Xmas, New Year, BHs
Additional: Children welcome

Club Gasçon

Map F4

"One of the most enjoyable visits I have ever done" testified one seasoned inspector after a meal here. Sure enough, the menu style - a multitude of mini-courses - is just the thing to excite even the most jaded palate. 'la route de sel', 'le potager' and of course 'les foies gras' are amongst the layers with the first of these featuring a "superb" pot au feu of duck, lavender and asparagus and the second "ultra crisp" fat chips with fleur de sel. 'Les foies gras' is the biggest section on the menu and more than upholds the south west France credentials with for instance, mi cuit duck foie gras with piquillo pepper. 'L'Oceane' features grilled scallops with caviar cream and 'Les Paturages' offers the slow cooked dishes ("spectacular" braised lamb with orange and crystallised garlic for example) so typical of the region. The surroundings too are an eye-opener, deeply cool with marbled walls a stunning feature bar and a bold combination of colours.

57 West Smithfield, EC1A 9DS
Tel: 020 7796 0600
Fax: 020 7796 0601
Chef(s): Pascal Aussignac
Owner(s): P Aussignac & V Labeyrie
Cost: Alc £35, set price L & D £30. ☺ H/wine £12.50
Times: Noon-2pm/7-10pm. Closed Sun, L Sat
Additional: Children welcome
Seats: 60
Style: Modern, Chic
Smoking: No pipes; Air conditioning
Directions: Nearest tube: Barbican or Farringdon

WINE AWARD BEST REGIONAL FRENCH

Gaudi Restaurante

Map E4

63 Clerkenwell Road, EC1M 5PT
Tel: 020 7608 3220
Fax: 020 7250 1057
✉ gaudi@turnmills.co.uk
Chef(s): Nacho Martinez
Owner(s): John Newman
Cost: Alc £35, set price L £15. ☺ H/wine £11.50
Times: Last orders L 2.30pm/D 10.30pm. Closed Sun, L Sat, Xmas, Easter, BHs

In homage to the great Catalan architect of the same name, the interior explodes in a sensual riot of wrought ironwork, tiles, stained-glass windows, fantastic shaped pillars (a massive ram's horn winding round the bar) and a pastiche art collection. Chef Nacho Martinez was one of the best modern Spanish cooks in Madrid before he was lured to London where's he is offering the capital the sort of light and vivid Spanish food rarely found outside of the country. Martinez is a thoughtful chef who takes all kinds of liberties, combining modern techniques and

England

inspirations with his Spanish heritage to produce an exciting hybrid. Traditional ingredients are there but lined up in an untraditional way. Starters can be subtle as in baby artichokes with black truffle on a thyme scented confit cep. Mains are triumphant, with fish dishes handled lovingly and cooked precisely - baked sea bream with cod mousse, confit of piquillo peppers and griddled razor clams with bacon for example. Desserts can also hold their own, with an outstanding example being crêpes filled with crème rice pudding, crystallised caramel nest and orange sauce. The Spanish wine list is remarkably well priced.

Additional: Children 5 yrs+
Seats: 70. Private dining room 45. Jacket and tie preferred
Style: Modern Spanish
Smoking: No-smoking area; no pipes; no cigars; Air conditioning
Directions: Nearest tube: Farringdon. 2mins walk. 1st L into Turnmill St. Situated on corner with Clerkenwell Rd

Maison Novelli

Map GtL D3

Stylish restaurant on Clerkenwell Green, the frontage taking in the whole corner site with distinctive blue canopies capping the windows. Inside are the trademark hyacinth blue walls, with cream drapes, white linen and wooden floors. Staff are professional but approachable, and personable enough to cause a flutter among the diners. The *carte* is simpler than it used to be with well-executed dishes - potato and foie gras terrine with hazelnut dressing, and a coarse-textured smoked haddock fishcake with a dollop of good tartare sauce. One highlight was chocolate fondant with white chocolate ice cream and a spun sugar and tuile sail. Good to see the talented chef back at the stove.

Directions: Nearest Tube: Farringdon

29 Clerkenwell Green,
EC1R 0DU
Tel: 020 7251 6606
Fax: 020 7490 1083
 maisonnovelli@hotmail.com
Chef(s): Jean Christophe Novelli
Owner(s): Jean Christophe Novelli
Cost: Alc £50. H/wine £14.95
Times: Noon-3pm/6-11pm.
Closed Sun, L Sat
Additional: Children 5yrs+
Seats: 30-72
Style: Modern, French
Smoking: No pipes; no cigars; Air conditioning

Moro

Map E5

A packed restaurant is bound to have its imitators and such has been the case with Moro. Mimics should take care though - raiding the cuisine of Spain and North Africa will not be enough. Quality of produce, honesty and value for money are harder to reproduce but they are the real root of Moro's success. Dishes range from the perfectly simple (Serrano ham with dressed broad beans) to the more intricate (a brik of tuna, chopped egg and anchovy) with the wood-fired oven providing much of the inspiration for the cooking of some carefully sourced meats. Saucing, naturally, tends to be spicy. The wine list is enterprising, Spanish biased and reasonably priced.

Smoking: No pipes; no cigars; Air conditioning
Directions: Nearest tube: Farringdon or Angel. 5 minutes walk from Sadlers Wells theatre, between Farringdon Road & Rosebery Avenue. Bus routes nos. 19, 38, 341, 63.

34/36 Exmouth Market, EC1R 4QE
Tel: 020 7833 8336
Fax: 020 7833 9338
 mororestaurant@hotmail.com
Chef(s): S Clark
Owner(s): Mr & Mrs S Clark & Mark Sainsbury
Cost: Alc £24. ☺
Times: 12.30-2.30pm/7-10.30pm. Closed Sun, L Sat, Xmas, New Year, BHs
Additional: Bar food. Children welcome
Seats: 90. Private dining room 14
Style: Modern

Quality Chop House

Map E4

Jellied eels and Sevruga caviar rub comfortable shoulders at this original Victorian eating house where black and white tiles, booths and plenty of frosted glass betray its origins. An eclectic menu offers lobster and rocket salad, grilled kippers and poached egg, and French black pudding with apple compôte, plus an extended fish repertoire. Smart, relaxed staff.

Seats: 66. **Style:** Classic, Traditional
Smoking: No-smoking area; Air conditioning
Directions: Nearest tube: Farringdon. North end of Farringdon Road

94 Farringdon Road, EC1 3EA
Tel: 020 7837 5093
Fax: 020 7833 8748
Chef(s): Charles Fontaine
Owner(s): Charles Fontaine
Cost: Alc £27. ☺ ☺ H/wine £11
Times: Noon-3pm/6.30-11.30pm. Closed L Sat, 24 Dec-3 Jan
Additional: Sunday L. Children welcome

LONDON EC1 *Continued*

Smiths of Smithfield   NEW   Map F4

Roaming over four floors and invariably packed on every one. From the ground floor bar serving easygoing meals (from breakfast at 7am to hotpots and pasties at lunch) through the first floor champagne bar and second floor brasserie (lots of shared dishes), the degree of formality escalates as you ascend. The third floor is where the serious dining takes place with crisp, white clothed tables and knowledgeable staff. Expect plenty of quality meat and seafood in punchy combinations. Starters have included an accomplished lobster omelette with Thai basil and star anise and amongst the mains an Islay sirloin with a decent béarnaise and fat chips was noted as "deeply satisfying". Terrific fun.

Directions: Nearest tube: Farringdon & Barbican

67-77 Charterhouse Street,
EC1M 6HJ
Tel: 020 7236 6666
Fax: 020 7236 5666
Chef(s): Tony Moyse, Ashley Shergold
Owner(s): John Torode
Cost: Alc £36. H/wine £13.75
Times: Noon-3pm/7-10.30pm.
Closed L Sat, Xmas, New Year
Additional: Sunday L.
Children welcome
Seats: 78. Private dining room 30
Style: Modern
Smoking: Air conditioning

St John   Map F5

A former smokehouse provides an appropriately earthy setting for this triumphantly unpretentious restaurant. Fergus Henderson's sturdy take on British cooking is justly celebrated for its honesty and fathom-deep flavours. Roast bone marrow salad and dried kid's liver with radishes and boiled egg are not the type of dishes you see every day (after a visit here you may well be asking why). Whilst a main course of pot roast Gloucester Old Spot with butterbeans may be more familiar it's rare to see it treated with such obvious affection. Marvellous relaxed atmosphere too.

Directions: Nearest tube: Farringdon. 100 metres from Smithfield Market on the north side

26 St John Street, EC1M 4AY
Tel: 020 7251 0848
Fax: 020 7251 4090
e tg@johnrestaurant.co.uk
Chef(s): Fergus Henderson
Owner(s): T Gulliver & F Henderson
Cost: Alc £26. ☺ ☺ H/wine £11
Times: Noon-3pm/6-11pm.
Closed Sun, L Sat, Xmas, New Year
Additional: Bar food. Children welcome
Seats: 100. Private dining room 18
Smoking: Air conditioning

Tatsuso Restaurant   Map G4

Busy, buzzing Japanese restaurant directly adjacent to Liverpool Street station. The restaurant comprises a variety of dining areas - go traditional in the downstairs sushi bar and restaurant or, should you anticipate the need for distraction, the upstairs teppanyaki bar affords a view of the chef at work. A typical selection from the set menu might include a small appetiser of simmered hijiki (sweet seaweed), sashimi, tempura, Japanese clear soup and toban yaki (sliced beef served in a casserole.)

Style: Modern, Oriental
Smoking: No pipes; Air conditioning
Directions: Nearest tube: Liverpool St. Ground floor of Broadgate Circle

32 Broadgate Circle,
EC1M 6BT
Tel: 020 7638 5863
Fax: 020 7638 5864
Chef(s): Nobuyuki Yamanaka
Owner(s): Terutso Fujii
Cost: Alc £38, set price L £38-£80/ D £36-£80. H/wine £14
Times: 11.30-2.30pm/6-9.45pm.
Closed Sat & Sun, Xmax, New Year, BHs
Additional: Children 10 yrs+. Vegetarian by request only
Seats: 100. Private dining room 8.
Jacket and tie preferred

LONDON EC2

Aurora   Map GtL D3

Aurora is a vast, palatial room with pillars, high arched windows and pastoral friezes, crowned by a beautiful stained glass dome. Tractor wheel-size lampshades keep the effect

at Great Eastern Hotel,
Liverpool Street, EC2M 7QN
Tel: 020 7618 5000
Fax: 020 7618 5001

contemporary, with black suede chairs, white antimacassars and smart monogrammed tableware. It gets very busy, but there are abundant staff and the quality of the food is unaffected by the rush. Try terrine of ham hock with smoked eel wrapped in leek - succulent and full of flavour - or roast quail, breasts boned with a white pudding under the skin, served with pommes Anna, artichoke mousseline finished with truffle oil, and an accomplished tarragon sauce.

Civil licence: 160
Accommodation: 267 rooms (267 en suite) ★ ★ ★ ★ ★
Directions: Nearest tube: Liverpool St

e sales@great-eastern-hotel.co.uk
Chef(s): Robert Stirrup
Owner(s): Wyndham Conran
Cost: Alc £45, set price D £34-£58. H/wine £14
Times: Noon-2.45pm/6.45-10.45pm. Closed Sat, Sun, Xmas, New Year
Additional: Children welcome
Seats: 170. Jacket and tie preferred
Style: Modern
Smoking: Air conditioning

Fish Market   NEW   Map GtL D3

The ocean theme extends beyond the food to the interior design that features a crustacean altar, fish mosaics and sea-blue bar. Huge platters of fruits de mer are carried at shoulder height by young Kenzo-clad waiters (deep blue shirts, silk waistcoats and long white aprons), and the menu is dedicated to the sea. Lobster and crab spring rolls with plum sauce are an upmarket marine version of the Chinese staple starter, with seabass with tapenade and chive mash as fresh a main dish as could be hoped for. For those in a hurry the less formal Champagne bar offers the same menu more speedily.

at Great Eastern Hotel,
40 Liverpool Street, EC2M 7QN
Tel: 0207 618 7200
Telephone for further details

Restaurant Twentyfour   Map G4

Spectacular setting on the 24th floor of the City's tallest building, with terrific views all around. A contemporary interior with clean lines and soft tones offers sophistication. Menus deserve the same adjective with lobster tortellini, tomato and tarragon consommé sitting happily alongside pan-fried sea bream on purple mash, crispy leek and citrus dressing.

Additional: Bar food D. Children welcome
Seats: 72. Private dining room 18. **Style:** Modern, Minimalist
Smoking: No pipes; no cigars; Air conditioning
Directions: Nearest tube: Bank, Liverpool Street.

Tower 42, Old Broad Street,
EC2N 1HQ
Tel: 020 7877 2424/7703
Fax: 020 7877 7742
Chef(s): Jeremy Ford
Owner(s): Tower Ltd Partnership/ Roux Fine Dining
Cost: Alc £38, set price L £26. H/wine £13.95
Times: 11.45am-2.30pm/6-9.30pm. Closed Sat-Sun, Xmas-New Year

LONDON EC3

1 Lombard Street   NEW   Map GtL G3

Former banking hall with a Grade II listed neo-classical interior, which suits the business set particularly well. An informal brasserie is filled with City types networking and relaxing with champagnes and wines. The good, bustling atmosphere is a complete contrast to the exceedingly formal restaurant where service can be starchy, although professional. Simply clothed tables with brown lining plates and paper sealed napkins, along with menus and wine lists aspiring to haute dining are all part of the central theme. The food is appropriately classical and soundly based on French technique. Try perhaps a sauté of lobster and langoustines in Sauternes, with carrot tagliatelle – where a velvety sauce enhances the partially shelled seafood. Flavours and combinations are well balanced throughout, even down to some delightful petits four.

1 Lombard Street,
EC3V 9AA
Tel: 020 7929 6611
Fax: 020 7929 6611
e hb@1lombardstreet.com
Chef(s): Herbert Berger
Owner(s): Jessen & Co
Cost: Alc £50, set price L £38/ D £32. H/wine £17
Times: Noon-3pm/6-10pm. Closed Sat-Sun, Xmas, New Year, BHs
Additional: Children welcome
Seats: 40
Style: Modern
Smoking: Air conditioning
Directions: Nearest tube: Bank

England

LONDON EC3 *Continued*

1 Lombard Street – The Brasserie

Map GtL G3

An impressive glass domed roof above a circular bar is the striking feature of this simply decorated modern brasserie, located next door to its fine dining alter ego. All age groups are represented in the buzz of the closely packed restaurant, served by a young and well-organised team. The fairly lengthy menu draws influences from all over Europe, with picturesque options like feuilleté of Burgundy snails from the 'Egg & Pasta' selection to 'Specials' of paella (for two), braised oxtail, or suckling pig stuffed with bread and wild mushrooms and served with warm cabbage salad.

Directions: Nearest tube: Bank. Opposite Bank of England

1 Lombard Street,
EC3V 9AA
Tel: 020 7929 6611
Fax: 020 7929 6622
e hb@1lombardstreet.com
Chef(s): Herbert Berger
Owner(s): Jessen & Co
Cost: *Alc* £35. ☺ H/wine £17
Times: Noon-3pm/6-10pm. Closed Sat-Sun, 1 wk Xmas
Additional: Bar food. Children welcome
Seats: 150. Private dining room 36
Smoking: No pipes; Air conditioning

LONDON EC4

City Rhodes Restaurant

Map E4

1 New Street Square, EC4A 3JB
Tel: 020 7583 1313
Fax: 020 7353 1662
Chef(s): Gary Rhodes
Owner(s): Sodexho
Cost: *Alc* £70 H/wine £16.50
Times: Noon-2.30pm/6-9pm. Closed Sat-Sun, Xmas, New Year
Additional: Children welcome
Seats: 90. Private dining room 12
Style: Modern
Smoking: No pipes; no cigars; Air conditioning
Directions: Off Shoe Lane, behind International Press Centre

The entrance is done up as a sort of shrine to Gary Rhodes, but there is much more to the first-floor restaurant than celebrity hype. The room is sleek and well-groomed, a minimalist backdrop to some serious cooking which is good enough to silence the sceptics. Luxury items mingle temptingly on the menu with more robust ingredients, but everything receives the same competent handling: foie gras appears roasted on a potato cake with macerated grapes, or in a shallot tart with roast chump of lamb; ox tongue is braised in a salad, and there's champagne and caviar linguini, and lobster with black trompette mushrooms for the uninhibited hedonist. Desserts range through chocolate plate (superb) to champagne crème brûlée with raspberries, and there are ten dessert wines by the glass. Charming youthful staff are the icing on the cake.

The Don

NEW Map G3

Approached via a quaint cobbled courtyard, The Don was once the cellar for Sandeman's famous port and wine company in 1798. True to tradition, a wine bar occupies the ground floor, while the upstairs restaurant, with its polished wooden floors

The Courtyard, 20 St Swithins Lane,
EC4 8AD
Tel: 0207 626 2606
Fax: 0207 626 2616
Chef(s): Matt Burns

England

and impressive stainless steel ceiling sculpture, is the setting for enjoyable Mediterranean inspired food. Expect fish soup, roasted halibut with risotto, seared sea bass with balsamic and pesto dressing, and banana tatin.

Directions: Nearest tube: Bank

Owner(s): R & R Wilson
Cost: Set price D £17.95
Times: Noon-3pm/6-11pm.
Closed Sat-Sun, Xmas-New Year

LONDON N1

Frederick's Restaurant   Map GtL D3

Long-established Camden restaurant, which sits in a listed building. Inside, the décor is cheery and colourful with bold abstract art dotted around, and Frederick's has an impressive conservatory overlooking a walled garden. Menus reveal a mix of classic flavours and imaginative twists, pleasing customers which tend to be both businessmen and casual shoppers. Modern British food with the usual Mediterranean influences happily cropping up in, say, spiced crab bisque baked with a Gruyère crust, served with rouille, while local flavours appear in dishes like Scottish venison, chestnut and foie gras Wellington with pickled walnut jus.

Smoking: No-smoking area; Air conditioning. **Civil licence:** 40
Directions: Nearest Tube: Angel. 2 mins walk to Camden Passage. Restaurant among the antique shops

Camden Passage, Islington,
N1 8EG
Tel: 020 7359 2888
Fax: 020 7359 5173
e eat@fredericks.co.uk
Chef(s): Andrew Jeffs
Owner(s): Louis Segal
Cost: Alc £30, set price L £15.50/
D £15. ☺ ☺ H/wine £10.95
Times: Noon-2.30pm/5.45pm-1am.
Closed Sun, Xmas, New Year, BHs
Additional: Bar food. Children welcome
Seats: 150. Private dining room 30
Style: Modern

Granita   Map GtL D3

Attracts a chic, young crowd to its minimalist enclave in Islington, where both business and arty types seem to mix happily. Pale blue walls, plain wooden flooring and tables along with a steel bar counter give Granita a clean, stream-lined feel. Concise menus reveal a predisposition towards the Med - both east and west, with options such as hummus with lemon, olive oil and garlic, crispy onion, olives and flat bread or chump of lamb chargrilled with braised green beans, tomato and cos. Precision is the key to all the dishes, including puds like cranberry and almond tart with vanilla ice cream.

Directions: Nearest tube: Highbury & Islington, Angel. Opposite St Mary's Church

127 Upper Street, Islington, N1 1QP
Tel: 020 7226 3222
Chef(s): Ahmed Kharshoum
Owner(s): Ms V Leffman
Cost: Alc £16.90, set price L £14.95.
☺ ☺ H/wine £10.95
Times: 12.30-2.30pm/6.30-10.30pm.
Closed Mon, L Tue, D Mon, 10 days Xmas, 1 wk Easter & 2 wks Aug
Additional: Sunday L.
Seats: 72
Style: Modern
Smoking: No pipes; no cigars;
Air conditioning

Lola's   Map GtL D3

359 Upper Street, Islington,
N1 2UD
Tel: 020 7359 1932
Fax: 020 7359 2209
e lolasrest.uk@btinternet.com
Chef(s): Gary Lee
Owner(s): Morfudd Richards & Carol George
Cost: Alc £25, set price L £15. ☺ ☺
H/wine £10.50
Times: Noon-2.30pm/6-11pm.
Closed 25-26 Dec, 1 Jan, BHs
Additional: Sunday L. Bar food. Children welcome

England

LONDON N1 *Continued*

Amidst the hustle and bustle of Camden passage with a great setting on the upper floor of an old tram shed. Pastel shades and a generally airy interior give an impression of space and light. Express menus offer an ideal option for business lunches or pre-theatre suppers, whilst a slightly larger *carte* provides more choice. Mediterranean influences abound with ideas from more than a few countries in the region.

Seats: 80
Style: Smart, informal
Smoking: Air conditioning
Directions: Nearest tube: Angel

The Real Greek

Map G5

15 Hoxton Market, N1 6HG
Tel: 020 7739 8212
Fax: 020 7739 4910
e the.realgreek@talk21.com
Chef(s): Theodore Kyriakou
Owner(s): Theodore Kyriakou &
Paloma Campbell
Cost: *Alc* £30. ☺ ☺ H/wine £12.50
Times: Noon-3pm/5.30-10.30pm.
Closed Sun, 23 Dec-2 Jan, BHs
Additional: Children welcome
Seats: 65. Private dining room 8
Style: Traditional, Greek
Smoking: No pipes; no cigars

A reminder, if any was needed, that there is more to Greek food than kebabs and vine leaves. The menu of this welcoming, relaxed restaurant comprises a page of Mezedes (little appetisers served in threes and fours), then Fagakia (small dishes), and finally the main courses. The vibrant, tasty cooking is truly inspiring: a 'succulent' half lobster comes roasted with tomatoes and served with aubergine imam, whilst a calf and lamb's liver faggot is accompanied by puréed liver, spinach, yogurt and pistachio. The equally imaginative desserts might include panacotta served with chilli-poached apples and green chillis. You'll be spoilt for choice.

Directions: Nearest tube: Old Street. Situated in square behind Holiday Inn Express on Old Street. From tube station walk down Old Street past Shoreditch Fire Station then 1st L, 1st R to the back of Inn

White Onion

Map GtL D3

297 Upper Street, Islington,
N1 2TU
Tel: 020 7359 3533
Fax: 020 7359 3533
Chef(s): Santino Busciglio
Owner(s): Bijan Bezhadi
Cost: *Alc* £27.70, set price L £17.95/
D £27.70. ☺ ☺ H/wine £14.50
Times: L until 2.30pm/D until
10.30pm. Closed L Mon-Fri, Xmas,
BHs
Additional: Sunday L.
Children welcome
Seats: 62. Private dining room 40.
Jacket and tie preferred

Fashionable Islington eaterie with understated décor and a mezzanine floor. The menu has morphed from modern French to Italian, with some salady starters and a few pasta dishes - lemon linguine with crab, sweet chilli and rocket - and a risotto con zucca (if you can take the 25-minute wait). Mains run along the lines of cod fillet wrapped in aubergine and roasted with baby vegetables and tomato brodo, or breast of guinea fowl with duck liver stuffing, wrapped in pancetta and served with roasted artichoke. Finish with pannacotta flavoured with grappa and served with exotic fruit.

Style: Modern, Italian
Smoking: No pipes; no cigars; Air conditioning
Directions: Nearest tube: Angel/Highbury & Islington (midway between two). Close to Almeida Street

LONDON N4

La Ventura Restaurant

Map GtL D4

28 Crouch Hill,
N4 4AU
Tel: 020 7281 5811
Fax: 0207 272 1878
Chef(s): Frank Gonsalves
Owner(s): Frank Gonsalves &
John Hadjiahannis

Unpretentious restaurant where the simple décor plays second fiddle to the highly enjoyable modern European cooking. Various menus offer a good value choice of dishes, including ravioli of gorgonzola and walnut with leek and Gruyère fondue, fresh salmon fishcake with buttered spinach, aïoli and aged balsamic, and a recommended celery and blue cheese risotto starter. Short traditional wine list, reasonably priced.

continued

Cost: Set price L £10.95 (£13.95 Mon-Wed)/D £13.95-£15.95. ☺ ☺ H/wine £9.95
Times: 11-4pm/6-midnight. Closed L Mon, D Sun
Additional: Sunday L. Children welcome
Seats: 55. Private dining room 18
Style: Modern, French
Smoking: No-smoking area
Directions: Nearest station: Finsbury Park. At junction of Crouch Hill and Japan Crescent.

LONDON N16

The Fox Reformed

Map GtL D4

No-frills high street restaurant serving simple, value-for-money food with a dash of adventure. The short menu supplemented by blackboard specials might serve up chicken livers in brandy cream sauce, followed by calves' liver with port, provençale fish stew, or braised duck leg with apple and prunes. Some very good red wines by the glass, and quality cappuccino.

Seats: 40
Directions: On No 73 bus route. Opposite the junction with Woodlea Road

176 Stoke Newington Church St, N16 0JL
Tel: 020 7254 5975
Fax: 020 7254 5975
Chef(s): Mark Kelly
Owner(s): Mr & Mrs R Richards
Cost: Alc £21.50. ☺ ☺ H/wine £9.25
Times: Closed L Mon-Fri, 25-26 Dec
Additional: Sunday L. Bar food. Children welcome

LONDON NW1

The Black Truffle

Map GtL C4

Cool black is the theme here - walls, tables and blinds - for modern Italian chic. In an upmarket residential area and part of a cluster of stylish restaurants, Black Truffle's speciality is fish, as in mosaic of raw fish with fennel and French beans or baby squid with courgettes tempura and mint. The eponymous black truffle may appear with a main dish of grilled divers' scallops with French beans and green apple sauce. The cooking is careful, reflecting all that is best in modern Italian cooking - first class breads, ravioli and other pastas served with meat, fish or plenty of grilled vegetables

Smoking: No pipes; no cigars; Air conditioning
Directions: Nearest Tube: Chalk Farm. Off Regent Park Rd

40 Chalcot Road, NW1 8LS
Tel: 020 7483 0077
Fax: 0207 483 0088
Chef(s): Tommaso Maddalena
Owner(s): Bijan Behzadi
Cost: Alc £27, set price L £17/ D £24.50-£28.50 H/wine £12.50
Times: Noon-2.30pm/7-10.45pm. Closed Sun, L Sat, Xmas, BHs
Additional: Children welcome
Seats: 45
Style: Modern, Italian

John Burton-Race at The Landmark

NEW Map E4

No questioning the courage of John Burton-Race. With the general trend being to up-sticks and move to the country the decision to leave cosy Shinfield and and head for London looks all the more intrepid. Happily, given the level of investment (personal as much as financial) the indications are of a resounding success. The dining room, once noted as lacking in charm, has benefited from a wittily ostentatious makeover and

222 Marylebone Road, NW1 6JQ
Tel: 020 723 7800
Fax: 020 723 4700
Chef(s): John Burton-Race
Owner(s): John Burton-Race
Cost: Alc £75, set price L £29.50/ D £48 (£160 for 2, 7-course tasting menu)

England

LONDON NW1 *Continued*

the feel is glitzy and resolutely fun. The food is perhaps more relaxed than at L'Ortolan, certainly less elaborate but the great strength is in doing the classics that much better than just about anyone else. Not that there is a lack of imagination, hot smoked fillet of salmon comes with a grilled langoustine and a "hugely successful" sardine and olive oil dressing. More familiar fare such as roasted scallops on truffled mash with chicken jus or a main course of squab pigeon breast and foie gras wrapped in savoy cabbage, also stood out for pinpoint accuracy and fathom deep flavour. The dessert menu seems to offer little in the way of surprises but the revelation comes on the plate with the likes of spiced roast pineapple with a light crème brûlée. None of this comes cheap, but the whole package (which includes some consummate service) adds up to quite an occasion and you're unlikely to feel cheated.

Times: 12.15-2.15pm/7-10.30pm. Closed Sun, L Sat, BHs
Additional: Children welcome
Seats: 80. Private dining room 25
Style: Classic, French
Smoking: No pipes; Air conditioning
Accommodation: 299 rooms (299 en suite) ★ ★ ★ ★ ★
Directions: Nearest tube: Marylebone. Hotel opposite station

Lemonia

Map GtL C3

No shortage of choice at this capacious Mediterranean restaurant. Kick off with a plate of olives and radishes together with decent hot pitta bread. Keftedakia (deep-fried minced chicken), and Alfelia (diced pork cooked in wine and coriander) are typical of the good value lunch menu. If you're going for the works, don't miss the deliciously sticky baklava.

Seats: 140. Private dining room 40
Style: Mediterranean
Smoking: No pipes; no cigars; Air conditioning
Directions: Nearest tube: Chalk Farm. 200 metres from Primrose Hill Park

89 Regent's Park Road, NW1 8UY
Tel: 020 7586 7454
Fax: 020 7483 2630
Chef(s): A Evangelou, A Mittas
Owner(s): Mr & Mrs Evangelou
Cost: Set price L £7.95/D £13.50. ☺ ☺ H/wine £12
Times: Noon-3pm/6-11.30pm. Closed L Sat, D Sun, 25-26 Dec
Additional: Sunday L. Children welcome

Meliá White House
Regents Park

Map D4

This hotel began life as an apartment building in 1936. The White House restaurant serves an ambitious and interesting selection of food, much of it French-influenced: perhaps foie gras followed by roasted duck with garlic dauphinoise. The lunchtime menu offers 'old fashioned favourites from the carving trolley' and traditional British dishes such as steak, mushroom and Guinness pie. Desserts may not be the greatest strength, but good coffee with home made chocolates is a consolation. Service is professional and very polished.

Accommodation: 582 rooms (582 en suite) ★ ★ ★ ★
Directions: Nearest tube: Great Portland Street

Albany Street, Regents Park, NW1 3UP
Tel: 020 7387 1200
Fax: 020 7388 0091
e melia.white.house@solmelia.es
Chef(s): Colin Norman
Owner(s): Mr P Lister
Times: 12.30-2.30pm/6.30-11pm. Closed Sun, L Sat
Additional: Children welcome
Seats: 70
Style: Classic, Traditional

Odettes

Map C4

This is still a tremendously popular place to eat, so it's wise to book a table in advance. The front room of Odette's is painted green and filled with dozens of gilt framed mirrors, but descend into the conservatory and you'll find yourself in a bright white room, full of pictures and arty photos. The menu is original and exciting, modern European in flavour and offering a 'fantastic value' lunch. Dinner is more elaborate and might include

130 Regents Park Road, NW1 8XL
Tel: 020 7586 5486
Fax: 020 7586 2578
e r.bouler@aol.com
Chef(s): Simon Bradley
Owner(s): Mr S Green

ballotine of foie gras and ham hock with toasted brioche, rhubarb and Sauternes compôte, followed by roasted black leg chicken with artichokes, salsify and braised celery.

Style: Modern
Smoking: No pipes; no cigars
Directions: Nearest tube: Chalk Farm. By Primrose Hill

Cost: *Alc* £35, set price L £12.50. ☺ H/wine £11.95
Times: 12.30-2.30pm/7-11pm. Closed L Sat, D Sun, 10 days Xmas/New Year
Additional: Sunday L. Children welcome
Seats: 65. Private dining room 30

Sauce
Map GtL C3

More a café bar/diner than a restaurant, Sauce produces wholly organic food in various combinations. There's a special children's menu, and a *carte* featuring burgers, wraps and sandwiches, all-day brunch salads, vegetarian dishes, and main dishes. Also fresh organic fruit juices and smoothies, and puddings like chocolate and nut torte with crème fraîche.

Seats: 60
Style: Modern
Smoking: No pipes; no cigars; Air conditioning
Directions: Nearest tube: Camden Town. Turn right, approx 150 yards on right. Just before traffic lights

214 Camden High Street, NW1 8QR
Tel: 020 7482 0777
e dining@sauce.prestel.co.uk
Owner(s): Karen & Ross Doherty, Rose Murphy
Cost: *Alc* £30, set price L £7.50/ D £7.50. ☺ ☺ H/wine £10.95
Times: Noon-11pm.
Closed D Sun, 25-26 Dec
Additional: Sunday L.
Children welcome

LONDON NW2

Quincy's Restaurant
Map GtL C4

Quincy's Restaurant homes in on all that is modish today, within a modern European context. A concise menu offers simple yet enticing choices. Caramelised red onion tarte Tatin with peach chutney and wild game and Armagnac pâté with beetroot.

Style: Traditional
Smoking: No pipes; no cigars; Air conditioning
Directions: Situated between Hendon Way and Cricklewood Lane

675 Finchley Road, NW2 2JP
Tel: 020 7794 8499
Chef(s): Aaron Claxton
Owner(s): Aaron Claxton
Cost: Set price D £25. H/wine £10
Times: Dinner only, 7-Midnight.
Closed Sun
Additional: Children 14+
Seats: 35. Jacket and tie preferred

LONDON NW3

Cucina
Map GtL C4

Fusion may have its detractors, but Cucina proves that the concept can really work. An understated, modern interior hides an ensuing flash of flavours. Covering much of the globe, the menu instantly generates interest with its unusual yet sound combinations. Dishes live up to expectations, revealing imagination and cogent practice alike. Reworkings of ubiquitous dishes delight, for instance fishcakes that comprise plenty of meaty crab and salt cod with contrasting gazpacho relish and saffron aïoli. Travelling to the East for its inspiration, roast miso marinated cod with sticky rice, seaweed aïoli and coconut vinegar is colourful yet restrained - a definite treat overall.

Smoking: No pipes; no cigars; Air conditioning
Directions: Opposite Hampstead BR Station

45a South End Road, Hampstead, NW3 2QB
Tel: 020 7435 7814
Fax: 020 7435 7147
e enquiries@cucina.uk.com
Chef(s): Andrew Poole
Owner(s): Andrew Poole & Vernon Mascarenhas
Cost: *Alc* £21. ☺ ☺ H/wine £11.95
Times: L from noon, 7pm-late.
Closed D Sun
Additional: Sunday L. Children welcome
Seats: 80
Style: Modern

LONDON NW3 *Continued*

Gresslin's

Map GtL C4

On Hampstead's bustling main street, the modern, simple style of Gresslin's complements the menu of modern European cuisine. Quality, fresh ingredients are used in dishes such as sea bass with confit of sweet potato and cucumber and sour cream. Desserts may include rice pudding with plum compôte or pear Tatin with crème fraîche.

Additional: Sunday L. Children welcome
Style: Chic, Modern
Smoking: No smoking in dining room; Air conditioning
Directions: Nearest tube: Hampstead, Halfway down Park Lane

13 Heath Street, Hampstead,
NW3 6TP
Tel: 020 7794 8386
Fax: 020 7433 3282
e restaurant@gresslins.co.uk
Chef(s): Michael Gresslin
Cost: *Alc* £26 H/wine £10.75
Times: Noon-2.30pm/7-10.30pm.
Closed L Mon, D Sun, BHs (ex 25
Dec, last 2wks in Aug

Manna

Map GtL C3

A cross between a conservatory and a Swiss chalet, this restaurant in a side street off the main drag in Primrose Hill serves a vegetarian menu. Stripped pine predominates inside, while the music is ethnic and the service relaxed and friendly. The manna meze is ideal for trying new dishes, while mains include slow baked aubergines, green coconut laksa, or Mexican tortilla galette.

Seats: 50
Style: Chic, Informal
Smoking: No smoking in dining room; Air conditioning
Directions: Nearest tube: Chalk Farm.Telephone for further directions

4 Erskine Road,
Primrose Hill, NW3 3AJ
Tel: 020 7722 8028
Fax: 020 7722 8028
Chef(s): Matthew Kay
Owner(s): S.Hague, R.Swallow,
M.Kay
Cost: *Alc* £23.50. ☺ ☺
H/wine £10.50
Times: 12.30-3pm/6.30-11pm.
Closed L Mon-Fri, 25-26 Dec
Additional: Sunday L. Children
welcome

LONDON NW6

Organic Café

Map GtL C3

The first organic restaurant to be accredited by the Soil Association is to be applauded for its honest, simple, clean approach to food. A warm atmosphere is created by the colourful walls and the wooden floors and furniture. The snack lunch and fuller dinner menu are supplemented by chalked up specials, and main courses are predominantly fish or vegetarian dishes. Expect the likes of smoked salmon with soda bread and tartare sauce or pan-fried mackerel fillet with garlic mash, crispy bacon and salsa verde.

Style: Chic, Bistro-Style
Smoking: No-smoking area; no pipes
Directions: Telephone for directions

25 Lonsdale Road,
NW6 6RA
Tel: 020 7372 1232
Fax: 0207 372 1081
e info@organic_cafe.co.uk
Chef(s): Issa Ciskocho
Owner(s): Charlton Family
Cost: *Alc* £25. ☺ H/wine £13.8
Times: 9.30am-4.30pm/7-Midnight
Additional: Sunday L. Bar food.
Children welcome. Vegetarian by
request only
Seats: 70. Private dining room 50

Indicates a restaurant that has told us that 50% or more of their ingredients are organically sourced

Prices quoted in the guide are for guidance only and are subject to change without notice

England

Singapore Garden Restaurant

Map GtL C4

A mélange of Singapore, Malaysian and Chinese cuisines defines this chic Swiss Cottage restaurant. A lengthy menu includes over a dozen specials, like Teochew braised pig's trotters, claypot prawns and scallops with 'glass' noodles, and wok-fried dumplings filled with minced pork and served with ginger vinegar. Bargain fixed-price lunches are also available.

Style: Chic. **Smoking:** No cigars; Air conditioning
Directions: Nearest tube: Swiss Cottage or Finchley Road. Off Finchley Road, on R before Belsize Park rdbt. No parking restrictions

83/83a Fairfax Road, NW6 4DY
Tel: 020 7328 5314
Fax: 020 7624 0656
e tohfamily@aol.com
Chef(s): Siam Kiang Lim
Owner(s): Mr Lim
Cost: Alc £25, set price L £8.50-£18.50/D £18.50-£22.50. ☺ ☺ H/wine £11.50
Times: Noon-2.45pm/6-10.45pm.
Additional: Sunday L. Children welcome
Seats: 100. Private dining room 6

LONDON NW8

Rosmarino

Map A1

Split-level Italian restaurant with wooden floors, pale walls and a large canopy over the entrance providing for outdoor eating in warmer weather. A large polished wood bar is the focal point of the room, taking up a lot of space, while tables are quite closely packed. A basket of good breads with olive oil for dunking is provided, and the *carte* offers around seven starters and five pasta dishes, the latter including the likes of gnocchi with black truffle and Valtellina fondue. Mains encompass chargrilled chicken paillarde, and pan-fried fillet of red snapper with sweet potatoes, leeks and thyme.

1 Blenheim Terrace, NW8 0EH
Tel: 020 7328 5014
Fax: 020 7625 2639
e rosmarinonw8@hotmail.com
Chef(s): Marzio Zacchi, Stefano Stecca
Owner(s): Giuliano Lotto
Cost: Alc £27.50, set price L £25-£28/D £25-£28. H/wine £12.5
Times: Noon-2.30pm/7-10.30pm.
Closed Easter, 25 Dec, 1 Jan, BHs
Additional: Sunday L.
Children welcome
Seats: 50
Style: Modern, Italian-Style
Smoking: No pipes; Air conditioning
Directions: Nearest tube: St John's Wood. Off Abbey Road

The Salt House

Map A5

A relaxed and friendly brasserie serving trendy beers and interesting wines with a simple daily-changing menu. Try perhaps, ham and parsley terrine set in jelly with onion marmalade and toasted brioche, or roasted wing of skate with peas pudding and drizzled nut butter. A short pudding list might include the highly rated lemon pannacotta with shortbread.

Style: Traditional
Smoking: No pipes; no cigars; Air conditioning
Directions: Telephone for directions

63 Abbey Road, NW8 0AE
Tel: 020 7328 6626
Fax: 020 7625 9168
Chef(s): Andrew Green
Owner(s): Robinson Restaurants
Cost: Alc £25, set price L £11.95.
☺ ☺ H/wine £9.75
Times: 12.30-3pm/6.30-10.30pm.
Closed 25-26 Dec, 1 Jan
Additional: Sunday L. Bar food.
Children welcome
Seats: 44. Private dining room 25

England

LONDON NW10

Sabras Restaurant

Map GtL C3 ◎◎

Longing for a really good Indian meal? Then try Sabras, an unpretentious family-run restaurant, which has been serving fresh and tasty vegetarian dishes for 27 years. It is very popular with locals and has a regular clientele who come from far and wide. Many of the ingredients are organic, everything is freshly prepared and the use of oil is restrained. Specialities from south and north India are included along with dishes from Gujarat, the owners' birthplace. Careful use of spices allows individual flavours to come through and the plate of assorted starters is a fine opportunity to taste differences in seasoning.

263 High Road, Willesden Green, NW10 2RX
Tel: 020 8459 0340
Chef(s): Mr & Mrs H Desai
Owner(s): Mr & Mrs H Desai
Times: Dinner only, 6.30-10.30pm. Closed Mon
Additional: Children welcome
Seats: 32
Smoking: No-smoking area

Directions: Nearest tube: Dollis Hill

LONDON SE1

Blue Print Café

Map G3 ◎

A bustling, stylish Conran restaurant with views to die for - unrivalled vistas across the Thames to Tower Bridge and the City. The décor is sophisticated and simple, as is the menu, which is written without elaboration. Changing twice daily, modern British dishes with Middle Eastern and Asian influences are presented in a straightforward manner such as rabbit cooked with peppers, black olives and basil.

The Design Museum,
28 Shad Thames, SE1 2YD
Tel: 020 7378 7031
Fax: 020 7357 8810
Chef(s): Jeremy Lee
Owner(s): Conran Restaurants
Cost: Alc £30, set price L £19.50. H/wine £14.50
Times: Noon-3pm/6-11pm. Closed D Sun, 25-28 Dec, 1 Jan

Additional: Sunday L. Children welcome
Seats: 120
Style: Modern, Minimalist
Directions: SE of Tower Bridge. On Mezzanine level of Design Museum

Butlers Wharf Chop House

Map D3 ◎

Good views of the river from this traditional restaurant, and there's an al fresco option when the weather allows. A strongly British menu offers starters like chicken livers on toast, potted Morecambe Bay shrimps and Jerusalem artichoke soup, followed by fish and chips with tartare sauce and watercress, steak and kidney pudding, and roast rib of beef. Good globetrotting wine list.

The Butlers Wharf Building,
36e Shad Thames, SE1 2YE
Tel: 020 7403 3403
Fax: 020 7403 3414
🄴 bwchophouse@ conran-restaurants.co.uk
Chef(s): Andy Rose
Owner(s): Conran Restaurants
Cost: Alc £30, set price L £23.75.
☺ ☺ H/wine £14.95
Times: Noon-3pm/6-11pm. Closed L Sat, D Sun, Good Friday

Additional: Sunday L. Bar food. Children welcome
Seats: 110
Style: Traditional
Directions: Nearest tubes: Tower Hill or London Bridge. On river front, SE side of Tower Bridge

England

Cantina del Ponte

Map GtL G3

Italian/Mediterranean-style food dominates the menu at this unpretentious Conran restaurant next to Tower Bridge, and bright murals accentuate its riverside setting. Sample the likes of pancetta and potato raviolo with white bean purée, and grilled pork with bean cassoulet and Toulouse sausage. Desserts like a faithful chocolate tart should please, but where was the Marsala in the tiramisu?

Additional: Children welcome
Seats: 95
Style: Rustic Italian
Directions: Nearest tubes: Tower Hill or London Bridge. SE side of Tower Bridge, by riverfront

The Butlers Wharf Building,
36c Shad Thames,
SE1 2YE
Tel: 020 7403 5403
Fax: 020 7403 0267
Owner(s): Sir Terence Conran
Cost: Alc £27.50, set price L
£32.50/D £32.50. ☺ ☺
H/wine £12.95
Times: Noon-3pm/6-11pm. Closed D
Sun, 24-26 Dec

Cantina Vinopolis

Map F3

The huge two-roomed restaurant in the Vinipolis wine museum is part of a suitably huge complex that also houses a gallery and a shop. The restaurant itself is decked out with honey-coloured bare brick walls, terracotta floor tiles, burgundy-coloured suede banquettes and solid wooden tables. More notable, perhaps, are the inescapable rows of wine bottles that line the establishment. The cuisine does justice to the stylish surroundings. Grilled tuna niçoise with salad of potato, French beans, anchovies and black olive tapenade is fairly typical of the style. Expect full flavours, consistent quality and generous portions.

Smoking: No-smoking area; no pipes; no cigars;
Air conditioning
Directions: Nearest tube: London Bridge

1 Bankside, SE1 9BU
Tel: 020 7940 8333
Fax: 020 7940 8334
🖃 cantina@vinopolis.co.uk
Chef(s): Annie Sheenan
Owner(s): T Gulliver & C Pulze
Cost: Alc £25. ☺ ☺ H/wine £10
Times: Noon-3pm/6-10.30pm.
Closed D Sun, BHs
Additional: Sunday L.
Children welcome
Seats: 160. Private dining room 160
Style: Modern, Brasserie

Champor Champor NEW Map G2

There is a sense of otherworldliness on stepping into this unusual restaurant and the effect is quite refreshing. Champor Champor means mix and match in Malay and this is religiously translated into the restaurant's eclectic decorative and culinary styles. Dishes from a number of Far Eastern countries are featured, including Thailand (Penang 'padi chicken' - crispy frogs legs served with Thai sweet chilli dip), Indonesia (Avocado and Nutmeg Tiramisu - derived from a creamy Indonesian avocado drink), Japan (calamari and burnt garlic miso soup), as well as the various regions within Malaysia itself (Malacan-Portugese fish).

Smoking: No pipes; no cigars
Directions: 3 mins walk from London Bridge Station. Leave station via Joiner St. Follow St. Thomas Street & 1st R into Weston Street. Restaurant 100yds on L

62 Weston Street,
SE1 3QJ
Tel: 020 7403 4600
🖃 mail@champor-champor.com
Chef(s): Amran Hassan
Owner(s): Charles Tyler &
Amran Hassan
Cost: Set price L £15/D £22.50. ☺ ☺
H/wine £9.50
Times: 12.30-3pm/6.30-Midnight.
Closed Sun, L Mon, Xmax-New Year
(10 days) Easter (4 days)
Additional: Children welcome.
Vegetarian by request only
Seats: 24
Style: Chic, Eclectic

England

LONDON SE1 *Continued*

Fire Station

Map E2

150 Waterloo Road,
SE1 8SB
Tel: 0207 620 2226
Fax: 0207 633 9161
e firestation@regent-inns.plc
Chef(s): Neil Pearson
Owner(s): Regent Inns Plc
Cost: *Alc* £25, set price L £13.50/
D £13.50. ☺ ☺
H/wine £10.45
Times: Noon-4pm/5.30-Midnight.

Former fire station located just south of the main entrance of
Waterloo Station. While the original structure is still quite
recognisable, it is now very much a pub in the outer section and
a diner in the inner area, with an open plan kitchen and rooms
available for private functions. Good food in generous portions
reflects an Eastern influence.

Additional: Sunday L. Bar food L. Children welcome
Seats: 100. Private dining room 90
Style: Modern
Smoking: No pipes; no cigars; Air conditioning
Directions: Nearest tube: Waterloo

London Marriott Hotel County Hall

Map E2

County Hall, SE1 7PB
Tel: 020 7902 8000
Fax: 020 7928 5300
Chef(s): Gregg Brown
Owner(s): Whitbread Hotels Plc
Cost: *Alc* £40, set price L £30/D £35.
H/wine £18
Times: Noon-2.30pm/5-11pm.
Additional: Sunday L. Bar food.
Children welcome
Seats: 90. Private dining room 80
Style: Modern, European
Smoking: No-smoking area; Air
conditioning
Civil licence: 150

Could one ask for a more enviable London location? This
Marriott hotel sits within a grade II listed building that
overlooks Big Ben and the Thames, and is adjacent to the
London Eye. All mod cons inside - including excellent leisure
facilities and splendid views from many rooms. Staff in the oak
panelled restaurant are cheerful and attentive which is welcome
in a hotel of this calibre. Contemporary British or modern
European - take your pick - define the style of cooking with the
simplest of dishes succeeding most. County Hall tiramisu is a
particular hit.

Accommodation: 200 rooms (200 en suite) ★ ★ ★ ★ ★
Directions: Nearest tube: Waterloo, Westminster. Situated next
to Westminster Bridge on the South Bank.

The Oxo Tower Restaurant

Map E3

8th Floor,
Oxo Tower Wharf,
Barge House Street SE1 9PH
Tel: 020 7803 3888
Fax: 020 7803 3838
e oxo.reservations@
harveynichols.co.uk

Perched high in the Oxo Tower and with a floor to ceiling glass
wall overlooking the river and the city beyond, the views here
are simply breathtaking (with dining on the terrace in fine
weather). Luckily the food is also noteworthy, with modern but
never outlandish combinations yielding consistent results.
Lobster, tomato and basil jelly and Sevruga caviar complement

each other well, as do whole lemon sole and sea urchin with wasabi butter, and roast scallops and langoustine tails with ratatouille ravioli and sauce Nantua. Try crab cake with tomato beurre blanc, and roast guinea fowl with crêpe parmentier and curly kale sauce.

Chef(s): Simon Arkless
Owner(s): Harvey Nichols & Co Ltd
Cost: *Alc* £38, set price L £27.50-£37.50. H/wine £12.50
Times: Noon-3pm/6-11pm.
Closed L Sat, 25-26 Dec
Additional: Sunday L.
Children welcome
Seats: 130
Style: Modern

Smoking: No pipes; Air conditioning
Directions: Nearest tube: Blackfriars. Between Blackfriars & Waterloo bridge

Neat   NEW   Map E3

Quite a homecoming was on the cards as we went to press. Richard Neat's youthful achievements at Pied à Terre still engender happy memories for those who ate there in the first half of the 1990s. Two years in India were followed by the audacious opening of the celebrated Neat in Cannes and his London return sees him ensconced on the 2nd floor of Oxo Tower Wharf. Neat itself is a 120-cover restaurant serving an unashamedly classic French menu that is likely to exhibit the trademark bold use of flavours and technical dexterity. A 150-seater brasserie will have simpler food and also offer breakfast and afternoon tea.

Directions: Nearest tube: Blackfriars. Between Blackfriars & Waterloo bridge

2nd Floor, Oxo Tower Wharf, Barge House Street, SE1 9PH
Tel: 020 7928 5533
🅴 eat@neatrestaurant.co.uk
Chef(s): Richard Neat
Cost: *Alc* £75
Times: Noon-2pm/7-10pm.
Closed Sun, L Sat
Additional: Vegetarian by request only. Jacket and tie preferred
Seats: 100. Private dining room 25
Style: Chic

The People's Palace   Map E3

Its outstanding South Bank location and a window seat providing fantastic views of the Thames alone should be enough to justify a visit to this minimalist restaurant. You can also pre-order meals for post-theatre convenience. Contemporary menu with a nod to British tradition in the likes of haunch of venison with braised red cabbage and mulled wine jus.

Seats: 240
Style: Modern, Minimalist
Smoking: No-smoking area; Air conditioning
Directions: Level 3 of the Royal Festival Hall

Royal Festival Hall,
Belvedere Road, SE1 8XX
Tel: 020 7928 9999
Fax: 020 7928 2355
🅴 reservations@peoplespalace.co.uk
Chef(s): Guy Bossom
Owner(s): Mr. Levin
Cost: *Alc* £25, set price L £17.50/D £21.50. ☺ ☺ H/wine £11.50
Times: Noon-3pm/5.30-11pm
Additional: Sunday L. Bar food.
Children welcome

England

LONDON SE1 *Continued*

Le Pont de la Tour

Map **G3**

The Butlers Wharf Building,
36d Shad Thames SE1 2YE
Tel: 020 7403 8403
Fax: 020 7403 0267
Chef(s): Tim Powell
Owner(s): Sir Terence Conran
Cost: *Alc* £45, set price L £28.50/
D £19.50 (pre/post theatre). ☺
H/wine £12.95
Times: Noon-3pm/6-11.30pm.
Closed L Sat, 25-26 Dec, Good Friday
Additional: Sunday L. Bar food.
Children welcome
Seats: 105. Private dining room 20

Thames-side brasserie-style restaurant with superb views of
Tower Bridge and the boating traffic of the river. An
understandably popular spot, the restaurant can get very busy,
though service is good and the rush is handled pretty well.
Cooking is simple and skilful - a basket brimful of delicious
rustic breads sets the scene - and seafood is a speciality of the
seasonal menu. Irish oysters, Cornish crab and wonderfully
fresh lobster - with mayonnaise, fennel and lemon salad - all
make an appearance. There is a separate vegetarian menu and
dishes of roast lamb, or venison casserole with juniper and
glazed parsnips

Style: Modern, Formal
Smoking: Air conditioning
Directions: SE of Tower Bridge. Nearest tube: Tower Hill

RSJ, The Restaurant on the South Bank

Map **E3**

13a Coin Street, SE1 8YQ
Tel: 020 7928 4554
Fax: 020 7401 2455
Telephone for further details

A converted stable setting has allowed for a spacious, modern
design with the restaurant spread over three floors. A modern
approach to cuisine does not preclude hearty satisfaction as in
an exquisitely tender cut of roast venison, and a really quite
rustic prune and orange brûlée - a tad messy but great flavours.

LONDON SE3

Chapter Two

Map **GtL E3**

43-45 Montpelier Vale,
Blackheath Village,
SE3 0TJ
Tel: 020 8333 2666
Fax: 020 8355 8399
Chef(s): Derek Baker
Owner(s): Selective Restaurants
Group
Cost: *Alc* £14.50-£22.50. ☺ ☺
H/wine £13.50

Just some five minutes' walk from Blackheath rail station, this
dapper restaurant sits at the fringe of the village. With attentive,
professional service - and a recent change of chef - it continues
to produce bright and crisply presented food. Stand-out dishes
include a Thai crab ravioli with galchan dressing and salmon
pavé, crisp and moist, laid over a potato mash dressed with
lobster morsels. Dinner menus command a fixed price (more
expensive at weekends) that may offer quail salad with pickled

vegetables and whole Jersey plaice on aïoli potatoes with braised leek vinaigrette. Chocolate-chip ice cream accompanies Bakewell cheesecake and fresh walnut bread comes with a trio of well-chosen cheeses.

Smoking: No-smoking area; no pipes; no cigars; Air conditioning
Directions: 5 min walk from Blackheath Rail Station.

Times: Noon-3.30pm/6.30-10.30pm.
Closed 1-4 Jan
Additional: Sunday L.
Children welcome
Seats: 70
Style: Modern, Chic

Laicram Thai Restaurant   Map GtL E2

This diminutive restaurant has a cottage feel to it with carved wooden panels and Thai china. The menu is fairly lengthy with plenty to hold one's interest such as chicken slices blended with galigaleroot, herbs, lemon grass, lemon juice, chilli and coconut. A light jelly flavoured with lotus flower made an enlightening dessert.

Seats: 50
Style: Traditional
Smoking: Air conditioning
Directions: Off main shopping street, in a side road near the Post Office. Opposite station

1 Blackheath Grove,
Blackheath, SE3 0DD
Tel: 020 8852 4710
Chef(s): Mrs S Dhirabutra
Owner(s): Mr D Dhirabutra
Cost: Alc £20. ☺ ☺ H/wine £9.50
Times: Noon-2.30pm/6-11pm.
Closed Mon, BHs
Additional: Sunday L.
Children welcome

LONDON SE21

Belair House   Map GtL D2

In a classic, though rebuilt, 1785 Palladian villa overlooking Belair Park, a stylish and airy setting in sunshine yellow and navy blue with bold modern European menus. At set prices for lunch and dinner, choices include langoustine ravioli, braised duck with chanterelles and truffle risotto and pear tarte Tatin.

Gallery Road, SE21 7AB
Tel: 020 8299 9788
Fax: 020 8299 6793
e belairhouse@aol.com
Chef(s): Zak Elhamoou
Owner(s): Gary Cady
Cost: Alc £32.45, set price L £21.95-£29.95. H/wine £16
Times: Noon-2.30pm/7-10.30pm.
Closed D Sun Winter
Additional: Sunday L. Children welcome
Seats: 100. Private dining room 85
Style: Classic, French
Smoking: No pipes; no cigars
Directions: From Brixton, Gallery Road is the 1st turning off the South Circular after passing West Dulwich train station. From Catford: 1st turning off South Circular after Dulwich College

LONDON SE23

Babur Brasserie   Map GtL D2

Renowned south London Indian restaurant with a colourful menu 'celebrating spice'. A tiger's head motif denotes the strength of the more challenging dishes (one head for hot and two for roaring). In the temperate zone is caldine, an aristocratic maritime dish of medallions of monkfish with a piquant sauce combining jeera, tamarind, coriander and coconut milk. For a more searing experience try chicken peri

119 Brockley Rise,
Forest Hill, SE23 1JP
Tel: 020 8291 2400
Fax: 020 8291 4881
e babur_brasserie@compuserve.com
Chef(s): Enam Rahman
Owner(s): Babur 1998 Ltd
Cost: Alc £22.25. ☺ ☺ H/wine £7.95

England

LONDON SE23 *Continued*

Babur Brasserie

peri - the Portuguese approach to chicken curry. A popular option for Sunday is the buffet lunch, where kids of seven or younger eat free.

Smoking: No-smoking area; Air conditioning
Directions: 5 mins walk from Honor Oak BR Station, where parking is available

Times: Noon-2.30pm/6-11.30pm.
Closed L Fri, 25-26 Dec
Additional: Sunday L.
Children welcome
Seats: 56
Style: Modern

LONDON SE24

3 Monkeys Restaurant

Map GtL D2

136-140 Herne Hill, SE24 9QH

Striking Indian restaurant with white minimalism spiced up by waiters' purple shirts and bows around napkins. The menu wanders around the sub-continent with karhai dishes from the Northwest Frontier, fish curry from Goa, soup (tamater ka rasam) and lamb (narial ka bunha gosht) from South India, and even a street dish (dhaba murg). Sensational naan bread, and over forty wines.

Tel: 020 7738 5500
Fax: 020 7738 5505
📧 jpeacock@monkeys3.demon.co.uk
Chef(s): Sanjay Gupta
Owner(s): Jan Peacock
Cost: Alc £24, set price L £9.95/D £18.95. ☺ ☺ H/wine £12.95
Times: Noon-3pm/6-10.30pm. Closed L Mon-Sat, 25-26 Dec, 1 Jan
Additional: Sunday L. Bar food D. Children welcome
Seats: 100
Style: Modern
Smoking: No-smoking area; no pipes; Air conditioning
Directions: Adjacent to Herne Hill Station

LONDON SW1

Al Duca

Map D4

4/5 Duke of York Street,
SW1Y 6LA
Tel: 020 7839 3090
Fax: 020 7839 4050
Chef(s): Michele Franzolin
Owner(s): Cuisine Collection

'Damn good value' is the judgement on this modern Italian restaurant. The cooking is not overly complicated but is none the worse for that, with well-conceived dishes full of fresh natural flavours from first-rate raw materials. Beautifully roasted, crisp-skinned cod - the nicest bit of fish had in a while -

was served with fresh tomato, sautéed new potatoes, green olives and basil, all in a light dressing. Like the cooking, the décor is unfussy but stylish, focusing around the glass-fronted wine cupboards. Wines are exclusively Italian (save for the fizz) with a good spread of prices, and service is urbane and attentive.

Directions: Nearest Tube: Green Park. 5 mins walk from station towards Piccadilly. R into St James', L into Jermyn St. Duke of York St, halfway along on R

Cost: Set price L £18-£21/D £21-£24.
☺ H/wine £12.50
Times: Noon-2.30pm/6-10.30pm.
Closed L Sun, BHs
Additional: Children welcome
Seats: 56
Style: Modern
Smoking: No pipes; no cigars; Air conditioning

The Avenue

Map C3

7-9 St James's Street,
SW1A 1EE
Fax: 020 7321 2500
Telephone for further details

It may be unusual to recommend a restaurant that serves fish fingers but the Avenue's home-made variation are a popular choice. The modern European menu also offers crispy duck pancakes with sweet soy sauce or calves' liver with champ and bacon. This large restaurant, with its long bar, large window and grand piano, has a lively atmosphere.

Directions: Nearest tube: Green Park. Turn R past The Ritz, 2nd turning into St James' Street

Bank Westminster & Zander Bar

Map C2

Buckingham Gate, SW1E 6BS
Tel: 020 7379 9797
Fax: 020 7240 7001
e westres@bankrestaurants.com
Chef(s): Matthew Dawson
Owner(s): Bank Restaurant Group
Cost: Alc £40, set price L £17.50/
D £17.50. ☺ H/wine £12.50
Times: Noon-3pm/5.30-11.30pm.
Additional: Sunday L. Bar food.
Children welcome

A bright, modern setting with lemon-yellow walls and well-placed modern art prints. The hotel restaurant maintains high-flying credentials - our inspector enjoyed an excellent piece of baked cod as the centrepiece of a classy meal.

Seats: 136. Private dining room 40
Style: Modern, Chic
Smoking: No-smoking area; Air conditioning
Accommodation: 342 rooms (342 en suite) ★ ★ ★ ★
Directions: 5 minutes from Victoria BR Station. L out of St James Park station, down Petty France and L into Buckingham Gate

Boisdale

Map C2

15 Eccleston Street,
SW1W 9LX
Tel: 020 7730 6922
Fax: 020 7730 0548
e info@boisdale.co.uk
Chef(s): Ronald Irvine
Owner(s): Mr R Macdonald
Cost: Alc £30, set price L £17.45/
D £17.45. ☺ ☺ H/wine £12.90
Times: Noon-2.30pm/7-Midnight.
Closed Sun, L Sat , Xmas, New Year,
BHs

A clubhouse atmosphere, live jazz music, supposedly, the oldest cigar bar in London and over 200 single malts in the Macdonald bar are amongst the attractions. The menu is patriotically Caledonian too, with everything from Scotch woodcock to Lochcarnan hot smoked salmon. Gentler handling of such prime, raw materials would be welcome, but careful sourcing of the finest Scottish produce is laudable.

Additional: Bar food. Children welcome
Seats: 100. Private dining room 22
Style: Scottish, Country-house
Smoking: Air conditioning
Directions: Nearest tube: Victoria, turn L along Buckingham Palace Road heading W, Eccleston Street is 1st on the R

LONDON SW1 *Continued*

The Cadogan Hotel

Map B2

75 Sloane Street, SW1X 9SG
Tel: 020 7235 7141
Fax: 020 7245 0994
e info@cadogan.com
Chef(s): Graham Thompson
Owner(s): Historic House Hotels Ltd
Cost: *Alc* £40, set price L £18.90/
D £27. H/wine £13.50
Times: 12.30-2pm/5.30-10pm.
Closed L Sat
Additional: Sunday L. Bar food.
Children 10yrs+
Seats: 40. Private dining room 36.
Jacket and tie preferred
Style: Edwardian
Smoking: No pipes; no cigars;
Air conditioning

Oscar Wilde and Lillie Langtry were two celebrated visitors to this delightful Victorian hotel, still noted for its elegance and style. The Edwardian restaurant exudes an ageless chic, though modern British influences have raised the classic cuisine to new heights. From a concise menu consider mille-feuille of wild mushrooms, squab pigeon (stunningly tender), or crab ravioli with lobster cappuccino. Follow this with roasted salmon with broad bean risotto and caviar cream, or pan-fried monkfish with creamy curried mussels. Look out for desserts like raspberry soufflé with sorbet, or orange mousse with praline, and enjoy some highly professional service.

Civil licence: 40
Accommodation: 65 rooms (65 en suite) ★ ★ ★ ★
Directions: Nearest tube: Sloane Square, Knightsbridge

Le Caprice Restaurant

Map C3

Arlington House,
Arlington Street,
SW1A 1RT
Tel: 020 7629 2239
Fax: 020 7493 9040
Chef(s): Elliot Ketley, Mark Hix
Owner(s): Belgo Group Plc
Cost: *Alc* £35. H/wine £11.25
Times: Noon-3pm/5.30-Midnight.
Closed Aug BHs, D 24 Dec,
25-26 Dec, 1 Jan
Additional: Bar food.
Children welcome
Seats: 80
Style: Classic
Smoking: No pipes; Air conditioning

The magnetic attraction of this celebrity restaurant means the place is usually heaving - book well in advance to ensure a table. Star's photos adorn the walls, and the focal point is a long bar where to see and be seen is the point. The food is almost a side issue, but it's much better than that, as a glance at the trendy menu suggests. The unpretentious features alongside the classy, in dishes like champagne risotto with black Perigord truffles, lobster thermidor with chips, and oysters Rockerfeller. Expect also upbeat versions of the commonplace with deep-fried haddock with chips, grilled rib-eye steak, roasted fillet of cod with lobster mash, and chopped steak Americaine, a posh version of the ubiquitous burger. There's a separate Sunday brunch menu, ranging from bagel with smoked salmon and cream cheese to eggs Benedict, or creamed linguini with lobster and tarragon, and puddings like mousse aux deux chocolats.

Directions: Nearest tube: Green Park. Arlington St runs beside The Ritz, Le Caprice is at end

Caraffini

Map B2

61-63 Lower Sloane Street,
SW1W 8DH
Tel: 020 7259 0235

Friendly staff, and stylish interiors with yellows, blues, greens, and wooden floors combine to create a warm atmosphere here.

The food is similarly benevolent. A typical generous offering of risotto with porcini mushrooms might be followed by rack of lamb with a crust of fresh herbs.

Fax: 020 7259 0236
Chef(s): John Patino, Serafino Ramalhoto
Owner(s): F Di Rienzo & Paolo Caraffini
Cost: Alc £25. ☺ ☺ H/wine £10.15
Times: 12.15-2.30pm/6.30-11.30pm. Closed Sun, BHs
Additional: Children welcome
Seats: 70
Style: Italian
Smoking: No pipes; Air conditioning
Directions: Nearest tube: Sloane Square

The Cavendish St James's   Map D3

A stylish, modern hotel whose restaurant features traditional decor, plenty of natural daylight and views over Jermyn Street. The menu is European in style, but occasionally imports ideas from further afield (as in a starter of chargrilled king prawn and sesame brochette with Thai sauce). Other dishes might include garlic studded mini roast lamb or roast salmon with basil and chorizo.

81 Jermyn Street, SW1Y 6JF
Tel: 020 7930 2111
Fax: 020 7839 4551
e guests@cavendishstjames.co.uk
Chef(s): Gary McGuinness
Owner(s): De Vere Hotels & Leisure Ltd
Cost: Alc £35, set price L £24.50-£35/D £24.50-£35. ☺ H/wine £13.95
Times: Noon-2.30pm/6-10.30pm. Closed L Sat-Sun
Additional: Bar food. Children welcome. Vegetarian by request only
Seats: 80. Private dining room 80
Style: Traditional, Classic
Smoking: No-smoking area; no pipes; no cigars; Air conditioning
Accommodation: 251 rooms (251 en suite) ★★★★
Directions: Nearest tube: Green Park, Piccadilly Circus

Drones   **NEW**   Map B2

Like some kind of benevolent cuckoo, Marco Pierre White has revived another legendary nest - this one opened in the 70's by Pink Floyd's Dave Gilmour. The recipe might be familiar (MPW reworkings of the classic and the comfortable) but it is none the less welcome for that and the food, like the service and interior is confident and stylish. The menu is spectacularly good value, especially at lunch and will offer you the likes of a sturdy dish of smoked haddock with colcannon potatoes, sublime roast chicken with bread sauce, the ubiquitous but brilliant tarte Tatin of pears with vanilla or an exquisite treacle tart with clotted cream. Cornel Lucas's alluring showbiz photos glamourise the walls, whilst the boutiques of nearby Sloane Street do the same for much of the clientele. The great virtue is that you don't need that kind of purchasing power to eat here.

1 Pont Street, SW1X 9EJ
Tel: 020 7235 9555
Fax: 020 7235 9566
Chef(s): Joseph Croan
Owner(s): White Star Line Restaurant Ltd.
Cost: Alc £45, set price L £17.95-£19.50. ☺ H/wine £15.50
Times: Noon-2.30pm/6-11pm. Closed 1 Jan
Additional: Sunday L. Children welcome
Seats: 100. Private dining room 40
Style: Classic, French
Smoking: Air conditioning

Directions: Nearest tube: Knightsbridge & Sloane Square

LONDON SW1 *Continued*

The Fifth Floor Restaurant

Map B2

Harvey Nichols,
Knightsbridge, SW1X 7RJ
Tel: 020 7235 5250
Fax: 020 7823 2207
Chef(s): Simon Shaw
Owner(s): Harvey Nichols & Co Ltd.
Cost: *Alc* £37.50, set price L £24.50.
H/wine £12.50
Times: Noon-3pm/6.30-11.30pm.
Closed D Sun, 25-26 Dec
Additional: Sunday L. Bar food L.
Children welcome
Seats: 110
Style: Modern, Chic
Smoking: No-smoking area; no pipes;
Air conditioning
Directions: Nearest tube:
Knightsbridge. Entrance on Sloane
Street

The ambience at this Harvey Nichols restaurant, five floors over Knightsbridge, may be a little more sedate these days but retains a certain chic along with its reclaimed teak parquet. The *carte* reads seductively enough with starters of warm roast pumpkin and chorizo salad, or rabbit, foie gras and potato terrine. A choice of around a dozen mains might field roasted cod with tomato and anchovy tart, or pork tenderloin with apple mash and glazed chestnuts. Don't miss out on the sweet stuff either, the kitchen is strong in the pastry department and there are suggestions from the sommelier for appropriate accompaniments.

Goring Hotel

Map C2

Beeston Place, Grosvenor Gardens,
SW1W 0JW
Tel: 020 7396 9000
Fax: 020 7834 4393
e reception@goringhotel.co.uk
Chef(s): Derek Quelch
Owner(s): Mr G E Goring
Cost: Set price L £25-£29/D £38.
H/wine £19.50
Times: 12.30-2.30pm/6-10pm.
Closed L Sat

Recently refurbished restaurant in gentle creams, yellows and gold leaf, with light streaming in through huge windows. The look is classical, and the pomp and ceremony provided by the formal service have probably changed little since the hotel opened. The menu is typically British with many dishes crafted from fine UK produce, but in recent times there has been a drift to more contemporary dishes. The wine list is extensive and relates particularly well to the menu. A high level of skill was apparent in a starter of rillette of rabbit with vegetable vinaigrette, which was served at just the right temperature (not too cold). Main courses comprise a good choice of fish, vegetarian and meat dishes, perhaps fillet of sea bass with Provençale vegetables, glazed wild mushroom and leek tart, and noisettes of lamb with coriander polenta.

Directions: Nearest tube: Victoria – onto Victoria St, turn L into Grosvenor Gdns, cross Buckingham Palace Rd, 75yds turn L into Beeston Place

Additional: Sunday L. Bar food. Children welcome
Seats: 70. Private dining room 50
Style: Traditional
Smoking: No pipes; Air conditioning
Civil licence: 50
Accommodation: 74 rooms (74 en suite) ★ ★ ★ ★

Green's Restaurant & Oyster Bar

Map C3

36 Duke Street, SW1Y 6DF
Tel: 020 7930 4566
Fax: 020 7491 7463
e greens@greens.org.uk
Chef(s): Eddie Bleackley
Owner(s): Mr S Parker-Bowles
Additional: Children welcome
Seats: 64
Smoking: No-smoking area

Exceedingly reliable restaurant in the club land section of the West End. Two main rooms offer contrasting settings, one which is more 'clubby' with green leather and wood panelling, and the other showing off pale yellow walls and a lighter style. Generous portions of straightforward food are to be expected from menus that also provide plenty of choice. Top-notch ingredients are soundly cooked, from herrings that are soused and served with beetroot and ginger relish to whole lobster served cold. Although the menu majors on fish, there are also some worthy meat dishes like pan-fried lamb with lentil, vegetable and barley broth.

Directions: Nearest tube: Piccadilly. Near Fortnum & Mason. Opposite the Cavendish Hotel

Grissini

Map B2

at Hyatt Carlton Tower Hotel, Cadogan Place, SW1X 9PY
Tel: 020 7858 7171/7172
Fax: 020 7235 9129
e grissini@hytlondon.co.uk
Chef(s): Donato Russo
Owner(s): Francesco Miglionico
Cost: Alc £35, set price L £16-£21. H/wine £30
Times: 12.30-2.45pm/6.30-10.30pm. Closed L Sat, D Sun, Easter
Additional: Sunday L. Bar food. Children welcome
Seats: 80. Private dining room 45
Style: Modern, Italian

Grissini is the conservatory restaurant at the Hyatt Carlton Tower Hotel, overlooking Cadogan Gardens and serving contemporary Italian cooking. The menu is fresh and imaginative, kicking off with good home-made breads and, of course, freshly baked grissini. Fish is of good quality and sympathetically treated - sea bass, simply baked with herbs, olive oil and lemon, resting on tender fennel stalks. A choice of accompaniments might include light olive mash with sun-dried tomatoes, with a garnish of fresh basil, niçoise olives and tomato concasse. Desserts have won praise too - crumbly polenta cake served with marinated pear and a vibrant grappa sorbet.

Smoking: No-smoking area; Air conditioning
Civil licence: 360
Accommodation: 220 rooms (220 en suite) ★ ★ ★ ★ ★
Directions: Nearest tube: Knightsbridge, Sloane Square. From Knightsbridge Station down Sloane St. Hotel entrance is 2nd L

Il Convivio

NEW Map C1

113 Ebury Street, SW1W 9QN
Tel: 020 7730 4099
Fax: 020 7730 4103
e comments@etruscagroup.co.uk
Chef(s): Lukas Pfaff
Owner(s): Piero & Enzo Quaradeghini

A glass fronted restaurant stylishly decorated with red and cream walls and light wooden flooring. A glass ceiling at the back lets in plenty of natural light. The menu is, of course, Italian, and offers a broad selection of pasta, fish and meat dishes. The friendly waiters (also Italian) are happy to help guests choose between mouthwatering offerings such as roasted duck breast with zolfini beans and a fig sauce or risotto with

England

LONDON SW1 *Continued*

farigliano cheese and a duck foie gras. The wine list also sticks to the Italian theme and includes some interesting, lesser known indigenous grapes.

Il Convivio

Cost: Set price L £16.50-£20/ D £29.50-£35. H/wine £14.50
Times: Closed Sun, Xmas, New Year, BHs
Additional: Children welcome
Seats: 65. Private dining room 14
Style: Modern, Chic, Formal
Smoking: No-smoking area;
Air conditioning
Directions: 7 min walk from Victoria Station – corner of Ebury St and Elizabeth St.

Isola

Map E2

The interior design is American, the food Italian and the chef French, but it all works rather well. It's hard to walk past this slick, glass fronted restaurant without being tranfixed by the smooth lines of the retro, red leather seating, mirrored pillars and parquet walls. The staff occupy the same time capsule, buttoned up to the chest in grey waistcoats and providing an efficient, 'old school' style of service. Don't expect pasta that's had an olive waved at it; this is Italian cooking with integrity - elaborate dishes such as stuffed saddle of rabbit or lobster cannelloni invite leisurely, enthusiastic eating.

145 Knightsbridge,
SW1X 7PA
Tel: 020 7838 1044
Fax: 020 7838 1099
e reception_isola@lineone.net
Chef(s): Bruno Loobet
Owner(s): Oliver Peyton
Cost: *Alc* £32. ☺ H/wine £13.50
Times: Dinner only, 6-Midnight.
Closed Sun
Additional: Children welcome
Seats: 110
Style: Modern, Minimalist
Smoking: Air conditioning
Directions: Nearest tube:
Knightsbridge. On the corner of Brompton Rd and Knightsbridge

Jak's

Map B1

Serious restaurant with a relaxed atmosphere in an upmarket residential district. The main dining areas are located in the basement, with some tables at the ground floor entrance, and there's a good bar area for meeting up with friends for a pre-meal drink. The sensibly short menu bears out the commitment

77 Lower Sloane Street,
SW1W 8DA
Tel: 020 7730 9476
Fax: 020 7823 5040
e info@jaksclub.com
Chef(s): Adrian Jones

England

to freshly cooked dishes from quality produce. Kick off with home-made bread and take your choice from the simply described dishes: 'home-cured beef, warm foie gras, red onion chutney', or 'grilled cod, peppers, new potatoes, Parma ham', and let the flavours speak for themselves.

Seats: 56. Private dining room 8
Style: Modern, Minimalist
Smoking: No-smoking area; Air conditioning
Directions: Nearest tube: Sloane Square

Owner(s): Justin Wheeler
Cost: *Alc* £30, set price L £15-£20/ D £25-£30. ☺ H/wine £13.50
Times: Noon-2.15pm/6.30pm-1am. Closed Sat, D Sun, 25 Dec
Additional: Sunday L. Bar food L. Children welcome

Just St James   NEW   Map C3

An old bank in the heart of St James', with huge marble pillars and arched windows, is the cavernous setting for some rather grand dining. Large storm lamps, and a gold, cream and terracotta décor soften the immense space, where modern British reinterpretations of some classic dishes are well received. Foie gras on dill pancakes, and seared scallops on pak choi with papaya might precede shank of lamb with red wine and shallots, fillet of beef Wellington with julienne of garlic potatoes, and seared calves' liver with smoked bacon. Bitter prune and Armagnac tart with clotted cream, and treacle sponge pudding follow.

Directions: Nearest Tube: Green Park – Turn R on Piccadilly towards Piccadilly Circus, then R into St James St. Restaurant on corner of St James St & King St

12 St James Street, SW1
Tel: 020 7976 2222
Fax: 020 7976 2020
🅔 bookings@juststjames.com
Chef(s): Peter Gladwin
Owner(s): Peter Gladwin
Cost: *Alc* £45, set price L £20.50. ☺ ☺ H/wine £14.50
Times: Noon-4pm/6-midnight. Closed D Sun, Xmas
Additional: Sunday L. Bar food. Children welcome
Seats: 120. Private dining room 120
Style: Classic, Oriental
Smoking: Air conditioning

The Lanesborough   Map C3

The soothing sounds of running water and a tinkling piano lull the senses in this conservatory restaurant at the centre of a fabulous old building. Light and airy with lots of levels, it serves traditional dishes based on reliable ingredients with a good balance between surf and turf. A concise set menu is offered alongside the snappy *carte*, with vegetarians carefully considered in both. The likes of rustic Tuscan pasta with sautéed shellfish, chilli and basil, and king prawn salad with green mango and mint yuzu dressing show the range of starters, while tamarind barbecued duck with spicy greens and caramelised pineapple, and baked Swiss chard and mascarpone rotolo with sage and Parmesan are typical main courses. Earl Grey panacotta was a superbly subtle recent dessert, served with a slightly tart orange marmalade.

Hyde Park Corner, SW1X 7TA
Tel: 020 7259 5599
Fax: 020 7259 5606
🅔 info@lanesborough.co.uk

Chef(s): Paul Gayler
Cost: *Alc* £55, set price L £31/D £34-£48. H/wine £21.50
Times: Noon-2.30pm/6.30-11.30pm.
Additional: Sunday brunch. Children welcome
Seats: 104. Private dining room 100. Jacket and tie preferred
Style: Oriental
Smoking: Air conditioning
Civil licence: 100
Accommodation: 95 rooms (95 en suite) ★ ★ ★ ★ ★
Directions: Nearest tube: Hyde Park Corner. On Hyde Park corner

LONDON SW1 *Continued*

Mandarin Oriental Hyde Park

Map B2

Adam Tihany (famous for his work at Le Cirque in New York and Spago in Las Vegas) was imported for the revamp of this famous venue and has split the critics on the results. The restaurant is on two levels with the leaf theme abundant in both. Walls are clad with glass panels sandwiching white silk leaves between the panes and these are lit to reflect the seasons (golds and reds in autumn etc). The bar is incredibly busy and you will do well to find space to take a pre-dinner drink. The menu is a satisfying take on classic French cuisine, there are few innovations but the pinpoint execution and depth of flavour achieved are more than enough compensation for that. Foie gras, for instance, comes 'three ways' – terrine on finely chopped chives with truffle jelly, seared on celeriac mousseline and marinated in port – a combination that has been described as "stunning" and that comes with a recommendation from the waiter as to the order in which to eat it "for best effect". Top-notch ingredients are allowed to speak for themselves in dishes like an "accomplished" main course of veal sweetbreads with a ravioli of ceps, roast shallots, braised cos and Sauternes cream – sturdy stuff indeed. Great dexterity apparent in the desserts which feature caramelised polenta cake with poached apricots, almond sorbet and a sabayon of Sauternes or a sesame and white chocolate mille feuille with blood orange jelly that has been noted as lacking a little balance flavour wise. Good petits fours arrive in a natty little oriental box with a china lid. The wine list is unashamedly francophile but given the location is not too aggressive with the mark-ups.

66 Knightsbridge, SW1X 7LA
Tel: 020 7235 2000
Fax: 020 7235 4552
e reserve-molon@mohg.com
Chef(s): David Nicholls
Cost: *Alc* £50, set price L £19-£23.50/D £37.50. H/wine £16
Times: Noon-2.30pm/7-10.30pm. Closed Sun, L Sat
Additional: Bar food. Children welcome
Seats: 46. Private dining room 250
Style: Modern, European
Smoking: No-smoking area; no pipes; no cigars; Air conditioning
Civil licence: 200
Accommodation: 200 rooms (200 en suite) ★ ★ ★ ★ ★
Directions: Nearest Tube: Knightsbridge

Matsuri

Map D3

The ideal introduction to Japanese food, Matsuri has a smart sushi bar and chic basement restaurant with a huge papier-mâché artwork on the stairs. Staff are particularly helpful and pleased to guide newcomers around the menu. The centrepiece of any meal is teppanyaki, with lobster and assorted seafood, steak, duck, chicken or pork all grilled on a hot plate. The tempura is great, and there's good sushi, sashimi, and that holy trinity of Japanese meals: miso soup, steamed rice and mixed pickles. The highpoint this time was succulent and superbly flavoured teppanyaki Scottish sirloin steak, served with stir-fried vegetables.

Directions: Nearest tube: Green Park. Towards Piccadilly Circus, R into St James', 1st L into Jermyn St, 1st R

15 Bury Street, SW1Y 6AL
Tel: 020 7839 1101
Fax: 020 7930 7010
e matsuri@japanglobe.net
Chef(s): Kanehiro Takase
Owner(s): JRK (UK) Ltd
Cost: *Alc* £30, set price L £20-£45/D £30-£50. ☺ ☺ H/wine £18
Times: Noon-2.30pm/6-10.30pm. Closed Sun, BHs, Xmas, New Year
Additional: Children welcome
Seats: 133. Private dining room 18
Style: Modern, Japanese
Smoking: Air conditioning

☺ Indicates a restaurant that has told us they offer a two-course lunch for less than £15

☺ Indicates a restaurant that has told us they offer a three-course dinner for less than £25

England

Memories of China Restaurant

Map C2 ◉◉

Still a leader in Chinese cooking offering modern dishes with influences from all over China. The décor of this smart restaurant is very simple, with bare white walls only interrupted by a few red-painted Chinese calligraphic signs, and some carved screens strategically placed to break up the room. The menu, written in plain English, offers a number of set meals, though none are for one person; and several specialities. Among these are delicious fried courgettes stuffed with prawn mince, Mongolian barbecue of shredded lamb in lettuce puffs and spicy bean curd casserole.

Directions: Nearest tube: Sloane Square, Victoria. At the junction of Ebury Street & Eccleston Street

67 Ebury Street,
SW1W 0NZ
Tel: 020 7730 7734
Fax: 020 7730 2992
Cost: Alc £30, set price L £19.50-£21.50/D £30-£34. ☺ ☺
H/wine £13.50
Times: Noon-2.30pm/7-11pm.
Closed L Sun, BHs, 25 Dec
Additional: Children welcome
Seats: 100. Private dining room 20
Style: Modern, Chic
Smoking: Air conditioning

Mitsukoshi

Map D3 ◉◉

Uncompromising Japanese restaurant where the uninitiated are welcome but not pandered to. Ninety-percent of the customers are Japanese so don't expect detailed Anglicised descriptions on the menu. On the other hand you can expect a good value, no-nonsense dose of the genuine article. The tempura set meal could open with miso soup (dashi based with fermented bean curd, wakame and small dice of tofu) followed by a tempura of enormous top quality prawns, aubergine, green pepper and onion. The décor is simple, light and tasteful and the restaurant is housed in the basement of a Japanese department store.

Style: Classic, Japanese
Smoking: No pipes; no cigars; Air conditioning
Directions: Nearest tube: Piccadilly Circus

Dorland House, 14-20
Lower Regent Street, SW1Y 4PH
Tel: 020 7930 0317
Fax: 020 7839 1167
🄴 lonrest@mitsukoshi.co.jp
Chef(s): Mr Motohashi
Owner(s): Mitsukoshi (UK) Ltd.
Cost: Alc £25, set price L £9.90-£35/D £20-£35. ☺ ☺ H/wine £12
Times: Noon-3pm/6-10.30pm.
Closed Sun, Xmas, Easter, New Year
Additional: Children welcome
Seats: 56. Private dining room 32

Mju at Millennium Knightsbridge

Map B2

Exciting cross continental developments as we went to press with Tetsuya Wakuda (widely held to be Australia's finest and most innovative chef) due to take over the refurbished and renamed 90 cover restaurant. Wakuda's cooking marries the Japanese philosophy of the ultra fresh ingredients with classic French techniques. Expect a quite different dining procedure with a series of dishes (around eight at dinner) arriving in turn with no choice at any point.

Additional: Children welcome
Seats: 100. Private dining room 100
Smoking: No-smoking area; Air conditioning
Accommodation: 222 rooms (222 en suite) ★ ★ ★ ★
Directions: 200yds from Kensington Stn/near Harrods

17 Sloane Street, Knightbridge,
SW1X 9NU
Tel: 020 7201 6330
Fax: 020 7235 3705
Chef(s): Paul Bates
Owner(s): Millennium & Copthorne Hotels
Cost: Alc £40, set price L £18-£25/D £35. H/wine £18
Times: Noon-2.30pm/7-10.30pm.
Closed Sun, L Sat, BHs

LONDON SW1 *Continued*

Monte's

Map B2

164 Sloane Street, SW1X 9QB
Tel: 020 7245 0896
Telephone for further details

A private club fronted by Jamie Oliver, and only open to non-members for lunch. The spacious first floor restaurant specialises in Italian-influenced food like maltagliati (rough-cut pasta) with vine tomato sauce, fried aubergine, basil and salted ricotta. Simple, fresh, well-made desserts, like classic pear and almond tarte Tatin.

Nahm

NEW Map GtL C2

At The Halkin Hotel,
Halkin Street, Belgravia,
SW1X 7DJ
Tel: 020 7333 1000
Telephone for further details

All change at The Halkin Hotel as we went to press with David Thompson flying in from Australia to bring his take on Thai cooking to this venerable London setting. Renowned as one of the world's leading experts on the cuisine of Thailand, particularly its Royal Cuisine, his background suggests a more complex approach than commonly found in modern Thai cooking. An exciting prospect.

L'Oranger

Map C3

5 St James's Street, SW1A 1EF
Tel: 020 7839 3774
Fax: 020 7839 4330
Chef(s): Kamel Benamar
Owner(s): A-Z Restaurants Ltd.
Cost: Set price L £20-£24.50-£37 H/wine £16
Times: Noon-2.30pm/6-10.45pm. Closed Sun, L Sat, Xmas, BHs
Additional: Children 6 yrs+. Vegetarian not available
Seats: 55. Private dining room 20
Style: French
Smoking: No pipes; no cigars; Air conditioning
Directions: Nearest tube: Green Pk access by car via Pall Mall

Modern, sophisticated and filled with natural light from a skylight, L'Oranger provides an oasis of calm in the busy West End. The secret of the modern *carte* is not only the fresh high-quality ingredients but also the precisely composed dishes.

Opening with starters such as potato salad with poached egg, caviar and red wine vinaigrette, the menu leads on to roast loin of pork wrapped in bacon and sage with Vichy carrots or roast fillet of John Dory with mange-tout and jus de ceps. From the dessert menu, lemon thyme crème caramel and caramelised pineapple sablé with exotic fruit sorbet are typical examples of the accurate and carefully balanced cooking.

Pétrus

Restaurant of the Year for England - see page 27 for entry

Quaglino's

Map C3

Oh, the glamour! Descend a sweeping staircase into this chic icon of gastronomy whose menu ranges from caviar to fish and chips. Despite its grand age (71 years) Quaglino's menu is fresh and modern. As well as all the seafood, you'll encounter grills, rotisseries and a fixed price menu that includes curried parsnip soup, confit of duck and sticky toffee pudding.

Additional: Sunday L. Bar food. Children welcome
Seats: 267. Private dining room 44
Style: Modern, Chic
Smoking: Air conditioning
Directions: Nearest tube: Green Park. Bury St is off Jermyn St

16 Bury Street, St James's
SW1Y 6AJ
Tel: 020 7930 6767
Fax: 020 7839 2866
Chef(s): Julian O'Neil
Owner(s): Sir Terence Conran
Cost: Alc £36, set price L £15/D £15.
☺ ☺ H/wine £13.50
Times: Noon-3pm/5.30-Midnight.
Closed 25 Dec

Rhodes in the Square

Map D1

Dolphin Square, Chichester Street,
SW1V 3LX
Tel: 020 7798 6767
Fax: 020 7798 5685
e rhodesinthesquare@
sodexho-uk.com
Chef(s): Michael James
Owner(s): Gary Rhodes
Cost: Alc £35, set price L £19.50/
D £33.50. H/wine £17.50
Times: Noon-2.30pm/7-10pm.
Closed Sun-Mon, L Sat, BHs
Additional: Children welcome
Seats: 70
Style: Classic, Modern
Smoking: No pipes; Air conditioning

Gary Rhodes' expanding group of restaurants continue to do him credit. The Dolphin Square version stays faithful to the modern British cooking for which the TV chef is known. A sky-blue interior with numerous small ceiling lights twinkling like stars creates a soothing effect that the balanced menu does nothing to disturb. Look for crab risotto, a super creamy starter with strong flavours, and braised oxtail with buttered root vegetables. Also featured might be roast skate wing with crispy shrimps, and confit of duck leg on braised red cabbage and red wine sauce, all served with ultra smooth and creamy mashed potato.

Civil licence: 100
Accommodation: 200 rooms
Directions: Nearest tube: Pimlico

LONDON SW1 *Continued*

Ristorante L'Incontro

Map C1

87 Pimlico Road, SW1W 8PH
Tel: 020 7730 3663
Fax: 020 7730 5062
Chef(s): Simone Rettore
Owner(s): Mr G Santin
Cost: *Alc* £40, set price L £18.50. ☺
H/wine £15.75
Times: 12.30-2.30pm/7-11.30pm.
Closed L Sat & Sun, Xmas, 1 Jan,
Easter
Additional: Children welcome
Seats: 60. Private dining room 35.
Jacket and tie preferred
Style: Modern, Chic
Smoking: No pipes; Air conditioning
Directions: Nearest tube: Sloane
Square. From Lower Sloane Street, L
into Pimlico Road, restaurant is on
the R

The original black and white photos of famous meetings between the likes of Nixon and Khruschev, go along with the theme of Ristorante L'Incontro which is Italian for 'the encounter'. This is an airy yet fairly intimate restaurant with warm apricot and taupe upholstery - as classy looking as its clientele. The understated and stylish décor suits the service and the simply presented, predominantly Venetian cuisine. Natural flavours are allowed to stand out in, say, grilled king prawns with cannellini beans, frisée, oil and lemon or cuttlefish in ink sauce with polenta. Choose from antipasti, pasta, fish and meat dishes and, classically, desserts, cheese or fresh fruit.

Give us your views!

All the restaurants in this guide have been visited by one of the AA's team of professional inspectors but we want to hear from you too. Use the report forms in the back of the guide or email us at lifestyleguides@theAA.com with your comments on any of the establishments featured or other restaurants that you feel are worthy of an entry. We would also be pleased to receive your views on the guide itself and suggestions for any other information you would like to see included.

England

Roussillon

Map C1

It's difficult to imagine the actual restaurants of the Roussillon region being quite this earnest about the source of their produce (the menu even invites you to ask the restaurant manager for certificates) but then they probably take good produce for granted. This style of earthy cooking does rely heavily on the excellence of the raw materials and fortunately this is a notable strength of this discreet Belgravia restaurant. The elemental theme stretches to a menu that features "Garden", "Sea" and "Land" options along with "Classics" and a seasonal *carte*. No prizes for guessing which one a "sensationally light" ravioli of Kentish greens comes from or a dark and rich dish of slow-cooked hare with shallots and turnips. Similarly to the point, a straightforward treatment of grilled "biodynamic" lamb with button onions and chard. A mainly French wine list featuring some good value from Roussillon. Where else?

16 St Barnabas Street,
SW1W 8PB
Tel: 020 7730 5550
Fax: 020 7824 8617
e alexis@roussillon.co.uk
Chef(s): Alexis Gauthier
Owner(s): Alexis Gauthier,
J & A Palmer
Cost: *Alc* £35, set price L £18/
D £35-£42. H/wine £13.50
Times: Noon-2.30pm/6.45-10.30pm.
Closed Sun, L Sat, 24 Dec-5 Jan
Additional: Children 6 yrs+
Seats: 46. Private dining room 30
Style: Classic
Smoking: No-smoking area; no pipes;
no cigars; Air conditioning

Directions: Nearest tube: Sloane Square. Off Pimlico Road

Royal Horseguards

Map D3

A fusion of Asian and pukka English influences inspire the cooking at this top class Whitehall hotel. Classics like Caesar salad and smoked Scottish salmon blend effortlessly with monkfish cooked in coconut milk and garam masala with bok choi, black linguini and chilli jam, and vegetarian spicy potato cake with chick peas and pepper coulis.

Whitehall Court, SW1A 2EJ
Tel: 020 7839 3400
Fax: 020 7925 2263
e royal.horseguards@thistle.co.uk
Chef(s): Graham Burst
Cost: *Alc* £30, set price L £19.50/
D £26.50. H/wine £18
Times: Noon-2.30pm/6-11.30pm.
Closed L Sat-Sun & L 2-8 Jan
Additional: Bar food. Children
welcome

Seats: 85. Private dining room 16. Jacket and tie preferred
Style: Modern, Asian
Smoking: No-smoking area; Air conditioning
Accommodation: 280 rooms ★ ★ ★ ★
Directions: Nearest tube: Embankment

The Rubens at the Palace

Map C2

After descending a spiral staircase you are immediately hit by the luxurious setting of the 'Library Restaurant.' Rich warm fabrics set the tone, complemented by soft lighting, attractive table presentation and live background piano. Cuisine combines English and international styles producing signature dishes such as the 'Rubens House Salad' featuring scallops, crayfish, crispy pancetta, and toasted pine nuts. Simple, well executed dishes such as pan-fried fillet of brill with woodland mushrooms, shallots and a red wine jus make for robust centre-pieces to the meal, whilst a new take on an old favourite (crème brûlée scented with ginger accompanied by a rhubarb compôte) rounds things off nicely.

39 Buckingham Palace Road,
SW1W 0PS
Tel: 020 7834 6600
Telephone for further details

England

Salloos Restaurant

Map B2

Long established family-run Pakistani restaurant tucked away in a secluded Belgravia mews. Rich reds, dark wood, cream table linen and polite, helpful service characterise the mood at this timeless haven of authentic cuisine. Tandoori charcoal grills (without colourings) prove an enduring highlight (try the Tandoori chops), as do house specialities such as Haleem Akbari (a shredded lamb dish) and Chicken Karahi served sizzling in an iron karahi.

Smoking: No pipes; no cigars; Air conditioning
Directions: Nearest tube: Knightsbridge

62-64 Kinnerton Street, SW1X 8ER
Tel: 020 7235 4444
Fax: 020 7259 5703
Chef(s): Abdul Aziz
Owner(s): Mr & Mrs M Salahuddin
Cost: *Alc* £35, set price L £16. ☺ ☺
H/wine £12.50
Times: Noon-2.30pm/7-11.30pm.
Closed Sun, BHs, Xmas
Additional: Children 6 yrs+
Seats: 65
Style: Formal, Classic

Santini

Map C1

Italian cuisine is more fashionable than ever judging by the number of Italian eateries visible throughout the capital. Santini is yet another, but distinguishes itself with its elegance, and cool, uncluttered style. A marble floor, maple staircase and mustard and blue upholstery all add to the simple charm. The menu is a sensible length with five or six choices in four traditionally Italian sections. There is much to please in both service and judiciously prepared dishes. Try perhaps speck with rocket and Parmesan, garganelli pasta with tomatoes, aubergine and mozzarella or pot roasted rabbit with Savoy cabbage and Italian smoked pancetta.

29 Ebury Street, SW1W 0NZ
Tel: 020 7730 4094
Fax: 020 7730 5062
Chef(s): Giuseppe Rosselli,
Giuliano Vilardo
Owner(s): Mr G Santin
Cost: *Alc* £40, set price L £19.75.
H/wine £15.75
Times: 12.30-2.30pm/7-11.30pm.
Closed L Sat-Sun, Xmas, 1 Jan,
Easter Sun
Additional: Children welcome
Seats: 65. Private dining room 35.
Jacket and tie preferred
Smoking: No pipes; Air conditioning
Directions: On the corner of Edbury
St and Lower Belgrave St.
Nearest tube: Victoria

Shepherds

Map D2

Tradition reigns supreme at this long-established restaurant close to the Tate Gallery. Expect good old-fashioned service and classic English dishes - chicken liver pâté with Cumberland sauce, braised oxtail with turnips, and 'nursery' puddings like bread and butter pudding or spotted dick.

Additional: Bar food. Children welcome
Seats: 50. Private dining room 32
Style: Traditional
Smoking: No-smoking area; Air conditioning
Directions: Near Tate Gallery and Westminster Hospital.
Nearest tube: Pimlico

Marsham Court,
Marsham Street, SW1P 4LA
Tel: 020 7834 9552
Fax: 020 7233 6047
Chef(s): Jeremy Stent
Owner(s): Mr R Shepherd
Cost: Set price L & D £23.50-£25.50.
H/wine £10.50
Times: 12.15-2.45pm/6.30-11pm.
Closed Sat & Sun, BHs

England

Sheraton Park Tower,
Restaurant One-O-One

Map B2

The striking circular shape of this modern hotel blends surprisingly well with the traditional buildings along Knightsbridge. The famous thoroughfare is also the view from the street-level One-O-One restaurant, where the specialist 'cuisine de la mer' has achieved a well-deserved reputation. Needless to say, the emphasis is very much on fresh fish, although don't be surprised to find a delicate slice of foie gras amongst the canapés. A signature dish of warm king crab royal leg with black truffle risotto, small egg pancake and Parmesan makes an exhilarating start to a meal that might continue with pan-roasted ligne seabass with watercress truffle salad, buttered mash, caramelised shallots and natural jus - the starring fish flavours standing out from the supporting cast. Expect a delicious charge from desserts like warm moelleux, Caribbean Monjari chocolate with pink grapefruit sorbet, and a strong finish from espresso and petit fours.

Accommodation: 289 rooms (289 en suite) ★★★★★
Directions: Nearest tube: Knightsbridge. E, just after Harvey Nichols

101 Knightsbridge,
SW1X 7RN
Tel: 020 7235 8050
Fax: 020 7235 8231
e morten.ettesen@luxurycollection.com
Chef(s): Pascal Proyart
Owner(s): Starwood Hotel and Resorts
Cost: Alc £50, set price L £19.50-£25. H/wine £19.50
Times: Noon-2.30pm/7-10.30pm.
Additional: Sunday L. Children welcome
Seats: 70
Style: Modern
Smoking: No-smoking area; Air conditioning

Simply Nico

Map D2

Even on a cold and damp winter's evening 'Simply Nico' bustles with activity. Whether it's the warm yellow décor beckoning passers-by in from the cold, or its justly high reputation shining like a beacon into the dark London streets; those who cross the threshold are rewarded with consistently high quality cooking served by focused, hard working and able staff. Fresh clean tastes abound - gâteau of crab with pak choi, soya bean salad for instance. The successful simplicity of many of the dishes - witness roast corn-fed chicken with risotto - is testament to the confidence of a kitchen happy to play it straight.

Directions: Nearest tube: Victoria. From Victoria Station take Vauxhall Bridge Road – 2nd on L at 2nd set of lights

48a Rochester Row,
SW1P 1JU
Tel: 020 7630 8061
Fax: 020 7828 8541
Chef(s): Jean Luc Hoez
Cost: Alc £27.75, set price L £23.50/D £26.50. H/wine £13.50
Times: Noon-2pm/6-11pm.
Closed Sun, L Sat, Xmas, Easter
Additional: Children welcome
Seats: 45
Style: Bistro, French
Smoking: No-smoking area; no pipes; no cigars; Air conditioning

The Stafford

Map D4

Understated luxury, country house style, in London's St James's, close to Green Park. The American bar is best known for its celebrity photos and mean dry Martini, while the restaurant picks up a classic theme with Grecian statues, pillars, a ceiling painting and trompe l'oeil window. Restaurant service is accomplished and well paced, and the kitchen team produce an interesting choice of dishes from carte and fixed-price menus. A series of private dining rooms includes a central chamber in the 350-year-old cellars - an atmospheric setting for a candlelit dinner - approached through the extensive wine collection.

Civil licence: 60
Accommodation: 81 rooms (81 en suite) ★★★★
Directions: Nearest tube: Green Park. 5 mins St James' Palace

16-18 St James's Place, SW1A 1NJ
Tel: 020 7493 0111
Fax: 020 7493 7121
e info@thestaffordhotel.co.uk
Chef(s): Chris Oakes
Cost: Alc £48, set price L £28/D £34. H/wine £19.50
Times: 12.30-2.30pm/6-10.30pm.
Closed L Sat
Additional: Sunday L. Bar food. Children 8 yrs+
Seats: 50. Private dining room 44. Jacket and tie preferred
Style: Classic, Formal
Smoking: No-smoking area; no pipes; no cigars; Air conditioning

England

Suntory Restaurant

Map C3 ◉◉

With twenty-four years' experience in serving top quality, reasonably priced Japanese food Suntory has built up quite a fan base. One night in the company of crystal clear dashi soup (packed with flavour), foie gras with teriyaki sauce, and fillet steak with fried rice is likely to recruit you to the fan club. The menu covers much familiar ground but all the dishes are cooked to perfection, full of flavour and very enjoyable. The *carte* and lunch menus offer a particularly affordable taste of Japan. On the other hand the appropriately named 'Royal' set menu option caters well for those with bulging wallets.

Smoking: No pipes; Air conditioning
Directions: Nearest tube: Green Park

72 St James's Street, SW1A 1PH
Tel: 020 7409 0201
Fax: 020 7499 0208
Chef(s): K Kanno
Cost: *Alc* £43, set price L £18-£38/ D £53-£65. H/wine £19
Times: Noon-3pm/6-10pm. Closed L Sun, Xmas, L BH, Easter
Additional: Children 6 yrs+
Seats: 130. Private dining room 12. Jacket and tie preferred
Style: Traditional, Japanese

La Tante Claire

Map B2 ◉◉◉

The quiet craft of Pierre Koffmann has been something to behold over the years and his impact on British cooking cannot be overestimated. Whilst there is still much to admire in this incarnation of La Tante Claire the renowned consistency has been questioned on more than one occasion in recent times. The menu is as unashamedly French classic as ever and descriptions remain in French only and the procedure is for the waiting staff to offer lengthy translations of the dishes at the table. The selection of breads (delivered on a trolley with some theatricality) continues to amaze and delight. Luxury ingredients abound throughout the menus, for instance, an amuse of lobster ravioli with a crab bisque and classic starters like seared foie gras with a Sauternes sauce. Those seeking signature dishes like the legendary Koffmann pig's trotter or an exemplary and classic tournedos Rossini won't be disappointed. Service is as correct as you might expect and the wine list exhaustive.

Directions: Nearest tube: Hyde Park Corner. 300 metres from Hyde Park Corner along Knightsbridge

The Berkeley, Wilton Place, Knightsbridge SW1X 7RL
Tel: 020 7823 2003
Fax: 020 7823 2001
Chef(s): Pierre Koffmann
Cost: *Alc* £65, set price L £28. H/wine £20
Times: 12.30-2pm/7-11pm. Closed Sun, L Sat, 2 wks Xmas, BHs
Additional: Children welcome. Vegetarian by request only
Seats: 60. Private dining room 16. Jacket and tie preferred
Style: Modern
Smoking: No pipes; no cigars; Air conditioning
Accommodation: 168 rooms (168 en suite) ★ ★ ★ ★ ★

Vong

Map B2 ◉◉

Indian spice colours and Spanish limestone tables make a refreshing change from today's mono steel and frosted glass style. The food here is also distinctive with the sheer variety of flavours making it an intensely sensual experience. The Black Plate of five signature starters is a great place to begin, with crab spring roll and skewered shrimp (plus dips) to stimulate the palate. Chicken marinated in ginger, chilli and lemongrass then roasted is served with sticky coconut rice in a banana leaf, a faultless dish. Valrhona chocolate cake, normally something of a cliché, is an exceptional version

Smoking: No-smoking area; no pipes; no cigars; Air conditioning
Accommodation: 168 rooms (168 en suite) ★ ★ ★ ★ ★
Directions: Nearest tube: Hyde Park Corner

The Berkeley, Wilton Place, Knightsbridge SW1X 7RL
Tel: 020 7235 1010
Fax: 020 7235 1011
Chef(s): J-G Vongerichten
Owner(s): The Berkeley Hotel
Cost: *Alc* £45, set price L £21/ pre-theatre D £21.50. H/wine £24
Times: Noon-2.30pm/6-11.30pm. Closed 25-26 Dec, 1 Jan
Additional: Sun L. Children welcome
Seats: 140
Style: Minimalist

England

Wiltons

Map C3

Say it softly, but subtle changes have been carried out at this favourite haunt of the Establishment, and renowned fish and game restaurant. The hushed atmosphere of the gentleman's club remains, but it's brighter now, with new carpets and curtains. The food has changed too. A selection of lighter dishes supplements the traditional menu: think sun-dried tomato risotto, grilled goats' cheese salad, and steamed scallops with ginger and spring onions. Stalwarts need not worry though. Smoked salmon, lobster bisque, and grilled lambs' kidneys are still there, plus that old favourite, sherry trifle. A mainly French wine list, and impressive selection of cigars.

55 Jermyn Street, SW1Y 6LX
Tel: 020 7629 9955
Fax: 020 7495 6233
e wiltons@wiltons.co.uk
Chef(s): Ross Hayden
Owner(s): The Hambro Family
Cost: *Alc* £60. ☺ H/wine £17.50
Times: Noon-2.30pm/6-10.30.
Closed Sat, Xmas, New Year
Additional: Sunday L. Bar food.
Children welcome
Seats: 90. Private dining room 18.
Jacket and tie preferred
Style: Traditional, Formal
Smoking: No pipes; Air conditioning
Directions: Nearest tube: Green Park.
Near the Ritz Hotel and Piccadilly
Circus. Opposite Turnbull & Asser
(shirtmakers).

Zafferano

Map B2

To judge by the difficulty in securing a table for lunch at this Knightsbridge Italian, it's clear that something special is cooking here. Sure enough, the place is packed for all the right reasons. The cooking is exceptional: a merger of quality ingredients and simple execution produces dishes with fresh, clean flavours and some inspirational saucing. A dash of spontaneity married a quenelle of tomato and aubergine purée to a chargrilled lamb fillet on a bed of roasted peppers, then added a small pile of dressed leaves and a superb tomato sauce with exquisite results. Similarly baby artichoke salad with fresh Parmesan and rocket leaves and a side plate of focaccia, ciabatta and rich olive oil left nothing to be desired. You can eat plainly or extravagantly, and enjoy very good Italian wines.

15 Lowndes Street,
SW1X 9EY
Tel: 020 7235 5800
Fax: 020 7235 1971
Chef(s): Andrew Needham
Owner(s): Atoz Restaurants
Cost: Set price L £23.50/D £35.50-
£39.50. ☺ ☺ H/wine £12.50
Times: Noon-2.30pm/7-11pm.
Closed Xmas, New Year
Additional: Sunday L. Children
welcome
Seats: 55. Jacket and tie preferred
Style: Modern, Italian
Smoking: No pipes; no cigars;
Air conditioning
Directions: Nearest Tube:
Knightsbridge. Exit Harvey Nichols.
Restaurant is just behind Harvey
Nichols

England

LONDON SW3

Bibendum

Map A1

Michelin House,
81 Fulham Road, SW3 6RD
Tel: 020 7581 5817
Fax: 020 7823 7925
e manager@bibendum.co.uk
Chef(s): Matthew Harris
Owner(s): Sir Terence Conran,
Lord Hamlyn, Simon Hopkinson,
Graham Williams
Cost: Alc £38, set price L £28.
H/wine £11.95
Times: Noon-2.30pm/7-11.30pm.
Closed Xmas
Additional: Sunday L.
Children welcome
Seats: 76
Style: Classic
Smoking: No pipes; Air conditioning
Directions: Nearest tube: South
Kensington

The world still goes to Bibendum. No real wonder, it still has a lively atmosphere and a name that resonates. It's not cheap, but there remain sufficient merits to pull in a dedicated clientele. The menu is extensive in a broadly European mould and the dishes that continue to win praise would still form a long list, (especially the all time favourites of deep fried plaice with chips and tartare sauce, Baltic herrings à la creme, fillet steak au-poivre). Mention though should also be made of some notable lapses, especially sauces lacking in intensity and depth of flavour. It is possible to leave with both spirits and the wallet a little deflated. Service is typically pleasant and efficient. Impressive wine list with wide selection of quality vintages and good estates.

Bluebird

Map B1

Chelsea gastrodome including a flower shop, café, kitchen shop and exclusive supemarket. Overlooking all this is the vast 240-seater restaurant, all neutral tones (wear black, everyone else does), natural light, and giant bluebird kites soaring overhead. It is a busy and impersonal operation, but popular despite the prices. There's a good choice of crustacea - rock and native oysters, potted shrimps, lobster, cracked crab, and a plateau de fruit de mer for two. Mains range from pumpkin and coriander risotto, through saddle of rabbit, Suffolk bacon, braised beans and chorizo, to Chateaubriand with béarnaise sauce and matchstick frites.

Smoking: Air conditioning
Directions: Nearest tube: Sloane Square

350 King's Road,
SW3 5UU
Tel: 020 7559 1000
Fax: 020 7559 1111
e enquiries@bluebird-store.co.uk
Chef(s): Blair Smethurst
Owner(s): Sir Terence Conran
Cost: Alc £35, set price L £21.50. ☺
H/wine £12.75
Times: Noon-3pm/6-11pm.
Additional: Sunday brunch. Children
welcome
Seats: 260. Private dining room 32
Style: Modern, Minimalist

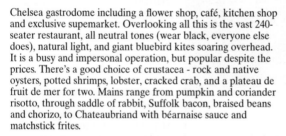

The finest wine lists

The AA wine awards recognise some of the finest wine lists in the country. As well as the winners for England, Scotland and Wales you will find this symbol throughout the guide indicating those restaurants who reached the final shortlist and others that were recognised for their excellence in specialist areas. The AA wine awards are sponsored by T&W wines of Thetford.

England

The Capital

Map B2

Basil Street, Knightsbridge,
SW3 1AT
Tel: 020 7589 5171
Fax: 020 7225 0011
e reservations@
capitalhotel.co.uk
Chef(s): Eric Chavot
Owner(s): Mr D Levin & Mr J Levin
Cost: *Alc* £56, set price L £24.50-£32.
H/wine £14.50
Times: Noon-2.30pm/7-11.15pm.
Closed D 25 Dec
Additional: Sunday L. Bar food L.
Children welcome
Seats: 35. Private dining room 24
Style: Classic, Formal
Smoking: No pipes; no cigars; Air
conditioning
Accommodation: 48 rooms (48 en
suite) ★ ★ ★ ★

Harrods and Harvey Nicks are just round the corner, so this
luxurious little hotel restaurant is just the place to recharge the
batteries after some serious shopping. There's a discreet and
intimate atmosphere, and it's always busy (booking is essential).
The look is grand traditional - think large chandeliers, tall old
mirrors, crisp linen and silverware, but the cooking is inspired
and innovative. A 'menu dégustation' is a tempting alternative
to the set menus, but the latter will not disappoint: expect pan-
fried snails and sweetbreads with potato gnocchi and tomato
sauce (tasty), langoustine ravioli with cream jus (delicate, good
strong flavours), turbot fillet on spinach (delicious), and saddle
of lamb with onion pastilla and thyme jus. Pastry is a real
strength, as in mille-feuille with pain d'épice brulée and apple
sorbet. The wine catalogue is not for the faint-hearted, but well
worth a perusal for its châteaux and really good vintages.
Definitely one to watch.

Directions: Nearest tube: Knightsbridge. Off Sloane St, beside
Harrods

The Collection

Map B1

264 Brompton Road, SW3 2AS
Tel: 020 7225 1212
Fax: 020 7225 1050
Chef(s): Warren Lee, Paul Shields
Owner(s): Belgo Group Plc
Cost: *Alc* £40, set price D £35.
H/wine £12.95
Times: Dinner only, 6.30-11pm.
Closed 25-26 Dec, 1 Jan
Additional: Sunday brunch.
Bar food D
Seats: 160
Style: Modern
Smoking: Air conditioning
Directions: Nearest Tube: South
Kensington, Pelham St to traffic lights
and turn L

Urban warehouse restaurant introduced via a long, tunnel-like
passageway with an under-lit glass walkway over pebbles.
Overlooking the bar is the stylish mezzanine restaurant where
the menus take a global stance, but with a pronounced
Mediterranean overtone. Try anything from seared tuna sashimi
with shiitake, mooli and cucumber to lamb Merguez. Canapés,
brunch and fun drinks menus add to the allure.

England

LONDON SW3 *Continued*

Dans Restaurant

Map B1

Long established restaurant with a secure team in the kitchen, a
friendly proprietor and a regular clientele. Interconnecting
rooms lead through to the garden where outside eating is an
option. There's a mirrored conservatory, bare-board floors and
a collection of old farm animal prints. The frequently changing
menu encompasses marinated king prawns with Thai dressing,
pan-fried calves' liver with crispy bacon and parsley mash, and
breast of free range chicken stuffed with wild mushrooms and
sun-dried tomato. The good-value fixed-price lunch menu is
worth a look, as is the very approachable wine list - mostly
French with a sprinkling by the glass and reasonable number of
halves.

Directions: Nearest Tube: South Kensington or Sloane Square,
off King's Road

119 Sydney Street,
SW3 6NR
Tel: 020 7352 2718
Fax: 020 7352 3265
e sagem084410@talk21.com
Chef(s): Yehia M Ali
Owner(s): Dan Whitehead
Cost: *Alc* £25, set price L £16. ☺ ☺
H/wine £12.50
Times: 12.15-2.30pm/7.15-10.30pm.
Closed Sun in winter, L Sat in winter,
Xmas, New Year, BHs
Additional: Children welcome
Seats: 50. Private dining room 23.
Jacket and tie preferred
Style: Traditional, Rustic

English Garden Restaurant

Map B1

Close to Sloane Square, just five minutes' walk down the King's
Road, is this newly established restaurant with a timeless air
epitomised by cream décor, a dark redwood floor and intimate
banquette seating. Both dining sessions involve fixed-price,
daily changing menus that are scarcely short of ambition. At
lunchtime, stuffed baby squid with feta, mussels and garlic;
rabbit leg with Serrano ham, gratin potato, mustard and thyme,
and toffee banana crumble. The night's choices then run to foie
gras and chicken livers with fig chutney, John Dory with curried
spinach, yoghurt and harissa and chocolate fondant with
Bailey's cream mousse. Private dining in The Terrace and The
Lincoln rooms.

Smoking: No pipes; Air conditioning
Directions: Nearest tube: Sloane Square

10 Lincoln Street, SW3 2TS
Tel: 020 7584 7272
Fax: 020 7584 1961
e english.garden@ukgateway. net
Chef(s): Malcolm Starmer
Owner(s): Richard Corrigan
Cost: *Alc* £35, set price L £19.50/
D £27.50. ☺ H/wine £14.50
Times: Noon-3pm/6.30-11pm.
Closed L Mon, 2 wks Aug
Additional: Sunday L.
Children welcome
Seats: 45. Private dining room 34
Style: Modern

Floriana

Map C3

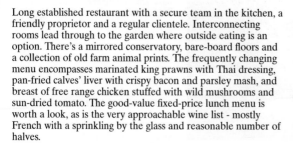

15 Beauchamp Place,
SW3 1NQ
Tel: 020 7838 1500
Fax: 020 7584 1464

Floriana's posh-shop façade and smart canopy merge with
those of its high-class Knightsbridge neighbours, making it hard

to spot in upmarket Beauchamp Place. Persevere, and be rewarded with designer chic, a huge indoor tree surrounded by an atrium and Italian food that is a real tonic. Large bottles of bubbly signed by the rich and famous adorn the front counter, and slick waiters glide amongst well-spaced tables. The typically Italian menu covering antipasti, risotto/pasta starters, seafood, meat and grills, disguises the actual content, where quality ingredients meet impeccable cooking. Look for sautéed mixed vegetables with asparagus and salad leaves, a clear and vibrant starter, and sea bass in cartoccio with clams, fennel and olives - a tricky dish that worked a treat. Roast rack of lamb with black truffle, and pan-fried calves' liver with moscato grapes, receive the same deft touch, and the pannacotta is manna from heaven.

Chef(s): Graziano Bonacina
Owner(s): R Mazzuccelli & S Hawa
Cost: Alc £45, set price L £15-£19.50. H/wine £18
Times: 12.30-3pm/7-11pm.
Additional: Sunday L. Children welcome
Seats: 100. Private dining room 24
Style: Italian
Smoking: Air conditioning
Directions: Nearest tube: Knightsbridge

The House

Map B1

3 Milner Street, SW3 2QA
Tel: 020 7584 3002
Fax: 020 7581 2848
Chef(s): Graham Garrett
Owner(s): Searcy-Corrigan Restaurants
Cost: Alc £25, set price L £18/D £27. H/wine £13.50
Times: Noon-2.30pm/6-11pm. Closed Sun, L Sat, 26 Dec-2 Jan, 2 wks Aug
Additional: Children welcome
Seats: 26. Private dining room 12
Style: Classic, Country-house
Smoking: No pipes; no cigars

Take a step back in time at this small cottage-cum-house tucked away in a quiet backwater off Cadogan Square. Fabric covered walls, period furnishings, fireplace and leafy plants create a charming, old English mood. Graham Garrett's cooking by contrast has a contemporary edge with occasional Mediterranean forays; roasted belly of Gloucester Old Spot with scallops and pancetta show the style. The compact, fixed-price dinner menu displays artful presentation, balance, innovation and a lightness of touch. Try wild garlic soup with ham toastie and grilled pineapple with chilli syrup and coconut sorbet. A well-healed local clientele combined with knowledgeable service adds up to a cosy, friendly atmosphere.

Directions: Nearest tube: South Kensington or Sloane Square

 Indicates a restaurant that has told us that 50% or more of their ingredients are organically sourced

Prices quoted in the guide are for guidance only and are subject to change without notice

England

LONDON SW3 *Continued*

The Parisienne Chop House

NEW Map B2

Easy going and admirably honest in style, this new eatery attracts a buzzy crowd with its wide-ranging French country cooking. No fewer than twenty-two starters include frogs' legs, moules marinière, whitebait, jambon persillé (parsley), and gratinée Normande a l'onion, moving on to various meats and grills like côte de veau and steak tartare, skate Grenobloise, and several rôtisseries for two: gigot d'agneau, and côte de boeuf à la Moelle perhaps. Soupe de poisson with rouille was a superb example of a French classic, and gelée de fruits rouges, framboise sirope an intensely-flavoured and satisfying dessert.

Smoking: Air conditioning
Directions: Telephone for directions

3 Yeoman's Row, Brompton Road, SW3 3AL
Tel: 0207 590 9999
Fax: 0207 590 9900
Chef(s): Adam Clark
Owner(s): Marco Pierre White
Cost: *Alc* £24, set price L £13.50. ☺
H/wine £12.50
Times: Noon-2.30pm/5.30-11pm.
Additional: Sunday L.
Children welcome
Seats: 120. Private dining room 12
Style: Classic, French

Restaurant Gordon Ramsay Map B1

Gordon Ramsay may be sprinting across to Claridges (see entry London, Central) and overseeing Amaryllis (see entry

68 Royal Hospital Road, SW3 4HP
Tel: 020 7352 4441
Fax: 020 7352 3334
Chef(s): Gordon Ramsay
Owner(s): Gordon Ramsay
Cost: *Alc* £75, set price L £35/D £85.
H/wine £20
Times: Noon-2.30pm/6.45-11pm.
Closed Sat, Sun, BHs, 2 wks Xmas
Additional: Children welcome.
Vegetarian by request only
Seats: 44. Jacket and tie preferred
Style: Modern, Chic
Smoking: No pipes; no cigars;
Air conditioning
Directions: Nearest tube: Sloane Square. Near Royal Army Museum

Scotland, Glasgow) but there is no hint that the dilution of his energies is having an impact on his eponymous Chelsea restaurant. The former La Tante Claire is a compact premises, stylishly attired and almost overrun at times by a highly skilled team of front of house staff who are much more successful at coupling professionalism with affability than some in the Capital. This is arguably the most precise cooking in the country, dishes can look shockingly good and the beauty without tends to reflect beauty within. A shining silver fillet of sea bass screamed "perfect timing" for instance and came in the well-judged company, of basil leaves, steamed new potatoes, celeriac purée, baby pak choi, crème fraîche and caviar sauce. It isn't the innovation that excites so much as the fact that the familiar is taken to new levels: a warm salad of calf's sweetbreads with crispy scallops, grilled asparagus and a sweet and sour vinaigrette for example, where every element was "as good as it gets". Signature dishes are as fresh as ever (slowly braised pork belly with spices, sautéed langoustine brushed with coral, haricots blanc à la crème still gets described as "brilliant") and the menu prestige gives you a seven course tour. Desserts are remarkably deft and run from the vanilla crème brûlée to caramelised pineapple with its own granité, with an assiette of desserts available for two. Serious wine list but with some reasonable value and character at the cheaper end.

England

St Quentin Brasserie

Map B2

After spending an hour or two in the classical French surroundings of this rather distinguished restaurant, you could be forgiven for forgetting that you are in London. Walls are heavily wooded and highly polished windows jostle for wall-space with bright, quirky artwork. Tables are quite close together but this only adds to the cheerful continental atmosphere and charm of the place. Expect consistently high quality cuisine throughout the courses but also throughout each particular dish. Take for example duck liver terrine - not only was the terrine fantastic but accompaniments of sweet white wine jelly and toasted brioche were well matched and carefully prepared.

243 Brompton Road,
SW3 2EP
Tel: 020 7589 8005
Telephone for further details

Turners Restaurant

Map A1

TV celebrity chef Brian Turner owns, hosts - and occasionally does a stint in the kitchen in his Walton Street restaurant. A cosy venue in a fashionable area, comfortable banquettes covered in rich woven fabric complement the yellow and blue décor which evokes more than a hint of the Mediterranean. Service is attentive and the menu features interesting creations: grilled Mediterranean vegetables with quails' eggs or tower of scallops, smoked haddock and sole in a champagne butter sauce. Enjoy perfectly cooked, artfully arranged vegetables and choose from a predominantly French wine list, which caters for a range of budgets.

Directions: Nearest tube: South Kensington, Knightsbridge. Behind Harrods

87-89 Walton Street, SW3 2HP
Tel: 020 7584 6711
Fax: 020 7584 4441
e turnerrest@aol.com
Chef(s): Jon Lucas, Brian Turner
Owner(s): Brian Turner
Cost: *Alc* £45, set price L £17.50/ D £29.50-£32.50. H/wine £15.50
Times: 12.30-2.30pm/7.30-11pm. Closed Sun, L Sat, BHs, Xmas
Additional: Children welcome
Seats: 52. Jacket and tie preferred
Smoking: Air conditioning

Zaika

Map A1

Make no mistake, Vineet Bhatia's Fulham Road restaurant is as exciting and inventive as ever. The elegant entrance with its stylishly-attired hostess taking coats is a long way from the flock-wallpaper school of Indian restaurant design: rich colours, earth tones and ethnic touches are appropriate for its smart-set following. Inspired cooking can be sampled on the five-course Jugalbandi: stunning scallops poached in lemon and chilli-scented coconut milk with masala mashed potato (Mulayam Rattan), Indian risotto with red onion and coriander (Jhinga Khichdi), grilled black-spiced chicken, marinated in tamarind, with milk fritters and saffron and cardamom yoghurt (Kala Murg), tandoori breast of pheasant with a rich black lentil and morel sauce (Titar Mussalam), and crispy Hawaiian soft-shell crab and seared spicy scallops (Samundri Khazana). The *carte* includes these and more, and chocolate samosas, mango and coconut rice pudding, and crispy stuffed dates are original desserts. Great stuff.

Directions: Nearest tube: South Kensington

257-259 Fulham Road,
SW3 6HY
Tel: 020 7351 7823
Fax: 020 7376 4971
Chef(s): Vineet Bhatia
Owner(s): Claudio Pulze, Ras Sharma, Vineet Bhatia
Cost: *Alc* £35, set price L £14-£28.
☺ ☺
Times: noon-2.30pm/6.30-10.30pm. Closed L Sat, BHs, Xmas, New Year
Additional: Children welcome
Seats: 70. Private dining room 20
Style: Modern, Chic
Smoking: No pipes; no cigars; Air conditioning

LONDON SW5

Cambio De Tercio

Map A1

Friendly Spanish restaurant with mustard yellow walls and a burgundy ceiling (matching the undercloths) and bullfighting paraphernalia on display. A feature of the carte is jamón de jabugo 'jjjj' ham, more exclusive even than Serrano ham, produced from a rare breed of black pig. Each 'j' relates to how long the pig has been fed exclusively on acorns.

Seats: 45. Private dining room 22
Style: Modern, Spanish
Smoking: No pipes
Directions: Nearest tube: Gloucester Road. Close to junction with Drayton Gardens

163 Old Brompton Road,
SW5 0LJ
Tel: 020 7244 8970
Fax: 020 7373 8817
Chef(s): Javier Jimenez, Ignacio Arce
Owner(s): Abel Lusa & David Rivero
Cost: Alc £28. ☺ ☺ H/wine £12.90
Times: Noon-2.30pm/7-11.30pm.
Closed Xmas, New Year
Additional: Sunday L.
Children welcome

Catch

Map A1

Cosy yet modern neighbourhood restaurant with seven tables. Although the name implies plenty of seafood, there are abundant meat dishes too to suit all tastes. Besides a good range of fishy starters and mains, diners can splash out on a dozen oysters or purse-busting caviar. Wafer-thin marinated tuna and roasted sea bass go down particularly well.

Seats: 40. Private dining room 18
Style: Modern, Rustic
Smoking: No pipes; Air conditioning
Directions: Nearest tube: Gloucester Road

158 Old Brompton Road, SW5 0BA
Tel: 020 7370 3300
Fax: 020 7370 3377
Chef(s): Stephen Barfoot
Owner(s): Sophie Burrell &
Annie Foster-Firth
Cost: Alc £30. ☺ H/wine £12.50
Times: Dinner only, 6.30-11.30pm.
Closed Sun, 24 Dec-2 Jan, BHs
Additional: Bar food D. Children welcome. Vegetarian by request only

The Hogarth

Map GtL C3

Stripped wooden floors, tables and chairs fit with a very informal approach to dining. Large windows looking out onto the passing life of the street make for calming yet compulsive diversion whilst awaiting the likes of pan-fried fillet of sea bass with smooth mashed potato and a tarragon beurre blanc.

33 Hogarth Road,
Kensington, SW5 0QQ
Tel: 020 7370 6831
Telephone for further details

Swallow International Hotel

Map A2

Two distinct eating options at the hotel include Blayneys, an attractive modern restaurant with piano music drifting from the nearby cocktail bar - very soothing after a busy day in the capital. Seared peppered pork might come with a hot spicy pear chutney, and the main course, baked whole red snapper, was noted as a real success.

Accommodation: 419 rooms (419 en suite) ★★★★
Directions: Nearest tube: Gloucester Rd/Earls Court. Near Cromwell Hospital

Cromwell Road, SW5 0TH
Tel: 020 7973 1000
Fax: 020 7370 1685
 international@
swallow-hotels.co.uk
Telephone for further details

England

LONDON SW6

Restaurant 755

Map A1

No shrinking violet this, bold and blue, Restaurant 755 is an up-to-the-minute restaurant in an up-to-the-minute area. The interior is equally vibrant and stylish with colourful paintings, modern cutlery and glassware. The modern French menu is complemented by a predominantly French wine list. Our spring visit started with some interesting breads and a vegetable soup with truffle oil which was delightfully frothy. The ballotine of trout with celeriac remoulade, glazed chicken and mussel dressing that followed was an excellent foil to the main course of duck breast with Parmesan risotto. An amusingly presented rich chocolate cappuccino dessert proved irresistible.

Style: Classic, French
Smoking: Air conditioning
Directions: Nearest tube: Parsons Green

755 Fulham Road,
Parsons Green, SW6 5UU
Tel: 020 7371 0755
Fax: 020 7371 0695
Chef(s): Mark McCann
Owner(s): Mr & Mrs McCann
Cost: Alc £32.50, set price L
£12.50/D £30. ☺ H/wine £15
Times: Noon-3pm/7-late. Closed Sun,
Mon, 10 days Xmas, 2 wks summer
Additional: Children welcome
Seats: 40. Private dining room 30

LONDON SW7

Bistro 190

Map A1 ☺

The lofty front room of the Gore Hotel is the setting for this laid-back bistro. Expect wooden floors, an interesting mixture of simple furniture, huge windows overlooking elegant Queen's Gate, and yellow walls strewn with old prints and mirrors. A twice-daily menu of Mediterranean-inspired dishes is offered along with a short wine list, including house wines by the two-glass pichet.

Seats: 60. Private dining room 24
Directions: Nearest tube: South Kensington. Next to Gore Hotel on Queensgate

190 Queen's Gate,
SW7 5EU
Tel: 020 7581 5666
Fax: 020 7581 8172
Chef(s): Michael Moore
Owner(s): Simpson of Cornhill
Cost: Alc £22. ☺ H/wine £13
Times: Noon-Midnight.
Closed 25-Dec
Additional: Sunday L. Bar food.
Children welcome. Vegetarian by
request only

Hilaire

Map A1 ☺☺

68 Old Brompton Road,
SW7 3LQ
Tel: 020 7584 8993
Fax: 020 7581 2949
Chef(s): Bryan Webb
Owner(s): Brian & Susan Webb

A cheery and informal restaurant behind its curved glass Victorian shop front with heavy drapes, fresh flowers and candlelit by night, this remains as popular a venue as ever. After 14 years Bryan Webb retains his approach of quality ingredients, many of them organic, used simply and to good

LONDON SW7 *Continued*

effect. Busy at lunchtimes, popular dishes include parfait of foie gras and chicken livers, roast sea bass with lentils, salsa verde and rocket and calves' liver with pancetta and fried sage, followed perhaps by rhubarb fool or prune and almond tart. Dinners take in smoked eel, new potato and bacon salad and pigeon, artichoke and French bean salad preceding turbot fillet with pea mashed potato, dill and mustard, duck breast with apple and cider sauce or leg of rabbit with black pudding wrapped in Parma ham. Early and late evening supper menus include daily soups, saffron risotto, tagliatelli with crab and rib-eye steak au poivre, followed by desserts such as steamed ginger pudding and custard, ice cream, unusual sorbets and British cheeses from Neals Yard. A comprehensive wine list starts with over a dozen house selections.

Cost: *Alc* £43, set price L £24/D £40. H/wine £14.5
Times: 12.15-2.30pm/6.30-11pm. Closed Sun, L Sat, 10 days Xmas, 2 wks Aug, BHs
Additional: Children welcome
Seats: 50. Private dining room 20
Style: Modern, Classic
Smoking: No pipes; no cigars; Air conditioning
Directions: Nearest tube: South Kensington. Opposite Christie's auction rooms

Radisson Edwardian Vanderbilt Hotel NEW Map A2

Good use of fresh ingredients and sound technical skills are promising features of the kitchen at this Victorian hotel. Follow a well flavoured and textured haricot soup or smoked chicken ravioli with basil butter sauce, with red mullet served on a potato cake with jambalaya sauce, and finish with tamarillo mousse with poached tamarillo on shortbread. Cheerful, well-motivated young staff.

Additional: Bar food. Children welcome
Seats: 102. Private dining rooms
Style: Modern
Smoking: No-smoking area; Air conditioning
Accommodation: 114 rooms (114 en suite) ★★★★
Directions: Telephone for directions

68/86 Cromwell Road, SW7 5BT
Tel: 020 7761 9000
Fax: 020 7761 9001
e 68/86cromwellroad@radisson.com
Chef(s): Robert Ciegan
Owner(s): Jasmineer Singhg/Radisson Edwardian
Cost: *Alc* £40, set price L £14-£19.50/D £14-£19.50. ☺ ☺
H/wine £15.5
Times: 12.30-2.30pm/5.30-10pm. Closed L Sat-Sun

Swag and Tails Map B2

Peaceful pub in Knightbridge village with informality and relaxation at the heart of its operation. A constantly changing blackboard makes a good partner to the regular pub menu with plenty of Mediterranean style dishes on offer. Hummus and marinated olives to chargrilled calves' liver with crispy pancetta mash and sage sum up the range.

10-11 Fairholt Street, SW7 1EG
Tel: 020 7584 6926
Fax: 020 7584 6926
e Swag&tails@mway.com
Chef(s): Anthony Shaw
Owner(s): Annemaria & Stuart Booker Davies
Cost: *Alc* £23.75. ☺ ☺ H/wine £9.95
Times: Noon-3pm/6-10pm. Closed Sat-Sun, BHs
Additional: Bar food. Children welcome
Seats: 32
Style: Classic, Bistro-Style
Smoking: No-smoking area; no pipes; no cigars
Directions: Nearest tube: Knightsbridge

LONDON SW8

The Stepping Stone

Map GtL C2

Still cool in that primary colour/minimalist décor and hard surfaces sort of way, the Stepping Stone is a popular venue for local dining and the odd business lunch. The relaxed, informal service suits the lively atmosphere and it is perhaps not surprising that the food appears to be effortlessly thrown together rather than painstakingly 'created'. The style is broadly British but naturally there are no tight constraints, and many dishes show an imaginative mind at work: scallops might come with pepperonata and couscous; tuna with sauteed potatoes and chorizo. Among the desserts, look out for the 'delightfully moist' chocolate pud.

Directions: Nearest tube: Clapham Common. From Lavender Hill/Wandsworth Road crossroads, up Queenstown Road towards Chelsea Bridge. Restaurant on L after 0.5 mile

123 Queenstown Road, SW8 3RH
Tel: 020 7622 0555
Fax: 020 7622 4230
e thesteppingstone@aol.com
Chef(s): Michael Bird
Owner(s): Mr G Levy
Cost: *Alc* £28, set price L £12.75. ☺
☺ H/wine £10.95
Times: Noon-2.30pm/7-11pm. Closed L Sat, D Sun, BHs, 5 days Xmas
Additional: Sunday L. Children welcome
Seats: 65
Style: Modern, Chic
Smoking: No-smoking area; no pipes; no cigars; Air conditioning

LONDON SW10

Aubergine

Map A1

11 Park Walk, SW10 0AJ
Tel: 020 7352 3449
Fax: 020 7351 1770
Chef(s): William Drabble
Cost: Set price L £22.50/D £45 H/wine £16
Times: Noon-2pm/7-10.30pm. Closed Sun, L Sat, 2wks end Aug, 1wk Xmas, BHs
Additional: Children 10+. Vegetarian not available
Seats: 55. Jacket and tie preferred
Style: Formal
Smoking: No pipes; no cigars; Air conditioning
Directions: W along Fulham Road, 2nd road L after MGM cinema

The trademark aubergine canopy and front door are a reminder of past glories. Taking on a venue with this sort of semi-legendary status is a steep challenge, so extra credit is due to William Drabble for quickly establishing himself and making his own indelible mark on the London scene. This is a serious dining venue in the modern mode. Wooden floors, sunshine yellow walls and Provençal style artwork on the walls mixed with crisp table settings and formal service make for an almost

reverential atmosphere. The cooking style is a similar mix of the vibrant and the restrained. Take for instance an amuse of red mullet ceviche with tomato, coriander, onion and wine vinegar "exploding with fresh flavours" or a "simply stunning" mousse of foie gras with broad beans, morels and chicken livers which managed the important trick of being "richly flavoured but light". The style can be beautifully economic, sea bass coming roasted with baby artichokes, confit tomatoes and sweet pepper sauce in a perfectly balanced combination with every element playing its part. Further incidentals might include a pre-dessert of prunes in Armagnac with Armagnac ice cream. Desserts are a strength with, for instance, roasted figs in red wine with liquorice, fromage blanc mousse and gingerbread crisps being "perfectly balanced". A second coming for Aubergine.

LONDON SW10 *Continued*

Chez Max

Map C2

168 Ifield Road,
SW10 9AF
Tel: 020 7835 0874
Fax: 020 7244 0618
📧 chezmax1@aol.com
Chef(s): Nick Reeves
Owner(s): Graham Thomson &
Steven Smith
Cost: Set price D £29.50-£35.
H/wine £12.50
Times: Dinner only, 7-11pm.
Closed Sun, 25 Dec, BHs
Additional: Children welcome

Surbiton, a London suburb trying hard to retain its Surrey leafiness, is well worth exploring and the restaurant Chez Max is worth seeking out. It is unrelated to Chez Max in Chelsea or Le Petit Max in Hampton Wick but is a sister establishment to C'est La Vie in Ewell in Surrey which serves French-style cooking. A typical meal could be salad of goats' cheese or fricassée of snails, followed perhaps by lamb in a creamy garlic sauce or beef in red wine sauce. Fish is well represented on the *carte*, and desserts include superior versions of crème brûlée, strawberry gâteaux and chocolate charlotte.

Seats: 50. Private dining room 16
Style: French
Smoking: No pipes; no cigars; Air conditioning
Directions: Nearest Tube: Earls Crt. Nr West Brompton Cemetery. Turn off Fulham Rd into Ifield Rd, 500yds on L

Chutney Mary Restaurant

Map GtL C2 ⊚

535 Kings Road, Chelsea,
SW10 0SZ
Tel: 020 7351 3113
Fax: 020 7351 7694
📧 action@realindianfood.com
Chef(s): N Panjabi
Owner(s): R Mathrani & N Panjabi
Cost: Alc £35, set price L £14. ☺ ☺
H/wine £11.50
Times: 12.30-2.30pm/6.30-11.30pm.
Additional: Sunday L. Children welcome. Vegetarian by request only
Seats: 150. Private dining room 36
Smoking: No-smoking area; no pipes; no cigars; Air conditioning
Directions: On the corner of King's Road and Lots Road; 2 mins from Chelsea Harbour. Nearest tube: Fulham Broadway

Established Anglo-Indian restaurant evocative of the 1920's Raj era, decorated with large murals and a romantic garden conservatory. Anglo dishes like goats' cheese salad with cashews, mixed leaves and roasted peppers or kebab of fresh baby corn and spiced mash sit cosily next to more pointedly Indian creations such as moong bhel - a popular Bombay street snack - or tandoori kebabs.

Conrad International London

Map GtL C2 ⊚

Chelsea Harbour, SW10 0XG
Tel: 020 7823 3000
Fax: 020 7351 6525
Chef(s): Ray Neve, Roger Serjent
Cost: Alc £32, set price L £19/D £25.
☺ H/wine £12

A corporate setting for modish cuisine, with influences from the Mediterranean and Asia. A bold approach is mostly successful (tandoori monkfish with lentils and cucumber ratia) though just occasionally a little heavy-handed (Kafar lime leaf and lemon grass citrus tart with a large crescent of saffron parfait).

continued

England

Times: 12.30-3.30pm/7-11.45pm.
Closed D Sun
Additional: Sunday brunch. Bar food.
Children welcome
Seats: 64. Private dining room 14
Smoking: No-smoking area;
Air conditioning
Civil licence: 180
Accommodation: 160 rooms (160 en
suite) ★ ★ ★ ★ ★
Directions: Nearest tube: Fulham
Broadway, Earls Court

Vama

Map C3

A restaurant that makes a statement with its beautifully
decorated interior, resplendent in rich ochre, with teak chairs,
hand-made crockery, antique Indian frames and a fossil
flagstone floor. The menu claims to be unique too with a host
of Northwest Frontier dishes ranging from game rarely seen in
Indian eateries like tandoori quail or royal hunt-style venison to
more familiar sounding choices like murg tikka makhni.

438 King's Road, SW10 0LJ
Tel: 020 7351 4118/7565 8500
Fax: 020 7565 8501
e andyv@aol.com
Chef(s): Andy Varma
Owner(s): Andy Varma, Arjun Varma,
Ritu Dalmia
Cost: Alc £30. ☺ ☺ H/wine £13
Times: Noon-3.30pm/6.30-11.30pm.
Closed 25-26 Dec, 1 Jan
Additional: Sunday L. Bar food L.
Children welcome
Seats: 120. Private dining room 35
Style: Modern
Smoking: Air conditioning
Directions: Nearest tube: Sloane
Square. Approx 20-minute walk down
King's Road, ot take a No 11 or 22
Bus

LONDON SW11
Osteria Antica Bologna

Map GtL C2

Stripped wooden floors and tables and plenty of wrought iron
add to the rustic appeal of this Italian restaurant. Providing real
interest are the menus, which focus on some ancient Roman
specialities like In Ventrem Elius Fractas Olivas Mittis - boned
quail stuffed with bread and herbs, wrapped in pancetta, with
chickpeas and greens.

Smoking: No pipes; no cigars; Air conditioning
Directions: Off Battersea Rise, between Wandsworth and
Clapham Commons

23 Northcote Road, SW11 1NG
Tel: 020 7978 4771
Fax: 020 7978 4771
Chef(s): Mr Cabrera, Ms Barone
Cost: Alc £25. ☺ ☺ H/wine £9.50
Times: Noon-3pm/6-11pm.
Closed 10 days Xmas-New Year
Additional: Sunday L. Children
welcome
Seats: 75. **Style:** Traditional, Italian

Ransome's Dock

Map GtL C2

Cool (well it is a former ice cream factory) and airy in that
familiar Matisse-blue, parquet flooring, polished wooden
tables kind of way, but with an uncommonly vibrant feel. A

Battersea, SW11 4NP
Tel: 020 7223 1611
Fax: 020 7924 2614
e martinlam@compuserve.com

England

LONDON SW11 *Continued*

lively modern European *carte* is supplemented by daily specials, a set-price lunch, and a superlative wine list. Successes include tender, pink duck with parsnip purée, earthy lentils and root vegetables. Hot prune soufflé fluffy and well risen, comes with a potent Armagnac whipped cream.

Style: Modern. **Smoking:** No pipes; Air conditioning
Directions: Nearest tube: Sloane Square. Between Albert Bridge & Battersea Bridge

Chef(s): Martin Lam
Owner(s): Mr & Mrs M Lam
Cost: *Alc* £30, set price L £13.50.
☺ ☺ H/wine £13.50
Times: 11am-11pm
Closed D Sun, Xmas
Additional: Sunday L.
Children welcome
Seats: 55

LONDON SW12

Bombay Bicycle Club

Map G3

95 Nightingale Lane, SW12 8NX

A fresh and airy listed building filled with cut flowers. Specialities include Barra Channa Shahi, the restaurant's renowned tender knuckle of lamb with chickpeas and fresh curry leaves, and Bulsari Salmon, spiced fresh salmon brochette marinated in strained yoghurt and cooked over charcoal. The Indian cooking also includes plenty of familiar favourites.

Smoking: No pipes; no cigars
Directions: Telephone for directions

Tel: 020 8673 6217
Fax: 020 8673 9100
Chef(s): B J Gurung
Owner(s): J Cahn & D Sawuck
Cost: *Alc* £22.50. ☺ H/wine £11
Times: Dinner only, 7pm-12.30am.
Closed Sun, Xmas for 1 wk
Additional: Children welcome
Seats: 100. Private dining room 22

LONDON SW13

Riva Restaurant

Map GtL C3

169 Church Road, Barnes, SW13 9HR

Calling itself a café restaurant, Riva is a tiny and plain but pleasingly busy Italian eatery. A laid back approach and casual setting accompany a short yet sweet menu with quite a few options to offer interest. Try for example the brodetto mare nostrum - a saffron flavoured chunky fish soup or a mixed meat platter including culatello ham and dried figs, unusual smoked goose prosciutto and burrata tartufata with chicory and nuts. Pasta and risotto or a short selection of fish, meat and poultry dishes make up the mains, while puddings take up a larger chunk of the menu.

Directions: Nearest tube: Hammersmith. Barnes Bridge British Rail. Junction of Church Rd with Castlenau Road, Hammersmith

Tel: 020 8748 0434
Fax: 020 8748 0434
Chef(s): Franceso Zanchetta
Owner(s): Adrea Riva
Cost: *Alc* £30. ☺ H/wine £11.50
Times: Noon-2.30pm/7-11pm. Closed
L Sat, Xmas, Easter, last 2wks in Aug
Additional: Sunday L. Children
welcome
Seats: 50
Style: Italian
Smoking: No pipes; no cigars;
Air conditioning

Sonny's Restaurant

Map C3

94 Church Road, Barnes, SW13 0DQ

With its stylish, frosted windows and adjacent black-canopied food store, Sonny's is the model of modern chic. The fashionable café, serves up-to-the-minute snacks, and the light, airy restaurant, displaying a range of modern art is popular for both sociable lunches and cosy dinners. The emphasis is on contemporary cuisine with a strong Mediterranean slant. Service is efficient, yet relaxed and friendly. Try confit of rabbit ravioli, girolles, swiss chard and pearl barley broth to begin, then perhaps roasted fillet of salmon, with saffron and courgette risotto. Both vegetarians and meat-lovers will find appealing dishes complemented by a varied selection of desserts and wines.

Directions: Nearest Tube: Hammersmith. From Castlenau end of Church Road, on left by shops

Tel: 020 8748 0393
Fax: 020 8748 2698
Chef(s): Leigh Diggins
Owner(s): Rebecca Mascrenhas,
James Harris
Cost: *Alc* £30, set price L £16. ☺ ☺
H/wine £10.50
Times: 12.30-3pm/7.30-11pm.
Closed D Sun, BHs
Additional: Sunday L. Children
welcome. Vegetarian by request only
Seats: 100. Private dining room 20
Style: Chic, Minimalist
Smoking: Air conditioning

LONDON SW14

Crowthers Restaurant

Map GtL B2

Small shop parade restaurant, beautifully kept with handsome furnishings and quality china. Front of house service is provided by Shirley Crowther while husband Philip produces carefully executed dishes from a classic menu priced for two or three courses. The choice of aperitifs is a feature, and the short wine list offers a fair proportion of halves

Seats: 30. **Style:** Traditional
Smoking: No pipes; no cigars; Air conditioning
Directions: Train to Mortlake, train or tube to Richmond. Between junction of Sheen Lane & Clifford Ave

481 Upper Richmond Road West, East Sheen, SW14 7PU
Tel: 020 8876 6372
Fax: 020 8876 6372
Chef(s): Philip Crowther
Owner(s): Mr & Mrs P Crowther
Cost: *Alc* £26.60, set price D £24.75. H/wine £11
Times: Dinner only, 7-10.30pm. Closed 1 wk Xmas, 2 wks Aug
Additional: Children welcome

The Depot Waterfront Brasserie

Map GtL C2

Thameside restaurant, just off the High Street, with river views from many tables. Choose from a *carte*, two-course lunch or short set dinner. Intercontinental options include pan-fried Thai marinated salmon with Asian greens, yam and sweetcorn croquettes with coconut chutney, and chargrilled calves' liver with pancetta.

Tideway Yard, Mortlake High Street, SW14 8SN
Tel: 020 8878 9462
Fax: 020 8392 1361
Chef(s): Robert Veint
Owner(s): Tideway Restaurants Ltd.
Cost: *Alc* £25, set price D £13.50.
☺ ☺ H/wine £10.50
Times: 11am-3pm/6-11pm.
Closed 24-26 Dec
Additional: Sunday L. Bar food. Children welcome
Seats: 120. Private dining room 120
Style: Modern, Rustic
Smoking: No-smoking area; Air conditioning
Directions: Between Barnes Bridge & Mortlake stations

Redmond's

Map GtL B2

Popular neighbourhood local delivering a touch of the Mediterranean to leafy suburbia. Pavement plants provide a green canopy to the glass-fronted restaurant, while inside vibrant colours create warm and sunny first impressions. Polished blonde floorboards, designer-style leather chairs, white tablecloths and colourful contemporary abstracts cut an informal, upbeat mood. Redmond Hayward's modern, eclectic, fixed-priced menus provide imaginative and assured cooking with a nod to the Mediterranean and beyond. Must tries include roast pepper soup with seared goats cheese, and roast, boned and stuffed saddle of lamb with shallots, rosemary and truffle oil, tian of Mediterranean vegetables and lamb jus. Front of house is run with panache by wife Pippa, expect a vibrant, buzzy and noisy atmosphere at dinner.

Directions: Located half way between Putney and Richmond. On the South Circular Road at the Barnes end of Sheen

170 Upper Richmond Road West, SW14 8AW
Tel: 020 8878 1922
Fax: 020 8878 1133
✉ pippahayward@btconnect.com
Chef(s): Redmond Hayward
Owner(s): Mr R Hayward, Mrs P Hayward
Cost: Set price L £21.50/ D £27.50-£30. ☺
Times: Noon-2pm/7-10.30pm. Closed L Sat, D Sun, 4 days Xmas
Additional: Sunday L. Children welcome
Seats: 54
Style: Modern
Smoking: No-smoking area; no pipes; no cigars; Air conditioning

England

LONDON SW15

Phoenix Bar & Grill

Map GtL C2

Up-tempo and consciously cool décor (white walls, contemporary art) with food to match. What's on offer depends on when you come. Whether its the *carte*, set lunch (Monday to Friday), early bird (Sunday to Thursday) or Saturday brunch expect dishes along the lines of wild mushroom risotto, smoked haddock with saffron mash, and apple and Calvados parfait with apple fritters.

Seats: 100
Style: Modern
Smoking: No-smoking area; no pipes; Air conditioning
Directions: Telephone for directions

162 Pentlow Street,
Putney SW15 1LY
Tel: 020 8780 3131
Fax: 020 8780 1114
Chef(s): Carol Craddock
Owner(s): Rebecca Mascarenhas & James Harris
Cost: *Alc* £30, set price L £15. ☺
H/wine £10.50
Times: 12.30-2.30pm/7-11pm.
Closed BHs, 24-26 Dec, 1 Jan
Additional: Sunday L. Children welcome

Putney Bridge

Map GtL C2

Smack bang on the river with boat style architecture to match, giving the dining room a long narrow emphasis with consistent views over the Thames. Anthony Demetre provides the real excitement with a classic French approach being just the foundation for a plethora of extra dimensions that are guaranteed to excite and sometimes amaze. There is plenty of theatre in a menu that is not overlong but is supplemented at dinner by two amuse and two pre-desserts. The menu dégustation offers a ten course odyssey and is well judged enough to have diners "eagerly anticipating" the delivery of each new dish. There is a lot going on but the disparate elements tend to knit very well. Take for instance, brochette of diver-caught scallops, chorizo and snails with carrot and coral purée founded on the strong basis of "super sweet" scallops, judiciously spiced and with "a marvellous range of textures". Roast wild duck with boudin blanc, confit cabbage and Armagnac received a rapturous reception not least for "the best duck ever encountered" and a faithful daube of beef with sweet potato purée, red wine and parsley sauce also won plaudits. Amongst the desserts, warm Valrhona chocolate moelleux with soft turrón ice cream was described as "simply unctuous". Lunch is marvellous value and staff are both chirpy and knowledgeable.

The Embankment, SW15 1LB
Tel: 020 8780 1811
Fax: 020 8780 1211
🅴 demetre@globalnet.co.uk
Chef(s): Anthony Demetre
Owner(s): Gerald Davidson
Cost: *Alc* £46, set price L £18.50. ☺
H/wine £15
Times: Noon-2.30pm/7-10.30pm.
Closed Mon, D Sun, Xmas, New Year
Additional: Sunday L. Children 5 yrs+
Seats: 100
Style: Modern
Smoking: No pipes; Air conditioning
Directions: Nearest tube: Putney Bridge. From station cross bridge. Restaurant is 1st building on R, facing onto river

LONDON SW17

Chez Bruce

Map GtL C2

Behind the small red-fronted exterior facing onto Wandsworth Common is a colourful, busy restaurant serving, in the main, salubrious locals. The smart rustic décor favours dark wooden shutters, cast iron chandeliers and a plain wooden floor, with the slight tightness of space lending an intimate feel. The simple menu offers some interesting combinations, using mainly French but also other European influences. Cured foie gras and ham hock ballotine with pear chutney juggles contrasts effectively, as does rare-grilled tunas with avocado, crème fraîche and salsa, another delicious starter. Braised lamb shank with truffled mash and glazed endive produced wonderfully intense flavours. Seafood is well-handled in the likes of roast cod with fondant leek and wild mushroom risotto, and choucroute of fish with shrimp beurre blanc and chives. The long wine list makes a confusing read, but there's a good choice of mainly French halves and wines by the glass. Service can occasionally be rushed.

Directions: Nearest tube: Balham. Near Wandsworth Common B.R. station

2 Bellevue Road, Wandsworth Common, SW17 7EG
Tel: 020 8672 0114
Fax: 020 8767 6648
Chef(s): Bruce Poole
Owner(s): Bruce Poole
Cost: Set price L £21.50-£27.50/ D £27.50-£33.50. H/wine £14
Times: Noon-2pm/7-10.30pm. Closed D Sun, BHs, 23-30 Dec
Additional: Sunday L. Children welcome at L
Seats: 75. Private dining room 18
Style: Modern
Smoking: No pipes; no cigars; Air conditioning

Kastoori

Map GtL C2

A purely vegetarian restaurant with its main roots in the Indian sub-continent, and a daily special with Ugandan influences. Everything is appealingly fresh, ranging from curries (fresh tomato, or cauliflower with cream) through various thalis (several small dishes making a fixed meal), with soft chapaties, crisp papadams, and perfect rice.

Seats: 82. Jacket and tie preferred
Smoking: Air conditioning
Directions: Nearest Tube: Tooting Bec & Tooting Broadway. Situated between tube stations

188 Upper Tooting Road, SW17 7EJ
Tel: 020 8767 7027
Fax: 020 8767 7027
Chef(s): Manoj Thanki
Owner(s): Mr D Thanki
Cost: ☺ ☺ H/wine £7.75
Times: 12.30-2.30pm/6-10.30pm. Closed L Mon & Tue
Additional: Sunday L. Children welcome

LONDON SW19

Cannizaro House

Map GtL C2

Impressive house with a long tradition of accommodating and entertaining the upper echelons of London society. The dining room is traditional in style with a massive central chandelier, large tables dressed in crisp white linen, and flowers arranged in a silver chalice. Trolleys and cloches are all part of the paraphernalia, and piano music drifting in from the lounge seems like an echo of a bygone age. Rigorous standards extend to the cuisine. Contemporary flavours are well represented, but old favourites are not forgotten, with smoked salmon, fillet of Aberdeen Angus with bordelaise sauce; and crêpes Suzette flambéed at the table.

Smoking: No smoking in dining room
Civil licence: 60
Accommodation: 45 rooms (45 en suite) ★ ★ ★ ★
Directions: From A3 (London Rd) Tibbets Corner, take A219 (Parkside) R into Cannizaro Rd, then R into West Side

West Side, Wimbledon Common, SW19 4UE
Tel: 020 8879 1464
Fax: 020 8879 7338
✉ cannizaro.house@thistle.co.uk
Chef(s): Stephen Kitchen
Owner(s): Thistle Hotels
Cost: Alc £45, set price L £22.75/ D £24.75. ☺ ☺ H/wine £17.95
Times: Noon-2pm/7-11.30pm.
Additional: Sunday L. Children 14yrs+
Seats: 50. Private dining room 96
Style: Traditional, Country-house

England

LONDON SW19 *Continued*

The Lighthouse
Restaurant NEW Map GtL C2

75-77 The Ridgeway, Wimbledon,
SW19 4ST
Tel: 020 8944 6338
Fax: 020 8946 4440
✉ lightrest@aol.com
Chef(s): Gianni Vatteroni
Owner(s): Mr Finch & Mr Taylor
Additional: Sunday L. Children
welcome
Seats: 80
Style: Modern, Minimalist
Smoking: No-smoking area; no pipes;
no cigars
Directions: Telephone for directions

Decorated in modern, minimalist style with limestone, slate and
blonde wood, the Lighthouse is a stylish setting for a meal. The
menu travels the world, offering interesting modern dishes such
as green beans, enoki mushrooms and sweet potato tempura
with vanilla sweet soy, or roast rack of lamb with cassava chips,
field mushrooms, rocket and salsa verdi. The strongest
influence, however, is Italian - as is evident in dishes such as
braised octopus, lemon grass and mushroom risotto or egg
tagliatelli with confit of baby fennel, porcini and graveria. The
globe-trotting wine list favours France.

LONDON W1

Alastair Little Soho Map D4

Alastair Little's original Soho restaurant. On an inspection visit,
the buzz and thrill of previous meals seemed rather lacking.
Breads are delicious, but there was little inspiration in the
Caesar salad, roast breast of chicken with potato gratin and
wild mushroom sauce, or a bourride of sliced fish, prawns and
mussels. Other dishes, perhaps more typical of the Little stamp,
include grilled sardines with salsa verde, six native oysters with
spicy sausages and shallot relish, and skate wing with rocket
and herb dressed potatoes. From the dessert list, Venetian rice
pudding with blood orange salad still conjures up the simple,
sunny flavours with which his name is associated.

Directions: Nearest tube: Tottenham Court Rd. Near Ronnie
Scott's Jazz Club

49 Frith Street, W1V 5TE
Tel: 020 7734 5183
Fax: 020 7734 5206
Chef(s): Ed Rugg, Alastair Little
Owner(s): A Little, K Pedersen,
M. André-Vega
Cost: Set price L £27/D £35.
H/wine £14
Times: Noon-3pm/6-11pm.
Closed Sun, L Sat, BHs
Additional: Children welcome
Seats: 65. Private dining room 25
Style: Minimalist, Italian
Smoking: No pipes; Air conditioning

☺ Indicates a restaurant that has told us they offer a two-course lunch for
less than £15

☺ Indicates a restaurant that has told us they offer a three-course dinner for
less than £25

England

Alloro

NEW Map C3

Modern décor of marble sculpted bay leaves marks out this new Italian venue with an added twist of imagination and spark. Fresh ciabatta and focaccia accompany black tagliolini with crab, with Ossobuco alla Milanese and Orata (sea bream) con stufatino prominent among main dishes "full of sunshine". Friendly, relaxed service.

20 Dover Street,
W1X 3PB
Tel: 020 7495 4768
Fax: 020 7629 5348
Chef(s): Michele Brogi
Owner(s): A to Z Restaurants Ltd.
Cost: Set price L £19.50-£23.50/D £23-£32. H/wine £15
Times: Noon-2.30pm/7-10.30pm. Closed Sun, Xmas, New Year, BHs
Additional: Bar food L. Children welcome
Seats: 70. Private dining room 18
Style: Modern, Italian
Smoking: No pipes; no cigars; Air conditioning
Directions: Nearest tube: Green Park. From station towards Piccadilly Circus, Dover St is on L. Alloro is halfway down Dover St.

L'Anis

Map GtL C3

A considered balance of new and old, L'Anis' offers a classical menu with modern touches. Take the tortellini of herbs with roasted red mullet, ratatouille and black olive consommé, for example, in which flavours are sophisticated without ... they could be more pronounced. Quite enjoyable is a pud like banana cream with banana and passion fruit sorbet and chocolate and saffron sauce.

CLOSED

Style: Chic, French
Smoking: No pipes; no cigars; Air conditioning
Directions: Nearest tube: High Street Kensington. Opposite Royal Garden Hotel & Kensington Palace

1 Kensington High Street, W8 5NP
Tel: 020 7795 6533
Fax: 020 795 8854
Owner(s): C. Schulze & R. Shama
Cost: c £?, set price L £25.50/ D £25.50 ☺ H/wine £13.50
Times: Noon-2.45pm/6-10.45pm. Closed L Sat, D Sun, Xmas, New Year
Additional: Sunday L. Bar food. Children welcome
Seats: 70

Archipelago

NEW Map C3

Boldly coloured peacock feathers, candles, mirrors and masks hang from corners and ceilings, and there are trinkets everywhere. In this eclectic setting it's no wonder that the food is somewhat outlandish, made from exotic ingredients and cryptically described on the menu: swamp fever - green-laden Vietnamese chicken; Berber tents - spicy lamb in an Injera pancake; Cayman Islands - pan-fried crocodile wrapped in vine leaves; hot marsupial - kangaroo rump on kumura. Bizarre desserts include chocolate-covered scorpion (crispy, but no real taste) and the enigmatically titled 'A Visit from the Doctor'.

Smoking: No-smoking area; no pipes; no cigars; Air conditioning
Directions: Nearest tube: Warren Street. South along Tottenham Court Road. 1st R into Grafton Way. 1st L into Whitfield St

110 Whitfield Street,
W1T 5ED
Tel: 020 7383 3346
Fax: 020 7383 7181
Chef(s): Campbell Starr
Owner(s): Bruce Alexander
Cost: Set price L £19.50/D £38.50 ☺ H/wine £18.50
Times: Noon-4.30pm/6pm-late. Closed Sun, L Sat, Xmas, New Year
Additional: Children welcome
Seats: 38
Style: Eclectic

England

LONDON W1 *Continued*

Aroma II

Map D3

Watch the chef hand-pulling noodles (Tues & Thurs pm) at this authentic Chinese restaurant specialising in Peking, Cantonese and Szechuan cooking. Some variations on the norm, including whole suckling pig at a cool £128, spicy shredded jellyfish with Arctic clam, and lobster sashimi. Usual set menus, and dishes listed by type.

118 Shaftesbury Avenue, W1V 7DJ
Tel: 020 7437 0377
Fax: 020 7437 0377
 booking@aromarestaurant.co.uk
Chef(s): David Tam
Cost: *Alc* from £15. ☺ ☺ H/wine £9
Times: Noon-11.30pm
Additional: Sunday L. Children welcome. Vegetarian by request only
Seats: 120. Private dining room 40
Style: Modern, Informal
Smoking: No-smoking area; Air conditioning
Directions: Nearest tube: Leicester Square. North along Charing Cross Road, then left into Shaftesbury Avenue at Cambridge Circus

Athenaeum Hotel, Bullochs @ 116

Map C3

A discreet address in the heart of Mayfair, and preferred staging post for the rich and famous. Bullochs is intimate and friendly, with oil lamps, candles and the odd alcove for privacy. As you would expect, the cooking is competent, with dishes coming from far flung points of the globe. Try the mildly illegal-sounding gianuja mousse, a wicked dessert.

116 Piccadilly, W1V 0BJ
Tel: 020 7499 3464
Fax: 020 7493 1860
 info@athenaeumhotel.com
Chef(s): David Marshall
Cost: *Alc* £30, set price L £14-£17/ D £15-£20 (pre-theatre). ☺ ☺ H/wine £13
Times: 12.30-2.30pm/5.30-11pm. Closed L Sat & Sun
Additional: Children welcome
Seats: 50. Private dining room 14
Style: Modern, Mediterranean
Smoking: No pipes; Air conditioning
Civil licence: 55
Accommodation: 157 rooms (157 en suite) ★ ★ ★ ★
Directions: Nearest tube: Hyde Park Corner, Green Park

Atlantic Bar & Grill

Map D3

This cavernous Art Deco style venue with its original 1920's marble pillars is still pulling them in. At night, it's something of a crush but for many that's the whole point. Food amounts to a broadly modern British brasserie menu with the likes of fillet of

20 Glasshouse Street, W1R 5RQ
Tel: 020 7734 4888
Fax: 0207 734 5400
 LOZ@atlanticbar.freeserve.co.uk

beef with pea purée and good chips. Good range of wines by the glass.

Seats: 200
Private dining room 70
Style: Art deco. **Smoking:** Air conditioning
Directions: Nearest tube: Piccadilly Circus

Chef(s): Stephen Carter
Owner(s): Oliver Peyton
Cost: *Alc* £40, set price L £14.50/
D £14.50-£40. ☺ ☺ H/wine £13.50
Times: Noon-2.45pm/6-Midnight.
Closed L Sat-Sun
Additional: Bar food.
Children welcome

Bentley's
Map C3

☺☺
11/15 Swallow Street, W1R 7HD
Tel: 020 7734 4756
Telephone for further details

Bentley's is a bit of a seafood lover's paradise, with fish everywhere on the menu and only the slightest nod towards carnivores. An oyster bar sits beneath the formal first floor restaurant, where booths occupy the outside of the room and tables are scattered in the centre. It's very classic in style, like the extensive wine list which offers some decent growers and vintages. Expect the likes of crab risotto with saffron and red peppers, and a herb-roasted royal bream Niçoise which shows fine attention to detail. A classic crème brûlée might complete a meal, and there's good espresso coffee.

The Berners Hotel
Map D4

Berners Street, W1A 3BE
Tel: 020 7666 2000
Fax: 020 7666 2001
e berners@berners.co.uk
Chef(s): John Brodie
Cost: *Alc* £27, set price L £16.95-
£19.70/D £10.25-£16.70. ☺ ☺
H/wine £14.50
Times: 12.30-2.30pm/5.30-10pm.
Additional: Sunday L. Bar food.
Children welcome
Seats: 110. Private dining room 150
Style: Chic
Smoking: No-smoking area; no pipes;
Air conditioning
Civil licence: 70
Accommodation: 217 rooms (217 en
suite) ★ ★ ★ ★
Directions: Off Oxford Street

Reflections is the name of the dining room and it doesn't take a detective to work out why, with the marble floor and stunning moulded ceiling reflected in the etched silver wall mirrors. Fresh ingredients and skilled execution are evident in dishes of smoked duck breast with beetroot mousse and herb salad, and red mullet with wilted greens and baby squid stuffed with lemon couscous.

England

LONDON W1 *Continued*

Bice

Map C3

13 Albemarle Street, W1X 3HA
Tel: 020 7409 1011
Telephone for further details

The first Bice opened in Milan in 1926 and now there are some 20 of them scattered across the globe (Paris, Beverley Hills, Tokyo amongst others). This basement venue in Mayfair retains a restrained 1920's feel with pale wood panelling, banquettes and bevelled mirrors. The menu is packed with familiar favourites (liguine alle vongole, minestrone, veal cutlet Milanese style and pannacotta with pear in red wine) along with more contemporary offerings. It doesn't feel old fashioned though and the likes of seared scallops with porcini, lambs lettuce and green beans are praised for their freshness and vibrancy. Medallions of veal might come in a pungent combination with smoked cheese, new potatoes and a robust balsamic sauce. Good breads include focaccia with a variety of toppings.

Blues Bistro & Bar

Map D4

42-43 Dean Street, W1V 5AP
Tel: 020 7494 1966
Fax: 020 7494 0717
e info@bluesbistro.com
Chef(s): Gerry Dowd
Owner(s): Anthony Whitehouse
Cost: *Alc* £35, set price L £23.50-£38.
☺ ☺ H/wine £10.95
Times: 12.30-4.30pm/5.30pm-Midnight. Closed L Sat & Sun, BHs
Additional: Bar food. Children welcome
Seats: 100. Private dining room 45
Style: Modern
Smoking: No pipes; no cigars; Air conditioning
Directions: From Shaftesbury Avenue into Dean St, past Old Compton St, 20yds on the L

Amiable and efficient restaurant with a New York brasserie feel. A contemporary approach and a menu spanning the globe is the name of the game here, with Mediterranean choices such as warm haloumi salad with avocado and marinated red onion coupled with Stateside influences in, say, Maryland chicken with corn fritter and bacon.

Restaurant 1837
@ Brown's Hotel

Map C3

Albemarle Street,
Dover Street, W1A 4BP
Tel: 020 7408 1837
Fax: 020 7408 1838
e 1837@brownshotel.com
Chef(s): Andrew Turner
Owner(s): Raffles International
Cost: *Alc* £45, set price L £20-£30/ D £39-£49. H/wine £25

Refurbished a couple of years back but still with a clubby feel. Many will be reassured to find that service is as correct as ever and the clientele continues to comprise a mix of pin-striped businessmen and American tourists. The menu is enormous and retains the old favourites like grilled Dover sole alongside the more adventurous dishes such as parfait of smoked sturgeon with black olive and caviar or velouté of rabbit and truffle. The real strength is the quality of the raw materials and the technical precision of the cooking. Take for example milk-fed veal with morels, asparagus and broad beans that feature "impeccable" saucing or seared confit of wild salmon with langoustine risotto and a tarragon veal jus that stands out for its delicate balance of flavours. Desserts tend towards the classic with a plate of miniature rhubarb puddings that include rhubarb crumble, iced rhubarb parfait and a mousse with a rhubarb crisp. The wine list is stunning with about 100 available by the glass.

Times: 12.30-2pm/7-10pm.
Closed Sun, L Sat, BHs
Additional: Children welcome.
Vegetarian by request only
Seats: 70. Private dining room 12
Style: Classic
Smoking: No-smoking area; no pipes; no cigars; Air conditioning
Civil licence: 70
Accommodation: 118 rooms (118 en suite) ★ ★ ★ ★
Directions: Near Piccadilly Circus. Nearest tube: Green Park

Caviar House

Map C3

161 Piccadilly, W1V 9DF
Tel: 020 7409 0445
Telephone for further details

An exotic little shop sells various Balik specialities (vodka, caviar, salmon etc), while the stylish eatery serves the same luxury produce and other excellent quality meats and fish. Lots of vibrant blues, funky lighting and mirrors suggest the sea in the light and airy restaurant, and there are two menus to choose between: the more expensive *carte* and a good value set menu which offers a taster of the specialities as well as some classic dishes. Lobster bisque cappuccino with fresh Sevruga caviar to start, perhaps, then roasted breast of wild duck with port and raspberry sauce, and Charlotte Russe with berries.

Caviar Kaspia

NEW Map C3

18-18a Bruton Place, W1X 7AH
Tel: 020 7493 2612
Fax: 0207 408 1627
✉ london@caviarkaspia.com
Chef(s): Willian Cooper
Owner(s): Madame Fixon
Cost: *Alc* £45, (caviar menus) set price L £39.90-£72.50/D £43-£144. H/wine £16
Times: Noon-3pm/7-11.30pm.
Closed Sun, Xmas, Aug

Set in a quiet back street off Berkeley Square, Kaspia is a shop specialising in Baltic foods and a formal restaurant rolled into one. Its name gives away its passion for the produce of the Caspian Sea with, you guessed it, first-rate caviar taking centre stage. There is also a *carte*, which is modern European with many more seafood options.

Additional: Children welcome
Seats: 50. Private dining room. Jacket and tie preferred
Style: Classic, French
Smoking: No-smoking area; no pipes; Air conditioning
Directions: Nearest tube: Green Park. Off Berkeley Square

LONDON W1 *Continued*

Cecconi's   NEW   Map C3

5a Burlington Gardens, W1X 1LE
Tel: 0171 434 1509
Telephone for further details

'No fusion, no mixture, no fuss' sums up the cuisine and ambience at this elegant, minimalist restaurant with svelte décor, a long welcoming bar, capacious leather chairs and carefully spaced tables. Refined regional cooking is the theme, and the menu combines respected Italian dishes (minestrone, cotoletta alla Milanese), home-made pasta (priced for starter or main) and more modern ideas (outstanding olive oil with focaccia, roast duck with spelt and balsamic vinegar). Flavours and presentation are fresh and uncomplicated, and torta al limone and excellent regional cheeses make good choices to finish. A fine Italian wine list includes some seductive Super-Tuscans.

Chesterfield Hotel   Map C3

35 Charles Street,
Mayfair, W1X 8LX
Tel: 020 7491 2622
Fax: 020 7491 4793
e reservations@chesterfield.
redcarnationhotels.com
Chef(s): Stephen Henderson
Owner(s): RCH Hotels
Cost: *Alc* £27, set price L £17.50/
D £22.50. ☺ H/wine £16.50
Times: Noon-2.30pm/5.30-10.30pm.
Closed L Sat

An elegant restaurant with an exclusive atmosphere and a unique wine room for tasting wines before dinner. There are plenty of adventurous dishes on the modern menu - try courgette flowers in batter with dolcelatte cheese, or beetroot-cured salmon with mustard and dill. A spring menu offered new-season rump of lamb with lentils, sage and spiced quince.

Additional: Sunday L. Bar food. Children welcome
Seats: 85. Private dining room 28
Style: Classic, Traditional
Smoking: No pipes; Air conditioning
Civil licence: 120
Accommodation: 110 rooms (110 en suite) ★★★★
Directions: Nearest tube: Green Park. Bottom of Berkeley Square, on corner of Charles Street & Queen Street.

cheznico   Map B3

90 Park Lane, W1A 3AA
Tel: 020 7409 1290
Fax: 020 7355 4877
e cheznico@globalnet.co.uk
Chef(s): Paul Rhodes
Owner(s): Nico & Dinah-Jane Ladenis
Cost: Set price L £43/D £62.
H/wine £17
Times: Noon-2pm/7-11pm.
Closed Sun, L Sat, 10 days Xmas,
4 days Easter, BHs
Additional: Children welcome
Seats: 85. Private dining room 20
Style: Classic, Traditional
Smoking: No pipes; Air conditioning

Just the place to spend a few hours and a few quid (but not as many as you might expect). The friendly French staff wax lyrical about the food as they deliver the menu, and there's none of the snobbishness sometimes associated with restaurants of this renown. Green and sage are the predominant colours, and the signature mirrored dado of all Nico's outlets is there too. The cooking continues to be distinguished by accurate flavours and obvious attention to detail. Exceptionally good bread is always an indication of good things to come and so it is here, with first class baking followed by pinpoint starters like tortellini of langoustine with lobster sauce (wafer-thin saffron pasta and a velvety sauce). An "exemplary" osso buco with Parmesan risotto exhibits the ideal mixture of unctuous and tender meat, marrow and perfect risotto with marvellously intense flavours. Desserts continue in the classic vein with lemon tart and raspberry sauce being a pretty much benchmark example. Service is neatly balanced, being professional but unstuffy and the wine list offers heaps of quality but at a price.

Directions: Nearest Tube: Marble Arch. On Corner Park Lane.
Part of Grosvenor House Hotel

England

Chor Bizarre

Map C2

16 Albermarle Street,
Mayfair, W1X 3HA
Tel: 020 7629 9802
Fax: 020 7493 7756
e chorbizarrelondon@
oldworldhospitality.com
Chef(s): Deepinder Sondhi
Owner(s): India's Restaurants Ltd.
Cost: Alc £22. ☺ ☺ H/wine £14.50
Times: Noon-3pm/6-11.30pm.
Closed 25-26 Dec, BHs
Additional: Sunday L. Bar food.
Children welcome
Seats: 70. Private dining room 30
Smoking: No-smoking area; no pipes;
no cigars; Air conditioning
Directions: Telephone for directions

Yes, a pun on the word bazaar, and taking its inspiration from India's labyrinthine markets, this well received Indian restaurant in Mayfair is full of imagination and fun. The menu strays far from the usual curry house fare. Dakshni scallops with garlic, lime, green pepper and spices offers 'perfectly cooked scallops', and chicken chettinad is 'pungent but not overpowering'.

Churchill Inter-Continental, The Terrace

Map B4

30 Portman Square, W1A 4ZX
Tel: 020 7486 5800
Fax: 020 7486 1255
e churchill@interconti.com
Chef(s): Justin Higgens
Cost: Alc £45. H/wine £17.50
Times: 12.30-3pm/6-11pm.
Additional: Sunday L. Bar food.
Children welcome
Seats: 120
Style: Modern, Chic

A great haunt for weekenders, with all the comforts of a London hotel and character befitting a 16th-century coaching inn. The restaurant combines opulence with contemporary art and food. The kitchen may sometimes stumble with complex combinations, but finds its feet in knockout puddings — cleverly prepared and presented. Don't miss the poached pear with five-spice sabayon and lemongrass ice cream.

Smoking: No-smoking area; Air conditioning
Civil licence: 180
Accommodation: 445 rooms (445 en suite) ★★★★★
Directions: Close to Marble Arch, just off Oxford Street.

Claridge's

Map C3

Brook Street, W1A 2JQ
Tel: 020 7629 8860
Fax: 020 7499 2210
e info@claridges.co.uk
Chef(s): John Williams
Owner(s): Marco Piras
Cost: Alc £50, set price L £28.75/
D £35. H/wine £19.5
Times: 12.30-2.45pm/7-11pm.
Additional: Sunday L. Bar food.
Children welcome
Seats: 100. Private dining room 150
Style: Formal, Chic
Smoking: Air conditioning

The elegant and very comfortable art deco restaurant at Claridge's was designed in 1926 and is being refurbished for the 2002 season. A major change for what is an institution, perhaps even more so given that the new operation will be overseen by no less than Gordon Ramsay. It is likely that the revamped restaurant will be called Gordon Ramsay at Claridge's (not many surprises there) and the menu is likely to feature a mix of Ramsay originals and signature dishes in the modern European style.

Civil licence: 200
Accommodation: 197 rooms (197 en suite) ★★★★★
Directions: Two minutes from Bond Street tube, at the corner of Brook & Davies Streets

LONDON W1 *Continued*

The Connaught

Map C3

The Connaught dining experience is special - well worth the time and money. The stunning service, classic elegance, lavish artwork and exemplary napiery are a working memorial to those who set the standard a century before. Michel Bourdin (due to retire at the end of 2001) provides a menu as rich in tradition as is it is in calories, all elaborate garnishing and swathes of complex French terminology, though some lapses in the execution of dishes were noted - a dull sauce here and ill-timed scallops there. Equally extravagant is the wine list, made accessible by the good choice by the glass.

Smoking: Air conditioning
Accommodation: 92 rooms (92 en suite) ★ ★ ★ ★ ★
Directions: Nearest tube: Bond Street/Green Park. On corner of Mount Street and Carlos Place

Carlos Place, W1Y 6AL
Tel: 020 7499 7070
Fax: 020 7495 3262
e info@the-connaught.co.uk
Chef(s): Michel Bourdin
Cost: *Alc* £60, set price L £50-£70/ D £58-£80
Times: 12.30-2.30pm/6-10.45pm. Closed L Sat Grill Room
Additional: Sunday L. Bar food. Children welcome
Seats: 70. Private dining room 22. Jacket and tie preferred
Style: Traditional, French

The Criterion

Map C3

One of Marco Pierre White's string of restaurants, the Criterion is a stunning neo-Byzantine creation, its grand entrance flanked by potted palms leading into a vast bar topped with great drum lamps. The main room evokes the magic of the Arabian Nights with ornate marble walls and exquisite mosaics. The menu reads well, with plenty to get your teeth into - turmeric-roasted brill with mussel and clam fondue, or roast suckling pig with Stilton creamed leeks and jus gras. There have been occasional lapses in execution but the kitchen generally delivers. Serious wine list with depth in vintages and a global sweep.

Smoking: Air conditioning
Directions: Nearest tube: Piccadilly Circus

224 Piccadilly, W1V 9LB
Tel: 020 7930 0488
Fax: 020 7930 8380
Chef(s): Peter Reffel
Owner(s): Marco Pierre White
Cost: *Alc* £35, set price L £17.95/ D £17.95. ☺ ☺ H/wine £15
Times: Noon-2.30pm/5.30-11.30pm. Closed L Sun, 25-26 Dec, 1 Jan
Additional: Children welcome
Seats: 160
Style: neo-Byzantine

The Dorchester, Grill Room

Map C3

The dramatically opulent décor of the Dorchester Grill has remained unchanged since the hotel opened 70 years ago. It is elaborately gilded in the Spanish Baroque style, hung with Flemish tapestries and furnished with deep burgundy velvet

The Dorchester, Park Lane, W1A 2HJ
Tel: 020 7629 8888
Fax: 020 7317 6363
e foodandbeverage@ dorchesterhotel.com
Chef(s): Henry Brosi
Owner(s): Dorchester Group
Cost: *Alc* £45, set price L £32.50/ D £39.50. H/wine £20
Times: 12.30-2.30pm/6-11pm.
Additional: Sunday L. Children welcome
Seats: 81
Style: Traditional
Smoking: Air conditioning
Civil licence: 500
Accommodation: 250 rooms (250 en suite) ★ ★ ★ ★ ★

and leather. The menu and most attentive service uphold traditional standards and a mixed clientele comprises business people, tourists and often a number of elderly gentlemen dining alone. Braised oxtail wrapped around a mousse of herbs, shredded oxtail and cheese, made for a very rich but successful dish, thankfully served with a lighter jus to counteract the lip-smacking qualities.

Directions: Nearest Tube: Hyde Park Corner. Two-thirds of the way down Park Lane, fronting a small island garden.

The Dorchester, The Oriental Map C3

Park Lane, W1A 2HJ
Tel: 020 7629 8888
Fax: 020 7317 6363
e foodandbeveridge@
dorchesterhotel.com
Chef(s): Henry Brosi & Kenneth Poon
Owner(s): Dorchester Group
Cost: Alc £60, set price L £25/
D £43-£95. H/wine £27.50
Times: Noon-2.30pm/7-11pm.
Closed Sun, L Sat, Aug, Xmas,
New Year, BHs
Additional: Children welcome
Seats: 81. Private dining room 16
Style: Modern, Cantonese
Smoking: Air conditioning
Civil licence: 500
Accommodation: 250 rooms (250 en suite) ★ ★ ★ ★ ★
Directions: Nearest tube: Hyde Park Corner. Two-thirds of the way down Park Lane, fronting a small island garden

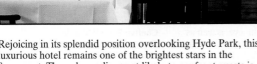

Rejoicing in its splendid position overlooking Hyde Park, this luxurious hotel remains one of the brightest stars in the firmament. The only predicament likely to confront guests is the one of where to eat, since this great institution boasts several quality options. The finest is undoubtedly the acclaimed Cantonese cooking of The Oriental, where set menus called 'Forbidden City', 'Imperial Phoenix' and 'Mandarin's Tale' offer an alluring but restrained range of dishes. Balance is the keyword here, and flavours are mutually supportive rather than overwhelming. Memorable recent dishes included prawn and chicken dumplings in ginger and spring onion, king prawns yin yang, and chicken with snow peas and oyster sauce, served with an uplifting version of oriental fried rice. A dessert of red bean paste and coconut parcel is an innovation that might not appeal to everyone's taste. Guests are welcomed with a handshake from the maitre d', and eased through the ordering process by knowledgeable staff.

L'Escargot – The Ground Floor Restaurant Map D4

48 Greek Street, W1V 5LQ
Tel: 020 7439 7474
Fax: 020 7437 0790
Chef(s): Andrew Thompson
Owner(s): Jimmy Lahoud
Cost: Alc £29, set price L £17.95/
D £17.95. ☺ ☺ H/wine £14
Times: 12.15-2.15pm/6-11.30pm.
Closed Sun, L Sat, 25-26 Dec, 1 Jan
Additional: Children welcome
Seats: 70. Private dining room 60
Style: French
Smoking: Air conditioning

1927 vintage and still going strong. With its original artwork (Miró, Matisse and Hockney included) this is a genuine destination restaurant that scarcely moves with the times. Dishes tend to be elaborate with starters such as an escargot tartlet "signature de la maison", sesame-coated goats' cheese with aged balsamic vinegar and warmed oxtail terrine with shaved foie gras. Mains include seared red mullet with sweet-and-sour aubergines and crisp suckling pig with celeriac and apple purée. Watch out for supplements on the menu and don't expect to find too many bargains on the wine list.

Directions: Nearest tube: Tottenham Court Rd, Leicester Square

England

LONDON W1 *Continued*

L'Escargot –
The Picasso Room

Map D4

48 Greek Street, W1D 4EF
Tel: 020 7439 7474
Fax: 020 7437 0790
Chef(s): Jeff Galvin
Owner(s): Jimmy Lahoud
Cost: *Alc* £46, set price L £25.50/
D £42
Times: Noon-2.15pm/7-11pm. Closed
Sun, Mon, L Sat, 24-26 Dec,1 Jan,
Aug
Additional: Children welcome
Seats: 30. Jacket and tie preferred
Style: Modern, French

Journey up the short flight of stairs from L'Escargot, and you enter another world. The understated elegance of the small dining room, with its paintings by Picasso and other fine pieces of art are balanced by a very serious attitude towards dining. The impressive and extensive wine list supports food that gives cause for rhapsody. Roast escalope of foie gras with lentils and caramelised onions was one such starter, while red mullet croustillant came with the purest essence of tomatoes in a silky butter sauce. There were raptures over raspberry soufflé too, while espresso coffee and petit fours live up to expectations.

Smoking: No pipes; no cigars; Air conditioning
Directions: Nearest tube: Tottenham Court Rd, Leicester Sq

Four Seasons Hotel

Map C3

Hamilton Place, Park Lane,
W1A 1AZ
Tel: 020 7499 0888
Fax: 020 7493 1895
 fsh.london@fourseasons.com
Chef(s): Eric Deblonde
Cost: *Alc* £32, set price L £36/D £33.
H/wine £16
Times: Noon-2.30pm/6-11pm.
Additional: Sunday L. Bar food.
Children welcome
Seats: 55. Private dining room 300.
Jacket and tie preferred
Style: Modern French
Smoking: No-smoking area; no pipes;
Air conditioning

Lanes Restaurant remains as distinctive as ever with its stained glass, marbling and wood panelling in cranberry, bottle green and deep blue. With its collection of glassware and modern ice sculpture as well as views over Hyde Park and the hotel's own private garden, there is plenty here to feast the eye as well as the appetite. The menu features modern British cuisine, with some European influences. Grilled diver-caught scallops, game consommé with cep ravioli, baked halibut with mixed seafood and lentils, and traditional roast fore-rib of Scottish beef are all worth trying.

Civil licence: 400
Accommodation: 220 rooms (220 en suite) ★ ★ ★ ★ ★
Directions: Nearest tube: Green Park, Hyde Park

The French House
Dining Room

Map D4

49 Dean Street, W1D 5BG
Tel: 020 7437 2477
Fax: 020 7287 9109
Chef(s): Margot Henderson
Owner(s): M Henderson & M Arnold
Cost: *Alc* £25. ☺ ☺ H/wine £11.25
Times: Noon-4.30pm/6-12.30am.
Closed Sun, Xmas, New Year, BHs
Additional: Bar food. Children
welcome

First-floor restaurant over well-known Soho pub, with Victorian panels, burgundy paintwork and a bohemian feel. The menu is refreshingly 'what-you-see-is-what-you-get' with a dearth of inane garnishes. The rustic approach works well in the likes of chicken, broad bean and rocket salad with pungent garlic mayonnaise and other simple dishes from baked mackerel to devilled kidneys.

Seats: 28. Private dining room 30. **Style:** Classic
Directions: Above the French House Pub. Nearest Tube:
Leicester Square, Piccadilly Circus

Le Gavroche Restaurant

Map B3

43 Upper Brook Street,
W1K 7QR
Tel: 020 7408 0881
Fax: 020 7491 4387
 gavroche@cwcom.net
Chef(s): Michel Roux

What of Le Gavroche in the 21st Century? Much has changed in British cuisine in the last 30 odd years, and a large part of it can be attributed to the hugely benevolent effect of the brothers Roux. This legacy in itself is reason enough to visit the spring from which so much talent has emerged, but perhaps

England

more than that, Le Gavroche epitomises a style of classic French cooking (and service) that is close to unique in the UK. Not surprising then that those looking for the vivacity and lightness of touch apparent in some of the more contemporary restaurants at the top end of British cooking, can come away disappointed. There is though, still plenty of evidence of the famed technical dexterity and accuracy in the execution of dishes such as artichoke hearts with foie gras, truffles and chicken mousse or "Les Trois Petits Delicasies de la Mer", the latter comprising oysters with caviar, langoustine with salad and grilled scallops with bacon. Dishes singled out for praise in recent times have included sea bass with tiger prawns and five spice and roast saddle of rabbit with crispy potatoes and Parmesan. Service, can be surprisingly varied, but at its best remains as assured as ever and the wine list remains a treasure chest (and is priced accordingly).

Owner(s): Le Gavroche Ltd
Cost: *Alc* £100, set price L £38.50. H/wine £30
Times: Noon-2pm/7-11pm. Closed Sat, Sun, Xmas, New Year, BHs
Additional: Children welcome
Seats: 60. Private dining room 20. Jacket and tie preferred
Style: Classic, French
Smoking: No pipes; no cigars; Air conditioning
Directions: Nearest Tube: Marble Arch. From Park Lane into Upper Brook St (one way), restaurant on R.

Greenhouse Restaurant   Map C3

The Greenhouse sits in the heart of Mayfair, in a tranquil setting featuring dark wood, marble and a stone floor. This restaurant takes its food, service and decor seriously, yet it is suitable for all age groups. Noted for 'some superbly balanced flavours', the kitchen turns out around eight or nine starters, mains and desserts. Some apposite combinations reveal a knowledge of unusual partnerships e.g. whole orange cake with candied fennel which works like a dream. Try too the likes of pan-fried sea bass on sag aloo with onion bhaji and tomato pickle.

Smoking: No pipes; Air conditioning
Directions: Behind Dorchester Hotel just off Hill St. Nearest tube: Green Park, Hyde Park

27a Hay's Mews, W1X 7RJ
Tel: 020 7499 3331
Fax: 020 7499 5368
Chef(s): Paul Merrett
Owner(s): David Levin
Cost: *Alc* £55, set price L £23.50 H/wine £13.50
Times: Noon-2.30pm/6.30-11pm. Closed L Sat, 26 Dec-31 Dec, BHs
Additional: Sunday L. Children welcome
Seats: 95
Style: Classic, Country-house

Hakkasan   NEW   Map D4

This clubby restaurant is concealed in a dark corner off Tottenham Court Road, and the shadowy theme continues inside. Black-clad waiters, black polished stone staircase and black Chinese screens all contribute to the cave-like atmosphere, and there's a steady background beat of music. The menu divides into small eats, soup, seafood, meat, noodles, vegetables, and rice, with lots of exotic ingredients like lotus root, lily bulb, and dried lily flower to add cachet to a dish. Pan-fried beef rib-eye with sweet soya and almond falls apart under chopsticks (black), and stir-fried spicy prawn with lily bulb (like cashews) also works well. It has been a long wait for this kind of approach but there is little doubt that this is the most innovative Chinese food in the UK and may well be the start of something of a trend.

No 8 Hanway Place, W1T 9DH
Tel: 0207 927 7000
Telephone for further details

Hotel Inter-Continental, Le Soufflé   Map C2

Prominently positioned five-star hotel on Hyde Park Corner. The jewel in its crown is undoubtedly Le Soufflé restaurant, with its classical French repertoire, plus vegetarian and designated healthy dishes. The muted colour scheme and display of cigars gives the place something of a masculine feel. Neither the game and foie gras mosaic, nor the sole stuffed with

1 Hamilton Place, Hyde Park Corner, W1J 7QY
Tel: 020 7409 3131
Fax: 020 7491 0926
e london@interconti.com
Chef(s): Peter Kromberg
Owner(s): Bass Hotels & Resorts

England

LONDON W1 *Continued*

lobster mousse quite scaled the heights of a flawless Grand Marnier mousse. Chocolate truffles hidden inside adding to the wow factor of a stunning dish.

Smoking: No-smoking area; no pipes; Air conditioning
Accommodation: 460 rooms (460 en suite) ★ ★ ★ ★ ★
Directions: Nearest tube: Hyde Park Corner

Cost: *Alc* £45, set price L £29.50-£33.50/D £40-£47. H/wine £19.50
Times: 12.30-2.30pm/7-10.30pm. Closed Mon, L Sat, D Sun, Xmas, BHs
Additional: Sunday L. Bar food. Children 5 yrs+
Seats: 80. Jacket and tie preferred
Style: Modern, Formal

Hush   NEW   Map A3   ◉

A fashionable little mews housing a busy two-pronged eating outlet - brasserie-style downstairs and slightly more formal upstairs. The menu offers plenty of choice, including 'comforts' - Guinness and parsley sausages with colcannon, goats' cheese boulangere, and grilled rib-eye steak in a mushroom bun with Roquefort. Black pepper and rum pannacotta is a warming dessert that has won praise.

8 Lancashire Court, Brook Street, W1S 1EY
Tel: 020 7659 1500
Telephone for further details

Il Forno   Map D4   ◉

63-64 Frith Street, W1V 5TA
Tel: 020 7734 4545
Fax: 020 7287 8624
Chef(s): Marco Stucchi
Owner(s): Claudio Pulze & Raj Sharma
Cost: *Alc* £20. ☺ ☺ H/wine £12.50
Times: Noon-2.30pm/6pm-11pm. Closed L Sat & Sun, BHs
Additional: Children welcome
Seats: 70
Style: Modern
Smoking:; Air conditioning
Directions: Nearest tube: Tottenham Court Rd

A light n' easy Italian restaurant with a modern take on the traditional pasta/pizza repertoire, plus some other interesting interpretations. Poached egg with crispy Parmesan, pancetta and aromatic leaves, roasted duck leg with lentils, and fresh flat pasta with peas and bacon are fairly typical, and buffalo ricotta pudding has been a success.

Kai Mayfair   Map C3   ◉

65 South Audley Street, W1Y 5FD
Tel: 020 7493 8988
Fax: 020 7493 1456
e kai@kaimayfair.co.uk
Chef(s): K H Huang
Owner(s): Bernard Yeoh
Cost: *Alc* £40, set price L £30-£50/ D £30-£50. H/wine £17.50
Times: Noon-2.30pm/6.30-11.30pm. Closed 25-26 Dec, New Year
Additional: Children welcome. Vegetarian by request only
Seats: 110. Private dining room 12
Style: Chic
Smoking: Air conditioning

Tastefully redecorated into a sleek, modern affair, this long-established Chinese restaurant aims to highlight the many different cooking styles of the People's Republic. Although more distinctive flavours would be welcome at times, dishes with names like 'enrichment of the surprised piglet' and the 'goat on the great wall' generally live up to their billing.

Directions: Nearest tube: Marble Arch. Situated behind The Dorchester

Levant   NEW   Map C4

The scent of rose petals and spices greets you on entering this atmospheric Lebanese restaurant. Subdued lighting, regional music and middle eastern decoration complete the scene. A meal begins with bowls of pickles, breads, pretzels and a choice of freshly made dips, but leave room for the array of other dishes on the menu - perhaps fatayer (a pastry stuffed with ewes' cheese and spinach) followed by yakhnet al samac (fish stew with chilli, saffron and tomato). Vibrant, well-balanced flavouring and waiters who are willing to offer suggestions make this a rewarding experience. A truly interesting, relaxed restaurant.

Smoking: Air conditioning
Directions: Nearest tube: Bond Street. Cross into Oxford St., through St Christophers Place to Wigmore St. Jason Court is directly opposite

Jason Court, 76 Wigmore Street, W1H 9DQ
Tel: 020 7224 1111
Fax: 020 7486 1216
Chef(s): Michael Smith
Owner(s): Mrs D Learner & Tony Kitous
Cost: Alc £22, set price L £15.50/ D £15.50. ☺ ☺ H/wine £12.50
Times: Noon-11.30pm. Closed Sun, L Sat, Xmas, New Year
Additional: Bar food. Children welcome
Seats: 90. Private dining room 8
Style: Lebanese

Lindsay House Restaurant   Map D3

The discreet signage and menu give the game away at this unassuming town house, and one has to ring the doorbell for admittance. Once inside it's all unadulterated gold-leaf decorations, gilt-framed mirrors and fine modern paintings. With such emphasis on ambient elegance the food could easily be a let-down, but all kitchen forces have been mobilised to create a terrific sense of adventure. A seam of delicacy runs through tortellini of crab, saffron pistou and sweet pepper, while complex combinations are deftly handled in roast pigeon with crubeen (pig's trotter), apple and pumpkin chutney; even an amuse - demitasse of leek and potato soup with haddock and scrambled egg - was a delightful orchestration of distinct flavours. Blue cheese bavarois, and stuffed vine tomatoes with spiced autumnal fruit might be eye-popping desserts, but caramelised banana soufflé should hit home.

21 Romilly Street, W1V 5TG
Tel: 020 7439 0450
Fax: 020 7437 7349
Chef(s): Richard Corrigan
Owner(s): Searcys-Corrigan
Cost: Set price L £23/D £44. H/wine £16
Times: Noon-2.30pm/6-11pm. Closed Sun, L Sat, 1wk Xmas, 1wk Easter, 2 wks summer
Additional: Children welcome
Seats: 50. Private dining room 40. Jacket and tie preferred
Style: British, Town House
Smoking: No-smoking area; no pipes; no cigars; Air conditioning
Directions: Nearest tube: Leicester Square

England

LONDON W1 *Continued*

London Marriott Hotel
Grosvenor Square

Map C3

Grosvenor Square, W1K 6JP
Tel: 020 7493 1232
Fax: 020 7491 3201
 businesscentre@londonmarriott.
co.uk
Chef(s): David Dent
Cost: *A/c* £25, set price L £25.50/
D £12.95. ☺ H/wine £21.50
Times: Noon-10.30pm. Closed L Sat
Additional: Sunday L. Bar food.
Children welcome
Seats: 80. Private dining room 40
Style: Classic, Traditional
Smoking: No-smoking area; Air
conditioning
Accommodation: 221 rooms (221 en
suite) ★ ★ ★ ★
Directions: Nearest tube: Bond Street.
Hotel entrance is on Duke Street, off
Oxford Street

Situated in the famous garden square at the heart of exclusive
Mayfair, you'll find the Marriott rubbing shoulders with foreign
embassies and the capital's most desirable residences. The
panelled Diplomat Restaurant on the mezzanine floor is clubby
without being the least bit stuffy. The simple, well-executed
dishes offer everything promised in the menu of roasts, grills,
and dishes such as fillet of sea bass with fennel crust, red onion
and dill salad and caper beurre blanc, or the award-winning loin
of Herdwick lamb with potato and shallot galette, tomato jam
and balsamic jus.

Mash

Map C3

19-20 Great Portland Street,
W1N 5AB
Tel: 020 7637 5555
Telephone for further details

Imagine 'Thunderbirds' meets 'Star Trek' and you have an idea
of the design of this funky restaurant. Set above a vast, trendy
floor serving drinks and snacks, the more serious upstairs part
of Mash offers a contemporary Mediterranean style of food:
expect carpaccio of marinated swordfish and rocket, and grilled
salmon with chilli tamarind sauce.

England

May Fair Inter-Continental, Opus 70

Map C3

There's a globe-trotting feel to the menu of this modern restaurant, which travels from Cornish crab, through sushi, tortellini and crispy duck before returning home to pork with apple purée. Perhaps overwhelmed by the variety, the kitchen sometimes displays some uncertainty in flavouring and temperature, but if you enjoy an interesting, international menu, this could be the place.

Stratton Street, W1J 8LA
Tel: 020 7344 7070
Fax: 020 7344 7071

e mayfair@interconti.com
Chef(s): Michael Coaker
Owner(s): Intercontinental Hotel
Cost: Alc £30, set price L £20/(early) D £20. H/wine £17.50
Times: Noon-2.30pm/6-11pm. Closed L Sat & BHs
Additional: Sunday L. Bar food. Children welcome
Seats: 80. Private dining room 14
Style: Modern
Smoking: No-smoking area; no pipes; no cigars; Air conditioning
Civil licence: 400
Accommodation: 290 rooms (290 en suite) ★★★★★
Directions: Nearest Tube: Green Park. From Hyde Park Corner, turn L off Piccadilly, just below Green Park tube station

Le Meridien Piccadilly – The Oak Room

Map D3

One of the capital's grandest hotels that offers several dining options, of which The Oak Room is the classiest, with oak panelling from floor to ceiling, glittering chandeliers and unashamed glitz. The legacy of Marco Pierre White's tutelage lives on in cooking that is technically very accomplished with some genuine touches of magic. The more successful instances have included panache of langoustines and pork belly with pomme purée, fillet of sole with sea scallops, cabbage embeuree and jus de nage and Bresse pigeon with thyme, braised cabbage and petit pain of foie gras. Soufflé of chocolate amer with glace au lait rose to the occasion and lemon tart was a pretty textbook version. Classic supplementary dishes include mille-feuille of crab and tomato with tomato vinaigrette, grilled lobster with herbs, garlic and béarnaise mousseline and roast guinea fowl en cocotte (for two) with herb risotto, young leeks and fresh girolles. Lunchtime, in particular, is something of a bargain.

Directions: Nearest tube: Piccadilly Circus

21 Piccadilly, W1V 0BH
Tel: 020 7437 0202
Fax: 020 7851 3141
Chef(s): Robert Reid
Owner(s): Marco Pierre White
Cost: Alc £44, set price L £27.50-£48/D £38-£48. H/wine £18
Times: Noon-2.30pm/7-11.15pm. Closed Sun, L Sat, 2 wks Xmas, BHs Mon
Additional: Children welcome
Seats: 70
Style: Classic, Traditional
Smoking: No pipes; Air conditioning
Civil licence: 200
Accommodation: 235 rooms (235 en suite) ★★★★★

WINE AWARD FINALIST

Le Meridien Piccadilly – The Terrace

Map D3

Anyone who has ever walked along Piccadilly could not have failed to notice the enormous conservatory on the second floor of the hotel. This sense of scale is not lost inside the airy, split-level restaurant and if the setting is impressive, the standard of food is consistently good and rarely falters. The menu style is modern

Le Meridien Piccadilly, 21 Piccadilly, W1J 0BH
Tel: 0171 734 8000
Telephone for further details

LONDON W1 *Continued*

French and offers a range of tempting treats to appeal to most palates. Diners are also offered a choice of portion sizes with many dishes available as both a starter and as a main course.

Mezzo

Map D3 ◎◎

An elegant, mirrored basement restaurant with all that's expected of a Conran establishment. Chic and fashionable, it offers the more refined option of two restaurants built on the site of the famous Marquee Club. A theatrical feel emanates through a glass wall, behind which chefs perform their art. Dishes may be presented in a trendy 'tower', which clearly works in say smoked duck breast, pine nuts, fine beans and rhubarb dressing where all the ingredients are expertly stacked. Diners also have a choice of crustacea, caviar, rotisseries and grills, in a departure from the upstairs Mezzanine restaurant.

The Clove Building,
100 Wardour Street, W1V 3LE
Tel: 020 7314 4000
Fax: 020 7314 4040
📧 catherineh@conran-restaurants.co.uk
Chef(s): David Laris
Owner(s): Sir Terence Conran
Cost: *Alc* £30, set price L £15.50/D £15.50. ☺ ☺ H/wine £13.50
Times: Noon-3pm/6-Midnight. Closed L Sat, Mon & Tue, Xmas, 1 Jan
Additional: Sunday L. Bar food. Children welcome

Seats: 350. Private dining room 44. **Style:** Modern
Smoking: Air conditioning
Directions: Nearest tube: Piccadilly, Shaftsbury Avenue exit

Millennium Hotel London Mayfair

Map C3 ◎◎

Grosvenor Square, W1A 3AN

The impressive Georgian façade of the Millennium Hotel overlooks Grosvenor Square in the heart of exclusive Mayfair. The hotel offers a choice of restaurants, but it is The Shogun that merits the Two Rosette award for its authentic Japanese cooking - among the best to be had in London. (A view endorsed by the strength of its Japanese clientele.) There is none of the understated chic you might expect from the genre - here kyudo archery arrows divide the room and a statue of a samurai warrior oversees the proceedings. Despite the ferocity of the décor the service is very friendly and professionally managed.

Tel: 020 7629 9400
Fax: 020 7629 7736
📧 britannia.sales@mill-cop.com
Chef(s): Neil Gray
Cost: *Alc* £35, set price L £23/D £23. ☺ H/wine £18.50
Times: Noon-2.30pm/6pm-late. Closed L Sat
Additional: Sunday L. Bar food L. Children welcome
Seats: 90. Private dining room 400
Style: Traditional
Smoking: No-smoking area; no pipes; Air conditioning
Civil licence: 400
Accommodation: 348 rooms (348 en suite) ★ ★ ★ ★
Directions: Nearest tube: Bond St, Green Park. Facing American Embassy

Mirabelle

Map C3 ◎◎◎

56 Curzon Street,
W1Y 8PA
Tel: 020 7499 4636
Fax: 020 7499 5449
Chef(s): Martin Caws
Owner(s): Marco Pierre White

The Marco Pierre White experience comes in an increasing variety of wrappings but you can't help but feel that Mirabelle is the epitome of the style. Perhaps it's the way that the interior (classically elegant with added wit) seems to echo the archetypal MPW menu (classically French with added guile).

England

Whatever the root, the success of the equation is indisputable and when coupled with commendable consistency and sleek service, the package is hard to resist. Typically, there's not too much mucking about and nothing is superfluous, with dishes such as a quiche of scallops and langoustine exhibiting a characteristic precision in balancing fragile flavours. It is the extra depth of flavour that really impresses though, especially in meat dishes such as a mighty bressoles of bresse pigeon with a foie gras parcel, pomme pureé and a fumet of truffle. Desserts hold their own, with for example, a tarte Tatin bursting with toffee apple aromas. A wine list of world classics offers plenty of opportunity to bash the credit card, with the sommeliers selection offering the best value.

Cost: Alc £35, set price L £16.95-£19.50. H/wine £18.50
Times: Noon-2.30pm/6-11.30pm.
Additional: Sunday L. Children welcome
Seats: 110. Private dining room 48
Style: French
Smoking: No pipes; Air conditioning
Directions: Nearest tube: Green Park

Montcalm Hotel Nikko London, The Crescent

Map B4 ⊛⊛

Great Cumberland Place, W1A 2LF
Tel: 020 7402 4288
Telephone for further details

A charming Georgian hotel in a secluded crescent off Marble Arch with a decidedly upbeat attitude towards food. The very modern menu makes daring and ambitious forays around the world, drawing strength from the East and the Mediterranean in its British-based repertoire. Salt cod fish cake with spiced tomato coulis, and red mullet with crispy salmon lardoons, tabouleh, tomatoes and a hint of harissa show the kitchen's bold style, while several head-turning desserts include a striking crisp tuille tube filled with lush coffee/caramel crème served with passion fruit sorbet. A decent shot of espresso to finish.

Mortons

Map C3 ⊛⊛

Set on the first floor of a private club, this restaurant has an exclusive feel: you'll pass a doorman and formal reception area before ascending to the high-ceilinged restaurant on the first floor. Here, a modern menu draws inspiration from Europe and Asia: dishes might include tataki of yellow fin tuna with oshatashi and wasabi, or griddled calves' liver with semolina gnocchi and mustard fruits. The wine list is thoughtfully composed and based mostly in the old world. Friendly, professional service and impressive views of Berkeley Square should keep your mind off the prices.

Style: Chic, Minamalist. **Smoking:** No-smoking area
Directions: Nearest tube: Bond Street. On the northen side of Berkeley Square

The Restaurant,
28 Berkeley Square,
W1X 5HA
Tel: 020 7499 0363
Fax: 020 7495 3160
e reception@mortonsclub.com
Chef(s): Mark Broadbent
Owner(s): Jeffery Pattinson
Cost: Alc £35, set price L £19.50. H/wine £15
Times: Noon-2.30pm/7-10.30pm. Closed Sun, L Sat, Xmas, BHs
Additional: Children welcome
Seats: 60. Private dining room 30. Jacket and tie preferred

LONDON W1 *Continued*

New World

Map D3

1 Gerrard Place, W1V 7LL
Tel: 020 7434 2508
Telephone for further details

Waitresses parade the floor with aluminium carts piled high with all manner of steamed and fried dim sum delicacies. Non-Chinese customers are thoughtfully treated though it is down to the diner to pace his or herself - no easy task with such a myriad of tempting dishes available in an almost constant flow.

Nico Central

Map C4

This chic modern restaurant is decorated in minimalist style, its walls adorned with abstract art. The interesting French cuisine is complemented by a good wine list. Dishes might include braised rabbit with macaroni, tomato and olives or roast pigeon with swede purée, confit of fennel and walnut. Staff are smart and attentive.

35 Great Portland Street,
W1N 5DD
Tel: 020 7436 8846
Fax: 020 7436 3455
Chef(s): Nigel Trimble
Owner(s): The Resaurant Partnership
Cost: *Alc* £32, set price L £14.50-£18.50. ☺ H/wine £15.50
Times: Noon-2.30pm/6-10.30pm. Closed L Sat-Sun, D Sun, Xmas, New Year, BHs
Additional: Children 8 yrs+

Seats: 50. Private dining room 10. Jacket and tie preferred
Style: Classic, Chic
Smoking: No pipes; no cigars; Air conditioning
Directions: Oxford St end of Portland St. Nearest tube: Oxford Circus

Nicole's

Map D4

158 New Bond Street,
W1 9PA
Tel: 020 7499 8408
Fax: 020 7409 0381
Chef(s): Annie Wayte
Owner(s): Stephen Marks
Cost: *Alc* £37 ☺ H/wine £12.50
Times: Noon-3.30pm/6.30-10.45pm. Closed Sun, D Sat, BHs
Additional: Bar food L. Children welcome

Serious eatery for Bond Street's footsore shoppers, beneath the Nicole Fahri shop, entered through the shop door. The winding stone staircase takes you down to the restaurant and gives it a nautical feel, as do the wall of ships' mirrors. Grilled tuna with roasted globe artichokes, and pan-fried calves' liver saltimbocca are typical dishes.

Seats: 65. Private dining room 80
Style: Modern, Chic
Smoking: No-smoking area; no pipes; Air conditioning
Directions: Nearest tube: Green Park, Bond St. Between Hermes Shop & Asprey

Noble Rot

Map C3

Named after 'the fungus to which great dessert wines owe their sweetness', it stands to reason that sweet wines feature heavily at Noble Rot. No surprise either to find many of the classic dishes associated with the likes of Sauternes and Barsac listed on the menu. Foie gras, lobster, truffle and green bean salad is a typically light and deliciously simple starter whilst roast cod with fennel seeds, pistachio crust and saffron mash features excellent fish and a subtle Madeira sauce. Great desserts might include a skilful chocolate and peanut cheesecake with caramelised banana and caramel sauce.

3-5 Mill Street, W1R 9TS
Tel: 020 7629 8877
Fax: 0207 629 8878
☑ noblerot@noblerot.com
Chef(s): Matthew Owsley-Brown
Owner(s): Søren Jessen
Times: Closed Sun, 25 Dec, New Year, BHs
Additional: Bar food D. Children welcome

Seats: 60
Smoking: Air conditioning
Directions: Nearest tube: Oxford Circus. Follow Regent Street, 3rd R into Maddox St, 1st L is Mill Street

Nobu

Map C3

Two things you can be sure of. Firstly you'll need to book well in advance and secondly it will be packed wall to wall when you do get there. It's great fun if you like to people watch (if you don't spot somebody famous then you'll have been very unlucky - or lucky, depending on your viewpoint), and it is a venue awash with various interpretations of glamour. There can be something of a canteen feel to the occasionally harassed service but staff are exceptionally well trained and knowledgeable. The latter is of course an especially good thing when faced with a menu that doesn't obey western conventions of starter, main course and dessert. The uncertain should feel free to rely on the waiting staff, or plump for the omakase menu (it looks expensive but you'll find it hard to spend much less) which gives you a stream of chef's selections. The raw elements of sashimi and sushi can hit the heights of freshness and clarity (although there have been one or two recent disappointments) and the dexterity with which some intense flavours (black cod in a sweet miso sauce, rock shrimp tempura and a spicy creamy sauce) are combined is masterful.

Old Park Lane, W1Y 4LB
Tel: 020 7447 4747
Fax: 020 7447 4749
Chef(s): Mark Edwards
Owner(s): Nobuyuki Matsuhisa, Robert de Niro, Drew Nieporent
Cost: *Alc* £70, set price L £23.50-£25. H/wine £14.50
Times: Noon-2.15pm/6-10.15pm. Closed L Sat & Sun, BHs
Additional: Children welcome
Seats: 150. Private dining room 40
Style: Modern, Chic
Smoking: No-smoking area; Air conditioning
Directions: Nearest tube: Hyde Park, Green Park

L'Odéon

Map C3

Calm, uncluttered and modern is the feel of L'Odéon and a window seat has possibly the best vantage point in London - looking over Regent Street and Piccadilly Circus. Broadly sophisticated modern European in style there are enough global influences to make for a varied *carte*. Baked scallop on spinach with truffles or warm Mediterranean vegetable torte are representative of some direct and flavour-intensive starters. From the main courses, fillet of sea bass with five-spice vegetables or pan-fried liver, chorizo and sweet potato mash are similarly direct in style but delivered with a level of precision and balance that marks them out from the crowd. Careful preparation shows in desserts such as a sophisticated L'Odéon chocolate plate. The wine list covers most bases and offers a particularly strong Australian selection.

65 Regent Street, W1R 7HH
Tel: 020 7287 1400
Fax: 020 7287 1300
Chef(s): Franco Montone
Owner(s): Pierre & Kathleen Condou
Cost: *Alc* £30, set price L £15.50-£19.50. H/wine £16
Times: Noon-2.45pm/5.30-11.30pm. Closed Sun, BHs
Additional: Bar food. Children welcome
Seats: 250. Private dining room 20
Style: Chic, Modern

Smoking: No-smoking area; no pipes; no cigars; Air conditioning
Directions: Piccadilly Circus, opposite Cafe Royal

The Orient

Map C3 ⊚

Well-furnished spacious restaurant with friendly service and an excellent value set-price lunch menu. Vast choice of cuisine featuring everything from seared mahi mahi with rice wine soy to garlic marinated lamb. Oriental flavours with a European presentation.

Additional: Bar food. Children welcome
Seats: 120. Private dining room 18. Jacket and tie preferred
Style: Modern, Chic
Smoking: Air conditioning
Directions: Nearest tube: Green Park. Next to The Ritz Hotel

China House, 160 Piccadilly, W1V 9DF
Tel: 020 7499 6888
Fax: 020 7659 9300
🖂 chinahouse@chinahouse.co.uk
Chef(s): Chris Kwan
Owner(s): Eddie Wat, Saeb Eigner
Cost: *Alc* £35. ☺ ☺ H/wine £16
Times: Noon-2.30pm/6-11.30pm. Closed Sun, L Sat, Xmas, New Year, BHs

LONDON W1 *Continued*

Orrery

Map B4

Part of Conran's restaurant empire above the Marylebone shop, Orrery has been a model of consistency since its 1997 opening. The dining-room is fairly formal with the majority of tables along one side wall and a few circular tables overlooking the street. Service is attentive and efficient "without being in your face" and food continues to impress. Canapé of tuna carpaccio has been found to be "exquisitely" fresh and cep consomme with Jerusalem artichoke and chestnut agnolotti has stood out for it's remarkable depth of flavour. Main dishes take in sea bass with lasagne of wild mushroom and chard, meat and game such as venison saddle with quince, polenta, artichoke and sauce poivrade, and poultry creations epitomised by breast of duck with red onion tarte Tatin, foie gras and black figs. Blueberry soufflé, still soft in the middle, with home-made vanilla ice cream might typically round off a meal of notable accuracy. For an entire table, the Menu Gourmand, complete with inspired wines matched to each course, makes mouth-watering reading for solo diners.

55-57 Marylebone
High Street, W1M 3AE
Tel: 020 7616 8000
Fax: 020 7616 8080
e patrickf@conran-restaurants.co.uk
Chef(s): Chris Galvin
Owner(s): Chris Galvin, Conrad Restaurants

Cost: *Alc* £50, set price L £23.50/D £28.50-£55. H/wine £13
Times: Noon-3pm/7-11pm. Closed 25-26 Dec, Good Friday
Additional: Sunday L. Bar food. Children welcome
Seats: 80
Style: Modern, Elegant
Smoking: No pipes
Directions: Nearest tube: Baker St & Regents Park. At the northern end of Marylebone High Street

Ozer

Map C4

Exotic flavours from the Middle East and North Africa are blended with the Mediterranean and given a contemporary twist at this striking restaurant. Friendly, knowledgeable staff dressed smartly in black, dispense an awesome range of menus, covering set meals, grills, mezze (hot or cold) and a *carte*. Expect seared tuna in a spiced filo crust with a ginger, fig and lime chutney, and grilled fillet of lamb with basmati rice and chilli sauce. Confit of pumpkin with walnuts is another unusual concept, but like everything else here, well worth sampling. Finish with mint tea, pistachio Turkish delight, and pomegranate pips.

5 Langham Place,
W1N 7DD
Tel: 020 7323 0505
Fax: 020 7323 0111
e res@ozer.co.uk
Chef(s): Jerome Tauvron
Owner(s): Mr Ozer
Cost: *Alc* £25. ☺ ☺ H/wine £14
Times: Noon-midnight
Additional: Sunday L. Bar food. Children welcome
Seats: 100. Jacket and tie preferred
Style: Modern, Turkish
Smoking: No-smoking area; Air conditioning
Directions: Nearest tube: Oxford circus. 2 min walk towards Upper Regent Street

The Park Lane Hotel NEW Map C3

The 'Citrus' restaurant is a light, bright and informal venue offering an eclectic range of enjoyable dishes based around the flavours and styles of the Mediterranean. A roast loin of venison is cooked to perfection and benefits from potato stuffed with goats' cheese, truffle mash and red cabbage Tatin.

Style: Modern, Mediterranean
Smoking: No-smoking area; no pipes; no cigars;
Air conditioning
Civil licence: 450
Accommodation: 307 rooms (307 en suite) ★ ★ ★ ★ ★
Directions: Telephone for directions

Piccadilly, W1J 7BX
Tel: 020 7290 7364
Fax: 020 7499 1965
e citrus.parklane@sheraton.com
Chef(s): Andrew Bennett
Owner(s): The Park Lane Hotel, Sheraton
Cost: Alc £23.50, set price L £18/ D £22. ☺ ☺ H/wine £18
Times: Noon-3pm/5.30-11.30pm
Additional: Sunday L.
Children welcome
Seats: 60. Private dining room 400

Passione NEW Map C4

The name says it all: as soon as you walk in the door you sense the passionate attitude towards food. Herbs grow in little pots on the tables, the cool, pale turquoise walls sport foodie pictures, and the chef - Gennaro Contaldo - was one of Jamie Oliver's mentors. Pasta is his speciality, as in the sophisticated agnolini riieni di selvaggina con salsa al tortufo (parcels filled with game stuffing, with truffle sauce), while the rustic is also successful - freshly-flavoured John Dory with tomato and basil. A small selection of desserts include pears cooked in red wine, or orange pannacotta, and sound espresso to finish.

Directions: Nearest tube: Goodge Street. 5 mins walk

10 Charlotte Street, W1T 2LT
Tel: 020 7636 2833
Fax: 020 7636 2889
e liz.przybylskie@lineone.net
Chef(s): Gennaro Contaldo
Owner(s): Gennaro Contaldo, G Diursot, Liz Przybylskie
Cost: Alc £35 H/wine £11.50
Times: 12.30-2.15pm/7-10.15pm. Closed Sun, L Sat, 1 wk Xmas, BHs
Additional: Children welcome
Seats: 40. Private dining room 12
Style: Modern
Smoking: No pipes; no cigars

Pescatori Map C4 – D3

57 Charlotte Street, Fitzrovia, W1P 1LA
Tel: 020 7580 3289
Fax: 020 7580 0539
Chef(s): Michele Espenica
Owner(s): Lavarini/Olivelli/Fraquelli
Cost: Alc £35, set price L £17.50/ D £29.50. H/wine £11.75
Times: Noon-3pm/6-11pm. Closed Sun, L Sat, Easter, Xmas, Bhs
Additional: Children welcome
Seats: 130. Private dining room 50
Smoking: No-smoking area; no pipes; no cigars; Air conditioning

In a restaurant themed around a Mediterranean fishing village, the display of fresh fish and seafood packed in ice makes an impressive central feature. The fairly lengthy menu delivers all it promises and makes few concessions to non-fish eaters. It offers a couple of risottos, and from the pasta selection maybe scallop and lobster ravioli, or fettuccine al salmon flavoured with truffle oil and grappa. Main courses feature pan-fried red snapper, and plaice and chips with fried zucchini, though the starring dish is undoubtedly the shellfish platter. The good choice of home-made desserts should not be overlooked.

Directions: Nearest Tube: Goodge Street. From station turn R and into Goodge St, then 2nd R into Charlotte St. Restaurant on L

LONDON W1 *Continued*

Pied à Terre

Map C4

34 Charlotte Street, W1P 1HJ
Tel: 020 7636 1178
Fax: 020 7916 1171
e p-a-t@dircon.co.uk
Chef(s): Shane Osborn
Owner(s): David Moore
Cost: *Alc* £55, set price L £23/D £50.
H/wine £18
Times: 12.15-2.30pm/7-11pm. Closed
Sun, L Sat, 2 wks Xmas & New Year
Additional: Children welcome
Seats: 38. Private dining room 15
Style: Modern, Chic
Smoking: Air conditioning
Directions: Nearest tube: Goodge
Street. S of BT Tower.

Approaching a decade in the same ownership, this stylish restaurant continues to move with the times and achieve a remarkable degree of consistency even through a number of changes of chef. Somewhat minimalist décor has been up-dated and there is a warmer feel to the place these days that makes for a less severe dining experience. Menus are deceptively simple in concept, with trompette canelloni with hazelnut emulsion at luncheon followed perhaps by roast brill fillet with cauliflower purée and red wine sauce, belying an intricacy and depth of flavour seldom seen. "Stellar" roast quail breast with boudin of black leg chicken and foie gras had one correspondent in raptures and monkfish fillets with cep risotto, onion purée and rosemary sauce has proved to be both "technically faultless" and perfectly balanced. Slivers of mango enveloped in creamy rice pudding have similarly impressed amongst some imaginative desserts. Attention to detail, flair and innovative ideas marks out David Moore's restaurant for special mention. The wine list is strong with some great Burgundy and wine recommendations are appended to each dish.

La Porte des Indes

Map D4

32 Bryanston Street, W1H 7AE

Spectacular Indian restaurant, the sheer size of which is belied by its modest exterior. A stairway with a glass cupola above leads down through a large galleried opening to the floor below where there is also a comfortable bar area with Douanier Rousseau-style wall panels, and a marble waterfall extending to the height of the two floors. Seating is be-cushioned rattan and there are lots of potted palms and colourful paintings on the walls. The *carte* menu is wide ranging, but with an emphasis on the French-Creole cuisine of Pondicherry, the last of the French enclaves on the subcontinent.

Tel: 020 7224 0055
Fax: 020 7224 1144
e pilondon@aol.com
Chef(s): Mehernosh Mody
Owner(s): The Blue Elephant Group
Cost: *Alc* £35, set price L £16.75/D £30-£34. ☺ H/wine £10.50
Times: Noon-2.30pm/7-11.30pm. Closed L Sat, 25-26 Dec, 1 Jan
Additional: Sunday L. Bar food. Children welcome   *continued*

England

Seats: 300. Private dining room 12
Style: Old Colonial. **Smoking:** Air conditioning
Directions: Nearest tube: Marble Arch

The Purple Sage

Map C3

92 Wigmore Street, W1H 9DR
Tel: 020 7486 1912
Fax: 020 7486 1913
Chef(s): Paul Holmes
Cost: *Alc* £26, set price L £15.50.
☺ ☺ H/wine £9.90
Times: Noon-2.30pm/6-10.30pm.
Closed Sun, L Sat, Xmas
Additional: Children welcome

Bare brick walls and solid wood furniture fit right in at this modern restaurant. Simplicity and fresh raw materials lie behind the dependable cooking. Italianesque favourites like crostini and wild rocket and Parmesan salad sit cosily beside Oriental flavours, as in tiger prawn pancake rolls with tuna tataki, bok choy and pickled cucumber.

Seats: 85. Private dining room 35. **Style:** Rustic, Italian
Directions: Nearest tube: Bond Street

Quo Vadis

Map D4

26-29 Dean Street, W1V 6LL
Tel: 020 7437 9585
Fax: 0207 734 7593
 sales@whitestarline.org.uk
Chef(s): Charlie Rushton
Owner(s): Mr J Lahoud & Marco Pierre White
Cost: Set price L £17.50/D £17.50.
☺ ☺ H/wine £14.50
Times: Noon-2.30pm/5.30-11.30pm.
Closed Sun, L Sat, 24-25 Dec, 1 Jan
Additional: Children welcome
Seats: 80. Private dining room 100
Style: Chic, Bistro
Smoking: No pipes; Air conditioning
Directions: Nearest tube: Leicester Square

In premises once occupied by Karl Marx, the three floor restaurant and private dining-rooms remains a showcase for Marco Pierre White's collection of original Warhol paintings and an increasing number of his own. The chic, bistro-style main room still invokes conversation with its reptile skeletons, chicken skulls and pictures made from real butterflies. The menu continues to carry some trademark dishes typified by an accomplished terrine of foie gras with "tongue-tingling" Sauternes jelly and toasted brioche, peppered magret duck with caramelised peaches, and a mouth-watering lemon tart of light, buttery pastry and superb citrus flavour. Less complex but none the worse for that, are soups of truffled parsley or red mullet with saffron, asparagus risotto with Parmesan, smoked haddock with colcannon and poached egg and roast rump of lamb with clams and roasting juices: gelée of red fruits and apple tarte Tatin to round off. Classic wines, strong espresso and efficient, friendly staff with a good line in banter.

Radisson Edwardian
Berkshire Hotel

Map C3

350 Oxford Street, W1N 0BY
Tel: 020 7514 3456
Fax: 020 7629 8156
Chef(s): Steve White
Owner(s): Radisson Edwardian
Cost: *Alc* £45, set price L £25/D £25.
H/wine £15.75
Times: 12.30-2.30pm/5.30-10.30pm.
Closed L Sat & Sun
Additional: Bar food. Children welcome
Seats: 45. Private dining room 20
Style: Modern

Ideal location for shopping therapy, sandwiched between two Oxford Street department stores, this friendly hotel features recently refurbished public rooms including a contemporary-style drawing room and the first floor Ascot restaurant and cocktail bar. A modern British menu ranges through fried monkfish with bacon, cabbage, herbs and vanilla, and cannon of lamb with vegetable stew and a colcannon potato cake. For a sweet finish try bramley tart with Bushmills, accompanied by toffee sauce and vanilla ice cream. Professional service is particularly impressive.

Smoking: No-smoking area; no pipes; Air conditioning
Accommodation: 148 rooms (148 en suite) ★ ★ ★ ★
Directions: Nearest tube: Bond Street (opposite)

England

LONDON W1 *Continued*

Rasa Sumudra

Map C4 ⑨⑨

5 Charlotte Street, W1P 1HD
Tel: 020 7637 0222
Fax: 020 7637 0224
e dasrasa@hotmail.com
Chef(s): Narayanan Karolil
Owner(s): Das Shreedharan
Cost: *Alc* £35. H/wine £11.50
Times: Noon-3pm/6-11pm.
Closed L Sun, 2 wks Dec
Additional: Sunday L. Bar food.
Children welcome
Seats: 100. Private dining room 70
Style: Classic, Indian

Rasa (meaning taste) Sumudra brings you the food of the south west Indian state of Kerala, a vegetarian menu from a tropical region, which has 250 types of banana, spice plantations and coconut groves in abundance, and is also the cashew capital of the subcontinent. A typical meal comprises a selection of pickles and chutneys, rice, dhal, yoghurt to balance the hotter curries and a range of crisp savouries. Add to this the choice of Indian breads, and you get a flavour of the menu. Curries includes avial, a festive dish of vegetables, green bananas and drumsticks, mixed with fresh coconut, chillies and home-made yoghurt.

Smoking: No smoking area
Civil licence: 200
Directions: Nearest tube: Tottenham Court Road, Goodge Street

Rasa W1

Map C4 ⑨⑨

6 Dering Street, W1R 9AB
Tel: 020 7629 1346
Fax: 020 7491 9540
e dasrasa@hotmail.com
Chef(s): Rajan Karatil
Owner(s): Das Shreedharan
Cost: *Alc* £25. ☺ ☺ H/wine £10.95
Times: Noon-3pm/6-11pm. Closed L
Sun, Xmas, New Year
Additional: Children welcome
Seats: 75. Jacket and tie preferred
Style: Indian
Smoking: No smoking in dining room;
Air conditioning

Two Rasa restaurants - one in Stoke Newington, the other in the West End - both serving good-value, authentic vegetarian food from Kerala in Southern India. Despite their differing styles (Rasa WI is more refined) both do a superb tasting menu: try Rasa Kayi, spicy mixed vegetable curry in a garlic, ginger and fennel sauce, Baga Baingan, aubergine cooked in a paste of roast onion, coriander seed, chillies and tamarind in a yoghurt and cashew nut sauce, and to finish spiced rice pudding flavoured with raisins and cashew nuts. Flavours are clean and defined, and the uniformed staff are attentive and courteous. The Stoke Newington branch is at 55 Stoke Newington, Church Street, London N16 0AR. Tel: 020 7249 0344.

Directions: Nearest tube: Bond Street

The Red Room

Map C3 ⑥

Waterstone's,
Lower Ground Floor,
203-206 Piccadilly W1V 9LE
Tel: 020 7851 2464
Fax: 020 7851 2469
e searcys_waterstones@talk21.com
Chef(s): Barry Atkins
Owner(s): Searcy's
Cost: *Alc* £26, set price L £20.50/
D £21.50. ☺ H/wine £12.50
Times: Noon-3pm/5-11pm.
Closed Sun, Xmas, Easter

Pleasant unfussy restaurant on the lower ground floor of a large bookshop. The service is informal and friendly, with the whole affair operating more as a relaxed lounge bar in the evenings. The menu includes the likes of mini salmon fishcakes with lemon mayonnaise, and smoked duck salad with cranberry chutney.

Additional: Bar food. Children welcome.
Vegetarian by request only
Seats: 80. Private dining room 14
Style: Modern, Chic
Smoking: No-smoking area; Air conditioning
Directions: Nearest tube: Piccadilly Circus

Restaurant 1837 @ Brown's Hotel

See pages 318-319 for entry

The Ritz

Map C3

150 Piccadilly, W1J 9BR
Tel: 020 7493 8181
Fax: 020 7493 2687
 enquire@theritzlondon.com
Chef(s): Giles Thompson
Cost: *Alc* £51, set price L £35/D £43.
H/wine £22
Times: 12.30-2.30pm/6-11pm.
Additional: Sunday L. Children
welcome
Seats: 130. Private dining room 50.
Jacket and tie preferred
Style: Traditional
Smoking: Air conditioning
Civil licence: 50

It claims to be one of the most beautiful dining rooms in the world, and if the ruched grandeur of Versailles is your thing then you will not be disappointed. Tailcoated staff and classically based cuisine complete a scene which easily lives up to The Ritz's reputation for opulence and sophistication. Everything from the throne-like chairs to the ornate coving is painted gold. The gold trimmed menu might include a reassuringly expensive tournedos of beef, supreme of guinea fowl, or Royal Beluga caviar, alongside more modern creations such as consommé of langoustine, scallops and ginger or tarragon ravioli with summer vegetables and leek sabayon.

Accommodation: 133 rooms (133 en suite) ★ ★ ★ ★ ★
Directions: Nearest tube: Green Park. Ten minutes walk from Picadilly Circus

RK Stanleys

Map B3

6 Little Portland Street,
W1N 5AG
Tel: 020 7462 0099
Fax: 020 7462 0088
 fred@rkstanleys.co.uk
Chef(s): Ebrima Njie,
Daniel Mayas Johnson
Cost: *Alc* £17.50. ☺ ☺
H/wine £10.95
Times: Noon-3.30pm/6-11.30pm.
Closed Sun, L Sat, BHs, Xmas,
New Year

Dine out on bangers and mash with pride! Not just any sausage and mash though - seasonal game sausage of venison, rabbit and hare with mustard mash is just one of eight similarly tempting variations on the classic theme. Fish and chips and spotted dick with custard are other old favourites that get the no-nonsense high quality treatment.

Additional: Bar food. Children welcome
Seats: 140. **Style:** Modern
Smoking: No-smoking area; no pipes; no cigars; Air conditioning
Directions: Nearest tube: Oxford Circus

Sartoria

Map D3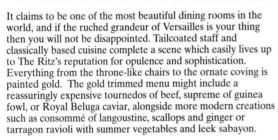

20 Savile Row, W1X 1AE
Tel: 020 7534 7000
Fax: 020 7534 7070
Chef(s): Piero Boi
Owner(s): Sir Terence Conran
Cost: Set price L £18.50-£22.50/D
£14.95-£19.50 H/wine £14
Times: Noon-3pm/6.30-Closed L Sun
Additional: Bar food. Children
welcome
Seats: 120. Private dining room 32
Style: Modern, Minimalist
Smoking: Air conditioning

Flashy interior design - Italian theme tempered by Japanese-style screens – and couture clichés are everywhere. Plenty of temptation in the sophisticated Italian cuisine happily based on quality produce. Freshness and flavour are retained in simple but well-timed dishes such as grilled quail with a mousseline stuffing. Intelligent accompaniments (such as a pancake of polenta Tortina with Portabello mushrooms and chopped basil) and decent desserts (perhaps a moist and airy chocolate and hazelnut sponge) add up to an accomplished (but not cheap) collection.

Directions: Nearest tube: Oxford Circus, Piccadilly Circus.
5 minutes' walk

England

LONDON W1 *Continued*

Scotts

Map C3

Glitzy Mayfair fish restaurant frequented by affluent city types, specialising in seafood. The classical enjoys a contemporary twist, as in grilled squid with spiced aubergine and a chilli salsa, and grilled monkfish with bubble and squeak and bacon. Expect the lightest of touches and bursting flavours in puddings like lemon and whisky parfait with lavender shortbread.

Seats: 140. Private dining room 20
Style: Modern, Chic
Smoking: No-smoking area; Air conditioning
Directions: Nearest tube: Green Park

20 Mount Street, W1Y 6HE
Tel: 020 7629 5248
Fax: 020 7499 8248
Chef(s): Adrian Martin
Owner(s): Group Chez Gerard
Cost: *Alc* £32, set price L £21.50-£26.50. H/wine £16.50
Times: Noon-3pm/6-11pm.
Closed 25-26 Dec, Good Friday
Additional: Sunday L. Bar food.
Children welcome

Six-13

NEW Map C4

A French art deco interior replete with velvet, Mocassar ebony and antique marble may beckon at Six-13, but it's the unusual kosher-fusion menu that really takes the stage. Already the restaurant is popular amongst Jewish communities. One could easily jump from seared tuna with Japanese vegetables to chicken consommé with matzo balls. Try the lockshen pudding for interest.

19 Wigmore Street, W1H 9LA
Tel: 020 7629 6133
Fax: 020 7629 6135
e susan@six13.com
Chef(s): Stephen Collins
Owner(s): Susan & Kenneth Arfin, Jay Sinclair
Cost: *Alc* £35, set price L £18.50/ D £18.50 (pre-theatre). ☺
H/wine £18.50
Times: Noon-3pm/5.30-11pm.
Closed Sat in Summer, L Sat in Winter, D Fri in Winter
Additional: Sunday L.
Children welcome
Seats: 150. Private dining room 20
Style: Modern, Minimalist
Smoking: No-smoking area; Air conditioning
Directions: Nearest tube: Oxford Circus or Bond Street. Restaurant behind John Lewis store

Spiga

Map D4

Wood burning pizza ovens entice customers to Spiga, a contemporary Italian restaurant which majors on now popular basics like buffalo mozzarella or chargrilled veg starters to pizza margherita and spaghetti pomodoro. Desserts are also pleasingly familiar from gelati and omnipresent tiramisu to simple tarts and cakes like lemon and mascarpone or chocolate.

Seats: 120. **Style:** Modern, Minimalist
Smoking: No pipes; no cigars; Air conditioning
Directions: In the Shaftesbury Ave end of Wardour St

84/86 Wardour Street, W1V 3LF
Tel: 020 7734 3444
Fax: 020 7734 3332
Chef(s): Nick Melmott Coombs
Owner(s): Giorgio Locatelli, A-Z Partnership
Cost: *Alc* £25. H/wine £12
Times: Noon-3pm/6-Midnight. Closed Xmas, New Year
Additional: Sunday L. Bar food.
Children welcome

La Spighetta

Map B4

Although just off busy Baker Street, La Spighetta has a real taste of Italy. White walls, tiled floors, volcanic rock décor and

43 Blandford Street, W1H 3AE
Tel: 020 7486 7340
Fax: 020 7486 7340

the smell of pizzas cooking in the wood-burning oven make one think of sunnier climes! Among a strong selection of pizzas is the signature, thin, crispy pizza buffala. Of course pasta is not neglected and the tiramisu is excellent.

Style: Contemporary, Italian
Directions: Nearest tube: Baker Street

Chef(s): Valerio Daroz
Cost: Alc £20 H/wine £11.50
Times: 10.30-2.30pm/6.30-10.30pm.
Closed L Sun
Additional: Children welcome
Seats: 85

Spoon + at Sanderson   NEW   Map D4

Sharing an open plan space with the glamorous bar of the Sanderson Hotel this is an interesting restaurant with a singular approach to dining. A 'create your own dish' system sounds complicated but, when coupled with helpful advice, it can result in excellent results such as fillet of ostrich with a sweet and sour sauce plus pumpkin and turnip fondant.

Style: Modern
Smoking: Air conditioning
Accommodation: 150 rooms (150 en suite)
Directions: Nearest Tube: Oxford Circus or Tottenham Court Rd. Sanderson is on Berners St off Oxford St, next to the plaza on Oxford St

50 Berners Street, W1T 3NG
Tel: 020 7300 1444
Fax: 020 7300 1479
Chef(s): Laurent Anore
Owner(s): Jeffrey Chodorow/
SC London Ltd
Cost: Alc £70, set price D £70.
H/wine £28
Times: Noon-3pm/6-11pm.
Additional: Sunday brunch. Bar food.
Children welcome
Seats: 135. Private dining room 28

The Square   Map C3

Classical and modern worlds converge at this corner restaurant off Bond Street, where abstract paintings and fine table settings, French-style menus and well-heeled clientele rub comfortable shoulders together. The food is pricey, and so is the wine, with a glass of Montrachet weighing in at £14 a glass, and the cheapest bottle costing £30. Eight choices at each course plus a tasting menu and various specials might include lasagne of crab with a mousseline of scallops, cappuccino of shellfish, and basil (soft and delicate), and velouté of globe artichoke with chanterelles and soft-poached truffled egg, to start with. The menu moves on to roast loin of venison with caramelised root vegetables, an exceptionally refined and tender main course, or fillet of John Dory morels, risotto and Parmesan, and you'd have to toss a coin between equally wonderful desserts like lemon tart, and millefeuille of caramelised apple with raisin puree and apple sorbet. Return to earth with coffee, truffles and nougat.

Directions: Nearest tube: Bond St

6-10 Bruton Street, W1J 6PU
Tel: 020 7495 7100
Fax: 020 7495 7150
e squarethe@aol.com
Chef(s): Philip Howard
Owner(s): Mr N Platts-Martin &
Philip Howard
Cost: Alc £53, set price L £25/D £50.
H/wine £17.50
Times: Noon-2.45pm/6.30-10.45pm.
Closed L Sat & Sun, 24-26 Dec,1 Jan
Additional: Children welcome
Seats: 70. Private dining room 15.
Jacket and tie preferred
Style: Modern, Formal
Smoking: No pipes; no cigars;
Air conditioning

Stephen Bull Restaurant   Map B4

The restrained décor of pastel walls, black leather chairs, crisp white tablecloths, all reflected in mirrors, continues to establish the consistent nature of Stephen Bull's premier restaurant. The daily-changing *carte* supports popular dishes as well as newcomers. Roasted rabbit with red onion marmalade, butter beans and black pudding or pan-fried sea bass, pesto risotto, grilled fennel and chorizo are interesting main courses. The rice pudding brûlée with plums in red wine certainly adds a twist to that old favourite. The wine list has a good selection from around the world and offers ten wines by the glass.

Directions: Nearest tube: Bond Street

5-7 Blandford Street, W1U 3DB
Tel: 020 7486 9696
Fax: 020 7486 5067
e sb2@compuserve.com
Chef(s): Robert Jones
Cost: Alc £40. H/wine £14
Times: 12.15-2.30pm/6.30-10.30pm.
Closed Sun, L Sat
Additional: Children welcome
Seats: 56
Style: Modern, British

England

The Sugar Club

Map GtL C3 ⊕⊕

So, you really fancy kangaroo? Well, here's your chance: spicy kangaroo salad with mint, peanuts and lime-chilli dressing. Sophisticated minimalist, this studiously chic, Soho venue is a place to be seen - and it's a cool scene: adventurous fusion food leans towards the Orient with a New Zealand touch. Giving the kangaroo a miss, you could opt instead for pan-roast cod with turmeric crushed charlotte potatoes, bok choi and red pepper curry. Alternatively, pan-fried monkfish on vanilla braised butter beans, and fennel with salsify crisps. For dessert, the mango and white chocolate crème brûlée is to die for.

Smoking: No-smoking area; no pipes; no cigars; Air conditioning
Directions: Nearest tube: Oxford Circus

21 Warwick Street,
West Soho W1R 5RB
Tel: 020 7437 7776
Fax: 020 7437 7778
Chef(s): David Selex
Owner(s): Vivienne Hayman & Ashley Sumner
Cost: *Alc* £35. H/wine £12.50
Times: Noon-3pm/6-11pm
Additional: Sunday L.
Children welcome
Seats: 120. Private dining room 55
Style: Modern, Chic

Tajine

Map B4 ⊕

A small, cosy restaurant with a real buzz about it serving authentic Moroccan/North African cuisine. A dish of tender grains of cous-cous topped with chicken, lamb, spicy merguez sausage, herbs and vegetables is one good example of the kind of vibrant cuisine you can expect to find here.

7a Dorset Street, W1H 3FE
Tel: 020 7935 1545
Telephone for further details

Tamarind

Map C3 ⊕⊕

Setting out to "change the perception of Indian dining," Tamarind is an exotic fruit in the heart of Mayfair. The décor combines Eastern and European influences and, like the food, mixes contemporary and traditional styles. In the designer basement restaurant with its elegant gold pillars, tan leather and wrought iron chairs and its beautifully clothed tables, the numerous staff attend to your every need. Great food, beautifully presented, is cooked North West Indian style in Tandoor ovens. Familiar dishes sit alongside the less usual guinea fowl in fenugreek sauce or John Dory with crisp spinach for instance. Exciting food and a choice of good wines.

20 Queen Street, Mayfair,
W1X 7PJ
Tel: 020 7629 3561
Fax: 020 7499 5034
 tamarind.restaurant@virgin.net
Chef(s): Atul Kochhar
Owner(s): Indian Cuisine Ltd.
Cost: *Alc* £35, set price L £14.50/ D £34.50-£45. ☺ ☺ H/wine £14.50
Times: Noon-3pm/6-11.30pm. Closed L Sat, 25-26 Dec
Additional: Sunday L.
Children 10 yrs+
Seats: 90. Jacket and tie preferred
Style: Modern, Chic
Smoking: No pipes; no cigars; Air conditioning
Directions: Nearest tube: Green Park. Head for Hyde Park, and turn 4th R into Half Moon St and walk to end (Curzon St). Turn L. Queen St is 1st R

England

Teatro

Map C3 @@

Typically modern, trendy London restaurant with banquet seating, opaque glass and bare wooden floor. Set lunch and pre-theatre addendums to the menu offer easy, quick options for the busy diner. The normal *carte* offers a decent range of dishes with at least three salads and nine additional starters and mains to choose from. Foie gras seems to crop up quite a bit, along with other luxuries like caviar with blinis and crème fraîche. However, there is enough of a mix of influences in dishes like warm tart of feta cheese and aubergine with a red pepper pesto, to keep everyone happy.

Additional: Bar food. Children welcome. **Seats:** 100
Style: Miniamlist, Chic. **Smoking:** No pipes; Air conditioning
Directions: Nearest tube: Leicester Square, Piccadilly Circus

93-107 Shaftesbury Avenue, W1V 8BT
Tel: 020 7494 3040
Fax: 020 7494 3050
e teatroclub@msn.com
Chef(s): Stuart Gillies & John Newton
Owner(s): Lee Chapman & Lesley Ash
Cost: *Alc* £37, set price L £16/D £16.
☺ ☺ H/wine £13.50
Times: Noon-3pm/5.30-11.45pm.
Closed Sun, L Sat, 24-26 Dec, 1 Jan, Easter Day, BHs

Teca

Map C3 @@

Teca embodies modern Italian cuisine. The menu features many types of pasta, all freshly home-made, while breads are baked twice daily. Risottos are also a speciality, a particular favourite being squid ink. Another popular dish is duck which is presented in two parts - the breast is carved at the table and served with spinach and a timbale of potato and aubergine, while the legs are taken back for further roasting before reappearing with a mixed green salad. Wines from the list of 300 are displayed as part of the décor.

54 Brooks Mews, W1Y 1LE
Tel: 020 7495 4774
Fax: 020 7491 3545
Chef(s): Marco Torri
Cost: Set price L £19.50-£23.50/D £25-£33. H/wine £15
Times: Noon-2.30pm/7-10.30pm.
Closed Sun, L Sat,
Additional: Children welcome
Seats: 65
Style: Modern
Smoking: Air conditioning
Directions: Nearest tube: Bond Street

Vasco & Piero's Pavilion

Map GtL D4 @@

A well-established restaurant that stands out for all the right reasons; quality ingredients combined with love and intelligence, and a warm and inviting environment that buzzes. A bright, sunny dining-room features abstract pictures that reflect the cuisine of Umbria. Starters make use of stunning produce, as in a carefully sliced tuna carpaccio of well-defined flavour and ravioli of ricotta and asparagus. Parmesan and rocket dress a fine Angus steak, while market-fresh roast cod sports a sensational herb crust. To follow, the chocolate mousse is full of flavour as is the espresso, served with crisp Italian biscuits.

Directions: Nearest tube: Oxford Circus. On corner of Great Marlborough Street & Noel Street

15 Poland Street, W1V 3DE
Tel: 020 7437 8774
Fax: 020 7287 2577
Chef(s): Vasco Matteucci
Owner(s): Vasco Matteucci
Cost: *Alc* £30, set price D £21.50. ☺ H/wine £11.50
Times: Noon-3pm/6-11pm.
Closed Sun, L Sat, BHs
Additional: Children 5 yrs+.
Vegetarian by request only
Seats: 50. Private dining room 36
Style: Modern
Smoking: No pipes; Air conditioning

England

LONDON W1 *Continued*

Veeraswamy Restaurant

Map C3

Britain's oldest Indian restaurant refashioned into a contemporary concept with stripped wood, vivid colours and Indian antiques on sandblasted glass. The menu is sensibly divided into grills and roasts, spicy specialities from South India and classic dishes from the North. Unusual ideas include swordfish with turmeric, cumin and lemon or Malabar lobster curry with turmeric and raw mango.

Mezzanine Floor, Victory House,
99 Regent Street W1B 4RS
Tel: 020 7734 1401
Fax: 020 7439 8434
e action@realindianfood.com
Chef(s): N Panjabi
Owner(s): R Mathrani & N Panjabi
Cost: *Alc* £35, set price L £14/D £14.
☺ ☺ H/wine £11.50
Times: Noon-2.30pm/5.30-11.30pm
Additional: Sunday L.
Children welcome
Seats: 130. Private dining room 36
Style: Modern
Smoking: No pipes; no cigars;
Air conditioning
Directions: Entrance near junction of
Swallow St and Regent St, located in
Victory House. Entrance in Swallow
St. Nearest tube: Piccadilly

Villandry

Map C4

Food store, florist and glass fronted restaurant with stone floor, white walls and simple wooden chairs and tables. This place has a real buzz about it, despite a sometimes austere service style. Reasonably simple dishes well executed, such as a well-flavoured fresh fillet of halibut set on really good buttery mash.

170 Great Portland Street, W1N 5TB
Tel: 020 7631 3131
Fax: 020 7631 3030
e villandry.com
Chef(s): Steve Evenett Watts
Owner(s): J Sinclair, Martha Greene
Cost: Set price L £25. ☺ ☺
H/wine £14
Times: Noon-3pm/6.30-11pm.
Closed D Sun, Xmas
Additional: Sunday L. Bar food.
Children welcome
Seats: 100. Private dining room 20
Style: Modern, Chic
Smoking: No smoking in dining room;
Air conditioning
Directions: Nearest tube: Great
Portland Street. Restaurant entrance at
91 Bolsover Street

Westbury Hotel

Map C3

Surrounded by Versace and friends in its prime location on Bond Street, this reputable hotel manages to muster a remarkably relaxing atmosphere inside its airy restaurant. Menus are ambitious, offering a wide range of both traditional and more adventurous dishes. The cannon of lamb, scented with celery and mint is a particular success.

Bond Street,
W1S 2YF
Tel: 020 7629 7755
Fax: 020 7495 1163
e westburysales@compuserve.com
Chef(s): Jon McCann
Owner(s): Cola Holdings Ltd.

continued

Cost: *Alc* £30, set price L £19.50/
D £21.50. ☺ H/wine £16.50
Times: 12.30-2.30pm/6-10.30pm
Additional: Sunday L. Bar food.
Children welcome
Style: Traditional
Smoking: No-smoking area; no pipes;
no cigars; Air conditioning
Accommodation: 254 rooms (254 en
suite) ★ ★ ★ ★
Directions: Nearest tube: Oxford
Circus, Piccadily Circus, Bond Street

YMing

Map D4

35-36 Greek Street,
W1V 5LN
Tel: 020 7734 2721
Fax: 020 7437 0292
e cyming2000@aol.com
Chef(s): Yip Keng Heng
Owner(s): Christine Yau
Cost: *Alc* £15, set price L £10-£20/
D £15-£20. ☺ ☺ H/wine £9.50
Times: Open all day. Closed Sun (ex
Chinese New Year), 25-26 Dec
Additional: Children welcome
Seats: 60. Private dining room 25
Smoking: No-smoking area;
Air conditioning
Directions: Nearest tube: Piccadilly
Circus. Opposite Palace Theatre

Fashionable, relaxed Chinese restaurant in the heart of Soho.
The extensive menu (including Mongolian, Szechuan and
Hunan dishes) allows you to play it safe with the likes of
barbeque ribs and crispy duck, or sample more imaginative
dishes such as an 18th-century royal recipe for lamb. The
dessert menu might include bananas or apples in toffee.

Yumi Restaurant

Map B4

110 George Street, W1H 5RL
Tel: 020 7935 8320
Telephone for further details

The ambience is largely that of a neighbourhood restaurant
although the handful of private dining rooms offer an element
of authenticity with their tatami mat floors. The décor is
minimalist (with some rather curious montages on the walls)
whilst the cuisine is fresh, varied and vibrant. A chirashi sushi
dish features thin slices of fresh salmon, squid, tuna and
cucumber whilst ebi tempura is a dish well endowed with
enormous king prawns. This place is certainly not cheap, but the
freshness and the quality of the ingredients and the great skill
and experience of the kitchen makes it well worth a visit.

England

LONDON W2

Amandier et Bistro Daniel

Map A3

Decide between the small but elegant upstairs restaurant (Amandier) and the informal basement bistro, then settle down to enjoy some classical French cooking with a distinct Provençal bias (more rustic and gutsy downstairs). Chef Daniel Gobet services both from one kitchen, and his expert use of quality produce in seasonally changing menus demonstrates unquestionable talent. Expect soufflé of goats' cheese and prunes with chive butter sauce, and papillotte of sea bream fillet à la Provençal from the restaurant, and perhaps homemade country-style terrine and gherkins, with braised knuckle of lamb with carrots and thyme jus from the bistro. Good selection of French cheeses.

Directions: Nearest tube: Lancaster Gate. Corner of Stanhope Terrace

26 Sussex Place, W2 2TH
Tel: 020 7262 6073
Fax: 020 7723 8395
Chef(s): Daniel Gobet
Owner(s): Daniel Gobet, D Azziz
Cost: Set price L £18/D £30.50. ☺
H/wine £12.95
Times: Noon-2.30pm/7-10.30pm.
Closed Sun, L Sat, Bhs
Additional: Children welcome
Seats: 25. Private dining room 17
Style: Classic French
Smoking: No pipes; no cigars; Air conditioning

Assaggi

Map GtL C3

It's easy to see why this contemporary Sardinian restaurant is so popular and why it keeps getting such good reviews. The emphasis is very much on simple, uncomplicated cooking, fresh ingredients and clear flavours. With an entirely Italian menu to choose from, non-Italian speakers may find a little help from the friendly and patient staff welcome.

Seats: 35
Style: Italian
Smoking: No pipes; no cigars; Air conditioning
Directions: Telephone for directions

39 Chepstow Place, W2 4TS
Tel: 020 7792 5501
📧 nino@assaggi.demon.co.uk
Chef(s): Nino Sassu
Owner(s): Nino Sassu &
Pietro Fraccari
Cost: Alc £35. ☺ ☺ H/wine £10.95
Times: 12.30-4pm/7.30pm-12.30am.
Closed Sun, BHs, 2 wks Xmas
Additional: Children welcome

40° at Veronica's

Map GtL C3

An interesting restaurant offering dishes plucked from 2000 years of cooking in the British Isles replete with informative historical notes. You might for example try a Roman recipe for chargrilled tuna served with 14th century style beans. Dessert aficionados might be interested in an apple and custard tart from the kitchen of Joan Cromwell (wife of Oliver).

📧 veronicas@appleonline.net
Chef(s): Antonio Feliccio
Owner(s): Ms V Shaw
Cost: Alc £35, set price L £18.50/D £18.50. ☺ ☺
H/wine £10.50
Times: Noon-2.30pm/6-11.30pm.
Closed Sun, L Sat, BHs, 2 days Xmas
Additional: Children welcome
Seats: 70. Private dining room 35
Style: Modern, Rustic
Smoking: No pipes; no cigars
Directions: Nearest Tube: Bayswater, Queensway. Hereford Rd runs parallel to Queensway in between Bayswater Rd and Westbourne Grove

3 Hereford Road,
Bayswater, W2 4AB
Tel: 020 7229 5079
Fax: 020 7229 1210

Nipa Thai Restaurant **NEW** Map GtL C3

at The Royal Lancaster Hotel, Lancaster Terrace, W2 2TY
Tel: 020 7551 6039
Fax: 020 7724 3191
📧 fanb@royallancaster.com
Chef(s): Nongyao Thoopchoi
Owner(s): Lancaster Landmark Hotel Co Ltd
Cost: Alc £25, set price (min 2 people) L £12.65-£14.30/D £12.65-£14.30. ☺ ☺ H/wine £19.50
Times: Noon-2pm/6.30-10.30pm. Closed Sat-Sun
Additional: Children welcome
Seats: 55
Style: Traditional, Thai
Smoking: Air conditioning
Accommodation: 416 rooms (416 en suite) ★★★★
Directions: Nearest tube: Lancaster Gate. Opposite Hyde Park on Bayswater Road. On 1st floor of hotel

A sister restaurant to the famous Nipa Restaurant at Bangkok's Landmark, the interior is full of wood and Thai artefacts. The fairly lengthy menu has plenty of interesting dishes with appetisers, exciting salads, soups, curries, noodle and rice dishes and plenty of seafood, beef, pork and chicken all receiving authentic Thai treatment. Plenty of clear fresh flavours.

Park Restaurant Map GtL C3

at The Royal Lancaster Hotel, Lancaster Terrace, W2 2TY
Tel: 020 7551 6037
Fax: 020 7724 3191
📧 fanb@royallancaster.com
Chef(s): John Robinson
Owner(s): Lancaster Landmark Hotel Co. Ltd.
Cost: Set price L £25.90/D £25.90 H/wine £19.50
Times: L from 12.30/D from 6.30. Closed Sun, BHs
Additional: Bar food. Children welcome
Seats: 60. Private dining room 12
Style: Traditional, Classic
Smoking: Air conditioning
Accommodation: 416 rooms (416 en suite) ★★★★
Directions: Nearest tube: Lancaster Gate. Opposite Hyde Park on the Bayswater Road. On 1st floor of hotel

The Park Restaurant overlooks the elegant fountains of the Italian gardens and the tree-lined avenues of Hyde Park. Scallops with roasted saffron potatoes, lambs lettuce and balsamic dressing is a good example of the style of modern British cuisine served here. Beautifully tender marinated cannon of lamb is amongst the more traditional main course options.

 Indicates a restaurant that has told us that 50% or more of their ingredients are organically sourced

Prices quoted in the guide are for guidance only and are subject to change without notice

England

LONDON W4

The Chiswick

Map B3 ◉

A real find. This straightforward, relaxed restaurant offers a warm welcome and good quality ingredients, carefully prepared and presented. The modern, European style menu might include roast skate wing (highly recommended), baked aubergine or poached salt duck with beetroot and mint dumplings. The bread comes fresh, chunky and warm.

Additional: Sunday L. Children welcome
Seats: 74. **Style:** Modern
Smoking: No-smoking area; no pipes; no cigars; Air conditioning
Directions: Nearest tube: Turnham Green. On Chiswick High Road close to junction with Turnham Green Terrace

131/133 Chiswick High Road, W4 2ED
Tel: 020 8994 6887
Fax: 020 8994 5504
e thechiswick@talk21.com
Chef(s): Jim Garvan
Owner(s): Mr A Robinson
Cost: Alc £27, set price L £12.95/D £12.95-£15.50. ☺ ☺ H/wine £11.50
Times: 12.30-2.45pm/7-11pm. Closed L Sat, D Sun, 1 week Xmas, BHs

Pug

NEW Map GtL C3 ◉

A large open plan area divided between a modern, minimalist restaurant (with soft lighting, black unclothed tables and leather seating), a less formal lounge area and a front bay. A modern British approach taking in fusion influences results in the likes of grilled swordfish with basil mash and a lime, pine-nut and coriander dressing.

Seats: 120
Style: Modern, Bistro-Style
Smoking: No pipes; no cigars; Air conditioning
Directions: Nearest tube: Stanford Brook

68 Chiswick High Road, W4 5RG
Tel: 0208 987 9988
Fax: 0208 987 9911
Chef(s): Lee Bearman
Owner(s): M. Milton, G. Harward, P. Lancashire, G. Barlow, N. Taylor
Cost: Alc £23, set price L £9.95/D £14.50. ☺ ☺ H/wine £11.95
Times: Noon-3pm/6.30-10.30pm.
Additional: Sunday L. Bar food. Children welcome

Riso Restaurant

Map A1 ◉◉

A cheery mood characterises this popular, neighbourhood Italian restaurant. Wooden furniture and terracotta tiles complement the sunny yellow walls, which sport vibrant modern canvasses. On the food front, the freshness and immediacy of the cooking are evident across all courses. Delicious starters include frittata with sun-dried tomatoes and courgettes, and grilled polenta with pan-fried spicy sausage and goats' cheese. Various enticing pasta dishes may be ordered as starters or mains and pizzas abound. Worthy of particular note, and highly recommended, is the intriguing and elegant dessert: taleggio cheese with sugar syrup-preserved fruit and mustard essence.

Smoking: No-smoking area; no pipes
Directions: Nearest tube: Chiswick Park. Turn L, Restaurant 400 metres on L

76 South Parade, W4 5LF
Tel: 020 8742 2121
Fax: 020 8742 2121
Chef(s): Sandro Medda
Owner(s): Mauro Santoliquido, Maurizo Rimerici
Cost: Alc £19.50, set price L £19.50-£24.50/D £19.50-£24.50. ☺ H/wine £11.50
Times: Noon-2.30pm/7-10.30pm. Closed Mon, L Tue-Sat, Xmas, Easter
Additional: Sunday L. Children welcome
Seats: 66
Style: Modern

La Trompette

NEW Map GtL C3 ◉◉

A quiet side street in Chiswick is the venue for this smart looking restaurant, from a pedigree stable. The décor follows the modern trend for neutral and earth tones and the combination of oak floor, chocolate leather banquet seating and reed-effect papered walls is very effective. Sliding glass doors open onto a small paved area shielded from the road by a row of box trees - useful for al fresco dining in fine weather. A dish

5-7 Devonshire Road, Chiswick, W4 2EQ
Tel: 020 8747 1836
Fax: 020 8995 8097
Chef(s): Oliver Couillaud
Owner(s): Nigel Platts-Martin & Bruce Poole

of roast cod is a good example of the cuisine - quality fish perfectly timed with a super crisp coating and blobs of tapenade to give real bite. Tomato salsa, couscous and grilled aubergines accompany.

Smoking: No pipes; no cigars; Air conditioning
Directions: Telephone for directions

Cost: Set price L £19.50/D £25. ☺
H/wine £11.50
Times: Noon-2.30pm/6.30-10.30pm.
Closed D Sun, 3 days at Xmas
Additional: Sunday L. Children welcome at L
Seats: 72. **Style:** Chic

LONDON W5

Gilbey's

Map GtL B3

Few restaurants can boast such an individual wine list: Gilbey's imports wines from France and even has its own vineyard (Peasants Ridge near Henley on Thames). The European menu favours dishes which are quick to assemble, but the quality of ingredients is good and the cooking exact: a meal might include a well risen Roquefort and walnut soufflé followed by a good cut of cod, roasted and served on Puy lentils with sun dried and sun warmed tomatoes. The setting is light and airy, with wicker chairs, wooden floors and paintings by Alexandra Haynes. Seating is also available in the conservatory and the peaceful (heated) garden.

WINE AWARD
BEST VALUE

77 The Grove, Ealing,
W5 5LL
Fax: 020 8840 1905
e gilbeyselg@cs.com
Chef(s): Neil Gill
Owner(s): The Hon. Michael & Linda Gilbey, The Hon. William & Caroline Gilbey
Cost: Alc £23.75, set price L £14.75/D £14.75. ☺ ☺ H/wine £6.80
Times: 12.15-2.45pm/7-10.30pm.
Closed Mon, D Sun, 4 days Xmas, 1 Jan
Additional: Sunday L. Children welcome
Seats: 50. Private dining room 26
Style: Modern, Chic
Smoking: No-smoking area; no pipes; no cigars; Air conditioning
Directions: Nearest tube: Ealing Broadway. Behind Ealing Centre

Momo

Map GtL B3

Functional urban Japanese restaurant popular with the Japanese community. A choice of set lunches is offered, all served with boiled rice, soya bean soup, Japanese pickles and dessert. A separate vegetarian selection is available in addition to the comprehensive *carte*. The latter features sushi, and nabemono, specialities prepared at the table for a minimum of two people.

Seats: 30. **Style:** Modern, Minimalist
Directions: Nearest tube: North Ealing

14 Queens Parade, Ealing,
W5 3HU
Tel: 020 8997 0206
Fax: 020 8997 0206
Chef(s): Toyosaku Asari
Owner(s): Toyosaku Asari
Cost: Alc £25, set price L £7.50-£16/D £16-£30. ☺ ☺ H/wine £9.90
Times: Noon-3pm/6-10.30pm.
Closed Sun, 1 wk Xmas,1 wk Aug
Additional: Children welcome

Parade

Map GtL B3

With its small glass lobby opening onto a bright room full of modern paintings and prints, it would be easy to mistake Parade for an art gallery. The stylish bar at the front of the restaurant is furnished with comfy armchairs and occasional tables where diners can enjoy pre-dinner drinks or a light snack

18-19 The Mall, Ealing,
W5 2PJ
Tel: 020 8810 0202
Fax: 020 8810 0303
e parade@sonnys.co.uk
Chef(s): Robert Jones

England

LONDON W5 *Continued*

and coffee. A popular venue filled with people of every age and occupation, it offers an exciting selection of European style dishes such as Irish stew with stuffed cabbage or pan-fried sea bass with truffle oil mash, crispy onions and red wine sauce. Service is friendly and attentive.

Seats: 100. Private dining room 40
Style: Modern, Minimalist
Smoking: No pipes; no cigars; Air conditioning
Directions: Nearest tube: Ealing Broadway. Turn L from tube station along High Street, turn L into The Mall. Restaurant on L

Owner(s): Rebecca Mascarenhas & James Harris
Cost: *Alc* £24, set price L £15. ☺ ☺ H/wine £10.50
Times: 12.30-2.30pm/7-11pm. Closed D Sun, BHs
Additional: Sunday L. Bar food. Children welcome

LONDON W6

Anglesea Arms

Map GtL C3

What looks like a normal pub from the outside is quite remarkable inside. There's a bar serving real ale and wines by the glass, and beyond this a simply appointed restaurant (large mural, wooden floors, skylights), heaving with customers from 7.30 onwards. Good fresh food, well presented, includes Gloucester Old Spot bacon, whole roast John Dory, and stuffed saddle of lamb.

Seats: 70
Style: Rustic, Minimalist
Smoking: No pipes; no cigars; Air conditioning
Directions: Nearest tube: Goldhawk Road, Ravenscourt Park. Off Goldhawk Road

35 Wingate Road, W6 0UR
Tel: 020 8749 1291
Fax: 020 8749 1254
e fievons@aol.com
Chef(s): Dan Evans, Luke Smith
Owner(s): Dan & Fiona Evans
Cost: *Alc* £20. ☺ ☺ H/wine £10.25
Times: 12.30-2.45pm/7.30-10.45pm. Closed 24-31 Dec
Additional: Sunday L. Bar food. Children welcome

The Gate

Map GtL C3 🏵

An "electric" atmosphere no less, at this exemplary vegetarian restaurant. There's a broadly Mediterranean feel to many of the dishes with some bright combinations, crisp textures and robust flavours. Wild mushroom tart has come "quiche like" with walnuts, leeks and trompette de mort, whilst a saffron ravioli with artichokes and mozzarella has been described as a "highlight".

51 Caroline Street, W6 9QL
Tel: 020 8748 6932
Telephone for further details

River Café

Map GtL C3 🏵🏵🏵

Longevity is something of an achievement in the sometimes faddish world of London restaurants. Impressive then to find that River Café feels as fresh as ever, and remains an example to others of its type. Many of the dishes on the concise menu are simple, and involve little in the way of last-minute cooking, but when they are as successful as a 'brilliantly' fresh crab salad with artichokes, or main courses that feature sea bass and scallops of the highest order, it's hard to argue with the formula. The slick service is designed to speed you through your meal (there are two evening sittings), but you won't have to leave before meeting a chocolate nemesis (as good as ever),

Thames Wharf Studios,
Rainville Road,
Hammersmith W6 9HA
Tel: 020 7386 4200
Fax: 020 7386 4201
e info@rivercafe.co.uk
Chef(s): Rose Gray, Ruth Rogers
Owner(s): Rose Gray, Ruth Rogers
Cost: *Alc* £70 H/wine £10.5
Times: 12.30-2.30pm/7-9.15pm. Closed D Sun, 22 Dec-3 Jan, BHs

England

or excellent coffee. The hand-written menu changes twice daily, focusing on fish but with a few meat choices. The wine list is (happily) chauvinistically Italian and fairly marked-up.

Directions: Nearest Tube: Hammersmith. 10 min walk. (Restaurant in converted warehouse so not obvious from road). Entrance on south side of Ramville Road at junction with Bowfell Road

Additional: Sunday L. Children welcome
Seats: 108
Style: Modern, Minimalist
Smoking: No pipes; no cigars; Air conditioning

LONDON W8

Belvedere

Map GtL C3

Marco Pierre White seems dedicated to saving London's gastro-architectural heritage as the latest owner (with Jimmy Lahoud) of this grand garden pavilion. In a unique arcadian setting amongst the lawns and woodlands of Holland Park, inside it's all vaulted ceilings, high windows and flashes of colour. Echoes of Marco's culinary lineage drift across the menu: langoustine tagliatelle, endive tarte Tatin, pigs trotters aux saveurs de terroir, caramelised apple tart. Dishes show high technical skills, artistic appearance and clear flavours, and lunch offers terrific value. As expected at all MPW eateries, service is professional and the wine list significant.

Directions: Nearest tube: Holland Park. On the Kensington High Street side of Holland Park

Abbotsbury Road, Holland House, Holland Park W8 6LU
Tel: 020 7602 1238
Fax: 020 7610 4382
Chef(s): Jeremy Brown
Owner(s): Marco Pierre White & Jimmy Lahoud
Cost: Alc £33, set price L £17.95. ☺ H/wine £14.50
Times: Noon-2.30pm/6-11pm
Additional: Sunday L. Children welcome. Vegetarian by request only
Seats: 90. **Style:** Classic
Smoking: Air conditioning
Civil licence: 150

Clarke's

Map GtL C3

As her award winning book testifies, Sally Clarke is a master when it comes to creating simple dishes with top quality ingredients. For further proof, try a meal at Clarke's, where fresh ingredients are used to create unfussy dishes of real clarity and flair. The balance of the menu is slick, with no repetition of styles or flavours. Dishes might include loin of roe deer with red wine glaze and pickled quince, or fillet of halibut roasted with white wine, black truffle and chive sauce. A stylish, welcoming haven away from the bustle of Kensington Church Street.

Smoking: No smoking in dining room at D; Air conditioning
Directions: Nearest tube: Notting Hill Gate

124 Kensington Church Street, W8 4BH
Tel: 020 7221 9225
Fax: 020 7229 4564
🄴 restaurant@sallyclarke.com
Chef(s): Sally Clarke, Elizabeth Payne
Owner(s): Sally Clarke
Cost: Alc L £38.50/D £55
Times: 12.30-2pm/7-10pm. Closed Sat, Sun, L Sat, 10 days Xmas, Aug 2 wks
Additional: Children welcome
Seats: 90

Kensington Place

Map GtL C3

The large glass-fronted room with views onto the pavement is ideal for diners who want to be seen to be here. The retro furniture is a little flimsy - even school-like - but with the no-nonsense food and friendly staff this is definitely a fun place to eat. The menu style is sort of modern European, but doesn't rule out more traditional stuff. There's plenty to choose from - steamed hake with khichiri, garam masala and cardamon butter, rump point of beef with roast shallots, colcannon and red wine gravy, and cabbage cake with truffles and Mozzarella.

Style: Modern. **Smoking:** Air conditioning
Directions: Nearest tube: Notting Hill Gate

201-5 Kensington Church Street, W8 7LX
Tel: 020 7727 3184
Fax: 020 7229 2025
🄴 kpr@placerestaurants.com
Chef(s): Rowley Leigh
Owner(s): Place Restaurants Ltd.
Cost: Alc £30, set price L £16. ☺ ☺ H/wine £12.50
Times: Closed 4 days Xmas
Additional: Sunday L. Bar food. Children welcome
Seats: 140. Private dining room 40

England

LONDON W8 *Continued*

Launceston Place Restaurant Map A2

1A Launceston Place, W8 5RL
Tel: 020 7937 6912
Fax: 020 7938 2412
e lpr@place-restaurants.co.uk
Chef(s): Philip Reed
Owner(s): Christopher Booker
Cost: *Alc* £30, set price L £18.50/
D £18.50. ☺ H/wine £14.50
Times: 12.30-2.30pm/7-11.30pm.
Closed L Sat, D Sun, Xmas, Easter
Additional: Sunday L.
Children welcome
Seats: 85. Private dining room 30
Style: Town-house
Smoking: No pipes; no cigars;
Air conditioning
Directions: Nearest tube: Gloucester
Road, High Street Kensington. Just
south of Kensington Palace

Consistently excellent. The menu is largely traditional British in content but the occasional splash of modern bravado gives it real lift and excitement. A starter of scallops served with delicate fine noodles, shavings of ginger and chilli stood out for the freshness and quality of the raw materials. An excellent main of roast monkfish (lightly cooked - really fresh and juicy) was enhanced by a side order of accurately seasoned young wilted spinach and beautifully textured mashed potato. Desserts include a faithful tarte Tatin, chocolate pecan pie and apple charlotte with rum and raisin ice cream.

Royal Garden Hotel, Tenth Floor Restaurant Map GtL C3

2-24 Kensington High Street,
W8 4PT
Tel: 020 7937 8000
Fax: 020 7361 1991
e guest@royalgardenhotel.co.uk
Chef(s): Norman Farquharson
Owner(s): Mr G Bamford
Cost: *Alc* £35, set price L £19.75.
☺ H/wine £15
Times: Noon-2.30pm/5.30-11pm.
Closed Sun, L Sat, 2 wks Aug,
2 wks Jan
Additional: Children welcome

A hotel of real style and elegance and nowhere more so than in the restaurant, sensibly housed on the tenth floor to take full advantage of stunning views. A chrome rail around the dance floor gives the feel of an ocean liner, and tables are well spaced and professionally served. The cooking style embraces a classical repertoire with skilfully executed modern and oriental ideas, with some brilliant results. It was hard to fault a starter of wild mushroom boudin with butter bean broth, which followed hard on the heels of a 'heavenly' lobster cappuccino amuse bouche. Breast of duck with a Thai slant (coriander and galangal), rack of New Forest venison with a juniper berry

England

sauce, and grilled fillet of beef on horseradish pommes purée and a morel sauce feature amongst imaginative main courses. A choice of chilled desserts includes mulled pear with ginger snap ice cream, and crème brulée with a tropical fruit tower.

Accommodation: 396 rooms (396 en suite) ★ ★ ★ ★ ★
Directions: Nearest tube: Kensington High Street

Seats: 100
Style: Modern
Smoking: No-smoking area; Air conditioning
Civil licence: 100

Stratfords
Map GtL C3

7 Stratford Road, W8 6RF
Tel: 020 7937 6388
Fax: 020 7938 3435
e stratfords@
stratfords-restaurant.com
Chef(s): Alain Patrat
Owner(s): Mrs E Martin
Cost: Alc £25, set price L £12.50/
D £12.50. ☺ ☺ H/wine £10.80
Times: L from noon/D from 6pm.
Closed Xmas
Additional: Sunday L.
Children welcome
Seats: 55. Private dining room 30
Style: Classic
Smoking: No-smoking area; no pipes; no cigars
Directions: Nearest tube: High Street Kensington

This quintessentially French restaurant pays homage to its culinary roots with a classic, unpretentious menu that resists all fads and fashions. Seafood is a speciality - an extensive range of fish come grilled or poached with a choice of sauces - but traditional meats such as steak and duck also feature. As you might hope, the wine list is good.

LONDON W9

Green Olive
Map GtL C3

5 Warwick Place, W9 2PX
Tel: 020 7289 2469
Fax: 020 7289 2469
Chef(s): Morelli Apreda
Owner(s): Benjan Bezhadi
Cost: Alc £29.50, set price L £19/
D £26.50. H/wine £14
Times: Noon-2.30pm/7-10.30pm.
Closed L Sat, BHs
Additional: Sunday L.
Children 5yrs+
Seats: 50
Style: Traditional, Rustic
Smoking: No pipes; no cigars

Situated near 'Little Venice', Green Olive entices a real mixture of customers. This is not surprising, given the friendly atmosphere and straightforward cooking. Dishes arrive just as described with minimal fuss. Menus are printed in both Italian and English and divided traditionally into antipasti, primi piatti (pastas and soups), secondi di pesce (fish) and secondi di carne (meat), yet veer towards updated Italian fare. Flavours reminiscent of sun-soaked holidays reign as in baby octopus stew with chick peas and lettuce or roast wild duck with chicory and lentil timbale, vin santo and dry figs.

Directions: Nearest tube: Warwick Avenue

The Red Pepper
Map GtL C3

8 Formosa Street, W9 1EE
Tel: 020 7266 2708
Fax: 020 7266 5522
Chef(s): Pasquale Manni
Owner(s): Bijan Behzadi
Cost: Alc £22. ☺ ☺ H/wine £9.50
Times: 12.30-2.30pm/6.30-10.45pm.
Closed L Mon-Fri, 25-26 Dec,1 Jan
Additional: Sunday L. Children welcome
Seats: 50. Private dining room 25

Great neighbourhood restaurant characterised by efficient service and friendly staff. Youthful regulars clamber for fresh, bold flavours, popular pizzas and pasta. Punchy combinations on offer in the likes of seared carpaccio of beef with porcini and artichokes or pizza with tomato, Mozzarella, anchovies, capers and oregano.

Style: Traditional, Rustic
Smoking: No pipes; no cigars; Air conditioning
Directions: Nearest tube: Warwick Avenue

England

LONDON W10

Rain

Map GtL C3

Pretty, underwater themed fusion restaurant on the outer edge of Notting Hill. There's a value-led weekend lunch/brunch menu, but more complex evening dishes really sum up the philosophy of the place: Hunanese roast rack of lamb with aromatic spices, Vietnamese glazed pumpkin and okra tempura.

Additional: Bar food. Children 12 yrs+
Seats: 42. Private dining room 14. **Style:** Chic
Smoking: No pipes; Air conditioning
Directions: Nearest tube: Ladbroke Grove. N end of Portobello Road

303 Portobello Road,
Notting Hill, W10 5TD
Tel: 020 8968 2001
Fax: 020 7449 6961
enqs@rain.uk.com
Chef(s): Sameer Vaswani,
Gunda Weninger
Owner(s): Sameer Vaswani
Cost: Alc £26, set price D £19.50.
☺ ☺
Times: Noon-3pm/7-Midnight.
Closed Sun, L Mon-Thu

LONDON W11

Alastair Little W11

Map C2

136a Lancaster Road,
W11 1QU
Tel: 020 7243 2220
Fax: 020 7792 4535
Chef(s): Tony Abarno,
Luigi Del Giudice
Owner(s): Mr A Little, Ms K Pedersen
& Ms M André-Vega
Cost: Alc £26, set price D £28.50. ☺
H/wine £14
Times: Noon-2.30pm/7-11pm.
Closed D Sun, BHs
Additional: Sunday L.
Children welcome
Seats: 40

The name is synonymous with expert cooking, Italian simplicity and style. Spacious and light with white linen, blue chairs and '60s lights, Alistair Little is evidently popular and a firmly established, quintessential neighbourhood restaurant. The emphasis has always been and remains on first-rate ingredients treated with respect, and using what's best in season. Menus are short but tempting with dishes such as pappardelle with game salamis (mallard, pheasant, hare) and sea bass with Sicilian style fennel and orange salad. Puds also stick to the Italian ethos in, say, affogato al caffe with a few departures like chocolate brownie and espresso ice cream.

Style: Minimalist, Italian
Smoking: No pipes; Air conditioning
Directions: Nearest tube: Ladbroke Grove. From tube turn R, Lancaster Rd is 1st R

Chez Moi

Map GtL C3

Some of the regulars have been coming since the restaurant opened 30 years ago, and it is easy to see why it inspires such loyalty. Chez Moi is a lively setting, with leopard skin head cushions, deep red walls and gilt framed pictures. The service is formal and efficient but also friendly - the manager greets regulars by name - and the menu offers plenty of classic French dishes (terrine of foie gras; rack of lamb coated with Dijon mustard) alongside international curiosities such as chicken dhosa and Moroccan lamb tagine.

Smoking: No pipes; no cigars; Air conditioning
Directions: Nearest tube: Holland Pk. Opp. Kensington Hilton

1 Addison Avenue, W11 4QS
Tel: 020 7603 8267
Fax: 020 7603 3898
chezmoi_rest@hotmail.com
Chef(s): Richard Walton
Owner(s): Mr R Walton, Mr C Smith
Cost: Alc £31, set price L £15.
H/wine £10.75
Times: 12.30pm-2pm/7pm-11pm.
Closed Sun, L Sat & Mon, BHs
Additional: Children welcome (no babies). Vegetarian by request only
Seats: 45

Dakota

Map GtL C3

Suggestive photos of Marilyn Monroe, bound pieces of bark, and tables decorated with brown wrapping paper and jubilee clips make a definite statement at this interesting restaurant.

127 Ledbury Road, W11 2AQ
Tel: 020 7792 9191
Telephone for further details

Quite what they are getting at is anyone's guess, but the food also takes pleasing flights of fancy. A light lunch menu and more extensive evening list are enhanced by daily specials, offering exciting dishes like corn blini with tequila cured salmon, horseradish cream and avocado salsa, and chargrilled tuna with wild rice salad and nectarine and fig relish.

Halcyon Hotel

Map GtL C3

81 Holland Park, W11 3RZ
Tel: 020 7727 7288
Fax: 020 7229 8516
✉ information@thehalcyon.com
Chef(s): Nigel Davis
Owner(s): Mr V Khanna
Cost: Set price L £10/D £10. ☺ ☺
H/wine £14.95
Times: Noon-2.30pm/6.30-10.30pm.
Closed L Sat,
Additional: Sunday L. Bar food.
Children welcome
Seats: 60. Private dining room 12
Style: Bistro, French
Smoking: No-smoking area; no pipes; no cigars; Air conditioning

Faithfully restored and set in fashionable Holland Park, this elegant hotel remains ever popular. The restaurant has been revamped, and its new name - Aix en Provence - indicates the direction the food is taking. The style is rustic French and a restrained fixed menu offers excellent value alongside the lengthier *carte* which changes with the seasons. A spring vegetable and herb risotto might open a meal followed by roast bass with sea kale and cherry-vine tomatoes. Amongst the desserts expect fine apple tart with caramel cream and blueberries or croustade of winter fruits with cinnamon and vanilla cream.

Accommodation: 42 rooms (42 en suite) ★★★★
Directions: Nearest tube: Holland Park. 200 metres up Holland Park Ave from Shepherds Bush rdbt

Orsino

Map GtL C3

119 Portland Road,
W11 4LN
Tel: 020 7221 3299
Fax: 020 7229 9414
✉ joeallen.ldn@btinternet.com
Chef(s): Anne Kettle
Cost: H/wine £12
Times: Noon-11.30pm.
Closed 24-25 Dec
Additional: Children welcome
Seats: 100. Private dining room 36

Unassuming, yet spacious and bright Italian eatery with a good mixture of clients. Terracotta and wood emphasise the Mediterranean atmosphere, along with the brasserie style set-up. Along with mainstays like various pizzas and pastas, one could opt for a typically modern dish like roast sea bass with fennel, lime leaves and new potatoes. The pannacotta is a particular strength.

Style: Modern
Smoking: No-smoking area; no pipes; no cigars; Air conditioning
Directions: Nearest tube: Holland Park

England

Pharmacy Restaurant

Map GtL C3

Another Damien Hirst extravaganza with a nifty pharmaceutical concept that has persisted rather longer than some predicted. Pill-shaped bar stools, cabinets filled with medicine pots, medical crosses for banisters and unusual cocktails make for eye-catching design. The seasonal menu is petite, with a host of trendy dishes from carpaccio of fish or Caesar salad to risotto and spit-roast suckling pig.

Seats: 120
Style: Modern, Chic
Smoking: Air conditioning
Directions: Nearest tube: Notting Hill. From station walk towards Holland Park. Restaurant directly opposite Camden Hill Rd

150 Notting Hill Gate, W11 3QG
Tel: 020 7221 2442
Fax: 020 7243 2345
e mail@pharmacylondon.com
Chef(s): Micheal McEneary
Owner(s): Hartford Group
Cost: Alc £30, set price L £27.50/ D £37.50. ☺ ☺ H/wine £14
Times: Noon-5pm/6.45-Midnight. Closed BHs, 25-26 Dec, 1 Jan
Additional: Sunday L. Bar food D. Children welcome

Chinon Restaurant

Map GtL C3

Mute lighting and carefully chosen music calm the nerves at this easygoing and unassuming restaurant. The menu is similarly down to earth and offers the kind of understatement that suggests that the dishes may well exceed their humble billing. Stunning starters like crab ravioli – fragile pasta bulging with crab meat – served with a pot of crab bisque "spicy and flavour packed", mussels with cream and wine, smoked salmon with fresh crab and salmon caviar, and "excellent" fried squid in tomato soup all do exactly that. Lamb cooked French style comes in "deeply satisfying combinations" with harissa, aubergine, and puréed potato wrapped in cabbage leaves and fillet of sea bass arrives with scallops, pak choi, shitake, spring onions and ginger. Pastry is a great strength and a trembling chocolate custard tart might take the breath away. The wine list has an understandable French bias, but offers some decent New World selections and is marked-up with restraint.

23 Richmond Way, W14 0AS
Tel: 020 7602 5968
Fax: 020 7602 4082
e johnchinon@hotmail.com
Chef(s): John Hayes
Owner(s): John Hayes, Barbara Deane
Cost: Alc £27.50. ☺ H/wine £14
Times: Dinner only, 7-10.45pm. Closed Xmas, New Year, BHs
Additional: Children 10yrs+. Vegetarian by request only
Seats: 60. Private dining room 30
Style: Modern
Directions: Nearest tube: Shepherd's Bush. Off Blythe Road which is off Shepherd's Bush Road

Cibo

Map GtL C3

Don't be deceived by the white walls, white tiled floors and white tablecloths: there is Italian colour and passion in this cooking. Cibo has been going for 12 years now and remains an exciting place to eat. A meal could begin with porcini mushroom risotto, followed by 'superb' half moon pasta sachets of crab and ricotta topped with a sauce of cherry tomatoes, clams and baby squid. With at least 15 main courses to choose from, there's a good chance you'll be planning a return visit. The wine list also inspires curiosity: it includes wines from lesser known regions such as Molise and Basilicata.

Directions: Russell Gardens is a residential area off Holland Road, Kensington (Olympia) Shepherd's Bus

3 Russell Gardens, W14 8EZ
Tel: 020 7371 2085
Fax: 020 7602 1371
Chef(s): Roberto Federici
Owner(s): Gino Taddei
Cost: Alc £27.50, set price L £14.50. ☺ ☺ H/wine £11.50
Times: 12.15-2.30pm/7-11pm. Closed L Sat, D Sun, Xmas
Additional: Sunday L. Children welcome
Seats: 55. Private dining room 16
Style: Modern, Chic
Smoking: No pipes; Air conditioning

England

LONDON WC1

aka

Map E4

18 West Central Street, WC1A 1JJ
Tel: 020 7836 0110
Fax: 020 7419 9099
Chef(s): Thierry Brun
Owner(s): Heathcote Advisers
Cost: Alc £21.50/D £25.50. ☺
H/wine £12.50
Times: Dinner only, 7-Midnight.
Closed Sat-Mon, Xmas, BHs
Additional: Bar food D
Seats: 60

Trendy, young restaurant where the loud music and smoky interior does not overshadow the palpably good food. From humble starters such as hummus with wafer-thin chorizo to perfectly executed fish dishes like chargrilled swordfish on Swiss chard with oregano and sundried tomato oil, the cooking sings out with flavour. Some funky flavour combinations can be surprisingly appealing as in Charentais melon sorbet with pepper vodka.

Style: Modern
Smoking: No pipes; Air conditioning
Directions: Telephone for directions

Cigala

NEW Map E4

54 Lambs Conduit Street,
WC1N 3LW
Tel: 020 7405 1717
Fax: 020 7242 9949
e cigala@cigala.com
Chef(s): Jake Hodges
Owner(s): Jake Hodges
Cost: Alc £27, set price L £15-£18
H/wine £12.50
Times: Noon-2.45pm/6-10.45pm.
Closed Xmas, New Year, Easter, BHs

A stylish, open plan restaurant with polished light wood flooring and full length windows on two sides. Mains such as sea bass a la plancha with braised spinach, pine nuts and raisins, and braised monkfish in salsa verde hit all the right notes.

Additional: Sunday L. Children welcome.
Vegetarian by request only
Seats: 66
Style: Modern, Spanish
Directions: Nearest tube: Holborn St. Right from station into Southampton Row, R into Theobalds Rd. L at L.A. Gym. 2 mins walk

LONDON WC2

The Admiralty Restaurant

NEW Map E3

Somerset House, The Strand,
WC2R 1LA
Tel: 020 7845 4646
Telephone for further details

A nautical-style restaurant in the museum part of Somerset House, serving honest, French country cooking based on decent ingredients. Expect cream of pumpkin soup with cheese and parsley ravioli, duck leg confit with pan-fried potatoes, and chocolate mousse (French with English subtitles). Also terrines, moules marinière, grilled tuna, and rack of lamb.

England

LONDON WC2 *Continued*

Asia de Cuba   NEW   Map D3

There is no sign outside this new boutique-style hotel, so you would have to be in the know to recognise it as a haunt of the rich and famous. The restaurant décor is a step beyond minimalist, with bare light bulbs hanging over the tables, plain white walls, and everything else either white or very pale. The food is a blend of Japanese, Chinese, Thai and Cuban, with a lot of exotic combinations, and plenty of choice: Margarita-marinated salmon and beef rolls to start, perhaps, then palomillo of lamb, or wok-fried sea bass with a pocket full of crab escabeche. Mainly chocolate desserts.

Accommodation: 205 rooms (205 en suite)
Directions: Nearest tube: Covent Garden

St Martin's Hotel,
45 St Martin's Lane,
WC2N 4HX
Tel: 020 7300 5588
Fax: 020 7300 5540
Chef(s): Shaun Gilmore
Owner(s): Ian Schrager
Cost: ☺ H/wine £15
Times: Noon-2.30pm/6-12.30am.
Closed L Sat & Sun, Xmas
Additional: Children welcome
Seats: 150. Private dining room 48
Style: Asian, Cuban
Smoking: Air conditioning

Bank Restaurant   Map E4

As lively a venue as ever. A huge bar at the front, an open plan kitchen with glass walls, and an amazing 20-tonne chandelier snaking from the bar to the restaurant. There is a hefty menu ranging from caviar to brasserie-style fare - salt cod fritters with some spicy tomato salsa, and glazed belly of pork with Chinese cabbage - great fun at lunchtime.

Additional: Sunday brunch. Bar food. Children welcome
Seats: 220
Style: Modern, Chic
Smoking: Air conditioning
Directions: Nearest tube: Holborn, 2 mins from The Strand

1 Kingsway, WC2B 6XF
Tel: 020 7379 9797
Fax: 020 7379 5070
e banklondon@bankrestaurant.co.uk
Chef(s): Lee Ward
Cost: Alc £45, set price L £17.50/
D £17.50. ☺ H/wine £13
Times: Noon-2.45pm/5.30-11.15pm.
Closed BHs

Christopher's   Map E3

Theatrical setting with sweeping stone staircase and high ceilings, not to mention an interesting past as London's first gaming house. Calling itself an American grill, Christophers definitely majors on large steaks. Expect fries, New England clam bakes and, of course, brownies and pecan pie. Excellent selection of wines by the glass.

Additional: Sunday brunch. Bar food. Children welcome
Seats: 160. Private dining room 50
Style: Classic
Smoking: Air conditioning
Directions: Nearest tube: Embankment. Opposite the Lyceum Theatre

18 Wellington Street,
Covent Garden, WC2E 7DD
Tel: 020 7240 4222
Fax: 020 7836 3558
e info@christophers.uk.net
Chef(s): Gary King, Adrian Searing
Owner(s): Christopher Gilmour
Cost: Alc £40, set price L £14.50-
£18.50. ☺ ☺ H/wine £14
Times: Noon-3pm/5-11.30pm.
Closed D Sun, Xmas, New Year

Incognico   NEW   Map D3

A rather unassuming (but very popular - booking essential) restaurant at the top end of Shaftesbury Avenue with (Nico Ladenis) quality stamped everywhere, particularly on the food. Straightforward classical dishes with a remarkable depth of flavour are the forte of the well-paced kitchen, and service is also slick and professional. Expect top-class ingredients and

117 Shaftesbury Avenue,
Cambridge Circus, WC2H 8AD
Tel: 020 7836 8866
Telephone for further details

clever contrasts in seared scallops with garlic butter and rocket salad, and pan-fried escalope of foie gras with brioche and orange, while osso bucco with Parmesan risotto and grilled baby Dover sole with tartare sauce are also sure-fire successes. Disappointing, then, to find some desserts occasionally lacking the expected intense flavours.

The Ivy

Map D3

A legend, and still amongst the most sought after seats in London. A sophisticated setting with formal staff and simple décor (wooden floors, leather chairs and stained glass windows). The menu echoes this understated style, condensing ideas from around the world onto a brasserie style page of salads, soups, seafood, roasts and more. Expect cod with parsley sauce or braised beef in Guinness. More surprising, perhaps, are the vegan and vegetarian dishes, which include thyme roasted vegetables with spiced lentil salsa or roasted squash with Amaretti crust. There are good wines by the glass and some nicely priced bottles - many under £20. Round off with great espresso or speciality tea.

Directions: Off Cambridge Circus. Nearest tube: Leicester Square, Covent Garden

1 West Street, Covent Garden, WC2H 9NE
Tel: 020 7836 4751
Fax: 020 7240 9333
📧 mailbox@caprice.co.uk
Chef(s): Alan Bird, Des McDonald
Owner(s): Belgo Group Plc
Cost: Alc £34, set price L £18 (Sat-Sun only)
Times: Noon-3pm/5.30-Midnight. Closed 25-26 Dec,1 Jan, Aug BH
Additional: Sunday L. Bar food. Children welcome
Seats: 100. Private dining room 60
Style: Modern, Traditional
Smoking: Air conditioning

J. Sheekey

Map D3

From the doorman who welcomes you, to the wooden panelling, burgundy leather banquettes and black and white theatre photos, J. Sheekey is traditional with a capital T. However, dishes are presented in a modern fashion and the seafood is as fresh as it comes. Plenty of shellfish appears on the menu including Cornish cock-crab and Colchester native oysters, while you can also indulge in good old British favourites from jellied eels to Morecambe Bay potted shrimps. The likes of organic Irish salmon and salt baked wild sea bass with fennel hearts also make an impression, while puds like spotted dick are there for pure comfort.

Directions: Nearest tube: Leicester Square

St Martin's Court, WC2N 4AL
Tel: 020 7240 2565
Fax: 020 7240 8114
Chef(s): Tim Hughes
Owner(s): Belgo Group Plc
Cost: Alc £35, set price L £14.50. ☺ H/wine £11.25
Times: Noon-3pm/5.30-Midnight. Closed 25-26 Dec, 1 Jan, BHs
Additional: Sunday L. Children welcome
Seats: 105
Style: Classic, Traditional
Smoking: No pipes; Air conditioning

Kingsway Hall   NEW

Map E4

Smart Covent Garden hotel within easy reach of Oxford Street and Theatreland. Expect a high standard of accommodation and a stylish restaurant where modern European cooking with distinct classical influences is reflected in the seasonally changing *carte* and daily fixed-price menus. A winter meal took in a timbale of marinated salmon, smoked eel and langoustine, served with avocado salsa and lemon balm sauce. Next up was pan-fried calves' liver, perfectly cooked and accompanied by spiced couscous and a well executed onion lentil jus. A creamy smooth iced pear parfait with a rich and well balanced butterscotch sauce, followed by decent espresso coffee and hand-made petit fours rounded off a sound meal.

Accommodation: 170 rooms (170 en suite) ★ ★ ★ ★
Directions: Telephone for directions

Great Queen Street, Covent Garden, WC2B 5BZ
Tel: 020 7309 0909
Fax: 020 7309 9696
Chef(s): Ian Hunt
Cost: Alc £26, set price L £16.50/ D £22. H/wine £13.50
Times: 12.30-2pm/5.30-10pm. Closed L Sat-Sun
Additional: Bar food. Children welcome
Seats: 130. Private dining room 120
Smoking: No-smoking area; no pipes; no cigars; Air conditioning

LONDON WC2 *Continued*

Mela

NEW Map D3

Country style Indian cuisine with rich textures, vibrant colours, earthy flavours and truly authentic tastes. A stunning wall painting by an acclaimed folk artist is very much in keeping with the style and concept of the operation. Expect the likes of breast of guinea fowl seasoned with jaipur spices, skewered with pepper, tomatoes and mushroom.

152-156 Shaftesbury Avenue, WC2H 8HL
Tel: 020 7836 8635
Fax: 020 7379 0527
e info@wwwmelarestaurant.co.uk
Chef(s): Kuldeep Singh
Owner(s): Kuldeep Singh
Cost: *Alc* £14, set price D £14.95.
☺ ☺ H/wine £8.90
Times: Noon-11.30pm.
Closed 25 Dec, L 26 Dec
Additional: Sunday L. Children welcome
Seats: 105. Private dining room 35
Style: Modern
Smoking: No-smoking area; Air conditioning
Directions: Telephone for directions

Le Meridien Waldorf

Map E4

Forget chilly English weather when you enter the glorious colonial setting of the Palm Court with its giant palms, marble floors and intense lightness. The food covers an eclectic mix of the traditional (parfait of chicken livers and foie gras), the simple (langoustine in their shells with mayonnaise) and even the oriental (spring rolls with salmon, ginger and chilli sauce). Main courses like rump of lamb, grilled lobster with café de Paris butter, and halibut fillet with boulangère potato cake show adventure and enterprise, while a classic lemon tart was a good example of the timeless dessert.

Aldwych, WC2B 4DD
Tel: 0870 4008484
Telephone for further details

Mon Plaisir

Map D4

Four very different rooms make up this smart/casual very French bistro with a mezzanine loft and tucked-away back room hung with large abstract paintings. The same family has been at the helm for a quarter of a century and the service is relaxed and friendly, yet by today's standards some will find it dated and slow to come to the boil. Pre-theatre dinners take in fresh daily soups, bream fillet with tomato and balsamic dressing and strawberry parfait. The French-language *carte* with sub-titles invites choice from grilled quail and foie gras terrine, turbot fillet on crab risotto, roast rabbit leg saltimbocca with Parmesan polenta and an orange and vanilla crème brulée.

Style: Traditional, French-Style
Smoking: No pipes; no cigars; Air conditioning
Directions: Nearest tube: Leicester Square. Off Seven Dials

21 Monmouth Street, WC2H 9DD
Tel: 020 7836 7243
Fax: 020 7240 4774
e eatafrog@mail.com
Chef(s): Richard Sawyer
Owner(s): Alain Lhermitte
Cost: *Alc* £35, set price L £15.95/ D £15.95. ☺ H/wine £11.50
Times: Noon-4.30pm/5.45- Closed Sun, L Sat, BHs, Xmas, New Year
Additional: Children welcome
Seats: 100

England

Neal Street Restaurant

Map D4

Baskets of breads, mushrooms and asparagus displayed at the entrance of Antonio Carluccio's restaurant reflect his culinary passions, notably for funghi, plenty of which features in the Italian menu. Perhaps in a starter of warm mushroom and crispy Italian bacon salad; a pasta dish of pappardelle al funghi; a fish course of baked pike with morel sauce, and a vegetarian option of chickpea panelle with tomatoes and funghi. For something completely different check out pork loin and Italian boiled sausage with cured Tirolean cabbage, or braised veal cutlet with sage fritters and sautéed potatoes.

26 Neal Street, WC2H 9PS
Tel: 020 7836 8368
Fax: 020 7240 3964
e gisellebd@nealstreet.co.uk
Chef(s): Flavio Giacoletto
Owner(s): Antonio Carluccio
Cost: Alc £40. H/wine £13
Times: 12.30-2.30pm/6-11pm.
Closed Sun, 25 Dec-2 Jan
Additional: Children welcome
Seats: 65. Private dining room 24

Style: Modern, Italian
Smoking: No pipes; Air conditioning
Directions: Nearest tube: Covent Garden (2 mins)

One Aldwych – Axis

Map E3

The restaurant is a dramatic double-height space, with a vast mural on one wall entitled 'Secret City'. The use of wood, muted colours, and black leather chairs makes for a very defined and urban look. Impressive though it is, the place is easy to feel part of with a simply set out menu and knowledgeable service - and it couldn't be more convenient for the theatres. There's a choice of main courses from the grill - steak, Barbary duck breast and organic salmon - along with options of roast venison, Japanese Saikyo cod with udon noodles, and cauliflower, spinach and baked Gruyère cheese soufflé.

1 Aldwych, WC2B 4RH
Tel: 020 7300 0300
Fax: 020 7300 0301
e sales@onealdwych.co.uk
Chef(s): Mark Gregory
Owner(s): Gordon Campbell-Gray
Cost: Alc £30, set price L £19.75-£23.75. H/wine £19.95
Times: Noon-3pm/5.45-11.30pm.
Closed Sun, L Sat, Xmas, New Year
Additional: Children welcome
Seats: 116. Private dining room 50
Style: Modern, Chic
Smoking: Air conditioning
Civil licence: 60

Accommodation: 105 rooms (105 en suite) ★ ★ ★ ★ ★
Directions: Nearest tube: Covent Garden Station. On corner of Aldwych & Wellington Street, opposite Lyceum Theatre

One Aldwych – Indigo

Map E3

At the former home of the Morning Post, with striking views over Waterloo Bridge and Covent Garden, spectacular restoration has created a fine, sophisticated hotel. Of two dining outlets -see "Axis" above - Indigo is arguably the less formal, located on the hotel's mezzanine. Many of its most popular dishes come in both small and large portions, with options to gorge on crab cakes with sweetcorn and coriander relish, wild mushroom risotto and classic Caesar salad with fresh anchovies. Also roast organic salmon and fillets of Scottish beef with optional side orders, perhaps French beans, spinach or roasted swede.

1 Aldwych, WC2B 4BH
Tel: 020 7300 0400
Fax: 020 7300 0401
e indigorestaurant@onealdwych.co.uk
Chef(s): Julian Jenkins
Cost: Alc £32. ☺ ☺ H/wine £19.50
Times: Noon-3pm/6-11.15pm
Additional: Sunday L.
Children welcome
Seats: 62
Style: Modern
Smoking: No pipes; no cigars; Air conditioning
Civil licence: 60

Accommodation: 105 rooms (105 en suite) ★ ★ ★ ★ ★
Directions: Nearest tube: Covent Garden Station. On corner of Aldwych & Wellington Street, opposite Lyceum Theatre

England

Orso Restaurant

Map D3 ◉◉

A long-established, all-day Italian restaurant right in the heart of Covent Garden with white tiling on walls and pillars and otherwise fairly neutral décor. Its bilingual menu changes daily, offering Prosecco with blood orange juice to accompany pre-theatre two and three-course meals at set prices. Sardine fillets with lemon zest, Parmesan and parsley, and white crabmeat saffron risotto are likely to precede roast sea bass with spinach and saddle of rabbit with porcini and polenta. Italian desserts are pretty limited - unlike a serious Italian wine list that offers some great wines at corresponding prices.

Directions: Nearest tube: Covent Garden

27 Wellington Street, WC2E 7DB
Tel: 020 7240 5269
Fax: 020 7497 2148
e joeallen.ldn@btinternet.com
Chef(s): Martin Wilson
Owner(s): Ms L Thorne
Cost: *Alc* £30. ☺ H/wine £12.50
Times: Noon-Midnight.
Closed 24 & 25 Dec
Additional: Children welcome
Seats: 100
Style: Modern
Smoking: No-smoking area

Radisson Edwardian Mountbatten Hotel

Map E3 ◉◉

Ultra modern dining at Dials Bar and Restaurant, which is busiest in the pre-theatre period. Coolly clad staff in Armani look-alike uniforms are well versed in the social skills department. The dark chocolate floor and spotlighting achieve a similar effect to other Radisson dining outlets. Menus offer plenty of variety from the set and *carte* selections, the bar menu utilising some of the starters and less sophisticated items. The quality of the fish impressed in a dish of roast fillet of sea bass, though there was little evidence of crab in the accompanying potato crabmeat rösti.

Smoking: No-smoking area; Air conditioning
Accommodation: 128 rooms (7 en suite) ★★★★
Directions: Nearest tube: Leicester Square

Monmouth Street, Seven Dials,
Covent Garden WC2H 9HD
Tel: 020 7845 8607
Fax: 020 7240 3540
e crivarir@radisson.com
Chef(s): Lhadi Rouane
Owner(s): Radisson Edwardian Hotels
Cost: *Alc* £35, set price L £24.95/
D £24.95. H/wine £15.75
Times: Noon-2.30pm/5.30-11pm.
Closed L Sat & Sun
Additional: Bar food.
Children welcome
Seats: 70. Private dining room 70
Style: Modern

The Red Cube

NEW Map D3 ◉

Strong two-tone red decor is lightened by natural wood floors, wicker chairs and lively modern prints. Overall the atmosphere is fiercely trendy with unusually passionate undertones. A familiar take on modern British cuisine with classical French influences is as successful as ever - crab risotto with beignets of scallop, lobster and oyster for example. Great fun.

Style: Modern
Smoking: Air conditioning
Directions: Nearest tube: Leicester Square. 2 mins walk though the Square

1 Leicester Place,
Leicester Square, WC2H 7BP
Tel: 020 7287 0101
Fax: 020 7287 0100
Chef(s): Gary Hollihead
Owner(s): White Star Line Restaurants
Cost: *Alc* £35. H/wine £14
Times: Dinner only, 6pm-Midnight.
Closed Sun-Mon
Additional: Older children welcome
Seats: 180

Savoy Grill

Map E3 ◉◉

With its richly panelled walls and semi-private booths, the Savoy Grill provides the venue for traditional dining in elegant opulence. You could be forgiven for imagining yourself in a select gentleman's club. Abundant trolleys glide past transporting plats du jour, and service, as you'd expect, is prompt and attentive. The menu offers a tempting array of dishes. Plump, moist, pink chicken livers with red wine shallot

1 Savoy Hill, Strand,
WC2R 0EU
Tel: 020 7836 4343
Fax: 020 7240 6040
e f&b@the-savoy.co.uk
Chef(s): Simon Scott
Cost: *Alc* £45, set price (pre-theatre)
D £29.75. H/wine £20.50

England

dressing provide a simple, but delicious starter leading seamlessly into, say pan-fried fillet of sea bass with winter cabbage and girolles. Meat and poultry, grills, shellfish, egg, pasta or rice dishes are also available. All exude class and are reliably executed.

Directions: Nearest Tube: Embankment. Walk E through the riverside gardens to the hotel

Times: 12.30-2.30pm/6-11.15pm.
Closed Sun, L Sat, Aug
Additional: Children 12 yrs+
Seats: 100. Jacket and tie preferred
Style: Traditional
Smoking: No pipes; Air conditioning
Accommodation: 228 rooms (228 en suite) ★ ★ ★ ★

The Savoy,
The River Restaurant

Map E3

Strand, WC2R 0EU
Tel: 020 7420 2698
Fax: 020 7420 2450
e dgarlinski@ the.savoy.co.uk
Chef(s): Anton Edelmann
Cost: *Alc* £33, set price L £29.75/ D £39.50 H/wine £20.50
Times: 12.30-2.30pm/6-11.30pm
Additional: Sunday L. Children welcome
Seats: 150. Jacket and tie preferred
Style: Classic
Smoking: No-smoking area; no pipes; Air conditioning
Accommodation: 228 rooms (228 en suite) ★ ★ ★ ★

Succumb to intense competition for the social cachet of a riverside table, or accept the inevitable and opt for a better view of who's coming and going. Either way you're assured of an enjoyable experience at this colossus of a hotel restaurant, and the set menu is hardly going to break the bank (although the *carte* might!). The repertoire remains faithful to tradition - the daily roast is still carved at your table - but there are modern influences too: cappuccino soup of wild mushrooms with pesto croutons shows decided innovation, while roasted spiced cod on lentils with oxtail pea purée, and cannon of lamb with egg plant tart and curried carrot sauce are piquant main choices. Red wine poached pear with grappa sabayon and basil ice cream was a formidable example of the River's desserts, all distinct flavours marrying perfectly. Expect unsurpassable service from a professional team; relax and enjoy being pampered.

Directions: Nearest Tube: Embankment. Walk E through the riverside gardens to the hotel

BARNET

Map GtL C4

Mims

The black-painted frontage at Mims lends a stylish air to this good, unpretentious restaurant. Inside, the tiled floors, granite-topped tables and contemporary prints give an uncluttered modern feel. The cooking is skilled, with an intelligent approach to combinations and the results are noteworthy. On the daily-changing menu there may be squid stuffed with trout served with lemon and dill or aubergine pancakes with tomato, Mozzarella and oregano. A wood-burning oven is used in dishes such as wood-roasted chicken with herb noodles or smoked shoulder of lamb with Lyonnaise potatoes and baby spinach. Strawberry cheesecake with lemon sorbet is a refreshing dessert.

Directions: On East Barnet Road, next to garage and almost opposite Sainsbury's

63 East Barnet Road, New Barnet, EN4 8RN
Tel: 020 8449 2974
Fax: 020 8449 2974
Chef(s): Ali Alsersy
Cost: Set price L £10.50/D £14. ☺ ☺ H/wine £9.50
Times: 12.30-2.30pm/6.30-10.30pm (12.30-10.30pm Sat-Sun). Closed Mon
Additional: Children 7 yrs+. Vegetarian by request only
Seats: 45
Style: Informal, Minimalist
Smoking: No-smoking area; no pipes; no cigars

England

BROMLEY
Map GtL E3

Chapter One
NEW

Mock Tudor on the outside, genuine modern European within. Andrew McLeish (ex Chez Nico, The Ritz) has been at the helm since mid-2000 and has quickly established an impressive line in intelligent, classic cooking. Interior design is cool but not precious and coupled with unstuffy service, it's easy to relax. The food too offers plenty of comfort, majoring on enduring combinations in for instance, a well defined pressed terrine of ham hock with foie gras, apple purée and truffle cream. Fish has been noted as a strength, in particular a beautifully seasoned roasted fillet of sea bass with saffron sautéed leeks and a bouillabaisse sauce. It's the kind of cooking where the success lies in consistent execution and depth of flavour, plenty of which were in evidence in a cognac parfait with hot chocolate ravioli and a zippy, apricot compôte. A well-chosen wine list completes the happy picture.

Directions: Situated on A21, 3 miles from Bromley. From M25 J4 onto A21 for 5 miles. (rail Bromley South Station)

Farnborough Common, Locksbottom, BR6 8NF
Tel: 01689 854848
Fax: 01689 858439
✉ pennyatch1@aol.com
Chef(s): Andrew McLeish
Owner(s): Selective Restaurants Group
Cost: Alc £25.55, set price L £19.50/D £23.95. ☺ H/wine £12
Times: Noon-2.30pm/6.30-11pm. Closed 1-4 Jan
Additional: Sunday L. Bar food L. Children welcome
Seats: 120. Private dining room 55
Style: Modern, Chic
Smoking: No pipes; no cigars; Air conditioning

CROYDON
Map GtL D1

Coulsdon Manor

This Victorian manor house has a deserved reputation for high standards of service and hospitality. Despite its parkland setting and the classic décor of the restaurant, there are many modern, European ideas in the cooking: a meal might include chicken liver parfait with a celery and grain mustard chutney followed by poached lamb with red wine gravy, home sun-dried tomatoes and Lyonnaise potatoes. Other treats include some inspiring vegetarian options and elaborate desserts such as vanilla and cherry zucotto with Glayva sabayon. A great place to dine after a round of golf or a relaxing walk.

Smoking: No smoking in dining room
Civil licence: 60
Accommodation: 35 rooms (35 en suite) ★★★★
Directions: M23 N until road becomes A23. After 2.5 miles, R after Coulsdon S Railway Station onto B2030 (Purley). Follow uphill 1 mile, L past pond, 0.5 mile, and turn R into Coulsdon Court Rd

Coulsdon Court Road, Coulsdon, CR5 2LL
Tel: 020 8668 0414
Fax: 020 8668 3118
✉ coulsdonmanor@marstonhotels.com
Chef(s): Neil Bradshaw
Owner(s): Marston Hotels
Cost: Alc £32.50, set price L £19.50-£31.50/D £27-£33. H/wine £12.60
Times: 12.30-2.30pm/7-9.30pm. Closed L Sat
Additional: Sunday L. Bar food. Children welcome
Seats: 80. Private dining room 60. Jacket and tie preferred
Style: Modern, Classic

England

CROYDON   Map GtL D1
Selsdon Park Hotel

Selsdon Park, an imposing Jacobean mansion has long been looked on as grand, with its 18-hole championship golf course and extensive leisure and conference facilities. More to its credit that it still treats restaurant guests as individuals in such potentially intimidating surroundings. Fennel and bacon quiche, sweet pepper and Bayonne ham brandade, black bream fillet with courgette and lime pickle potatoes and poached beef fillet with white wine, tarragon and shallots do not exactly come cheap: exactitude, however, does shine through in their execution. Round off with bitter chocolate terrine or mango souffle with kumquat marmalade.

Smoking: No smoking in dining room; Air conditioning
Civil licence: 100
Accommodation: 204 rooms (204 en suite) ★★★★
Directions: 3 miles SE of Croydon off A2022

Addington Road, Sanderstead,
CR2 8YA
Tel: 020 8657 8811
Fax: 020 8657 3401
e sales.selsdonpark@
principalhotels.co.uk
Chef(s): Alan White
Cost: Alc £30, set price L £22/D £26.
☺ ☺ H/wine £14
Times: Noon-2pm/7-10pm.
Additional: Sunday L. Bar food.
Children welcome
Seats: 220. Private dining room 160.
Jacket and tie preferred
Style: Formal, Country-house

HADLEY WOOD   MapGtL C5
West Lodge Park Hotel, The Cedar Restaurant

Country house hotel, set in 35 acres of parkland including a mature arboretum, just 12 miles from London and a few minutes' drive from the M25. The Cedar Restaurant is a little like an alpine lodge, with a timbered ceiling, exposed brickwork, huge floor to ceiling windows and heavily draped curtains. It's a popular venue so booking is advisable even for residents. The fixed-price four-course dinner could offer salmon terrine wrapped in sushi nori with lobster dressing, and saffron spiced lamb rump, with bubble and squeak, roasted green beans and tomato jus.

Smoking: No smoking in dining room; Air conditioning
Civil licence: 60
Accommodation: 55 rooms (55 en suite) ★★★★
Directions: On A111, 1mile S of M25 J24

Cockfosters Road, EN4 0PY
Tel: 020 8216 3900
Fax: 020 8216 3937
e info@westlodgepark.com
Chef(s): Paul Tuthill
Owner(s): Beales Group
Cost: Alc £35, set price L £23.95/
D £27.50-£30.25. ☺ H/wine £13.90
Times: 12.30-2pm/7.15-9.30pm.
Restricted opening 21-30 Dec
Additional: Sunday L. Bar food.
Children welcome
Seats: 65. Private dining room 54.
Jacket and tie preferred
Style: Modern, Traditional

HAMPTON   Map GtL B1
Monsieur Max

A mixture of original French fittings c1900-1950, along with a warm yellow entrance and big windows bring an air of authenticity to this formal restaurant. The atmosphere and style is sophisticated Gallic, with cuisine bourgeoisie and an impressive fourteen-page wine list to match. Fine ingredients make themselves known in the likes of Cantabrian anchovies with shallots and échiré butter or a delicious seared South Coast diver-caught scallop, chorizo, endive and asparagus tart with celeriac purée and thyme beurre blanc. Desserts are every inch classical French.

Style: French
Smoking: No pipes; no cigars; Air conditioning
Directions: On W side of Bushy Park

133 High Street, Hampton Hill,
TW12 1NJ
Tel: 020 8979 5546
Fax: 020 8979 3747
e monsmax@aol.com
Chef(s): Alex Bentley, Max Renzland
Owner(s): Max Renzland
Cost: Set price L £25/D £35.
H/wine £14.50
Times: Noon-2pm/7-9.30pm. Closed
Mon, L Sat, D Sun, Xmas, 3 wks Aug
Additional: Sunday L. Children 8 yrs+
Seats: 70

England

Crowne Plaza London-Heathrow

Food is cooked in full view of diners in the theatre kitchen of this colourful modern restaurant. The menu reads well and suggests a promise that is generally fulfilled. Check out the roasted sea bass, or breast of corn-fed chicken with Szechuan vegetables, both come with Good Karma recommendations for the 'well-being of mind, body and soul'.

Style: Modern
Smoking: No-smoking area; Air conditioning
Accommodation: 458 rooms (458 en suite) ★ ★ ★ ★
Directions: From M25 J15 take M4. At J4 take A408. Straight on at traffic lights. Hotel on slip road on L

Stockley Road, UB7 9NA
Tel: 01895 445555
Fax: 01895 445122
e cplhr@netscapeonline.co.uk
Chef(s): Murdo Macsween
Owner(s): Bass Hotels and Resorts
Times: 11am-11.30pm/11am-11.30pm
Additional: Sunday L. Bar food. Children welcome
Seats: 180. Private dining room 180

London Heathrow Marriott Hotel

Enlivened by an open kitchen and live piano playing from the atrium, the restaurant is light and airy with a 'rustic brasserie' concept. The menu shows a degree of eclecticism with a broth of flageolet bean, potato and yellow and green courgette, or pan-fried king prawn in chilli oil with basil and shallot with rocket salad among the starters. Similarly, from the main courses comes osso bucco in tomato, white wine and mixed vegetable sauce, and lamb's cutlets coated in polenta on green fettucini with mint and red pepper dressing. Good desserts - apple and pine nut tart for instance - make a fitting end.

Bath Road, UB3 5AN
Tel: 020 8990 1100
Telephone for further details

The Glasshouse

As the name suggests, this is an airy, glass fronted restaurant, whose walls are hung with bold modern paintings. The cooking is, of course, totally up to date, and has a definite European slant: dishes might include roast pheasant with braised celery, Puy lentils and game chips or escalope of veal Holstein with sweetbreads, salsify, sauté potatoes and Madeira. The staff are clearly happy to be there, and succeed in being both chatty and professional. The meals impress right down to the finer details such as crusty homemade breads or good espresso.

Smoking: No pipes; no cigars; Air conditioning
Directions: Nearest tube: Kew Garden

14 Station Road, TW9 3PZ
Tel: 020 8940 6777
Fax: 020 8940 3833
Chef(s): Anthony Boyd
Owner(s): Larkbrace Ltd
Cost: Set price L £19.50/D £25. H/wine £13.50
Times: Noon-2.30pm/7-10.30pm. Closed D Sun, Xmas, New Year
Additional: Children 10 yrs+
Seats: 60
Style: Modern

England

KINGSTON UPON THAMES   Map GtL B2
Ayudhya Thai

14 Kingston Hill, KT2 7NH
Tel: 020 8546 5878
Fax: 020 8546 5878
Chef(s): Miss S Thanpho
Owner(s): Miss S Thanpho
Cost: Set price L £25-£35.
H/wine £9.95
Times: Noon-3pm/6.30-11pm.
Closed Mon, Xmas, BHs
Additional: Sunday L. Bar food.
Children welcome
Seats: 70
Style: Thai
Smoking: No pipes; no cigars
Directions: 0.5 mile from Kingston
town centre on A308, and 2.5 miles
from Robin Hood rdbt at junction
of A3

A small temple shrine, wood carvings and glowing candles create an atmosphere as authentically Thai as the food. Unobtrusive staff in traditional costume complete the scene. Choices from the exciting and exhaustive menu might include Gung Hom Pa (prawns with crab meat, minced pork, spring onion and coriander wrapped in a fine rice pancake then deep fried) followed by Gai Yang (a baby spring chicken marinated in Thai herbs and spices then grilled 'to perfection'). The traditional Thai desserts, such as banana and toasted sesame seeds in coconut milk, are unusual and well worth a go.

KINGSTON UPON THAMES   Map GtL B2
Frère Jacques

10-12 Riverside Walk,
Off Bishops Hall,
KT1 1QN
Tel: 020 8546 1332
Fax: 020 8546 1956
e john@frerejaques.co.uk
Chef(s): Yves Tatard
Owner(s): Mr J Scott
Cost: Alc £18.90, set price L £9.90/
D £17.50. ☺ ☺ H/wine £10.90
Times: Noon-7pm/7-11pm.
Closed D 24, 25 Dec, 1 Jan
Additional: Sunday L.
Children welcome
Seats: 55 (100 Terrace)
Style: Bistro-Style
Smoking: No-smoking area; no pipes;
no cigars; Air conditioning

This lively brasserie is right by the river in the town centre and has outside tables in good weather. French favourites, such as steak and frites, fish soup and tarte Tatin, are offered à la *carte* and in good value set-price menus. French music and staff add to the atmosphere.

Directions: 50metres S of the Kingston side of Kingston Bridge, by the river

PINNER

Map GtL A4

Friends Restaurant

11 High Street, HA5 5PJ
Tel: 020 8866 0286
Fax: 020 8866 0286
 friends@pinnerii.freeserve.co.uk
Chef(s): Terry Farr
Owner(s): Terry Farr
Cost: Alc £30, set price L £16.50/
D £25. H/wine £12
Times: Noon-2.30pm/6.30-10pm.
Closed Mon, D Sun, 25 Dec,
4-19 Aug, BHs
Additional: Sunday L.
Children welcome
Seats: 50. Private dining room 25
Style: Traditional
Smoking: No-smoking area; no pipes;
no cigars
Directions: In centre of Pinner.
2 minutes walk from Pinner
Metropolitan Line Station

Well-supported local restaurant with a genuinely friendly atmosphere, located on two floors of a 400-year-old building. Beams and whitewashed walls provide the wholesome backdrop for simple cooking from fresh ingredients - perhaps roast pheasant with caramelised apples, prunes and Calvados sauce, or roast sea bass with beetroot mash and tarragon butter, from a choice of menus.

RICHMOND UPON THAMES

Map GtL B2

Nightingales   NEW

Nightingales is a grand restaurant within the Petersham hotel, a striking building with a prominent position on the edge of Richmond. At the restaurant, guests get to enjoy fantastic views of the Thames, sit comfortably in richly upholstered chairs and relax in an atmosphere that is warm and friendly, even though service may be a bit formal at times. A concise fixed-price menu and good length *carte* veer towards modern British options with classical undertones. Hence you may find breast of chicken and mushroom risotto - juicy and perfectly cooked meat and technically precise risotto - along with perhaps Calvados crème brûlée with thin apple crisps.

Style: Formal, Traditional
Smoking: No pipes; no cigars; Air conditioning
Accommodation: 61 rooms (61 en suite)
Directions: Telephone for directions

The Petersham Hotel,
Nighingale Lane,
Richmond on Thames TW10 6UZ
Tel: 020 8939 1084
Fax: 020 8939 1098
 enq@petershamhotel.co.uk
Chef(s): Andy Johns
Owner(s): Dare Family
Cost: Alc £30, set price L £20. ☺ ☺
H/wine £17.50
Times: 12.15-2.15pm/7-9.45pm.
Closed D Sun, 25-26 Dec
Additional: Sunday L. Bar food L.
Children welcome
Seats: 74. Private dining room 30

RICHMOND UPON THAMES

Map GtL B2

Richmond Gate Hotel

Richmond Hill, TW10 6RP
Tel: 020 8940 0061
Fax: 020 8332 0354
 richmondgate@corus.co.uk
Chef(s): Christopher Basten
Owner(s): Corus & Regal Hotels
Cost: Set price L £19.75/D £31-£36
H/wine £14.75

Shades of yellow, sage green and white lend a slightly dream-like elegance to the restaurant contrasting with the very bold contemporary cooking that takes place there. The self-confidence of the kitchen is evident in the brief, almost cursory descriptions on the menu. The food certainly speaks for itself with starters such as tuna spring roll and trio of quail benefiting from real clarity of flavour. Chicken breast sliced onto a small

England

tian of fluffy potato with sage and basil proved a strong centrepiece to a main course which also featured chicken leg stuffed with wild mushroom mousse and wrapped in crispy pancetta.

Times: 12.30-2.30pm/7-9.30pm.
Closed L Sat, BHs L
Additional: Sunday L. Bar food.
Children welcome
Seats: 30. Private dining room 70
Style: Traditional, Country-house
Smoking: No smoking in dining room;
Air conditioning

Accommodation: 68 rooms (68 en suite) ★ ★ ★ ★
Directions: At top of Richmond Hill, opposite Star and Garter, just opposite Richmond Park

---

TWICKENHAM   Map GtL B2

McClements Restaurant   NEW   ◎◎

2 Whitton Road, TW1 1BJ
Tel: 020 8744 9610
Fax: 020 8744 9598
e johnmac21@aol.com

Even when it's packed out on a Saturday night, McClements retains an air of quiet respectability. Candles burning on clothed tables create a cosy, intimate atmosphere, and a meal is something of a ritual, with its generous supply of canapés, cleansing, frothy inter-course drink, and pre-dessert. It all goes down very well with the customers, and importantly, the food takes centre stage. Roast tranche of foie gras, roast saddle of rabbit, and suckling pig with pig ravioli are balanced with lighter options like caramelised scallops, sea bream with oyster tempura, and monkfish with langoustine cannelloni.

Chef(s): John McClements
Owner(s): John McClements
Cost: *Alc* £32, set price L £20/£25
Times: Noon-2.30pm/6.30-11pm
Additional: Children welcome.
Jacket & tie preferred
Seats: 40
Style: French
Smoking: No-smoking area;
Air conditioning

Civil licence: 80
Directions: Telephone for directions

☺   Indicates a restaurant that has told us they offer a two-course lunch for less than £15

☺   Indicates a restaurant that has told us they offer a three-course dinner for less than £25

✎   Indicates a restaurant that has told us that 50% or more of their ingredients are organically sourced

Prices quoted in the guide are for guidance only and are subject to change without notice

England

MERSEYSIDE

LIVERPOOL
Map 7 SJ39

Liverpool Marriott City Centre

Modern hotel with the familiar open-plan cocktail bar and restaurant. Raised areas with low-level partitions manage to create a feeling of some intimacy without losing the sense of space. Good canapés and warm, home-made breads are a promise of things to come, including an excellent confit of shoulder of lamb, cooked almost like Peking duck, crisp on the outside and succulent within.

Smoking: No smoking in dining room; Air conditioning
Civil licence: 200
Accommodation: 146 rooms (146 en suite) ★ ★ ★ ★
Directions: From City centre, follow signs for Queen Square Parking

1 Queens Square, L1 1RH
Tel: 0151 476 8000
Fax: 0151 474 5000
Chef(s): Gerard O'Sullivan
Owner(s): Marriott Hotels
Cost: Alc £30, set price D £23.50.
☺ ☺ H/wine £12.75
Times: Noon-3pm/6.30-10pm.
Closed L Sat,
Additional: Sunday L.
Children welcome
Seats: 104
Style: Modern, Chic

Simply Heathcotes NEW

It's a little bit of Brookside meets Chelsea Harbour at this chic, glass-fronted brasserie with some of Merseyside's elite for neighbours. Entry is via a spacious courtyard complete with fountain, and inside it's light and modern, with smart young suited staff. Classic Heathcote favourites are there, like roast Goosnargh duckling breast, and bread and butter pudding with apricot compôte and clotted cream. Mainly British starters include potted shrimp risotto, and terrine of wild mushrooms (lovely truffle flavour), followed by seared cod with buttered spinach, and artichoke and leek tart. Baked raspberry and polenta Bakewell with vanilla ice cream made for an "ace" dessert.

Style: Modern Chic
Smoking: No pipes; no cigars; Air conditioning
Directions: Opposite pier head

25 The Strand, L2 0XL
Tel: 0151 236 3536
Fax: 0151 2363534
📧 liverpool@simplyheathcotes.co.uk
Chef(s): Andrew McGuiness
Owner(s): Paul Heathcote
Cost: Alc £26.50, set price L £15.50.
☺ ☺ H/wine £11.50
Times: noon-2.30pm/7-10pm.
Closed BHs, 25 Dec, 1 Jan
Additional: Sunday L.
Children welcome
Seats: 72. Private dining room 24

60 Hope Street

60 Hope Street, L1 9BZ
Tel: 0151 707 6060
Fax: 0151 707 6016
📧 info@60hopestreet.com
Chef(s): Steven Mcabe
Owner(s): Colin & Gary Manning
Cost: Alc £30, set price L £13.95.
☺ ☺ H/wine £13.50
Times: Noon-2.30pm/7-10.30pm.
Closed Mon, L Sat, D Sun,
25 Dec until early Jan
Additional: Sunday L. Bar food.
Children welcome
Seats: 80. Private dining room 30.
Jacket and tie preferred

Looking more like an upmarket town house than a restaurant, 60 Hope Street is a Georgian Grade II listed building located

between the two cathedrals. Inside it is modern and airy with walls of white, cream, violet and burgundy. Semi-spiral staircases lead up to the private dining room and down to the basement café-bar. Service is provided by knowledgeable staff in pale blue who offer an interesting wine list along with a choice of menus. Expect the likes of wild sea bass with roast Jerusalem artichoke, or saddle of rabbit with black pudding, creamed parsnip and Madeira jus.

Style: Modern, Minimalist
Smoking: No-smoking area; no pipes; no cigars; Air conditioning
Directions: From M62 follow city centre signs, then brown tourist signs for Cathedral. Hope St near Cathedral

Ziba

Car showroom converted to create a two-tier open-plan brasserie and bar. The uncompromising décor is reflected in the direct approach of the cooking, with interesting options like pan-fried foie gras, haricot blanc purée and casserole of ceps; brill with kohlrabi fondant, creamed lentils and herb gnocchi, and plum sable with liquorice.

Additional: Children welcome
Seats: 120. Private dining room 12
Style: Modern, Chic
Smoking: No-smoking area; no pipes; no cigars
Directions: Telephone for directions

15-19 Berry Street, L1 9DF
Tel: 0151 708 8870
Fax: 707 9926
Chef(s): Glenn Futter
Owner(s): Martin Ainscough
Cost: *Alc* £30, set price L £16.50/ D £16.50. ☺ ☺ H/wine £10.50
Times: Noon-2pm/6-10pm.
Closed Sun, BHs, 25-26 Dec, 1 Jan

NORFOLK

BLAKENEY   Map 9 TG04

Morston Hall

Set in a quiet and secluded position close to the coast, this brick and flint 17th-century country house features a bright, uncluttered dining-room with well-spaced tables and local artwork displayed on orange pastel walls. Aperitifs, served with olives and capers in the lounge, precede a set four-course meal served at 8pm. As a result, the bread comes piping hot to accompany the likes of a "stunning" seared scallop appetiser with guacamole followed by foie gras and confit duck terrine with toasted brioche. An intermediate fish course might then be poached haddock fillet with poached egg and chive hollandaise, preceding roast loin of milk-fed lamb with fondant potato and aubergine caviar. For those foregoing the bourbon vanilla soufflé or a classic orange tart with lemon curd ice cream, there is a selection of European cheeses with home-made biscuits and more bread. Throughout, these are well crafted dishes served in a courteous, discreet and knowledgeable style.

Directions: On coastal road, A149 between Blakeney & Wells

Morston, Holt,
NR25 7AA
Tel: 01263 741041
Fax: 01263 740419
✉ reception@morstonhall.com
Chef(s): Galton Blackiston
Owner(s): Mrs T Blackiston
Cost: Set price L £22/D £36.
H/wine £11
Times: D from 7.30pm.
Closed 2 wks Jan
Additional: Sunday L.
Children welcome
Seats: 35. Private dining room 20
Style: Classic
Smoking: No smoking in dining room
Accommodation: 6 rooms (6 en suite)
★ ★

England

BURNHAM MARKET
Map 9 TF84

Hoste Arms Hotel

Set in the heart of Lord Nelson's Norfolk, a 17th-century Inn overlooking the green. Wood panelling, stone floors, open fires combine the stylish and the comfortable with a down to earth atmosphere. Add a mix of restaurant, hotel and trad pub, and you can soon see why the place is always buzzing. Variety also applies to the food with oriental flavours (Chinese, Thai and Japanese) mingling with all things European. Local and North Sea ingredients constitute the kitchen's bedrock; dressed Cromer crab, mussels and oysters all abound. A signature dish of salmon and chilli fishcakes, with sweet-salt spinach and tzatziki, sets the tone. Very good wine list with keenly priced fine wines.

The Green, PE31 8HD
Tel: 01328 738777
Fax: 01328 730103
106504.2472@compuserve.com
Chef(s): Andrew McPherson
Owner(s): Mr P D Whittome
Cost: Alc £21. ☺ ☺ H/wine £9.95
Times: Noon-2pm/7-9pm.
Closed L New Years Eve,
Additional: Sunday L.
Children welcome
Seats: 140
Style: Rustic
Smoking: No-smoking area;
Air conditioning
Accommodation: 28 rooms (28 en suite) ★ ★
Directions: 2m from A149 between Burnham & Wells

COLTISHALL
Map 9 TG21

Kings Head
NEW

Fish is a recurring theme at this 17th-century inn, from the angling paraphernalia on display to the piscine choice from an imaginative menu. You can eat in the bar, the adjacent restaurant or upstairs, and besides the seafood options - pan-fried skate wing with apples, prawns and capers for instance - you might try roast fillet of beef with spinach, potato rösti, mushrooms and Madeira sauce.

Smoking: No smoking in dining room
Accommodation: 4 rooms (2 en suite) ♦♦♦
Directions: From Norwich take B1150 to Coltishall, approx 10 miles

26 Wroxham Road,
NR12 7EA
Tel: 01603 737426
Fax: 01603 736542
Chef(s): Kevin Gardner
Owner(s): Kevin & Susan Gardner
Cost: Alc £22.50. ☺ ☺ H/wine £9.75
Times: noon-3pm/6-11.30pm.
Additional: Sunday L. Bar food L.
Children welcome
Seats: 50. Private dining room 24
Style: Rustic

Norfolk Mead Hotel

On a quiet edge of the Norfolk Broads leading to the River Bure, a delightful Georgian manor house with a candlelit restaurant. The best of local produce goes into a frequently changing range of dishes, such as chicken liver parfait with tawny port, and turbot parcels on asparagus. Save space for some excellent desserts.

Style: Classical. **Smoking:** No smoking in dining room
Accommodation: 9 rooms (9 en suite) ★ ★
Directions: From Norwich take B1150. In Coltishall turn R after humpbacked bridge. Hotel 600yds on R just before church

Church Lane, NR12 7DN
Tel: 01603 737531
Fax: 01603 737521
info@norfolkmead.co.uk
Chef(s): Mark Sayers
Owner(s): Mr & Mrs D Fleming
Cost: Alc £26, set price D £25. ☺ ☺
H/wine £12.95
Times: Noon-1.45pm/7-8.30pm.
Closed L Mon,
Additional: Sunday L. Bar food L.
Children welcome
Seats: 40. Private dining room 20

ERPINGHAM
Map 9 TG13

Ark Restaurant

Norfolk is regularly scoured for tip-top ingredients to supply this small restaurant, and what is not purchased locally is probably grown in the garden. Elizabeth David is Sheila Kidd's muse, and there's a distinctly European flavour to many of her dishes. Mousseline of smoked haddock with mango salsa is a typically adventurous starter, while creamy lamb with aubergine, or nut pâté en croute with mushrooms, leeks and pine nuts makes a versatile main course. Expect mouthwatering desserts, like old English ratafia trifle.

Style: Rustic. **Smoking:** No smoking in dining room
Accommodation: 3 rooms. **Directions:** Off A140, 4m N of Aylsham

The Street, NR11 7QB
Tel: 01263 761535
Fax: 01263 761535
Chef(s): Sheila Kidd
Owner(s): Sheila & Michael Kidd
Cost: A/c £26.75, set price L £15.25/D £25-£28. ☺ H/wine £11
Times: 7-9.30pm. Closed Mon-Tue, D Sun, 25-26 Dec
Additional: Sunday L. Children welcome
Seats: 26. Private dining room 12

GREAT YARMOUTH
Map 5 TG50

Imperial Hotel

Fancy taking a step back in time to traditional silver service, steaks flambéed at the table, trifle and profiteroles? If so then this is the place for you. The menus offer a good choice of well-executed dishes with a French influence, including vineyard snails with herb butter, and frogs' legs deep-fried, piled high, with a savoury jus.

North Drive, NR30 1EQ
Tel: 01493 851113
Fax: 01493 852229
e imperial@scs-datacom.co.uk
Chef(s): Stephen Duffield
Owner(s): Mr R S Mobbs
Cost: A/c £25, set price L £16/D £21. ☺ ☺ H/wine £14
Times: Noon-2pm/7-10pm. Closed L Sat
Additional: Sunday L. Bar food. Children welcome
Seats: 60. Private dining room 140
Style: Modern, French
Smoking: No-smoking area; Air conditioning
Accommodation: 39 rooms (39 en suite) ★★★
Directions: North end of Great Yarmouth seafront

GRIMSTON
Map 9 TF72

Congham Hall

A thoroughly accommodating country house hotel. The lunch menu invites diners to sit wherever they fancy - bar, lounge or restaurant, whilst the evening menu assures guests that 'the table you have reserved is yours for the evening.' This relaxing, pampered atmosphere is enhanced by warm, unfussy decor, attentive staff and panoramic views of the garden (which apparently supplies the kitchen with 700 varieties of herbs). A meal includes canapés, an amuse bouche and modern European creations such as fillet of beef with an oxtail macaire, cassis shallots and a jus rôti. There's plenty to interest everyone, from the seasoned carnivore to the devout vegetarian.

Smoking: No smoking in dining room
Civil licence: 70. **Accommodation:** 14 rooms (14 en suite) ★★★
Directions: 6 miles NE of King's Lynn on A14, turn R toward Grimston. Hotel is 2.5 miles on L; don't go to Longham

Lynn Road, PE32 1AH
Tel: 01485 600250
Fax: 01485 601191
e reception@conghamhallhotel.co.uk
Chef(s): James Parkinson
Owner(s): Von Essen Hotels
Cost: A/c £20, set price L £13.50-£29.95/D £34-£39.95. ☺ ☺ H/wine £14.50
Times: Noon-2pm/7-9.30pm. Closed D Xmas Day
Additional: Sunday L. Bar food. Children 7yrs+
Seats: 50. Private dining room 18
Style: Modern, Country-house

England

Map 9 TG03

HOLT

Yetman's

Expect no nonsense at this intimate, theatrical restaurant where seasonal fresh produce is transformed into honest traditional dishes. Two small cottages, the oldest parts Tudor, have been knocked together, and brightened with yellow décor and loads of fresh flowers. A short, snappy menu featuring various well-described wines by the glass, touches on fish, meat, vegetarian choices and half a dozen desserts. Local cockles and mussels, poached separately in wine, seared fresh scallops, and twice-baked cheese soufflé are inviting starters, and there might be grilled haddock and poached turbot, or roasted apple-fed Hereford duck to follow. A lengthy, mainly New World wine list.

37 Norwich Road, NR25 6SA
Tel: 01263 713320
Chef(s): Alison Yetman
Owner(s): Alison & Peter Yetman
Cost: Set price L £30-£35/D £30-£35
Times: 12.30-2pm/7-9.30pm.
Closed Mon-Tue, D Sun, 25-26 Dec, 3wks in Aug
Additional: Sunday L.
Children welcome. **Seats:** 32
Smoking: No smoking in dining room
Directions: Village centre

HORNING

Map 9 TG31

Taps

Busy neighbourhood restaurant that goes from strength to strength. Open just over two years, there have been real signs of a kitchen on the way up. Paul has taken over front of house providing relaxed and attentive service, while Terry remains in the kitchen and produces food that on the surface can appear fussy, but in actuality works very well. Mussel ravioli with sauerkraut and marinière sauce. Roast fillet of turbot with crab and sweetcorn blinis, butter and horseradish sauce, set the pace for an intricate and memorable dining experience. Chic modern décor with wicker furniture in the reception area and a light coloured two-tone effect in the restaurant.

Directions: From Norwich follow signs to 'The Broads' on A1151. Through Wroxham and turn R to Horning & Ludham. After 3 miles turn R into Horning, Lower St 500yds on L

25 Lower Street,
NR12 8AA
Tel: 01692 630219
Chef(s): Terry Westall & Paul Yaxley
Owner(s): Terry Westall & Paul Yaxley
Cost: Alc £23.50, set price L £12.95/D £35. ☺ ☺ H/wine £9.50
Times: Noon-4.30pm/7-midnight.
Closed Mon, D Sun,
Additional: Sunday L.
Children welcome
Seats: 40
Style: Modern, Chic
Smoking: No smoking in dining room

KING'S LYNN

Map 9 TF62

Rococo

Although it's set in a 17th-century cottage, this restaurant has a modern feel, the bright walls adorned with contemporary paintings. The cheerful, confident staff are 'delightful', and can be relied upon for advice on menus and cooking methods. Quality ingredients and careful cooking much in evidence. The modern British menu offers confident, unfussy interpretations of old favourites such as seared king scallops with pea purée, fried courgettes and Avruga or lamb chump with preserved lemons, olives and a ginger jus. Desserts might include freshly made lemon tart or caramelised pear and pecan tart with a poire William sauce.

Directions: Follow Signs to The Old Town, next to Tourist Information

11 Saturday Market Place, PE30 5DQ
Tel: 01553 771483
Fax: 01553 771483
🄴 rococorest@aol.com
Chef(s): Nick Anderson
Owner(s): Nick & Anne Anderson
Cost: Set price D £30.50-£34.50. ☺
Times: Noon-2pm/6.30-10pm.
Closed Sun-Mon,
Additional: Bar food L.
Children welcome
Seats: 40
Style: Modern, British
Smoking: No smoking in dining room

NORTH WALSHAM

Map 9 TG23

Beechwood Hotel

Agatha Christie used this elegant country house as her Norfolk hideaway, and the ivy-clad building with its stylish lemon and

Cromer Road, NR28 0HD
Tel: 01692 403231
Fax: 01692 407284

blue furnishings is as welcoming as ever. The restaurant is rather grand, with its Victorian furniture and smartly-set tables, and the classically English food is very much in keeping with its surroundings. The daily set menu offers good value in simple but well-made dishes like celery apple and stilton soup, and chargrilled rib eye on horseradish mash with a quenelle of caramelised onion and rich Madeira jus. Puddings (crème brûlée with Amaretto), petit fours and coffee all keep their end up.

Chef(s): Steven Norgate
Owner(s): Don Birch & Lindsay Spalding
Cost: Set price L £12.50/D £24.
☺ ☺ H/wine £12.90
Times: Noon-2pm/7-9pm.
Closed L Mon & Sat,
Additional: Sunday L. Children welcome. Vegetarian by request only
Seats: 40. Private dining room 14
Style: Traditional, Country-house
Smoking: No smoking in dining room
Accommodation: 10 rooms (10 en suite) ★ ★
Directions: From Norwich on B1150, 13m to N Walsham. Turn L at lights and next R. Hotel 150mtrs on L

NORWICH
Map 5 TG20
Adlard's Restaurant

On a quiet street close to the city centre stands this well-established restaurant hosted by the affable David Adlard, whose enthusiastic wine recommendations - particularly from the New World - add an extra dimension to dining out on Modern British cooking with distinctly classical influences. A sympathetically modern setting of pine flooring and stripped walls adorned with geometric paintings, features well-spaced, attractively presented tables lit mostly by individual table lamps. The sensibly limited *carte*, relying on careful shopping for the best seasonal produce, is imaginatively balanced with accurately cooked results. Following perhaps confit of chicken terrine with celeriac remoulade and delicately roast turbot with roast shallots and deep-fried salsify, salad or a selection of British and Irish cheeses may be taken as an intermediate course, prior to chocolate fondant with pistachio ice cream and good coffee served with petits fours. Relaxed, friendly service adds to a sense of occasion that puts everyone at their ease.

79 Upper St Giles Street, NR2 1AB
Tel: 01603 633522
Fax: 01603 617733
e info@adlards.co.uk
Chef(s): Roger Hickman
Owner(s): David Adlard
Cost: *Alc* £37.75, set price L £19/ D £25. H/wine £14
Times: 12.30-4pm/7.30-Midnight.
Closed Sun, L Mon, 1 wk after Xmas
Additional: Children welcome. Vegetarian by request only
Seats: 40
Style: Modern
Smoking: No pipes; no cigars; Air conditioning
Directions: City centre, 200 yds behind the City Hall

Annesley House Hotel

Smart conservatory restaurant overlooking the gardens of this Georgian hotel. Marble effect tables, pastel colours and 'superb' ceiling lights and fans create a Mediterranean atmosphere which is reflected in much of the cooking. Elsewhere, local ingredients are championed - as in a crispy Norfolk duck breast served with parsnip crisps and redcurrant sauce.

Smoking: No smoking in dining room
Accommodation: 26 rooms ★ ★ ★
Directions: On A11 close to city centre

6 Newmarket Road, NR2 2LA
Tel: 01603 624553
Fax: 01603 621577
Chef(s): Simon Woodward
Owner(s): Mr & Mrs D Reynolds
Cost: *Alc* £25. ☺ ☺ H/wine £9.50
Times: Noon-2pm/7-9pm.
Closed Xmas
Additional: Sunday L. Bar food. Children welcome
Seats: 40. Private dining room 18

Beeches Hotel & Victorian Gardens

Bistro-style restaurant in a conservatory with French doors leading to the patio and garden. The food is an appealing blend of traditional British with Mediterranean influences: smoked bacon and red pepper risotto, and pork loin with potato and apple rösti followed by hot rum and sultana rice pudding.

Additional: Bar food. Children 14yrs+.
Vegetarian by request only
Seats: 30
Smoking: No smoking in dining room
Accommodation: 35 rooms (35 en suite) ★★★
Directions: W of City on B1108, behind St Johns R C Cathedral

2-6 Earlham Road, NR2 3DB
Tel: 01603 621167
Fax: 01603 620151
e reception@beeches.co.uk
Chef(s): Claire Whibley
Owner(s): Mr & Mrs K R Hill
Cost: ☺
Times: Lunch by arrangement,
D 6-9pm. Closed Xmas, New Year

Brummells Seafood Restaurant

A building dating back to the 11th century is the charming, intimate setting for this renowned seafood restaurant. The atmosphere is romantic and the welcome hospitable, setting the stage for an enjoyable romp through an exciting array of fishy treats. Stewed cuttlefish in wine and black ink, deep-fried breaded oysters, and monkfish fritters with roast tomato relish are innovative starters, while the dozen or so main courses might include Scottish salmon fillet with a Creole mustard sauce, chargrilled tuna with compôte of fruity curry marmalade, and the more straightforward pan-fried skate wing with black butter, and simply grilled Dover sole.

Directions: In city centre, 40yds from Colegate

7 Magdalen Street, NR3 1LE
Tel: 01603 625555
Fax: 01603 766260
e brummell@brummells.co.uk
Chef(s): A Brummell, J O'Sullivan
Owner(s): Mr A Brummell
Cost: *Alc* £29.90. H/wine £11.95
Times: L from noon, D from 6pm
Additional: Sunday L.
Children welcome
Seats: 30. Jacket and tie preferred
Style: Rustic
Smoking: No-smoking area;
Air conditioning

By Appointment

A warren of heavily-beamed rooms decorated in bold colours distinguishes this intimate restaurant in a former merchant's house. Expect a dash of theatre with your food, from a short choice of mainly English dishes like smoked breast of duck with Oriental mango, and supreme of chicken with pistachio nuts and apricots.

Smoking: No smoking in dining room
Accommodation: 4 rooms (2 en suite)
Directions: City centre. Entrance rear of Merchants House

27-29 St George's Street, NR3 1AB
Tel: 01603 630730
Fax: 01603 630730
Chef(s): Timothy Brown, Robert Culyer
Owner(s): Timothy Brown,
Robert Culyer
Cost: *Alc* £26.50. ☺ H/wine £9.50
Times: Closed L All Week, 25 Dec
Additional: Children 12yrs+
Seats: 50. Private dining room 36
Style: Traditional, Formal

Cumberland Hotel

Jovial warmth and hospitality define a night out at this vibrant restaurant. Smoked pigeon, bacon and pine kernel salad might precede baked venison sausages with button mushrooms and shallots.

Additional: Children 13yrs+
Seats: 48. Private dining room 18.
Accommodation: 25 rooms (25 en suite) ★★
Directions: 1m E of city centre on A47 to Yarmouth. Close to Railway station and Football Club

212-216 Thorpe Road, NR1 1TJ
Tel: 01603 434560
Fax: 01603 433355
e cumberland@paston.co.uk
Chef(s): Craig Robinson
Owner(s): Michael A Price
Cost: *Alc* £24.50, set price L
£12.95/D £17.95-£22.95. ☺ ☺
H/wine £11.95
Times: Lunch by arrangement, 6.30-9.30pm. Closed Xmas

England

Femi's

A busy city centre restaurant with a pleasant ambience. The varied menu continues to offer its perennial favourite - blinis. Other options may be crispy duck salad or roast dishes such as loin of pork wrapped in bacon with cider and brandy sauce or rump of spiced lamb with shallots and aubergine.

Seats: 50. Private dining room 20
Style: Modern
Smoking: No-smoking area; no pipes; Air conditioning
Directions: City centre, 200yds from castle & cathedral. Behind Anglia Television

42 King Street, NR1 1PD
Tel: 01603 766010
Fax: 01603 766010
Chef(s): Femi Abodunde
Owner(s): Mr Femi Abodunde
Cost: Alc £22.50, set price L £10-£24.50/D £17.50-£32. ☺ ☺ H/wine £8.95
Times: Noon-3pm/6-11pm. Closed L Sun-Mon, D Sun,
Additional: Children welcome

Marco's Restaurant

The rent on this classic Georgian house was once sixteen shillings and five fat hens a year. Nowadays the hens are likely to feature as pan-fried escalopes of chicken breast in Parma ham, or sautéed with pine nuts and chopped shallots. Don't expect to find standard Italian fare at this fine restaurant, where prime ingredients from local sources receive the lightest touch. Instead you can try wild boar with Parmesan cheese, smoked salmon on a potato pancake, or main dishes like pan-roasted breast of Gressingham duck with wine, orange and Morello cherry sauce. There's also terrific value from the set menu.

Directions: City centre: From market place facing Guildhall, turn R then L into Pottergate

17 Pottergate, NR2 1DS
Tel: 01603 624044
Chef(s): Marco Vessalio
Owner(s): Marco Vessalio
Cost: Alc £26, set price L £16. ☺ ☺ H/wine £12.50
Times: Noon-2pm/7-10pm. Closed Sun, Mon, Xmas & BHs
Additional: Children welcome
Seats: 22
Style: Classic, Italian

Marriott Sprowston Manor Hotel

Plush restaurant in an impressive hotel and leisure complex set amidst attractive grounds and parkland. Ample skill as well as real imagination are evident in a smooth, full flavoured duck liver parfait with toasted brioche and a fennel and gooseberry marmalade for example.

Sprowston Park, Wroxham Road, Sprowston NR7 8RP
Tel: 01603 410871
Telephone for further details

Old Rectory

This Georgian house dates back to 1754 and stands in mature gardens by the river Yare. Its intimate dining room offers an interesting selection of British and Mediterranean cooking, including home-made desserts such as apple crumble, fresh from the oven. The short wine list includes well-chosen bins of the month available by the glass. Staff are personable and professional.

Seats: 16. Private dining room 16. Jacket and tie preferred
Style: Classic
Smoking: No smoking in dining room
Accommodation: 8 rooms (8 en suite) ★ ★
Directions: from A147 take A1242 to Thorpe. Hotel on L after church

103 Yarmouth Road, Thorpe St Andrew, NR7 0HF
Tel: 01603 700772
Fax: 01603 300772
e rectoryh@aol.com
Chef(s): Andy Clegg
Owner(s): Chris Entwistle
Cost: Set price D £18.50-£20.45. ☺ H/wine £11.50
Times: Dinner only, 7-9.30pm. Closed Sun, Xmas, New Year
Additional: Children 12yrs+

England

St Benedicts Restaurant

St Benedicts has been totally refurbished this year and has a fresher more contemporary feel, with glass screens bearing the SBR logo. The menu is wide ranging and there is a good choice of wines. Notable dishes include a tartlet of smoked chicken and Jerusalem artichoke, and salmon fishcakes served with excellent hand-made chips.

Seats: 42. Private dining room 24
Style: Modern
Smoking: No-smoking area; no pipes; no cigars
Directions: At city end of St Benedicts. Nearest car park Duke Street (day), on street (evening)

9 St Benedicts Street,
NR2 4PE
Tel: 01603 765377
Fax: 01603 765377
e nigel@nraffles.freeserve.co.uk
Chef(s): Nigel Raffles
Owner(s): Nigel & Joyne Raffles
Cost: *Alc* £21. ☺ ☺ H/wine £9.25
Times: noon-2pm/7-10pm.
Closed Sun-Mon, 25 Dec-31 Dec
Additional: Children welcome

SWAFFHAM   Map 9 TF80

Romford House

A 400-year-old beamed property with an intimate feel fostered by open fires and pretty fabrics. Blackboard specials like black pudding fritters, and breast of pigeon with a blackcurrant sauce make a delicious alternative to the standard menu where you'll find warm crab and spring onion tarts, and chicken breast stuffed with grapes and onions.

Style: Traditional, French
Smoking: No smoking in dining room
Directions: 16 miles from King's Lynn, in the main market place

5 London Street, PE37 7DD
Tel: 01760 722552
e peter.rose@ukgateway.net
Chef(s): Jane Rose
Owner(s): Jane Rose
Cost: *Alc* £22. ☺ ☺ H/wine £8.95
Times: L from 11.30, D from 7pm.
Closed Sun, L Mon,
Additional: Children welcome
Seats: 38. Private dining room 22

THORNHAM   Map 9 TF74

Lifeboat Inn

A distant glimpse of Thornham harbour across the open meadows will put you in mind of the generations of smugglers who sought refuge in this delightful 16th-century alehouse. The attraction these days is some sturdy and honest cooking with the likes of spiced crab and ginger fishcakes or Morrocan spiced shank of lamb.

Seats: 70. Private dining room 18
Style: Traditional, Rustic
Smoking: No smoking in dining room
Accommodation: 22 rooms (22 en suite) ★ ★
Directions: Take A149 from Kings Lynn to Hunstanton. Carry on through Hunstanton on A149 to Thornham. Take first left turn

Ship Lane, PE36 6LT
Tel: 01485 512236
Fax: 01485 512323
e reception@lifeboatinn.co.uk
Chef(s): Paul Atkins,
Michael Sherman
Owner(s): Charles & Angie Coker
Cost: Set price D £22. ☺ ☺
H/wine £10.50
Times: Noon-2.30pm (bar only)/
7-9.30pm
Additional: Sunday L. Bar food.
Children welcome

THORPE MARKET   Map 9 TG23

Elderton Lodge Hotel

Lillie Langtry entertained Edward VII here, and this warm, intimate former hunting lodge retains its attraction as a peaceful refuge. Dine by candlelight in the beautiful panelled restaurant, on seared loin of venison, or Oriental roasted pork

Gunton Park,
NR11 8TZ
Tel: 01263 833547
Fax: 01263 834673
e enquiries@eldertonlodge.co.uk

fillet from the *carte* perhaps, and dark Belgian chocolate torte to finish.

Chef(s): Robbie Richardson, Louise Cradock
Owner(s): Mr & Mrs M H Worby
Cost: Alc £32.50, set price L £14.50/ D £30. ☺ ☺ H/wine £13.95
Times: Noon-2pm/7-9.30pm. Closed 3 Wks Jan
Additional: Sunday L. Children 10yrs+
Seats: 50. Private dining room 25
Style: Country-house, Classic
Smoking: No smoking in dining room
Accommodation: 11 rooms (11 en suite) ★ ★
Directions: On A149 (Cromer/North Walsham Road), 1 mile South of village

TITCHWELL
Map 9 TF74

Titchwell Manor Hotel

Seafood and fish caught in local waters offer a strong incentive to dine at this charming hotel looking out over marshland. Game (pot-roasted pheasant) and meat (chargrilled steak) are available, but the menu concentrates on whitebait, mussels (poached or tossed in chilli), oysters, Brancaster crab and Whitby scampi.

PE31 8BB
Tel: 01485 210221
Fax: 01485 210104
e margaret@titchwellmanor.co.uk
Chef(s): Chris King
Owner(s): Margaret & Ian Swaith
Cost: Alc £24, set price L £15/ D £23-£25. ☺ ☺ H/wine £12.50
Additional: Sunday L. Bar food. Children welcome
Seats: 50
Style: Modern
Smoking: No smoking in dining room
Accommodation: 16 rooms (16 en suite) ★ ★
Directions: On the A149 coast road between Brancaster and Thornham

UPPER SHERINGHAM
Map 9 TG14

Dales Country House Hotel   NEW

Hidden within extensive grounds but with magnificent coastal and countryside views, this impressive hotel serves fine food, well presented. Plenty to choose from, like pork and prune terrine, course duck breast with honey sauce, and monkfish and Parma ham, much of it local produce. Service is very attentive.

Smoking: No smoking in dining room
Accommodation: 17 rooms (17 en suite) ★ ★ ★
Directions: Situated on B1157, 1 mile S of Sheringham. From A148 Cromer to Holt road, take turn at entrance to Sheringham Park. After 0.5 mile restaurant on L

NR26 8TJ
Tel: 01263 824555
Fax: 01263 822647
Chef(s): Derek Byrne
Owner(s): Mr & Mrs Mackenzie
Cost: Alc £25. ☺ ☺ H/wine £10.95
Times: Noon-2pm/7-9.30pm.
Additional: Sunday L. Bar food L. Children welcome
Seats: 40. Private dining room 40
Style: Classic, Country-house

England

WYMONDHAM
Map 5 TG10

Number Twenty Four

An informal restaurant in pretty gold and cream colours, run by a competent husband and wife team. Richard Hughes produces quality food while Sue is a relaxed host, serving the likes of creamy leek and Stilton risotto with roasted pear, and pan-fried lambs' liver with sausage and mash.

Additional: Children welcome. **Seats:** 60. Private dining room 20
Style: French. **Smoking:** No-smoking area
Directions: Town centre opposite war memorial

24 Middleton Street, NR18 0BH
Tel: 01953 607750
Fax: 01953 607750
e numb24@msn.com
Chef(s): Richard Hughes
Owner(s): Richard & Sue Hughes
Cost: Alc £21, set price L £14.95/
D £18.95. ☺ ☺ H/wine £9.50
Times: Noon-2.30pm/7-9.30pm.
Closed Sun-Tue, 24-31 Dec

NORTHAMPTONSHIRE

DAVENTRY
Map 4 SP85

Fawsley Hall Hotel

Fawsley, NN11 3BA
Tel: 01327 892000

Enter through the Norman arch into the early 16th-century heart of the manor. The attractive restaurant area boasts stone flags, a beamed ceiling and an original fireplace - all as might be expected from an establishment that includes Elizabeth I in its list of past clientele. Ingredients are first class (sea bass for example) and the dishes well executed (said sea bass being perfectly cooked and seasoned with a nicely crisped skin and accompaniments of sweet and sour vine tomatoes, baby fennel and black olives.) Flavours are generally well balanced and vibrant with attention to detail from the canapés to the chocolate truffles in evidence.

Fax: 01327 892001
e reservations@fawsleyhall.com
Chef(s): Richard Turner
Cost: Alc £41.00, set price L £14.95/D £31. ☺ H/wine £17.50
Times: Noon-2pm/7-9.30pm
Additional: Sunday L. Children welcome
Seats: 70. Private dining room 60. Jacket and tie preferred
Style: Country House. **Smoking:** No smoking in dining room
Civil licence: 140. **Accommodation:** 30 rooms (30 en suite) ★★★★
Directions: From M40 J11 take A361, follow for 12 miles. Turn R towards Fawsley Hall

FOTHERINGHAY
Map 4 TL09

The Falcon Inn

PE8 5HZ
Tel: 01832 226254
Fax: 01832 226046
Chef(s): Ray Smikle
Owner(s): John Hoskins & Ray Smikle
Cost: Alc £22, set price L £13.25.
☺ ☺ H/wine £11
Times: Noon-3pm/7-10.30pm.
Closed Mon (winter)
Additional: Sunday L. Bar food.
Children welcome
Seats: 45. Private dining room 25
Style: Modern
Smoking: No smoking in dining room

Attractive 18th-century stone pub in an historic village, part of the Huntsbridge Inns' winning formula of offering innovative food in a relaxed pub environment. You can eat what you like, where you like, and accompany it with excellent wines or a decent glass of ale. It's still the village local, and you can pop in for a snack, or go the whole hog and settle for three courses. An imaginative menu changes monthly, offering robust dishes veering towards the Mediterranean. Crispy spring duck rolls with spiced Asian coleslaw, and calves' liver with olive oil mash and bacon are typical of the style.

Directions: Off A605 follow signpost Fotheringhay

KETTERING — Map 4 SP87

Kettering Park Hotel

Dining in the open plan restaurant is a largely informal affair with an airy and tranquil Mediterranean atmosphere. A lengthy menu featuring both classical and contemporary dishes ensures that most tastes are catered for, though fish fans will be particularly gratified with daily deliveries from Brixham ensuring real freshness.

Kettering Parkway, NN15 6XT
Tel: 01536 416666
Fax: 01536 416171
Telephone for further details

MARSTON TRUSSELL — Map 4 SP68

The Sun Inn

Rural English inn combining character and modern comforts, with a choice of restaurant or bar in which to dine. Deep radiant colours in the restaurant exude warmth. Guests may choose traditional options from whitebait to rump of lamb, which vie for attention with more contemporary flavours such as crisp Thai fishcakes with searing chilli dressing.

Seats: 60. Private dining room 70. **Style:** Classic, Country-house
Smoking: No-smoking area
Accommodation: 20 rooms (20 en suite) ★ ★
Directions: Off A4304, between the villages of Lubenham & Theddingworth

Main Street, LE16 9TY
Tel: 01858 465531
Fax: 01858 433155
e manager@suninn.com
Chef(s): John Bumpstead, Suzanne Bell
Owner(s): Bernard Gover
Cost: Alc £20, set price L £13.95/ D £17.95. ☺ ☺ H/wine £10.95
Times: Noon-6pm/6-10pm. Closed Xmas, 1 Jan
Additional: Sunday L. Bar food L. Children welcome

NORTHAMPTON — Map 4 SP76

Northampton Marriott

There is now an informal Mediterranean feel to the recently re-themed restaurant. The menu offers dishes such as roast duck breast with confit leg, Savoy cabbage, apple brandy jus or monkfish with saffron potatoes and coriander & lime dressing. While for dessert perhaps an individual white chocolate mousse served with raspberries.

Eagle Drive, NN4 7HW
Tel: 01604 768700
Fax: 01604 769011
Telephone for further details

ROADE — Map 4 SP75

Roade House Restaurant

Come rain or shine, this restaurant is always popular, and a sample of the food shows why. Quality ingredients are prepared with skill, resulting in a tasty poached fillet of smoked haddock, chorizo and Gruyère salad, and pan-fried calves' liver with caramelized apple. Date and walnut pudding (rich and gooey!).

Additional: Sunday L. Children welcome.
Vegetarian by request only. Jacket and tie preferred
Seats: 50. **Style:** Modern
Smoking: No smoking in dining room; Air conditioning
Accommodation: 9 rooms (9 en suite)
Directions: M1/J15 (A508 Milton Keynes) to Roade, L at mini rdbt 500yds on the R

16 High Street, NN7 2NW
Tel: 01604 863372
Fax: 01604 862421
e chris@roadehousehotel.demon. co.uk
Chef(s): Chris Kewley
Owner(s): Mr & Mrs C M Kewley
Cost: Alc £27, set price L £16.50/ D £27. H/wine £10.50
Times: Noon-1.45pm/7-10pm. Closed L Mon & Sat, D Sun, 1 wk Xmas

STOKE BRUERNE

Map 4 SP74

Bruernes Lock Restaurant

The Canalside, NN12 7SB
Tel: 01604 863654
Fax: 01604 863330
e bruernlock@aol.com
Chef(s): Nicholas Collingwood
Owner(s): Mr N Hollick &
Mr Harry Thuillier
Cost: Alc £29, set price L £17-£19.50/
D £20. ☺ ☺ H/wine £12.75
Times: 12.15-2pm/7.15-9.30pm.
Closed Mon, L Sat, D Sun, Last wk
Dec, 1 wk Jan, 1 wk Oct, 1 wk Mar
Additional: Sunday L. Bar food L.
Children welcome
Seats: 50. Private dining room 12
Smoking: No smoking in dining room
Directions: On A508 between
Northhampton & Milton Keynes

Situated by the canal in Stoke Bruerne, this restaurant offers a
mixed bag of dishes from Britain, France and further afield.
Moroccan roast chicken, steak diane, Chinese style pork and
seared lamb's liver illustrate the global sweep, as does the 'far
reaching' selection of British cheeses and the variety of teas
and coffees.

TOWCESTER

Map 4 SP64

Vine House Restaurant

100 High St, Paulerspury,
NN12 7NA
Tel: 01327 811267
Fax: 01327 811309
Chef(s): Marcus Springett
Owner(s): Mr M & Mr J Springett
Cost: Set price L £25.95/D £25.95.
H/wine £11.95
Times: 12.30-2pm/7.30-9pm.
Closed Sun, L Sat-Wed,
2 wks from 24 Dec
Additional: Children welcome.
Vegetarian by request only
Seats: 45. Private dining room 11
Style: Modern

The low, mellow limestone exterior and immaculate gardens of
this 16th-century building present a welcoming sight. In this
case appearances are not deceptive, and the modern British
cooking with French and Oriental tinges more than meets
expectations. The small selection on the fixed-price menu
ensures a consistently good standard, and the cooking rarely
falters. Begin, perhaps, with sticky Thai rice with prawns coated
in sesame seeds with a honey, soy and sesame oil dressing, then
move on to, say, breast of pheasant with a chestnut bubble and
squeak, cranberry sauce and sage gravy. Finish with vanilla
pannacotta with lexus raisins for example.

Smoking: No smoking in dining room
Accommodation: 6 rooms (6 en suite)
Directions: 2m S of Towcester, just off A5

NORTHUMBERLAND

BAMBURGH
Map 12 NU13

Victoria Hotel

Close to Bamburgh Castle and the Grace Darling Museum, this friendly hotel serves skillfully prepared food in its conservatory brasserie. Popular locally (booking essential, even in winter) for dishes like Seahouses smoked haddock soup, and North Sea cod chunk with sautéed herb potatoes. Finish with vanilla pannacotta with spiced apricots.

Front Street, NE69 7BP
Tel: 01668 214431
Fax: 01668 214404
e enquiries@victoriahotel.net
Chef(s): Peter Airey
Owner(s): Elizabeth & John Sanderson
Cost: Alc £23. ☺ ☺ H/wine £10.50
Times: Dinner only, 7-9pm
Additional: Sunday L. Bar food. Children welcome
Seats: 80. Private dining room 20
Style: Modern, Bistro
Smoking: No smoking in dining room
Accommodation: 29 rooms (29 en suite) ★★
Directions: Turn off A1, north of Alnwick onto B1342 follow signs to Bamburgh. Hotel opposite village green

BELFORD
Map 12 NU13

Blue Bell Hotel   NEW

A range of menus provides an extensive choice of food at this town-centre coaching inn. The elegant restaurant offers a fairly classic four-course dinner, with coffee and mints in the lounge after. Some complex compositions include poached pavé of salmon with a walnut and mozzarella gratin and a soft leek and vermouth cream sauce.

Style: Classic
Smoking: No smoking in dining room
Accommodation: 17 rooms (17 en suite) ★★★
Directions: Telephone for directions

Market Place, NE70 7NE
Tel: 01668 213543
Fax: 01668 213787
e bluebel@globalnet.co.uk
Chef(s): Steve Owens
Owner(s): Mrs J Shirley
Cost: Alc £26. ☺ ☺ H/wine £11.95
Times: Noon-2pm/6.30-10pm.
Additional: Sunday L. Bar food. Children welcome
Seats: 36. Private dining room 36

BELLINGHAM
Map 12 NY88

Riverdale Hall Hotel

Cosy Victorian hotel with log fires and views over the Tyne. The menus offer a wide selection, using some of the local produce, and including some imaginative vegetarian choices and Thai specialities. Dishes range from mushroom and Stilton soup to red Thai chicken curry with steamed rice.

Additional: Sunday L. Bar food. Children welcome
Seats: 45. Private dining room 20
Style: Traditional, French
Smoking: No-smoking area; no pipes; no cigars
Accommodation: 20 rooms (20 en suite) ★★
Directions: Turn off B6320, after bridge, hotel on L

NE48 2JT
Tel: 01434 220254
Fax: 01434 220457
e iben@riverdalehall.demon.co.uk
Chef(s): Iben Cocker
Owner(s): Iben Cocker
Cost: Alc £12.95, set price L £11.95-£19.95/D £12.95-£21.95. ☺ ☺ H/wine £8.90
Times: Noon-2.30pm/6.45-9.30pm

England

CHOLLERFORD

Swallow George Hotel

Map 12 NY96

A long established hotel enjoying a riverside setting and attractive gardens. A good selection of interesting dishes is on offer with presentation a particular strong point, as in highly artistic blueberry and lime tart with raspberry coulis.

NE46 4EW
Tel: 01434 681611
Fax: 01434 681727
Telephone for further details

CORNHILL-ON-TWEED

Tillmouth Park Hotel

Map 12 NT83

Gracious surroundings (a magnificent nineteenth century country mansion) and trad hotel dining. Expect the likes of warm salad of avocado, croutons and shaved parmesan, grilled lamb cutlets with mint couscous, parsnip and rosemary. Desserts are along the lines of chocolate and praline bavarois with caramel.

Seats: 40. Private dining room 20
Style: Classic, Country-house
Civil licence: 60
Accommodation: 14 rooms (14 en suite) ★ ★ ★
Directions: A698, 3m E from Cornhill-On-Tweed

TD12 4UU
Tel: 01890 882255
Fax: 01890 882540
e reception@tillmouthpark.force9.co.uk
Chef(s): Martin Furlong, Tony McKay
Cost: Alc £25, set price D £26. ☺ ☺ H/wine £10.50
Times: Dinner only, 7-8.45pm
Additional: Sunday L. Children welcome

HEXHAM

De Vere Slaley Hall

Map 12 NY96

The new restaurant looks very impressive, and makes a superior addition to this popular hotel. The quality of food remains unchanged, with the short daily-changing menu offering some fine dishes: pressed ham shank terrine with yellow peas and Cumberland sauce to start, or salmon and sole with creamed leeks.

Style: Modern
Smoking: No-smoking area; Air conditioning
Civil licence: 250
Accommodation: 139 rooms (139 en suite) ★ ★ ★ ★
Directions: From A69 take A68 towards Darlington, follow signs to Slaley Hall

Slaley, NE47 0BY
Tel: 01434 673350
Fax: 01434 673050
e slaley.hall@devere-hotels.com
Chef(s): Tony Binks
Owner(s): De Vere Group Plc
Cost: Alc £30/D £23.50. ☺ H/wine £12.95
Times: Dinner only, 7-10pm
Additional: Sunday L. Children welcome
Seats: 125. Private dining room 250. Jacket and tie preferred

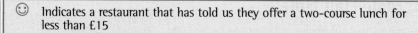
☺ Indicates a restaurant that has told us they offer a two-course lunch for less than £15

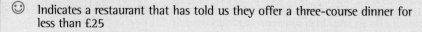
☺ Indicates a restaurant that has told us they offer a three-course dinner for less than £25

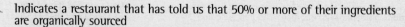
Indicates a restaurant that has told us that 50% or more of their ingredients are organically sourced

Prices quoted in the guide are for guidance only and are subject to change without notice

NOTTINGHAMSHIRE

LANGAR

Map 8 SK73

Langar Hall

NG13 9HG
Tel: 01949 860559
Fax: 01949 861045
e langarhall-hotel@ndirect.co.uk
Chef(s): Toby Garratt & Chris Ansell
Owner(s): Imogen Skirving
Cost: Alc £30, set price L £12.50-£22.50. ☺ ☺ H/wine £10.50
Times: Noon-3pm/7-11pm
Additional: Sunday L.
Children welcome
Seats: 30. Private dining room 20
Style: Country-house
Smoking: No smoking in dining room
Civil licence: 40
Accommodation: 10 rooms (10 en suite) ★ ★ ★
Directions: Off A46 & A52 in village centre (behind church)

An elegant dining room in a 19th-century country house hotel with an abundance of pictures and large stone figures. Much use is made of local produce, including the sheep that can be seen grazing from the hotel windows. An excellent twice-baked soufflé won praise, "beautifully presented, light and fluffy throughout". Top quality sea bass features as a main course, served on creamed pasta strips with a sweet and sour sauce - a better match than it sounds. Further evidence of a skilled approach in the kitchen in a dessert of poached pear, filled with a crème brûlée and set on a caramelised pecan sauce.

NOTTINGHAM

Map 8 SK53

Hart's Restaurant

1 Standard Court,
Park Row, NG1 6GN
Tel: 0115 9110666
Fax: 0115 9110611
Chef(s): Mark Gough
Owner(s): Tim Hart
Cost: Alc £25, set price L £14.95. ☺ ☺ H/wine £12.50

Bright brasserie style cooking well suited to the setting with its bold colours, abstract paintings and polished wooden floors. An informal, breezy atmosphere with service dispensed by waiting staff in shirts, ties and long aprons. Vibrant flavours define the style of dishes like pan-fried squid with mini chorizo sausages that has come with a satisfying basil mash and pan fried sea

NOTTINGHAM *Continued*   Map 8 SK53

bass with saffron potatoes, wilted pak choi and a smooth basil and tomato sauce. Amongst the desserts, banana tarte Tatin with butterscotch sauce and coconut ice cream excites. A simple wine list offers a reasonable selection of decent bins that are fairly priced.

Directions: Follow signs for Castle and from Maid Marian Way take last L after casino into Park Row. At the top turn L into side of old General Hospital

Times: Noon-2pm/7-10.30pm.
Closed 26 Dec, 1 Jan
Additional: Sunday L.
Children welcome
Seats: 80. Private dining room 50
Style: Modern
Smoking: No-smoking area; no pipes; no cigars; Air conditioning
Civil licence: 60

Hotel des Clos   NEW

Old Lenton Lane,
NG7 2SA
Tel: 0115 986 6566
Fax: 0115 986 0343
e danralley@hoteldesclos.com
Chef(s): Sat Bains
Owner(s): Mr D Ralley
Cost: *Alc* £38.50, set price L £18.95/D £35. ☺ H/wine £11
Times: Noon-2pm/7-9.30pm.
Closed Sun, L Sat, BHs
Additional: Children 8 yrs+
Seats: 40. Private dining room 14
Style: Classic
Smoking: No smoking in dining room

Award-winning head chef Sat Bains has an impressive CV. He was a member of the team that opened the first of Raymond Blanc's brasseries. Now he has arrived at this attractive restaurant, situated in converted Victorian farm buildings, and his enthusiasm for food shines through in a lively menu. Modern European in style, it might include roasted scallops with braised oxtail or pigeon with Puy lentils, roast baby onions and beetroot jus. Among the desserts you might find apple and marmalade ginger crumble or a 'superbly flavoured' pistachio crème brûlée.

Accommodation: 8 rooms (8 en suite) ★★
Directions: Telephone for directions

Merchants Restaurant

This is definitely the place to be seen in. An ultra modern eatery in the old lace market area, the Merchant's Restaurant boasts polished wooden floors, high-backed chairs, and an adventurous range of modern British food. Butternut squash soup might be followed by sea bass with crab couscous, and lemon tart.

Seats: 70. Private dining room 20. **Style:** Modern, Chic
Smoking: Air conditioning
Accommodation: 29 rooms (29 en suite) ★★★★
Directions: Follow town centre signs for Galleries of Justice, entrance is opposite

29/31 High Pavement, NG1 1HE
Tel: 0115 9589898
Fax: 0115 8523223
e reservations@lacemarkethotel.co.uk
Chef(s): Dean Rogers
Owner(s): Lace Market Hotel Ltd
Cost: *Alc* £22, set price L £12.50. ☺ ☺ H/wine £9.95
Times: Noon-2.30pm/6.30-10.30pm.
Closed L Sat
Additional: Sunday L. Bar food.
Children welcome

Rutland Square Hotel by the Castle NEW

St James Street, NG1 6FJ
Tel: 0115 941 1114
Fax: 0115 941 0014
 rutlandsquare@zoffanyhotels.co.uk
Chef(s): Adrian Todd
Owner(s): Zoffany Hotels
Cost: *Alc* £27, set price D £16.95. ☺
H/wine £12
Times: Dinner only, 7-10pm
Additional: Sunday L. Bar food.
Children welcome

Tucked behind the Regency facade is a comfortable, modern hotel. Dine in the informal Terrace Bar or the bright and stylish Woods Restaurant, where a modern menu offers plenty of Eastern spice (Lan Gui Fong King Scallops; breast of chicken marinated in ginger and oriental spices) as well as classics such as pan-fried foie gras or confit of duck.

Seats: 28. Private dining room 48
Style: Modern, Chic
Smoking: No smoking in dining room
Accommodation: 105 rooms (105 en suite) ★ ★ ★
Directions: Telephone for directions

Sonny's

3 Carlton Street, Hockley, NG1 1NL
Tel: 0115 947 3041
Fax: 0115 950 7776
Chef(s): David Hodgins
Owner(s): Ms R Mascarenhas
Cost: *Alc* £27.50, set price L £13.95.
☺ ☺ H/wine £10.45
Times: Noon-2.30pm/7-10.30pm.
Closed BHs
Additional: Sunday L. Children
welcome
Seats: 80
Style: Modern, Minimalist

Simple and arty, with attentive and friendly service, Sonny's is deservedly recognised as one of the county's best, housed in a handsome Grade II listed building. Both café and restaurant menus exhibit an awareness of modern trends, as in chick-pea, feta, red onion, tomato and chilli salad or chicken liver and foie gras parfait served with fig chutney. Main dishes take in chargrilled salmon with spinach and chive beurre blanc and pork saltimbocca with honey roast parsnips and cream sauce: seasonal vegetables or a salad of plum tomato, shallots and basil accompany. Dark chocolate brûlée and warm plum tart with pecan ice cream are typical desserts.

Smoking: No-smoking area; Air conditioning
Directions: Central Nottingham

RADCLIFFE ON TRENT   Map 8 SK63

The Yew Trees NEW

16 Shelford Road,
NG12 1BA

A village centre setting for this reincarnated guest house, comprising a delightful conservatory restaurant with palms and terracotta wash walls, a bar area and traditional dining room for small parties. An interesting modern British *carte* ranges through confit leg of duck with hoi-sin dressing, traditional sausage and mash, and naturally smoked haddock with cheese and tomato crust.

Tel: 0115 9333818
Fax: 0115 9333818
Chef(s): Clive Bernard Wisdom
Owner(s): Sonia Holmes
Cost: *Alc* £28. ☺ ☺ H/wine £9.95
Times: 12.15-1.30pm/7-9.30pm.
Closed Mon, L Tue & Sat, D Sun, New Year, BHs
Additional: Sunday L. Children welcome
Seats: 54. Private dining room
Style: Bistro Style, Modern
Smoking: No smoking in dining room; Air conditioning
Directions: From Nottingham take A52 towards Grantham. Take 1st turn signed to Radcliffe-on-Trent. In centre turn L into Shelford Road

England

OXFORDSHIRE

BANBURY
Map 4 SP44

Wroxton House Hotel

Hotel created from three cottages of golden Cotswold stone, with the addition of a clock tower and a conservatory lounge. The restaurant too, comprises three adjoining rooms with original beams and inglenook fireplaces. Fresh local produce is put to use in some robust fare, such as roasted saddle of Cotswold rabbit with lightly spiced Puy lentils, wild mushrooms and roasted baby navets coated in Madeira sauce. Pan-fried pheasant marinated in juniper and tarragon, and served on fondant potato and celeriac purée with foie gras comes with a rich and distinctive bay sauce.

Smoking: No smoking in dining room. Jacket and tie preferred
Civil licence: 50
Accommodation: 32 rooms (32 en suite) ★★★
Directions: From M40 J11 follow A422 (signposted Banbury, then Wroxton). After 3 miles, hotel on 1st right bend

Wroxton St Mary,
OX15 6QB
Tel: 01295 730777
Fax: 01295 730800
Chef(s): Hylton Bradley
Cost: Alc £39, set price L £13.95/ D £26. ☺ H/wine £12
Times: Noon-2pm/7-9.30pm.
Closed L Sat, 26 Dec-4 Jan
Additional: Sunday L. Bar food. Children welcome
Seats: 50. Private dining room 20
Style: Traditional, Country-house

BICESTER
Map 4 SP52

Bignell Park Hotel

With a dramatic gallery as a backdrop, the stage is set for a bit of culinary theatre at this beamed and painting-packed restaurant. Certainly the desserts in particular don't disappoint, with pastry outstanding in dishes like frangipane and fruit tart with ice cream. Portions are generous, and the menu offers fresh takes on confidently cooked dishes.

Chesterton, OX6 8UE
Tel: 01869 241444
Fax: 01869 241444
Chef(s): Graham Thomson
Owner(s): E.K Sorensen & M.A Young
Cost: Alc £30, set price L £20/ D £20. ☺ H/wine £11
Times: Noon-2pm/7-9.30pm.
Closed L Sun
Additional: Bar food L. Children 6 yrs+. Jacket and tie preferred
Seats: 60. Private dining room 16
Style: Country-house
Smoking: No smoking in dining room
Accommodation: 23 rooms (23 en suite) ★★
Directions: On A4095, Witney Road

BLEWBURY
Map 4 SU58

Blewbury Inn

A subtle Mediterranean feel to the décor, a brasher, earthy approach to the cooking. The menu changes weekly with a typical evening meal offering not insubstantial interest and adventure. Most dishes are not for the faint-hearted - a typical meal might open with onion and organic cider soup with a cheddar crust, this could be followed by medallions of beef fillet with truffle mash, red onion marmalade, broad beans and a port

London Road,
OX11 9PD
Tel: 01235 850496
Fax: 01235 850496
Chef(s): Franck Peigne
Owner(s): Mr & Mrs F R Peigne
Cost: Alc £25, set price L £25/D £25. ☺ ☺ H/wine £11.20

jus. Desserts are along trad lines with the likes of crème brûlée with blackcurrant sorbet. Lunchtime dishes tend towards a lighter style with baguettes, pasta and salads dominating.

Times: Noon-3pm/6-11pm.
Closed L Mon, D Sun
Additional: Sunday L. Bar food L.
Seats: 24. Private dining room 24
Style: Rustic, Country-house
Smoking: No smoking in dining room

Accommodation: 2 rooms (2 en suite)
Directions: On A417 between Wantage and Reading

BRITWELL SALOME   Map 4 SU69

The Goose

OX9 5LG
Tel: 01491 612304
Fax: 01491 614822
e barber@thegoose.freeserve.co.uk
Chef(s): Christopher Barber &
Michael North
Owner(s): Chris Barber
Cost: Alc £27.50, set price L £10/
D £25. ☺ H/wine £10.50
Times: Noon-3pm/6-11pm. Closed
Mon, D Sun, 25-26 Dec, 2-4 Jan

This popular lunch destination, close to the M40 - more intimate and atmospheric at night - delivers up-to-date traditional menus at kind, fixed prices. Terrine of foie gras with chicken and quince, rack of lamb on parsnip mash and a sharp lemon tart exceeded expectations. A friendly, informal team keeps a close eye on the service.

Additional: Sunday L. Bar food L. Children welcome
Seats: 30
Style: Modern
Smoking: No smoking in dining room. Jacket and tie preferred
Directions: M40 J6 take B4009 to Watlington and on towards Benson. Pub on R, 1.5 miles

---

BURFORD   Map 4 SP21

The Bay Tree

12-14 Sheep Street,
OX18 4LW
Tel: 01993 822791
Fax: 01993 823008
e baytree@cotswold-inns-
hotels.co.uk
Chef(s): Brian Andrews
Owner(s): Cotswold Inns & Hotels
Cost: Alc £35, set price L £15.95/
D £24.95. ☺
Times: Noon-1.45pm/7-9pm.
Additional: Sunday L. Bar food L.
Children welcome

With low ceilings, real fires and flagstone floors, this is everything a Cotswold inn ought to be. The restaurant overlooks a walled garden and serves a selection of modern, British based dishes. These might include twice baked goats' cheese soufflé with tomato salad, followed by a trio of fillets with wild garlic rösti and baby vegetables.

Seats: 70. Private dining room 8. Jacket and tie preferred
Style: Traditional
Smoking: No smoking in dining room
Civil licence: 30
Accommodation: 21 rooms (21 en suite) ★ ★ ★
Directions: Sheep St off main street in centre of Burford

England

England

Inn For All Seasons

The Barringtons,
OX18 4TN
Tel: 01451 844324
Fax: 01451 844375
e sharp@innforallseasons.com
Chef(s): Matthew Sharp
Owner(s): Matthew Sharp
Cost: *Alc* £19.50. ☺ ☺ H/wine £9.95
Times: 11.30-2.30pm/6-9.30pm.
Additional: Sunday L. Bar food.
Children welcome
Seats: 40. Private dining room 50
Style: Traditional, Rustic
Smoking: No-smoking area; no pipes
Accommodation: 10 rooms (10 en
suite) ★ ★ ★
Directions: On A40 Cheltenham, 3m
from Burford

Taking justifiable pride in providing a warm, homely
atmosphere, this former coaching inn is a good choice for those
seeking stress-free dining (without any loss of quality.) Expect
grilled Hereford rump steak with a shallot and Brouilly wine
sauce, or tagliatelle in a creamy wild mushroom sauce and
Parmesan shavings.

Jonathan's at the Angel

14 Witney Street,
OX18 4SN
Tel: 01993 822714
Fax: 01993 822069
e jo@theangel-uk.com
Chef(s): Jonathan Lewis &
Adam Strange
Owner(s): Jonathan &
Josephine Lewis
Cost: *Alc* £19.95. ☺ ☺
H/wine £12.75
Times: Noon-2pm/7-9.30pm.
Closed Mon, L Tue-Wed,
D Sun, 20 Jan-9 Feb
Additional: Sunday L. Bar food L.
Children 9 yrs+
Seats: 34. Private dining room 18

The exterior of this 16th-century coaching inn entices visitors
with its pale Cotswold stone, pretty window boxes and painted
signs. Inside you'll find a brasserie style restaurant of three
cosy rooms, each with white walls, a beamed ceiling and chunky
pine tables. There's also a pretty walled garden for summer
dining. The menu reflects the simple, earthy style of the décor:
European dishes might include an 'excellent' fish soup, brought
to the table in a huge terrine for you to help yourself, or pan
fried rib steak with girolle mushrooms. Look out for intriguing
desserts such as coffee and cardamom ice cream.

Style: Rustic, French
Smoking: No smoking in dining room
Accommodation: 3 rooms (3 en suite) ♦♦♦♦
Directions: From A40, turn off at Burford rdbt, down hill 1st R
into Swan Lane, 1st L to Pytts Lane, L at end into Witney Street

England

The Lamb Inn

A fine 15th-century Cotswold stone inn with flagstone floors, log fires and gleaming antiques. Light lunches are normally taken in the bar, while restaurant dining justifiably retains its touch of traditional formality. Two or three courses at fixed prices offer the likes of rabbit and chicken gallantine with cranberry and truffle oil dressing, followed by braised shin of veal or halibut fillet with a creamy scallop and dill risotto. Desserts follow classical lines, as in an apricot tarte Tatin or mango cheesecake with raspberry sauce; alternatively a platter of British cheeses with spiced apple chutney.

Smoking: No smoking in dining room
Accommodation: 15 rooms ★ ★ ★
Directions: 1st L as you descend on the High Street

Sheep Street, OX18 4LR
Tel: 01993 823155
Fax: 01993 822228
Chef(s): Pascal Clavaud
Owner(s): Mr & Mrs R de Wolf
Cost: Set price L £20/D £27.
H/wine £10
Times: Dinner only, 7-9pm.
Closed 25-26 Dec
Additional: Sunday L. Bar food L.
Children welcome
Seats: 50
Style: Traditional

CHALGROVE   Map 4 SU69

Red Lion Inn

115 High Street, OX44 7SS
Tel: 01865 890625
Fax: 01865 890795
Chef(s): James Barter
Owner(s): Jonathan & Maggie Hewitt
Cost: Alc £18. ☺ ☺ H/wine £9.75
Times: Noon-2pm/7-11pm.
Closed D Sun, Xmas, New Year
Additional: Sunday L. Bar food.
Children welcome
Seats: 50
Style: Rustic
Smoking: No smoking in dining room
Directions: Telephone for directions

Expect an imaginative pub menu offering perennial favourites with a modern twist at this civilised rural hostelry set back from the village street and a babbling brook. Served in smart, modern and informal surroundings, dishes range from old Oxford sausages with spicy red cabbage and mash or fresh beer-battered cod and chips, to seared loin of lamb with roasted spiced aubergine and port jus. Desserts include a delicious melting chocolate tart with home-made ice cream. Lighter lunchtime options.

CHINNOR   Map 4 SP70

Sir Charles Napier

A rustic setting with intimate lighting and a hint of wood smoke in winter. The furnishings are eclectic: interesting old chairs and tables are surrounded by a changing display of modern paintings and sculptures, many of which are for sale. The menu reflects this variety, combining ideas from Britain, France and Europe: a meal might include Mediterranean fish soup, lamb shank and vanilla crème brûlée. Flavours are well balanced and ingredients of the highest quality. Over 400 wines add to the enjoyment, as does the professional, attentive service.

Smoking: No-smoking area; no pipes; Air conditioning
Directions: M40 J6 to Chinnor. Turn R at rdbt, up hill for 2 miles to Sprigg's Alley

Sprigg's Alley, OX9 4BX
Tel: 01494 483011
Fax: 01494 485311
Chef(s): Jose Cau
Owner(s): Julie Griffiths
Cost: Alc £28.50, set price L
£14.50/D £15.50. ☺ ☺
H/wine £12.95
Times: Noon-2.30pm/6.30-10pm.
Closed Mon, D Sun, 25-26 Dec
Additional: Sunday L. Bar food L.
Children 7yrs+
Seats: 75. Private dining room 45
Style: Traditional

England

CHIPPING NORTON

Map 4 SP32

Chav Brasserie

NEW

The black-and-white fronted building with its trendy signage at the top end of town is beamed inside and painted in sunny yellow and blue. A comfortable combination of old and new runs from the fine art on show to a jazzy bistro menu that relies in large part on up-to-date continental influences. Home-cured bresaola with Parmesan and mustard mayonnaise vies for attention with Thai-spiced prawn samosas with lime pickle amongst the half dozen starters; with smoked haddock with potato and chive tortilla, penne pasta with baby artichokes, spinach and roquefort and confit duck with chick peas, tomato and coriander typical of choices that follow. To round off, various European cheeses are served with toasted onion bread; lemongrass, lime leaf and coconut brûlée comes with almond biscuits and stem ginger sorbet; and home-made fudge accompanies the selection of continental coffees. Some twenty wines, including champagne, served by the glass offer compelling options from old and new worlds. These premises formerly housed Chavignol which has moved to Shipston on Stour, Warwickshire.

Lovells Ltd, 7 Horsefair, OX7 5AL
Tel: 01608 645968
Fax: 01608 646794
e chavignol@virginbiz.com
Chef(s): Paul Haywood
Owner(s): Chavignol Ltd
Cost: *Alc* £18. ☺ ☺ H/wine £8.50
Times: 11.30-2.30pm/6.30-10pm.
Closed Sun, L Mon
Additional: Children welcome
Seats: 30
Style: French
Smoking: No smoking in dining room
Directions: Main road on Banbury side

CLANFIELD

Map 4 SP20

Plough at Clanfield

A stone-built Elizabethan manor house standing proud in its Cotswold village position. The restaurant décor is traditional (with its white and pink linen and padded leather menus) tying in with a largely classical French and traditional English approach to cuisine. Duck and wild mushroom pâté with red onion marmalade and continental leaves is one of a number of well judged starters to make a regular appearance on the menu. Mains such as fillet of Aberdeen Angus beef with fresh tagliatelle and a green peppercorn sauce are complemented nicely by the likes of crème brûlée with baby figs marinated in rum.

Smoking: No smoking in dining room
Accommodation: 12 rooms (12 en suite) ★ ★ ★
Directions: At Junct of B4020 & A4095, between Farringdon and Witney. 15 miles W of OXford

Bourton Road, OX18 2RB
Tel: 01367 810222
Fax: 01367 810596
e ploughatclanfield@hotmail.com
Chef(s): Rosemary Hodges
Owner(s): Mr & Mrs J C Hodges
Cost: Set price L £17.50/D £32.50.
☺ H/wine £11.75
Times: Noon-2pm/7-9.30pm.
Closed L Mon, 26-29 Dec
Additional: Sunday L. Bar food L.
Children 12 yrs+. Vegetarian by request only
Seats: 35. Private dining room 10
Style: Country-House

DEDDINGTON

Map 4 SP43

Dexters Restaurant

The first thing that strikes the eye when entering Dexters is the bar top created from a huge piece of rough hewn wood. In this dramatic bar lighter dishes are available, but the serious eating takes place upstairs in the bright modern restaurant. Changing every four weeks, the *carte* has a generous display of fashionable dishes such as Thai fish cakes or red onion and Mozzarella tart. A popular dish is an open ravioli of asparagus, artichokes and roast peppers, glazed with crème fraîche and Parmesan, or try wild sea bass on a ratatouille sauce with basil oil and Modena vinegar.

Directions: Village centre, A4260 from Banbury. L at lights

Market Place, OX15 0SE
Tel: 01869 338813
Chef(s): Jamie Dexter Harrison
Owner(s): J D Harrison, R Blackburn
Cost: *Alc* £26.50, set price L
£15.50/D £19.50. ☺ H/wine £11.50
Times: Noon-2.15pm/7-9.15pm.
Closed Sun-Mon
Additional: Bar food L.
Seats: 60
Style: Informal, Modern
Smoking: No pipes; no cigars

DORCHESTER-ON-THAMES   Map 4 SU59

George Hotel

Honest and accomplished cooking is served in this lofty beamed restaurant in the centre of the village. Fresh produce is a strong feature and presentation is very good. Start with char-grilled scallops with pancetta bacon and asparagus and follow with the likes of pan-fried halibut fillet on parsley mash with morel mushroom sauce.

Additional: Sunday L. Bar food. Children welcome
Seats: 35. Private dining room 30
Style: Modern
Smoking: No smoking in dining room
Accommodation: 18 rooms (18 en suite) ★ ★ ★
Directions: In the town centre

25 High Street, OX10 7HH
Tel: 01865 340404
Fax: 01865 341620
Chef(s): Simon Quarrie
Owner(s): Brian Griffin
Cost: Alc £30, set price D £20-£30.
☺ ☺ H/wine £9.10
Times: Dinner only, 7-9.30pm.
Closed Xmas, New Year

White Hart Hotel

An historic inn that seems quite at home sharing this charming village with the well-known abbey and a plethora of antique shops. Ancient setting, modern cooking - an appealing combination as ever, here yielding the likes of warm salad of beef fillet, and leek and smoked duck tagliatelle.

Tel: 01865 340074
Fax: 01865 341082
e whitehart.dorchester@virgin.net
Chef(s): Sean Harris
Owner(s): Tasty Blackboard Co Ltd.
Cost: Alc £22.50. ☺ H/wine £10.50
Times: Noon-2.30pm/6.30-9.30pm.
Additional: Sunday L. Bar food. Children welcome
Seats: 40. Private dining room 16
Style: Country-House
Smoking: No-smoking area
Accommodation: 24 rooms (24 en suite) ★ ★ ★
Directions: Village centre, just off A415/ A4074

High Street, OX10 7HN

FARINGDON   Map 4 SU29

The Lamb
at Buckland

If a short stroll round a pretty village followed by an excellent meal in a traditional country pub is what you seek you need look no further. Look forward to the likes of roast breast of Lunesdale duckling with an apple and Calvados sauce, or lobster and shellfish fricassée.

Seats: 65. Private dining room 18
Smoking: No smoking in dining room
Accommodation: 4 rooms
Directions: Midway between Oxford and Swindon on A420. 4 miles E of Faringdon

Buckland, SN7 8QN
Tel: 01367 870484
Fax: 01367 870675
Chef(s): Paul Barnard
Owner(s): Paul Barnard
Cost: Alc £25 H/wine £10.65
Times: Noon-2pm/7-9.30pm.
Closed 25-26 Dec
Additional: Sunday L. Bar food. Children welcome

England

FARINGDON *Continued*

Map 4 SU29

Sudbury House Hotel

A business function-minded hotel that has sensibly put some thought into making the restaurant a welcoming retreat for stressed delegates. The benefits may be shared by the casual diner and signature dishes such as Mediterranean style chicken fillets, home-made sausage of wild boar, and banana parfait certainly have strong appeal.

Seats: 150. Private dining room 50
Smoking: No smoking in dining room; Air conditioning
Accommodation: 49 rooms (49 en suite) ★★★
Directions: Off A420 signposted Folly Hill

London Street, SN7 8AA
Tel: 01367 241272
Fax: 01367 242346
e restaurant@sudburyhouse.co.uk
Chef(s): Karl Fox
Cost: Set price D £19.95. ☺ ☺
H/wine £11
Times: 12.30-1.45pm/7-9.15pm.
Closed L Sat
Additional: Sunday L. Bar food.
Children welcome

GORING

Map 4 SU68

The Leatherne Bottel

RG8 0HS
Tel: 01491 872667
Fax: 01491 875308
e leathernebottel@aol.com
Chef(s): Julia Storey
Owner(s): A Bonnet
Cost: *Alc* £45, set price D £19.50.
☺ ☺ H/wine £14.50
Times: 12.30-2pm/7-9pm.
Closed D Sun, 25 Dec, New Year
Additional: Children 10yrs+
Seats: 45
Style: Chic
Smoking: No pipes
Directions: M4 J12 or M40 J6, signposted from B4009 towards Wallingford

Charming restaurant on the banks of the Thames, approached by a winding lane. The style is modern British with some imaginative twists, and the dishes rely on quality ingredients, some of which are home-grown. Scallops with smoked paprika, fennel, cherry tomatoes, spring onion and mushrooms sounds a bit busy, but the dishes are generally well-conceived and vibrant. Main courses too are noted for their bright flavours and skilful execution - breast of chicken wrapped in pancetta served with lemon thyme for example. The pudding, a good lemon tart, was eclipsed by the accompanying sorbet - the very essence of melon.

GREAT MILTON

Map 4 SP60

Le Manoir Aux Quat' Saisons

@@@@@

OX44 7PD
Tel: 01844 278881
Fax: 01844 278847
e lemanoir@blanc.co.uk
Chef(s): Raymond Blanc &
Gary Jones
Owner(s): Raymond Blanc
Cost: *Alc* £85, set price L £42
Times: 12.15-2.45pm/7.15-9.45pm
Additional: Sunday L.
Children welcome
Seats: 100. Private dining room 50
Style: Modern French
Smoking: No smoking in dining room;
Air conditioning
Civil licence: 50

Whilst there has been much change in recent times - massive refurbishment with a cleaner more modish look - the heart of Le Manoir still beats the same rhythm. The only restaurant in this 10th edition of the AA guide to have started out with five Rosettes and still have them in this 2002 edition.

Take one look at the menu and it speaks of real affection for food, its preparation and its appreciation. The economy of the cooking style with the apparently simple treatment of the very best ingredients and complete absence of frippery is a lesson in the real laws of cooking at the highest level. Not that this is simply classic French cuisine; there is a lightness of touch and dexterity apparent that has a distinctly modern feel about it. Ballotine of foie gras, for instance arrives in a comfortable partnership with French beans and truffle salad, the whole dish lifted by a precision and balance that belies the fairly prosaic feel of the constituent parts. Similarly, langoustine ravioli comes with the shellfish wrapped in spinach and wafer thin pasta, a radiant shellfish *jus* and just a smidgen of tarragon sabayon in what has been described as an "exquisitely judged" combination.

Of course, the whole approach rests on having the best raw materials available and the advantages of an organic kitchen garden to die for are apparent in the likes of roasted monkfish with mustard beurre blanc and garden vegetables where the latter almost outshone the excellence of the fish itself. The menu gourmand with its eight sampler courses has its fair share of takers (unless you're going back regularly there's some sense in making the most of it) and some of the great dishes of the Manoir canon are featured in "Les Spécialitiés du Manoir". The atmosphere is not precious and staff (especially the sommeliers) are skilled and enthusiastic hosts. Le Manoir has become something of a legend, its achievement is that it continues to live up to its exalted status.

Accommodation: 32 rooms (32 en suite) ★ ★ ★ ★
Directions: From M40 J7 follow A329 towards Wallingford. At 1 mile turn R, signposted Great Milton Manor

HENLEY-ON-THAMES

Map 4 SU78

Red Lion Hotel

With the River Thames obligingly gliding past the hotel's doorstep a tranquil, even glamorous atmosphere is assured. The restaurant, like the hotel, is nicely decorated with period details a-plenty including exposed timbers, panelling and luxurious rugs. A confident, skilful approach in the kitchen results in simple, bold statements such as home-cured gravadlax with a dill mustard sauce followed perhaps by roast Norfolk turkey with a chestnut stuffing, cocotte potatoes and a just rôti. Raspberry crème brûlée with ginger biscuits or profiteroles filled with a white chocolate mousse also stand up well.

Smoking: No pipes; no cigars
Accommodation: 26 rooms (26 en suite) ★ ★ ★
Directions: On the R when entering Henley by the bridge

@@

Hart Street, RG9 2AR
Tel: 01491 572161
Fax: 01491 410039
e reservations@redlionhenley.co.uk
Chef(s): Stephen Fowler
Owner(s): The Miller Family
Cost: *Alc* £29.50, set price L £16. ☺
H/wine £12
Times: Noon-2.30pm/7-9.45pm.
Additional: Sunday L. Bar food L.
Children welcome
Seats: 35. Private dining room 80.
Jacket and tie preferred
Style: Modern

HORTON-CUM-STUDLEY

Map 4 SP51

Studley Priory Hotel

OX33 1AZ
Tel: 01865 351203
Fax: 01865 351613
e res@studley-priory.co.uk
Chef(s): Simon Crannage
Owner(s): Jason Adams
Cost: *Alc* £25, set price L £20/
D £27.50. H/wine £14
Times: Noon-1.45pm/7-9.30pm
Additional: Sunday L. Bar food.
Children welcome
Seats: 40. Private dining room 30
Style: Classic
Smoking: No smoking in dining room
Civil licence: 50
Accommodation: 18 rooms (18 en
suite) ★ ★ ★

Rising proudly above the rolling landscape, this Elizabethan house was founded in the 12th century as a Benedictine nunnery. It is now a beacon for travellers seeking a tasteful resting-place within its solid walls. Equally accomplished is the cooking, where top quality raw ingredients are transformed into dynamic and genuinely exciting dishes. Amidst starched table cloths, stone-mullioned windows and fresh flowers, the *carte* and set menus offer a vibrant contrast - curry and pea risotto with poached smoked haddock and egg ravioli, and roast venison with turnip fondant, carrot purée and port sauce. Canon of lamb recently approached perfection, served with wilted spinach and a stunning sage infused ravioli, whilst assiette of chocolate included both an exemplary tart and fondant. Other successes have included hot banana soufflé with coffee ice cream and butterscotch sauce, or maybe passion fruit and grenadine parfait. An extensive wine list matches the ambition of the food.

Directions: At top of hill in village

KINGHAM

Map 4 SP22

Mill House Hotel

A converted mill where the preservation of original details such as the wheel and ovens adds a great deal of character. For a former mill the bread is nothing out of the ordinary, but dishes such as baked fillet of salmon with a Champagne and tarragon-scented cream sauce are very successful.

OX7 6UH
Tel: 01608 658188
Fax: 01608 658492
e stay@millhousehotel.co.uk
Chef(s): Jeremy Collar
Owner(s): John Parslow
Cost: Set price L £13.95/D £22.75.
☺ ☺ H/wine £11.95
Times: Noon-2pm/7-9pm.
Additional: Sunday L. Bar food L.
Children welcome

Seats: 70. Private dining room 50
Style: Traditional
Smoking: No smoking in dining room
Accommodation: 23 rooms (23 en suite) ★ ★ ★
Directions: Just off B4450, on S outskirts of village

England

The Tollgate Inn **NEW**

Church Street, OX7 6YA
Tel: 01608 658389
Telephone for further details

Robust, full-flavoured dishes are skilfully prepared from local
organic produce at this stylishly refurbished small hotel set in
an off-the-beaten-track Cotswold village. Well balanced daily
menus may list a gutsy spiced chorizo sausage, chickpea, butter
bean and vegetable broth for starters, followed by a moist and
tender pork cutlet with caraway braised cabbage, black pudding
and paprika sauce, or grilled salmon with beetroot and
pancetta. Rhubarb and poached berry fruit fool or English
cheeses to finish.

MIDDLETON STONEY Map 4 SP52

Jersey Arms Hotel

OX6 8SE
Tel: 01869 343234
Fax: 01869 343565
e jerseyarms@bestwestern.co.uk
Chef(s): F Hamilton
Owner(s): Donald Livingstone
Cost: Alc £21. ☺ ☺ H/wine £9.75
Times: Noon-2.15pm/6.30-9.30pm.
Additional: Sunday L. Bar food.
Children welcome
Seats: 50. Private dining room 18
Style: Modern
Smoking: No smoking in dining room
Accommodation: 20 rooms (20 en
suite) ★ ★
Directions: On B430, 3 miles from
Bicester, 10 miles N of Oxford

There's a friendly, village inn feel to this hotel restaurant. The
décor is Mediterranean-meets-Old England, with bare beams
and warm terracotta walls. A similar diversity is evident in the
menu, which offers everything from Thai style crab cakes with
steamed rice and chilli sauce to rib eye steak with fries.

MILTON COMMON Map 4 SP60

The Oxford Belfry

OX9 2JW
Tel: 01844 279381
Fax: 01844 279624
e oxfordbelfry@marstonhotels.com
Chef(s): Robert Hubbard
Owner(s): Marston Hotels
Cost: Alc £34.50,
set price L £19.50/D £27.
H/wine £12.60
Times: Noon-2pm/7.30-9.30pm.
Closed L Sat
Additional: Sunday L. Bar food.
Children welcome
Seats: 130. Private dining room 50

Impressively smart and comfortable hotel with restaurant to
match. Modern British menus tempt with dishes like smoked
trout and mackerel mousse studded with pink peppercorns on a
salad with balsamic dressing, and seared calves' liver with
shallot and black pudding mash finished with root vegetables
and a redcurrant jus. A stunning courtyard is the place for a
pre-dinner drink.

Style: Formal, Country-house
Smoking: No smoking in dining room; Air conditioning
Civil licence: 400
Accommodation: 130 rooms (130 en suite) ★ ★ ★ ★
Directions: From S: M40 J7. Top of slip road turn R, immediate
L (50yds). From N: M40 J8a. Top of slip road turn 1st L after golf
club. Take 1st R, hotel 1m on L

OXFORD

Map 4 SP50

Cotswold Lodge Hotel

66a Banbury Road, OX2 6JP
Tel: 01865 512121
Fax: 01865 512490
e cotswoldlodge@netscapeonline.
co.uk
Chef(s): Garin Chapman
Owner(s): Mrs O Peros
Cost: Alc £35.75,
set price L £22.85/D £22.85. ☺
H/wine £13.95
Times: Noon-2.30pm/6.30-10.30pm.
Additional: Sunday L. Bar food.
Children welcome
Seats: 48. Private dining room 80.
Jacket and tie preferred
Style: Classic, Formal
Smoking: No smoking in dining room
Civil licence:
Accommodation: 49 rooms (49 en
suite) ★ ★ ★ ★

This Victorian house has been impressively restored and refurbished, the Georgian style restaurant offering a comfortable dining environment. An interesting selection of dishes combines ideas from Britain and the Mediterranean: perhaps seared foie gras with brioche and mango dressing followed by fillet of halibut with wilted spinach and a chardonnay sauce.

Directions: Take A4165 (Banbury Road) off A40 ring road, hotel 1.5m on left

Fallowfields
Country House Hotel

Faringdon Road,
Kingston Bagpuize,
Southmoor OX13 5BH
Tel: 01865 820416
Fax: 01865 321275
e stay@fallowfields.com
Chef(s): Alan Jefferson Mackney
Owner(s): Mr & Mrs A Lloyd
Cost: Alc £30, set price L £15-£25/
D £19.95-£29.95. ☺ ☺
H/wine £14.25
Times: Noon-2.30pm/6-9.30pm.
Closed 25-26 Dec
Additional: Bar food L.
Children 8yrs+
Seats: 72. Private dining room 12
Smoking: No smoking in dining room
Civil licence: 100
Accommodation: 10 rooms (10 en
suite) ★ ★ ★

The well tended gardens provide most of the kitchen's vegetables as well as an attractive view for diners. A supplier's list on the menu further demonstrates a genuine commitment to local sourcing. The standard does vary a little - it is always decent and occasionally excellent - with a subtle, perfectly seasoned chicken and leek spring roll being an example of the latter.

Directions: From A34 at Abingdon take A415 (Whitney). At mini roundabout in Kingston Bagpuize turn L. Fallowfields is 1 mile on L

England

Gee's Restaurant

61 Banbury Road, OX2 6PE
Tel: 01865 553540
Fax: 01865 310308
e info@gees-restaurant.co.uk
Chef(s): Michael Wright
Owner(s): Jeremy Mogford
Cost: *Alc* £30, set price L £9.50/
D £22.95. ☺ ☺ H/wine £12
Times: Noon-2.30pm/6-11pm.
Closed 25-26 Dec
Additional: Sunday L.
Children welcome
Seats: 75
Style: Chic
Smoking: No smoking in dining room;
Air conditioning
Directions: M40 J8. From Ring Road
take Banbury Rd to city centre. 1m R
after N Parade

Conservatory restaurant a few minutes' walk from the city centre. It dates from 1900 and was originally a florist and greengrocers. Excellent Tuscan bread puts the taste buds on alert for marinated aubergine with goats' cheese, basil and garlic, and a confit of lamb shank served with butter beans, mint pesto and tomato vinaigrette.

La Gousse d'Ail   NEW

268 Woodstock Road,
OX2 7NW
Tel: 01865 311936
Fax: 01865 516613
e info@lagoussedail.co.uk
Chef(s): Jonathan Wright
Owner(s): Jayne & Jonathan Wright
Cost: *Alc* £44, set price L £22.50-£55.
H/wine £12
Times: Noon-2.30pm/7-10.30pm.
Closed Mon, D Sun, 2 wks Jan
Additional: Sunday L. Children
welcome
Seats: 75
Style: Sophisticated, Contemporary
Smoking: No smoking in dining room
Civil licence: 100

With a glossy pedigree that includes head chef at Le Manoir aux Quat' Saisons, expectations were inevitably sky high when Jonathan Wright took over and renamed Oxford's successful Lemon Tree Restaurant. Since then he has scarcely put a foot wrong, and the cosmetic makeover from brash yellows to subtle browns and beiges is more than skin deep. Set lunch offers the best value (though a planned menu du jour will make dinner more affordable too), with its tiny selection covering parfait of foie gras, roast guinea fowl with fresh morels, and pan-fried skate with brandade. Foie gras features heavily on the *carte* too, along with sea bass, red mullet and brill appropriately dressed and sauced, and daily specials like roast saddle of lamb and côte de boeuf. Presentation is exceptional, and roast venison with caramelised endive was a picture of perfection. Desserts reach their own dizzy heights, and the wine list is fairly priced.

Directions: From London M40, take A40 to Oxford. Follow A40 towards Cheltenham but turn off onto Woodstock Rd toward city centre. 0.25 mile on L. Car park at rear

England

Old Bank Hotel

A skilfully restored former banking hall houses Quod, a brasserie that neighbours a peaceful courtyard for a welcome contrast to the hustle and bustle of the high street. A fairly cosmopolitan clientele tuck into a menu offering dishes such as pizza al salmone or a chargrilled rib-eye steak, served with home-made chips and sage butter.

Seats: 150. Private dining room 24
Style: Modern, Italian
Smoking: No-smoking area; no pipes; Air conditioning
Accommodation: 43 rooms (43 en suite) ★ ★ ★ ★
Directions: Approach city centre via Headington. Over Magdalen Bridge into high street. Hotel 75yds on L

92-94 High Street, OX1 4BN
Tel: 01865 799599
Fax: 01865 799598
e info@oldbank-hotel.co.uk
Chef(s): Alburto Brunelli
Owner(s): Mr J Mogford
Cost: *Alc* £20.50, set price L £12.70.
☺ ☺ H/wine £9.95
Times: Noon-11pm.
Closed 25-26 Dec
Additional: Children welcome

Le Petit Blanc

71-72 Walton Street, OX2 6AG
Tel: 01865 510999
Fax: 01865 510700
Chef(s): Martin White
Owner(s): M R Blanc
Cost: *Alc* £25, set price L £15/D £15.
☺ ☺ H/wine £10.20
Times: Noon-3pm/6-11pm.
Closed 25-Dec
Additional: Sunday L.
Children welcome
Seats: 150. Private dining room 20
Style: Modern, Bistro-Style

Of course the décor is cutting edge (Terence Conran), of course the cuisine is high quality. Perhaps less expected are the great efforts made to be genuinely accommodating to the customer such as the provision of a playroom for children on weekends between 12 noon and 3pm. The restaurant is not above providing a 'fresh fast food' option Monday to Friday (12 noon to 7pm) featuring a selection of salads. All of this makes for a friendly, buzzing atmosphere in which to enjoy the full dinner option, featuring brasserie style dishes along the lines of roast wild pigeon with cabbage, chestnuts and a port jus.

Smoking: No-smoking area; no cigars; Air conditioning
Directions: From centre of Oxford, N up St Giles, L down Little Clarendon St and R at end of Walton Street

 Indicates a restaurant that has told us they offer a two-course lunch for less than £15

 Indicates a restaurant that has told us they offer a three-course dinner for less than £25

STADHAMPTON
Map 4 SU69

The Crazy Bear Hotel

Bear Lane,
OX44 7UR
Tel: 01865 890714
Fax: 01865 400481

An unassuming 16th century pub exterior belies a strikingly flamboyant interior. Think zebra skin wall hanging, think stuffed bear, think subdued lighting. A selection from the fixed-price menu might open with roast pumpkin soup scented with rosemary and sweet chilli, followed by local wild mushroom risotto, or Cumberland sausages with pomme purée and onion gravy. The à la *carte* menu is more uncompromisingly French with the likes of whole lobster with a tomato and shallot sauce proving a great temptation. Chocolate crème brûlée, sticky toffee pudding and chocolate marquise typify the desserts.

Chef(s): Jason Fretwell
Owner(s): Jason Hunt
Cost: Set price L £18.95/D £18.95.
☺ ☺ H/wine £12.50

STOP PRESS
Change of Chef

Times: Noon-3pm/7pm-Midnight.
Closed Mon, D Sun, 24 Dec-4 Jan
Additional: Sunday L. Bar food. Children welcome
Seats: 50. Private dining room 36
Style: Chic
Smoking: No-smoking area; Air conditioning
Accommodation: 12 rooms (12 en suite) ♦♦♦
Directions: From London leave M40 at J7 turn L onto A329, continue for 5 miles, L after Petrol Station and L again into Bear Lane

Thai Thai
NEW

at The Crazy Bear Hotel,
Bear Lane, OX44 7UR

The Crazy Bear is a trendy pub with rooms and two busy eateries. Thai Thai, the cosy restaurant on the lower floor, offers an extensive menu of nearly 50 dishes and gets a 'some of the best Thai food I've tasted' rating, notably for the quality of the ingredients and the clarity of the flavours. Set menus include a plentiful variety of dishes and are particularly good value for money. Thai desserts are not available, and this is probably wise as they are a bit of an acquired taste.

Tel: 01865 890714
Fax: 01865 400481
Chef(s): Anusak Thepdamrongchaikagul
Owner(s): Jason Hunt
Cost: *Alc* £19.20, set price L £19/D £19. ☺ ☺ H/wine £12.50
Times: Noon-3pm/7-10pm. Closed L Sun
Additional: Bar food. Children welcome
Seats: 50. Private dining room 30
Style: Modern Chic
Smoking: No smoking in dining room; Air conditioning
Accommodation: 12 rooms (12 en suite) ♦♦♦♦
Directions: From London leave M40 at J7 turn L onto A329, continue for 5 miles, L after Petrol Station and L again into Bear Lane

England

STEEPLE ASTON
Map 4 SP42

The Holt Hotel

Hopcroft's Holt, OX25 5QQ
Tel: 01869 340259
Fax: 01869 340865
✉ info@holthotel-oxford.co.uk
Chef(s): Paul Sherriff
Cost: Alc £30, set price L £14.95/
D £24. ☺ ☺ H/wine £10.95
Times: 12.30-2pm/7-9.30pm.
Closed L Sat, D Sun, Xmas, New Year
Additional: Sunday L. Bar food.
Children welcome
Seats: 30. Private dining room 24.
Jacket and tie preferred
Style: Modern
Smoking: No smoking in dining room
Civil licence: 200
Accommodation: 86 rooms (86 en
suite) ★ ★ ★
Directions: 8 miles from J10 of the
M40 on the B430 and B4030.

The resident ghost of ruthless highwayman Claude Duval provides a theme for both the 'Highwayman's Bar' (serving decent pub grub) and the more formal Duval's Restaurant. Choose the latter if you are keen to plunder the riches of Scottish salmon and poached shellfish in a light saffron sauce and other similarly tempting dishes.

STONOR
Map 4 SU78

Stonor Arms Hotel

RG9 6HE
Tel: 01491 638866
Fax: 01491 638863
✉ stonorarms.hotel@virgin.net
Cost: Alc £36.50, set price L £15.95/
D £25. ☺ ☺ H/wine £11.50
Times: Noon-2pm/7-9.30pm.
Additional: Sunday L. Bar food.
Children welcome
Seats: 50. Private dining room 26
Style: Traditional
Smoking: No smoking in dining room
Civil licence: 50
Accommodation: 10 rooms (10 en
suite) ★ ★ ★
Directions: In centre of village

Rolling Oxfordshire countryside and a pretty village set the scene for this comfortable 18th-century inn-cum-country house. In summer, enjoy pre-prandial drinks in the well tended walled garden and then dine in the airy conservatory, while in winter retire from the cosy lounge into the traditionally-styled restaurant with its dark red walls and open fire. The kitchen weaves some interesting variations around French provincial cooking in terrine of foie gras, duck and quail, seared langoustine with confit tomato and truffle potato, and assiette of venison with white bean casserole. Alternatively, the carte may offer cannelloni of rabbit with watercress soup, roast scallops with pea purée, pancetta and red wine jus and, for pudding, pecan and praline parfait with prunes in syrup and caramelised pecans.

England

THAME
Map 4 SP70

Spread Eagle Hotel

Cornmarket, OX9 2BW
Tel: 01844 213661
Fax: 01844 261380
e enquiries@spreadeaglehotel.
fsnet.co.uk
Chef(s): Michael Thomas
Owner(s): Mr D Barrington
Cost: Alc £24.95, set price L £18.95-
£24.95/D £10.95-£24.95. ☺ ☺
H/wine £10.95
Times: 12.30-2pm/7.30-10pm.
Closed D Sun, 28-30 Dec
Additional: Sunday L. Bar food.
Children welcome
Seats: 65. Private dining room 20
Style: Traditional, French
Smoking: No pipes; no cigars
Civil licence: 200
Accommodation: 33 rooms (33 en
suite) ★ ★ ★

A relaxing, pine panelled restaurant that serving an inspiring selection of classic and modern dishes. British and French in style, these might include Dover sole pan-fried with nut brown butter or medallions of beef fillet with shallot, Dijon mustard crust and a Madeira jus. Pleasantly located in a red brick coaching inn.

Directions: M40 – J6 from S, J8 from N. Town centre on A418 (Oxford to Aylesbury road)

The Swan at Tetsworth   NEW

High Street, Tetsworth
Tel: 01844 281182
Fax: 01844 281770
e restaurant@theswan.co.uk
Chef(s): Naseem Salam
Owner(s): Swan Holdings Ltd.
Cost: Alc £25. ☺ ☺ H/wine £11.95
Times: Noon-2.15pm/7-9.30pm.
Closed D Sun, Mon, 25-26 Dec
Additional: Sunday L. Bar food.
Children welcome
Seats: 55. Private dining room 12
Style: Rustic, Country-House
Smoking: No-smoking area

This large rambling building in the heart of the village is as much vast antiques emporium as welcoming restaurant. The dining room has its fair share of antiquated charm with an original uneven wooden floor, exposed brickwork and large paintings glowing in the light of a roaring log fire. This is not the place to go for a speedy lunch - frenetic haste would seem something of an affront to the ancient dignity of the place - but it is ideal for a lazy Sunday afternoon. With dishes such as sea bass with olive mash and pesto this is also a good bet for a 'culinarily enlightening' night out.

Directions: From London – 3 miles from M40 J6. From Birmingham – 5 miles from M40 J8

WALLINGFORD
Map 4 SU68

Shillingford Bridge Hotel

Shillingford, OX10 8LZ
Tel: 01865 858567
Fax: 01865 858636
e shillingford.bridge@forestdale.com
Chef(s): Paul Jarvest
Owner(s): Mr G Rolfe
Cost: Set price L £20/D £20. ☺ ☺
H/wine £8.95
Times: 12.30-2pm/7.30-10pm.
Closed L Sat
Additional: Sunday L. Bar food.
Children welcome
Seats: 150. Private dining room 60

Photos of the hotel at various stages of its history are on display, some dating back to the early 1800's. Such longevity has a lot to do with the superb riverside views, but its continuing popularity today rests as much on the excellent cuisine such as pan-fried fillet steak with bubble and squeak and a thyme jus.

Style: Modern
Smoking: No smoking in dining room; no cigars
Accommodation: 42 rooms (42 en suite) ★ ★ ★
Directions: From the M4 J10 take the A329, through Wallingford towards Thame, from M40 J6 take B4009, then R on to A4074 then L at Shillingford Rdbt towards Wallingford

England

WALLINGFORD *Continued*　　　　Map 4 SU68

Springs Hotel

Country house hotel with a bright dining room that overlooks the gardens with its lake and wildfowl. The menu offers a range of fairly straightforward dishes in a broadly modern British style. Recent selections have included baked fillet of cod with potato and parsley crust and a warm pear and almond tart with clotted cream amongst the desserts..

Seats: 80. Private dining room 30. Jacket and tie preferred
Style: Modern
Smoking: No smoking in dining room; Air conditioning
Accommodation: 31 rooms (31 en suite) ★ ★ ★
Directions: Edge of village of North Stoke

Wallingford Road, North Stoke,
OX10 6BE
Tel: 01491 836687
Fax: 01491 836877
e info@thespringshotel.co.uk
Chef(s): Paul Franklin
Owner(s): S Wolf
Cost: Set price D £25. H/wine £14
Times: Noon-2pm/7-9.30pm
Additional: Sunday L. Bar food L.
Children welcome

WESTON-ON-THE-GREEN　　　　Map 4 SP51

Weston Manor Hotel

Once owned by Henry VIII, this imposing stone mansion has been the showpiece of the village since the 11th century. The magnificent vaulted ceiling of the restaurant combines with original panelling and well-chosen furnishings to produce an atmospheric yet comfortable venue for fine dining. After a stroll round the attractive gardens a starter of roasted red pepper and goats' cheese Charlotte with courgette and pesto salad makes for a light and delicate opening to the meal. Pan-fried duck breast with gratin dauphinoise and red wine jus might follow, with rich tangy lemon tart to close.

OX6 8QL
Tel: 01869 350621
Fax: 01869 350901
e westonmanor@hotmail.com
Chef(s): Michael Keenlyside
Owner(s): Mr & Mrs Osborn
Cost: Alc £35, set price L £25/
D £37.50. H/wine £15.95
Times: 12.30-2pm/7-9.30pm.
Closed L Sat & Sun
Additional: Bar food.
Seats: 60. Private dining room 32
Style: Country-house
Smoking: No smoking in dining room
Civil licence: 60
Accommodation: 35 rooms (35 en
suite) ★ ★ ★
Directions: 2 mins from the M40 J9,
via A34 (Oxford) on Weston-on-
Green; hotel in village centre

☺　Indicates a restaurant that has told us they offer a two-course lunch for less than £15

☺　Indicates a restaurant that has told us they offer a three-course dinner for less than £25

WOODSTOCK

Map 4 SP41

The Bear Hotel

⊛⊛
Park Street, OX20 1SZ
Tel: 0870 4008202
Fax: 01993 813380
e heritagehotels_woodstock.bear@
forte-hotels.com
Chef(s): David Morris
Owner(s): Heritage Hotels Ltd
Cost: Alc £29, set price L £10-£25/
D £20-£39. ☺ ☺ H/wine £14.50
Times: 12.30-2.30pm/6.30-10pm
Additional: Sunday L. Bar food L.
Children welcome
Seats: 80. Private dining room 20
Style: Traditional, Country-house
Smoking: No smoking in dining room
Accommodation: 54 rooms (54 en
suite) ★ ★ ★
Directions: Town centre, facing the
market square

Elizabeth Taylor and Richard Burton used this hotel as a
hideaway at the height of their love affair. It's easy to see why:
creepers wander across the higgledy-piggledy brickwork,
flowers grace the window boxes and the interior is all stone
fireplaces and beamed ceilings. The restaurant offers an
appropriately relaxed, romantic atmosphere - candlelit in the
evenings - and serves a good range of traditional European
dishes. These might include Scottish fillet steak with foie gras or
roast lamb with tomato and olive ragout.

Feathers Hotel

Market Street, OX20 1SX
Tel: 01993 812291
Fax: 01993 813158
Telephone for further details

As we went to press, it was the end of a highly successful era
at the Feathers as Mark Treasure departs and Darren Prideaux
(previously Holbeck Ghyll and Nanny Brow) takes up the reins.
No doubt though that top quality food will continue to be at the
centre of this special hotel with its warren of bedrooms,
lounges, bars and dining areas and its unforced English inn
charm. On a summer's evening take advantage of the terrace
for a pre-meal aperitif.

England

WOODSTOCK *Continued*   Map 4 SP41

Kings Head Inn

This traditional style inn dates back to the 16th century. A warm welcome from the staff is a solid foundation, as are a particularly impressive range of appetisers. The menu has an international feel, offering dishes such as roast rack of lamb with ratatouille or wild mushroom risotto with parmegiano. The in-house breads are a major strength.

Style: Rustic, Traditional. **Smoking:** No smoking in dining room
Accommodation: 3 rooms (3 en suite) ◆◆◆◆
Directions: On A44 2m N of Woodstock turn R to Wootton. The inn is located near church on Chapel Hill

Chapel Hill, Wootton, OX20 1DX
Tel: 01993 811340
Fax: 01993 813131
e t.fay@kings-head.co.uk
Chef(s): Tony Fay
Owner(s): Mr & Mrs T Fay
Cost: *Alc* £25. ☺ ☺ H/wine £10.95
Times: Noon-2pm/6-9pm.
Closed D Sun, Xmas
Additional: Sunday L. Bar food.
Children 12 yrs+
Seats: 45

RUTLAND

OAKHAM   Map 8 SK80

Barnsdale Lodge Hotel

Lovely hotel beside Rutland Water and restored tastefully throughout with an Edwardian theme. Eclectic menu offering the likes of rack of lamb with Cumbrian cured ham and a tomato and marjoram coulis followed by crème brûlée with a rhubarb sorbet.

The Avenue,
Rutland Water,
North Shore LE15 8AH
Tel: 01572 724678
Fax: 01572 724961
e barnsdale.lodge@btconnect.com
Chef(s): Robert Knowles
Owner(s): Mr R Reid
Cost: *Alc* £30. ☺ ☺ H/wine £11.50
Times: Noon-2.30pm/7-9.45pm.
Additional: Sunday L. Bar food.
Children welcome
Seats: 120. Private dining room 25
Style: Country-house
Smoking: No-smoking area; no pipes; no cigars
Civil licence: 100
Accommodation: 45 rooms (45 en suite) ★ ★ ★
Directions: Telephone for directions

Hambleton Hall Hotel

In sweeping landscaped grounds and overlooking Rutland water Hambleton Hall could pass for the epitome of an English country house hotel. Perhaps the biggest draw is Aaron Patterson's inspired cooking. Ingredients are second to none with a huge emphasis placed on local, seasonal and organic produce. The style, if it can be defined, is industrious modern British served in a relaxed, crisply presented dining room, where professional and attentive staff seem genuinely interested in making sure you enjoy yourself. The depth of ambition and technical proficiency is evident from the outset with precise canapés (mini-cottage pie, tapenade in a filo case, scrambled egg tartlet) that have the effect of creating great anticipation of what is ahead. Opinions vary on the worth of all the peripheral elements, but when they are as good as minestrone with langoustine served as an amuse, only the

Hambleton, LE15 8TH

churlish would argue. Starters might include a simple sounding but in fact mighty complex, pigeon and wild mushroom tartlet. This amounted to a "divine" thin and brittle pastry case filled with mushrooms and slices of tender pigeon on spinach and garnished with lardons of bacon, a shallot purée, tomato concasse, roasted shallots, and a rich and deep sauce. Amongst the mains braised turbot, baby leeks, herb risotto and a Sauternes jus included a faultlessly cooked piece of turbot with wilted spinach, a herb risotto and a sublime sauce. Desserts tend to be takes on the classic with caramelised apple tart, compôte of blackberries and vanilla ice-cream for instance creating a stunning impression. Predominately French wine list, but there's also a good showing from California, Italy and Spain.

Tel: 01572 756991
Fax: 01572 724721
 hotel@hambletonhall.com
Chef(s): Aaron Patterson
Owner(s): Mr T Hart
Cost: *Alc* £47, set price L £21.50/ D £35. H/wine £15
Times: Noon-2pm/7-9.30pm
Additional: Sunday L. Bar food. Children welcome
Seats: 60. Private dining room 24
Style: Classic, French
Smoking: No smoking in dining room
Civil licence: 64
Accommodation: 17 rooms (17 en suite) ★ ★ ★
Directions: From A1- A606 Oakham. After 8.4 miles take turning signed Hambleton/ Egleton only. Hotel on R in main street of Hambleton village

Whipper-In Hotel

A popular inn furnished in English country house style. An open fire in the lounge bar is a pleasant prelude to the interesting meals served in the modern informal brasserie and the candlelit restaurant. The latter offers main courses along the lines of grilled tuna steak with asparagus and wild mushroom sauce.

Seats: 60. Private dining room 30
Style: Traditional, Classic
Smoking: No smoking in dining room
Accommodation: 24 rooms (24 en suite) ★ ★ ★
Directions: Town centre in the market place

Market Place, LE15 6DT
Tel: 01572 756971
Fax: 01572 757759
 whipper.in@lineone.net
Chef(s): Michel Oliver
Owner(s): Brook Hotels
Cost: *Alc* £20.10, set price L £12.95-£21.95/D £18.50-£26.95. ☺ ☺
H/wine £9.95
Times: Noon-2pm/7-9.30pm. Closed D Sun
Additional: Sunday L. Bar food. Children welcome

STRETTON   **Map 8 SK91**

Ram Jam Inn

The charismatic Ram Jam has long been a landmark on the long haul up the A1, with the informal but stylish ambience of the bistro style restaurant calling siren-like to passing travellers. Somewhat rustic presentation belies a thoroughly modern, popularist approach to food with the quality of produce consistently high.

Style: Traditional, Bistro-Style
Smoking: No smoking in dining room
Accommodation: 7 rooms (7 en suite) ★ ★
Directions: On n'bound carriageway of A1, 8m N of Stamford; s'bound exit Oakham B668, follow signs under bridge to inn

Great North Road, LE15 7QX
Tel: 01780 410776
Fax: 01780 410361
e rji@rutnet.co.uk
Chef(s): Matt Chittock
Owner(s): Mr Littlemore & Mrs Cox
Cost: ☺ ☺ H/wine £10.95
Times: Noon-all day/9.30pm. Closed 25-Dec
Additional: Sunday L. Bar food. Children welcome
Seats: 120. Private dining room 60

England

UPPINGHAM

Map 4 SP89

Lake Isle Hotel

High Street East, LE15 9PZ
Tel: 01572 822951
Fax: 01572 822951
Chef(s): Gary Thomas
Owner(s): Richard Burton
Cost: Set price D £23.50-£27.50. ☺
☺ H/wine £11.50
Times: 12.15-1.45pm/7-9.15pm.
Closed L Mon, D Sun, BHs
Additional: Sunday L. Children
welcome
Seats: 40. Private dining room 10
Style: Traditional, Rustic
Smoking: No pipes; no cigars; Air
conditioning

Attractively domestic in décor, this town house restaurant sets a comfortable, rustic tone with pine furnishings and panelling complemented by earthy green floors. Cheerful and informal service adds to the homely charm to such an extent that it is easy to be slightly startled by the seriousness of the cuisine that is issued forth with such gaiety. Mains run along the lines of seared fillet of halibut with buttered spinach and a saffron and tomato cream, or roast breast of chicken with an orange and almond sauce. Revel in sticky toffee pudding with butterscotch sauce and caramel ice cream.

Accommodation: 12 rooms (12 en suite) ★ ★
Directions: Town centre, on foot via Reeves Yard, via Queens Street by car

SHROPSHIRE

CHURCH STRETTON

Map 7 SO49

Stretton Hall Hotel

The Lemon Tree Restaurant is very much the heart of this impressive country house hotel. The décor is in keeping with the Georgian setting but the choice of colours makes for a light, fresh atmosphere in which to enjoy such wonders as monkfish tails wrapped in pancetta and stuffed with chopped artichokes.

Seats: 60. Private dining room 14
Style: Classic, Country-house
Smoking: No smoking in dining room
Accommodation: 12 rooms (12 en suite) ★ ★ ★
Directions: Off A49 Ludlow to Shrewsbury Road, in village of Stretton

All Stretton, SY6 6HG
Tel: 01694 723224
Fax: 01694 724365
📧 enquiries@strettonhall.co.uk
Chef(s): Miles Holtby
Owner(s): Mr & Mrs C Baker-Vilain
Cost: *Alc* £20, set price L £17/D £19.
☺ ☺ H/wine £9.95
Times: 12.30-2pm/7-9pm.
Additional: Sunday L. Bar food.
Children welcome

The Studio

59 High Street, SY6 6BY

The Studio is just the kind of place that in a perfect world, would be found in the High Street of every town. Honest, full-flavoured cooking that might feature leek and mustard soup, pan fried monkfish with smoked bacon and a white wine sauce and an "excellent" iced lemon soufflé. Mistakenly shown as 2 Rosettes last year, for which we apologise.

Tel: 01694 722672
Fax: 01694 722672
Chef(s): Ed Van Doesburg
Owner(s): Ed & Jane Van Doesburg
Cost: Alc £23.50, set price L £12.50. ☺ ☺ H/wine £9.50
Times: Noon-2pm/7-10pm. Closed Mon, Sun, Xmas, BHs
Additional: Children welcome
Seats: 35
Style: Informal
Smoking: No smoking in dining room
Directions: From A49 into village. L at crossroads into High Street

---

CLEOBURY MORTIMER   Map 7 SO67

The Crown Inn

Hopton Wafers, DY14 0NB

A 16th-century inn set in immaculate gardens. The interior fits the setting, with exposed beams and real fires. Eat in the smart dining room or the informal rent room, where the local landowner used to meet tenants to collect rent and taxes. The imaginative cooking ranges from British to Oriental and makes impressive use of local ingredients.

Tel: 01299 270372
Fax: 01299 271127
Chef(s): Steven Griffiths
Owner(s): Mr & Mrs A C Matthews
Cost: Alc £23.70. ☺ H/wine £11.95
Times: Dinner only 7-9.15pm. Closed Mon-Wed, D Sun, 25 Dec
Additional: Sunday L. Bar food. Children welcome

Seats: 36. Private dining room 36
Style: Classic, Traditional
Smoking: No smoking in dining room
Accommodation: 7 rooms (7 en suite) ♦♦♦♦
Directions: Telephone for directions

DORRINGTON   Map 7 SJ40

Country Friends Restaurant

SY5 7JD

An ancient beamed building retaining a great deal of historic charm inside and out. Simplicity reaps dividends in a light and accurate twice-baked leek and Llanboidy soufflé whilst a fresh and full-flavoured sea bass is royally treated - pan fried with a nicely textured mussel sauce. Apparently ordinary puddings such as lemon torte often reveal hidden depths - in this case a mousse-like texture combining well with tuile biscuits to unite in an accurate, tangy flavour. A detailed wine list is also a strong feature.

Tel: 01743 718707
Fax: 01743 718707
e whittaker@countryfriends.demon.co.uk
Chef(s): Charles Whittaker
Owner(s): Mr & Mrs C Whittaker
Cost: Set price L £31.50-£35/D £31.50-£35. H/wine £12.75
Times: Noon-2pm/7-9pm. Closed Sun & Mon, L Tue, 2 wks mid July
Additional: Bar food L. Children welcome
Seats: 35

Style: Modern
Smoking: No smoking in dining room
Accommodation: 1 room
Directions: 6m S of Shrewsbury on A49, in village centre

England

LLANFAIR WATERDINE
Map 6 SO27

The Waterdine
NEW

Ken Adams has taken to the hills following his departure from the culinary hothouse of Ludlow. Quite a location, with entrancing views over the river and hills, a vegetable garden and an orchard. The menu features an abundance of organic and locally sourced produce. Dishes are appealingly straightforward in conception but impressively accurate in their execution. Lunch offers especially good value and could comprise a "super tasty" poached egg in puff pastry with mushroom duxelle and hollandaise followed by "so tender" Trelough duck braised in red wine with celeriac and carrots and a dessert of chocolate and hazelnut pithivier with a hazelnut sauce. Well worth seeking out.

Directions: 4 miles from Knighton on B4355. Turn R in Lloyney. Last property in village opposite the church

LD7 1TU
Tel: 01547 528214
Chef(s): Ken Adams
Owner(s): Ken Adams
Cost: Set price D £25 ☺
Times: Noon-1.45pm/7-9pm.
Closed Mon, D Sun,
Additional: Bar food. Children 8yrs+
Seats: 20
Smoking: No smoking in dining room
Accommodation: 3 rooms (3 en suite)

LUDLOW
Map 7 SO57

The Cookhouse

There's something for everyone at this busy roadside operation, with a popular café and bar, and a bright restaurant with large flower prints to give the place a summery feel. Expect clear flavours from purée of vegetable soup with pesto swirl, and smoked salmon mousse with lemon dressing. Main courses include tartlet of vegetables with cheese sauce, and chicken breast with shallots, white wine and mushroom sauce.

Seats: 40. **Style:** Modern, Minimalist
Directions: 1m N of Ludlow, on A49 towards Shrewsbury

Bromfield, SY7 8LR
Tel: 01584 856565
Fax: 01584 856661
Chef(s): Peter Gartell
Owner(s): Paul & Barbara Brooks
Cost: Alc £23.50, set price L £14.25.
☺ ☺ H/wine £9.75
Times: Noon-2.30pm/7-9.30pm.
Closed 25 Dec evening
Additional: Sunday L. Bar food.
Children welcome

The Courtyard

Set in a courtyard development close to Ludlow's Butter Cross - bistro-style at lunchtime and a little more formal in the evening. Expect the likes of a delicate spinach and nutmeg soup, and a tasty salmon fishcake with an accurate caper hollandaise. A "pretty much classic" creamy vanilla crème brûlée starred amongst the puds.

Smoking: No smoking in dining room; Air conditioning
Directions: Town centre, off Market Place

Quality Square, SY8 1AR
Tel: 01584 878080
Chef(s): Philip Woodhall
Owner(s): Ms J Lloyd
Cost: Alc £20.90. ☺ ☺ H/wine £9.50
Times: Noon-2pm/7-9pm.
Closed Sun, D Mon-Wed,
25-26 Dec, 1 Jan, May BH Mon
Additional: Children welcome
Seats: 30. **Style:** Bistro

Dinham Hall Hotel

This handsome small hotel, close to Ludlow's Castle grounds and dating from 1792, holds its own in a town commonly described as the gastronomic capital of the Welsh Marches (at the very least). Novel menus reflecting the chef's French origins, display careful sourcing of fresh seasonal produce prepared with skill and confidence. A foie gras terrine was described as "close to top-notch", turbot with langoustines and Chinese sauce as "a greater challenge to the taste-buds". Garnishes to both starters and desserts - such as an apple tarte Tatin - labelled as reminiscent of a florist's shop, yet their flavours are accurately crafted, with proper care and attention taken to the finer details.

Accommodation: 15 rooms (15 en suite) ★ ★ ★
Directions: Town centre, off Market Place

By the Castle, SY8 1EJ
Tel: 01584 876464
Fax: 01584 876019
Chef(s): Olivier Bossut
Owner(s): Mr J Mifsud
Cost: Alc £31.25 H/wine £13.50
Times: 12.30-2.30pm/7-9pm.
Additional: Children 8 yrs+.
Vegetarian by request only
Seats: 30. Private dining room 26.
Jacket and tie preferred
Style: Classic, Country-house
Smoking: No smoking in dining room
Civil licence: 40

Hibiscus

Is there no limit to the magnetism of this little market town? Well, on this evidence, the appeal has spread to France at least. Claude Bosi took the helm here in the middle of 2000 and has quickly established himself in what was The Oaks. Contemporary oils and stylish table presentations add freshness and vitality to the wooden panels, and there is bright, unassuming service to match. There is a welcome lightness to the cooking too, so it's not necessary to feel daunted by the option of a 7-course menu dégustation. Classic French is coupled with some demanding combinations like a daring (but immensely successful) amuse bouche of chilled melon soup with green chartreuse, olive oil and black pepper. Similar deftness in a typically delicate but intense roasted lobster with a white bean velouté and a main course of roast Welsh lamb with an almond crust plus top quality girolles. Well kept British, French and Italian cheeses precede desserts that might feature warm chocolate tart with star anise or avocado (yes avocado) soufflé with chocolate ice creams. One to watch.

Directions: Town centre, bottom of hill below Feathers Hotel

17 Corve Street, SY8 1DA
Tel: 01584 872325
Fax: 01568 874024
Chef(s): Claude Bosi
Owner(s): Claude Bosi & Claire Crosby
Cost: Alc £32.50, set price L £25/D £32.50 H/wine £13.50
Times: 12.30-1.30pm/7.30-10pm. Closed L Sun-Tues, D Sun, 1 wk Spring, 1-2 wks Autumn
Additional: Children welcome Children 8 yrs+. Vegetarian by request only
Seats: 30
Style: Chic, French
Smoking: No smoking in dining room

Merchant House

62 Lower Corve Street, SY8 1DU
Tel: 01584 875438
Fax: 01584 876927
Chef(s): Shaun Hill
Owner(s): Shaun Hill
Cost: Set price L £31.50/D £31.50
Times: 12.30-2pm/7-9pm. Closed Sun & Mon, L Tue-Thu, 1 wk Xmas, 1 wk Spring
Additional: Vegetarian by request only
Seats: 24
Smoking: No smoking in dining room
Directions: Town centre, next to Unicorn Pub

The restrained style of Shaun Hill's restaurant - well-polished tables, linen placemats, and a beautiful log-burner fireplace - is a pretty much perfect match for the understated style of cooking. Both are a tribute to impeccable taste and a chef that has the confidence to keep it simple. Add top-notch ingredients and a hefty portion of talent to the pot, and you get the sort of results other places dream of. Luxury produce and more humble foods merge effortlessly on the short menu, producing harmonious starters like sea bass and basil with crème fraîche, and calves' sweetbreads with watercress sauce. Seasonal main dishes like summery wild salmon with a sorrel beurre blanc use the freshest of ingredients to great effect, and there is a penetrating honesty to the likes of English grey partridge with potato and celeriac cake and morel mushroom sauce.
Puds seem to excite the greatest superlatives with the likes of apricot tart with amaretto ice cream - sending some into raptures. Service is friendly and unpretentious. An example to others.

LUDLOW *Continued*   Map 7 SO57

Mr Underhills

Out of the town proper, at the foot of the castle and with gardens that roll down to the river, lies Christopher and Judy Bradley's recently refurbished restaurant with rooms. It's a relaxed and auberge-like setting for food that offers few surprises but is distinguished by the quality of the raw materials and consistent accurate cooking. There is a choice at dessert only but likes and dislikes will be checked in advance and your menu will come personalised with your name at the top. Starters tend to focus on fish and might include warm smoked salmon with coriander, noodles and ginger or lemon sole with leeks and a champagne chive beurre blanc. Local bounty is a feature whether it be saddle of wild Shropshire venison with sauce poivrade and roasted roots or fillet of Shropshire beef with tarragon and mushrooms scented with white truffle. The aforementioned list of desserts again tends towards the classic and might include poached pears with lemon grass, vanilla and pistachio ice cream or lemon tart. The wine list favours character over the commercial, offers some lesser known bins and is fairly marked-up.

Dinham Weir SY8 1EH
Tel: 01584 874431
Chef(s): Christopher bradley
Owner(s): Christopher & Judy Bradley
Cost: Set price L £27.50/D £27.50.
H/wine £12.50
Times: Lunch by arrangement,
D 7pm-midnight. Closed D Tue
Additional: Children welcome.
Vegetarian by request only
Seats: 20
Smoking: No smoking in dining room
Accommodation: 6 rooms (6 en suite)
Directions: From Castle Square: with Castle in front, turn immediately L, proceed round castle, turn R before bridge, restaurant on L

Overton Grange Hotel

Hospitality and impressive levels of service continue to be worthy of note at this handsome Edwardian mansion that stands in mature grounds with fine views out across the Shropshire countryside. The re-modelled "Les Marches" restaurant is the setting for equally stylish food that makes intelligent use of fresh produce, much of it from the locality from which it derives its name. Simply described dishes are mouth-wateringly balanced without undue complication - allowing, for instance, cannelloni of quail with lentils, smoked bacon and white truffle oil, and seared scallops with white vichyssoise and oyster beignet to speak for themselves. Seared turbot with braised salsify and roast onion purée and local venison with morels, cabbage confit and snail bourguignonne similarly typify the quality and balance of main dishes, with fine French and British cheeses offered as alternatives to the pineapple frangipane, black pepper caramel and coconut ice cream that epitomises some well-worked desserts.

Hereford Road, SY8 4AD
Tel: 01584 873500
Fax: 01584 873524
Chef(s): Wayne Vicarage
Cost: A/c £35, set price L £25-£30/
D £32.50-£40. ☺ H/wine £15
Times: Noon-1.45pm/7-9.30pm.
Closed L Mon & Sat, 2 wks Jan
Additional: Sunday L. Children welcome. Vegetarian by request only
Seats: 35. Private dining room 18
Style: Modern
Smoking: No smoking in dining room
Accommodation: 14 rooms (14 en suite) ★★★
Directions: On B4361 adjacent to garage, approximately 1.5 miles from Ludlow

Roebuck Inn Restaurant

Something of a pioneer of gastropubs. Terracotta walls, wooden floors and cane seating give a conservatory feel which, coupled with informal but attentive service, creates a conducive atmosphere in which to enjoy a good variety of modern and traditional dishes. The variety of home-made breads (including light textured walnut and apricot) is a fitting precursor to pan-seared scallops, steamed steak and mushroom suet pudding and mouthwatering bread-and-butter pudding. The ample menu is further enhanced by specials such as fresh crab and avocado gâteau, and crisply grilled fillets of sea bass on a liquorice scented risotto.

Accommodation: 3 rooms (3 en suite) ♦♦♦
Directions: Just off A49 between Ludlow & Leominster

Brimfield, SY8 4NE
Tel: 01584 711230
Fax: 01584 711654
e dave@roebuckinn.demon.co.uk
Chef(s): J Waters & D Willson-Lloyd
Owner(s): Mr & Mrs D Willson-Lloyd
Cost: Alc £23, set price L £17.50/ D £24. ☺ ☺ H/wine £9.95
Times: Noon-2.30pm/7-9.30pm.
Additional: Sunday L. Bar food.
Children welcome
Seats: 46. Private dining room 16
Style: Chic, Modern
Smoking: No smoking in dining room

MARKET DRAYTON Map 7 SJ63

Goldstone Hall

Nothing pretentious about this charming family-run hotel. The restaurant with its original country house furnishings, offers a relaxed dining atmosphere. The menu makes good use of fresh local ingredients, for which the hotel has a well-deserved reputation. An impressive fire and views across an expanse of countryside provide a warm backdrop to which you may enjoy the likes of steamed red mullet with soy, chilli and ginger, or roast leg of lamb with garden mint and crab apple jelly.

Smoking: No smoking in dining room
Civil licence: 100
Accommodation: 8 rooms (8 en suite) ★★★
Directions: From A529, 4 miles S of Market Drayton, follow signs for Goldstone Hall Gardens

Goldstone, TF9 2NA
Tel: 01630 661202
Fax: 01630 661585
e enquiries@goldstonehall.com
Chef(s): Carl Fitzgerald-Bloomer
Owner(s): Mr J Cushing & Mrs H Ward
Cost: Alc £25, set price L £15.95/ D £13.50. ☺ ☺ H/wine £11.25
Times: Noon-2.30pm/7.30-10.30pm.
Additional: Sunday L.
Children welcome
Seats: 40. Private dining room 20
Style: Traditional, Country-house

Rosehill Manor

A rather splendid country house boasting historic architectural details (in some cases 16th-century) and 1.5 acres of private gardens. The dining room is plush and formal and might lead you to anticipate a fairly traditional British approach to cuisine. You'd be right; expect tenderloin of pork with an apricot and apple stuffing and a Calvados cream sauce.

Smoking: No smoking in dining room
Civil licence: 90
Accommodation: 9 rooms (9 en suite) ★★
Directions: From roundabout at Turnhill take A35/41 towards Newport, hotel on right.

Rosehill, Ternhill, TF9 2JF
Tel: 01630 638532
Fax: 01630 637008
Chef(s): Hazel Francis
Owner(s): Mr & Mrs P Eardley
Cost: Alc £23, set price L £14.95/ D £23. ☺ ☺ H/wine £10.50
Times: Noon-2pm/7-9pm.
Closed L Mon-Sat, D Sun
Additional: Sunday L.Bar food D.
Children welcome
Seats: 70. Private dining room
Style: Traditional, Country-house

 Indicates a restaurant that has told us that 50% or more of their ingredients are organically sourced

Prices quoted in the guide are for guidance only and are subject to change without notice

England

Raven Hotel

30 Barrow Street, TF13 6EN
Tel: 01952 727251
Fax: 01952 728416
Chef(s): Steve Biggs
Cost: *Alc* £20, set price L £15. ☺
H/wine £12
Times: Noon-2pm/7-9.15pm.
Closed 25-26 Dec
Additional: Sunday L. Bar food L.
Seats: 40. Jacket and tie preferred
Smoking: No smoking in dining room
Accommodation: 15 rooms (15 en
suite) ★ ★ ★

Choose between eating inside lovely old almshouses beside a large open fire or, on a balmy evening, outside in a charming courtyard. These are the options at the Raven. Whatever the weather, the menu is lively and the dishes are well executed and restrained: dishes such as braised shank of lamb with redcurrant, butter bean and rosemary casserole or pot-roast chicken breast wrapped in bacon and served with orange sauce. Among the starters may be escabèche of Scottish salmon marinated in white wine and sweet peppers with olive and anchovy crostini, while hazelnut meringue with clotted cream and strawberries makes a deceptively simple dessert.

Directions: Town centre

Hundred House Hotel

Bridgnorth Road, TF11 9EE
Tel: 01952 730353
Fax: 01952 730355
🄴 hphundredhouse@
compuserve.com
Chef(s): Stuart Phillips
Owner(s): Mr H Phillips
Cost: *Alc* £30. ☺ ☺ H/wine £12.50
Additional: Sunday L. Bar food.
Children welcome

The enthusiasm of the friendly family team at this hotel restaurant is admirable. A memorable meal can be enjoyed in one of the intimate dining areas of this primarily Georgian building. The *carte* menu provides an extensive variety of dishes to choose from. The clear flavours of a carrot and coriander soup might be enjoyed before embarking on a "melt-in-the-mouth" braised shank of lamb, served with a robustly flavoured basil tomato sauce and accompanied by polenta and spinach.

England

Such choices are further supplemented by an impressive list of daily specials. The food is competently and skilfully prepared from quality produce.

Directions: Midway between Telford & Bridgenorth on A442. In centre of village

Seats: 60. Private dining room 30
Smoking: No-smoking area
Accommodation: 10 rooms (10 en suite) ★ ★

OSWESTRY
Map 7 SJ22

Pen-y-Dyffryn Country Hotel

This charming old house dates back to the 1840s, when it was built as a rectory. It stands in five acres of grounds and is quietly located on the edge of Rhydycroesau village, three miles west of Oswestry. The warm and friendly hospitality of the proprietors and staff make it an appealing place to eat. The menu has a British flavour, with a sprinkling of European ideas. A typical menu might include starters of white onion soup with melted cheddar cheese or grilled free-range Shropshire fallow deer, followed by main courses such as grilled sea bass or rack of Welsh lamb.

Accommodation: 10 rooms (10 en suite) ★ ★ ★
Directions: 3m W of Oswestry on B4580

Rhydycroesau, SY10 7JD
Tel: 01691 653700
Fax: 01691 650066
e stay@peny.co.uk
Chef(s): David Morris
Owner(s): Mr & Mrs M J Hunter
Cost: Set price D £22-£26. ☺
H/wine £11
Times: Dinner only, 6.45-11.30pm
Additional: Children welcome
Seats: 25
Style: Country-house
Smoking: No smoking in dining room

Sebastian's Hotel & Restaurant
NEW

Parts of this town centre property date back to 1640. Now a privately run hotel, its wealth of charm and character is enhanced by original features such as exposed beams and oak panelling. The French based menu might include dishes such as roast fillet of turbot with tagliatelli and asparagus or roast breast of duck with a calvados and cider sauce.

45 Willow Street, SY11 1AQ
Tel: 01691 655444
Fax: 01691 653452
e sebastians.rest@virgin.net
Chef(s): Mark Sebastian Fisher
Owner(s): Mark & Michelle Fisher
Cost: Set price D £25-£31.25.
H/wine £11.50
Times: Dinner only, 6.30-12.30am.
Closed Sun & Mon, Xmas
Additional: Children welcome
Seats: 40. Jacket and tie preferred
Style: French
Smoking: No smoking in dining room;
Air conditioning
Accommodation: 8 rooms (8 en suite)
★ ★
Directions: Telephone for directions

☺ Indicates a restaurant that has told us they offer a two-course lunch for less than £15

☺ Indicates a restaurant that has told us they offer a three-course dinner for less than £25

England

OSWESTRY *Continued*   Map 7 SJ22

Wynnstay Hotel

Church Street, SY11 2SZ
Tel: 01691 655261
Fax: 01691 670606
e info@wynnstayhotel.com
Chef(s): Martin Harrop
Owner(s): Earlymulti Plc
Cost: Set price L £13.95/D £18.50.
☺ ☺ H/wine £9.25
Times: Noon-2pm/7-9.30pm.
Closed D Sun
Additional: Sunday L. Bar food.
Children welcome
Seats: 46. Private dining room 200
Style: Country-house
Smoking: No smoking in dining room
Civil licence: 90
Accommodation: 29 rooms (29 en
suite) ★ ★ ★
Directions: In centre of town,
opposite the church

Once a well known posting house on the Liverpool to Cardiff route, this Georgian coaching inn is decorated in period style throughout, so it's a surprise to find that many of the dishes are Italian. A meal might include a warm tart of tomato, mozzarella and black olives followed by grilled fillet steak with straw potatoes, grilled tomatoes and garlic cream mushrooms.

SHIFNAL   Map 7 SJ70

Park House Hotel

Once two separate houses, which have been successfully combined, Park House Hotel evokes the grandeur of a bygone age. There are imposing high ceilings and glittering chandeliers to make this a fine dining experience. A good variety of modern British dishes is available on the menu with starters such as wild mushroom and smoked chicken ravioli or Toulouse sausage and ham hock terrine with plum chutney and yoghurt dressing. Main courses too have a contemporary air, with pork fillet served with apple mille-feuille, celeriac mash and garlic and thyme jus, while seared scallops are presented with saffron noodles and aubergine caviar

Park Street, TF11 9BA
Tel: 01952 460128
Fax: 01952 461658
Chef(s): Kevin Baggot
Cost: *Alc* £40, set price L £14.50/
D £18. ☺ ☺ H/wine £14.50
Times: Noon-2pm/7-10pm.
Closed L Sat
Additional: Sunday L. Bar food.
Children welcome
Seats: 50. Private dining room 180.
Jacket and tie preferred
Style: Classic
Smoking: No smoking in dining room

Civil licence: 150
Accommodation: 54 rooms (54 en suite) ★ ★ ★ ★
Directions: From M54 J4 take A464 through Shifnal; hotel is 200 yards after railway bridge

SHREWSBURY   Map 7 SJ41

Albright Hussey Hotel

First recorded in Domesday Book, this splendid property thrived under the Husseys' ownership until the 17th century, when it was converted to a farm. Under present direction for over a decade, it sports a Tudor-style restaurant overlooking four acres of mature, landscaped gardens. A la *carte* menus follow the seasons with consistent results backed up by friendly, attentive service. Cuisine is basically modern British with French overtones, as in duck liver parfait with hazelnuts and green bean salad, followed by sole fillets with asparagus, vermouth and saffron cream. Chocolate marquise with a raspberry truffle and Shrewsbury cake have both attracted warm praise.

Ellesmere Road, SY4 3AF
Tel: 01939 290571
Fax: 01939 291143
e abhhotel@aol.com
Chef(s): David Burns & Paul Davies
Owner(s): Franco, Vera &
Paul Subbiani
Cost: *Alc* £25, set price L £12.50-
£17.50/D £16-£23. ☺ ☺
H/wine £11.95
Times: Noon-2.15pm/7-10pm.
Additional: Sunday L. Bar food L.
Children welcome

England

Seats: 80. Private dining room 40. Jacket and tie preferred
Accommodation: 14 rooms (14 en suite) ★ ★ ★
Directions: On A528, 2 miles from centre of Shrewsbury

Style: Country-house, Italian
Smoking: No smoking in dining room
Civil licence: 200

Rowton Castle Hotel

Halfway House, SY5 9EP
Tel: 01743 884044
Fax: 01743 884949
e post@rowtoncastle.co.uk
Chef(s): Steve Parke
Owner(s): Mr J DeSousa
Cost: Alc £25.95, set price L £15.50/
D £25.95. ☺ H/wine £11.50
Times: Noon-2pm/7-9.30pm
Additional: Sunday L. Bar food.
Children welcome.
Vegetarian by request only
Seats: 32. Private dining room 20

18th-century luxury in the oak panelled restaurant. Sample peppercorn studded terrine of wild boar as you gaze over the formal gardens. Desserts are generally of the sturdy variety with the likes of steamed almond pudding served with an Amaretti scented custard.

Smoking: No smoking in dining room
Civil licence: 110
Accommodation: 19 rooms (19 en suite) ★ ★ ★
Directions: From Birmingham, take M6 west. Follow M54 and A5 to Shrewsbury. Continue on A5 and exit at the 6th rdbt. Take A458 to Welshpool. Rowton Castle is 4 miles on R

Sol Restaurant

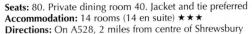

82 Wyle Cop, SY1 1UT
Tel: 01743 340560
Fax: 01743 340552
e john@solrestaurant.co.uk
Chef(s): John Williams
Owner(s): John & Debbie Williams
Cost: Alc £30, set price L £15/
D £28.50-£33. ☺ H/wine £9.95
Times: 12.30-2pm/7-9.30pm.
Closed Sun & Mon, 1 wk winter,
1 wk summer
Additional: Children 8 yrs+.
Vegetarian by request only
Seats: 45. Private dining room 20
Style: Modern
Smoking: No smoking in dining room;
no cigars
Directions: From A5 bypass follow town centre signs, cross English bridge and restaurant is at the top of hill on L after Lion Hotel. Advisable to park at bottom and walk up

Warm oranges and yellows, plus the bright blues of temperate oceans have brought a welcome touch of the Mediterranean to this corner of Shrewsbury. It might be wishful thinking to call an English restaurant 'Sol', but this one does manage to impart a radiant quality to its interior, housed in a set of preserved old buildings in the city centre. Informality is the key, with well-spaced bare tables and easy-going staff, while kitchen skills achieve a high level of precision judging by the clear flavours in

England

SHREWSBURY *Continued*

Map 7 SJ41

well-balanced dishes. The short lunch and dinner menus are similar in style, offering perhaps marble of ham hock with root vegetables and sherry vinegar syrup followed by corn-fed guinea fowl cooked three ways, or medallion of Ludlow venison with a pavé of winter vegetables and parsnip mash. Errors occasionally creep in (a vanilla parfait was a little over-chilled) but there's plenty to cheer about. A short wine list offers reliable selection at fair mark-ups.

TELFORD

Map 7 SJ60

Valley Hotel

Innovation without fuss is the order of the day at this hotel restaurant near the famous iron bridge. Quality ingredients shine through daily-changing dishes which span the globe, and there's a good choice including vegetarian options. Try Thai crab cakes with a green curry and coconut sauce, and fillet of pork wrapped in panchetta and a crisp filo pastry, served with a balsamic reduction and roasted tomatoes. Also recommended is the summer pudding with clotted cream, a deliciously refreshing dessert. Other choices might include roast rump of lamb with roasted vegetables, bubble and squeak and a port and rosemary jus.

Smoking: No smoking in dining room. **Civil licence:** 120
Accommodation: 35 rooms (35 en suite) ★ ★ ★
Directions: Follow signs to Ironbridge Gorge. At mini rdbt at bottom turn L, hotel 200 yds on L

TF8 7DW
Tel: 01952 432247
Fax: 01952 432308
e valley-hotel@ironbridge.
fsnet.co.uk
Chef(s): Barry Workman
Owner(s): Philip & Lesley Casson
Cost: *Alc* £25, set price L £21/D £21.
☺ ☺ H/wine £8.95
Times: Noon-2pm/7-9.30pm.
Closed L Sat, 26 Dec-2 Jan
Additional: Sunday L. Bar food L.
Children welcome. Vegetarian by request only
Seats: 50. Private dining room 120.
Jacket and tie preferred
Style: Classic, Country-house

WORFIELD

Map 7 SO79

Old Vicarage Hotel

There is something delicious about this brasserie-style restaurant in a country house hotel, even before the food is sampled. From the moment you pass through the door, the pampering begins with service that is always attentive and hospitality that could reasonably be described as refined. There is a sense of comfortable well-being in the restaurant, where polished wooden floors and antique tables dressed with silver cutlery and white napkins suggest that dining is taken seriously but not obsessively. The cooking takes a fresh look at the

WV15 5JZ
Tel: 01746 716497
Fax: 01746 716552
e admin@the-old-vicarage.
demon.co.uk
Chef(s): Blaine Reed
Owner(s): Mr D Blakstad
Cost: Set price L £19.75/D £25-£30.
H/wine £15.75
Times: Noon-2.30pm/7-9pm.
Additional: Sunday L. Children welcome
Seats: 42. Private dining room 14.
Jacket and tie preferred
Style: Country-house
Smoking: No smoking in dining room
Accommodation: 14 rooms (14 en suite) ★ ★ ★
Directions: From Wolverhampton take A454 Bridgnorth Rd, from M54 J4 take A442 towards Kidderminster

traditional, as in griddled king scallops with mango salsa and rocket pesto, and fillet of Brixham brill with a fricassée of puglia pasta, crayfish tails and basil. Parfait of chicken livers with apricot chutney and brioche will not disappoint and loin of venison with braised red cabbage, creamed truffle celeriac and red wine jus was a melt-in-the-mouth main dish. Finish on a high with some irresistible petit fours.

SOMERSET

BATH

Map 3 ST76

Bath Priory

Executive chef Robert Clayton's stated ambition is to create well-presented dishes, which explore and exploit exquisite flavours, and few would argue with his success. He doesn't stint on quality, relying on the freshest of fine ingredients to articulate his culinary designs: pan-fried scallops, diver-caught, with a confit of garlic parcels and a Jerusalem artichoke velouté is faultless, the latter a frothy creation which unites the whole starter. Roast loin of venison with a mushroom and goats' cheese risotto and lemon and thyme sauce was another well-chosen dish. A real treat came in the dollop of malted milk ice cream that accompanied a hot chocolate fondant, and impressive cheeses from home and abroad are worth trying. Meals are taken in the comfortable, sprawling dining room where relaxing sofas blend with more formal seating in luxurious surroundings. While service is impeccably orchestrated it can occasionally be a little stiff.

Weston Road, BA1 2XT
Tel: 01225 331922
Fax: 01225 448276
e bathprioryhotel@compuserve.com
Chef(s): Robert Clayton
Owner(s): Mr T Pettifer
Cost: Set price L £22.50/D £42. H/wine £15
Times: Noon-2pm/7-10pm.
Additional: Sunday L. Bar food. Children welcome
Seats: 40. Private dining room 60. Jacket and tie preferred
Style: Classic
Smoking: No smoking in dining room
Accommodation: 28 rooms (28 en suite) ★ ★ ★ ★

Directions: At the top of Park Lane, on W side of Victoria Park, turn L into Weston Rd. 300 Yds on the L

Bath Spa Hotel

Sydney Road, BA2 6JF
Tel: 0870 4008222
Fax: 01225 444006
e fivestar@bathspa.u-net.com
Chef(s): Andrew Hamer
Owner(s): Forte Hotels
Cost: Alc £45, set price L £17.95/ D £35. H/wine £19.50
Times: 12.30-2pm/7-10pm. Closed L Mon-Sat

Located in the ballroom of this mansion house, the Velore restaurant is a vivid reminder of Bath's reputation for Regency splendour. Traditional linen covered tables, tall white columns and heavy fabrics create a grand setting, but the staff are disarmingly friendly and relaxed. The chef concentrates on quality rather than number of choices, offering a restrained, English menu with an undercurrent of Italian passion (carpaccio of blue fin tuna; tomato risotto with spinach and wild

England

BATH *Continued*   Map 3 ST76

mushrooms). Dishes such as Cornish monkfish or roast chump of West Country lamb show off the finest local ingredients, whilst the extensive, good value wine list is equipped to complement any choice.

Accommodation: 102 rooms (102 en suite) ★ ★ ★ ★ ★
Directions: From A4 turn L onto A36 Warminster, R at mini rdbt and pass fire station, turn L into Sydney Place

Restaurant le Clos

Close to the Theatre Royal, Le Clos enjoys a peaceful environment, offering under its new owners a refreshing amalgam of French and modern British cuisine in recently refurbished surroundings. The popular range of menus offers fairly-priced set meals with alternatives on the *carte*. No little elaboration goes into starters such as Parmesan risotto with roast vegetables, followed by plaice fillets stuffed with salmon mousseline on deep-fried watercress and lamb noisettes with rosemary and bread sauce. Cointreau roulade with chocolate ganache and raspberry coulis typifies similarly convoluted yet successful desserts. Classic range of mainly French wines.

Directions: Next to the Theatre Royal

Combe Grove Manor Hotel

Georgian manor house set in over 80 acres of gardens and meadows. The formal restaurant is British and European influenced, offering some unusual combinations (among the canapés, a salsa style tartlet and salmon with rice). Flavours could occasionally be better balanced, as in a dish of partridge served with a very mild whisky cream sauce. Pleasing views and period decoration.

Smoking: No smoking in dining room
Civil licence: 50
Accommodation: 40 rooms (40 en suite) ★ ★ ★ ★
Directions: A4 from Bristol to roundabout (Newton St Loe), 2nd exit for Combe Down (5 miles). At Combe Down continue for 1.5 miles, hotel entrance on R

Additional: Sunday L.
Children welcome
Seats: 80. Private dining room 120.
Jacket and tie preferred
Style: Traditional
Smoking: No smoking in dining room; Air conditioning
Civil licence: 100

1 Seven Dials, Saw Close, BA1 1EN
Tel: 01225 444450
Fax: 01225 404044
Chef(s): Peter Quinion
Owner(s): Mr. D Gerhardt
Cost: *Alc* £30, set price L £13.95/ D £19.50. ☺ ☺ H/wine £10
Times: Noon-2.30pm/6-10pm.
Closed D Sun, 26 Dec, 1 Jan
Additional: Sunday L.
Children welcome
Seats: 70
Style: Classic, French
Smoking: No-smoking area; no pipes

Brassknocker Hill,
Monkton Combe, BA2 7HS
Tel: 01225 834644
Fax: 01225 834961
🇪 reservations@combegrovemanor.com
Chef(s): Kate Vaughan, Elvis Mayers
Owner(s): Mr J Parker
Cost: *Alc* £36.50, set price L £18/ D £27.50. H/wine £14.50
Times: Noon-2pm7-9.30pm.
Closed L Mon-Sat
Additional: Sunday L. Children 7 yrs+
Seats: 28. Private dining room 18
Style: Modern

Dukes' Hotel & Fitzroys NEW

Great Pulteney Street, BA2 4DN
Tel: 01225 787960
Telephone for further details

Martin Blunos of Lettonie fame brings his considerable talents and experience to this basement venue in the Dukes' Hotel. The room has undergone a complete transformation accordingly, with a "kind of Indian safari theme" featuring ornamental elephants, animal pictures and subtle lighting - mysterious and intimate stuff. A sensibly short menu offers a range of reassuringly straightforward dishes such as scallops with a fennel and butter sauce or shoulder of lamb off the bone with haricot beans and "terrific" Jersey Royals. Bread and butter pud has come apricot glazed, nutmeg infused and with a generous dollop of clotted cream. Sheer indulgence.

Lucknam Park

For **Lucknam Park** *see* entry under **Colerne, Gloucestershire**

The Moody Goose

7A Kingsmead Square, BA1 2AB
Tel: 01225 466688
Fax: 01225 466688
e moody-goose@excite.co.uk
Chef(s): Stephen Shore
Owner(s): Stephen & Victoria Shore
Cost: *Alc* £33, set price L £16-£18.50/D £24. ☺ ☺ H/wine £12
Times: Noon-2.30pm/6pm-Midnight. Closed Sun, 2wks Jan, BHs (except Good Friday)
Additional: Children 8 yrs+
Seats: 30. Private dining room 8
Style: Classic, Formal
Smoking: No smoking in dining room
Directions: Town centre

"A refreshing lack of pretension" is amongst much praise sung for a restaurant that lets the food do most of the talking. Staff go about their business with a quiet efficiency delivering an understated menu of balanced and intelligently conceived dishes. There is a deft touch at work in the likes of tempura of scallops with a surprisingly delicate sweet and sour cucumber sauce and an honest roast rump of lamb with root veg and a caper and grain mustard crust. Particular praise for some pinpoint desserts, including an excellent lemon tart with lime syrup and a "wonderful" tarragon sorbet.

England

No 5 Bistro

A great choice if you're after high quality cuisine without any of the trappings of formal restaurant etiquette. The informality here even extends to bring-your-own wine nights on Monday and Tuesday evenings (optional, no corkage charge) and at all times the service is merrily executed by casual but efficient, jeans-clad staff. The approach to food is anything but casual as demonstrated by an accomplished dish of roast chicken breast filled with goats' cheese wrapped in Coppa ham and served with balsamic vinegar and shallot dressing. Desserts are along the lines of iced hazelnut parfait with a dark chocolate sauce, or white chocolate terrine with dark chocolate sorbet.

5 Argyle Street, BA2 4BA
Tel: 01225 444499
Fax: 01225 318668
charleshome@no-5-bistro.fsbusiness.co.uk
Chef(s): S Smith & Paul Hearne
Owner(s): S Smith & C home
Cost: *Alc* £26. ☺ ☺ H/wine £11.25
Times: Closed Sun, L Mon,
1 wk Xmas
Additional: Children welcome
Seats: 35
Style: Bistro
Smoking: No smoking in dining room
Directions: 30yds from Pulteney Bridge towards Laura Place

The Olive Tree at the Queensberry Hotel

Russel Street, BA1 2QF
Tel: 01225 447928
Fax: 01225 446065
queensberry@dial.pipex.com
Chef(s): Jason Horne
Owner(s): Mr & Mrs S W Ross
Cost: *Alc* £30, set price L £13.50/
D £24. ☺ ☺ H/wine £12.50
Times: Noon-2pm/7-10pm.
Closed L Sun & BHs, 4 days Xmas
Additional: Children welcome
Seats: 60. Private dining room 30
Style: British
Smoking: No smoking in dining room
Accommodation: 29 rooms ★ ★ ★

Bright and airy restaurant with oriental rugs on the white tiled floor and lovely paintings by local artist Deidre Dyson. A colourful, modern mood prevails in the cooking too, with Mediterranean flavours at the fore. A meal might include a starter of saffron risotto with mussels, cockles and fresh herbs followed by pheasant with braised baby savoy cabbage and smoked bacon. The dessert menu features traditional puds (sticky toffee pudding, for example) alongside more elaborate options such as baked prune and Armagnac cream with ginger florentines. A popular place, frequented by locals as well as guests of the hotel.

Directions: City centre 100 yards N of Assembly Rooms in Lower Lansdown

Restaurant Lettonie

Wit and attention to detail are the defining characteristics of the cooking here, but it extends further than the plate with the entire dining experience expertly choreographed. Hot and cold canapés are served in the bar with its leather tub chairs and sofas where you are to peruse a menu that offers intricate but intelligent combinations with an endearing quirkiness and more than a hint of the Latvian roots of Martin Blunos. A seven course gastronomic menu offers the opportunity to get the broadest experience of dishes that run from salmon tortellinis with a rocket cream sauce, through rabbit rillettes with grain mustard and toasted brioche to rump of lamb with a mini shepherd's pie. The mock "boiled egg and soldiers" that is in fact a vanilla cream with mango mousse, strips of shortbread and sugar and chocolate replacing the salt and pepper also features as a pre-dessert and "pretty much sums up the approach" according to one reporter. Yes, there is much complexity, but it says a lot for the chef's technical dexterity and understanding of flavours that there is rarely an imbalance or clash. Some of the cooking is also "beautifully economic" as in seared fillets of red mullet with a white wine cream sauce for instance. The intelligence extends to a carefully selected wine list offering depth and variety from across the globe.

@@@@
35 Kelston Road, BA1 3QH
Tel: 01225 446676
Fax: 01225 447541
e Sian@lettonie.co.uk
Chef(s): Martin Blunos
Owner(s): Sian & Martin Blunos
Cost: Set price L £25/D £47.50-£60.
H/wine £19.50
Times: Noon-2pm/6.30-9.30pm.
Closed Sun, Mon, Xmas, New Year
Additional: Children welcome.
Vegetarian by request only
Seats: 40. Private dining room 12
Style: Classic
Smoking: No smoking in dining room
Accommodation: 4 rooms (4 en suite)
Directions: 2 miles from Bath on
A431 Bilton Road

Royal Crescent Hotel – Pimpernels

@@@

Relocated to the more capacious surroundings of the Dower House (where it has replaced the Brasserie) Pimpernels retains its Eastern take on modern British cooking. Whatever the influences there is a lightness of touch and accuracy apparent that has impressed in starters like "wonderfully fresh" seared tuna with a purée of carrot and a soy dressing or "meltingly tender" strips of braised belly pork with wilted Chinese greens and lardons. Desserts too can have a fusion twist but are just as likely to include a refined take on the likes of blackberry and apple crumble which might as a filo "cup" with a nutty crumble and blackberry ripple ice cream. Admirable wine list of tremendous depth.

Civil licence: 90
Accommodation: 45 rooms (45 en suite) ★ ★ ★ ★ ★
Directions: In city centre follow signs to Royal Crescent

16 Royal Crescent,
BA1 2LS
Tel: 01225 823333
Fax: 01225 339401
e reservations@royalcrescent.co.uk
Chef(s): Steven Blake
Owner(s): Mr. L Beere
Cost: Alc £45, set price L £25.
H/wine £23
Times: 12.30-2pm/7-10pm.
(Opening times vary at Xmas-New Year)
Additional: Sunday L.
Children welcome
Seats: 70. Private dining room 35
Style: Modern, Chic
Smoking: No smoking in dining room;
Air conditioning

England

BATH *Continued*   Map 3 ST76

Woods Restaurant

◉
9-13 Alfred Street, BA1 2QX
Tel: 01225 314812
Fax: 01225 443146
Telephone for further details

A bistro feel and ambience permeates the three separate dining areas suiting the cosmopolitan, city centre location. Good quality fresh, simple food is increasingly the norm here with a thick leek and potato soup yielding well-defined flavours and a mushroom goulash with garam masala proving to be suitably spicy, without going overboard.

BECKINGTON   Map 3 ST85

Woolpack Inn

◉
BA3 6SP
Tel: 01373 831244
Fax: 01373 831223
Telephone for further details

An old coaching inn that has been brought up-to-date while keeping its open fires, beams and flagstones. Eat in the bar, the glass-roofed Garden Room or the intimate Oak Room. Everything is freshly cooked - try confit of roasted vegetables with fresh thyme, olive oil and balsamic dressing or roast fresh monkfish on a potato galette with a sweet shallot cream.

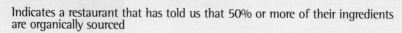
Indicates a restaurant that has told us that 50% or more of their ingredients are organically sourced

Prices quoted in the guide are for guidance only and are subject to change without notice

England

BRUTON
Map 3 ST63

Truffles

Gallery-style restaurant on two levels, decked out in suburban cream and terracotta. Monthly menus are based on local produce together with fresh fish from Brixham and meat from Smithfield. A vigorous cooking style offers up game terrine with layers of pigeon, partridge and pheasant, and seared fillet of sea bass with salmon mousse on a bed of fennel and spinach with Pernod sauce.

Additional: Sunday L. Children 6 yrs+
Seats: 30. Private dining room 12
Style: Modern
Smoking: No smoking in dining room; Air conditioning
Directions: Bruton centre, at start of one-way system, on L

95 High Street, BA10 0AR
Tel: 01749 812255
Fax: 01749 812255
e trufflesbruton@tinyworld.co.uk
Chef(s): Martin Bottrill
Owner(s): Mr & Mrs Bottrill
Cost: Alc £26.30, set price L £14.95/D £24.95. ☺ ☺
H/wine £12.95
Times: Noon-2pm/7-11pm. Closed Mon, D Sun, L Tue-Sat 2 wks Feb, 1 wk Oct

DULVERTON
Map 3 SS92

Ashwick House Hotel

A small, simple, south-facing dining room with beautiful views over swaying trees to a rich and varied slice of Exmoor countryside. Local produce is prepared with great care. Dishes such as smoked haddock soufflé wrapped in smoked salmon, and Somerset pork fillet with a prune and redcurrant sauce are the pleasing result.

Seats: 30. Private dining room 10. Jacket and tie preferred
Style: Country-house
Smoking: No smoking in dining room
Accommodation: 6 rooms (6 en suite) ★★
Directions: From M5 J27 follow signs to Dulverton, then take B3223 Lynton road and turn L after 2nd cattle grid

TA22 9QD
Tel: 01398 323868
Fax: 01398 323868
e ashwickhouse@talk21.com
Chef(s): Richard Sherwood
Owner(s): Richard Sherwood
Cost: Set price L £14.95/D £12.95. ☺ ☺ H/wine £10.50
Times: 12.30-1.45pm/7.15-8.30pm. Closed L Mon-Sat
Additional: Sunday L. Children 8 yrs+. Vegetarian by request only

EXFORD
Map 3 SS83

Crown Hotel

Views of the attractive terrace and water garden add to the palpable sense of tranquillity in the spacious restaurant. Alongside the decent bar food the kitchen works hard to achieve stylish restaurant cuisine using good fresh ingredients. Chargrilled chick pea cakes with a Parmesan and pancetta salad are an original and successful opening to a meal that might also feature crispy aromatic duck with creamy mustard onions and haricot vert. If you should feel desserts such as rich dark chocolate marquise with pistachio ice cream are excessively indulgent a selection of West Country cheeses offer a decent alternative.

Style: Modern, Chic
Smoking: No-smoking area
Accommodation: 17 rooms (16 en suite) ★★★
Directions: Village centre, facing the green

Park Street, TA24 7PP
Tel: 01643 831554
Fax: 01643 831665
e bradleyhotelsexmoor@easynet.co.uk
Chef(s): Gary Fisher
Owner(s): Mr. M Bradley
Cost: Set price L £18.50/D £25-£32.50. H/wine £11.25
Times: Dinner only, 7-9pm
Additional: Sunday L from noon. Bar food. Children welcome
Seats: 28. Private dining room 16. Jacket and tie preferred

STOP PRESS Change of Chef

England

FROME
Map 3 ST74

Talbot Inn Restaurant

Mells, BA11 3PN
Tel: 01373 812254
Fax: 01373 813599
✉ talbot.inn@lineone.net
Chef(s): Mark Jones
Cost: H/wine £9.50
Times: Closed 25-Dec
Additional: Children welcome
Seats: 65
Accommodation: 8 rooms ♦♦♦♦
Directions: From M5 J23 follow Wells
& Shepton Mallet signs towards
Frome. Before Frome turn left to Mells

A 15th-century inn with bags of character, and lots of little stone-flagged, beamed eating areas. A long *carte* and daily fish choice offer the likes of ravioli of wild mushroom, fillet of pork in puff pastry with sage and onion stuffing and Calvados sauce, and banana cheesecake. A buzzy, pleasant atmosphere.

HINTON CHARTERHOUSE
Map 3 ST75

Homewood Park

In a delightfully rural setting of mature gardens and woodland, yet only a few minutes' drive from historic Bath, well-loved Homewood Park remains a perennial draw for lovers of fine food. In particular, the eight-course tasting dinner is not to be missed by those endowed with large appetites and deep pockets. A confident and accomplished kitchen makes everything from canapés and breads to ice creams and petits fours and produces modern, yet timeless, interpretations of classical dishes with faultless accuracy. Pan-fried Isle of Skye langoustines with toasted hazelnuts and tarragon ravioli in a lightly frothed bouillon is described as a minor triumph, and the following rump of West Country lamb with fondant potato and white haricot bean sauce as suitably robust without ever being overpowering. Original oil paintings and antique furniture with white tablecloths, fresh flowers and candles lend a formal air to the restaurant, which nonetheless has a relaxed feel, matched by service that exudes unstuffy efficiency and professionalism.

BA3 6BB
Tel: 01225 723731
Fax: 01225 723820
✉ res@homewoodpark.com
Chef(s): Nigel Godwin
Owner(s): Mr A Moxon &
Mr Carvella
Cost: *Alc* £50, set price L £19.50.
H/wine £16
Times: Noon-1.30pm/7-9.30pm
Additional: Sunday L. Bar food.
Children welcome
Seats: 60. Private dining room 40
Style: Country-house
Smoking: No smoking in dining room
Civil licence: 50
Accommodation: 19 rooms (19 en
suite) ★ ★ ★

Directions: 5 miles SE of Bath off A36, turn by marked sharpstone

HOLCOMBE
Map 3 ST64

The Ring O'Roses
Country Inn
NEW

On the outside it's very much a village inn dating from the 16th century. Inside you'll find a spacious restaurant serving vibrant food using lots of fresh ingredients. Thai fish cake with ginger and coriander might be followed by grilled calves' liver with bacon, and apple and apricot pie, all beautifully presented.

Stratton Road, BA3 5EB
Tel: 01761 232478
Telephone for further details

England

The finest wine lists

The AA wine awards recognise some of the finest wine lists in the country. As well as the winners for England, Scotland and Wales you will find this symbol throughout the guide indicating those restaurants who reached the final shortlist and others that were recognised for their excellence in specialist areas. The AA wine awards are sponsored by T&W wines of Thetford.

HUNSTRETE   Map 3 ST66

Hunstrete House

A change at the stove saw Phil Hobson taking over the reins from Stewart Eddy at this classic country house setting. It's a formal, but not over stuffy dining experience with mainly French staff dispensing professional and attentive service. The menu offers some intricate combinations in the country house style with the likes of a crispy potato parcel with chicken, wild mushrooms, a cep sauce and crispy pancetta amongst the starters and a main course of sautéed John Dory fillets with pommes Parisienne and a light red wine jus featuring "first-rate" fish. Desserts have included an "accomplished" chocolate and caramel delice with earl grey sorbet. Heavyweight wine list offers bags of quality

BS39 4NS
Tel: 01761 490490
Fax: 01761 490732
e user@hunstretehouse.co.uk
Chef(s): Phillip Hobson
Owner(s): Mr R Gillis
Cost: Alc £40, set price L £19.95.
H/wine £14.95
Times: Noon-2pm/7-9.30pm.
Additional: Sunday L.
Children welcome
Seats: 50. Private dining room 30.
Jacket and tie preferred
Style: Country-house
Smoking: No smoking in dining room
Civil licence: 50
Accommodation: 22 rooms (22 en suite) ★ ★ ★
Directions: On A368 – 8 miles from Bath

MINEHEAD   Map 3 SS94

Periton Park Hotel

An elevated position affords pleasant views of the wooded grounds with an interesting selection of dishes based on fresh local produce appropriate to the rural situation. Roasted Exmoor goats' cheese might be followed by West Country lamb fillet with a port and redcurrant glaze.

Style: Country-house
Smoking: No smoking in dining room
Accommodation: 8 rooms (8 en suite) ★ ★
Directions: Off A39. Signposted Porlock & Lynmouth. Hotel about 1mile on the L

Middlecombe, TA24 8SW
Tel: 01643 706885
Fax: 01643 706885
Chef(s): Angela Hunt
Owner(s): Mr & Mrs Hunt
Cost: Alc £23. ☺ H/wine £9.50
Times: Dinner only, 7-9pm.
Closed Jan
Additional: Children 12 yrs+
Seats: 30. Private dining room 14

England

PORLOCK

Map 3 SS84

Andrews on the Weir

Porlock Weir, TA24 8PB
Tel: 01643 863300
Fax: 01643 863311
e information@andrewsontheweir.co.uk
Chef(s): Andrew Dixon
Owner(s): Mr A Dixon &
Mr Rodney Sens
Cost: Alc £35, set price L £14/D £25.
☺ H/wine £11.50
Times: Noon-2.30pm/7-9.30pm.
Closed Mon, D Sun, 2nd-3rd wk Jan,
2nd-3rd wk Nov
Additional: Sunday L.
Children 12 yrs+
Seats: 30
Style: French, Country-house
Smoking: No smoking in dining room
Accommodation: 5 rooms (5 en suite)
◆◆◆◆

In an elegant Georgian building beside Porlock Harbour, Andrew Dixon and Sarah Baudins run a commendable restaurant-with-rooms, with splendid views across the Bristol Channel to the South Wales coast. Fresh sea bass, literally landed on the quay opposite, is treated with the reverence it deserves, alongside locally reared beef, lamb from the surrounding Exmoor hills and some superb West Country cheeses. Andrew's cooking, full of creativity and not a little daring, produces amongst the starters oven roasted quail cooked to perfection with great depth of flavour and sauced with truffle, cabbage, bacon and a dinky quail's egg. In early spring, the Exmoor lamb is unmissable - full of sweet grassy flavour and dressed with ravioli of its sweetbreads and a superbly restrained tarragon jus and garlic velouté. Desserts are a strength and accomplished petits fours come with good espresso.

Directions: From M5 J25 follow A358 towards Minehead, then take A39 through Porlock and onto Porlock Weir. Hotel is 1.5m further

The Oaks Hotel

Fresh flowers crown the traditional décor and wonderful views of Porlock Weir are an added bonus. It is the quality of ingredients that really win through here, with a fillet of beef (provided by the local butcher) hitting all the right notes and a béarnaise sauce and accurately cooked vegetables complementing well.

TA24 8ES
Tel: 01643 862265
Fax: 01643 863131
e oakshotel@aol.com
Chef(s): Anne Riley
Owner(s): Tim & Anne Riley
Cost: Set price D £25. ☺ H/wine £9
Times: Dinner only, 7-8.30pm.
Closed Nov-Mar
Additional: Children 8 yrs+

Seats: 22. **Style:** Traditional, Country-house
Smoking: No smoking in dining room
Accommodation: 9 rooms (9 en suite) ★★
Directions: At bottom of Dunstersteepe Road, on L on entering Porlock from Minehead

SHAPWICK

Map 3 ST43

Shapwick House Hotel

A stone manor house dating back to the 15th century with a Georgian dining room offering views to the Mendips. An

Monks Drive, TA7 9NL
Tel: 01458 210321
Fax: 01458 210729

imaginative fixed-price menu. Mains such as paupiette of lemon sole with wilted spinach and Champagne sauce remain memorable, even after a luscious iced lemon soufflé with home-made shortbread.

Style: Country-house
Smoking: No smoking in dining room
Accommodation: 12 rooms (12 en suite) ★ ★
Directions: From M5 J23 follow signs to Glastonbury, L onto A39. After 5 miles hotel signed on the L

 keith@shapwickhouse.free-on-line.co.uk
Chef(s): Keith Gibson
Owner(s): Mr & Mrs K T Gibson
Cost: Alc £25, set price D £25-£35.
☺ H/wine £10.50
Times: Dinner only, 6.30-8.30pm
Closed Sun
Additional: Children 8 yrs+
Seats: 30. Private dining room 20

SHEPTON MALLET

Map 3 ST64

Bowlish House

You could be forgiven for feeling slightly swamped by the imposing nature of this old Georgian house and the extensive nature of the menus. Fear not, although the interior is formal and elegant, it is both snug in atmosphere and unpretentious in attitude. A roast fillet of brill set on a bed of spaghetti courgettes in a chive cream sauce is a particular success.

Seats: 30. Private dining room 24. Jacket and tie preferred
Style: Classic. **Smoking:** No smoking in dining room
Accommodation: 3 rooms (3 en suite)
Directions: 0.25 mile from town centre on A371 Wells road

Bowlish, BA4 5JD
Tel: 01749 342022
Fax: 01749 342022
Chef(s): Deirdre Forde
Owner(s): John & Deidre Forde
Cost: Alc £27.50/D £21-£30.
H/wine £10.95
Times: Dinner only, 7-9.30pm.
Closed Sun-Mon, 1-2 wks Winter
Additional: Children welcome.
Vegetarian by request only

Charlton House Hotel

Not a place for the indecisive diner, this country hotel restaurant offers a choice of three eating areas including the conservatory, and a set of menus with several tempting options. There's the lengthy 'menu gourmand' for the serious foodie, then a set vegetarian selection which might also persuade meat eaters, and a seasonal fixed-price menu, all offering accomplished and imaginative cooking. The simplest dishes are the strongest, as in lentil broth served with foie gras and confit of duck and leek terrine, a terrific composition. Minced lamb kofta with blackened aubergine and Greek yoghurt might also feature, or straightforward ballotine of Scottish salmon, while loin of veal poached in milk, wrapped in pancetta and roasted, then served with cocotte potato and veal jus was a triumph. Complexity occasionally outweighs simplicity, and passion fruit sorbet with several accompaniments was enjoyable if a little over elaborate.

Charlton Road, BA4 4PR
Tel: 01749 342008
Fax: 01749 346362
 enquiries@chaltonhouse.com
Chef(s): Adam Fellows
Owner(s): Roger Saul
Cost: Alc £38.50, set price L £16.50/D £35.50-£55. ☺ H/wine £15
Times: Noon-2pm/7.30-9.30pm.
Additional: Sunday L. Bar food L.
Children welcome
Seats: 84. Private dining room 36
Style: Chic, Country house
Smoking: No smoking in dining room
Civil licence: 75
Accommodation: 16 rooms (16 en suite) ★ ★ ★
Directions: M4 J17, follow A350 S at Trowbridge join A361. Hotel is located 1 mile before Shepton Mallet on the L

SHIPHAM
Map 3 ST45

Daneswood House Hotel

Cuck Hill, BS25 1RD
Tel: 01934 843145
Fax: 01934 843824
e info@daneswoodhotel.co.uk
Chef(s): Heather Matthews &
Mrs E Hodges
Owner(s): D. Hodges & E. Hodges
Cost: Set price L £19.95/D £29.95. ☺
H/wine £10.50
Times: Noon-2pm/7-9.30pm.
Closed 26 Dec-4 Jan
Additional: Sunday L.
Children welcome
Seats: 50. Private dining room 30.
Jacket and tie preferred
Style: Traditional, Country-house
Smoking: No smoking in dining room
Accommodation: 17 rooms (17 en
suite) ★ ★ ★
Directions: 1m from A38 between
Bristol & Bridgwater

An Edwardian mansion occupying an elevated position in both geographical and culinary terms. The former affords stunning views across delightful countryside to the Bristol Channel in the far distance, the latter a fair panorama of taste and texture. Take for example a main dish of poached fillets of turbot with fresh wilted spinach - a good central concept complemented by a cake of purée of cauliflower with ground almonds, a pool of coconut sauce and tiny mounds of fresh pasta. Intriguing and successful desserts such as warm brioche butter pudding and honey yoghurt bavarois are an added attraction.

STON EASTON
Map 3 ST65

Ston Easton Park

The fine plasterwork and soft furnishings of the dining room are very much in keeping with the 18th-century grandeur of the house which is set in impressive landscaped gardens and parkland. Imagination and considered care are in strong evidence in starters such as beetroot soup with confit duck raviolis and Cornish scallops with roasted salsify and vanilla butter. Expect mains along the lines of herb crusted turbot on a leek and pear compôte with Poire William butter sauce. An iced parfait of white chocolate and lemons set on caramelised pineapple brings things to a close in successful fashion.

Civil licence: 60
Accommodation: 23 rooms (23 en suite) ★ ★ ★ ★
Directions: On A37 from Bristol to Shepton Mallet, about 6 miles from Wells

BA3 4DF
Tel: 01761 241631
Fax: 01761 241377
e stoneastonpark@stoneaston.co.uk
Chef(s): Garry Cook
Owner(s): Van Essen Hotels
Cost: Alc £42, set price L £16-£39.50.
H/wine £20
Times: Noon-2pm/7-9.30pm
Additional: Sunday L. Children 7yrs+
Seats: 40. Private dining room 24.
Jacket and tie preferred
Style: Traditional, European
Smoking: No smoking in dining room

TAUNTON
Map 3 ST22

Brazz

A lively, buzzing restaurant whose bright yellow walls are adorned with equally bright pictures. The sparky setting also includes Brazz's trademark fish tank and a domed ceiling full of star-like lights. Brasserie style menus cater for breakfast, coffee

Castle Bow, TA1 1NF
Tel: 01823 252000
Fax: 01823 336066
Owner(s): Mr K Chapman
Cost: Alc £22. ☺ ☺ H/wine £11

England

breaks and evening meals - the latter ranging from grills to the likes of moules marinière.

Times: 11.30-3pm/6.30-10.30pm.
Closed 25 Dec
Additional: Sunday L. Bar food.
Children welcome
Seats: 100
Style: Modern, Chic
Smoking: Air conditioning
Directions: Follow signs for town centre, castle & museum

Castle Hotel

Castle Green, TA1 1NF
Tel: 01823 272671
Fax: 01823 336066
 reception@the-castle-hotel.com
Chef(s): Richard Guest
Owner(s): Mr C H Chapman
Cost: Set price L £22/D £32.
H/wine £12.50
Times: 12.30-2pm/7-9.30pm.
Additional: Sunday L.
Children welcome
Seats: 60. Private dining room 12.
Jacket and tie preferred
Style: Classic, Formal
Smoking: No smoking in dining room
Accommodation: 44 rooms (44 en suite) ★ ★ ★
Directions: M5 J25, follow signs for town centre/castle

The heavily-scented flowers of an old wisteria cover the front of this town-centre hotel from late spring onwards, but even when the petals have fallen Kit Chapman's Castle remains a landmark of modern British cooking. Following the well-worn path trodden by Gary Rhodes and Phil Vickery, Richard Guest has now settled in at the helm. There's no shortage of imagination or ambition, although menu descriptions along the lines of "Great British Beef!" and "Orange! Orange! Orange!" might grate with some. The somewhat calmer hues of the restaurant encourage you to take a relaxed approach (this is not an experience to rush) and there are few distraction from the food. That is undoubtedly a good thing - there is enough going on the plate to require your full attention. Take for instance, starters like a delicately flavoured pyramid of jellied tomato consommé with flakes of Brixham crab and honest, sturdy main courses such as saddle of rabbit with liver parfait on braised vegetables or a highly successful dish of spiced pig's trotter with apricots and pork belly on apple cream. Peripherals come in the form of a sharp amuse bouche of cucumber water laced with lime juice and a touch of vanilla and some excellent petit fours. And as for the "Orange! Orange! Orange!" it's an elaborate hemisphere of chocolate and orange with enough tang to justify the exclamation marks.

TAUNTON *Continued* Map 3 ST22

Mount Somerset Hotel

Henlade, TA3 5NB
Tel: 01823 442500
Fax: 01823 442900
Chef(s): Richard Herkes
Owner(s): The Von Essen Group
Cost: *Alc* £30.35, set price L £22/
D £27.50. H/wine £15
Times: Noon-2pm/7-9.30pm
Additional: Sunday L.
Children welcome
Seats: 40. Private dining room 30
Style: Modern, Country-house
Accommodation: 11 rooms (11 en
suite) ★ ★ ★
Directions: 3 miles SE of Taunton.
From M5 J25 take A358 (Chard); turn
R in Henlade (Stoke St Mary), then
turn L at T-junction, Hotel entrance
400yds on R

The hotel is a classic Regency building with sumptuous
furnishings and impressive views over Taunton Vale from the
panelled Somerset Restaurant. Quality table appointments are
enhanced by fresh flowers and candles, and the *carte* is
supplemented by a menu du jour. A typically ambitious dish
would be guinea fowl and wild mushroom sausage with pearl
barley risotto.

WELLINGTON Map 3 ST12

Bindon House

Langford Budville, TA21 0RU
Tel: 01823 400070
Fax: 01823 400071
🄴 stay@bindon.com
Chef(s): Patrick Roberts
Owner(s): Lynn & Mark Jaffa
Cost: *Alc* £45, set price L £12.95/
D £29.95. H/wine £13.50
Times: Noon-2pm/7.30-9pm.
Additional: Sunday L.
Children 10yrs+
Seats: 50. Private dining room 29
Style: Traditional Country-house
Smoking: No smoking in dining room
Civil licence: 50
Accommodation: 12 rooms (12 en
suite) ★ ★ ★

A most unusual, baroque country house in a fabulous setting,
Bindon Hotel is dominated by memorabilia of the Duke of
Wellington. Naturally, Beef Wellington is a popular favourite on
the generally classic menu. Not that modern influences are
ignored: a trilogy of duck with roast potatoes, fig Tatin and foie
gras sauce or pan-fried tenderloin of pork stuffed with
mushrooms on a bed of tartlets of roast apples and cider cream
sauce are among the modern European dishes one can expect.
While luxurious puddings such as gourmandises on caramel -
baby crème caramel, caramel ice cream, vanilla mousse and
caramel parfait are a great temptation.

Directions: From Wellington B3187 to Langville Budville,
through village & R towards Wiveliscombe, R at Jct, past Bindon
Farm R after 450 yds

WELLS Map 3 ST54

Market Place Hotel

 One Market Place, BA5 2RW
Tel: 01749 836300
Fax: 01749 836301
e marketplace@bhere.co.uk
Chef(s): Paul Mungo-West
Owner(s): Christopher Chapman
Cost: Alc £24.50. ☺ H/wine £11
Times: Dinner only, 7-10pm.
Closed 28-31 Dec
Additional: Bar food D.
Children welcome
Seats: 60
Style: Modern, Scandanavian
Smoking: No smoking in dining room
Accommodation: 38 rooms (38 en
suite) ★ ★ ★
Directions: A39-A371 in centre of
town, on one-way system. Directly in
front of conduit in market square

A unique hotel seamlessly combining modern style and
elegance with the character and appeal of a building built over
500 years ago. Dishes such as a smooth parfait of duck livers on
a salad of pink grapefruit and sugar-snap peas are well designed
to wake up the taste buds.

WILLITON Map 3 ST04

White House Hotel

 Long Street, TA4 4QW
Tel: 01984 632306
Chef(s): Dick & Kay smith
Owner(s): Dick & Kay Smith
Cost: Set price D £34. H/wine £14
Times: Dinner only, 7.30-8.30pm.
Closed early Nov-mid May
Additional: Children welcome
Seats: 26
Style: Classic, Chic
Smoking: No smoking in dining room
Accommodation: 10 rooms (10 en
suite) ★ ★
Directions: On A39 in centre of
village

After some thirty years, Dick and Kay Smith's modest roadside
inn remains a one-off; a restaurant-with-rooms long before such
terminology was ever thought of, with an annually up-dated
wine list that bears the stamp of a connoisseur, and cooking
that relies on local shopping, careful planning through the day
and boundless enthusiasm in preparation and service. The
restaurant's sandstone walls provide the backdrop for a fine
collection of oil and watercolour paintings that include Hans
Schwarz originals. Though less original, much thought goes into
preparing nightly menus that might include a tartlet of fresh
Brixham crab and prawns or the ever-popular Withycombe
asparagus with hollandaise. This might be followed by lightly
roasted, boned loin of local spring lamb - perfectly cooked and
enticingly pink -or escalope of wild salmon baked in pastry with
fresh lime and ginger. Follow with a rich compôte of damsons
accompanied by textured almond and polenta cake of a peasant
origin that pre-dates many more modish fabrications.

England

WINCANTON
Map 3 ST72

Holbrook House Hotel

A stunning range of leisure facilities makes this hotel a must for both the keep-fit fanatic and those in serious need of pampering. Perhaps the best medicine for the jaded and the hyper-active lies beyond the health club, where the cuisine presented in the formal dining room is a tonic in itself. Look out for the likes of pigeon breast with ceps and pan-fried fillet of sea bass with seared calamari and sauce vierge. Desserts include some innovative takes on the classics like baked Alaska with pear ice cream and griottine cherries.

Civil licence: 60
Accommodation: 20 rooms (20 en suite) ★ ★ ★
Directions: From A303 at Wincanton, turn left on A371 towards Castle Cary and Shepton Mallet.

Holbrook, BA9 8BS
Tel: 01963 32377
Fax: 01963 32681
e Reception@Holbrookhouse.co.uk
Chef(s): Mark Harrington
Owner(s): Mr & Mrs John McGinley
Cost: Set price L £16/D £25.95. ☺
H/wine £15
Times: 12.30-2pm/7.30-9.30pm.
Additional: Sunday L. Bar food. Children welcome
Seats: 35. Private dining room 150. Jacket and tie preferred
Style: Country-house
Smoking: No smoking in dining room

WINSFORD
Map 3 SS93

Karslake House NEW

Snug 15th-century malthouse set in the beautiful Exmoor National Park. The bowed windows of the spacious restaurant look out on to the lane and cobbles. Dishes worthy of note include a wild mushroom risotto, tender new season lamb with a redcurrant reduction, and a cherry and almond tart.

Additional: Children 12yrs+. **Seats:** 18
Style: Country House
Smoking: No smoking in dining room
Accommodation: 6 rooms (4 en suite) ♦♦♦♦
Directions: A361 to Winsford. L at garage. R at Royal Oak

Halse Lane, TA24 7JE
Tel: 01643 851242
Fax: 01643 851242
e karslakehouse@aol.com
Chef(s): Nikki Plumb & Juliette Mountford
Owner(s): Mr & Mrs F N G Mountford
Cost: Set price D £27.50.
H/wine £14.50
Times: Dinner only, 7-10pm.
Closed Feb, March & Xmas

WITHYPOOL
Map 3 SS93

Royal Oak Inn

Although the adjoining bar areas are very much the quintessential village inn, the 'Acorn Restaurant' errs more on the side of comfort and simple modern décor. Meat and fish is sourced locally and a careful approach to preparation and presentation is apparent in dishes like slow roasted pheasant, on a bed of tagliatelle with cider cream sauce.

TA24 7QP
Tel: 01643 831506
Fax: 01643 831659
e enquiries@royaloakwithypool. co.uk
Chef(s): Oliver Knell
Owner(s): Mrs G Slogett
Cost: A/c £28, set price L £11.95/D £19.50-£21.50. ☺ ☺ H/wine £9.80
Times: Noon-2pm/7-9pm.
Closed L Mon-Sat
Additional: Sunday L. Bar food. Children welcome. Vegetarian by request only
Seats: 32. Private dining room 32
Style: Modern
Smoking: No smoking in dining room
Accommodation: 8 rooms (7 en suite) ★ ★
Directions: A361 via S Molton, N Molton to Withypool. M5 J25, take A358 then B3224 to Withypool

WIVELISCOMBE   Map 3 ST02

Langley House Hotel

Tranquil charm exudes from every inch of this idyllic property - from the gentle curves of the Brendon Hills glimpsed through landscaped gardens, to the pastel shades of the comfortable restaurant. Fresh produce including herbs and vegetables from the kitchen garden provide a strong basis for quality cuisine, ably forged into well balanced dishes by skilful hands. A four-course meal might open simply with an avocado and orange salad, followed by roasted cod with a sun-dried tomato topping. Mignons of (top-notch) Aberdeen Angus Beef might be followed by elderflower and elderberry syllabub.

Accommodation: 8 rooms (8 en suite) ★ ★
Directions: Off B3277, 0.5m from Wiveliscombe on the Langley Marsh Rd

Langley Marsh, TA4 2UF
Tel: 01984 623318
Fax: 01984 624573
e user@langley.in2home.co.uk
Chef(s): Peter Wilson
Owner(s): Mr & Mrs P Wilson
Cost: Set price D £27.50-£32.50. H/wine £12.50
Times: Dinner only, 7.30-8.30pm
Additional: Bar food L.
Children 7 yrs+
Seats: 18. Private dining room 18
Style: Country-house
Smoking: No smoking in dining room

YEOVIL   Map 3 ST51

Little Barwick House

Tim and Emma Ford have a good pedigree, but even so their delightful Georgian dower house restaurant far exceeds expectations. From the spontaneity of their hospitality to the classiness of the cuisine, they consistently make an impact. The place could be a million miles from nearby Yeovil, and the farmyard behind the house promises fresh flavours and wholesome produce. A set menu offers two or three courses priced accordingly. Terrine of duck confit and foie gras with sweet and sour plums has worked well, and pink roasted rump of lamb with aubergine confit and black olive jus on fresh spinach looked as good as it tasted. Other daily-changing dishes like warm salad of pan-fried scallops, and grilled fillets of Cornish red mullet should please, while banana tarte Tatin comes with a sensational star anise ice cream. Good house wines, and some realistically priced clarets and Burgundies.

Barwick Village,
BA22 9TD
Tel: 01935 423902
Fax: 01935 420908
Chef(s): Timothy Ford
Owner(s): Emma & Timothy Ford
Cost: Set price L £13.95/D £27.95.
☺ ☺ H/wine £11.60
Times: Closed L Mon, D Mon
Additional: Sunday L. Bar food L.
Children welcome
Seats: 40
Smoking: No-smoking area
Civil licence: 40
Accommodation: 6 rooms ★
Directions: Turn off A371 Yeovil to Dorchester opp Red House pub, 0.25m on L

England

YEOVIL *Continued*   Map 3 ST51

Priory House   NEW

Small restaurant in a quiet Somerset village, serving imaginative food that hits all the right spots. Within weeks of opening it was already pulling in the punters, though at this early stage the atmosphere was a little subdued. Not so the cooking: whole grilled scallops wrapped in smoked salmon with tartar sauce, and sautéed foie gras with toasted brioche and caramelised orange caused a stir, while escalope of brill with baby leek, savoy cabbage and chive velouté exceeded expectations. The wine list is very attractively priced, with plenty of good choice under £20.

Directions: Follow signposts to Stoke-sub-Hamdon, off A303. 1 mile

Stoke Sub Hamdon,
Tel: 01935 822826
Fax: 01935 822826
Chef(s): Martin Hadden
Owner(s): Martin & Michele Hadden
Cost: Set price L £18-£28/D £28. ☺ H/wine £13
Times: Noon-2pm/7-9pm.
Closed Sun-Mon, 2Wks Aug, 2Wks Xmas, BHs
Additional: Children welcome
Seats: 30
Style: French
Smoking: No smoking in dining room

Yeovil Court Hotel

Something of a scattergun menu catering for a diverse clientele. Dishes range through Thai fishcakes with couscous and sundried tomato dressing, to fillet of pork stuffed with apricot crumble and served with Madeira jus. Interesting vegetables included beetroot in batter, dauphinoise potatoes, red cabbage and cauliflower, all notably crisp and fresh.

West Coker Road, BA20 2HE
Tel: 01935 863746
Fax: 01935 863990
e verve@yeovilcourt.freeserve.co.uk
Chef(s): Steve McGuire
Owner(s): Brian & Carol Devonport
Cost: A/c £20, set price L £10.50/ D £25. ☺ ☺ H/wine £10.90
Times: Noon-1.45pm/7-9.30pm.
Closed L Sat, 26-30 Dec
Additional: Sunday L. Children welcome
Seats: 50. Private dining room 40
Style: Traditional, Country-house
Smoking: No smoking in dining room
Accommodation: 30 rooms (30 en suite) ★★★
Directions: 2m west of Yeovil on A30

STAFFORDSHIRE

LEEK   Map SJ95

Three Horseshoes Inn

A family-run hostelry with an extensive menu ranging from the resolutely traditional such as chilled melon served in port, to the satisfyingly robust like herb crusted chicken breast served on a bed of tagliatelle with mild cheeses, asparagus, sun-dried tomato and mushrooms.

Buxton Road, Blackshaw Moor,
ST13 8TW
Tel: 01538 300296
Fax: 01538 300320
Chef(s): Mark & Stephen Kirk

Owner(s): Bill & Jill Kirk
Cost: Alc £25. ☺ H/wine £12.50
Times: Noon-1.30pm/7-9pm.
Closed L Mon-Sat, 26 Dec-30 Dec
Additional: Sunday L. Bar food.
Children welcome
Seats: 100
Style: Traditional
Smoking: No smoking in dining room
Accommodation: 6 rooms (6 en suite)
★ ★

Directions: M6 J15 or 16 onto A500. Exit A53 towards Leek.
Turn L onto A50 (Burslem)

STAFFORD
Map 7 SJ92

Moat House

A large, attractively designed conservatory is a successful
addition to the 15th century moated manor house. Views of the
adjacent canal coupled with marquee-style drapery create a
bright and appealing environment in which to dine. The menu
maintains a close relationship with the seasons although even in
winter light dishes such as sun-dried tomato muffin with
Parmesan rarebit and rocket pistou are available alongside
more hearty offerings of pheasant breast with ballotine of
guinea fowl leg, leek mousse and a juniper scented sauce, and
the like. Desserts tend towards the robust, along the lines of
steamed sticky toffee and apple sponge with caramel ice cream
and banana crisps.

Civil licence: 120
Accommodation: 32 rooms (32 en suite) ★ ★ ★ ★
Directions: M6 J13 towards Stafford, 1st R to Acton Trussell,
Moat House by church

Lower Penkridge Road,
Acton Trussell, ST17 0RJ
Tel: 01785 712217
Fax: 01785 715344
e info@moathouse.co.uk
Chef(s): Matthew Davies
Owner(s): Mr C & Mr M Lewis
Cost: Alc £35.75, set price L £12.95-
£16.95/D £23.95. ☺ ☺
H/wine £14.95
Times: Noon-2pm/7-10pm.
Closed 25-26 Dec, 1 Jan
Additional: Sunday L. Bar food.
Children welcome
Seats: 120. Private dining room 150
Style: Classic
Smoking: No smoking in dining room;
Air conditioning

STOKE-ON-TRENT

Map 7 SJ84

Haydon House Hotel

Some might find it disconcerting, but you can always tell the time in this restaurant - there are clocks everywhere. The European influenced menu includes timeless classics such as tournados Rossini and Welsh rack of lamb. Assured cooking, a good wine list and smart, polite staff, make this a popular choice with locals and residents.

Smoking: No-smoking area; no pipes; no cigars; Air conditioning
Civil licence: 40
Accommodation: 23 rooms (23 en suite) ★ ★ ★
Directions: From M6 J15 A500 to Stoke-on-Trent, turn onto A53 Hanley/Newcastle, at roundabout take 1st exit, go up hill, take 2nd L at top of hill

Haydon Street, Basford,
ST4 6JD
Tel: 01782 711311
Fax: 01782 717470
Chef(s): John Wilson
Owner(s): Mr J F Machin
Cost: *Alc* £22, set price L £11.50/ D £15.90. ☺ ☺ H/wine £8.95
Times: Noon-2pm/7-9.30pm.
Closed L Sat & Sun
Additional: Bar food. Children welcome
Seats: 45. Private dining room 20.
Jacket and tie preferred
Style: Traditional

WATERHOUSES

Map 7 SK05

Old Beams Restaurant with Rooms

"As close to auberge style as can be found in the UK" has been remarked of this impressive, family-run, riverside restaurant. A huge central log fire dominates the beamed room - just the thing on a cold day when you want to linger over a meal. From start to finish the 'wow' factor is present in some classy cooking, and delicious home-made breads and amuse bouche hint at what is to come. The short menu might open with pressed terrine of venison with a beetroot marmalade, or pan-fried sea bass on basil mash with creamed leeks and chive sauce. Lightly roasted squab pigeon with port wine cabbage and potato galette, artichokes and ceps, was a main dish which recently scored right off the board. Rich dark chocolate gateau and iced nougat with pistachio sauce further illustrates the kitchen skills. All in all an invitation to indulge, with overnight accommodation just across the road.

Directions: On A523, Leek to Ashbourne Road

Leek Road, ST10 3HW
Tel: 01538 308254
Fax: 01538 308157
Chef(s): Nigel Wallis
Owner(s): Nigel & Ann Wallis
Cost: *Alc* £35, set price L £23. H/wine £15.95
Times: Noon-1.30pm/7-9pm.
Closed Mon, L Tue-Thu & Sat, D Sun, Jan
Additional: Sunday L. Children welcome.
Vegetarian by request only
Seats: 45. Private dining room 12
Style: Country-house
Smoking: No smoking in dining room
Accommodation: 5 rooms (5 en suite)
★ ★

England

SUFFOLK

ALDEBURGH

Map 5 TM45

Lighthouse

Six years ago, when they opened this acclaimed, bistro-style, fish restaurant, the owners decided that since Suffolk's trendiest seaside town lacked only a lighthouse they would give it one. Now, it's hard to get in without booking, yet the food remains as deceptively simple as ever: locally caught Dover soles in lemon and butter, skate with blackened butter and capers, bread-and-butter pudding made with brioche, marmalade and whisky.

Style: Modern, British
Smoking: No-smoking area; no pipes; no cigars; Air conditioning
Directions: From A12 take A1094 to Aldeburgh. Past church to T-jcnt. Turn R into High St. Hotel between cinema and garage

77 High Street, IP15 5AU
Tel: 01728 453377
Fax: 01728 453377
e sarafox@dircon.co.uk
Chef(s): Sara Fox, Guy Welsh, G Battle
Owner(s): Sara Fox & Peter Hill
Cost: Alc £15. ☺ ☺ H/wine £10.75
Times: Noon-2.30pm/7-10pm. Closed 2 wks Jan, 1 wk Oct
Additional: Sunday L. Children welcome
Seats: 90. Private dining room 25. Jacket and tie preferred

Regatta Restaurant

Nautical murals, pine floors and atmospheric sea views work well for this popular bistro. The menu is fairly eclectic featuring daily changing specials and making good use of local fish. What's more a busy events calendar offers weekly features such as 'crab week' and 'moules, frites and Belgian beer week' .

Additional: Sunday L. Bar food L. Children welcome
Seats: 90. Private dining room 30
Style: Bistro-Style
Smoking: No-smoking area; no pipes; no cigars; Air conditioning
Directions: Middle of High Street, town centre

171 High Street, IP15 5AN
Tel: 01728 452011
Fax: 01728 453324
e regatta.restaurant@aldeburgh. sagegost.co.uk
Chef(s): Robert Mabey
Owner(s): Mr & Mrs R Mabey
Cost: Alc £18/D £10. ☺ ☺ H/wine £9.50
Times: Noon-2pm/6-10pm. Restricted opening in winter

Wentworth Hotel

Charming hotel restaurant overlooking Aldeburgh beach. Brightly decorated with interesting paintings the atmosphere is well suited to the quality, unpretentious cuisine on offer. Don't expect too many frills or fancies, the flavours of dishes such as whole grilled plaice with parsley butter only benefit from the lack of culinary clutter.

Additional: Sunday L. Bar food L. Children welcome
Seats: 90. Private dining room 20. Jacket and tie preferred
Style: Classic
Smoking: No smoking in dining room
Accommodation: 37 rooms (35 en suite) ★ ★ ★
Directions: From A12 take A1094 to Aldeburgh. In Aldeburgh straight on at mini-rdbt, turn L at x-roads into Wentworth Rd, Hotel on R.

Wentworth Road, IP15 5BD
Tel: 01728 452312
Fax: 01728 454343
e wentworth.hotel@anglianet.co.uk
Chef(s): Kevan Pulfrey
Owner(s): Michael Pritt
Cost:, set price L £13.75-£19.75/ D £16.95-£24. ☺ ☺ H/wine £9.75
Times: Noon-3pm/7-10.30pm. Closed 28 Dec-5 Jan

England

BECCLES

Map 5 TM48

Swan House

Small wine bar style restaurant devoted to all good things artistic and cultural as well as Epicurean, including live musicians and regularly changing modern art. A fairly eclectic, modern selection of dishes generally offers simplicity coupled with excellent ingredients. Sample poached fillet of salmon served with a ginger and spring onion sauce.

By The Tower, NR34 9HE

Tel: 01502 713474
Fax: 01502 716400
e dining@swan-house.com
Chef(s): Alexander Smith
Owner(s): M R Blunk and Ms L Dumphie
Cost: *Alc* £23.50/D £15.90. ☺ ☺ H/wine £8.90
Times: Noon-2.15pm/6.45-9.30pm. Closed 1 Jan
Additional: Sunday L. Bar food L. Children 14 yrs+
Seats: 40
Style: Country-house
Smoking: No pipes; no cigars
Directions: Next to church tower in Market Place

STOP PRESS Change of Chef

BROME

Map 5 TM17

The Cornwallis Country Hotel

IP23 8AJ
Tel: 01379 870326
Fax: 01379 870051
e info@thecornwallis.com
Chef(s): Kevin Booth
Owner(s): Mr. J Ward and Mr. R Leslie
Cost: Set price L £23.50-£27.50/D £23.50-£27.50. ☺ H/wine £9.95
Times: Noon-2.30pm/6.30-10pm.
Additional: Sunday L. Bar food. Children welcome
Seats: 50. Private dining room 100
Style: Traditional, Country-house
Smoking: No smoking in dining room
Civil licence: 100
Accommodation: 16 rooms (16 en suite) ★ ★ ★
Directions: From A140 (Norwich to Ipswich road) take B1077 towards Eye. Hotel entrance on L

From pre-meal drinks in the vine-laden conservatory to good petits fours, there is quality in abundance. Starters such as a full flavoured tomato and basil soup accompanied with olive tapenade and a very spicy chorizo sausage set a very high standard. Succulent loin of pork served on a tian of diced black pudding with potato and diced roasted carrots has been noted as another success. A lemon tart with good sweet pastry and a beautifully textured zingy filling typifies the high quality desserts. The restaurant is elegantly open plan - part of a striking 16th-century dower house.

BUNGAY

Map 5 TM38

Earsham Street Café

NEW

A haven for food lovers, this friendly cafe adjoins a delicatessen so lunch could be followed by more indulgences. Bread is

11-13 Earsham Street, NR35 1AE
Tel: 01986 893103
Fax: 01986 896784

freshly baked and chunky, the wine list extensive and the menu an inspiring mix of British and Mediterranean flavours. Dishes might include seared tuna with mushroom risotto and Parmesan or roast pork with tomato and bean cassoulet.

Chef(s): Stephen David
Owner(s): Rebecca Mackenzie & Stephen David
Cost: Alc £12.50. ☺ H/wine £11.50
Times: 11am-3pm. Closed L Sun, Xmas, New Year, BHs
Additional: Children welcome
Seats: 32
Style: Modern, Bistro-Style
Smoking: No-smoking area; no pipes
Directions: In the centre of Bungay

St Peter's Hall NEW

A super place to visit: housed in a splendid medieval former monastery, complete with moat, stone floors and lofty ceilings. St Peter's Hall is noted for its brewery, but the restaurant is excellent too offering simple but well-executed dishes with vegetables and herbs from the garden. Roast locally barn reared turkey with prune and walnut stuffing and a cranberry and orange relish is an offering typical of the weekly-changing menu.

St Peter South Elmham, NR35 1NQ
Tel: 01986 782322
Fax: 01986 782505
🄴 beers@stpetersbrewery.co.uk
Chef(s): Alex Smith
Owner(s): St. Peter's Brewery Co Ltd.
Cost: Alc £27.50, set price L £15.95/ D £19.95. ☺ ☺ H/wine £11.95
Times: Noon-2.30pm/7-9.30pm. Closed Mon-Thu, D Sun, Last 2 wks Jan
Additional: Sunday L. Bar food L. Children welcome
Seats: 50. Private dining room 50
Style: Traditional, Country-house
Smoking: No pipes; no cigars
Civil licence: 70
Directions: 2.5 miles of Bungay. Follow brown tourist signs from A144

BURY ST EDMUNDS Map 5 TL86

Angel Hotel

The all new Abbeygate restaurant offers guests an opulent, if somewhat eccentric venue for dining. The décor is a veritable riot of colour and curiosities - rather overwhelming at first glance but surprisingly effective overall. Simple dishes such as seared sea bass on a bed of diced potatoes offer real quality.

Seats: 50. Private dining room 30. **Style:** Classic
Smoking: No smoking in dining room
Civil licence: 70
Accommodation: 66 rooms (66 en suite) ★ ★ ★
Directions: Town Centre, R from Northgate St traffic lights

Angel Hill, IP33 1LT
Tel: 01284 714000
Fax: 01284 714001
🄴 sales@theangel.co.uk
Chef(s): Simon Barker
Owner(s): Mrs Mary Gough
Cost: Alc £31, set price L £15/D £25. ☺ H/wine £10.95
Times: Noon-2pm/7-9.30pm. Closed L Sat, D Sun
Additional: Sunday L. Bar food L. Children welcome

England

42 Churchgate

42 Churchgate Street, IP33 1RG
Tel: 01284 764179
Fax: 01284 764179
Chef(s): Nigel Snook
Owner(s): Nigel & Samantha Snook
Cost: Set price L £12.75/D £22. ☺ ☺
H/wine £10.50
Times: Noon-2pm/7-9.30pm.
Closed Sun & Mon, 2 wks Jan,
2 wks Aug & Sept
Seats: 46
Style: Rustic
Smoking: No-smoking area; no pipes
Directions: Centre of Bury St
Edmunds opp Norman Tower

Pale lemon décor is well suited to the Mediterranean inspired
menu. Real talent is on display in starters such as a mixture of
lovely fresh pancetta, parmesan and mozzarella in an excellent
"crisp and delicious" savoury pastry. Desserts such as baked
white chocolate cheesecake are also notable for their good
honest flavours.

Leaping Hare Restaurant

Located in a lovely medieval barn on the Wyken estate, this
restaurant is reached via a country store full of foodstuffs, crafts
and wines from the nearby vineyard. The American and British
style menu might include Warm Wyken pheasant salad or
Dexter fillet steak with wild mushrooms and red wine sauce.
There is also the opportunity to sample the estate's award
winning wines.

Smoking: No smoking in dining room
Directions: 9 miles NE of Bury St Edmunds, 1 mile off A143.
Follow brown signs at Ixworth to Wyken vineyards

Stanton, IP31 2DW
Tel: 01359 250287
Fax: 01359 252372
Chef(s): Peter Harrison
Owner(s): Kenneth & Carla Carlisle
Cost: *Alc* £23. ☺ ☺ H/wine £10
Times: Noon-2.30pm/7-9pm. Closed
D Mon-Thu & Sun, 2 wks Xmas
Additional: Sunday L. Bar food L.
Children welcome
Seats: 55
Style: Chic, Country-house

Maison Bleue

No pretentions here. This friendly French restaurant serves
quality cooking, as honest and straightforward as the
descriptions on the menu. Fish and seafood dominate - there
are some tantalising mixed platters - but meat dishes such as
duck with a green peppercorn sauce also stand their ground.
Naturally, the coffee is excellent.

Additional: Children welcome
Seats: 65. Private dining room 35
Style: Traditional, French
Smoking: No smoking in dining room
Directions: Town centre. Churchgate Street is opposite
cathedral

30-31 Churchgate Street,
IP33 1RG
Tel: 01284 760623
Fax: 01284 761611
Chef(s): Pascal Canevet
Owner(s): Regis Crepy
Cost: *Alc* £25, set price L £14.95/
D £19.95. ☺ ☺ H/wine £9.95
Times: Noon-2.30pm/6.30-9.30pm.
Closed Sun-Mon, Jan

19 Angel Hill NEW

19-21 Angel Hill, IP33 1UZ
Tel: 01284 704870
Fax: 01284 755115
Chef(s): Peter Hewett
Owner(s): Peter & Joan Hewett
Cost: Alc £20, set price L £10. ☺ ☺
H/wine £9.75
Times: Noon-2pm/7-9.30pm.
Closed L Sat
Additional: Children welcome
Seats: 55. Private dining room 14
Style: Traditional
Smoking: No-smoking area; no pipes;
no cigars
Directions: Telephone for directions

A commitment to good food is clearly evident at this casual restaurant, where minimalist décor meets medieval beams and highly-polished furniture. The menus make for a good read: twice-baked cheese soufflé with tomato and basil pesto, or roasted tomato and eggplant tart from the starters, and earthy braised English lamb with bacon and onion, or picata of Suffolk pork with sage mashed potatoes from the mains; also plenty of vegetarian choices, like tagliatelle of leeks and roasted peppers. Home-made breads, fudge petit fours and espresso all add to a rewarding gastronomic experience, and service is as polished as the tables.

The Priory Hotel NEW

Lively country house hotel with an attractive conservatory restaurant. Some interesting output from the kitchen such as a starter of sweet potato and coconut chowder - pleasing natural sweetness and discernible coconut texture proving a successful precursor to chicken breast with prawn risotto and a tarragon jus.

Seats: 50. Private dining room 20. **Style:** Modern, Country-House
Smoking: No smoking in dining room
Accommodation: 39 rooms (39 en suite) ★ ★ ★
Directions: Telephone for directions

Tollgate, IP32 6EH
Tel: 01284 766181
Fax: 01284 767604
🖃 reservations@prioryhotel.co.uk
Chef(s): Jon Ellis
Owner(s): Eagle Hotels Ltd.
Cost: Alc £27, set price L £19.95/
D £23.25. ☺ H/wine £11.95
Times: 12.30-2.30pm/7-10pm.
Closed L Sat
Additional: Sunday L. Children
welcome

FRESSINGFIELD   Map 5 TM27

Fox & Goose Inn

Originally built in 1509 as an eating house for the nearby church, this historic inn serves up some classics - potted shrimps or creme brûlée - alongside more modern creations - salmon on a bed of cumin lentils or pan fried chicken in a creamy mustard sauce. There's a rustic feel to both the decor and the cooking: chips are chunky and hand cut; vegetables simply prepared. Desserts include cuddly comfort food such as warm rice pudding with rasberry jam or sticky toffee pudding with toffee sauce. Impressive, freshly ground coffee.

Smoking: No smoking in dining room
Directions: A140 & B1118 (Stradbroke) L after 6 miles – in village centre by church

IP21 5PB
Tel: 01379 586247
Fax: 01379 586688
🖃 fox@foxgoose.freeserve.co.uk
Chef(s): Maxwell Dougal
Owner(s): Tim & Pauline O' Leary
Cost: Alc £26, set price L £12.50/
D £17.50. ☺ ☺ H/wine £13.50
Times: Noon-2pm/7-9pm.
Closed 25-26 Dec
Additional: Sunday L. Bar food.
Children welcome
Seats: 40. Private dining room 20
Style: Rustic, Traditional

England

HINTLESHAM

Map 5 TM04

Hintlesham Hall

IP8 3NS
Tel: 01473 652268
Fax: 01473 652463
e reservations@hintlesham-hall.co.uk
Chef(s): Allan Ford
Owner(s): Mr D Allan
Cost: *Alc* £38, set price L £21/D £27. H/wine £12.90
Times: Noon-1.45pm/7-9.30pm. Closed L Sat
Additional: Sunday L. Children 10 yrs+
Seats: 80. Private dining room 40. Jacket and tie preferred
Style: Modern
Smoking: No smoking in dining room
Civil licence: 80
Accommodation: 33 rooms (33 en suite) ★ ★ ★ ★
Directions: 5m W of Ipswich on A1071

Until 1984 this was Robert Carrier's restaurant and cookery school. Whilst there is now much else to draw you to the Georgian façade of this plush hotel, food is still very much at the centre of things with the kitchen team delivering accomplished and consistent cooking that lives up to the grandeur of the setting. The formality is not overdone and staff whilst delivering due professionalism tend to succeed in fostering a relaxed atmosphere. The cooking is equally confident. It's a style that demands dexterity and lightness of touch but there is little in the way of over-complication or fussiness. Starters have a bright and often Mediterranean feel (warm tiger prawn and monkfish salad with sweet pimento dressing or char-grilled vegetable bruschetta with goats cheese rarebit) and there is a happy economy to dishes like shellfish risotto with saffron. A similarly vibrant style applies to mains too with the fish (supreme of cod with lemon scented mash and citrus beurre blanc) given suitably sensitive treatment. More heavyweight options are there though in the likes of venison loin with caramelised shallots, cranberry galette and mulled wine dressing or tournedos of Scottish beef with horseradish crust and white wine jus. Dessert wise expect some variations on familiar themes with the likes of Armagnac crème brulée with a crisp tuille.

IPSWICH

Map 5 TM14

Il Punto

Neptune Quay, IP4 1AX
Tel: 01473 289748
Fax: 01473 288919
Chef(s): F Lebrun
Owner(s): Mr R Crepy
Cost: *Alc* £21, set price L £14.95/D £19.95. ☺ ☺ H/wine £10.95
Times: Noon-2.30pm/7-Midnight. Closed Sun, L Sat, Jan
Additional: Sunday L. Bar food L. Children welcome
Seats: 80
Style: Traditional
Smoking: No-smoking area; no pipes; no cigars

Just a few minutes walk from the centre brings you to this delightful ship restaurant moored on the historic waterfront. The interior is styled after the fashion of a brasserie whilst incorporating many of the ship's original features. Dishes might include a well-timed roast fillet of sea bass with braised chicory and fennel.

Directions: Telephone for directions.

Marlborough Hotel

19th century building with a country house atmosphere, located in a quiet, residential area. The restaurant overlooks well tended gardens and offers a menu pretty much as classical as the décor. Meals begin with drinks in the smart modern bar, followed by dishes such as scallops with pancetta and chive oil dressing or noisettes of lamb with a Mediterranean vegetable gateau.

Style: Traditional
Smoking: No smoking in dining room. **Civil licence:** 70
Accommodation: 22 rooms (22 en suite) ★ ★ ★
Directions: Take A1156 from A14, or A1214 from A12. Turn R at Henley Road/A1214 crossroads

Henley Road, IP1 3SP
Tel: 01473 257677
Fax: 01473 226927
e reception@themarlborough.co.uk
Chef(s): Shaun Thurlow
Owner(s): Mr & Mrs R Gough
Cost: Alc £34, set price L £16.95/
D £24.95
Times: Noon-2pm/7-9.30pm.
Closed L Sat
Additional: Sunday L. Bar food.
Children welcome
Seats: 40. Jacket and tie preferred

Scott's Brasserie

Open beams and old world charm aplenty behind the Suffolk brick façade of this pleasant restaurant, where the bar has a Thames barge theme. Amongst the starters oriental duck samosa starred with a sharp cucumber and chilli dip. Robust main courses have included local naturally smoked cod with a Stilton and apple crust.

Style: Modern
Smoking: No smoking in dining room
Directions: SE of town centre

4a Orwell Place, IP4 1BB
Tel: 01473 230254
Fax: 01473 218851
Chef(s): Scott Davidson
Owner(s): C Lewis & S Davidson
Cost: Alc £23.50, set price L £17/
D £23.50. ☺ ☺ H/wine £9.95
Times: Noon-3pm/6.30-midnight.
Closed L Sat, D Sun
Additional: Children 14 yrs+
Seats: 80. Private dining room 40

IXWORTH Map 5 TL97

Theobalds Restaurant

68 High Street IP31 2HJ
Tel: 01359 231707
Fax: 01359 231707
e theorest@aol.com
Chef(s): Simon Theobald
Owner(s): Simon & Geraldine Theobald

Smart, upmarket restaurant housed in a 17th-century building in the heart of the village. The interior retains genuine period charm (exposed beams and upright timbers, inglenook fireplace etc.) whilst the menu does not confine itself to the traditional in its pursuit of interesting, well composed cuisine. Thus a starter

England

IXWORTH *Continued*

Map 5 TL97

of grilled scallops served on a bed of saffron and roast pepper risotto is quite at home alongside a simpler alternative of chicken and winter vegetable soup. Pan-fried fillet steak flamed with Cognac and served with a green peppercorn sauce is a characteristically robust main course.

Style: Modern. **Smoking:** No smoking in dining room
Directions: 7m from Bury St Edmunds on A143 Bury/Diss road

Cost: *Alc* £29, set price L £18.95.
☺ ☺ H/wine £11.25
Times: 12.15-1.30pm/7-9pm.
Closed Mon, L Sat, D Sun, 10 days in Summer
Additional: Sunday L.
Children 8yrs+ at D
Seats: 42. Private dining room 16

LAVENHAM

Map 5 TL94

Angel Hotel

A beautiful, heavily timbered building that stands out even in this well-preserved medieval town. First licensed in 1420, the Angel continues its proud tradition of hospitality offering a good choice of fresh dishes. Dishes range from home-smoked chicken and bacon salad to braised shank of lamb with redcurrant and rosemary jus.

Market Place, CO10 9QZ
Tel: 01787 247388
Fax: 01787 248344
e angellav@aol.com
Chef(s): Michael Pursell
Owner(s): Mr R Whitworth & Mr J Barry
Cost: *Alc* £17.75, set price L £17.75/D £17.75. ☺ ☺ H/wine £8.95
Times: Noon-2.15pm/6.45-9.15pm.
Closed 25-26 Dec
Additional: Sunday L. Bar food. Children welcome. Vegetarian by request only
Seats: 100. Private dining room 15
Style: Classic, Traditional
Smoking: No-smoking area; no pipes
Accommodation: 8 rooms (8 en suite)
★ ★
Directions: Town centre, close to Tourist Information

Great House Restaurant

A French restaurant with French staff in the most English of settings. A medieval house with an 18th-century façade, overlooking the marketplace, this is very much a restaurant with rooms, service oriented, with a panelled dining room dominated by a huge fireplace. Consistency is a virtue with each

Market Place,
CO10 9QZ
Tel: 01787 247431
Fax: 01787 248007
e info@greathouse.co.uk
Chef(s): Regis Crepy
Owner(s): Mr & Mrs Crepy

England

course holding its own, including a feuilleté of asparagus with a "perfectly poached egg" and hollandaise sauce, and a somewhat over-embellished chocolate terrine. Look out for pan-fried fillet of pink river trout served with a delicate white wine, bacon and cream sauce. Don't miss the impressive cheeseboard.

Smoking: No smoking in dining room
Accommodation: 5 rooms (5 en suite) ♦♦♦♦
Directions: In Market Place (turn onto Market Lane From High Street)

Cost: *Alc* £35, set price L £16/D £22.
☺ ☺ H/wine £10.50
Times: Noon-2.30pm/7-9.30pm.
Closed Mon, D Sun, 3 wks Jan
Additional: Sunday L.
Children welcome
Seats: 40
Style: Classic, Country-house

LONG MELFORD   Map 5 TL84

Chimneys Restaurant

Hall Street, CO10 9JR
Tel: 01787 379806
Fax: 01787 312294
Chef(s): Wayne Messenger
Owner(s): Samuel Chalmers
Cost: *Alc* £29.50, set price L £18.50-£21.45/D £18.50-£21.45. ☺ ☺
H/wine £11.75
Times: Noon-2pm/6-9pm.
Closed Sun, BHs
Additional: Children welcome
Seats: 45
Style: Classic, Traditional

No surprise, amongst the half-timbered charm of Long Melford, to find a restaurant trading on seductive log fires, an equally warm welcome and a menu that makes few concessions to fashion. Less predictable perhaps, to find it being done quite this well. Given up on the steak and mushroom pie? Lunch here may force you to rethink, with the first-rate pastry and properly braised beef being something of a revelation. Other stalwarts include calf's liver and bacon with a proper onion gravy or lamb chump with rosemary and thyme. Naturally, desserts feature both Bakewell tart and an "excellent" bread and butter pudding. How could it be otherwise?

Directions: Village centre

Scutchers Restaurant

Modern British cooking gets the positive treatment in this bright bistro outside Long Melford. Sautéed fois gras on a rösti with mushy peas, haggis and a caramelised shallot sauce might be a featured starter, with fillet of halibut lightly curried with a creamy crayfish sauce to follow. Bakewell tart and bread and butter pudding or cheeses to finish.

Additional: Children welcome
Seats: 70
Smoking: No pipes; no cigars; Air conditioning
Directions: About a mile from Long Melford towards Clare

Westgate Street, CO10 9DP
Tel: 01787 310200
Fax: 07000 785443
Chef(s): Nicholas Barrett
Owner(s): Nicholas & Diane Barrett
Cost: *Alc* £20.25. ☺ ☺
H/wine £11.80
Times: Noon-2pm/7-9.30pm.
Closed Sun-Mon, Xmas, 1st wk Jan, last wk Aug

England

LOWESTOFT
Map 5 TM59

Ivy House Farm

Ivy Lane, Beccles Road,
Oulton Broad NR33 8HY
Tel: 01502 501353
Fax: 01502 501539
e admin@ivyhousefarm.co.uk
Chef(s): Richard Pye
Owner(s): Caroline Sterry
Cost: Alc £30.35. ☺ ☺
H/wine £10.95
Times: Noon-1.45pm/7-9.30pm.
Closed 20 Dec-05 Jan
Additional: Sunday L.
Children welcome
Seats: 45. Private dining room 16
Style: Rustic, Traditional
Smoking: No smoking in dining room;
no cigars
Accommodation: 19 rooms (19 en
suite) ★ ★ ★
Directions: A146 into Ivy Lane

The restaurant is at the heart of the hotel, in an 18th-century
thatched barn with a heavily beamed interior and views of the
gardens. Two menus are offered, one bistro-style the other a
rather ambitious *carte*. The approach aims to please, with a
choice of portion size on the former and the option of one to
three courses on the latter

MILDENHALL
Map 5 TL77

Riverside Hotel

Mill Street, IP28 7DP
Tel: 01638 717274
Fax: 01638 715997
e bookings@riverside-hotel.net
Chef(s): Scott Pammenter
Owner(s): Mr B Keane
Cost: Alc £25, set price L £20.50/
D £20.50. ☺ H/wine £12.50
Times: Noon-2pm/6.30-9.30pm.
Additional: Sunday L. Bar food.
Children welcome
Seats: 100. Private dining room 50
Style: Modern

An imposing 18th century red brick Georgian building
overlooking the River Lark and attractive gardens. Although in
many ways a traditionally styled dining room, the restaurant
also has a conservatory feel to it thanks to an abundance of
glass panels and doors. Braised neck of lamb on a tarragon
mash demonstrated accuracy and quality.

Smoking: No-smoking area
Accommodation: 29 rooms (29 en suite) ★ ★ ★
Directions: From M11 J9 take A11 for Norwich. At Fiveways
Rdbt take A1101 into town. L at mini-rdbt, hotel last on L before
the bridge

NAYLAND
Map 5 TL93

White Hart Inn

High Street, CO6 4JF
Tel: 01206 263382
Fax: 01206 263638
e nayhart@aol.com
Chef(s): Neil Bishop
Owner(s): Mr M Roux
Cost: Alc £23.50, set price L
£13.50/D £21.50. ☺ ☺ H/wine £11
Times: Noon-2.30pm/6-9.30pm.
Closed Mon, 26 Dec-4 Jan
Additional: Sunday L. Children
welcome

Set on a narrow street of colour washed houses with a wealth of
overhanging timbers, this 15th century coaching inn houses a
cosy, bare beamed restaurant. Recent redecoration has
achieved a balance between period charm and modern style:
walls are whitewashed and the cellar is lit so that it can be
viewed through a glass cover. The cooking reflects the setting,
using French influences to polish the rough edges from
otherwise rustic dishes such as Nayland wood pigeon pan fried
with Savoy cabbage and bacon jus. Flavours are well defined
throughout and the friendly French staff make diners feel
cared for.

Accommodation: 6 rooms (6 en suite) ◆◆◆◆
Directions: 6m N of Colchester on A134 towards Sudbury

Seats: 55. Private dining room 36
Style: Modern, French
Smoking: No pipes

NEWMARKET
Map 5 TL66

Bedford Lodge Hotel

The Orangery Restaurant is a very tasteful affair with fruit trees, yellow ochre washed walls and limestone floors creating a light, contemporary space in which to enjoy fine food. The cuisine has a sturdy classical bent with oven roasted pheasant, braised haunch of venison and chargrilled tuna steak taking their places in the main course options.

Style: Bistro
Smoking: No smoking in dining room; Air conditioning
Accommodation: 56 rooms (56 en suite) ★ ★ ★
Directions: From town centre follow A1303 towards Bury St Edmunds for 0.5 mile

Bury Road, CB8 7BX
Tel: 01638 663175
Fax: 01638 667391
e info@bedfordlodgehotel.co.uk
Chef(s): Adrian Doughty
Owner(s): Barnham Brook Golf Club
Cost: Set price L £17.50/D £23.50.
☺ ☺
Times: Noon-2pm/7-9.30pm.
Closed L Sat
Additional: Sunday L. Bar food L.
Children welcome
Seats: 60. Private dining room 150

ORFORD
Map 5 TM45

The Crown & Castle

IP12 2LJ
Tel: 01394 450205
Fax: 01394 450176
e info@crownandcastlehotel.co.uk
Chef(s): Brendon Ansbro
Owner(s): David & Ruth Watson

This popular hotel dates back to Tudor times and has commanding views over the village, castle and marshes. The Trinity restaurant blends British, Italian and French influences on a user-friendly menu which invites guests to ask if they want something served more plainly. There is an emphasis on quality

England

ORFORD *Continued*   Map 5 TM45

produce, bought locally wherever possible, as in the bourride of
fresh cod and mussels or free-range chicken breast in leek and
tarragon sauce.   Slick service, a helpfully written wine list and a
friendly little menu for children all add to the feeling that you
are being well looked after.

Smoking: No pipes; no cigars
Accommodation: 18 rooms (18 en suite) ★ ★
Directions: Turn off B1084 in village

Cost: *Alc* £24, set price D £24. ☺ ☺
H/wine £9.90
Times: Noon-2.30pm/7-9pm. Closed
7 Jan-11 Jan
Additional: Sunday L. Bar food.
Children welcome
Seats: 60. Private dining room 12
Style: Bistro

POLSTEAD   Map 5 TM14

The Cock Inn

A 17th-century inn overlooking the village green, the Cock has
a Victorian restaurant extension providing a rustic setting
(scrubbed tables, quarry tile floors and open fireplaces) for
some country-style cooking. Winter vegetable soup was a
substantial starter, garnished with crispy bacon, and a main
course of chicken breast stuffed with cream cheese and sun-
dried vegetables was succulent and full of flavour.

Seats: 50. **Style:** Traditional
Smoking: No-smoking area; Air conditioning
Directions: Colchester/A134 towards Sudbury then R at
Nayland to Stoke-by-Nayland then L following brown tourist
signs to Cock Inn

The Green, CO6 5AL
Tel: 01206 263150
Fax: 01206 263150
e enquiries@the-cock-inn-polstead.
fsbusiness.co.uk
Chef(s): Mark Inwood, Karen Leafe
Owner(s): Mr M Inwood &
Miss J Leafe
Cost: *Alc* £20. ☺ ☺ H/wine £10.50
Times: 11-3pm/6-11pm.
Closed Mon (ex BHs),
Additional: Sunday L. Bar food L.
Children welcome

SOUTHWOLD   Map 5 TM57

The Crown

Old posting inn where the high quality restaurant co-habits
with both pub and wine bar. The food is unpretentious and of a
very high quality. A succulent pork fillet was very enjoyable
and the crème brûlée spot on.

Seats: 30. **Style:** Formal
Smoking: No smoking in dining room
Accommodation: 14 rooms (11 en suite) ★ ★
Directions: Take A1095 from A12; hotel at the top of High
Street.

90 High Street, IP18 6DP
Tel: 01502 722275
Fax: 01502 723603
Chef(s): Chris Coubrough
Owner(s): Adnams Hotels
Cost: Set price L £18.50/D £25.50
H/wine £8.95
Times: 12.15-2pm/7-9.30pm.
Additional: Sunday L. Bar food.
Children 5 yrs+

Swan Hotel

The elegant restaurant is traditional in style and features huge
bay windows to the front which overlook the busy market
square. A seasonally changing *carte* can include starters of foie
gras and chicken liver parfait, mains of roasted salmon fillet
with scallops, and desserts of glazed lemon tart with jersey
cream.

Style: Traditional, Country-house
Smoking: No smoking in dining room; Air conditioning
Accommodation: 43 rooms (41 en suite) ★ ★ ★
Directions: Take A1095 off A12: Follow High Street into market
place, hotel on the L

Market Place, IP18 6EG
Tel: 01502 722186
Fax: 01502 724800
Chef(s): Ian Howell
Owner(s): Adnams & Co PLC
Cost: Set price L £20/D £25.50.
H/wine £8.25
Times: Noon-1.30pm/7-9pm.
Closed Mid wk in Winter,
Additional: Sunday L. Bar food L.
Children 5 yrs+
Seats: 65. Private dining room 42.
Jacket and tie preferred

England

STOKE-BY-NAYLAND
Map 5 TL93

The Angel Inn
NEW

A 52 foot well, rough brick and timber add to the historical charm of this 16th-century inn. The restaurant and bar serve up some worthy dishes making good use of local seafood and game. Dishes might include brochette of scallops wrapped in bacon, steak and kidney pudding or ballontine of duckling with cassis sauce. Friendly, relaxed atmosphere.

Polstead Street,
CO6 4SA
Tel: 01206 263245
Fax: 01206 263373
Chef(s): Mark Johnson
Owner(s): Horizon Inns
Cost: *Alc* £13. ☺ ☺ H/wine £8.50
Times: Noon-3pm/6-11pm.
Closed 25-26 Dec, 1Jan
Additional: Sunday L. Bar food.
Children 8 yrs+

Seats: 28
Style: Traditional
Accommodation: 6 rooms (6 en suite) ♦♦♦♦
Directions: Telephone for directions

STOWMARKET
Map 5 TM05

Tot Hill House

Situated bang on the A14, you can't help but wish that Tot Hill would start a whole new trend in roadside eating. A forlorn hope perhaps, but this is honest, brasserie style cooking that doesn't disappoint. Smoked salmon on a potato cake with crème fraîche, beef fillet with bacon and liver ragout and a warm pear and almond tart sum up the style.

IP14 3QH
Tel: 01449 673375
Fax: 01449 673375
e marybruce@barclays.net
Chef(s): C Bruce
Owner(s): Mr & Mrs C Bruce
Cost: *Alc* £27.95, set price L £17.95/
D £25. ☺ ☺ H/wine £13.50
Times: Noon-1.30pm/7-9.00pm.
Closed Mon-Tue, L Sat, D Sun,
2 wks Jan, 1 wk Sept

Additional: Sunday L. Children welcome.
Vegetarian by request only
Seats: 34. Jacket and tie preferred
Style: Classic
Smoking: No smoking in dining room
Directions: On A14 between Ipwich & Bury St Edmunds

WESTLETON
Map 5 TM46

The Westleton Crown

IP17 3AD
Tel: 0800 328 6001
Fax: 01728 648239
Telephone for further details

Delightful inn steeped in charm and character. The daily changing menu is carefully focused and does great credit to excellent ingredients in dishes such as medallions of beef fillet on roasted root vegetables served with a rich jus. The dining area is more formal than the bar - both worth a visit.

England

WOODBRIDGE
Map 5 TM24

Captain's Table

Not much change here over the years and many will be grateful for that. The menu offers an eclectic range of punchy dishes with, if anything, a southern European bias. Starters might comprise a simple, pungent, French onion soup, steamed curried mussels or smoked salmon paté with a dill scone. Classic skate wing with black butter and capers has been praised for ultra-fresh fish "crisp without, moist within" and crème fraîche mousse with poached mixed berries has also been a success. Notable good value too.

Style: Bistro-Style
Smoking: No smoking in dining room
Directions: From A12, (Garden centre on left). Quay St is opposite rail station & theatre, restaurant 100 yds on L

3 Quay Street, IP12 1BX
Tel: 01394 383145
Fax: 01394 388508
Chef(s): Pascal Pommier
Owner(s): Mr P & Mrs J M Pommier
Cost: Alc £17. ☺ ☺ H/wine £8.95
Times: 12-2pm/6.30-9.30pm.
Closed Mon (ex BHs), D Sun (ex BHs), 1st 2 wks Jan
Additional: Sunday L. Bar food. Children welcome
Seats: 50. Private dining room 24

Seckford Hall Hotel

Attractive Tudor manor house with an elegant, traditionally styled restaurant. The eclectic menu has a strong classical feel to it but there is a lightness to the cooking that adds real distinctive interest. Beef on a polenta cake with balsamic shallots and a rich jus typifies the main course options.

Style: Classic, Traditional
Smoking: No smoking in dining room; Air conditioning
Civil licence: 125
Accommodation: 32 rooms (32 en suite) ★★★
Directions: Hotel signposted on A12 (Woodbridge by-pass). Do not follow signs for town centre

IP13 6NU
Tel: 01394 385678
Fax: 01394 380610
e reception@seckford.co.uk
Chef(s): Mark Archer
Owner(s): Mr & Mrs Bunn
Cost: Alc £28.45. ☺ H/wine £10.95
Times: 12.30-2pm/7.30-9pm.
Closed L Mon, 25-Dec
Additional: Sunday L. Bar food L. Children welcome
Seats: 70. Private dining room 100

YAXLEY
Map 5 TM17

The Bull Auberge

Ipswich Road, IP23 8BZ
Tel: 01379 783604
Fax: 01379 783604
Chef(s): John Stenhouse
Owner(s): John & Dee Stenhouse
Cost: Alc £25/D £16.75. ☺ ☺ H/wine £9.75
Times: Noon-2pm/7-9pm.
Closed Sun & Mon, L Sat,
Additional: Bar food L. Children welcome. Vegetarian by request only
Seats: 30. Jacket and tie preferred
Style: Country-house
Smoking: No smoking in dining room
Directions: Adjacent to A140, Norwich to Ipswich road on junction with B1117 to Eye

Whilst the *carte* in this 15th-century inn has much to recommend it, the weekday set menu is an appetising option too. Try guinea fowl terrine, followed by say, salmon and scallop gratin and you'd not go far wrong. Round off with bread and butter pudding, complemented by mango coulis.

YOXFORD
Map 5 TM36

Satis House Hotel

IP17 3EX
Tel: 01728 668418
Fax: 01728 668640
✉ yblackmore@aol.com
Chef(s): Debbie Ferrance &
Chiv Blackmore
Owner(s): Chris & Chiv Blackmore
Cost: Alc £22.50, set price D £21.50.
☺ ☺ H/wine £12.50
Times: Dinner only, 7-9.30pm.
Closed Sun
Additional: Children 5 yrs+
Seats: 30. Private dining room 16.
Jacket and tie preferred
Style: Malaysian
Smoking: No smoking in dining room
Accommodation: 8 rooms (8 en suite)
★★
Directions: On A12 N of village

Elegant 18th-century listed house with an Oriental makeover in the form of paintings and ornaments - not so eccentric as it sounds when you realise that the restaurant is totally focused on providing top quality Malaysian cuisine to its appreciative customers. A plate of appetisers is a seductive start with beef chicken satay, spare ribs, prawn samosa and duck spring roll all being excellent. Main courses are along the lines of succulent chicken in a light chilli sauce or sweet and sour king prawns with tomato.

SURREY

BAGSHOT
Map 4 SU96

Pennyhill Park Hotel

London Road,
GU19 5EU
Tel: 01276 471774
Fax: 01276 472317
✉ pennyhillpark@msn.com
Chef(s): Karl Edmunds
Owner(s): The Latymer Restaurant
Cost: Alc £50 H/wine £20
Times: 12.30-2.30pm/7-10.30pm.
Closed Sun-Mon, BHs

Incorporated into a country club whose leisure pursuits include horse-riding, golf and fishing on a private lake, this hotel of Victorian origins stands in mature parkland with Windsor Forest in the background. The Latymer Restaurant's French-influenced British cuisine remains a destination worth seeking out for its memorable warmth, hospitality and stylish country house food. The ambience may be steeped in tradition but the menu nevertheless exhibits some imagination and flair. Hand-

BAGSHOT *Continued*   Map 4 SU96

crafted raviolo of rabbit and crab comes dressed with lentils and Champagne sauce, and caramelised scallops are served with butternut squash and tarragon risotto. Tenderloin of pork might follow, with a sage-and-onion stuffing, confit of belly with crackling, girolles and red wine sauce. Elaborate fish dishes are along the lines of lemon sole with asparagus and langoustine soufflé and orange beurre blanc. Some of the most successful dishes are amongst the desserts including toasted pineapple with excellent Malibu ice cream and memorable petits fours.

Directions: On A30 between Bagshot & Camberley

Additional: Children 12 yrs+
Seats: 30. Private dining room 160. Jacket and tie preferred
Style: Traditional, Formal
Smoking: No smoking in dining room; Air conditioning
Civil licence: 100
Accommodation: 123 rooms (123 en suite) ★ ★ ★ ★ ★

CHURT   Map 4 SU84

Pride of the Valley Hotel

Baronial-style dining room making good use of seasonal items to produce quality, contemporary food. Enjoy the likes of sautéed calves' liver with an apricot and tarragon dressing, or half duckling served with a rich red-berry sauce. Desserts are also a strong point - sticky toffee pudding with a toffee sauce in particular.

Seats: 50. **Style:** Traditional
Smoking: No smoking in dining room
Accommodation: 16 rooms (16 en suite)
Directions: Telephone for directions

GU10 2LE
Tel: 01428 605799
Fax: 01428 605875
Chef(s): Chris Jackson
Owner(s): Mr. E Powell
Cost: *Alc* £25, set price L £12.50/ D £18.50. ☺ ☺ H/wine £10.95
Times: Noon-2pm/6-9.30pm. Closed D Sun
Additional: Sunday L. Bar food. Children welcome. Vegetarian by request only

CLAYGATE   Map 4 TQ16

Le Petit Pierrot Restaurant

Intimate French restaurant featuring a tented ceiling and, yes, Pierrot figures. The friendly, relaxed service is accompanied by sizzling sounds from the kitchen and the occasional emergence of the chef to shake hands with regulars. Classic French dishes might include fillet of sea bass with fennel and a Pernod cream or noisettes of venison with chestnuts and a poivrade sauce.

Seats: 32. **Style:** Chic, French
Smoking: No pipes
Directions: Telephone for directions

4 The Parade, KT10 0NU
Tel: 01372 465105
Fax: 01372 467642
Chef(s): Jean-Pierre Brichot & Eric Plantereux
Owner(s): Annie & Jean-Pierre Brichot
Cost:. ☺ ☺ H/wine £11.25
Times: 12.15-2pm/7.15-9.30pm. Closed Sun, L Sat, Xmas,1 Jan, BHs
Additional: Children 9 yrs+

EGHAM   Map 4 TQ07

Runnymede Hotel

A tranquil riverside setting with stylish aquatic themed décor and the kitchen in view. The modish menu includes asparagus risotto with truffle oil and shaved parmesan amongst an interesting selection of starters. Justice is done to the aquatic theme with mains of salmon fishcakes with saffron sauce and buttered spinach, and prosciutto wrapped monkfish with roasted summer vegetables. Carnivores fear not - fillet steak or breast of chicken stuffed with brie will satisfy. Classic desserts such as lemon tart and chocolate Napoleon conclude proceedings with a bang.

Windsor Road, TW20 0AG
Tel: 01784 436171
Fax: 01784 436340
e info@runnymedehotel.com
Chef(s): Laurence Curtis
Owner(s): Ralph Trustees Ltd
Cost: *Alc* £30, set price L £18.95/D £26. H/wine £13.95
Times: Noon-2.30pm/7-10.30pm. Closed L Sat, D Sun, Xmas, New Year
Additional: Sunday L. Children welcome

Civil licence: 150
Accommodation: 180 rooms (180 en suite) ★★★★
Directions: On A308 Windsor road from M25 J3

Seats: 150. Private dining room 300
Style: Modern, Chic
Smoking: No-smoking area; no pipes;
Air conditioning

EPSOM
Map 4 TQ26

Chalk Lane Farm
NEW

At the foot of the Epsom Downs in a truly unspoilt location lies this attractive complex of buildings, some of which date back to the 17th century. A simple, honest approach is evident in a crisp filo tart filled with plump mushrooms and finished with a port and honey dressing.

Style: Country-house
Smoking: No smoking in dining room
Accommodation: 22 rooms (22 en suite) ★★★
Directions: M25 J9 then A24 towards Ashtead & Epsom. Just in Epsom turn R at BP garage, then L into Avenue Road & follow hotel signs

Chalk Lane,
Woodcote End, KT18 7BB
Tel: 01372 721179
Fax: 01372 727878
e Chalklane@compuserve.com
Chef(s): Robert Hughes
Cost: *Alc* £30, set price L £16.95/
D £30-£35. ☺ ☺ H/wine £13.50
Times: 12.30-2.30pm/7-10pm.
Closed L Sat, D Sun
Additional: Sunday L. Children welcome
Seats: 40. Private dining room 20

FARNHAM
Map 4 SU84

Bishop's Table Hotel

27 West Street, GU9 7DR
Tel: 01252 710222
Fax: 01252 733494
e welcome@bishopstable.com
Chef(s): Brett Sutton
Owner(s): Mr K Verjee

Family-run Georgian townhouse with a restaurant offering an intelligent menu in a broadly modern European style. The dining room, whilst traditional in style is in no way stuffy and offers a bright setting lifted by crisp table appointments and

England

FARNHAM *Continued*

Map 4 SU84

fresh flowers. Sometimes the simpler dishes are the most successful, for instance, a weighty cassoulet of game with braised red cabbage was noted as a real success, whilst a starter of pigeon breast with chorizo sauerkraut and a beetroot chocolate sauce was perhaps a little over-ambitious. More plaudits though for some worthy puds such as a baby pear Tatin with poire William sorbet, toffee sauce and sugar spears.

Directions: In the centre of the town

Cost: *Alc* £30, set price L £12.50. ☺ H/wine £10.50
Times: 12.30-1.45pm/7-9.45pm. Closed L Mon, 26 Dec-3 Jan
Additional: Sunday L. Children welcome
Seats: 55. Private dining room 36
Style: Modern
Smoking: No smoking in dining room
Accommodation: 17 rooms (17 en suite) ★ ★

GUILDFORD

Map 4 SU94

The Angel Posting House

Historic coaching inn offering friendly service in the centre of Guildford's high-street . Some historical character remains with a Jacobean fireplace, a 17th-century Parliament clock and a 13th-century stone-vaulted crypt which is now the restaurant. The menu offers a broadly European range with dishes such as scallops with coriander and summer leaves or Gressingham duck breast with wilted leaves and a cassis sauce. Desserts are mainly familiar (sticky toffee pudding with a toffee sauce) and top-drawer extras include bread and pre-dinner nibbles. Inaccuracies can just occasionally take the gloss off the dining experience. Responsive and well-informed staff.

Accommodation: 21 rooms (21 en suite) ★ ★ ★
Directions: Town centre

91 High Street, GU1 3DP
Tel: 01483 564555
Fax: 01483 533770
e reservations@angelpostinghouse.com
Chef(s): David Edwards
Owner(s): Mr G Wiggington & Mr J Laird
Cost: Set price L £18.50/D £24.50. ☺ ☺ H/wine £10.50
Times: Noon-3pm/7-11pm. Closed D 24 Dec, 1 Jan
Additional: Sunday L. Bar food L. Children welcome
Seats: 32. Private dining room 80
Style: Classic
Smoking: No smoking in dining room

HASLEMERE

Map 4 SU93

Lythe Hill Hotel

A cluster of buildings share 20 acres of fine grounds including a bluebell wood and several lakes. It is the original 14th century black-and-white timbered farmhouse that hosts the Auberge de France restaurant - all oak panelling and antique tables as one might expect - and the refined atmosphere is well suited to the largely classical French cuisine on offer. Fresh peppered ravioli

Petworth Road, GU27 3BQ
Tel: 01428 651251
Fax: 01428 644131
e lythe@lythehill.co.uk
Chef(s): Roger Clarke
Cost: *Alc* £40, set price L £22.50/D £25. H/wine £12.50

filled with wild mushrooms and goats' cheese tossed in a truffle and herb dressing might lead into roast supreme of salmon wrapped with prosciutto ham and roasted asparagus with winter squash. Flaming crêpes suzette available for dessert.

Smoking: No smoking in dining room
Civil licence: 130
Accommodation: 41 rooms (41 en suite) ★ ★ ★ ★
Directions: 1 mile E of Haslemere on B2131

Times: 12.30-2.30pm/7.15pm-Midnight
Additional: Sunday L. Children welcome. Vegetarian by request only
Seats: 60. Private dining room 60. Jacket and tie preferred
Style: Modern-French

HORLEY
Map 4 TQ24

Langshott Manor

Langshott Lane, RH6 9LN
Tel: 01293 786680
Fax: 01293 783905
e admin@langshottmanor.com
Chef(s): Stephen Toward
Owner(s): Peter & Debra Hinchcliff
Cost: Alc £40, set price L £25/ D £37.50. H/wine £17
Times: Noon-2.30pm/7-9.30pm.
Additional: Sunday L. Bar food. Children welcome
Seats: 42. Private dining room 22. Jacket and tie preferred
Style: Country-house
Smoking: No smoking in dining room

Set in an Elizabethan wood framed manor house, this comfortable restaurant overlooks a medieval moat. The cooking is European in style and makes good use of local produce: a meal might include a 'stunning' sweetcorn and smoked bacon soup, followed by pan fried Cornish red mullet with carrot and coriander crust and crushed tomato sauce. Deep flavours and well matched vegetables complete a satisfying experience. Also worth sampling are the alluring desserts (they do a great crème brûlée), followed by quality coffee. If you have time, take a look at the beautiful gardens which surround this hotel.

Civil licence: 60
Accommodation: 15 rooms (15 en suite) ★ ★ ★
Directions: From A23, Horley, take Ladbroke Road turning off Chequers Hotel rndbt, 0.75 mile on R

OCKLEY
Map 4 TQ14

Bryce's Seafood Restaurant

The Old School House, RH5 5TH
Tel: 01306 627430
Fax: 01306 628274
e bryces.fish@virgin.net
Chef(s): B Bryce & Gregory Baverstock
Owner(s): Mr B Bryce
Cost: Alc £25.50, set price L £20.25/D £24. ☺ H/wine £10.95
Times: Noon-2.30pm/7-9.30pm. Closed D Sun in Nov, Jan & Feb, 25-26 Dec, 1-2 Jan
Additional: Sunday L. Bar food. Children welcome
Seats: 50
Style: Traditional
Smoking: No smoking in dining room
Directions: 8m S of Dorking on A29

The freshest seafood simply cooked is the admirable philosophy of this restaurant located in a former schoolhouse. Not surprisingly, it seems to work with the place noted as being absolutely packed, even on a Monday night. Take your fish grilled, steamed or poached, with the likes of spice-crusted crab cakes, monkfish in Parma ham, and zarzuela, a classic Catalonian fish stew.

England

OTTERSHAW
Map 4 TQ06

Foxhills

Stonehill Road, KT16 0EL
Tel: 01932 872050
Fax: 01932 874762
e reservations@foxhills.co.uk
Chef(s): Kevin Clark
Owner(s): Mr I Hayton
Cost: *Alc* £30.32, set price L £16/
D £16-£20. ☺ ☺ H/wine £12.50
Times: Noon-2.30pm/7-10pm.
Closed L Sat
Additional: Sunday L.
Children welcome
Seats: 80. Private dining room 50.
Jacket and tie preferred
Style: Traditional
Smoking: Air conditioning
Accommodation: 38 rooms (38 en
suite) ★ ★ ★ ★
Directions: A320 to Woking from
M25. At 2nd rdbt take last exit
Cobham Road, turn R into Foxhills
Rd, follow until T-junction, turn right
into Stonehill Rd

Situated in the manor house of what is more of a resort than a
hotel, the Manor Restaurant is a popular destination after a day
de-stressing on the golf course or by the pool. The light décor,
high ceilings and huge, arched windows give an air of
understated grandeur to what is one of several eating options at
Foxhills. Examples from the British based menu might include
a starter of smoked trout followed by lamb shank with parsnip
mash. However, hot smoked salmon with Asian pesto or
spiced pork with egg noodles also reveal some international
influences.

PEASLAKE
Map 4 TQ04

Hurtwood Inn Hotel

Walking Bottom, GU5 9RR
Tel: 01306 730851
Fax: 01306 731390
e sales@hurtwoodinnhotel.com
Chef(s): Robert Joynes
Owner(s): Mrs S Bell
Cost: *Alc* £27, set price L £15.95/
D £17. ☺ ☺ H/wine £10.75
Times: Dinner only, 7-9.30pm.
Closed D Sun
Additional: Sunday L. Bar food.
Children welcome
Seats: 30. Private dining room. Jacket
and tie preferred
Style: Classic, Formal
Smoking: No smoking in dining room
Accommodation: 17 rooms (17 en
suite) ★ ★ ★

Something of a timewarp, this attractive 1920s style restaurant
in a hotel of the same era, but the British based menu gives a
modern twist to many familiar dishes: salmon might be served
on wilted savoy cabbage; beef in a red wine and wild mushroom
jus; goats cheese with pepper coulis.

Directions: Leave A25 in Gomshall, follow signs to Peaslake,
turn opposite Jet Garage, follow hotel signs

England

REDHILL
Map 4 TQ35

Nutfield Priory

Nutfield, RH1 4EL
Tel: 01737 824400
Fax: 01737 823321
e nutpriory@aol.com
Chef(s): David Evans
Cost: Alc £37, set price L £16/
D £28.50. ☺ H/wine £12.95
Times: Noon-2pm/7-10pm.
Closed L Sat
Additional: Sunday L. Bar food L.
Children welcome
Seats: 60. Private dining room 100.
Jacket and tie preferred
Style: Country-house
Smoking: No smoking in dining room
Civil licence: 85
Accommodation: 60 rooms (60 en
suite) ★ ★ ★ ★
Directions: On A25, 1 mile E of
Redhill

An imposing century-old building houses the stone-framed, lead-windowed Cloisters restaurant. Service and presentation is fittingly formal with a grandly presented menu and quiet, respectful serving staff. Notable technical skill is apparent in a starter of sole mousse piped over brochette of langoustines with crayfish bavarois and saffron sauce. Mains might include poached fillet of roe deer with chervil mousse and, with a skilled pastry chef on board, the puddings are very strong across the menu. Coffee and petits fours in one of the three seating areas round off the meal nicely

REIGATE
Map 4 TQ25

The Dining Room

Ready Steady Cook chef Tony Tobin rustles up some impressive dishes in this first floor restaurant, tucked away at one end of the high street. The interior is smart and modern in style, as is the menu. Perhaps relieved by the abundance of ingredients, Mr Tobin offers a variety of dishes which blend European and Oriental ideas: seared scallops with crab and coconut cakes and a hot and sweet syrup might be followed by baby guinea fowl with mushroom fettuccine and essence of truffles. Look out for the impressive selection of breads.

Seats: 50. Jacket and tie preferred. **Style:** Modern
Smoking: No smoking in dining room; Air conditioning
Directions: 1st floor restaurant on Reigate High Street

59a High Street,
RH2 9AE
Tel: 01737 226650
Fax: 01737 226650
Chef(s): Tony Tobin
Owner(s): Paul Montalto
Cost: Alc £32, set price L £16.50/
D £22.95. ☺ ☺ H/wine £11.95
Times: Noon-3.30pm/7-Midnight.
Closed L Sat, D Sun, 1st 2 wks Aug,
Xmas
Additional: Sunday L.
Children welcome

Richmond Gate Hotel

For **Richmond Gate Hotel** see entry under
Richmond upon Thames, Greater London

RIPLEY
Map 4 TQ05

Michels' Restaurant

Classically French to the core, Eric Michel and family's eponymous restaurant is housed in a Georgian-fronted Queen Anne building full of fresh flowers and china ornaments and

13 High Street,
GU23 6AQ
Tel: 01483 224777
Fax: 01483 222940

RIPLEY *Continued*   Map 4 TQ05   *Michels' Restaurant*

hung throughout with many of Eric's original paintings. In summer guests can sit in the lovely walled garden. His cooking is stylish, bold and interesting, with perhaps the best choices to be found on a gourmet menu, including well-chosen complementary wines, that can be ordered by a whole table. To accompany wafer-thin crab biscuits layered with avocado mousse, a fresh Janus rosé; with plaice tempura and seaweed vinaigrette, organic Gascogne sauvignon; and Carinena Tinto to sample with cabbage parcels of turkey leg confit and foie gras. Classical alternatives on a monthly *carte* might include Bouchot mussel soufflé with curried butter sauce, or roast guinea fowl with buttered spinach leaves and pears flamed in cognac. Desserts might include vanilla custard cream with apple slices and apple sorbet.

Chef(s): Erik Michel
Owner(s): Mr & Mrs E Michel
Cost: *Alc* £42, set price L £21/ D £23-£33. ☺ H/wine £10.95
Times: 12.30-1.30pm/7.30-9pm. Closed Mon, L Sat, D Sun, Early Jan, 2 wks Aug
Additional: Children welcome
Seats: 45. Private dining room 12
Smoking: No smoking in dining room
Directions: M25 J10. 1mile towards Guildford. In centre of Ripley, by traffic lights

SHERE   Map 4 TQ04

Kinghams

A picturesque 17th-century cottage in a small village. An intimate and invariably busy restaurant is given warmth by low ceilings and open fireplaces. A range of tempting starters might include avocado and roasted tomato timbale served with mozzarella fritters, basil oil and deep fried herbs. Some well cooked main courses deliver all their promised flavours (roast best end of lamb marinated in rosemary and black pepper with roasted fennel, red pepper mousse and rosemary and green peppercorn sauce, for example).

Gomshall Lane, GU5 9HE
Tel: 01483 202168
e paul@kinghams-restaurant.co.uk
Chef(s): Paul Baker
Owner(s): Paul Baker
Cost: *Alc* £28, set price L £18.90/ D £20.90. ☺ ☺ H/wine £11.95
Times: 12.15-2.15pm/7-Midnight. Closed Mon, D Sun, 25 Dec-4 Jan
Additional: Sunday L. Children welcome
Seats: 48. Private dining room 24
Smoking: No smoking in dining room
Directions: From Dorking follow A25; from Guildford follow A246 then A25

STOKE D'ABERNON   Map 4 TQ15

Woodlands Park Hotel

The traditional setting of the Oak Room is notable for its attractive, Victorian style furnishings and expansive views over the gardens. Despite the setting the cuisine tends towards the modern with starters such as roasted partridge with caramelised chicory and pear, and mains of baked fillet of salmon with langoustine ravioli.

Smoking: No smoking in dining room
Civil licence: 110
Accommodation: 59 rooms
Directions: From M25 J10, A3 towards London. Through Cobham Centre and Stoke D'Aberton, L at garden centre into Woodlands Lane. Hotel 0.5 mile on L

Woodlands Lane,
KT11 3QB
Tel: 01372 843933
Fax: 01372 842704
e woodlands@arcadianhotels.co.uk
Chef(s): Marc Brown
Cost: *Alc* £32, set price L £21.95/ D £29.50. H/wine £14.95
Times: 12.15-2.30pm/7-10pm.
Closed D Sun, L Mon-Sat
Additional: Sunday L. Bar food L. Children welcome
Seats: 35. Private dining room 20

TADWORTH   Map 4 TQ25

Gemini

Set in a modest parade of shops, Gemini celebrated its tenth anniversary with a redecoration of the dining room in charming unfussy yellows and apricots. Chef Robert Foster combines technical skills from his time at Boulestin with a modern cooking style that might feature open ravioli of shellfish or lamb with gazpacho salsa. Desserts are not to be missed.

Seats: 50
Style: Modern
Smoking: No smoking in dining room
Directions: M25 J8, On Rdbt turn R to Sutton, on 3rd Rdbt take 2nd exit to Tadworth at lights turn R, restaurant on the L

28 Station Approach, KT20 5AH
Tel: 01737 812179
Fax: 01737 812179
Chef(s): Robert Foster
Owner(s): Mr R Foster
Cost: *Alc* £29, set price L £15.50/ D £28.50. ☺ ☺ H/wine £10.95
Times: Noon-2.30pm/7-9.30pm.
Closed Mon, L Sat, D Sun, 2 wks Xmas
Additional: Sunday L. Children welcome

WEYBRIDGE   Map 4 TQ06

Oatlands Park Hotel

18th-century elegance on the site of Henry VIII's Oatlands Palace Estate. The restaurant is a spacious and smart environment in which to enjoy modern European cuisine with a classical underpinning, such as loin of lamb with stuffed baby cabbage, fondant potatoes and a rosemary jus

Seats: 160
Style: Classic, Country-house
Smoking: No-smoking area
Civil licence: 200
Accommodation: 144 rooms (144 en suite) ★ ★ ★ ★
Directions: From Weybridge town centre approach Monument Hill, follow road to mini rdbt. 1st L into Oatlands Drive. Hotel 500 metres on L

146 Oatland Drive, KT13 9HB
Tel: 01932 847242
Fax: 01932 842252
e info@oatlandsparkhotel.com
Chef(s): John Hayes
Owner(s): Oatlands Investments Ltd
Cost: *Alc* £35, set price L £23/D £28. H/wine £15.75
Times: 12.30-2pm/7-9.30pm.
Additional: Sunday L. Bar food. Children welcome. Vegetarian by request only

England

SUSSEX, EAST

BATTLE

Map 5 TQ71

Powder Mills Hotel   NEW

Enormous plants and classical Greek statues adorn this Georgian orangery restaurant, with its marble floors and wicker chairs. There's a good choice from set-price and *carte* menus, offering the likes of rillet of pork with home-made chutney, and roast breast of guinea fowl with a crisp golden skin accompanied by a creamy sauce of chestnuts and artichokes.

Style: Country-house
Smoking: No smoking in dining room
Civil licence: 100
Accommodation: 35 rooms (35 en suite) ★ ★ ★
Directions: Telephone for directions

Powdermill Lane,
TN33 0SP
Tel: 01424 775511
Fax: 01424 774540
e powdc@aol.com
Chef(s): Daniel Alton
Owner(s): Mr & Mrs D Cowpland
Cost: *Alc* £27.50, set price L £15.50/
D £27.50. H/wine £11.25
Times: Noon-2pm/7-9pm.
Additional: Sunday L. Bar food L.
Children welcome
Seats: 90. Private dining room 16.
Jacket and tie preferred

BRIGHTON

Map 4 TQ30

Black Chapati

Steve Funnell and Laura Alker travelled extensively when they were younger, and their combined interests in food and travel provided the inspiration for the Black Chapati. The restaurant's name and location can both be deceptive - the menu extends far beyond India and the location is not the obvious venue for a restaurant of this quality. Malaysian, Thai, Japanese, Chinese, and North African influences are all brought to bear on a menu full of intelligent and accurately cooked dishes. Expect hot and sour soup with sea bass and rice noodles followed by braised pork belly with caramelised garlic, steamed rice and pak choi.

Seats: 32
Style: Modern, Minimalist
Smoking: No pipes; no cigars
Directions: Telephone for directions

12 Circus Parade,
New England Road, BN1 4GW
Tel: 01273 699011
Chef(s): Stephen Funnell
Owner(s): L Alker & S Funnell
Cost: *Alc* £25 H/wine £10.50
Times: Dinner only, 7-10pm.
Closed Sun-Mon, 2 wks Xmas,
2 wks Jul
Additional: Children welcome
Children 6yrs+

The Gingerman Restaurant   NEW

Modern British cooking and a well-balanced menu add up to a successful formula at this interesting restaurant. Tuna carpaccio with horseradish cream and mustard leaves, veal picatta with air-dried ham, sage runner beans and olive mash, and steamed sponge pudding with blueberries and port show the flavour. Lively wine list.

Additional: Children welcome
Seats: 32
Style: Modern, Chic
Smoking: No pipes; no cigars
Directions: Telephone for directions

21A Norfolk Square,
N1 2PD
Tel: 01273 326688
Fax: 01273 326688
Chef(s): Ben McKellar
Owner(s): Ben McKeller &
Pamela Abbott
Cost: Set price L £14.95/D £23.50.
☺ ☺ H/wine £9.95
Times: 12.30-1.45pm/7.30-10pm.
Closed Sun-Mon, 2Wks Winter,
2Wks Summer

La Marinade

Friendly, informal but smart atmosphere bringing in a cosmopolitan crowd. Bright fresh surroundings with stripped floorboards and modern pictures, and some punchy cooking along the lines of snails in parsley and garlic butter, pigeon breast with port, or wild sea trout fillet on a wild mushroom fricassée.

Additional: Sunday L. Children 3yrs+
Seats: 26. Private dining room 25. **Style:** Classic French
Smoking: No-smoking area; Air conditioning
Directions: From Palace Pier take direction of Marina, turn L at Royal Sussex Hospital sign, then 1st L

77 St George Road,
Kemp Town, BN2 1EF
Tel: 01273 600992
Fax: 01273 600992
 violavincent@yahoo.co.uk
Chef(s): LHuillery Vincent
Owner(s): LHuillery Vincent
Cost: Set price L £16/D £22. ☺ ☺
H/wine £10
Times: noon-2pm/7-10pm.
Closed Mon, L Tue, D Sun,
1 wk winter, 1 wk summer

One Paston Place

Fifty yards from the seafront lies a genuine star of the south coast. Whether it's the cool interior design (not so cool as to exclude views over a kitchen garden complete with chickens), efficient but easygoing service, or the French-rooted cooking, the feel is confident, contemporary, but ultimately relaxed. Hand-written menus offer the kind of spare, franglais descriptions ("roast cod, jus au pistou, roasted garlic mash") that often seem to coincide with clarity of purpose in the kitchen. Confirmation comes on the plate with some beautifully judged combinations. Dishes such as crab soup with roasted langoustines, crab dim sum and Thai spices, are a big ask in terms of balancing flavours but the required steady hand and lightness of touch are readily apparent. It's a finesse that runs through the repertoire and that is just as evident in the weightier dishes (pepper, almond juniper crusted canon of lamb with a sweet potato bubble and squeak) as in those that are more obviously in need of dexterity (a brilliant assiette chocolat). Take note, the menu du jour (lunch only) is something of a bargain.

1 Paston Place, BN2 1HA
Tel: 01273 606933
Fax: 01273 675686
Chef(s): Mark Emmerson
Owner(s): Mr & Mrs M Emmerson
Cost: Alc £42, set price L £21.
H/wine £14
Times: 12.30-1.45pm/7.30-9.45pm.
Closed Sun-Mon, 1-14 Jan, 1-14 Aug
Additional: Children 7yrs+.
Vegetarian by request only
Style: Chic
Smoking: No pipes; no cigars;
Air conditioning
Directions: Between Palace Pier &
Marina

Terre à Terre

Exciting vegetarian restaurant in the heart of Brighton. Stripped floors, terracotta walls and subtle spotlights create a modern atmosphere befitting the innovative, flavoursome food. Dishes such as Dosy Dunce Dosas are helpfully explained on the menu and for those who remain perplexed by the sheer choice, the Terre a Tapas offers a taste of many.

71 East Street, BN1 1HQ
Tel: 01273 729051
Fax: 01273 327561
Chef(s): P Morgan,
P Hodgson, L Glass
Owner(s): Ms A Powley &
Mr P Taylor
Cost: Alc £21. ☺ ☺ H/wine £10.25
Times: noon-6pm/6-midnight.
Closed L Mon, 24-26 Dec, 1 Jan
Additional: Sunday L.
Children welcome
Seats: 70
Style: Modern
Smoking: No-smoking area; no pipes;
no cigars; Air conditioning
Directions: Town centre near Cannon
cinema, close to palace pier

BRIGHTON *Continued*   Map 4 TQ30

Whytes

Small, simply decorated restaurant with red banquettes, white tablecloths and those arty sort of pictures that you admire but don't understand. Originally a fisherman's cottage, the building dates from the 18th century and is tucked away in a backstreet not far from the sea. A modern European carte, changing every six to eight weeks, offers the likes of pan-fried organic salmon with smoked salmon tortellini and baby chard broth, and light pepper smoked loin of venison with a cassis and liquorice scented game jus. The restaurant has a loyal following so advance booking is recommended, particularly at weekends.

Style: Modern, Chic
Smoking: No-smoking area; no pipes
Directions: From Brighton towards Hove. Western St is off seafront

33 Western Street, BN1 2PG
Tel: 01273 776618
Fax: 01273 776618
e janc-hong@lineone.net
Chef(s): Paul Gunn
Owner(s): John Anthony
Cost: *Alc* £25.50/D £24. ☺
H/wine £9.95
Times: Dinner only, 7pm-Midnight. Closed Sun, Mon, last 2 wks Feb, 26 Dec-5 Jan
Additional: Children welcome
Seats: 40. Private dining room 20

EASTBOURNE   Map 5 TV69

Grand Hotel

King Edward's Parade, BN21 4EQ
Tel: 01323 412345
Fax: 01323 412233
e reservations@grandeastbourne.com
Chef(s): Marc Wilkinson
Owner(s): Elite Hotels
Times: Closed Sun-Mon, 1-14 Jan
Additional: Children welcome
Seats: 50. Private dining room 50. Jacket and tie preferred
Style: Country-house
Smoking: No smoking in dining room; Air conditioning
Civil licence: 200

Proud of its 125-year history and traditional to the roots, the Grand has recently been restored to full and burnished glory. The Mirabelle restaurant, on the right wing, has its own entrance and dedicated lounge bar. Dining here is a refined experience, enhanced by polished service and live piano music. The wine list is large and serious, while the menu is moderately sized, showing respect for the seasons and a balance of ingredients. A well-timed main course of guinea fowl with basil risotto and black olive sauce has found favour, as has a harmonious dish of iced chocolate and tarragon parfait with pear soup.

Accommodation: 152 rooms (152 en suite) ★ ★ ★ ★ ★
Directions: Western end of the Seafront.

FOREST ROW

Map 5 TQ43

Ashdown Park Hotel

Wych Cross, RH18 5JR
Tel: 01342 824988
Fax: 01342 826206
 reservations@ashdownpark.com
Chef(s): John McManus
Cost: *Alc* £40, set price L £23/D £35.
H/wine £13.50
Times: 12.30-2pm/7.30-10pm.
Additional: Sunday L.
Children welcome
Seats: 120. Private dining room 160.
Jacket and tie preferred
Style: Traditional, Country-house
Smoking: No smoking in dining room
Civil licence: 150

This luxurious hotel stands in 186 acres of woods and lawns, among which you'll find lakes, streams, hidden gardens and a golf course. The impressive mansion is decorated in traditional, elegant style. A meal might begin with cocktails on the terrace or in one of the smart drawing rooms, before progressing to the Anderina restaurant. Wood panelling, an open fire and lovely views of the estate make this a pleasant setting. Naturally, the menu is full of classics: game terrine with pink peppercorn chutney followed by paupiette of sole and salmon with new potatoes and basil cream for example.

Accommodation: 107 rooms (107 en suite) ★ ★ ★ ★
Directions: From A22 at Wych Cross take Hartfield turning, hotel is 0.75 mile on R

HASTINGS & ST LEONARDS

Map 5 TQ80

Röser's Restaurant

64 Eversfield Place,
TN37 6DB
Tel: 01424 712218
Fax: 01424 713763
 gerald@roser.co.uk
Chef(s): Gerald Röser
Owner(s): Mr & Mrs Röser
Cost: *Alc* £36, set price L £20.95/
D £23.95. ☺ H/wine £11.50

Once again it's been a good year for the Rösers. All that glitters may not be gold, but it's also true that the plainest wrappings can hide the most precious gifts. So it is at this unprepossessing-looking jewel of a restaurant, the sort of place you might walk right past were you not in the know. Enter, and prepare for dining that still hits all the right notes. Home-made breads and tiny gorgeous soups are an excellent intro to Gerald Rösers

England

HASTINGS & ST LEONARDS *Continued* Map 5 TQ80

deceptively simple style. Deliciously silky starters like foie gras parfait with a hint of brandy are defined by a classical approach but with the odd twist along the way. Major successes have included blade of beef with creamed Savoy cabbage, rösti potato and foie gras sauce, a "superb" recent main dish. The menus range through port-marinated, smoked wild boar ham with fresh pear, to roast mallard with orange and port sauce, sweet-peppered pineapple with black pepper ice cream, and some wonderful petits fours. A serious wine list - more of a book really - has something for every palate and pocket.

Times: Noon-2pm/7-10pm. Closed Sun-Mon, L Sat, 1st 2wks Jan & 2wks June
Additional: Children welcome
Seats: 30. Private dining room 20
Style: Traditional
Smoking: No pipes; no cigars; Air conditioning
Directions: On the seafront, opposite Hastings Pier

HERSTMONCEUX Map 5 TQ61

Sundial Restaurant

A fish tank, leather chairs and bold patterned carpet lend a front room feel to this cute cottage restaurant nestling on Herstmonceux high street. Although au fait with the rules of classic cuisine, the French chef occasionally breaks free to create such surprisingly successful combinations as grilled ostrich with honey and lime, mango and papaya chutney or an appetiser of smoked duck with exotic fruit salsa and a hint of curry. More familiar dishes might include chicken ballotine with tarragon cream sauce or foie gras with brioche and muscat gelée. The serious, French biased wine list includes plenty of Bordeaux and some rare half bottles.

Accommodation: 1 rooms (1 en suite)
Directions: In centre of village, on A271

BN27 4LA
Tel: 01323 832217
Fax: 01323 832909
Chef(s): Vincent Rongier
Owner(s): Mr & Mrs V & Mary Rongier
Cost: *Alc* £35, set price L £19.50/ D £25.50. H/wine £13.25
Times: Noon-3.30pm/7-11.30pm. Closed Mon, D Sun
Additional: Sunday L. Children welcome
Seats: 50. Private dining room 22
Style: Chic, French
Smoking: No smoking in dining room

HOVE Map 4 TQ20

Quentin's

42 Western Road, BN3 1JD
Tel: 01273 822734
Fax: 01273 822734
e quentins@amserve.net
Chef(s): Anthony Sturge
Owner(s): Anthony Sturge
Cost: *Alc* £25/D £23.50. ☺
H/wine £11.50
Times: noon-2pm/7-9.30pm. Closed Sun & Mon, L Sat, 2 wk Xmas, 2 wks Aug
Seats: 29. Private dining room 25
Smoking: No pipes; no cigars
Directions: Telephone for directions

Modern British cuisine in a setting of stripped pine tables set on a wooden floor against burnt orange walls is as down to earth as its setting on Hove's main shopping street. Under the new ownership of chef Anthony Sturge it continues to produce monthly menus that are strongly produce orientated yet remain sensibly short for a dining-room of this size. Adventurous starters include crocodile with raspberry and red onion marmalade and chicken and green bean mousse with home-dried aubergine. Follow with oven-roasted cod on spiced beetroot salad or chicken breasts stuffed with ricotta and spinach. Finish with sweet potato pie with toffee pecans.

JEVINGTON
Map 4 TQ50

Hungry Monk Restaurant

BN26 5QF
Tel: 01323 482178
Fax: 01323 482178
Chef(s): G Fisher & N Sharman
Owner(s): Mr & Mrs N Mackenzie
Cost:, set price L £24.95/D £26.50.
H/wine £11
Times: Noon-5pm/6.45-1am.
Closed L Mon-Sat, BHs, 24-26 Dec
Additional: Sunday L. Children 4yrs+.
Vegetarian by request only
Seats: 38. Private dining room 16.
Jacket and tie preferred
Style: Country-house
Smoking: No smoking in dining room;
Air conditioning
Directions: Follow A22 towards
Eastbourne. Turn R on to B2105.
The restaurant is between Polegate
and Friston

Open fires and beamed ceilings create a cosy atmosphere at this pub-style restaurant, the home of the banoffi pie. Expect country starters like chorizo and bean soup, pork sausage and mustard Yorkshire, with perhaps rabbit roasted in prosciutto, stuffed with pea purée and leeks, and served with sage, apple and Calvados sauce. Try the homemade banoffi pie chocolates.

LEWES
Map 5 TQ41

Shelleys Hotel

High Street, BN7 1XS
Tel: 01273 472361
Fax: 01273 483152
Chef(s): Robert Pierce
Cost: Alc £30, set price D £28.50. ☺
H/wine £14.50
Times: Noon-2.15pm/7-9.15pm.
Additional: Sunday L. Bar food L.
Children welcome
Seats: 30. Private dining room 40.
Jacket and tie preferred
Style: Traditional Country-house
Smoking: No smoking in dining room

Elegant country house style dining with the wind whistling down the chimney into the huge fireplace, large chandeliers overhead and views of the delightful but compact gardens for the well positioned. The formality of good quality silverware, glassware and linen is soon softened by the friendliness of the staff. The cooking requires some dexterity- a risotto of sun dried tomato and basil - but generally hits the right balance. Desserts such as berry and mascarpone cheesecake with lemon curd ice cream are similarly accomplished.

Civil licence: 50. **Accommodation:** 19 rooms (19 en suite) ★ ★ ★
Directions: Town centre

England

NEWICK

Map 5 TQ42

Newick Park Country Estate

@@

BN8 4SB
Tel: 01825 723633
Fax: 01825 723969
e bookings@newickpark.co.uk
Chef(s): Tim Neil
Owner(s): Mr and Mrs Childs
Cost: *Alc* £43.50, set price L
£19.50/D £27.50. ☺ H/wine £9.75
Times: Noon-2.30pm/7-9.30pm.
Closed New Year
Additional: Sunday L. Children 1yr+
Seats: 60. Private dining room 54.
Jacket and tie preferred
Smoking: No smoking in dining room
Civil licence: 70

Food is at the centre of any visit to this secluded country house, much of it originating on the estate itself. Pork and game from the park, and fruit and vegetables from the organic walled garden, all make their way onto the plate, and everything else is as locally-sourced as possible. Unsurprising, then, to find that flavours are fresh and honest, as in pan-fried scallops with creamed cabbage and coral cappuccino, and thyme-roasted rump of lamb with garlic mash. The sea is raided for poached lobster salad, and grilled halibut, while sautéed local venison and roast pigeon smack of the countryside.

Accommodation: 16 rooms (16 en suite) ★ ★ ★
Directions: From Newick on A272 between Haywards Heath/ Uckfield, turn S on Church Rd, at end of road turn L. Hotel 0.25 mile on R

RYE

Map 5 TQ92

Landgate Bistro

Fresh ingredients and a nicely executed meal are what you can expect at the Landgate Bistro. Plain and white painted brick walls and heaps of modern pictures offer a simple backdrop for what promises to be a pleasurable visit. From either the set price or *carte* menu, choose such easy-going options as salmon and cod fishcakes or satisfying desserts like lemon and almond tart.

Directions: Telephone for directions

5-6 Landgate, TN31 7LH
Tel: 01797 227907
Chef(s): Toni Ferguson-Lees
Owner(s): Nick Parkin & Toni
Ferguson-Lees
Additional: Children welcome
Seats: 30
Style: Bistro, Modern
Smoking: No smoking in dining room

Mermaid Inn

Famous smugglers' inn where architectural glimpses of its rich history (beamed ceilings and attractive stone work) complement a contemporary approach to hospitality and cuisine. Great care is taken in assembling flavour, texture and colour - notably in a dish of pan-fried crab cake with mustard sauce, spinach and a walnut dressing.

Seats: 64. Private dining room 16. Jacket and tie preferred
Style: Traditional French. **Smoking:** No smoking in dining room
Accommodation: 31 rooms (31 en suite) ★ ★ ★
Directions: Town centre. Car park through archway

Mermaid Street, TN31 7EY
Tel: 01797 223065
Fax: 01797 225069
e mermaidinnrye@btclick.com
Chef(s): Robert Malyon
Owner(s): Mrs J Blincow &
Mr R I Pinwill
Cost: *Alc* £34, set price L £17.50/
D £35. ☺ H/wine £13
Times: Noon-2.30pm/7-9.30pm
Additional: Sunday L. Bar food.
Children welcome

TICEHURST
Map 5 TQ63

Dale Hill Hotel
NEW

Unpretentious hotel restaurant swimming in light and blessed with magnificent views over the Kentish Weald. 'Fresh, simple and enjoyable' sums up the approach with quality ingredients combining in a pleasing goats' cheese starter, or a succulent lamb main course with a full range of baby vegetable accompaniments.

TN5 7DQ
Tel: 01580 200112
Fax: 01580 201249
e info@dalehill.co.uk
Chef(s): Mark Carter
Cost: *Alc* £24, set price D £21.95. ☺
H/wine £11.25
Times: Dinner only, 6.30-9pm
Additional: Sunday L. Bar food. Children welcome
Seats: 80. Private dining room 120
Style: Modern
Smoking: No pipes; no cigars
Civil licence: 55
Accommodation: 32 rooms (32 en suite) ★★★★
Directions: At junction of A21 & B2087 follow signs for Ticehurst & Flimwell; Dale Hill is one mile on L

UCKFIELD
Map 5 TQ42

Buxted Park

A pleasant dining environment has been created at Buxted Park by locating the restaurant within the mansion's original orangery. The menu may offer starters such as ravioli of lobster, pan-fried sea bass with celeriac and chicken foie gras reduction as a main course. Desserts might include a white chocolate mousse with confit of orange.

Accommodation: 44 rooms (44 en suite) ★★★★
Directions: Turn off A22 Uckfield by-pass (London-Eastbourne road), then take A272 to Buxted. Cross set of traffic lights, entrance to hotel 1 mile on R

Buxted, TN22 4AY
Tel: 01825 732711
Fax: 01825 732770
Chef(s): Valentine Rodriguez
Cost: *Alc* £25 H/wine £14.50
Times: Noon-3pm/7-Midnight.
Additional: Sunday L. Bar food. Children welcome
Seats: 70
Style: Chic, Modern
Smoking: No smoking in dining room
Civil licence: 80

Horsted Place

A very fine example of Gothic revivalist architecture is the setting for a formal but not too stuffy country house-style dining room. Charismatic, personable staff are on hand to guide you through the *carte* and table d'hôte options as well as chef's seasonal signature dishes and a separate vegetarian menu. The flavour and texture of a terrine of chicken confit and foie gras demonstrated real technical flair whilst the choice of accompaniments (a quenelle of dense pesto, dressed leaves and fine dice of apple in a cider vinegar dressing) was genuinely imaginative. A main of seared scallops benefited from top quality fresh ingredients.

Little Horsted, TN22 5TS
Tel: 01825 750581
Fax: 01825 750459
Telephone for further details

England

The Wild Mushroom Restaurant   NEW

Refurbished rural restaurant set beside the A28 north of Hastings, with stripped wooden floors, a simple modern décor and a light and airy conservatory. Chef Paul Webbe, formerly at nearby Powder Mills Restaurant, has a loyal local following for his interesting and good value Sunday lunch menu (best to book) and daily set lunches. Enthusiasm and culinary expertise shine through on his varied and ambitious, evening *carte*. Modern British cooking with a nod to the Mediterranean are evident in such starters as duck liver and game terrine with Cumberland sauce and pan-fried scallops with gazpacho dressing and balsamic, or main dishes like braised rabbit with garlic confit, butter beans and tomato and thyme sauce. For pudding try the raspberry crème brûlée with Drambuie ice cream.

Directions: From Hastings take A21 towards London. On outskirts of Hastings turn R onto A28 towards Ashford (Westfield Lane). Restaurant 1.5 miles on L

Woodgate House,
Westfield Lane, TN35 4SB
Tel: 01424 751137
e info@wildmushroom.co.uk
Chef(s): Paul Webbe
Owner(s): Mr & Mrs Paul Webbe
Cost: *Alc* £26, set price L £16.95.
☺ ☺ H/wine £10.95
Times: Noon-2pm/7-10pm.
Closed Mon, L Sat, D Sun, 25 Dec,
2wks New Year
Additional: Sunday L.
Children welcome
Seats: 40
Style: Modern
Smoking: No smoking in dining room

Crossways Hotel

A 'gastronomic oasis in the heart of Cuckmere Valley' is how it describes itself, and few would argue with the claim; this small country hotel certainly exudes a warm, peaceful atmosphere. Much of the relaxing style is due to the friendly owners, David Stott and Clive James, and their successful recipe chimes comfortably with locals and visitors alike. The monthly-changing set price menu is offered in elegant surroundings, backed by a balanced wine list. Locally sourced produce is skillfully blended in seafood pancake, devilled breast of Gressingham duck, and white chocolate mousse with fresh raspberries, strawberries and a fruit coulis.

Accommodation: 7 rooms (7 en suite) ♦♦♦♦
Directions: A27, 2m W of Polegate

BN26 5SG
Tel: 01323 482455
Fax: 01323 487811
e dine@crosswayshotel.co.uk
Chef(s): David Stott & Juliet Anderson
Owner(s): David Stott & Clive James
Cost: Set price D £29.95.
H/wine £11.95
Times: Dinner only, 7.30-8.30pm.
Closed Sun & Mon, 24 Dec-24 Jan
Additional: Children 12yrs+
Seats: 22
Style: Modern
Smoking: No smoking in dining room

SUSSEX, WEST

Amberley Castle

This 11th century hotel is a treasure trove of history, from the impressive gatehouse (and portcullis) to the battlements with their lovely wield and downland views. The 12th century Queens Room restaurant has barvel vaulted ceilings and murals which date back several hundred years. It is a softly lit backdrop for the traditional French and British cooking. Dishes might include Southdown rabbit or quenelle of smoked haddock brandade with scallop tartare, spring leaves and herb vinaigrette. The extensive wine list is equipped to complement any choice. Other delights of the setting include magnificent 14th-century walls and a pretty, secluded garden.

continued

BN18 9ND
Tel: 01798 831992
Fax: 01798 831998
e info@amberleycastle.co.uk
Chef(s): James Peyton
Owner(s): Joy & Martin Cummings
Cost: *Alc* £45, set price L £15-
£23.10/D £35. ☺ H/wine £17.50
Times: 12.30-2pm/7-9.30pm.
Additional: Sunday L. Children 12yrs+
Seats: 39. Private dining room 48.
Jacket and tie preferred

Accommodation: 13 rooms (13 en suite) ★ ★ ★
Directions: Off B2139 between Amberley and Houghton

Style: Traditional, Country-house
Smoking: No smoking in dining room
Civil licence: 48

ARDINGLY Map 4 TQ32

Avins Bridge Restaurant

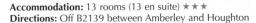

Relaxed dining with a good local following, in a luxurious
Victorian hotel. The food is wholesome, freshly-prepared and
unfussy, with unusual starters like red Leicester cheesecake, and
tuna steak with yellow pepper sauce offering a good mix of
flavours. Traditional puds like brandy snap basket with sorbets,
and fig pudding with cream.

Smoking: No-smoking area
Accommodation: 5 rooms (5 en suite) ◆◆◆◆◆
Directions: From A23 take Crawley/East Grinstead exit. At 2nd
rdbt take 3rd exit for Ardingly. Through village and turn R for
Ardingly College, restaurant 1 mile

College Road,
RH17 6SH
Tel: 01444 892393
e enquiries@theavinsbridge.co.uk
Chef(s): Chris Barnard
Owner(s): Mr and Mrs Barnard
Cost: Alc £25. ☺ H/wine £9
Times: Noon-2.30pm/7-9.30pm.
Closed Mon, D Sun, 24-30 Dec,
1-14 Jan
Additional: Sunday L. Children 6yrs+
Seats: 40
Style: Traditional

ARUNDEL Map 4 TQ00

Burpham Country House

Smart restaurant with attractive conservatory in a hotel dating
back to the 18th century. Crispy polenta cake with warm goats'
cheese, sun-dried tomato, basil, black olives and balsamic
dressing is representative of a largely modern approach to
cuisine although classics such as English rack of lamb on a
celeriac and parsnip mash also feature.

Old Down, Burpham, BN18 9RJ
Tel: 01903 882160
Fax: 01903 884627
Chef(s): Stephen Piggot
Owner(s): George &
Marianne Walker
Cost: Alc £25 H/wine £10.50
Times: Dinner only, 7.30-9pm.
Closed Mon, 22 Jan-5 Feb
Additional: Children 10yrs+
Seats: 30. Jacket and tie preferred
Style: Country-house
Smoking: No smoking in dining room
Accommodation: 10 rooms (10 en
suite) ★ ★ ★
Directions: 3 miles NE of Arundel,
off A27

BOSHAM

Map 4 SU80

Millstream Hotel

Attractive hotel in a delightful village setting right next to the water. A traditional dining room suits unpretentious fayre such as a well-balanced breast of duck with quince and plum sauce served with orange glazed carrots, gratin dauphinoise, broccoli and sugar snaps. Desserts include a milk chocolate and Baileys cheesecake.

Bosham Lane, PO18 8HL
Tel: 01243 573234
Fax: 01243 573459
e info@millstream-hotel.co.uk
Chef(s): Bev Boakes
Cost: Set price L £15.95/D £23.50.
☺ ☺ H/wine £11.50
Times: 12.30-3pm/7-11.30pm.
Additional: Sunday L. Bar food L. Children welcome
Seats: 60. Private dining room 92
Style: Classic country-house
Smoking: No smoking in dining room; Air conditioning
Civil licence: 80
Accommodation: 35 rooms (35 en suite) ★ ★ ★
Directions: Take A259 exit for Chichester rdbt and in village follow signs for Quay

BRACKLESHAM

Map 4 SZ89

Cliffords Cottage Restaurant

There is a warm and relaxed atmosphere at Clifford's Cottage and the staff are attentive. The thatched, low-beamed restaurant is often buzzing with the chatter of a regular local clientele and it is particularly popular at weekends. The fixed price menu and the carte both change regularly and are supported by a well balanced, reasonably priced wine list. Choices on the menu may include smoked chicken and avocado salad, venison steak with red onion compôte or pears on creamed rice with fresh raspberry sauce.

Smoking: No pipes; no cigars; Air conditioning
Directions: A27 follow signs for The Witterings. L at Birdham

Bracklesham Lane, PO20 8JA
Tel: 01243 670250
Chef(s): Tony Shanahan
Owner(s): Mr & Mrs Shanahan
Cost: Alc £28, set price L £12.50/D £19.50. ☺ ☺ H/wine £9.95
Times: 12.30-2pm/7-9.15pm.
Closed L Tue-Sat, D Sun, 1-14 Nov, 1-7 Feb
Additional: Sunday L. Children 5yrs+. Vegetarian by request only
Seats: 28
Style: Traditional

BURPHAM

Map 4 TQ00

George & Dragon

A charming old inn with a relatively modern restaurant area. The atmosphere is very much in keeping with the quiet village setting, with informal but attentive service. A strong French influence runs through the menu with dishes such as caramelised breast of Gressingham duck unlikely to disappoint.

Seats: 40
Smoking: No smoking in dining room
Directions: 2.5 miles up no-through road signposted Burpham off A27,1 mile E of Arundel

BN18 9RR
Tel: 01903 883131
Chef(s): Nick Markey
Owner(s): Kate Holle & James Rose
Cost: Alc £29, set price L £17.50. ☺ H/wine £11.50
Times: 12.15-2pm/7.15-9.45pm.
Closed L Mon-Sat, D Sun, 25 Dec, BHs
Additional: Sunday L. Bar food. Children 8yrs+

CHICHESTER Map 4 SU80

Comme Ça

True to its name this is an authentic little pocket of France. Shrouded in Virginia creeper a cosy French country cottage-style restaurant awaits as do the waistcoated waiters (largely French) and the talented French kitchen. Starters such as Normandy chicken liver pâté flavoured with Armagnac and presented with an apple jelly to be followed perhaps by grilled fillet of beef glazed with a Noilly Prat and Roquefort cream sauce. A well-made pastry with a half pear and frangipane filling topped with nicely thick crème anglaise is a pleasing way to end the meal.

Smoking: No smoking in dining room
Directions: On A286 near Festival Theatre

67 Broyle Road, PO19 4BD
Tel: 01243 788724
Fax: 01243 530052
e comme.ca@commeca.co.uk
Chef(s): M. Navet & O. Vennetier
Owner(s): Mr and Mrs Navet
Cost: Alc £24, set price L £17.95.
☺ H/wine £9.95
Times: Noon-3pm/6pm-Midnight.
Closed Mon, D Sun, BHs
Additional: Sunday L. Bar food L.
Children welcome
Seats: 100. Private dining room 14
Style: Chic

Croucher's Bottom Country Hotel

Homely, unpretentious conviviality is the strength here. That said the approach to cuisine is very serious with mains of roasted sea bass with salsa verde on a bed of sliced new potatoes demonstrating great skill in preparation and presentation.

Seats: 40. Private dining room 20. **Style:** Formal
Smoking: No smoking in dining room
Accommodation: 16 rooms (16 en suite) ★ ★ ★
Directions: From A27, S of Chichester, take A286 to The Witterings. Hotel 2 miles on L

Birdham Road, PO20 7EH
Tel: 01243 784995
Fax: 01243 539797
e crouchers_bottom@btconnect.com
Chef(s): Gavin Wilson
Owner(s): Mr D P Wilson
Cost: Alc £23.50, set price D £23.50-£46.75. ☺ H/wine £11.95
Times: Dinner only, 6-9.30pm
Additional: Bar food L.
Children welcome

Hallidays

Thatched cottage restaurant in the centre of the village, generally packed with locals. Perhaps they come for the impressive home-made breads or maybe the simple but effective combinations of toasted scallop and rocket salad with chilli jam, or sautéed calves' liver with bacon and mint purée. Full credit for an exceptional wine list that boasts several first growth clarets in a well-chosen selection.

Additional: Sunday L. Children welcome. **Seats:** 26
Style: Traditional Country-House. **Smoking:** No-smoking area

Funtington, PO18 9LF
Tel: 01243 575331
Chef(s): Andrew Stephenson
Owner(s): Mr A Stephenson &
Mr P Creech
Cost: Alc £28, set price L £13.50.
☺ ☺ H/wine £9.75
Times: noon-1.30pm/7-9pm.
Closed Mon, L Sat, D Sun, 1 wk Sep
& 2 wks Mar

The Ship Hotel

Former home of Nelson's right hand man, Sir George Murray, the building dates from 1780 and a subtle nautical theme runs throughout. Murray's restaurant offers some appropriately fishy fare (perhaps roast fillet of cod with crispy Parma ham and confit of fresh ceps) alongside the likes of roast free-range turkey and pan-fried English lamb.

Seats: 46. Private dining room 70. Jacket and tie preferred
Style: Traditional. **Smoking:** No smoking in dining room
Accommodation: 36 rooms (36 en suite) ★ ★ ★
Directions: At the inner ring road at large Northgate rdbt turn L into North Street, hotel on L

North Street, PO19 1NH
Tel: 01243 778000
Fax: 01243 788000
e bookings@shiphotel.com
Chef(s): Peter Broomhead
Owner(s): Paul & Jayne Addison
Cost: Alc £26, set price L £16.95/D £19.95. ☺ ☺ H/wine £10.50
Times: Noon-2pm/7.15-9.30pm.
Additional: Sunday L. Bar food.
Children welcome

England

CHILGROVE
Map 4 SU81

White Horse Inn

An attractive old coaching inn, off the road but visible from a distance, and a magnet for locals and passers by. The newly-extended bar offers plain seating or a plusher area, with blackboard specials like duck confit with raspberry sauce, and other seasonal offerings on the *carte*. Leave plenty of time to study the 500-odd wine choices.

Seats: 80
Smoking: No smoking in dining room; Air conditioning
Directions: On B2141 between Chichester & Petersfield

PO18 9HX
Tel: 01243 535219
Fax: 01243 535301
Chef(s): Dominique Willer
Cost: *Alc* £15, set price L £15/D £20. H/wine £12.50
Times: Noon-2pm/7-10pm. Closed Mon, D Sun
Additional: Sunday L. Bar food. Children welcome

COPTHORNE
Map 5 TQ33

Copthorne London Gatwick

Copthorne Way, RH10 3PG
Tel: 01342 348800
Fax: 01342 348833
✉ coplgw@mill-cop.com
Chef(s): Richard Duckworth
Owner(s): Millennium and Copthorne Hotels
Cost: *Alc* £28, set price L £18.50/D £24.50. ☺ ☺ H/wine £13.25
Times: 12.30-2pm/7-10pm. Closed Sun, L Sat, BHs
Additional: Sunday L. Bar food. Children welcome
Seats: 54. Private dining room 10. Jacket and tie preferred
Smoking: No pipes; Air conditioning

The hotel is a sprawling building built around a 16th-century farmhouse set amidst 100 acres of wooded, landscaped gardens. Soft furnishings give a cosy, intimate feel but the whole is fairly fresh looking with exposed beams adding character. The *carte* is extensive and wide ranging. Starters, for example, range from red lentil and coconut soup with chicken and coriander dumplings and chilli oil, to sweetbreads and duck liver with chanterelles mushrooms and marjoram. Baked salmon with an orange, horseradish and herb crust, red rice and pink peppercorn butter sauce demonstrates real attention to detail.

Civil licence: 120
Accommodation: 227 rooms (227 en suite) ★ ★ ★ ★
Directions: M23 J10 follow A264 signed East Grinstead, take 3rd exit off 1st rdbt

The Old House Restaurant

Careful interior renovations have created a winning combination of character and comfort in this superb half timbered building. The menu changes seasonally and reveals strong French influences: among the wide selection of dishes,

Effingham Road, RH10 3JB
Tel: 01342 712222
Fax: 01342 716493
✉ info@oldhouserestaurant.co.uk
Chef(s): Colin Gilbert

look out for the 'super smooth' chicken liver parfait or the escalopes of calves' liver with black pudding, braised red cabbage and cocotte potatoes. Other dishes might include paupiette of lemon sole filled with langoustine and served with a shellfish butter sauce, or Welsh lamb served on ratatouille with roasted garlic and potato fondant. Assured, professional service completes an enjoyable dining experience.

Owner(s): Mr & Mrs C Dorman
Cost: *Alc* £32, set price L £19/D £32.
H/wine £12
Times: 12.15-2pm/7-9.30pm.
Closed L Sat, D Sun, 1wk spring, BHs, Xmas, New Year
Additional: Sunday L.
Children 10 yrs+
Seats: 80. Private dining room 35.
Jacket and tie preferred
Style: Country-house
Smoking: No smoking in dining room; Air conditioning
Directions: From M23 J10 follow A264 to East Grinstead, take 1st at L at 2nd rdbt, L at crossroads, The Old House is 0.75 mile on L

CUCKFIELD

Map 4 TQ32

Taylors Barn Restaurant NEW

Brook Street, RH17 5JJ
Tel: 01444 455826
Fax: 01444 455826
 peter@taylorsbarn.co.uk
Chef(s): Sue Murray
Owner(s): Sue & Peter Murray
Cost: Set price L £23.50/D £32
H/wine £11.75
Times: 12.30-3pm/7.30-11.30pm.
Closed Sun, Mon, 25 Dec for 2wks
Additional: Children welcome
Seats: 12
Style: Rustic
Smoking: No smoking in dining room

It's worth the effort of finding Taylor's Barn, both for the setting and the food. Unusually, the restaurant is located in the owners' home, a splendid 15th-century timber-framed farmhouse with fine country views. Only 12 diners can be accommodated in the intimate beamed dining room, and it is generally full. Mr Murray presents you with the no choice dinner menu (lighter dishes at lunchtime) and a well-chosen list of wines. Mrs Murray prepares the carefully balanced dishes in her kitchen. Perhaps a warm salad of monkfish and dressed leaves, guinea fowl with herb polenta and spiced plums, and a rich dessert of pannacotta and raspberries.

Directions: From London M23, A23 follow signs for Cuckfield on B2125. L at 1st mini rdbt. 0.25 mile on R. From Brighton A23, A272 through Ansty, follow signs to village. Over 3 mini rdbts, 0.25 miles on R

England

EAST GRINSTEAD Map 5 TQ33

Gravetye Manor Hotel

RH19 4LJ
Tel: 01342 810567
Fax: 01342 810080
Chef(s): Mark Raffan
Owner(s): Mr P Herbert
Cost: *Alc* £56, set price L £27/D £37. H/wine £16.50
Times: 12.30-1.45pm/7-9.30pm. Closed 25 Dec eve to non-residents
Additional: Sunday L. Children 7 yrs+
Seats: 50. Private dining room 16. Jacket and tie preferred
Style: Classic, Country-house
Smoking: No smoking in dining room
Accommodation: 18 rooms (18 en suite) ★ ★ ★
Directions: From M23 J10 take A264 towards East Grinstead. After 2m take B2028 (signposted Haywards Heath/Brighton)

The magic of Gravetye Manor is hard to conjure up in a few words. Amazingly beautiful gardens, a forest setting, and the house itself - dating from 1598 and filled with antiques and open fires - are all woven into the spell. This might all be academic were it not for top-flight cooking which tends to deplete the most generous stock of superlatives. Everything served in the tiny restaurant speaks of attention to detail and the mouth-watering canapés and breads are a treasure in themselves. The cooking is intelligently conceived and precisely executed in dishes such as duck confit and foie gras terrine, where contrasting textures and super-intense flavours have been described as a clear winner. Similar praise has been forthcoming for another well judged combination of pan-fried fillet of sea bass on wilted spinach. Desserts offer some genuine leaps of imagination, especially in the pastry section. Top marks for an "irresistible" chocolate tian with a port reduction. True, none of this comes cheap, but with this consistency and quality you're hardly likely to feel cheated.

Findon Valley Hotel

For **Findon Valley Hotel** *see* entry under **Worthing - Sussex, West**

GOODWOOD Map 4 SU80

Marriott Goodwood Park Hotel

PO18 0QB
Tel: 01243 775537
Fax: 01243 520120
Chef(s): Matthew Carr
Owner(s): Marriott-Whitbread Hotel Co
Cost: Set price L £11.95-£15.95/ D £20-£27. ☺ ☺ H/wine £12.75
Times: Noon-2pm/7-9.30pm. Closed L Sat
Additional: Sunday L. Children welcome
Seats: 100. Private dining room 130
Style: Classic country-house
Smoking: No smoking in dining room
Civil licence: 120

The mixture of old and modern in the architecture is echoed in the mixture of rural grounds, golf course and modern leisure facilities. The restaurant itself is housed in a converted barn building boasting tastefully decorated exposed beams and modern, brightly patterned fabrics. A perfectly cooked assiette of duck rillettes was intelligently partnered with duck breast smoked on the premises and drizzled with port dressing, with delicious pan-seared foie gras served on a coarse celeriac purée, to make a starter packed with quality flavours and interest. Mains such as salmon and lobster ravioli on a tagliatelle of spring vegetables are similarly captivating.

Accommodation: 94 rooms (94 en suite) ★ ★ ★ ★
Directions: Just off A285, 3 miles NE of Chichester. Follow signs for Goodwood and once in estate follow signs for the hotel

---

HAYWARDS HEATH
Map 4 TQ32

Jeremy's at Borde Hill NEW

Naturally, being situated in the award winning Borde Hill gardens, there is a terrace overlooking the grounds for eating outside. Inside, the brightly coloured interior is modern and smart, as are the staff. An eclectic spring menu offered lamb's sweetbreads with an orange and Marsala sauce, guinea fowl with Madeira sauce and mash, and lemon tart with cinnamon crème fraîche.

Balcombe Road, RH16 1XP
Tel: 01444 441102
Fax: 01444 441102
Telephone for further details

HORSHAM
Map 4 TQ13

Les Deux Garçons NEW

Almost as many menus as dishes, including a gourmand, gourmet, grand gourmet and epicurean, so diners are spoilt for choice. Simpler style on weekdays which is when we visited. French-influenced mussels, pates and rustic soups alongside seared mignon of salmon, perhaps, and calves' liver with Ventreche ham, basil mash and plum chutney, then apple tart with vanilla ice cream.

Seats: 40. Private dining room 20. **Style:** Modern, Minimalist
Smoking: No smoking in dining room
Directions: Follow town centre signs, then sign for Piries Place & car park, situated bottom of car park at entrance to Piries Place

Piries Place, RH12 0DF
Tel: 01403 271125
Fax: 01403 271022
e nick@lesdeuxgarcons.com
Chef(s): David Lem
Owner(s): Nick Emmott
Cost: Alc £14, set price L £19-£27.50/D £19-£27.50. ☺ ☺
H/wine £11.50
Times: Noon-3pm/7-10pm.
Closed Sun,
Additional: Children welcome

LICKFOLD
Map 4 SU92

Lickfold Inn

A rustic pub is tucked away on a quiet country lane, but it's well worth tracking down. Its menu is an ever changing, colourful palette of international ideas, from French (char-grilled sirloin steak with au poivre sauce) to Japanese (Pepita seared salmon with Teryaki noodles). There's also a good value cold buffet.

Seats: 40. Private dining room 40
Style: Minimalist
Directions: NE of Midhurst, Lickfold signed from A286

Lickfold GU28 9EY
Tel: 01798 861285
Fax: 01798 861342
Chef(s): Edward Portman
Owner(s): Dops Limited
Cost: Alc £30. ☺ ☺ H/wine £10.50
Times: noon-2.30pm/7-9.30pm.
Closed 25-Dec
Additional: Sunday L. Bar food. Children welcome

England

LOWER BEEDING
Map 4 TQ22

The Camellia Restaurant at South Lodge Hotel

Brighton Road, RH13 6PS
Tel: 01403 891711
Fax: 01403 891766
e enquiries@southlodgehotel.co.uk
Chef(s): Lewis Hamblet
Owner(s): Mr. R Cox
Cost: *Alc* £45, set price L £24-£37.50.
H/wine £22.50
Times: Noon-2pm/7-10pm.
Additional: Sunday L. Bar food.
Children welcome
Seats: 40. Private dining room 10.
Jacket and tie preferred
Style: Classic, Country-house
Smoking: No smoking in dining room
Civil licence: 80
Accommodation: 41 rooms (41 en suite) ★ ★ ★ ★
Directions: From Horsham follow signs for Brighton on A281. After 6 miles South Lodge Hotel is signposted on R

A magnificent Victorian country house built in 1883, South Lodge has been acclaimed since its opening as a hotel some 100 years later. Standing in 90 acres of mature gardens and grounds it enjoys splendid views over the South Downs. The restaurant, named after the centuries-old camellia that has been preserved as a centrepiece of the south facing terrace, takes pride in its regular use of herbs, soft fruit and vegetables from the property's own walled garden - as good an indicator as any of the care taken over food preparation. Gratifying results on the plate are well illustrated by the speciality Camellia menu that offers choices of Caesar salad with crispy ham or curried parsnip soup followed by confit duck with orange and vanilla sauce or baked Atlantic cod with prawn, caper and pepper dressing and rounding off with bitter chocolate tart or raspberry roulade. A la *carte* alternatives that merit praise have included perfectly timed scallops with seafood rice and sweet-and-sour dressing, roe deer with foie gras, black trompettes and Madeira sauce and Belgian dark chocolate and orange parfait dressed with boozy black cherries marinated in kirsch.

MIDHURST
Map 4 SU82

Southdowns Country Hotel

Dumpford Lane, Trotton, GU31 5JN

Well tended gardens surrounded by arable farmland provide an idyllic setting for this attractive country house hotel. The combination of attractive floral displays, immaculate decor and top quality cuisine is an attractive mix. Starters include a chicken and vegetable terrine wrapped in leeks with red pepper and chilli jam or honeydew and cantaloup melon topped with gingered apples and finished with cassis coulis. Chicken supreme filled with Stilton and wrapped in Parma ham typifies the main course options.

Tel: 01730 821521
Fax: 01730 821790
e reception@southdownshotel.
freeserve.co.uk
Chef(s): Darren Lunn
Owner(s): R Lion
Cost: Alc £25, set price L £14.95/
D £25. ☺ ☺ H/wine £11.95
Times: Noon-2pm/7-9.30pm.
Additional: Sunday L. Bar food.
Children 10yrs+
Seats: 60. Private dining room 20
Smoking: No smoking in dining room;
Air conditioning
Civil licence: 100

Accommodation: 20 rooms (20 en suite) ★ ★ ★
Directions: 1 mile off A272, Petersfield Rd

PULBOROUGH
Map 4 TQ01

Chequers Hotel **NEW**

Old Rectory Lane, RH20 1AD
Tel: 01798 872486
Fax: 01798 872715
Chef(s): Jeff Welch
Owner(s): Martin & Pandora Pellett
Cost: Set price L £7/D £25.
H/wine £11.50
Times: Noon-2pm/7-8.30pm.
Additional: Sunday L.
Children welcome
Seats: 35. Private dining room 20
Style: Modern
Smoking: No smoking in dining room
Accommodation: 10 rooms (10 en
suite) ★ ★ ★
Directions: Telephone for directions

With views across the Arun Valley to the South Downs, this intimate, 16th-century hotel utilises fresh local produce in the careful preparation of dishes featured on daily-changing table d'hôte menus. Begin with monkfish and prawn cassoulet, move on to tender, well cooked shank of lamb with red wine jus, and round off a sound meal with iced prune and Armagnac parfait with orange tea syrup and spiced prunes

ROWHOOK
Map 4 TQ13

Chequers Inn

RH12 3PY
Tel: 01403 790480
Fax: 01403 790480
Cost: Alc £20
Times: Noon-2pm/7-9.30pm.
Closed D Sun
Additional: Sunday L. Bar food L.
Children welcome

Beamed ceilings and wooden floors ensure plenty of character in this inn dating from the 15th-century. The menu too has much to recommend it, offering dishes as varied as roast chump of lamb or fresh fish of the day niçoise in a basil and balsamic reduction. The emphasis is on simply prepared, high-quality fresh ingredients.

Directions: Telephone for directions

England

STORRINGTON

Map 4 TQ01

Fleur de Sel

Manleys Hill, RH20 4BT
Tel: 01903 742331
Fax: 01903 740649
Chef(s): Michel Perraud
Owner(s): Bernadette & Michel
Perraud
Cost: Alc £33, set price L £18.50-
£22.50/D £22.50. ☺ ☺
H/wine £12.50
Times: Noon-2pm/7-9.30pm.
Closed Mon, L Sat, D Sun, 2 wks Jan,
2wks Sep
Additional: Sunday L.
Children 10yrs+

Classical French cooking in a typically English setting. Pastel walls, beams, an inglenook fireplace, summer terrace and raised garden with pond and fountain. Guests are welcomed to the small bar area to peruse a fixed-price *carte*, written in French with English sub-titles. Main courses are likely to include roast Scottish salmon with honey and pink grapefruit and venison medallions with cranberry and chestnut sauce. Start out with saffron-flavoured fish bisque or foie gras escalope with elderberries and round off with a subtle orange and Grand Marnier soufflé with chocolate sorbet.

Seats: 54. Private dining room 18
Style: Country-House
Smoking: No smoking in dining room
Directions: On A283, off A24, just E of Storrington

Old Forge

As well as being responsible for some seriously good, imaginative cooking, industrious chef-patron Clive Roberts, also manages to run a wine business and organise food and wine trips abroad. The dining rooms are intimate and low beamed with pictures featuring the twin enthusiasms of cricket and South Africa. This is bright cooking with consistently lively flavours. Fairly typical of the style are a starter of 'rich and intense' smoked lamb with grape jelly and a successful main course of fillets of sole with lemon peppered couscous and an avocado sauce. Desserts have included a creditable raspberry and white chocolate tart. As might be expected, the wine list exhibits plenty of depth and character.

Style: Traditional, Rustic
Smoking: No-smoking area; no pipes
Directions: On a side street in the village centre

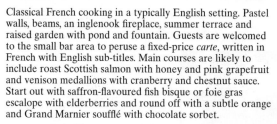

6 Church Street, RH20 4LA
Tel: 01903 743402
Fax: 01903 742540
e contact@oldforge.co.uk
Chef(s): Clive Roberts &
Will Murgatroyd
Owner(s): Mr & Mrs N C Roberts
Cost: Alc £30, set price L £14.50/
D £25 ☺ H/wine £12
Times: 12.15-1.15pm/7.15-9pm.
Closed Mon-Wed, L Sat, D Sun,
2 wks Spring, 2 wks Autumn,
Xmas-New Year
Additional: Sunday L. Children
welcome. Vegetarian not available
Seats: 34. Private dining room 12

England

TURNERS HILL
Map 4 TQ33

Alexander House

East Street, RH10 4QD
Tel: 01342 714914
Fax: 01342 717328
e info@alexanderhouse.co.uk
Chef(s): Neil Wiggins
Cost: H/wine £15.75
Additional: Sunday L. Bar food.
Children 7yrs+
Seats: 60. Private dining room 24.
Jacket and tie preferred
Smoking: No smoking in dining room
Civil licence: 60
Accommodation: 15 rooms (15 en suite) ★ ★ ★
Directions: On B2110 between Turners Hill and East Grinstead, 6 miles from M23 J10

There's a theatrical feel to this country house hotel at night, the long drive lit like a runway and the entrance dramatically bright. Inside it's all warm colours, soft lighting and muted sounds, a refined atmosphere that continues into the restaurant where diners can peruse the menu in peace. The food is a fresh interpretation of the traditional with an occasional hint of the exotic. Quality shines through such seafood concoctions as mussel and saffron soup, ravioli of crab with ginger and tarragon and warm salad with smoked salmon and seared scallops. Main dishes tend towards the meaty, as in tournedos of Scottish beef fillet, honey-glazed Gressingham duck breast, and loin of venison, with the odd fishy interloper like nage of Dover sole and langoustines with carrots and coriander. Skill is evident everywhere, especially the tiny, teasing amuse-bouche. The solid wine list has few surprises, and service is hands-on and generous.

WORTHING
Map 4 TQ10

Ardington Hotel

Steyne Gardens, BN11 3DZ
Tel: 01903 230451
Fax: 01903 526526
Telephone for further details

Attractive, spacious dining room looking out onto the street. The menu suffers a little from trying to be all things to all men but as long as you are careful in your selection good quality, interesting dishes such as seared tuna with cucumber spaghetti, soy sauce and roasted sesame seeds prove very enjoyable.

WORTHING *Continued*   Map 4 TQ10

Findon Manor Hotel

High Street, Findon, BN14 0TA
Tel: 01903 872733
Fax: 01903 877473
e findon@dircon.co.uk
Chef(s): Stanley Ball
Owner(s): Mike and Jan Parker-Hare
Cost: Set price L £19.50/D £22.50. ☺
H/wine £12
Times: Noon-2pm/7-9pm.
Additional: Sunday L. Bar food.
Children welcome
Seats: 45. Private dining room 34
Style: Country-house
Smoking: No smoking in dining room
Civil licence: 50

An oak-floored restaurant overlooks attractive gardens, a scene neatly reflected in the pale green décor of the interior. The menu descriptions are often complex but rest assured that at heart it is good quality ingredients sensibly and carefully manipulated that set the standard. A clear soup of smoked sausage, spices and duck might open, to be followed by the likes of poached supreme of chicken filled with foie gras and morels, topped with a truffle Madeira jus. A range of desserts is so packed with tempting, unusual offerings (elderberry and cardamom parfait with a caramelised orange jus for example) that a selection of miniature versions is an obliging alternative.

Accommodation: 11 rooms (11 en suite) ★★★
Directions: Town centre junction of A286 and A272

TYNE & WEAR

GATESHEAD   Map 12 NZ26

Eslington Villa Hotel

Refurbished small Edwardian hotel, where the quality of food and the ambience of the restaurant are great strengths. Fairly cosmopolitan menu with some enterprise. Risotto of finnan haddock with Parmesan typifies the style. Service is friendly and attentive.

Seats: 80. Private dining room 30
Style: Modern, Bistro-Style
Smoking: No smoking in dining room
Accommodation: 18 rooms (18 en suite) ★★
Directions: Off A1 (M) along Teme Valley, turn R at Eastern Avenue, then L into Station Road

8 Station Road, Low Fell, NE9 6DR
Tel: 0191 4876017
Fax: 0191 4200667
e admin@eslingtonvilla.fsnet.co.uk
Chef(s): Barry Forster
Owner(s): Mr & Mrs N Tulip
Cost: *Alc* £30, set price L £15.50/
D £20. ☺ ☺ H/wine £11.50
Times: Noon-2pm/7-10pm.
Closed L Sat, D Sun, 25-26 Dec,1 Jan,
BHs
Additional: Sunday L.
Children welcome

England

NEWCASTLE UPON TYNE Map 12 NZ26

Café 21

An informal cafe style restaurant with blackboard menus and light modern décor. A meal begins with a basket of French bread, a bowl of olives and a pot of butter then continues along Continental lines with dishes such as saffron risotto or slow cooked shoulder of lamb with Provençal vegetables.

Additional: Children welcome
Seats: 68
Style: Modern Bistro-style
Smoking: No-smoking area; no pipes
Directions: From A696, follow signs for Darras Hall. L at mini rdbt, restaurant is 200yds

35 The Broadway, Darras Hall,
Ponteland NE20 9PW
Tel: 01661 820357
Fax: 01661 820357
Chef(s): Michael Waugh
Owner(s): Terence Laybourne
Cost: Alc £20, set price L £13/D £13.
☺ ☺ H/wine £10.50
Times: Noon-2.30pm/5.30-10.30pm.
Closed Sun, L Mon-Fri, BHs

Café 21 Newcastle

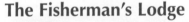

The switch to a more informal style has had the desired effect, and the quayside premises are packed at both lunch and dinner. A similar approach in terms of décor, menus and service as Café 21 (above). Expect salad of artichoke hearts with figs, grilled Toulouse sausage with mash and caramelised apple tart. Good fun.

Seats: 60
Style: Bistro-style
Smoking: No-smoking area; no pipes
Directions: Telephone for directions

Quayside, NE1 3UG
Tel: 0191 222 0755
Fax: 0191 221 0761
Chef(s): Christopher Dobson
Owner(s): Mr and Mrs T Laybourne
Cost: Alc £25, set price L £14.50.
☺ ☺ H/wine £10.50
Times: Noon-2.30pm/6-10.30pm.
Closed Sun, BHs
Additional: Children welcome

The Fisherman's Lodge

Jesmond Dene, Jesmond,
NE7 7BQ
Tel: 0191 281 3281
Fax: 0191 281 6410
e events@tomscompanies.com
Chef(s): Steven Jobson
Owner(s): Tom and Jocelyn Maxfield
Cost: Alc £40, set price L £19.50/
D £34. H/wine £14.50

A major redecoration has transformed this traditional Victorian house into a stylish modern hotel which still retains the best of its original features. Set in a wooded riverside ravine at the edge of the city, it offers bucketloads of peace and tranquility. The restaurant delivers a wide ranging selection of modern dishes - perhaps corn fed chicken breast with fondant potatoes, baby leeks and foie gras sauce or deep fried tempura of fish

England

NEWCASTLE UPON TYNE *Continued* Map 12 NZ26

with Chinese vegetables and sukiyaki sauce. Desserts might include apple sorbet, exotic fruit mousse or a chocolate choux bun.

Civil licence: 70
Directions: 2.5m from city centre, off A1058 (Tynemouth road) at Benton Bank, middle of Jesmond Dene Park

Times: Noon-2.30pm/7-10pm.
Closed D Sat
Additional: Children welcome
Seats: 60. Private dining room 40
Style: Chic
Smoking: No smoking in dining room

The Magpie Room

St James Park, NE1 4ST
Tel: 0191 201 8511
Fax: 0191 201 8611
Chef(s): Ian Lowery
Owner(s): Newcastle United
Cost: *Alc* £28, set price L £15/D £21.
☺ ☺ H/wine £13.95
Times: Noon-2.30pm/7-10.30pm.
Closed Mon, L Sat, D Sun, Xmas,
New Year
Additional: Sunday L.
Children welcome
Seats: 160. Private dining room 30.
Jacket and tie preferred
Style: Formal, Modern
Smoking: No-smoking area; no pipes;
Air conditioning
Civil licence: 500

Serious dining in a serious environment - albeit an unconventional one. The Magpie room is within Newcastle United's home ground and offers excellent views of the pitch. At the heart of the menu are key European players such as terrine of slow cooked duck, corn fed chicken and foie gras or sirloin steak with hand cut chips and sauce Béarnaise. Imports from further afield could include spiced lentil soup or breast of duck with Japanese five spice and vegetable spring rolls. The wine list is particularly good value, and features some of Newcastle United's own label wines (including Champagne). Service is prompt, efficient and friendly.

Directions: From S, follow Gateshead A1 signs then A692 over Redheugh Bridge, Blenheim St, then L on Bath Lane. Located within Newcastle United Football Ground

☺ Indicates a restaurant that has told us they offer a two-course lunch for less than £15

☺ Indicates a restaurant that has told us they offer a three-course dinner for less than £25

Indicates a restaurant that has told us that 50% or more of their ingredients are organically sourced

Prices quoted in the guide are for guidance only and are subject to change without notice

England

Malmaison Hotel

A striking modern hotel overlooking the redeveloped quayside. The sophisticated, contemporary atmosphere of the brasserie is enhanced by dark walls, white table cloths and the sound of jazz music. The equally modish French based menu might include citrus chicken with bang bang sauce or roasted artichokes and black eye bean stew. Service is slick and friendly.

Quayside, NE1 3DX
Tel: 0191 245 5000
Fax: 0191 245 4545
e malmaison.com
Chef(s): Gary Cook
Owner(s): Radisson-SAS/MWB
Cost: *Alc* £22, set price L £11.95/ D £12.95. ☺ ☺ H/wine £13.95
Times: Noon-2.30pm/6-11.00pm.
Additional: Sunday L. Bar food L. Children welcome
Seats: 147. Private dining room 12
Style: Modern, French
Smoking: Air conditioning
Accommodation: 116 rooms (116 en suite) ★ ★ ★
Directions: Telephone for further directions

Marriott Hotel, Gosforth Park   NEW

High Gosforth Park, Gosforth, NE3 5HN
Tel: 0191 236 4111
Fax: 0191 236 8192
Telephone for further details

The opulent surroundings of the Brandling Restaurant is where the main action is at this purpose-built hotel, set in landscaped grounds close to the A1 and the racecourse. Menus display a successful combination of both classical and modern cooking styles. A recent inspection meal yielded a good starter of strips of honey roast duck and chicken on a light duck liver pâté with oil dressed leaves. The highlight proved to be the main course of roasted medallions of monkfish wrapped in quality, oak flavoured smoked bacon, served with roasted fennel and a light and slightly sweet tomato fondue. Puddings include a traditional bread-and-butter pudding spiced with nutmeg and accompanied by a wholesome textured honey and oatmeal ice cream.

Treacle Moon

5-7 The Side, NE1 3JE
Tel: 0191 232 5537
Fax: 0191 221 1745
Chef(s): Patrice Buee
Owner(s): Tom and Jocelyn Maxfield
Cost: *Alc* £30, set price L £12.50/ D £12.50. ☺ ☺ H/wine £13.50
Times: Closed Sun, Mon, L Sat, BHs, Xmas, 2 wks Aug
Additional: Children welcome
Seats: 30
Style: Modern, Chic

Taken from Byron's description of his honeymoon at Seaham Sunderland, the name of this restaurant hints at the theme of its décor (Byron - not treacle). The room is lit by spotlights and decorated in mauve and brown, the walls adorned with quotes from the man himself. This stylish, contemporary atmosphere is echoed in the beautifully presented cooking. A meal might include red pepper and Stilton mille-feuille with Stilton sauce, followed by seared scallops with crab and fennel risotto. The well chosen wine list includes plenty of French classics as well as an interesting selection from the New World.

Smoking: No smoking in dining room; Air conditioning
Directions: Telephone for further directions

England

NEWCASTLE UPON TYNE *Continued* Map 12 NZ26

Vermont Hotel

Castle Garth, NE1 1RQ
Tel: 0191 233 1010
Fax: 0191 233 1234
e info@vermont-hotel.co.uk
Chef(s): David Ross
Owner(s): Lincoln Group
Cost: H/wine £14
Times: Dinner only, from 7pm.
Closed Sun-Mon, 1-14 Aug
Additional: Children welcome
Seats: 80. Private dining room 25.
Jacket and tie preferred
Style: Classic
Smoking: No-smoking area
Civil licence: 200
Accommodation: 101 rooms (101 en suite) ★★★★
Directions: City centre, by the castle and swing bridge

An historic landmark building with a striking façade close to the Castle Keep and with views across to the famous Tyne Bridge. A series of drinking and dining venues include Martha's bar, an all-day brasserie and the more sedate Blue Room. International cuisine in classic style is exemplified by Argyll smoked salmon with red onion marmalade, capers and fried quail egg, followed by roast loin of venison with sauté of girolle and parsnip and claret fumé. Vegetarian options might include aubergine, radicchio and goats' cheese mille-feuille with sweet pepper essence, while for the truly sweet-toothed there is 18th-century chocolate rum pie with white chocolate parfait and Kirsch anglaise.

SUNDERLAND   Map 12 NZ35

Brasserie 21

Wylam Wharf, Low Street, SR1 2AD
Tel: 0191 5676594
Telephone for further details

Terry Laybourne's Sunderland outlet offers a similar style to the other '21's' in Newcastle with a contemporary menu of punchy British cooking. Brasserie 21 occupies two floors of a converted warehouse and has a striking minimalist style of décor. Proximity to the quay makes for some good fish, in particular a mixed grill of seafood with basil and olive oil. Confit of duck with warm potato and shallot salad with red wine sauce is also praised.

Swallow Hotel

Queen's Parade, Seaburn,
SR6 8DB
Tel: 0191 529 2041
Telephone for further details

A Victorian bandstand commands the centre of this classic restaurant, where a gourmet menu offers bold and innovative flavour combinations. Pan-seared scallops work surprisingly well with rhubarb and a delicate curry butter sauce, and baked medallion of salmon comes with a mildly tangy lemon and dill sabayon. Strong coffee to finish.

England

WARWICKSHIRE

ABBOT'S SALFORD
Map 4 SP05

Salford Hall Hotel

It is rare to see a place as thoughtfully restored as this Tudor mansion: think log fires, leaded windows, tiled corridors and tapestries. The oak panelled restaurant serves British based cuisine which might occasionally benefit from a lighter touch (as in a fish casserole slightly overpowered by dill) but on the whole, meals are well presented and flavoursome. A typical menu might include rack of lamb or confit of duckling with Toulouse sausage. Desserts such as summer pudding or passion fruit tart are intense and cleansing. Other delights of this Grade I listed building include a priest's hole and Elizabethan stained glass.

Civil licence: 50
Accommodation: 34 rooms (34 en suite) ★★★
Directions: on A439, 8 miles W of Stratford-upon-Avon

WR11 5UT
Tel: 01386 871300
Fax: 01386 871301
e reception@salfordhall.co.uk
Chef(s): Robert Bean
Cost: Set price L £15.95/D £25-£28.
☺ ☺ H/wine £12.75
Times: Lunch only, 12.30-2pm.
Closed L Sat, Xmas
Additional: Sunday L. Bar food L.
Children 2yrs+
Seats: 50. Private dining room 50.
Jacket and tie preferred
Style: Traditional, Country-house
Smoking: No smoking in dining room

ALDERMINSTER
Map 4 SP24

Ettington Park Hotel

Friendly but discreet service attends diners at this magnificent Victorian mansion, set in 40 acres of parkland on the River Stour. The restaurant is an oak-panelled room with a rococo ceiling and two bay windows overlooking the 12th-century church. The menus offer a daily selection plus steaks and fish from the grill and a small *carte* of dishes at a supplement to the fixed price. Typical of these options are foie gras, leek and potato terrine with truffle dressing, and loin of veal with Puy lentils, fondant potatoes and garlic cream.

Accommodation: 48 rooms (48 en suite) ★★★★
Directions: 5 miles S of Stratford-upon-Avon

CV37 8BU
Tel: 01789 450123
Fax: 01789 450472
Chef(s): Chris Hudson
Owner(s): Hand Picked Hotels
Cost: *Alc* £35, set price L £20/
D £32-£45. H/wine £16.50
Times: Noon-2pm/7-9.30pm.
Closed L Mon-Sat
Additional: Sunday L. Bar food.
Children welcome
Seats: 60. Private dining room 80
Style: Classic, Country-house
Smoking: No smoking in dining room
Civil licence: 60

England

ATHERSTONE
Map 4 SP39

Chapel House Hotel

Friar's Gate, CV9 1EY
Tel: 01827 718949
Fax: 01827 717702
Chef(s): Adam Bennett
Owner(s): Mr D Arnold
Cost: Alc £27, set price L £17.50. ☺
H/wine £10.25
Times: Dinner only, 7-9.30pm.
Closed D Sun, 24-26 Dec, BHs
Additional: Sunday L.
Children 10yrs+
Seats: 50. Jacket and tie preferred
Style: Classic, Country-house
Smoking: No smoking in dining room

As its name suggests this hospitable hotel is situated right next to the church, its grounds partly enclosed by a high brick wall. The dining room, overlooking mature gardens, reflects the Georgian period style. An interesting monthly changing carte is supplemented by daily dishes and specialities. For those who prefer a lighter option, first course dishes may also be ordered as a second course - these could include Ribblesdale cheese croquettes, or smoked salmon with avocado and potato salad. More robust mains are pan-fried supreme of guinea fowl with pearl barley risotto, and rosette of beef with thyme mash and Puy lentils.

Accommodation: 14 rooms (14 en suite) ★★
Directions: Hotel is next to church, in market square

ILMINGTON
Map 4 SP24

The Howard Arms   NEW

Experienced hoteliers have successfully restored the fortunes of this rambling 17th-century stone inn overlooking the village green. Full of period charm with a relaxing atmosphere, it attracts discerning diners for modern, freshly prepared pub food. Blackboard menus may list guinea fowl and pork terrine with red onion marmalade, scallops with provençale sauce and couscous, chargrilled venison with parsnip purée and juniper and port sauce, and glazed lemon tart with orange compôte. Good list of house wines (10 by the glass).

Smoking: No smoking in dining room
Accommodation: 3 rooms (3 en suite)
Directions: Telephone for directions

Lower Green, CV36 4LT
Tel: 01608 682226
Fax: 01608 682226
e howard.arms@virgin.net
Chef(s): Sarah Keightley
Owner(s): Robert & Gill Greenstock
Cost: Alc £18, set price L £16.95.
☺ ☺ H/wine £9.95
Times: 11-3pm/6-11pm.
Closed L Mon-Sat, D Sun
Additional: Sunday L. Children
welcome. Vegetarian by request only
Seats: 90

KENILWORTH
Map 4 SP27

Restaurant Bosquet

Traditional front room-style restaurant run by husband and wife team Bernard and Jane Lignier. Jane provides attentive and chatty service while Bernard produces French cuisine from both fixed-price and carte menus. All the classic ingredients are

97a Warwick Road,
CV8 1HP
Tel: 01926 852463
Chef(s): Bernard Lignier
Owner(s): Bernard & Jane Lignier

there: starting with coquille St Jacques, leek salad and truffle dressing, or a salad of duck foie gras and confit. Mains include market fresh fish and favourites like filet de boeuf au vin rouge, and saddle of venison on a purée of celeriac and truffle with game sauce.

Style: Traditional
Smoking: No pipes; no cigars
Directions: In main street in the centre of Kenilworth

Cost: Alc £25, set price L £25/ D £25-£27.70
Times: Noon-1.15pm/7-9.15pm. Closed Sun & Mon, L Sat, 3 wks Aug, 1 wk Xmas
Additional: Children welcome. Vegetarian by request only
Seats: 26

Simpsons

A restaurant which 'oozes quality' - thanks to a recent refurbishment. A Mediterranean frontage with shutters and topiary box trees exudes classiness along with wooden floors, shining crystal and crisp table settings. The appearance and polish of the food gives away the chef's disciplined classical training with, vitally, visually stunning dishes pleasing the palate as much as the eye. Dishes may incorporate myriad flavours without being over complicated as in a salad of roast quail with its own egg, lentils, celeriac and walnut dressing - all of which come together beautifully. Exceptionally well-balanced flavours in intelligent combinations.

Directions: In main street in the centre of Kenilworth

Warwick Road, CV8 1HL
Tel: 01926 864567
Fax: 01926 864510
Chef(s): Andreas Antona
Owner(s): Andreas & Alison Antona
Cost: Set price L £20/D £33.75. H/wine £12.50
Times: 12.30-2pm/7-10pm.
Additional: Children welcome
Seats: 70. Private dining room 20
Style: Modern, Chic
Smoking: No-smoking area; no pipes; Air conditioning

ROYAL LEAMINGTON SPA   Map 4 SP36

Amor's   NEW

15 Dormer Place, CV32 5AA
Tel: 01926 778744
Fax: 01926 778744
Chef(s): Sami Amor, Christopher Harrod
Owner(s): Sami Amor
Cost: Alc £27.50, set price L £10.50/D £22.50. ☺ ☺ H/wine £12
Times: noon-2pm/7-10pm. Closed Sun, L Sat, BHs
Additional: Children welcome
Seats: 32. Jacket and tie preferred
Style: Modern French
Smoking: No-smoking area; no pipes; no cigars; Air conditioning
Directions: Off High St, opposite The Pump Room Gardens

Privately owned French restaurant offering continental calm in the heart of the Midlands. Warm, rustic flavours define carefully constructed dishes such as duck rillettes with finely chopped capers served on a galette of lentils. Dishes are generally well-balanced - pan-fried fillets of red mullet with roasted vegetables and jus niçoise for example - and traditional concepts such as pear and almond tart with caramel sauce are rendered accurately and with something of a flourish. Décor is crisply traditional (white linen and sparkling crystal) with hand-painted glass windows a happy distraction. Service is attentive yet nicely discreet.

England

ROYAL LEAMINGTON SPA *Continued* **Map 4 SP36**

Lansdowne Hotel

Small, cosy restaurant in an attractive terraced townhouse just off Leamington high street. Informal service complements a commendable emphasis on simplicity in the cuisine. Good ingredients manipulated in a skilful, unfussy fashion as with corn-fed chicken breast in a white wine and cream sauce. A loyal local clientele makes for an informal, cheerful atmosphere.

Style: Traditional
Smoking: No smoking in dining room
Accommodation: 14 rooms (14 en suite) ★★
Directions: Town centre, at crossroads of Warwick Street and Clarendon Street

87 Clarendon Street,
CV32 4PF
Tel: 01926 450505
Fax: 01926 421313
Chef(s): Perry Mehr
Owner(s): Ross Mehr
Cost: *A/c* £18.95,
set price D £18.95. ☺ ☺
H/wine £8.95
Times: Dinner only, 7-9pm.
Closed 25-26 Dec
Additional: Bar food D.
Children welcome
Seats: 20. Private dining room. Jacket and tie preferred

STOP PRESS Change of Chef

Leamington Hotel and Bistro

Simple Victorian house containing a traditional bistro-style restaurant. The menu offers everything from light lunches (spaghetti with fresh salmon and dill cream) to sandwiches, vegetarian food, and more substantial items (braised pheasant in rich smoked bacon and red wine sauce). The owners maintain a valuable personal touch in their operation.

Style: Bistro-Style, Traditional
Smoking: No pipes; no cigars
Civil licence: 65
Accommodation: 30 rooms (30 en suite) ★★★
Directions: Along Newbold Terrace, turn L at lights. Hotel on right-hand corner of Willes Road & Upper Holly Walk

64 Upper Holly Walk,
CV32 4JL
Tel: 01926 883777
Fax: 01926 330467
e leamington@bestwestern.co.uk
Chef(s): Robert Rouse
Owner(s): Frank Nixey
Cost: Set price L £12/D £15. ☺ ☺
H/wine £9.95
Times: Noon-2pm/7-10pm
Additional: Sunday L.
Children welcome
Seats: 40. Private dining room 36

Mallory Court Hotel

Harbury Lane,
Bishop's Tachbrook,
CV33 9QB
Tel: 01926 330214
Fax: 01926 451714
e reception@mallory.co.uk

An impeccable English country house hotel with a mellow atmosphere indoors and beautifully landscaped grounds outside. In this elegant, tranquil setting the excellent staff contrive to offer a memorable experience, not least in the dining room where the cuisine, like the service, is seamless. Expect the modern, like grilled goats' cheese with warm spiced pear and walnuts, and the classical - tournedos Rossini, Chateaubriand with béarnaise sauce (for two), or a marriage of both, as in noisettes of venison with chestnuts, spiced cranberries and Grand Veneur sauce, or pan-fried duck breast with figs and foie gras. Desserts are also innovative: caramel soufflé with praline ice cream, chocolate crème brûlée with prune and Armagnac ice cream, or exotic fruit salad with coconut ice cream. The wine list is extensive, with few surprises.

Accommodation: 18 rooms (18 en suite) ★ ★ ★
Directions: From M40 J13 (northbound) take A452 (signed Leamington Spa), next L into Oakley Wood Rd (B4087). R into Harbury Ln. Hotel on R. From M40 J14/A452 into Mallory Rd, then B4087

Chef(s): Allan Holland, Stephen Love
Owner(s): Mr J Mort, Mr A Holland
Cost: Alc £50, set price L £27.50/ D £38.50. H/wine £22
Times: Noon-2pm/7-10pm.
Additional: Sunday L. Bar food L. Children 9yrs+
Seats: 50. Private dining room 25
Style: Traditional, Country-house
Smoking: No smoking in dining room
Civil licence: 22

Solo   NEW

A chic restaurant with trendy clientele and a dramatic setting, along with hessian walls, chunky furniture and panels of colour adorning the walls. An open kitchen provides action with plenty of entertaining showmanship. Technical skill is evident in, say, well-judged lamb's kidney with cognac cream and watercress butter or a tail of monkfish, nicely cooked and accompanied by pak choi, sweet potato and sauce Oriental.

Style: Modern, Chic.
Smoking: No smoking in dining room
Directions: Telephone for directions

23 Dormer Place,
Tel: 01926 422422
Chef(s): Ian Wallace, Richard Ashfield
Owner(s): The Wallace Family
Cost: Set price L £18/D £25. H/wine £12
Times: Noon-2.30pm/7-9.30pm. Closed Sun, L Mon, Xmas, BHs
Additional: Children 12yrs+. Vegetarian by request only
Seats: 23

SHIPSTON ON STOUR   Map 4 SP24

Chavignol at
the Old Mill   NEW

The Maguires have flown from their Chipping Norton nest and landed just a few miles away at this delightful old mill where they were due to open a few weeks after we went to press. The original Chavignol is now reincarnated as a more informal affair (see entry Chavignol Brasserie) whilst Marcus Ashenford has made the move to Shipston on Stour. Expect the menu to continue to be defined by some bold takes on classic combinations and the cooking to be as robust in flavour and accurate in execution as ever.

Smoking: No smoking in dining room
Directions: Telephone for directions

Mill Street CV36 4AW
Tel: 01608 663888
Fax: 01608 663188
✉ chavignol@virgin.com
Chef(s): Marcus Ashenford
Cost: Alc £40, set price L £18-£25/ D £25. H/wine £14
Times: Noon-2pm/7-10pm
Additional: Sunday L. Children welcome
Seats: 34
Style: Classic

England

STRATFORD-UPON-AVON   Map 4 SP25

Billesley Manor Hotel

Billesley, Alcester, B49 6NF
Tel: 01789 279955
Fax: 01789 764145
✉ enquiries@billesleymanor.co.uk
Chef(s): Sean Cullum
Owner(s): Haydn Fentum
Cost: Alc £30, set price L £18.50/
D £22.95. ☺ ☺ H/wine £14.50
Times: 12.30-2pm/7-9.30pm.
Closed L Sat
Additional: Sunday L. Bar food L.
Children welcome
Seats: 42. Private dining room.
Jacket and tie preferred
Style: Traditional, Country-house
Smoking: No smoking in dining room

Historical links with Shakespeare and the immaculately kept gardens certainly add appeal but it is the restaurant that is the main attraction. Such diversions can easily be forgotten when confronted with an excellent terrine of foie gras with duck rillettes, Savoy cabbage and apple chutney. Mains such as belly pork with split pea purée, cider fondants and black pudding, or tarte Tatin of chicory, red wine lentils and glazed goats' cheese typify the sturdy style, whilst chocolate terrine with white chocolate ice-cream might prove an ideal stimulus for musings on gardening, literature or what you will.

Civil licence: 75
Accommodation: 61 rooms (61 en suite) ★ ★ ★ ★
Directions: 3m W of Stratford-upon-Avon on A46

Desports

13/14 Meer Street,
CV37 6QB
Tel: 01789 269304
Fax: 01789 269304
✉ bookings@desports.co.uk
Chef(s): Paul Desport
Owner(s): Paul & Julie Desport
Cost: Alc £35, set price L £14/
D £22.95-£27.95. ☺ ☺
H/wine £10.50
Times: Noon-2pm/6-9.30pm.
Closed Sun & Mon
Additional: Children welcome.
Vegetarian by request only
Seats: 50
Smoking: No-smoking area; no pipes;
no cigars
Directions: In town centre between
Market Place and Shakespeare Centre

Small market place restaurant with bright blue and yellow walls and vivid food to match. Colour, flavour and texture combine in the simplest of ways to produce real comfort food - but with a twist. Take for example cumin-crusted sea bass with shrimps on beetroot risotto with honey-roast pumpkin and tangerine oil - clear strong flavours, very well executed and nicely presented. The more classical combination of peppered beef fillet on a corn potato cake with pancetta and creamed parsnip is a real advertisement for clarity and simplicity - beautifully cooked with lots of contrasting flavours.

Fox and Goose   NEW

Armscote, CV37 8DD
Tel: 01608 682293
Fax: 01608 682121
Chef(s): Dean Hawker, Mark Smith
Owner(s): Sue Gray
Cost: Alc £22. ☺ ☺ H/wine £10
Times: Noon-2.30pm/7-9.30pm.
Closed 25-26 Dec, 1 Jan
Additional: Sunday L. Bar food.
Children welcome
Seats: 45. Private dining room 20
Style: Bistro-Style, Chic
Smoking: No-smoking area
Accommodation: 4 rooms (4 en suite)
Directions: From Stratford-upon-Avon take A3400 S for 7 miles. After Newbold-on-Stour turn R towards Armscote (signposted). 1mile to village

Traditional country village local transformed into a stylish pub-restaurant with a bright modern décor, a buzzy, cosmopolitan atmosphere, and an eclectic range of freshly prepared dishes listed on daily blackboard menus. Follow seafood terrine or whisky-scented gravadlax with blinis and dill crème fraîche with pan-roasted sea bream on wilted spinach with citrus sauce. Alternatively slow-roasted lamb shoulder with juniper berry and blackcurrant jus, and finish with a zesty glazed lemon tart.

Lambs of Sheep Street

The buzzy feel of this small, centrally located restaurant contributes to its relaxed, informal ambience. Popular with theatre-goers for early and late suppers, and noted, too, for its flexible lunch menus, which attract a wider clientèle, this is modern cuisine in a 16th-century setting. Expect the likes of salmon fishcakes with sorrel sauce and spinach.

Additional: Children welcome
Seats: 100. Private dining room 20
Style: Bistro-Style
Smoking: No pipes; no cigars
Directions: From Stratford town centre, towards 'Waterside' and 'Royal Shakespeare Theatre'. Sheep Street is 1st R on Waterside

12 Sheep Street, CV37 6EF
Tel: 01789 292554
Fax: 01789 292554
✉ lambs@ukgateway.net
Chef(s): Nigel Lambert
Owner(s): Nigel Lambert, Caroline Furby
Cost: Set price L £13.25/D £13.25.
☺ ☺ H/wine £8.95
Times: Noon-2pm/5-10pm.
Closed 25 Dec

The Shakespeare

Given the moniker, no surprise to find this is a black-and-white 18th-century building. The David Garrick Restaurant is simply appointed, with oak beams, an inglenook fireplace and leaded windows looking out on to the street. Terrine of duck confit has been singled out as a triumphant starter, and fillet of sea bass with seared scallops and roasted plum tomatoes, as one of those dishes you just want to go on and on. A carved winter fruit and pepper sabayon provided an interesting combination of

Chapel Street, CV37 6ER
Tel: 0870 4008182
Fax: 01789 415411
✉ heritage-hotels-stratford-upon-avon.shakespeare@forte-hotels.com
Chef(s): Graham Drewry
Cost: Alc £35, set price L £12/D £28.
☺ ☺ H/wine £14

England

STRATFORD-UPON-AVON *Continued*   Map 4 SP25

The Shakespeare

Times: 12.30-2pm/6-9.30pm.
Closed L Sat
Additional: Sunday L. Bar food.
Children welcome
Seats: 48. Private dining room 22
Style: Traditional
Smoking: No smoking in dining room
Civil licence: 45
Accommodation: 74 rooms (74 en suite) ★ ★ ★ ★
Directions: Follow signs to town centre. Round one-way system up Bridge St. At rdbt turn L. Hotel is 200yds on L

textures; finely sliced pears and plums in a brandy snap basket, drenched in sabayon and caramelised, the whole thing topped with a spun sugar basket drizzled in blackcurrant coulis.

Welcombe Hotel

Warwick Road, CV37 0NR
Tel: 01789 295252
Fax: 01789 414666
✉ sales@welcombe.co.uk
Chef(s): Colin Layfield
Cost: *Alc* £45, set price L £20/ D £35/£50 (Sat only). ☺ ☺
H/wine £16
Times: 12.30-2pm/6-9.30pm
Additional: Sunday L. Children 10yrs+. Vegetarian by request only
Seats: 60. Private dining room 60. Jacket and tie preferred
Style: Traditional French
Smoking: No smoking in dining room

This restaurant offers stunning views across terraced gardens, the golf course and far reaching countryside. The traditional but understated décor includes pastel colours, white linen and theatrically draped curtains, whilst staff dressed in white drill jackets with monogrammed breast pockets add to the air of mature refinement. The menu has a modern edge without losing sight of tradition. A meal might include white onion and sage soup followed by char-grilled pork cutlet with beetroot and red onion marmalade and carrot purée. Desserts such as pyramid nougat glace or pear and almond tart round off the meal in style, assisted by coffee with tasty petits fours.

Civil licence: 50
Accommodation: 64 rooms (64 en suite) ★ ★ ★ ★
Directions: 1 mile from Stratford-upon-Avon

WARWICK
Map 4 SP16

Ardencote Manor Hotel

Lye Green Road, CV35 8LS
Tel: 01926 843111
Fax: 01926 842646
e hotel@ardencote.com
Chef(s): Simon Douglas
Cost: *Alc* £32
Times: 12.30-2pm/7-9.30pm.
Additional: Sunday L.
Children 14yrs+. Vegetarian by request only
Seats: 28. Private dining room
Style: Modern, English
Smoking: No smoking in dining room
Civil licence: 150
Accommodation: 75 rooms (75 en suite) ★ ★ ★
Directions: Off A4189
(Warwick/Henley-in-Arden rd).
In Claverdon follow signs for
Shrewley and brown tourist signs for
Ardencote Manor. Approx 1.5 miles

As its name suggests, the Oak Room restaurant is an elegantly panelled room with a country house atmosphere. The cooking is French in essence with a modern English interpretation. A terrine of smoked haddock, salmon and chive, and an accurately cooked fillet of sea bass caught the eye, but biggest plaudits were reserved for desserts such as a knock out lemon and rosemary tart with the lightest pastry and creamiest filling.

WISHAW
Map 7 SP19

The De Vere Belfry

B76 9PR
Tel: 01675 470301
Fax: 01675 470256
e enquiries@thebelfry.com
Chef(s): Eric Bruce
Owner(s): De Vere Hotel Group
Cost: Set price L £15-£19/D £35. ☺
H/wine £14.95
Times: 12.30-2pm/7.30-10pm.
Closed L Sat, BHs
Additional: Sunday L.
Children 14yrs+
Seats: 70. Jacket and tie preferred
Style: Rustic, French
Smoking: No smoking in dining room
Civil licence: 70

The French restaurant is only one of several eating options at this busy resort hotel, but it is undoubtedly also the finest. Golfing fans staying here for the Ryder Cup, and others attracted by the top-class health and leisure club will enjoy the range and quality of dishes on offer. From the set menu sample carrot and Gruyère cheese timbale in watercress froth, moving on to tangerine and nettle sorbet before launching into collops of monkfish, coriander and cardamom risotto and lemon and lime cream, or vegetarian haggis with garlic cream. Classic desserts beckon, like crème brûlée with winter fruits.

Accommodation: 324 rooms (324 en suite) ★ ★ ★ ★
Directions: At junction of A446 & A4091, 1 mile NW of M42 J9

England

WEST MIDLANDS

BALSALL COMMON
Map 7 SP27

Haigs Hotel

Kenilworth Road,
CV7 7EL
Tel: 01676 533004
Fax: 01676 535132
Chef(s): Paul Hartup, Paul Foster
Owner(s): Alan & Hester Harris
Cost: Alc £31, set price D £24.50. ☺
H/wine £10.95
Times: 12.30-4pm/7.30-midnight.
Closed L Mon-Sat, D Sun, New Year
Additional: Sunday L. Children
welcome. Vegetarian by request only
Seats: 60. Private dining room 28.
Jacket and tie preferred
Style: Classic

Appropriately enough, Poppies Restaurant at Haigs Hotel has a floral theme to its décor. A choice of menus delivers an interesting range of dishes at a consistently high standard. Good examples are a parsnip and pear soup with fresh flavours and a good texture, and a main course of veal with grain mustard sauce topped with roast julienne of celeriac and served with a delicate cream sauce. The indecisive will appreciate the Chef's Surprise - a selection of small desserts - for instance, a grapefruit sorbet, citrus jelly, chocolate mousse, banana brûlée and fresh fruit tart.

Smoking: No smoking in dining room
Accommodation: 23 rooms (23 en suite) ★★
Directions: On A452, 4 miles N of NEC/Airport, on L before village centre

Nailcote Hall

This charming Elizabethan manor house is steeped in history and remains largely unspoilt, with heavy timbers and blazing open fires. The Oak Room is an intimate, candlelit retaurant with low beamed ceilings, an inglenook fireplace and dark green walls bearing superb Walter Dendy Sadler engravings. The menu is full of old favourites such as bangers and mash with creamed potato and caramelised onions or rump of lamb with field mushrooms, creamed potato and red wine jus. Desserts might include vanilla crème brûlée or autumn pudding with clotted cream. The staff add to the relaxing atmosphere with their spontaneous, cheerful service.

Style: Traditional
Smoking: No smoking in dining room
Civil licence: 120
Accommodation: 38 rooms (38 en suite) ★★★★
Directions: On B4101 towards Tile Hill/Coventry, 10 mins from NEC/Birmingham Airport

Nailcote Lane, Berkswell,
CV7 7DE
Tel: 024 7646 6174
Fax: 024 7647 0720
e info@nailcotehall.co.uk
Chef(s): Wayne Thomson
Owner(s): Mr R W Cressman
Cost: Alc £40, set price L £21.50/
D £29.50-£32.50. H/wine £13.50
Times: Noon-2.30pm/7-9.30pm.
Closed L Sat, D Sun
Additional: Sunday L. Bar food L.
Children welcome
Seats: 45. Private dining room.
Jacket and tie preferred

BARSTON

Map 4 SP27

The Malt Shovel

Barston Lane, B92 0JP
Tel: 01675 443223
Fax: 01675 443223
Chef(s): Kasu Chauda
Owner(s): Caroline & Chris Benbrook
Cost: Alc £28. ☺ ☺ H/wine £9.95
Times: Noon-3pm/7-late. Closed
Mon, L Tue-Thu & Sat, D Sun,
25-26 Dec, 1 Jan
Additional: Sunday L. Bar food.
Children 10yrs+
Seats: 40
Style: French-Style, Classic
Smoking: Air conditioning
Directions: From M42 J5, take turn
towards Knowle. 1st L on Jacobean
Lane, R turn at T-Jct (Hampton Lane).
Sharp L into Barston Lane. Restaurant
0.5 mile

Welcoming country pub with lots of cask conditioned ales and fine wines. You can eat in the bar or the restaurant, a stylish converted barn with modern soft furnishings. The menu includes favourites such as steak and chips alongside more creative European style dishes - perhaps tarte Tatin of shallots, wild mushrooms, baby leeks and tallegio. Excellent fish menu.

BIRMINGHAM

Map 7 SP08

Bank

Brindley Place is fast becoming the new trendy hangout in Birmingham, so it's no surprise that Bank is a stylish, futuristic affair. The stunning interior by Julyan Wickham combines Bond movie glamour with the hard lines of a multi storey car park, whilst the menu travels from sausages and mash to seared Thai tuna, stopping pretty much everywhere on the way: other dishes might include pumpkin risotto, chicken crostini or rump of lamb with Brinjal potatoes and mint yoghurt dressing. Interesting vegetarian options, a great value fixed-price menu and a thoughtful selection of children's dishes keeps everyone happy - as do the cheerful and knowledgeable staff.

Style: Modern
Smoking: No-smoking area; no pipes; Air conditioning
Directions: Brindley Place is just off Broad Street (A456)

4 Brindley Place, B1 2JB
Tel: 0121 633 7001
Fax: 0121 633 4465
e Info@birmingham.co.uk
Chef(s): Idris Caldora,
David Colcombe
Owner(s): Bank Restaurant Group
Cost: Alc £22.25, set price L £12.50/
D £12.50. ☺ ☺ H/wine £10.90
Times: Noon-3pm/5.30-11pm.
Closed D Sun, 1 Jan
Additional: Sunday brunch, Bar food.
Children welcome
Seats: 250. Private dining room 100

Birmingham Marriott

Pretension is completely absent from this elegant restaurant, where the fine French cuisine offers a lesson in simplicity. No dish suffers from fussy over-flavouring: it's just great food made from wonderfully fresh ingredients. Ravioli of goats' cheese poached in chicken bouillon with leeks prunes and marjoram shows the straightforward modern slant, as does sauté of foie gras with sweetcorn galette, cracked pepper and sherry vinegar jus. Inspired main courses are along the lines of Scotch beef fillet with girolles, pea purée and red wine and thyme jus, and John Dory with confit tomatoes, sauté potatoes, herb sauce and lemon oil. The standard never slips, and desserts like fabulous

12 Hagley Road, Five Ways,
B16 8SJ
Tel: 0121 452 1144
Fax: 0121 456 3442
e birmingham.marriott@whitbread.
com
Chef(s): Ian Mansfield
Owner(s): Marriot
Cost: Alc £43.75, set price L £22.50-
£32.50/D £32.50-£36.50.
H/wine £14.50
Times: Noon-2.30pm/7-10pm.

BIRMINGHAM *Continued*   Map 7 SP08   *Birmingham Marriott*

passion fruit soufflé show that all those extra luxury items can be superfluous. Good humour takes the severity off the very professional service, and split levels in the restaurant ensure that a cosy, intimate spot can be secured for privacy.

Additional: Sunday L. Bar food L. Children welcome
Seats: 60. Private dining room 25. Jacket and tie preferred
Style: Classic, Formal
Smoking: No-smoking area; Air conditioning

Accommodation: 98 rooms (98 en suite) ★ ★ ★ ★ ★
Directions: City end of A546, at the Five Ways roundabout

Langtry's at The Birmingham Marriott

The Edwardian elegance of this hotel is reflected in Langtry's, the less formal of its two restaurants. Yellow walls, green trellis work and plenty of foliage create a conservatory atmosphere, with subdued lighting and enormous art nouveau angels adding a distinctive character. The menu is predominantly British - dishes might include bubble and squeak or smoked haddock with a poached egg and a mustard and chive sauce - but an element of punch is added by dishes such as a sauté of chorizo, savoy cabbage, poached egg and Caesar dressing or char grilled tuna with a spiced lentil salsa.

Smoking: No smoking in dining room; Air conditioning
Accommodation: 98 rooms (98 en suite) ★ ★ ★ ★ ★
Directions: City end of A546, at the Five Ways roundabout

Birmingham Marriott Hotel, 12 Hagley Road, Five Ways B16 8SJ
Tel: 0121 452 1144
Fax: 0121 456 3442
e birmingham.marriott@whitbread.com
Chef(s): Ian Mansfield
Owner(s): Marriott
Cost: *Alc* £30. H/wine £17
Times: Noon-2.30pm/6-10pm. Closed Sun
Additional: Children welcome
Seats: 50. Private dining room 20
Style: Classic, Bistro-style

Chung Ying Garden

17 Thorp Street, B5 4AT
Tel: 0121 666 6622
Fax: 0121 622 5860
e chungying@aol.com
Chef(s): Mr Siu Chung Wong
Owner(s): Mr S C Wong
Cost: *Alc* £18. ☺ ☺ H/wine £9.50
Times: noon-midnight/noon-11pm. Closed Xmas
Additional: Sunday L. Children welcome
Seats: 350. Private dining room 200
Style: Oriental
Smoking: Air conditioning

Prepare to be amazed by the sheer vastness of the Cantonese range on offer at this gem in the Birmingham Chinese Quarter. Stamped with authenticity by the local Chinese community, it caters for every taste. Flavours are well judged and distinctive, as in steamed pork and prawn dumplings, or eel and belly of pork with garlic.

Directions: City centre, just off Hurst St, nr Hippodrome Theatre and shopping centre, just off A38

Copthorne Birmingham

Modern city-centre hotel with an informal brasserie and refined restaurant. The former delivers contemporary dishes like salad of tea-smoked duck with Chinese leaves or chocolate and mascarpone cheesecake. The latter veers towards classical tastes but with interesting additions as in baked sea bream with olive and citrus crust on champ mash and lobster hollandaise.

Additional: Sunday L. Bar food. Children welcome
Seats: 85
Style: Bistro-Style
Smoking: No-smoking area; Air conditioning
Accommodation: 212 rooms (212 en suite) ★ ★ ★ ★
Directions: In City centre, telephone for directions

Paradise Circus,
B3 3HJ
Tel: 0121 200 2727
Fax: 0121 200 1195
e sales.birmingham@mill-cop.com
Chef(s): Gerard Lee
Owner(s): Millenium Hotels and Resorts
Cost: Alc £15/D £15. ☺ ☺
H/wine £14.95
Times: 11-2.30pm/6-11pm.

Leftbank

This former banking hall stands in the centre of Birmingham and is decorated with a chic combination of rattan, polished floorboards and oil paintings. The cuisine is equally stylish and modern, combining British and European influences in dishes such as monkfish tail with French smoked bacon and Provençal vegetables or sirloin of beef with parsnips and Burgundy sauce.

Seats: 70. Private dining room 14
Style: Classic. **Smoking:** No pipes; no cigars
Directions: From M6 J6,follow signs City centre. Restaurant located in centre next to Novotel Hotel

79 Broad Street, B15 1AQ
Tel: 0121 643 4464
Fax: 0121 643 5793
Chef(s): Bill Marmion
Owner(s): Bobby-Browns Group
Cost: Alc £31, set price D £31. ☺
H/wine £12.50
Times: Noon-2pm/7-10pm.
Closed Sun, L Sat, BHs
Additional: Children welcome

Le Petit Blanc

Raymond Blanc's brasserie feels like a futuristic airport with its blue and red upholstery, utilitarian flooring and touches of chrome. Popular with diners of all ages and occupations (children are welcomed and have their own menu), this is a slick operation with friendly, efficient staff and reliably good food. The menu caters for most tastes: dishes might include crêpes with mushrooms, Gruyère cheese and ham and cream Kirsch sauce; confit guinea fowl with wild mushrooms and Madeira jus, or steak frites with Béarnaise sauce. Mouthwatering side orders (honey roasted parsnips; sautéed spinach) and equally enticing desserts complete an enjoyable meal.

Style: Modern Brasserie
Smoking: No-smoking area; no pipes; no cigars
Directions: Telephone for directions

9 Brindley Place, B1 2HS
Tel: 0121 633 7333
Fax: 0121 633 7444
e petitblanc.birmingham@virginnet.co.uk
Chef(s): Walter Blakemore, Peter Alcroft
Owner(s): Raymond Blanc
Cost: Alc £25, set price L £15. ☺ ☺
H/wine £11
Times: Noon-3pm/5.30-11.30pm.
Closed 25 Dec
Additional: Sunday L. Children welcome
Seats: 182. Private dining room 48

BIRMINGHAM *Continued*   Map 7 SP08

Shimla Pinks

214 Broad Street, B15 1AY
Tel: 0121 633 0366
Fax: 0121 643 3325
Chef(s): A S Sunner
Cost: *Alc* £14.95, set price L £6.95.
☺ H/wine £10.50
Times: Noon-3pm/6-11pm.
Closed L Sat-Sun
Additional: Children welcome
Seats: 350
Style: Chic, Modern
Smoking: Air conditioning
Directions: In City centre, opposite
Novotel and near the ICC

This very popular restaurant in the heart of Birmingham sets
out to be stylish and chic while maintaining the traditional
values of Indian service. The extensive menu offers plenty for
vegetarians and some unusual dishes such as Tikka Machi Ka -
pink Scottish salmon with a spicy marinade of dill, fennel and
ginger, roasted in the tandoor.

Thai Edge Restaurant   NEW

Sleek, well-run and oozing quality, this funky Thai restaurant
combines clean, fresh flavours with chilli-hot intensity. Chicken
satay, and deep-fried chicken wings with spicy minced pork
starters, then green papaya salad, and red curry with beef
cooked in coconut milk, are not for delicate palates. Cool down
with mango and papaya sorbet.

Brindley Place, B1
Tel: 0121 643 3993
Telephone for further details

La Toque d'Or   NEW

Fresh flowers adorn simple table settings under the high ceilings
and stained glass windows of this Parisian-style restaurant. A
whirl of fromage frais with roughly chopped basil, sage, sorrel
and mint served with a warm niçoise potato is a simple but
captivating opening to a meal. Excellent presentation is
apparent in a main of roast quail with spinach, mushrooms and
an incredibly potent truffle scented jus. With desserts such as
Calvados soufflé with an apple sorbet, and citrus fruit and
Grand Marnier Terrine with a mango sorbet this exciting
addition to the Birmingham scene is well worth investigating.

27 Warstone Lane,
B18 6JQ
Tel: 0121 233 3655
Fax: 0121 233 3655

e didier@latoquedor.co.uk
Chef(s): Didier Philipot
Owner(s): SSPG Consulting Ltd
Cost: Set price L £15.50/D £23.50. ☺ ☺ H/wine £12.50
Times: 12.30-2pm/7-9.30pm. Closed Sun-Mon, L Sat,
Xmas, 2wks Aug, 1wk Etr
Additional: Children welcome
Seats: 36
Style: French
Smoking: No pipes; no cigars; Air conditioning
Directions: 1m N of city centre, 400 metres from clock tower.
Telephone for further directions

La Toque d'Or

COVENTRY   Map 4 SP37

Brooklands Grange

Hidden behind a Jacobean façade is a modern business hotel with an up-to-the-minute attitude towards food. The friendly restaurant offers an innovative range of dishes, although results are occasionally inconsistent. Slow-cooked lamb shank with mild spices, wine jus and olive oil mash, and the day's special fish dish, sit alongside pan-fried sirloin steak with peppercorn cream sauce.

Style: Modern
Smoking: No smoking in dining room
Accommodation: 31 rooms (31 en suite) ★ ★ ★
Directions: Leav A5 at Oswestry, follow signs to Llansilin through town. Hotel is 3 miles W of Oswestry on B4580 Llansilin Rd

Holyhead Road, CV5 8HX
Tel: 024 7660 1601
Fax: 024 7660 1277
e enquiries@brooklands-grange.co.uk
Chef(s): Gina Kemp
Cost: Alc £25.90, set price L £18.50/D £18.50. ☺ ☺ H/wine £9.95
Times: Noon-2pm/7-10pm.
Closed L Sat, BHs
Additional: Sunday L. Bar food. Children welcome
Seats: 50. Private dining room 12

Hylands Hotel

This modern hotel houses an equally up to date restaurant: there's the feel of a London Brasserie to the décor, and the menu offers trendy, creative dishes such as fillet of cod with goats' cheese and chilli macaroni or corn fed chicken with herb and Swiss cheese risotto. Desserts might include summer-berry bavarois with an intensely flavoured liquorice scented berry compôte or chocolate brownie with rich chocolate sauce. A good range of speciality teas and coffees rounds off a satisfying dining experience. The hotel is convenient for the city centre and enjoys pleasant views over the Memorial park.

Smoking: No-smoking area; Air conditioning
Accommodation: 61 rooms (61 en suite) ★ ★ ★
Directions: On A429, 500yds from town centre ring road at J6, opposite Memorial Park

Warwick Road, CV3 6AU
Tel: 024 7650 1600
Fax: 024 7650 1027
e hylands@bestwestern.co.uk
Chef(s): Michael Batchelor
Cost: Alc £24.50, set price L £10.75/D £15.75. ☺ ☺ H/wine £11.95
Times: Noon-2.30pm/7-10pm.
Closed L Sat
Additional: Sunday L. Bar food. Children welcome
Seats: 80. Private dining room 30
Style: Modern, Chic

HOCKLEY HEATH   Map 7 SP17

Nuthurst Grange

Nuthurst Grange Lane, B94 5NL
Tel: 01564 783972
Fax: 01564 783919
e info@nuthurst-grange.co.uk

A long avenue drive brings you to Nuthurst, which stands in seven acres of landscaped gardens and woodlands. At its heart

England

HOCKLEY HEATH *Continued*　　　Map 7 SP17

is the restaurant, a comfortably traditional dining room with lovely countryside views. The menu makes impressive use of the freshest seasonal produce, delivering French and British based dishes such as fillet of beef with potato rösti, caramelised shallots, foie gras and rich red wine sauce or salmon with Puy lentils, green beans, aubergine caviar and red wine fish sauce. The set price menus include a wine inclusive dinner, which provides a great opportunity to sample some of the restaurant's fine selection of well chosen bins.

Civil licence: 90
Accommodation: 15 rooms (15 en suite) ★ ★ ★
Directions: Off A3400, 0.5 mile S of Hockley Heath, turn at sign into Nuthurst Grange Lane

Chef(s): David Randolph, Ben Davies
Owner(s): Mr & Mrs Randolph
Cost: Set price L £16.95/D £29.50. ☺
H/wine £14.50
Times: Noon-2pm/7-9.30pm.
Closed L Sat
Additional: Sunday L.
Children welcome
Seats: 60. Private dining room 95
Style: Country-house, modern
Smoking: No smoking in dining room

MERIDEN　　　Map 4 SP28

Manor Hotel

Main Road, CV7 7NH
Tel: 01676 522735
Fax: 01676 522186
📧 reservations@manorhotelmeriden.co.uk
Chef(s): Peter Griffiths
Owner(s): Mr C Dutton
Cost: *Alc* £28, set price L £22/D £22. ☺ H/wine £13.95
Times: Noon-2pm/7-10pm.
Closed L Sat, 27-30 Dec
Additional: Sunday L. Bar food.
Children welcome
Seats: 150. Private dining room 220
Smoking: No smoking in dining room; Air conditioning

A smart, sympathetically restored Georgian manor in a sleepy village, within easy reach of the NEC and motorway network. Service is professional, friendly and attentive, adding just that extra dimension to some imaginative food that offers a considerable range on both the fixed price menu and the *carte*. Accuracy and clarity of flavours are apparent in dishes such as avocado and crab galette, sea bass and scallops in creamed coriander sauce and white chocolate and iced lemon parfait. Alternatives on the set menu might include chicken and wild mushroom terrine and rump of lamb with pea and mint risotto.

Accommodation: 114 rooms (114 en suite) ★ ★ ★
Directions: From M42 J6 take A45 towards Coventry.0.5m after fly-over, turn R across dual carriageway onto B4104. Over mini rdbt. Hotel on L

　Indicates a restaurant that has told us that 50% or more of their ingredients are organically sourced

Prices quoted in the guide are for guidance only and are subject to change without notice

Marriott Forest of Arden Hotel

Maxstoke Lane, CV7 7HR
Tel: 016765 522335
Telephone for further details

The Broadwater Restaurant is spacious and expansive with high beamed ceilings and a terracotta colour tiled floor giving the room an earthy grandeur. Distinct sections prevent the vastness of the room from becoming overpowering. Beautifully moist pot-roasted chicken combined with braised barley is one of many successful main course options.

SUTTON COLDFIELD   Map 7 SP19

New Hall

Walmley Road, B76 1QX
Tel: 0121 378 2442
Fax: 0121 378 4637
e new.hall@thistle.co.uk
Chef(s): Simon Malin
Owner(s): Thistle Country House Hotels
Cost: *Alc* £42.75, set price L £29.50-£39.50/D £29.50-£39.50.
H/wine £17.50
Times: Noon-2pm/7-9.30pm.
Additional: Sunday L. Children 8yrs+.
Vegetarian by request only

Looking for a touch of glamour? How about eating foie gras in one of the oldest manor houses in the country only separated from the spectacular private gardens and open parkland by 12th-century stone-work and a lily-filled moat? The foie gras is of course optional and a twice baked Roquefort soufflé with a pear a walnut salad would be a perfectly respectable alternative. As for mains aromatic steamed bass with egg noodles, Asian greens and a light soy broth might feature, with iced cinnamon and apple parfait with hot apple fritters amongst the desserts.

Seats: 60. Private dining room 60. Jacket and tie preferred
Style: Country-house
Smoking: No smoking in dining room
Civil licence: 150
Accommodation: 60 rooms (60 en suite) ★ ★ ★ ★
Directions: On B4148, E of Sutton Coldfield, close to M6 & M42

☺   Indicates a restaurant that has told us they offer a two-course lunch for less than £15

☺   Indicates a restaurant that has told us they offer a three-course dinner for less than £25

England

WALSALL
Map 7 SP09

The Fairlawns at Aldridge

178 Little Aston Road,
Aldridge,
WS9 0NU
Tel: 01922 455122
Fax: 01922 743210
e welcome@fairlawns.co.uk
Chef(s): Mark Bradley
Owner(s): John Pette
Cost: Set price L £16.50/D £16.50-
£27.50. ☺ ☺ H/wine £12.50
Times: Noon-2pm/7-10pm.
Closed L Sat, 1 Jan, Good Fri, Easter
Monday, 1 May, BHs
Additional: Sunday L. Bar food.
Children welcome
Seats: 80. Private dining room 100.
Jacket and tie preferred
Style: Modern, Chic
Smoking: No pipes; Air conditioning

Rural surroundings and a dining room resplendent in its
contemporary elegance (large mirrors reflecting décor of
burgundy and gold) and a warm and welcoming atmosphere.
Dishes are all attractively presented in modern style, but
portions are gratifyingly generous. Starters might include a
well-balanced lobster and crab croquette with plum tomato and
red chilli salsa. Look out for a beautifully tender spiced rack of
Cornish lamb in a rich redcurrant and cumin marinade, or
perhaps char-grilled swordfish with stir fried vegetables and a
chilli and ginger sauce. Amongst the desserts a warm date and
toffee pudding served with home-made ice cream has
impressed.

Civil licence: 100
Accommodation: 50 rooms (50 en suite) ★ ★ ★
Directions: Outskirts of Aldridge, 400yds from crossroads of
A452 (Chester Rd) & A454 (Little Aston Road)

WIGHT, ISLE OF

RYDE
Map 4 SZ59

Biskra Beach Hotel

Elaborate menus often promise more than they perform -
happily not the case in this instance. It's a rustic but stylish
place to eat, with pale walls, chunky church candles, pine tables
and a real fire. The imaginative menu makes good use of local
produce, especially fish. Dishes might include seared scallops
with spicy pork ravioli or roasted duck breast with plum
chutney and maple glazed parsnips. A high degree of technical
skill is evident in the cooking and presentation, whilst efficient,
knowledgeable service adds to the atmosphere of relaxed
professionalism.

Smoking: No smoking in dining room
Civil licence: 50
Accommodation: 14 rooms (14 en suite) ★ ★
Directions: W from the Esplanade to Rdbt & into St Thomas's
St. Hotel on the R

17 Saint Thomas's Street,
PO33 2DL
Tel: 01983 567913
Fax: 01983 616976
e info@biskra-hotel.com
Chef(s): Lisa Roberts
Owner(s): Barbara Newman &
Hamish Kinghorn
Cost: Alc £27, set price L £13.95-
£18.50/D £26.95-£32.50. ☺ ☺
H/wine £9.75
Times: Noon-2pm/7-10pm.
Closed Xmas
Additional: Sunday L. Bar food.
Children welcome
Seats: 75. Private dining room 35
Style: Bistro-Style

SEAVIEW Map 4 SZ69

Priory Bay Hotel

An interesting menu makes much use of local produce at this comfortable hotel restaurant set in its own stretch of beach. Excellent veal escalopes come with a subtle mushroom sauce and might be preceded by a starter of intensely flavoured crab rillettes.

Style: Modern, Country-house
Smoking: No-smoking area; no pipes; no cigars
Civil licence: 60
Accommodation: 18 rooms (18 en suite) ★ ★ ★
Directions: On B3330 to Nettlestone, 0.5m from St Helens

Priory Drive, PO34 5BU
Tel: 01983 613146
Fax: 01983 616539
e enquiries@priorybay.co.uk
Chef(s): Amanda Webb
Owner(s): Mr R Palmer & Mr J Palmer
Cost: Alc £28, set price D £25. ☺ ☺
H/wine £12.50
Times: Noon-2pm/7.30-9.30pm.
Additional: Sunday L. Bar food L.
Children welcome
Seats: 70. Private dining room 40

Seaview Hotel

Lines of clinker built wooden dinghies bob invitingly as you enter this quiet seaside village. Two contrasting restaurants cater well for most dining occasions - the contemporary brightness of the original restaurant lending an air of sophistication, the ornate Sunshine room being more in tune with the traditional village surroundings. Either way the shared menu offers a good range of classic and modern dishes, often making good use of local specialities such as lobster, crab and sea bass. The starters tend towards the brasserie end of the market - pan-fried chicken livers, bacon and grapes with balsamic dressing for example. Mains are hearty and desserts rich and satisfying.

Smoking: No-smoking area; no pipes; Air conditioning
Accommodation: 16 rooms (16 en suite) ★ ★ ★
Directions: Take B3330 from Ryde to Seaview, L into Puckpool Hill & follow signs for Hotel

High Street, PO34 5EX
Tel: 01983 612711
Fax: 01983 613729
e reception@seaviewhotel.co.uk
Chef(s): Bob Rodwell,
Andy Holloway
Owner(s): Mr & Mrs Hayward
Cost: Alc £24. ☺ ☺ H/wine £9.75
Times: Noon-2pm/7.30-9.30pm.
Closed D Sun (ex BHs), 3 days Xmas
Additional: Sunday L. Bar food.
Children 5yrs at D
Seats: 80. Private dining room 40
Style: Modern, Classic

VENTNOR Map 4 SZ57

The Royal Hotel

Lovingly restored to its true Victorian splendour, this light and airy hotel stands in tranquil grounds on the southern coast of the Isle of Wight. The smart but relaxing restaurant is decorated in rich yellows and blues, with dramatically draped curtains framing pretty garden views. The menu offers a colourful selection of traditional and modern dishes: a meal might include a salad of chorizo and smoked bacon with poached egg and hollandaise sauce, followed by pan-fried rib eye steak with sautéed mushrooms, roasted cherry tomatoes and café de Paris butter.

Style: Traditional, Victorian
Smoking: No smoking in dining room
Accommodation: 55 rooms (55 en suite) ★ ★ ★ ★
Directions: On A3055 Coastal Road

Belgrave Road, PO38 1JJ
Tel: 01983 852186
Fax: 01983 855395
e royalhotel@zetnet.co.uk
Chef(s): Alan Staley
Owner(s): William Bailey
Cost: Set price L £15/D £27.50. ☺
H/wine £11
Times: Noon-2pm/7-9.15pm.
Closed L Mon-Sat in Apr-Oct,
2 wks Jan
Additional: Sunday L. Bar food.
Children welcome
Seats: 100. Private dining room 40.
Jacket and tie preferred

England

YARMOUTH
Map 4 SZ38

George Hotel

In a great location between the castle and quay of this picturesque yachting village, The George is just a short walk from the ferry terminal. The waterside garden and bright yellow-and-blue brasserie enjoy the best of the views, the latter offering informal eating options with a modern European slant and a decent daily set-lunch. Dinner is more formal in the smaller George restaurant, dramatic with its deep red panelling, white linen tablecloths and black candles. Some half dozen choices at each course of the fixed-price menu highlight well-sourced fresh produce and an assured approach to modern ideas and techniques. Delicious home-made bread accompanies starters such as roast scallops with fried wild mushrooms, flavoured with an unusual yet successful vanilla essence. Main courses might include fillet of sea bass with poached oyster, girolles and polenta crisps and a seasonal ballotine of local rabbit and its offal with thyme sweet potato, spinach and baby onions in a classy red wine reduction. Chestnut parfait with chocolate sauce and fromage blanc stands out amongst the desserts.

Quay Street, PO41 0PE
Tel: 01983 760331
Fax: 01983 760425
e res@thegeorge.co.uk
Chef(s): Kevin Mangeolles
Owner(s): Mr J Willcock, Mr J Illsley
Cost: Set price D £45. H/wine £12.95
Times: Dinner only, 7-10pm.
Closed Sun-Mon
Additional: Children 10 yrs+
Seats: 40. Private dining room 25
Style: Classic
Smoking: No smoking in dining room; Air conditioning
Civil licence: 100
Accommodation: 17 rooms (17 en suite) ★ ★ ★
Directions: Ferry from Lymington. Hotel visible from ferry between castle and pier

WILTSHIRE

ALDBOURNE
Map 4 SU27

Raffles Restaurant

Located in a Camberwick Green style village where little seems to have changed in the last 100 years, this cosy, traditional restaurant has an understandably loyal fan base. Sometimes the British and French dishes are given a modern twist, but the emphasis is always on traditional cooking methods with no short cuts, using only the best quality local ingredients. Regulars favour the Dutch calves' liver with oak smoked bacon and a dessert of home-made bread and butter pudding, but there are many other tempting options, such as loin of venison ('superb flavour') with game jus and a selection of vegetables.

Style: Traditional
Smoking: No-smoking area; no pipes; no cigars
Directions: On B4192 between J14 & 15 of M4

The Green, SN8 2BW
Tel: 01672 540700
Fax: 01672 540038
e mary@raffles-restaurant.fsnet.co.uk
Chef(s): James Hannan
Owner(s): James & Mary Hannan
Cost: Alc £20, set price L £10.50.
☺ ☺ H/wine £8.95
Times: 12.30-2pm/7-10pm.
Closed Mon, L Tue & Sat, 26 Dec-30 Jan & 1-14 Sep
Additional: Sunday L. Children welcome. Vegetarian by request only
Seats: 36. Private dining room 45

BRADFORD-ON-AVON
Map 3 ST86

Georgian Lodge

Set in a charming Georgian property, this stylish modern restaurant occupies two levels. Hessian coverings create a brasserie atmosphere on the lower floor, whilst the upper level is plush and a touch more traditional. Its location in the centre of beautiful Bradford-on-Avon makes it a busy little place, but the well-balanced menu and slick, friendly staff must take some credit for its popularity. Dishes might include roast chump of lamb with honey roasted parsnips, braised leeks and a lamb jus or grilled fillet of red mullet with seafood and coriander potato cake and lobster sauce. *continued*

25 Bridge Street, BA15 1BY
Tel: 01225 862268
Fax: 01225 862218
e georgianlodge.hotel@btinternet.com
Chef(s): Dan Copeland
Owner(s): Anthony Coates
Cost: Alc £22. ☺ ☺ H/wine £11
Times: Noon-3pm/6-9pm.
Closed L Mon

Style: Modern
Smoking: No smoking in dining room
Accommodation: 10 rooms (10 en suite)
Directions: Telephone for details

Additional: Sunday L.
Children welcome
Seats: 70. Private dining room 24

Woolley Grange

Woolley Green, BA15 1TX
Tel: 01225 864705
Telephone for further details

An exceptionally welcoming country house hotel in beautiful 17th-century Jacobean manor house. The formal dining room is elegant and comfortable with fresh flowers and crisp linen. There is also the option of eating in the Victorian conservatory or, in the summer, al fresco on the terrace. The kitchen has an enthusiastic commitment to good food with the cooking based on a firm classical foundation. Menu offerings may be rump veal, oxtail dumplings with ceps, shallot and port sauce or smoked garlic and Mrs Kirkham's Lancashire cheese tart, seared scallops with spiced lentils, coriander and mango fritters or Champagne mousse with strawberries.

CASTLE COMBE   Map 3 ST87

Castle Inn

SN14 7HN
Tel: 01249 783030
Fax: 01249 782315
e res@castle-inn.co.uk
Chef(s): Jamie Gemmell, Nicole Gillespie
Cost: Alc £19.50. ☺ ☺
H/wine £11.90
Times: Noon-2pm/7-9.30pm. Closed 25 Dec (ex residents)
Additional: Sunday L. Bar food. Children 4 yrs+
Seats: 28. Private dining room 20
Style: Rustic
Smoking: No smoking in dining room
Accommodation: 11 rooms (11 en suite) ★ ★ ★
Directions: M4 J17. In village centre

This famous 12th-century hostelry stands in the market place of historic Castle Coombe. The contemporary style conservatory restaurant offers a lengthy and thoughtful menu: choose from starters, an imaginative selection of 'middles' (perfect as light meals) and traditional style main courses. Dishes range from spicy oregano meatballs with tagliatelli to lamb shank with marjoram and honey stuffing.

England

Manor House Hotel

SN14 7HR
Tel: 01249 782206
Fax: 01249 782159
e enquiries@manor-house.co.uk
Chef(s): Mark Taylor
Cost: *Alc* £39.50-£49.50, set price L
£18.95. H/wine £19.75
Times: Noon-1.30pm/7-9pm.
Additional: Sunday L. Bar food.
Children welcome.
Vegetarian by request only
Seats: 75. Private dining room 30
Style: Traditional, French
Smoking: No smoking in dining room
Civil licence: 100
Accommodation: 47 rooms (47 en
suite) ★ ★ ★ ★

A truly lovely old manor house, with 14th-century origins and
some striking architecture from later periods. The grounds are
not to be missed, where waterfalls, meandering streams and a
romantic Italian garden are lovely at any time of the year.
Indoors it's all exposed stonework, mullioned windows, and a
high-ceilinged baronial hall where formal meals are served in
fairly awesome surroundings, softened by friendly staff. The crisp
menu is reassuringly straightforward: six choices at each level,
with an interesting selection of English and Irish cheeses to
finish off a meal. Some overzealous flavouring slightly swamped
an otherwise fresh and perfectly cooked terrine of red mullet,
but duck breast was deliciously tender, and tarte Tatin with ice
cream was excellent. Elsewhere on the menu expect cannelloni
of ceps, spinach, pine nuts and cep foam, and breast of guinea
fowl with crushed peas and fondant potato. The well-chosen
wine list offers some stately names that are priced accordingly.

Directions: Off B4039.Nr village centre, R immediately after
bridge

Lucknam Park

SN14 8AZ
Tel: 01225 742777
Fax: 01225 743536
e reservations@lucknampark.co.uk
Chef(s): Robin Zavou
Cost: *Alc* £45. H/wine £17.50
Times: 12.30-2.30pm/7.30-9.30pm.
Closed L Mon-Sat
Additional: Sunday L. Bar food.
Children 12yrs+
Seats: 64. Private dining room 30.
Jacket and tie preferred
Style: Classic, Country-house
Smoking: No smoking in dining room
Civil licence: 64
Accommodation: 41 rooms (41 en
suite) ★ ★ ★ ★

500 acres of glorious parkland and a magnificent Palladian
mansion lead you to expect something special, and fortunately

this restaurant delivers the goods. Furnished in the same lavish country house style as the rest of the hotel, the immaculate ex-ballroom features a hand-painted ceiling, crystal chandeliers and lovely views of the grounds. Naturally, the menu features time honoured classics such as braised turbot fillet filled with new season ceps and a light mushroom velouté or best end of Wiltshire lamb with a basil mousse and a piperade sauce. Highly efficient service and a comprehensive wine list complete the picture.

Directions: Follow M4 J17 take A350 to Chippenham, then A420 towards Bristol for 3 miles. At Ford turn L towards Colerne. After 3 miles turn R at crossroads. Hotel 0.25 mile on R

CRUDWELL   Map 3 ST99
The Old Rectory   NEW   ◎◎◎

SN16 9EP
Tel: 01666 577194
Fax: 01666 577853
Chef(s): Peter Fairclough
Owner(s): Derek & Karen Woods
Cost: Alc £27.95, set price L £18.50/ D £25. ☺ ☺ H/wine £12.25
Times: Noon-2pm/7-9.30pm.
Additional: Sunday L. Bar food. Children 6yrs+
Seats: 55. Private dining room 30
Style: Traditional, Country-house
Smoking: No smoking in dining room

This attractive 17th century stone rectory stands in three acres of walled Victorian gardens beside the village church. Dine in the conservatory or the wood panelled dining room, both of which have been refurbished to create a traditional but stylish setting. The imaginative menus offer dishes such as seared scallops with bubble and squeak, caramelised black pudding and minted pea purée or roasted canon of lamb with morteau sausage potato cake and a rosemary jus. The owners and their team of staff strike a pleasing balance between professional service and friendly informality.

Civil licence: 45
Accommodation: 12 rooms (12 en suite) ★ ★ ★
Directions: M4 J17, follow A429 to Cirencester. The Old Rectory is in the village centre, opposite The Plough

FORD   Map 3 ST87
White Hart Inn   ◎

SN14 8RP
Tel: 01249 782213
Telephone for further details

Mellow Cotswold stone, a babbling trout stream, beams and timbers provide an idyllic atmosphere at this friendly 15th century village inn. The cooking is more interesting than good pub food, but not too fussy for its traditional setting. Braised lamb shanks come with hotpot potatoes and leeks; salmon with cucumber and dill. Desserts are home-prepared.

HINDON

Map 3 ST93

The Grosvenor Arms

High Street, SP3 6DJ
Tel: 01747 820696
Fax: 01747 820869
Chef(s): Nick Robinson
Owner(s): Penny Simpson, Bill Laret, Jeff Fergus
Cost: Alc £22 H/wine £10.50
Times: Noon-2.30pm/7-9.30pm.
Additional: Sunday L. Bar food. Children 5yrs+
Seats: 42. Private dining room 20
Style: Bistro-Style, Informal
Smoking: No smoking in dining room
Accommodation: 10 rooms (10 en suite) ★★
Directions: 1 mile from both A350 & A303

Although a classic Georgian building, the interior of the hotel has been restored in a traditional style but with a contemporary feel. One unusual feature in a country restaurant is a glass-fronted, open plan kitchen where guests can watch their meal being prepared. Using first-class ingredients carefully sourced from local or independent suppliers, the style of cooking is modern - giving an added zest to traditional British dishes. Try roasted Cumberland sausages with mash and onion gravy or fillet of beef with shallot purée and tomato confit or cod fillet with Toulouse sausage and crispy pasta.

Lamb at Hindon Hotel

SP3 6DP
Tel: 01747 820573
Fax: 01747 820605
📧 cora@the-lamb.demon.co.uk
Chef(s): Trevor Baker, Ricardo Franco
Owner(s): Cora Scott
Cost: Set price D £19.95. ☺ ☺
H/wine £9.95
Times: Noon-1.45pm/7-9.30pm
Additional: Sunday L. Bar food. Children welcome
Seats: 40. Private dining room 30
Style: Traditional, Country-house
Smoking: No smoking in dining room
Accommodation: 14 rooms (14 en suite) ★★
Directions: In village centre, 1 mile off A303 & A350

A traditional inn at the heart of the village and justly popular with the locals. The menu offers some interesting takes on familiar dishes such as best end cutlets of lamb or a good blueberry crème brûlée. Service is friendly and relaxed with fresh flowers, candles and a huge inglenook fireplace all adding to the charm. Much use of local produce too.

England

LITTLE BEDWYN

Map 4 SU26

The Harrow Inn

SN8 3JP
Tel: 01672 870871
Fax: 01672 870871
e dining@harrowinn.co.uk
Chef(s): Roger Jones
Owner(s): Roger & Sue Jones
Cost: Alc £30, set price L £30/D £35.
☺ ☺ H/wine £12.50
Times: Noon-2pm/7-9pm.
Closed Mon, D Sun, 4 wks Xmas, Aug
Additional: Sunday L.
Children welcome
Seats: 32
Style: Country-house

This country pub down a narrow lane just hums with excitement. The fuss is all about seafood cooked to delectable standards, although meat will also feature, viz chargrilled Aberdeen Angus and roast woodcock. Exciting flavours burst from starters like fresh crevette, crab and lobster timbale, and seared scallops, chorizo and crème fraîche, while grilled fillet of sea bass and shellfish won ton with sweet chilli dressing offers equal allure. Try the spiced rice pudding with cardamom ice cream, or chocolate and raspberry terrine and you'll understand what all the commotion is about.

Smoking: No smoking in dining room; Air conditioning
Directions: Take Marlborough Road from Hungerford, after 2 miles Little Bedwyn signposted

MALMESBURY

Map 3 ST98

The Horse & Groom

As a place to finish a long walk, this popular village pub has it all: rustic charm, cheerful staff, real ale, home cooked food, wicked desserts and hot chocolate. Starters such as soup or salmon tagliatelli come in generous portions and can be ordered as light meals. Main courses include game casserole, chicken enchiladas and vegetable crumble.

Seats: 35. Private dining room 29
Style: Traditional, Rustic
Accommodation: 3 rooms (3 en suite) ♦♦♦♦♦
Directions: M4 J17, take 2nd roundabout exit, B4040 (Cricklade). 2 miles to Charlton, pub on L

The Street, Charlton, SN16 9DL
Tel: 01666 823904
Fax: 01666 823390
Chef(s): Robert Bieniasz
Owner(s): Nicola King &
Phillip Gilder
Cost: Alc £25. ☺ ☺ H/wine £7.95
Times: Noon-3pm/7-11pm
Additional: Sunday L. Bar food.
Children welcome

Knoll House Hotel

A hint of the Mediterranean informs the restaurant décor whilst large windows afford pleasing views of the hotel's resident cedar tree and the Cotswold countryside beyond. The hotel was originally home to an aristocratic family - the last three surviving members of which apparently only communicated with each other via their servants. However the dining room these days is conducive to good conversation and

Swindon Road, SN16 9LU
Tel: 01666 823114
Fax: 01666 823897
e knollhotel@malmesbury64.
freeserve.co.uk
Chef(s): Alan Johnson
Owner(s): Simon Haggarty
Cost: Alc £22.50. ☺ ☺ H/wine £10

England

MALMESBURY *Continued*   Map 3 ST98

relaxed enjoyment of some excellent bistro-style cuisine. Starters find strength in simplicity - oak smoked salmon and cream cheese on a toasted bagel for example. Similarly the mains where the likes of calves' liver and bacon on bubble n' squeak with onion gravy make a real impact.

Accommodation: 22 rooms (22 en suite) ★★★
Directions: From M4 J17 take A429 (Cirencester); turn onto B4042 (Swindon); hotel is 500 yds on L

Times: Noon-1.45pm/7-9pm.
Closed Dec 27-30
Additional: Bar food.
Children welcome
Seats: 30. Private dining room 30
Style: Modern, Bistro-Style
Smoking: No smoking in dining room

Mayfield House Hotel

Congenial haven nestling on the edge of the Cotswolds with a beamed bar and smart restaurant. A good variety of simple, classic dishes along the lines of grilled fillet of fresh mackerel with an aubergine and spring onion ragout and a white wine cream sauce.

Seats: 50. Private dining room 35
Style: Country-House
Smoking: No smoking in dining room
Accommodation: 24 rooms (24 en suite) ★★
Directions: 10 minutes from M4 J17. On A429 between Malmesbury and Cirencester, in village centre

Crudwell, SN16 9EW
Tel: 01666 577409
Fax: 01666 577977
📧 mayfield@callnetuk.com
Chef(s): Chris Amor
Owner(s): Mr Strelling
Cost: *Alc* £17.95, set price L £12/ D £17.95. ☺ ☺ H/wine £8.95
Times: Noon-2pm/6.30-8.45pm
Additional: Sunday L. Bar food. Children welcome

Old Bell Hotel

In 1220 the Abbot of Malmesbury ordered the holy brothers to tear down the Norman castle and, in its place, to build a guesthouse. Cultural vandalism perhaps but what's a Norman castle between friends when you've got a slow roasted cutlet of pork with a Parmesan crust, grilled pear and autumn vegetables to enjoy in the splendid surroundings of the oldest hotel in England (reputedly). An internationally influenced menu offers the likes of fettuccine with roasted vegetables and mozzarella served with a tomato and black olive sauce and a creditable lemon pannacotta with caramelised bananas amongst the desserts.

Accommodation: 31 rooms (31 en suite) ★★★
Directions: In centre of town

Abbey Row, SN16 0AG
Tel: 01666 822344
Fax: 01666 825145
📧 theoldbell@lnmplc.com
Chef(s): Michael Benjamin
Owner(s): Mr N Dickinson
Cost: *Alc* £26, set price L £15/ D £19.75. ☺ ☺ H/wine £15
Times: 12.30-2pm/7-9.30pm.
Closed 23-26 Dec, 30 Dec-1 Jan
Additional: Sunday L. Bar food
Seats: 60. Private dining room 24
Style: Classic
Smoking: No smoking in dining room
Civil licence: 50

England

MARLBOROUGH
Map 4 SU16

Ivy House Hotel

Built for the Earl of Aylesbury in 1707, this grade II listed property features a classic Palladian style restaurant with chandeliers, smartly dressed tables and an assortment of famous framed prints. The menu includes plenty of traditional dishes - perhaps best end of lamb with dauphinoise potato, roasted baby veg and a Puy lentil sauce - as well as more imaginative contemporary dishes such as stuffed Barbary duck leg with spinach linguini and a stir fry of pak choi and sweet peppers, or a warm salad of roasted vegetables with crisp polenta, tofu and and olive dressing. 'Utterly enjoyable' food, full of harmonious combinations

High Street, SN8 1HJ
Tel: 01672 515333
Fax: 01672 515338
e ivy.house@btconnect.com
Chef(s): Tony Cox
Owner(s): Mrs J Ball
Cost: A/c £26, set price L £12.95/ D £18. ☺ ☺ H/wine £9.50
Times: Noon-2pm/7-9.30pm.
Additional: Sunday L. Bar food. Children welcome
Seats: 60. Private dining room 20. Jacket and tie preferred
Style: Formal
Smoking: No smoking in dining room
Accommodation: 36 rooms (36 en suite) ★ ★ ★
Directions: Telephone for directions

MELKSHAM
Map 3 ST96

Shaw Country Hotel

Simply styled restaurant with pinks and greens echoing the Area of Outstanding Natural Beauty that it is set in. Dishes along the lines of breadcrumbed button mushrooms filled with Brie with a Cumberland sauce or halibut steak with a spicy fruit salsa.

Additional: Children welcome
Seats: 40. Private dining room 12. Jacket and tie preferred
Style: Modern.
Smoking: No smoking in dining room
Accommodation: 13 rooms (13 en suite) ★ ★
Directions: 1 mile NW of Melksham on A365, from M4 J17 or J18

Bath Road, Shaw, SN12 8EF
Tel: 01225 702836
Fax: 01225 790275
e info@shawcountryhotel.fsnet.co.uk
Chef(s): Nick & Paul Lewis
Owner(s): Mr & Mrs J Lewis
Cost: A/c £21.75, set price L £13.50/D £19.50. ☺ ☺ H/wine £8.95
Times: Noon-2pm/7pm-9pm.
Closed D Sun, 26-28 Dec, 1 Jan

PURTON
Map 4 SU08

The Pear Tree at Purton

This lovely Cotswold stone vicarage has been transformed into an elegant country retreat, whose conservatory restaurant overlooks delightful gardens. Despite the traditional setting, the menu offers plenty of exciting modern dishes - perhaps breast of wood pigeon with spiced green lentils and tawny port sauce or seared salmon with lobster sauce and crispy leeks. More familiar offerings might include roast rack of lamb with glazed baby onions, red wine jus and grain mustard. Desserts feature pear and almond tart or Champagne mousse trifle with

Church End, SN5 4ED
Tel: 01793 772100
Fax: 01793 772369
e stay@peartreepurton.co.uk
Chef(s): Alan Postill
Owner(s): Francis and Anne Young
Cost: Set price L £17.50/D £29.50. ☺ H/wine £11.50
Times: Noon-2pm/7-9.30pm.
Closed L Sat, 26-30 Dec

England

PURTON *Continued*   Map 4 SU08

The Pear Tree at Purton

strawberry jelly and crisp wafers. Friendly, attentive staff engender a relaxing atmosphere.

Accommodation: 18 rooms (18 en suite) ★★★
Directions: From M4 J16, follow signs to Purton. Turn R at Spa shop, hotel 0.25m on R

Additional: Sunday L.
Children welcome
Seats: 50. Private dining room 50
Style: Country-house
Smoking: No pipes; no cigars
Civil licence: 50

REDLYNCH   Map 4 SU22

Langley Wood Restaurant

Once upon a time this was a cottage in the forest, but extensions between the 17th and 19th centuries turned it into an equally pretty house. It retains five acres of wooded grounds through which deer roam freely. The restaurant's eclectic offerings might include fresh salmon roasted with sun dried tomato tapenade or guinea fowl stuffed with apricots and pine kernels

SP5 2PB
Tel: 01794 390348
📧 langleywood@lineone.net
Chef(s): Sylvia Rosen
Owner(s): David and Sylvia Rosen
Cost: *Alc* £25. ☺ ☺ H/wine £9.75
Times: 12.30-2pm/7-10pm.
Closed Mon & Tue, L Sat, D Sun,
Xmas-New Year
Additional: Sunday L.
Children welcome
Seats: 30
Style: Traditional, Country-house
Smoking: No smoking in dining room
Accommodation: 3 rooms
Directions: In village, between
Downton (on A338 Salisbury to
Bournemouth) and Landford (A36
Salisbury)

ROWDE   Map 3 ST96

George & Dragon

Local staff behind the bar, wooden floors and open fires exude an immediate sense of welcome where no-one stands on ceremony. Tim Withers' menus highlight fish delivered fresh from Cornwall, served perhaps on crostini with char-grilled red pepper and salsa verde to start, followed by steamed skate with

High Street,
SN10 2PN
Tel: 01380 723053
Fax: 01380 724738
📧 gd-rowde@lineone.net
Chef(s): Tim Withers

capers and black butter or monkfish with peppercorns, brandy and cream. Full marks, too, for the lobster bisque and Thai fish curry. The food here certainly doesn't conform, but there is a clarity of flavours that speaks volumes.

Owner(s): Tim & Helen Withers
Cost: Alc £26.50, set price L £12.50.
☺ ☺ H/wine £9.50
Times: Noon-3pm/7-11pm. Closed Sun & Mon, 25 Dec & Jan 1
Additional: Bar food. Children welcome
Seats: 35
Style: Traditional, Rustic
Smoking: No smoking in dining room
Directions: On A342 Devizes-Chippenham road.

SALISBURY   Map 4 SU12

Howard's House Hotel

Teffont Evias, SP3 5RJ
Tel: 01722 716392
Fax: 01722 716820
🄴 enq@howardshousehotel.com
Chef(s): Paul Firmin, Boyd McIntosh
Owner(s): Paul Firmin
Cost: Alc £33.80, set price L £18.50/ D £19.95. ☺ H/wine £9.95
Times: 12.30-1.45pm/7.30-9pm. Closed L Mon-Sat, Xmas
Additional: Sunday L. Children welcome
Seats: 30
Style: Modern, Country-house
Smoking: No smoking in dining room
Accommodation: 9 rooms (9 en suite)
★ ★

Time appears to have stood still in the very English village of Teffont Evias, home to this charming country hideaway. The levels of comfort in the hotel speak of a much newer age, however, and nowhere more so than in the dining room where the cooking receives well-deserved praise. Here, excellent ingredients and well-honed skills culminate in a refreshing array of dishes: terrine of marinated venison, pheasant and wild boar with pistachios, Muscat jelly and toasted cranberry brioche shows flair and imagination, while roast fillet of sea bass, watercress risotto and a caviar and lemon beurre blanc reveal modern overtones to classic concepts. The emphasis on fresh ingredients continues into the main courses, with grilled Dover sole with lemon, parsley and garlic butter and squid ink vermicelli, while irresistible desserts range from delice of passionfruit with poached raspberries, spun sugar, to hot Grand Marnier soufflé with a tangerine glaze and marmalade ice cream.

Directions: A36/A30 from Salisbury, turn onto B3089, 5 miles W of Wilton. In Teffont Evias follow brown tourist signs to hotel

England

Milford Hall Hotel

Smartly appointed hotel restaurant popular with locals and majoring on a welcoming atmosphere. The menu caters for a broad church and ranges from grilled fillet of Scottish salmon on a bed of julienne vegetables with an orange butter sauce to roast sirloin of beef with a shallot chutney and Yorkshire pudding.

Style: Modern French
Smoking: No smoking in dining room; Air conditioning
Civil licence: 50
Accommodation: 35 rooms (35 en suite) ★★★
Directions: At junction of Castle St, A30 ring rd & A345 (Amesbury), less than 0.5 mile from Market Square

206 Castle Street, SP1 3TE
Tel: 01722 417411
Fax: 01722 419444
🄴 milfordhallhotel@compuserve.com
Chef(s): Chris Gillbert
Owner(s): Mr S Hughes
Cost: *Alc* £20. ☺ ☺ H/wine £9.95
Times: Noon-2pm/6.30-9.30pm.
Additional: Sunday L.
Children welcome. Vegetarian by request only
Seats: 40. Private dining room 16.
Jacket and tie preferred

Blunsdon House Hotel

This vast, modern hotel and leisure club offers a variety of dining options. The Ridge restaurant is the more formal of these. A meal might begin with smoked salmon and goats' cheese croquette, followed by a main course of loin of venison on a wild mushroom risotto cake with redcurrant sauce. Good coffee and petits fours.

Style: California Grill
Smoking: No smoking in dining room
Accommodation: 120 rooms (120 en suite) ★★★★
Directions: 3 miles N of town centre. From A419 take turning signposted Broad Blunsdon, then first L

Blunsdon, SN26 7AS
Tel: 01793 721701
Fax: 01793 721056
🄴 info@blunsdonhouse.co.uk
Chef(s): Glen Bent
Owner(s): Mr & Mrs P Clifford
Cost: *Alc* £20, set price L £12/D £20.
☺ ☺ H/wine £11
Times: 12.15-2.15pm/7-9.45pm
Additional: Sunday L. Bar food.
Children welcome
Seats: 160

The Linnet   NEW

A sleepy village local that has been given a new lease of life by its new tenant and chef, Jonathan Furby. Purchasing of fresh ingredients, local where possible, shows on menus that are kept sensibly short and everything is freshly made on the premises, from a range of breads and pasta to ice cream. Follow duck pancakes with cucumber salsa and plum sauce, with lemon sole with crab and dill dumpling on a langoustine and chive sauce, rounding off with raspberry and Grand Marnier crème brûlée.

Smoking: No smoking in dining room; Air conditioning
Directions: Off A342, 4 miles W of Devizes

Great Hinton, BA14 6BU
Tel: 01380 870354
Chef(s): Jonathan Furby
Owner(s): Jonathan Furby
Cost: *Alc* £22, set price L £12.25-£14.15. ☺ ☺ H/wine £10.95
Times: Noon-2pm/6.30-10pm.
Closed Mon
Additional: Sunday L.
Children welcome
Seats: 40
Style: Formal, Country-house

WARMINSTER   Map 3 ST84

Angel Inn

Recently refurbished 16th-century coaching inn with big beams and feature fireplaces. Both bar and restaurant are informal in style with natural wood flooring and a mixture of pine tables and chairs. Typical offerings are baked avocado with spicy prawns, excellent fillet steak with foie gras and Madeira sauce, and reassuringly old-fashioned spotted dick.

Smoking: No-smoking area
Accommodation: 10 rooms (10 en suite) ♦♦♦♦♦
Directions: From either A36 or A350 follow signs for Upton Scudamore. Inn in village centre

Upton Scudamore, BA12 0AG
Tel: 01985 213225
Fax: 01985 218182
Chef(s): Eamonn Redden
Owner(s): Charlie Berkshire
Cost: Alc £21.50. ☺ ☺ H/wine £9.75
Times: Noon-3pm/7-11pm.
Closed 25 Dec
Additional: Sunday L. Bar food L.
Children welcome
Seats: 60
Style: Bistro-Style

Bishopstrow House Hotel

A fine example of a classical Georgian home set in 27 acres of peaceful countryside. With interior features such as antique furniture, log fires and classical music the word refined comes to mind. The menu is similarly cultured though never staid with a range of influences producing the likes of grilled sea bass with crab risotto, blue foot mushrooms and baby bok choi. The ingredients demonstrate a great commitment to quality sourcing with a starter of crostini of chargrilled scallops offering some of the most fresh, succulent, large scallops around, with a well thought-out accompaniment of asparagus and a not-too-sweet chilli jam.

Civil licence: 65
Accommodation: 32 rooms (32 en suite) ★ ★ ★ ★
Directions: From Warminster take B3414 (Salisbury). Hotel is signposted

BA12 9HH
Tel: 01985 212312
Fax: 01985 216769
e reservations@bishopstrow.co.uk
Chef(s): Chris Suter
Owner(s): Mr D Dowden
Cost: Alc £38. ☺ H/wine £14
Times: Noon-2.15pm/7.30-9.30pm.
Additional: Sunday L. Bar food.
Children welcome
Seats: 65. Private dining room 28
Style: Country-House
Smoking: No smoking in dining room

WHITLEY   Map 3 ST86

The Pear Tree

Popular country pub tucked away in its small village, where the fine food is complemented by the welcoming atmosphere generated by friendly staff. Robust offerings along the lines of fillet of beef with a creamy garlic mash, baby carrots and a port sauce and a poached pear in spiced red wine with a bramley apple sorbet.

Top Lane, SN12 8QX
Tel: 01225 709131
Fax: 01225 702276
Chef(s): Sebastien Rouxel
Owner(s): Mr M Still
Cost: Alc £25.17, set price L £11.50.
☺ ☺ H/wine £9.95
Times: 11am-2.30pm/6-11pm.
Closed 25-26 Dec, 1 Jan
Additional: Sunday L. Bar food.
Children welcome
Seats: 60. Private dining room 40.
Jacket and tie preferred
Smoking: No-smoking area
Directions: Telephone for directions

WORCESTERSHIRE

BROADWAY   Map 4 SP03

Dormy House Hotel

Willersey Hill, WR12 7LF
Tel: 01386 852171
Fax: 01386 858636
 reservations@dormyhouse.co.uk
Chef(s): Alan Cutler
Owner(s): Mrs I Philip-Sorensen
Cost: *Alc* £36.45, set price L £19.95-
£32.50. H/wine £14.75
Times: 12.30-2pm/7-9.30pm.
Closed L Mon-Sat, 24-27 Dec
Additional: Sunday L. Bar food.
Children welcome
Seats: 70. Private dining room 14.
Jacket and tie preferred
Style: Formal
Smoking: No-smoking area; no pipes;
Air conditioning
Civil licence: 100
Accommodation: 48 rooms (48 en
suite) ★ ★ ★
Directions: A44, take turn 'Saintbury'
after 0.5 mile turn left

This converted farmhouse features lovely views of the
Cotswolds and an inviting restaurant, full of soft colours and
bare brickwork. The imaginative menu is classically based, but
makes occasional excursions to the East (as in a monkfish
terrine with curry spiced mousse and a mango and coriander
relish). Intense sauces (perhaps green peppercorn, rich
burgundy or green lentil and thyme) conspire with quality
ingredients and well-timed cooking to create rewarding, tasty
meals. Equally interesting desserts might include liquorice
mousse, freshly cooked banana and pecan tart, or hot Calvados
soufflé with apple sorbet.

Lygon Arms

The Great Hall, as impressive as the name suggests, is the main
dining room at the historic Lygon Arms in the heart of
beautiful Broadway. A large fireplace is the central feature
along with numerous suits of armour and deer head trophies
hung high on the walls. Service is confident and attentive, and
guests are presented with both fixed-price and *carte* menus
along with an extensive wine list of notable quality. Options
range from cutlet of Warwick pork with bubble 'n' squeak,
apple fondue and light cider cream to classic Chateaubriand for
two with French fries and Béarnaise sauce.

High Street, WR12 7DU
Tel: 01386 852255
Fax: 01386 858611
 info@the-lygon-arms.co.uk
Chef(s): Ian Samson
Owner(s): The Savoy Group
Cost: Set price L £22.50/D £39.50.
H/wine £15.50
Times: 12.30-2pm/7.30-9.15pm.
Closed L Sun-Fri
Additional: Bar food L.
Children 8yrs+ at D
Seats: 90. Private dining room.
Jacket and tie preferred

Style: Traditional
Smoking: No smoking in dining room. **Civil licence:** 80
Accommodation: 70 rooms (70 en suite) ★ ★ ★ ★
Directions: In the centre of the high street

Grafton Manor Restaurant

The restaurant in this 1727 manor displays an eclectic décor, in
keeping with the imaginative menu. The chef, also an Indian
cookery writer, combines his love of Indian cuisine with a
European interpretation, as well as presenting classic favourites

Grafton Lane, B61 7HA
Tel: 01527 579007
Fax: 01527 575221
Chef(s): Simon Morris,
William Henderson

England

such as Lord of Grafton whisky steamed pudding with a whisky cream, or roast duck breast with spinach purée, fondant potatoes and shallot sauce. For a touch of India, try Gujarati lentil pakora and curd curry or lamb with chick peas and couscous, while coconut and lime rice pudding with mango sorbet freshens the palate.

Style: Modern, Mediterranean
Smoking: No smoking in dining room
Civil licence: 80
Directions: Off B4091, 1.5 miles S of Bromsgrove

Owner(s): The Morris Family
Cost: Set price L £20.50/ D £27.85-£32.75. H/wine £9.80
Times: 12.30-1.30pm/7-9.30pm. Closed L Sat, BHs
Additional: Sunday L. Children welcome
Seats: 60. Private dining room 60

Hanover International   NEW

The functional M5-side setting disguises an attractively Mediterranean themed restaurant featuring vivid peach and tranquil blues. The simple menu offers a good selection of dishes along the lines of breast of chicken with a banana and Parma ham roulade on a light curry sauce. A broad selection of pasta dishes, salads and grills adds variety.

Kidderminster Road, B61 9AB
Tel: 01527 576600
Fax: 01527 878981
e enquiries.hanover-bromsgrove@virgin.net
Chef(s): Mark Higgins
Owner(s): Hanover Hotels & Clubs
Cost: Alc £25, set price L £15.50/ D £19.50. ☺ ☺ H/wine £11.75
Times: Noon-2pm/7-10pm. Closed L Sat
Additional: Sunday L. Bar food. Children welcome
Seats: 100. Private dining room 200
Style: Classic, Traditional
Smoking: No smoking in dining room; Air conditioning
Civil licence: 200
Accommodation: 114 rooms (114 en suite) ★★★★
Directions: On A448 Kidderminster road 1 mile W of Bromsgrove centre

CHADDESLEY CORBETT   Map 7 SO87

Brockencote Hall

DY10 4PY
Tel: 01562 777876
Fax: 01562 777872
e info@brockencotehall.com
Chef(s): Jerome Barbançon
Owner(s): Mr & Mrs Petitjean

An idyllic country retreat set in the grounds of a 17th-century estate, Brockencote Hall maintains high standards of hospitality and comfort. The restaurant itself is the gracious affair you would expect, with its well-proportioned dimensions, bright aspect onto a terrace, and superb views over parkland. In this

CHADDESLEY CORBETT *Continued*   Map 7 SO87

classic country house setting, the food is precisely cooked and served with great care and solicitude. From short set menus anticipate perhaps shitake and prosciutto ham risotto or marinated mackerel fillet with parmentier potato, followed by pan-fried tuna on basil-crushed potato with red pepper confit and sauce vierge. French influences are also clear in the *carte*: mosaic of squab pigeon and foie gras alongside honey-roast loin of venison with braised chicory, celeriac purée and juniper berry jus. Finish with poached winter fruit in spices, or bitter chocolate moelleux with pistachio ice cream and praline tuille. The wine list concentrates entirely on France.

Directions: On A448 just outside village, between Kidderminster & Bromsgrove (M5 J5, M42 J1)

Cost: *Alc* £27.50, set price L £17/ D £24.30. ☺ ☺ H/wine £12.80
Times: Noon-1.30pm/7-9.30pm.
Closed L Sat
Additional: Sunday L.
Children welcome
Seats: 60. Private dining room 30
Style: Classic, Country-house
Smoking: No smoking in dining room
Accommodation: 17 rooms (17 en suite) ★ ★ ★

EVESHAM   Map 4 SP04

The Evesham Hotel

Eccentric and determinedly unpretentious, this Regency style restaurant offers an exhaustive range of dishes. From the varied main menu (spring rolls, spicy meatballs, veal) to the aptly titled 'Un-Mucked About' menu, the focus is on top quality ingredients. Vegetarians have a whole page to choose from and there is a separate menu for children. Interesting wine list.

Style: Regency
Smoking: No smoking in dining room
Accommodation: 40 rooms (40 en suite) ★ ★ ★
Directions: Coopers Lane is off road along River Avon

Coopers Lane,
Off Waterside, WR11 6DA
Tel: 01386 765566
Fax: 01386 765443
🖃 reception@eveshamhotel.com
Chef(s): Ian Mann
Owner(s): John Jenkinson
Cost: *Alc* £24.50. ☺ ☺ H/wine £11
Times: 12.30-2pm/7-9.30pm.
Closed 25 & 26 Dec
Additional: Sunday L.
Children welcome
Seats: 55. Private dining room 12

Riverside Hotel

The hotel, a clever conversion of three cottages linked with the main house, has a lovely location in Evesham Abbey's 15th-century deer park overlooking the River Avon. There are river views from the restaurant, which offers a brasserie-style menu with an emphasis on local produce, notably Evesham asparagus in season. Crudités at the table are a bit of a trademark, followed by the likes of fresh crab and salmon fritters with sour cream and chives, and chargrilled Gressingham duck with fragrant couscous, mixed leaves and lime pickle dressing, the latter delivering something of "a taste explosion".

Style: Modern
Smoking: No smoking in dining room
Accommodation: 7 rooms (7 en suite) ★ ★
Directions: 2 miles from town centre on B4510 (Offenham). At end of narrow lane marked 'The Parks'

The Parks, Offenham Road,
WR11 5JP
Tel: 01386 446200
Fax: 01386 40021
🖃 river-side-hotel.co.uk
Chef(s): Rosemary Willmott
Owner(s): Vincent & Rosemary Wilmott
Cost: *Alc* £17.80, set price L £19.95/ D £29.95. H/wine £11.95
Times: 12.30-2pm/7.30-9pm.
Closed Mon, D Sun
Additional: Sunday L. Bar food L.
Children welcome. Vegetarian by request only
Seats: 48

Wood Norton Hall

Once the largest broadcasting centre in Europe, and still a training centre for the BBC, the Hall is filled with the splendours of a bygone age. In these impressive surroundings, the food more than competes. The varied, business-like menus (gourmand, lunch, vegetarian and *carte*) feature interesting,

Wood Norton,
WR11 4YB
Tel: 01386 420007
Fax: 01386 420190
🖃 woodnorton.hall@bbc.co.uk
Chef(s): Steve Waites

balanced dishes like chorizo, tomato and spring onion risotto (delicate but spicy), and brill wrapped in crisp potato discs with grilled leeks, fettuccini and ratatouille (vibrant and rich). Finish on a stunning note with pear, apple and peach tarte Tatin and pistachio ice cream, and relax with good coffee and superior petits fours.

Cost: Set price L £19.50/D £32.50. H/wine £15.70
Times: 12.30-2pm/7.30-9.30pm. Closed L Sat
Additional: Sunday L. Bar food. Children welcome
Seats: 72. Private dining room . Jacket and tie preferred
Style: Traditional, Country-house
Smoking: No smoking in dining room

Civil licence: 70
Accommodation: 45 rooms (45 en suite) ★ ★ ★ ★
Directions: 2 miles NW of Evesham on A4538. Hotel is 0.5 mile on R

MALVERN   Map 3 SO74

Colwall Park, Seasons Restaurant

◎◎
Walwyn Road, Colwall, WR13 6QG
Tel: 01684 540000
Fax: 01684 540847
e hotel@colwall.com
Chef(s): Matthew Weaver
Owner(s): Mr & Mrs I Nesbitt
Cost: Alc £30, set price L £14.95/ D £22.95. ☺ ☺ H/wine £10.95
Times: 12.30-2pm/7.30-9pm.
Additional: Sunday L. Bar food. Children welcome
Seats: 40. Private dining room 100
Style: Classic, Country-house
Smoking: No smoking in dining room

Colwall Park was purpose built as a hotel at the turn of the century and stands in gardens in the village of Colwall near the Malvern Hills. Over the past year, its new chef has further enhanced the restaurant's reputation for quality food. The menus offer a wide variety of dishes, from classics such as tournedos Rossini to modern creations such as steamed turbot on crab risotto with chilli jam. These are complemented by an impressive wine list and some great home-baked breads (tomato and rosemary, for example). Look out for the exquisite lemon curd ice cream.

Accommodation: 23 rooms (23 en suite) ★ ★ ★
Directions: On B4218 between Ledbury and Malvern

England

Cottage in the Wood

Few UK restaurants can experience so much pressure for a window seat. "The best view in Britain" might seem like so much hype, but really there can be few competitors for this dining room set halfway up the Malvern Hills with views across the Severn Valley and way beyond. The cooking does its best to distract, with a menu of robust, no-nonsense dishes in which punchy flavours are the order of the day. Typical of the approach are the likes of mussel, potato and scallop soup with saffron or rib eye of Herefordshire beef with champ, root vegetables and a heavyweight Guinness sauce. Desserts are in similar vein with chilled blackberry soup (served with blackberry and apple compôte) being a notable success.

Accommodation: 20 rooms (20 en suite) ★ ★ ★
Directions: 3miles S of Great Malvern off A449. From Great Malvern, take 3rd turning on R after Railway pub

Holywell Road,
Malvern Wells,
WR14 4LG
Tel: 01684 575859
Fax: 01684 560662
e proprietor@cottageinthewood.
co.uk
Chef(s): Dominic Pattin
Owner(s): The Pattin Family
Cost: *Alc* £32.50, set price L £13.95.
☺ H/wine £13.60
Times: 12.30-2pm/7-9pm.
Additional: Sunday L.
Children welcome
Seats: 45
Style: Country-house
Smoking: No smoking in dining room;
Air conditioning

Croque-en-Bouche Restaurant

A self-sufficient restaurant if ever there was one. There is much bounty from the restaurant's own garden and you will find Marion Jones at the stove whilst Robin deals admirably with front of house duties. Real craftsmanship is at the heart of the cooking and, at this level, prices are something of a steal. The menu form doesn't vary: there are sushi appetisers, then a soup (lettuce and pea for instance), a choice of three starters and three main courses before a salad, British cheese and a range of desserts. Within this framework though, the cooking renews itself by degrees building on excellent raw materials like Herefordshire Trelough duck or Welsh mountain lamb. The way the garden informs the cooking is a trait often remarked upon as is the lightness of touch and accuracy of flavours evident in the likes of Cornish turbot with minted broad beans and couscous or leg of young lamb in the Burgundian style. Desserts are a real strength with dexterity apparent in an apricot and almond tart that came with a "superlative" cinnamon and praline ice cream. The wine list is something else, over a thousand reasonably priced bins from all over the globe

221 Wells Road,
Malvern Wells,
WR14 4HF
Tel: 01684 565612
Fax: 0870 7066282
e mail@croque-en-bouche.co.uk
Chef(s): Marion Jones
Owner(s): Marion & Robin Jones
Cost: Set price D £27-£40
Times: Dinner only, 7-9.30pm.
Closed Sun-Wed, 1 wk Xmas,
1 wk May, 1 wk Sep
Additional: Children welcome.
Vegetarian by request only
Seats: 22. Private dining room 6
Style: Traditional, French
Smoking: No smoking in dining room
Directions: 2 miles S of Great
Malvern on A449

England

Foley Arms Hotel

14 Worcester Road, WR14 4QS
Tel: 01684 573397
Fax: 01684 569665
e reservations@foleyarmshotel.com
Chef(s): Terry Herbert, Kevin Ratcliffe
Owner(s): Nigel & Helen Thomas
Cost: *Alc* £19, set price L £12.50/
D £19. ☺ ☺ H/wine £8.75
Times: Noon-2pm/7-9.30pm.
Closed L Sat
Additional: Sunday L. Bar food.
Children welcome
Style: Classic, Country-house
Smoking: No smoking in dining room
Civil licence: 120
Accommodation: 28 rooms (28 en suite) ★ ★ ★
Directions: Telephone for directions

Terrific views across the Severn Valley in the comfort of an old, hospitable Georgian hotel. Salmon gravadlax served with a coarse grain mustard sauce, and oven roasted chicken roulade set on vegetable spaghetti with sweet red pepper and thyme sauce, are typical of the menu's wide and sometimes original selection.

Holdfast Cottage

Little Malvern, WR13 6NA
Tel: 01684 310288
Fax: 01684 311117
e holdcothot@aol.com
Chef(s): Jane Knowles
Owner(s): Jane & Stephen Knowles
Cost:-£25. ☺ H/wine £11.25
Times: Dinner only, 7-11pm.
Closed D Sun (ex residents)
Additional: Children welcome
Seats: 26. Private dining room 14
Style: Traditional, Country-house
Smoking: No smoking in dining room
Accommodation: 8 rooms (8 en suite)
★ ★
Directions: On A4104 midway between Welland and Little Malvern

This pretty, soft green restaurant is furnished with antique oak tables and looks across a terrace and gardens to the Malvern Hills. Fresh flowers and candlelight add to its charm. Fairly traditional in style, a meal might begin with home-smoked trout and leek scones, followed by a sorbet, before progressing to lamb cutlets with rosemary butternut squash and redcurrant, orange and mint jelly. High quality ingredients and well-balanced flavours are the strengths of a good selection of puds - a typical example being a rhubarb and fig crumble served in a filo basket with home made ginger ice cream.

 Indicates a restaurant that has told us that 50% or more of their ingredients are organically sourced

Prices quoted in the guide are for guidance only and are subject to change without notice

England

OMBERSLEY   Map 3 SO86

The Venture In Restaurant

This pretty Tudor building stands on the high street of picturesque Ombersley. The interior is as charming and antique as the wonky black and white exterior suggests: bare beams and plain, cream coloured walls reflecting the firelight create a cosy, inviting atmosphere. The modern menu is a colourful blend of

British and European flavours. A meal might include a seared medallion of tuna loin with cucumber and Gazpacho butter, followed by pan-fried fillet of beef with braised barley, wild mushrooms and a Madeira sauce. Leave room for desserts such as assiette of apple or glazed lemon tart.

Main Road, WR9 0EW
Tel: 01905 620552
Fax: 01905 620552
Chef(s): Toby William Fletcher
Owner(s): Toby William Fletcher
Cost: Set price L £17.95/D £27.95 ☺ H/wine £10.95
Times: Noon-2pm/7-9.45pm. Closed Mon, D Sun, BHs, 2wks Summer & 2wks Winter, 26 Dec
Additional: Sunday L. Children 8yrs+ at D
Seats: 32. Private dining room 32
Style: Traditional, Rustic
Smoking: No smoking in dining room; Air conditioning
Directions: From Worcester N towards Kidderminster – A449 (approx 5 miles). Turn L at Ombersley turning – 0.75m on R

TENBURY WELLS   Map 3 SO56

The Peacock Inn   NEW

A welcoming exterior of pretty shrubs, hanging baskets and ivy at this charming 14th century coaching inn. Modern British cuisine combines well with a hint of eastern influence - Thai fishcakes proving a most enjoyable starter. A main of breast of duck demonstrated excellence in sourcing with the flavour of the meat singularly full and natural.

Smoking: No-smoking area; Air conditioning
Accommodation: 3 rooms (3 en suite) ♦♦♦♦
Directions: On A456, 1 mile from Tenbury Wells towards Worcester

Worcester Road, Boraston, WR15 8LL
Tel: 01584 810506
Fax: 01584 811236
🅴 jvidler@fsbdial.co.uk
Chef(s): Eric Celton
Owner(s): Mr J Vidler
Cost: Alc £20. ☺ ☺ H/wine £10.75
Times: Noon-2.30pm/7-9.30pm.
Additional: Sunday L. Bar food. Children welcome
Seats: 40
Style: Bistro-Style, French

UPTON UPON SEVERN

Map 3 SO84

White Lion Hotel

The sedate Georgian façade conceals a 16th-century inn with a robust past as the boisterous inn depicted in Henry Fielding's Tom Jones. The contemporary menu also has plenty of character with dishes such as scallop, lobster and salmon roulade with spring onion butter sauce or peppered duck breast with chorizo sausage, sauerkraut and orange caramel sauce. Deep fried beignet soufflé is amongst the desserts.

Seats: 45. **Style:** Traditional, Rustic
Smoking: No smoking in dining room
Accommodation: 10 rooms (10 en suite) ★ ★ ★
Directions: From A422 take A38 towards Tewkesbury. After 8 miles take B4104 for 1mile, after bridge turn L to hotel

21 High Street, WR8 0HJ
Tel: 01684 592551
Fax: 01684 593333
e reservations@whitelionhotel. demon.co.uk
Chef(s): Jon Lear, Richard Thompson, Adam Robinson
Owner(s): Mr & Mrs Lear
Cost: *Alc* £23/D £19. ☺ ☺
H/wine £12.55
Times: Noon-2pm/7-9.15pm.
Closed 26 Dec, 1 Jan
Additional: Sunday L. Bar food.
Children welcome

WORCESTER

Map 3 SO85

Brown's Restaurant

Refreshingly simple cooking in an airy converted grain mill. A typical meal might consist of grilled sea bass on mixed leaves with balsamic dressing, followed by roast rump of lamb with winter vegetables and Puy lentils. Round off with warm chocolate brownies and vanilla ice cream.

Additional: Sunday L. Children 8 yrs+
Seats: 110
Smoking: No-smoking area; no pipes
Directions: City centre, along river bank, car park opposite

The Old Cornmill,
South Quay, WR1 2JJ
Tel: 01905 26263
Fax: 01905 25768
Chef(s): W R Tansley, L Jones
Owner(s): W R & P M Tansley
Cost: Set price L £19.50/D £35.50.
H/wine £11.50
Times: 12.30-1.45pm/7.30-9.45pm.
Closed Mon, L Sat, D Sun, 1wk Xmas

Glass House Restaurant

A modern restaurant in a 16th-century school house whose stylish interior includes polished floorboards and attractive stained glass windows. Dishes on the eclectic menu range from braised shank of lamb with garlic mash and Provençal vegetables to whole baked Thai sea bass with fragrant rice and dipping sauce.

Additional: Children welcome
Seats: 42
Style: Modern, Classic
Smoking: No smoking in dining room; Air conditioning
Directions: Off north end of High St, next to St Swithuns church

Church Street, WR1 2RH
Tel: 01905 611120
Fax: 01905 616616
e brandon.weston@talk21.com
Chef(s): Calum MacCrimmon
Owner(s): Brandon Weston, Calum MacCrimmon
Cost: *Alc* £25, set price L £12.50.
☺ ☺ H/wine £11.50
Times: Noon-2pm/7-10pm. Closed Sun-Mon, Xmas, 2 wks Jan

The finest wine lists

The AA wine awards recognise some of the finest wine lists in the country. As well as the winners for England, Scotland and Wales you will find this symbol throughout the guide indicating those restaurants who reached the final shortlist and others that were recognised for their excellence in specialist areas. The AA wine awards are sponsored by T&W wines of Thetford.

YORKSHIRE, EAST RIDING

England

BEVERLEY   Map 8 TA03

The Manor House

Northlands, Walkington, HU17 8RT
Tel: 01482 881645
Fax: 01482 866501
e derek@the-manor-house.co.uk
Chef(s): Derek Baugh
Owner(s): Derek Baugh
Cost: *Alc* £30, set price D £18.50-£30. ☺ H/wine £13.95
Times: Dinner only, 7-9.15pm.
Closed Sun, 24 Dec-2 Jan, BHs
Additional: Children 12 yrs+.
Vegetarian by request only
Seats: 50. Private dining room 24.
Jacket and tie preferred
Style: Country-house

A small savoury soufflé served in the lounge is a signature of a meal here and strikes a good opening note, being perfectly timed and extremely well-flavoured. In the conservatory restaurant, the menu lives up to the promise of the canapés, giving a modern twist to classic combinations such as tenderloin of lamb with mint roasted potato and red onion jus or fillet of beef on a galette of courgette and scallions with braised cherry tomatoes and basil. The delightful country house setting features a terrace, lawns and well tended gardens.

Smoking: No smoking in dining room
Civil licence:
Accommodation: 7 rooms (7 en suite) ★ ★
Directions: 4 miles SW off B1230.

Tickton Grange Hotel

Tickton, HU17 9SH
Tel: 01964 543666
Fax: 01964 542556
e maggy@tickton-grange.
demon.co.uk
Chef(s): David Nowell
Owner(s): Mr & Mrs Whymant
Cost: *Alc* £25, set price D £25. ☺ ☺
H/wine £11.75
Times: Noon-2pm/7-9.30pm
Additional: Children welcome
Seats: 45
Smoking: No-smoking area
Civil licence: 60
Accommodation: 17 rooms (17 en suite) ★ ★ ★

The smart but relaxed restaurant in this Georgian country house delivers modern British cuisine through a choice of menus. The classic *carte* might include oak smoked salmon, devilled chicken breast and crêpe suzette, whilst the fixed price 'Colours and Creations' has a hint of the exotic. Salmon wears a Kashmir dressing and the chicken is marinated in Thai spices. A 'Champagne Dinner', including a glass of bubbly was noted as particularly good value. Make sure you're in a decisive mood for the cheese course (there are 40 to choose from) and don't miss the Tickton truffles with coffee.

Directions: From Beverley take the A1035 towards Bridlington. Hotel on left, after 3 miles, just past the village of Tickton

England

WILLERBY
Map 8 TA07

Willerby Manor Hotel

A light and airy restaurant decorated in a warm beige colour with views over landscaped gardens. A good level of skill and attention is in evidence in a baked breast of corn-fed chicken stuffed with pancetta mousseline. Roasted aubergine and courgettes with basil tomatoes presented on creamed spinach typifies the vegetarian option.

Seats: 50. Private dining room 25. **Style:** Formal, Country-house **Smoking:** No pipes; no cigars; Air conditioning **Civil licence:** 300. **Accommodation:** 51 rooms (51 en suite) ★ ★ ★ **Directions:** From A63 take Humber Bridge/Beverley exit onto A164. From A15/A164 take 1st exit to Beverley/Humber Bridge. From York on A1079, at rdbt take A164 towards Humber Bridge, then 3rd exit onto B1232 and follow signs

Well Lane, HU10 6ER
Tel: 01482 652616
Fax: 01482 653901
e info@willerbymanor.co.uk
Chef(s): Peter Lingard
Cost: *Alc* £25, set price D £17.75. ☺
H/wine £9.95
Times: 12.30-2.30pm/7-9.30pm.
Closed L Mon-Sat, D Sun, BHs,
last 2 wks Aug, 1st wk Jan
Additional: Sunday L. Bar food.
Children welcome

YORKSHIRE, NORTH

ALDWARK
Map 8 SE46

Aldwark Manor Hotel

Used by the Royal Canadian Air Force during the war, this 19th-century manor house is now a 'lovely oasis' surrounded by an 18-hole golf course and an extensive leisure centre. The Rendlesham restaurant has a high ceiling with elegant crystal chandeliers and plaster panelled walls. As it only sits 48, an intimate atmosphere is guaranteed. Cooking is imaginative but classically based: a meal might include salmon and truffle ravioli with a langoustine dressing followed by pan-fried duck breast with a red onion tarte Tatin, Puy lentils and a thyme jus.

Accommodation: 28 rooms ★ ★ ★
Directions: From A1, A59 towards Green Hammerton, then B6265 towards Little Ouseburn, follow signs Aldwark Bridge/Manor. A19 through Linton on Ouse to Aldwark

YO61 1UF
Tel: 01347 838146
Fax: 01347 838867
e reception@aldwarkmanor.co.uk
Chef(s): Andrew Burton
Owner(s): Mr B Holbrook
Cost: Set price L £12.95/D £24.95.
☺ ☺ H/wine £9.95
Times: Noon-2pm/7-9.30pm.
Additional: Sunday L. Bar food L.
Children welcome
Seats: 48. Private dining room 20
Style: Traditional, Country-house
Smoking: No smoking in dining room
Civil licence: 60

ARNCLIFFE
Map 7 SD97

Amerdale House Hotel

The manor house of the Arndale estate is all lofty ceilings, elegant lounges and uninterrupted views of spectacular landscapes down the dale. Guest comfort is paramount, with furnishings chosen accordingly, and the collection of prints - mostly signed limited editions - is particularly interesting. Delicacies of the region include Dales lamb at its best - roast loin with minted couscous and a redcurrant and port jus - and a good Yorkshire curd tart with delicately flavoured cinnamon ice cream. The wine list isn't extensive but offers a good range of choice and price with a commendable selection of halves.

Accommodation: 11 rooms (11 en suite) ★ ★
Directions: On the outskirts of village

BD23 5QE
Tel: 01756 770250
Fax: 01756 770266
Chef(s): Nigel Crapper
Owner(s): Paula & Nigel Crapper
Cost: Set price D £30. H/wine £12.95
Times: Dinner only, 7.30pm-late.
Closed mid Nov-mid Mar
Additional: Children 8 yrs+.
Vegetarian not available
Seats: 24
Style: Traditional

England

ASENBY

Map 8 SE37

Crab and Lobster Restaurant

Dishforth Road, YO7 3QL
Tel: 01845 577286
Fax: 01845 577109
e reservations@crabandlobster.co.uk
Chef(s): Steven Dean
Owner(s): David & Jackie Barnard
Cost: Alc £25, set price L £12.50/
D £21.50. ☺ ☺ H/wine £11
Times: 11.30-3pm/6.30-11pm.
Additional: Sunday L. Bar food.
Children 12yrs+
Seats: 146. Private dining room 24
Style: Modern
Smoking: No smoking in dining room;
Air conditioning
Civil licence: 50

Delightfully bohemian thatched pub where accordions, parasols and other curios take the place of crystal chandeliers, but where the cuisine is quite worthy of a swanky hotel. Influences from Mediterranean and Thai cuisine combine with a firmly modern British approach to produce starters ranging from mussels with black beans and spring onions to tagliatelle egg pasta with artichokes, pesto, red peppers and aubergine. Mains are eclectic in scope with whole roasted sea bass (with a tropical fruit salsa) lying alongside 'posh' fish and chips with minted mushy peas. Desserts are bound to test your decision-making faculties to the limit, but chocolate croissant pudding with lavender crème anglaise must be a strong contender.

Accommodation: 12 rooms (12 en suite)
Directions: Leave A1 for A19 at Dishforth, just N of Boroughbridge & Ripon, take A19 towards Teeside, 1st L

BILBROUGH

Map 8 SE54

The Three Hares Country Inn NEW

Main Street, YO23 3PH
Tel: 01937 832128
Fax: 01937 834626
e info@thethreehares.co.uk
Chef(s): David Fullerton, Keith Paylor
Owner(s): Hugh & Sarah Mansford
Cost: Alc £20. ☺ ☺ H/wine £11.50

Awards and accolades have been heaped upon this country inn and it's easy to see why. It incorporates the old village forge, sympathetically converted to create an attractive dining room, and both the bar and restaurant are jam-packed with character, flagged floors and exposed brickwork. The cooking is modern in approach demonstrating both imagination and technical skill,

and there's a good choice from the specials board in addition to the regular *carte*. Successes amongst the starters have included peppered salmon, simply seared and topped with avocado and tomato salsa. For a trip down memory lane, try the superb braised oxtail, the meat fairly falling off the bone.

Directions: From York take A64 towards Leeds and follow signs for Bilbrough on R

BOLTON ABBEY
Map 7 SE05

Devonshire Arms

A private country house feel pervades this fine country mansion with stunning views over the Yorkshire Dales National Park. An elegant dining room consisting of four interconnecting rooms features well-spaced tables and polished, attentive service. Good quality seasonal ingredients are well used in an innovative choice of dishes in modern Anglo/French style. Expect all the incidental elements such as an amuse bouche of lobster with coriander jelly, crème fraîche and caviar that worked exceptionally well. Flavours are robust as in a tian of duck leg confit with salad of green beans and truffle or baked fillet of cod with langoustine jus and a creamy truffle mash. Desserts feature some classics like an accurate lemon and lime soufflé.

Accommodation: 41 rooms (41 en suite) ★ ★ ★
Directions: On B6160 to Bolton Abbey, 250yds N of junct with A59 rdbt junction

Near Skipton, BD23 6AJ
Tel: 01756 710441
Fax: 01756 710564
✉ sales@thedevonshirearms.co.uk
Chef(s): Steve Williams
Owner(s): Duke & Duchess of Devonshire
Cost: *Alc* £45, set price L £19.95-£28/ D £45. H/wine £15
Times: Noon-2.30pm/7-10pm.
Closed L Mon-Fri
Additional: Sunday L.
Children welcome
Seats: 70. Private dining room 90
Style: Classic
Smoking: No smoking in dining room
Civil licence: 120

BOROUGHBRIDGE
Map 8 SE36

The Dining Room

The town square's fountain is an appropriate sign post for a restaurant overflowing with fresh, simple ideas and clear, accurate execution. The décor is light, bright and inviting with neutral furnishings and eye-catching contemporary art. Starters such as carrot, honey and ginger soup with king scallops. Mains of lamb with candied aubergine and rosemary sauce.

Smoking: No smoking in dining room
Directions: A1(M) Boroughbridge Junction, sign to town. Opposite fountain in the town's square

20 St James Square, YO51 9AR
Tel: 01423 326426
✉ lisaastley@virgin.com
Chef(s): Christopher Astley
Owner(s): Mr & Mrs C Astley
Cost: *Alc* £25, set price L £12.50-£17.50/D £25-£35. ☺ ☺ H/wine £10
Times: Noon-2pm/6.30-9.30pm.
Closed Mon, D Sun, BH Mon
Additional: Sunday L. Children 3 yrs+
Seats: 32. **Style:** Chic, Formal

BUCKDEN
Map 7 SD97

The Buck Inn Hotel

Set amidst glorious Dales scenery, this Georgian inn offers a warm welcome and plenty of traditional charm. The restaurant is a cosy, country style room with whitewashed stone walls and a beamed ceiling, so it's no surprise that the menu features the likes of Beef Wellington and pan-roasted lamb with fondant potato and cranberry and mint sauce. There are, however, plenty of internationally inspired surprises - perhaps roast breast of duck with stir-fried noodles and oriental sauce or roast escalope of salmon on a cherry tomato and spring onion risotto with a white wine and tarragon sauce

Smoking: No smoking in dining room; Air conditioning
Accommodation: 14 rooms (14 en suite) ★ ★
Directions: In centre of village

BD23 5JA
Tel: 01756 760228
Fax: 01756 760227
✉ thebuckinn@buckden.yorks.net
Chef(s): William Mallinson
Owner(s): Mr & Mrs Hayton
Cost: *Alc* £23.95/D £23.95. ☺
H/wine £12.50
Times: Closed L all week,
Additional: Sunday L. Bar food.
Children welcome
Seats: 40. Private dining room 40
Style: Classic

Times: Noon-3pm/7-11pm.
Closed Mon (ex BHs), D Sun, 3wks in Jan-Feb
Additional: Sunday L. Bar food.
Children welcome
Seats: 34
Style: Classic, Rustic
Smoking: No smoking in dining room

England

BURNSALL

Map 7 SE06

Red Lion Hotel

Charming Dales inn dating back to the 16th century. Expect around eight starters, main courses and desserts from menus that offer simplicity and comfort. An excellent range of vegetables is a real strength. Try a taste of the region in, say, Pately bridge sausage, black pudding, apple sauce and mash or any of the moreish puds.

By the Bridge, BD23 6BU
Tel: 01756 720204
Fax: 01756 720292
e redlion@daelnet.co.uk
Chef(s): James Rowley
Owner(s): Andrew &
Elizabeth Grayshon
Cost: Alc £25.95, set price D £25.95.
☺ ☺
Times: Noon-2.30pm/6-11.30pm.
Additional: Sunday L. Bar food.
Children welcome
Style: Traditional
Smoking: No smoking in dining room
Civil licence: 100
Accommodation: 11 rooms (11 en suite) ★ ★
Directions: On B6160 between Bolton Abbey (A59) & Grassington

CRATHORNE

Map 8 NZ40

Crathorne Hall Hotel

A fine Edwardian hall with fabulous views over the Leven Valley. The regal dining room features wood panelling, oil paintings and a magnificent carved fireplace but pale yellow walls and fresh flower displays give the room a fresh, light feel. The classically based menu might include roasted saddle of lamb with caramelised red onions and crab apple jus or seared fillet of salmon with tomato, spring onions and chervil broth. Desserts have a sense of occasion: expect parfait of Montelimar nougat wrapped in dark and white chocolate or gratin of pineapple, mango and maracuja with a malibu sabayon. Service is friendly and attentive.

Yarm, TS15 0AR
Tel: 01642 700398
Fax: 01642 700814
e enquiries@crathornehall.com
Chef(s): David Spencer
Owner(s): Hand Picked Hotels
Cost: Alc £36, set price L £16.75/
D £27.50. ☺ H/wine £14.95
Times: 12.30-2.30pm/7.30-10pm.
Additional: Sunday L. Bar food.
Children welcome
Seats: 45. Private dining room 26
Style: Formal, Country-house

Smoking: No smoking in dining room. **Civil licence:** 140
Accommodation: 37 rooms (37 en suite) ★ ★ ★ ★
Directions: Off A19, 2 miles E of Yarm. Access to A19 via A66 or A1, Thirsk

England

EASINGTON
Map 8 NZ71

Grinkle Park Hotel

An elegant country house set in extensive grounds on the foothills between Whitby and the moors of North Yorkshire. The interior offers all the character you'd expect from a Victorian shooting lodge whilst the menu keeps things traditional with combinations such as lamb and rosemary or duck with a peppercorn sauce.

Style: Traditional, Country-house
Accommodation: 20 rooms (20 en suite) ★★★
Directions: 9 miles from Guisborough, signed off A171 Guisborough-Whitby Rd

TS13 4UB
Tel: 01287 640515
Fax: 01287 641278
e grinkle.parkhotel@bass.com
Chef(s): Timothy Backhouse
Cost: *Alc* £25, set price L £13.25/ D £20.50. ☺ ☺ H/wine £9.95
Times: 12.15-2pm/7.15-9pm.
Additional: Sunday L. Bar food.
Children welcome
Seats: 80. Private dining room 24.
Jacket and tie preferred

ESCRICK
Map 8 SE64

The Parsonage Hotel

An early 19th-century parsonage with a country house atmosphere, whose many charms include relaxing lounges, a spacious conservatory and well-tended grounds. Begin your evening with quality canapés and pre-dinner drinks in the bar where smart staff will ensure that your glass stays full. Despite the traditionally elegant style of the restaurant, the menu shows modern flair, offering unconventional combinations such as herb crusted pigeon breast with grape sausage and hazelnut salad or Gressingham duck breast with rhubarb tart, sage potatoes and peppercorns. As in the bar, service is attentive and efficient.

Civil licence: 100
Accommodation: 21 rooms (21 en suite) ★★★
Directions: S from York on A19, Parsonage on R, 4 miles out of town in Escrick village

York Road, YO19 6LF
Tel: 01904 728111
Fax: 01904 728151
e reservations@parsonagehotel.co.uk
Chef(s): Mark Caffrey
Owner(s): K Ridley
Cost: Set price L £14/D £24.50. ☺ ☺ H/wine £11.25
Times: Noon-2pm/7-9.30pm.
Additional: Sunday L. Bar food L.
Children welcome
Seats: 30. Private dining room 20.
Jacket and tie preferred
Style: Traditional, Country-house
Smoking: No smoking in dining room

HACKNESS
Map 8 SE99

Hackness Grange Country House

North York Moors National Park, YO13 0JW
Tel: 01723 882345
Fax: 01723 882391
Telephone for further details

Brightly furnished in golds and reds, this gracious hotel dining room boasts views onto the lawns and rose beds of the private gardens and of the hills beyond. The dinner menu features interesting, well-composed dishes such as citrus marinated salmon served with continental salad, and vegetable crêpes served with a tomato and onion salad.

England

Map 8 SE35

The Boar's Head Hotel

Ripley Castle Estate, HG3 3AY
Tel: 01423 771888
Fax: 01423 771509
e reservations@boarsheadripley.co.uk
Chef(s): Steve Chesnut, Jason Main
Owner(s): Sir Thomas Ingilby & Lady Ingilby
Cost: Alc £25, set price L £14/ D £20-£30. ☺ ☺ H/wine £12.75
Times: Noon-2pm/6.30-9.30pm.
Additional: Sunday L. Bar food. Children welcome
Seats: 40. Private dining room 40

Cheerful establishment that offers real quality throughout its creditably restrained menu. A notably hushed and intimate atmosphere prevails leaving you free to focus on enjoying the likes of pan-fried breast of Gressingham duckling without distraction. Cherry smoked duck breast with a kumquat and shallot relish, and mille-feuille of lemon sole are some of the alternatives. Desserts tend to be satisfyingly robust - hot banana fondant gateau or sticky toffee pudding soufflé.

Style: Classic, Chic
Smoking: No smoking in dining room
Civil licence: 100
Accommodation: 25 rooms (25 en suite) ★ ★ ★
Directions: Telephone for directions

The Courtyard

A beacon of modernity in an area dominated by antique shops. The good value menu is deliciously simple offering steamed tranche of salmon with lemon crème fraiche and soda bread for instance.

Additional: Children welcome
Seats: 28
Style: Modern, Bistro-Style
Smoking: No smoking in dining room
Directions: Telephone for directions

1 Montpellier Mews,
HG1 2TG
Tel: 01423 530708
Fax: 01423 530708
Chef(s): Jamie Dillasier
Owner(s): E Wadsworth & I Meyer
Cost: Alc £20, set price L £12.50/ D £12.50. ☺ ☺ H/wine £10.45
Times: Noon-2pm/6.30-10pm.
Closed Sun-Mon

Dusty Miller

Set in a pretty ivy-clad building built as a pub in the 1800s, the Dusty Miller has plenty of cottagey charm, including polished wood tables, fresh flowers, antiques and a roaring fire in the bar area. The short menu changes daily and makes good use of quality local ingredients. Dishes are immaculately presented and largely traditional in style. A meal could take in oak roast

Low-Laithe,
Summerbridge,
HG3 4BU
Tel: 01423 780837
Chef(s): Brian Dennison
Owner(s): Brian & Elizabeth Dennison

salmon with horseradish, followed by crisp roast duckling with apples and Calvados. Desserts might include roasted fruits with crème anglaise or a tangy lemon mousse

Style: Classic, Traditional
Smoking: No smoking in dining room
Directions: On B6165, 10 miles from Harrogate

Cost: *Alc* £32, set price D £24. ☺ ☺
H/wine £12.90
Times: Dinner only, 7-11pm.
Closed 2wks mid Aug
Additional: Children 9 yrs+
Seats: 28

Harrogate
Brasserie Hotel

Authentic brasserie, with a lively formula of intimate ambience, slick service, occasional live jazz and an honest seasonal menu. Autumn dishes included a rustic starter of grilled goats' cheese on brioche, flashed medallions of venison with a juniper sauce, and a clever chocolate cup filled with a light mousse.

Seats: 72. Private dining room 26
Style: French
Smoking: No pipes
Accommodation: 14 rooms (14 en suite) ★★
Directions: In town centre, 500 metres from railway station, behind Theatre

28-30 Cheltenham Parade, HG1 1DB
Tel: 01423 505041
Fax: 01423 722300
E brasserie@zoom.co.uk
Chef(s): Brian Dale
Owner(s): Mr & Mrs R Finney
Cost: *Alc* £18, set price L £18/D £18.
☺ ☺ H/wine £8.95
Times: Dinner only, 6-10pm.
Closed 26 Dec, 1 Jan, BHs
Additional: Children welcome

Rudding Park House

Rudding Park, Follifoot, HG3 1JH
Tel: 01423 871350
Fax: 01423 872286
E sales@ruddingpark.com
Chef(s): Matthew Benson-Smith
Owner(s): Simon Mackaness
Cost: *Alc* £24.50, set price L £13.50-£19.50/D £24.50-£30.50. ☺ ☺
H/wine £11.50
Times: 12.30-2pm/7-9.30pm.
Additional: Sunday L. Bar food.
Children welcome.
Vegetarian by request only
Seats: 90. Private dining room 250
Style: Modern, Chic
Smoking: No smoking in dining room; Air conditioning

Slick service and a cool ambience, add much to the experience at this magnificent Regency residence. A welcome focus on simplicity and attention to natural flavours is to be celebrated too, in a menu that puts a modish, pan-global spin on some familiar constituents. Fairly typical of the style is a starter of pan fried king scallops with a lively basil and tomato dressing that has been noted as "deliciously to the point" with similar praise for a main course of lamb shank with couscous and a Madeira sauce. Desserts hold their own in some well-worked variations of old favourites such as chocolate crème brûlée with shortbread and summer berries.

Civil licence: 200
Accommodation: 50 rooms (50 en suite) ★★★★
Directions: M1/A1(M)/A59/A658 follow signs 'Rudding Park'

England

HAWES
Map 7 SD88

Simonstone Hall Hotel

Creative dinner menu in a stylish Jacobean hunting lodge restaurant. Enjoy the wild Yorkshire moors from comfort of your table in front of an open fire selecting from wild boar, sautéed pigeon, char-grilled salmon and wild mushrooms amongst others. If you're all Wuthered-out the king prawns with Thai dressing offer a brief sojourn to warmer climes.

Style: Traditional, Formal
Smoking: No smoking in dining room.
Civil licence: 55
Accommodation: 18 rooms (18 en suite) ★ ★
Directions: 1.5m N of Hawes on road signed to Muker and Buttertubs

Simonstone, DL8 3LY
Tel: 01969 667255
Fax: 01969 667741
e simonstonehall@demon.co.uk
Chef(s): Robert Mountain
Cost: *Alc* £20/D £20-£30. ☺ ☺
H/wine £9.95
Times: Dinner only, 7-9pm
Additional: Children 6 yrs+
Seats: 40. Private dining room 22.
Jacket and tie preferred

HELMSLEY
Map 8 SE68

The Black Swan

Picture postcard stuff with the restaurant benefiting from a seductive view of a delightful little walled garden. The hotel is justly proud of the fact that two of its restaurant staff have a total of 97 years experience between them - a rarity in this day and age. Some accomplished cooking in evidence particularly in a baked chicken and seafood nage.

Smoking: No smoking in dining room
Accommodation: 45 rooms (45 en suite) ★ ★ ★
Directions: Take A170 from Scarborough or Thirsk; Black Swan is in centre of village, at top end of Market Place

Market Place, YO62 5BJ
Tel: 01439 770466
Fax: 01439 770174
Chef(s): Nigel Wright
Cost: *Alc* £30, set price L £6.95/D
£26. ☺ H/wine £15
Times: Noon-2pm/7-9pm.
Additional: Sunday L. Bar food L.
Children welcome
Seats: 75. Private dining room 22
Style: Traditional

Feversham Arms Hotel

A smart and comfortable hotel that has been popular with guests for many years. The restaurant is decorated in opulent colours with mahogany and velvet fittings, whilst the exciting and truly eclectic menu might include Thai green chicken curry or salt cod with boiled potatoes and parsley sauce.

Seats: 70. Private dining room 30.
Style: International
Smoking: No smoking in dining room
Accommodation: 17 rooms (17 en suite) ★ ★ ★
Directions: From A1(M) take A168 to Thirsk then A170 for 14 miles to Helmsley

1 High Street, YO62 5AG
Tel: 01439 770766
Fax: 01439 770346
e fevershamarms@hotmail.com
Chef(s): Andrew Bingham
Owner(s): Studford Inns
Cost: *Alc* £20, set price L £20/D £20.
☺ ☺ H/wine £10.95
Times: Noon-2pm/7-9.30pm.
Additional: Sunday L. Bar food.
Children welcome

The Star Inn

Apart from probably sustaining local thatching industry by itself, this peaceful low-beamed building houses a sophisticated restaurant surrounded by well-tended gardens. Simple strategies are often the most effective and here great results are achieved through selecting the best of British raw materials and employing great care and skill. A warm salad of grilled black

Harome,
YO6 5JE
Tel: 01439 770397
Fax: 01439 771833
Chef(s): Andrew Pern
Owner(s): A & J Pern
Cost: *Alc* £25. ☺ ☺ H/wine £11.50

pudding with pan-fried foie gras might precede a main of pan-fried fillet of beef with blue cheese butter, spinach and ham salad, and a foie gras dressing. Traditional, unfussy desserts such as poached winter fruits in a rum and vanilla syrup with oatmeal shortbread really hit the spot.

Times: 11.30-2pm/6.45-9.30pm. Closed Mon, D Sun, 2wks Jan, 25 Dec, BHs
Additional: Sunday L. Bar food. Children welcome. Vegetarian by request only
Seats: 36. Private dining room 10
Style: Traditional
Smoking: No smoking in dining room
Accommodation: 3 rooms (3 en suite)

Directions: From Helmsley take A170 towards Kirkbymoorside, after 1.5 miles turn R towards Harome. After 1.5 miles inn is 1st building on R

HETTON

Map 7 SD95

Angel Inn

BD23 6LT
Tel: 01756 730263
Fax: 01756 730363
Chef(s): J Topham & B Elsworth
Owner(s): Mr D Watkins
Cost: *Alc* £25. ☺ ☺ H/wine £10.50
Times: Noon-2pm/6-9pm. Closed L Mon-Sat, D Sun, 2wks Jan
Additional: Sunday L. Bar food. Children welcome
Seats: 56. Private dining room 36
Style: Rustic
Smoking: No-smoking area; no pipes; no cigars

WINE AWARD BEST PUB

Attractive 500-year-old building offering a 'gastro-pub' formula which has inspired many emulators. The intimate dining areas remain traditionally rustic with the ambience rural and relaxing despite slick, professional service. The menu continues to reflect true country cooking with a commendable emphasis on the provision of seafood in this, a land-locked county. The flavours speak for themselves in a crispy duck salad with chorizo and bacon lardons - the constituent elements working together with charm and character. A slow-cooked confit of lamb with thyme mash and winter roots was surprisingly light in texture with delicate flavours very much to the fore. Still an example to others.

Directions: In village centre, B6265 (Rylestone) from Skipton by-pass

England

HOVINGHAM
Map 8 SE67

Worsley Arms Hotel

High Street, YO62 4LA
Tel: 01653 628234
Fax: 01653 628130
e worsleyarms@aol.com
Chef(s): Andrew Porter
Owner(s): Mr & Mrs A Finn
Cost: Alc £25, set price L £16/D £25.
☺ ☺ H/wine £11.95
Times: Noon-2pm/7-9.30pm
Additional: Sunday L. Bar food.
Children welcome
Seats: 50. Private dining room 40
Style: Traditional, Country-house
Smoking: No smoking in dining room
Civil licence: 90
Accommodation: 19 rooms (19 en
suite) ★ ★ ★
Directions: On B1257

Everything is in place for the quintessential English village experience - the stately home, the village green and the cluster of lovely golden-coloured stone cottages. Expect starters along the lines of pressed terrine of Goosnargh duckling and roasted apple and some robust mains such as a classic beef stew (small pieces of tender rump steak in a rich sauce with two light suet dumplings.) Desserts are good too - raspberry and pistachio crème brûlée being one highlight.

KNARESBOROUGH
Map 8 SE35

Dower House Hotel

The Terrace Restaurant overlooks the gardens from a building dating in part from the 15th century. The setting is traditional but the food is modern, offered from a brasserie-style menu priced from one to three courses. Expect the likes of Nidderdale smoked Salmon, braised lamb shank with root vegetables, mixed beans and basil mash, and Bakewell tart on Amaretto cream.

Style: Traditional. **Smoking:** No smoking in dining room
Accommodation: 31 rooms (31 en suite) ★ ★ ★
Directions: At Harrogate end of Knaresborough High Street

Bond End, HG5 9AL
Tel: 01423 863302
Fax: 01423 867665
e enquiries@bwdowerhouse.co.uk
Chef(s): Richard Taylor
Owner(s): Mr N R Davies &
Mr M J Davies
Cost: Alc £21. ☺ ☺ H/wine £10.95
Times: Noon-2pm/7-9.30pm.
Additional: Sunday L. Bar food.
Children welcome
Seats: 100. Private dining room 20

General Tarleton Inn

A one-time coaching inn sympathetically extended to provide additional accommodation and a covered courtyard where light meals can be taken. The inn is renowned not only for the high standard of the restaurant food but also for its good bar meals. The beamed bars offer dishes of the day and specials shown on blackboards while the restaurant is much more formally appointed but still full of character with its exposed stone walls. Local game and locally farmed Birstwith sirloin steak features alongside Yorkshire Dales lamb. The freshly prepared puddings should not be missed.

Smoking: No smoking in dining room
Accommodation: 14 rooms (14 en suite) ★ ★ ★
Directions: From A1 J48 take A6055 towards Knaresborough.
Ferrensby 3 miles

Boroughbridge Road,
Ferrensby, HG5 0PZ
Tel: 01423 340284
Fax: 01423 340288
e gti@generaltarleton.co.uk
Chef(s): John Topham, Jason Moore
Owner(s): Mr Watkins & Mr Topham
Cost: Alc £25, set price L £17.50/D
£25-£39.50. ☺ ☺
Times: Noon-3pm/6-11.30pm.
Closed L Mon-Sat, D Sun, 25 Dec
Additional: Sunday L. Bar food.
Children welcome
Seats: 60. Private dining room 40
Style: Traditional, Country-house

MALTON
Map 8 SE77

Burythorpe House Hotel

Set in its own grounds on the edge of the village, this charming hotel includes a relaxing, oak panelled dining room. The food, skilfully cooked by the owner and his daughter, ranges from traditional (home-made steak and kidney pudding) to international (pan-fried salmon steak with oriental sauce and spring onions).

Seats: 60. Private dining room 20
Style: Traditional, Country-house
Smoking: No smoking in dining room; Air conditioning
Accommodation: 16 rooms (16 en suite) ★ ★ ★
Directions: Edge of Burythorpe village, 4 miles S of Malton

Burythorpe, YO17 9LB
Tel: 01653 658200
Fax: 01653 658204
e reception@burythorpehousehotel. com
Chef(s): Mr & Mrs T Austin
Owner(s): Mr & Mrs T Austin
Cost: Alc £18.50, set price L £12.75/ D £18.50. ☺ ☺ H/wine £10.50
Times: Noon-2pm/7-9.30pm
Additional: L by arrangement only. Sunday L. Children 7 yrs+. Vegetarian by request only

MARKINGTON
Map 8 SE26

Hob Green Hotel

A charming country house hotel situated in its own grounds and gardens amid 800 acres of beautiful rolling countryside. The traditional style restaurant offers creative cooking using plenty of produce from the hotel's own kitchen garden. Dishes might include sautéed supreme of chicken bonne femme or grilled trout fillets in a nut crumble with rosemary and redcurrant sauce.

Civil licence: 30
Accommodation: 12 rooms (12 en suite) ★ ★ ★
Directions: One mile W of village off A61

HG3 3PJ
Tel: 01423 770031
Fax: 01423 771589
e info@hobgreen.com
Chef(s): Chris Taylor
Cost: Alc £28.50, set price L £13.45-£16.90/D £23.50-£27.45. ☺ ☺ H/wine £11.95
Times: 12.30-2.30pm/7-9.30pm.

MIDDLEHAM
Map 7 SE18

Waterford House

Kirkgate, DL8 4PG
Tel: 01969 622090
Fax: 01969 624020
Telephone for further details

This delightful restaurant-with-rooms is located in an attractive period house just off the village square. Furnished with antiques, china and silver, its warm, restful atmosphere is enhanced by genuinely friendly service. A meal begins with tasty savouries served at your table, whilst the menu itself features well loved classics such as tournedos Rossini or rack of Yorkshire lamb, all done with balance and precision. Try to leave room for impressive home-made desserts such as

MIDDLEHAM *Continued* Map 7 SE18

raspberry crème brûlée. Also well worth sampling is the
extensive and inspiring selection of wines from the proprietor's
own shop.

MIDDLESBROUGH Map 8 NZ41

The Purple Onion

Only a stone's throw from the Riverside Stadium on one of the
centre's main streets. This cosmopolitan oasis presents a rich
mix of Moorish lampshades, old Tiffany gas lamps, weeping fig
trees and a strangely intimate atmosphere behind its Victorian
shop-front. The brasserie is racy and full of young movers-and-
shakers enjoying relaxed, casual dining at its best. The food,
best described as eclectic, comes in varied Mediterranean guises
such as chicken mousseline and vegetable terrine with fresh
tomato and oregano and pan-fried sea bass with coriander and
shellfish chowder, with brunoise of al dente vegetables and a
tartlet of tomato chutney. Rum and chocolate cheesecake with
a banana and vanilla cream was a highlight.

80 Corporation Road, TS1 2RF
Tel: 01642 222250
Fax: 01642 650188
e purpleonion@ndirect.co.uk
Chef(s): Tony Chapman, Darre Allen
Owner(s): Bruno McCoy
Cost: ☺ ☺ H/wine £10.95
Times: Noon-2.30pm/5.30-10pm.
Closed Sun, 25 Dec, 1 Jan
Additional: Bar food L.
Children welcome
Seats: 80
Style: Classic, French Brasserie
Smoking: Air conditioning
Civil licence: 50
Directions: Exit A66 at Hospitality Inn
near Riverside Football Stadium.
Restaurant located nr Law Courts &
Odeon cinema

NORTHALLERTON Map 9 SE39

The Golden Lion

Cosy inn standing at the head of Northallerton High Street. The
menus tend toward hearty fare to comfort northern souls, from
braised oxtail and baked grouse to hefty chargrilled steaks.
Lighter, modern dishes appear too, say crab and ginger
fishcakes, with an emphasis on fresh fish from turbot to sea
bass, most welcome.

Style: Classic
Smoking: No smoking in dining room
Civil licence: 30
Accommodation: 25 rooms (25 en suite) ★ ★
Directions: From A684 take A167 through built-up area, take
3rd exit on rdbt to town centre. At 3rd rdbt turn L into High St.

High Street, DL7 8PP
Tel: 01609 777411
Fax: 01609 773250
Chef(s): Mark Gazzard
Cost: *Alc* £19, set price D £14.95.
☺ ☺ H/wine £10.95
Times: Noon-2.30pm/7-9.30pm.
Closed D Sun
Additional: Sunday L. Bar food.
Children welcome
Seats: 45

England

The Three Tuns   NEW

9 South End, Osmotherly,
DL6 3BN
Tel: 01609 883301
Chef(s): Mr C Robinson
Owner(s): Mr D Brown
Cost: *Alc* £25. ☺ ☺ H/wine £11.50
Times: Noon-3pm/6-midnight
Additional: Sunday L. Bar food L.
Children welcome at L
Seats: 45
Style: Modern, Traditional
Smoking: Air conditioning
Accommodation: 7 rooms (7 en suite)
♦♦♦
Directions: Telephone for directions

Behind the cosy cottage facade hides a stylish restaurant with
warm lighting, restrained décor and lots of bare wood. The
menu is an assured blend of British and Mediterranean
influences (Angus beef steak, lobster and tiger prawn risotto)
with the occasional bit of spice (among the starters, seared
scallops with crispy leeks and curry butter). Don't miss the
interesting local cheeses.

PICKERING   Map 8 SE78

Fox & Hounds
Country Inn

You can eat well both in the bar and restaurant at this
attractive village inn. The menus offer a contemporary slant on
a good range of dishes. Try the chargrilled swordfish steak with
black olive, lemon and oregano mash, or pan-fried calves' liver
on black pudding with whole grain mustard and honey sauce
topped with pancetta.

Style: Modern
Smoking: No smoking in dining room
Accommodation: 10 rooms (10 en suite) ♦♦♦♦
Directions: In centre of Sinnington, 300yds off A170 between
Pickering and Helmsley

Main Street, Sinnington,
YO62 6SQ
Tel: 01751 431577
Fax: 01751 432791
Chef(s): Mark Wilson, Simon Buckley
Owner(s): Mr & Mrs A Stephens
Cost: *Alc* £20, set price L £10.95.
☺ ☺ H/wine £11
Times: Noon-2.30pm/6.30-9.30pm.
Additional: Sunday L. Bar food.
Children welcome. Vegetarian by
request only
Seats: 40. Private dining room 12

White Swan

The crisp perfection of linen-covered tables is softened here by
red walls and candlelight. A similar mixture of polish and
warmth is evident in the service. Dishes range from rack of
lamb to aubergine with curried lentils and include a wide choice
of vegetable accompaniments. Set in an attractive coaching inn
in the centre of town.

Style: Classic
Smoking: No smoking in dining room
Accommodation: 12 rooms (12 en suite) ★★
Directions: Between the church and steam railway station

Market Place, YO18 7AA
Tel: 01751 472288
Fax: 01751 475554
e welcome@white-swan.co.uk
Chef(s): Darren Clemmit
Owner(s): Buchanan Family
Cost: *Alc* £23.50. ☺ ☺
H/wine £11.95
Times: Noon-2pm/7-9pm.
Additional: Sunday L. Bar food.
Children welcome
Seats: 60. Private dining room 50

England

RAMSGILL
Map 7 SE17

Yorke Arms

HG3 5RL
Tel: 01423 755243
Fax: 01423 755330
e enquiries@yorkearms.co.uk
Chef(s): Frances Atkins
Owner(s): Mr & Mrs G Atkins
Cost: Alc £25. ☺ ☺ H/wine £12
Times: Noon-2pm/7-9pm.
Closed D Sun (ex residents)
Additional: Sunday L. Bar food L.
Children 12yrs+
Seats: 60. Jacket and tie preferred
Style: Traditional, Rustic
Smoking: No smoking in dining room

This attractive, creeper-clad hotel stands in peaceful Upper Nidderdale, close to the Gouthwaite reservoir. The building was originally used to make cheese for a monastery but takes its name from the family who used it as a shooting lodge in the 18th century. The restaurant is an inviting, wooden floored room dominated at one end by a 17th-century oak dresser. Patterned rugs and mismatched wooden tables add to its charm. Staff are friendly and obliging, whilst the kitchen delivers accomplished reworkings of classics such as roast saddle of rabbit or fillet of beef Rossini.

Accommodation: 13 rooms (13 en suite) ★ ★
Directions: Take B6265 from Ripon. Turn R in Pateley Bridge for Ramsgill

ROSEDALE ABBEY
Map 8 SE79

Milburn Arms Hotel

Imagine a restaurant serving high quality food, nestling between the panoramic hills of North Yorkshire, and with no reception for mobile phones. Bliss! Unless of course you should feel the need mid-meal to phone your friends and to wax lyrical about the steamed mussels in a cream and garlic sauce. Some good classical orientated cooking has produced the likes of marinated top-side of roast venison with nicely contrasting juniper berries. Desserts such as caramelised peach parfait are a strength and don't miss the excellent chocolates that arrive with coffee.

Directions: Village centre, 3m W of A170 at Pickering

YO18 8RA
Tel: 01751 417312
Fax: 01751 417312
Telephone for further details

🍴 Indicates a restaurant that has told us that 50% or more of their ingredients are organically sourced

Prices quoted in the guide are for guidance only and are subject to change without notice

England

SCARBOROUGH

Map 8 TA08

Beiderbecke's Hotel

NEW

1-3 The Crescent, YO11 2PW
Tel: 01723 365766
Telephone for further details

Set in The Crescent, a row of listed properties in the centre of Scarborough, this hotel has been lovingly refurbished including the very swish 'Marmalades' restaurant, resplendent in rich blue and gold. The oak-panelled bar is a convivial context in which to wait for your meal before being seated in the jazz-themed restaurant ready to enjoy the endeavours of the very able kitchen. If the bread is less than revelatory do not be disheartened - starters such as Thai fishcake on a red pepper sauce soon liven things up, ably followed by pot-roast local pheasant with red rice and a lovely, light parsnip tart.

Wrea Head Country Hotel

Scalby, YO13 0PB
Tel: 01723 378211
Fax: 01723 355935
Telephone for further details

Charming Victorian country house situated in fourteen acres of landscaped gardens amongst splendid scenery on the edge of the town. Friendly and enthusiastic staff serve up varied and interesting cuisine such as filo basket filled with Cajun red mullet on aubergine, or chef's own coq au vin.

☺ Indicates a restaurant that has told us they offer a two-course lunch for less than £15

☺ Indicates a restaurant that has told us they offer a three-course dinner for less than £25

England

SELBY

Map 8 SE63

Restaurant Martel

This family run Georgian hunting lodge may be off the beaten track but the restaurant makes it well worth a detour. Lofty ceilings, stunning flower arrangements and modern paintings create an impressive backdrop for the assured modern cooking. A meal might include a tian of crab with apple, mascarpone and Avruga caviar with chilled tomato essence, followed by braised pig's trotter stuffed with veal sweetbreads, black pudding and chicken with celeriac purée and essence of morelle. Round off with a 'wonderful' pyramid of honey nougat glace and lemon sorbet. A well chosen wine list and relaxed yet very skilful service complete the picture.

Accommodation: 3 rooms (3 en suite)
Directions: Signposted from petrol station in Monk Fryston on A63.

Gateforth YO8 9LJ
Tel: 01757 228225
Fax: 01757 228189
e martel@uk.packardbell.org
Chef(s): Martel Smith
Owner(s): Martel Smith
Cost: Alc £35, set price L £17 ☺
H/wine £12.75
Times: Noon-2pm/7-10pm. Closed Mon, L Sat, D Sun, 3 days Xmas, 10 days Jan
Additional: Sunday L. Children welcome
Seats: 42. Private dining room 22
Style: Modern, Country-house
Smoking: No-smoking area

SKIPTON

Map 7 SD95

Coniston Hall Lodge

A rugged Yorkshire landscape is the idyllic setting for this 17th-century stone barn housing a small bistro-style restaurant. The finest of local produce is available according to season with a high level of skill demonstrated, for example, by a beautifully light and even pastry case in a delicious plum tomato and red onion tartlet.

Style: Bistro-Style
Civil licence: 40
Accommodation: 40 rooms (40 en suite) ★ ★ ★
Directions: On A65, 5 miles NW of Skipton

Coniston Cold, BD23 4EB
Tel: 01756 748080
Fax: 01756 749487
e conistonhall@clara.net
Chef(s): Stephanie Moon
Owner(s): Tom Bannister
Cost: Alc £28, set price D £18.50. ☺ ☺ H/wine £10.50
Times: 11.30-5.30pm/6.30-10pm.
Additional: Sunday L. Bar food. Children welcome
Seats: 45. Private dining room 70

STADDLE BRIDGE

Map 8 SE49

McCoys (Tontine Inn)

A consistently good restaurant which draws diners from near and far. The cosy, bistro-style room has an informal atmosphere; with bare tables, laid-back staff and hand-written menus, but there is nothing casual about the cooking. This is sturdy, unpretentious food that rarely disappoints. A meal begins with warm, crunchy French bread followed by a starter such as fresh mussels or black pudding with ham tortellini. Main courses include fresh fish (Dover sole with Béarnaise sauce or pan-fried salmon with roasted salsify) and an eclectic selection of meat dishes - perhaps spicy marinated chicken with guacomole and a sweet chilli dressing or roast rack of lamb with tarragon jus.

Directions: At the junction of A19 & A172, Stokesley road

DL6 3JB
Tel: 01609 882671
Fax: 01609 882660
Chef(s): Marcus Bennett
Owner(s): Mr E & Mr T McCoy
Cost: Set price D £28. H/wine £12.50
Times: Dinner only on Fri & Sat (bistro opening hours differ). Closed 25-26 Dec,1 Jan
Additional: Sunday L. Bar food. Children welcome
Seats: 26. Private dining room 26
Style: Modern, Bistro-Style
Smoking: No pipes; Air conditioning
Accommodation: 6 rooms (6 en suite)

England

SUTTON-ON-THE-FOREST
Map 8 SE56

Rose & Crown

Main Street, YO61 1DP
Tel: 01347 811333
Fax: 01347 811444
e mail@rosecrown.co.uk
Chef(s): Stephen Harper
Owner(s): Ralph Magee
Cost: *Alc* £23, set price L £15.50/
D £21.50. ☺ ☺ H/wine £10.95
Times: Noon-2pm/7-9.30pm.
Closed Mon & Tue, D Sun, 25 Dec,
2 wks Jan-Feb, 1 wk Aug
Additional: Sunday L. Bar food.
Children welcome
Seats: 50
Style: Classic, Traditional

There are lots of nooks and crannies in this restaurant, so diners have a degree of privacy in which to enjoy the whole colourful experience. Don't be fooled by its name or the blackboard specials - this is no pub. The bright interior design points towards a modern, trendy style of cooking. At first glance, there may seem to be an English bias to the menu, but this is because of the emphasis on fresh local produce: dishes reveal plenty of European influences, and might include Yorkshire beef with a herb crust, garlic crushed potatoes and bourguignonne sauce, or honey glazed pork with black pudding, French onion and cider jus.

Smoking: No smoking in dining room
Directions: 8 miles N of York towards Helmsley on B1363

TADCASTER
Map 8 SE44

Hazlewood Castle

The combination of grand-scale castle and John Benson-Smith's cooking style has clearly hit the spot with most of Yorkshire, who all seemed to be eating here on the various nights we visited. In a style reminiscent of John Tovey, ingredients slug it out on the plate, trying to grab your attention. A rabbit terrine, for example, was excellent, delivering not only rillettes-style smooth liver and Parma wrap with chutney but also hazelnuts, redcurrant, shallot dressing and crispy pear slice. An open pie of very good local pigeon breasts (two and perfectly pink) and red cabbage comes with confit of duck. Red snapper, on the other hand was simpler in conception, crisp-skinned with a caramel and lime dressing working very well.

Paradise Lane, Hazlewood,
LS24 9NJ
Tel: 01937 535354
Fax: 01937 530630
e info@hazlewood-castle.co.uk
Chef(s): John Benson-Smith
Cost: *Alc* £29.50, set price L £17.50.
☺ H/wine £14.95
Times: Noon-2pm/6-9.30pm.
Closed Mon, L Tue-Sat, D Sun,
Additional: Sunday L. Children
welcome
Seats: 80. Private dining room 120
Style: Modern, Chic
Smoking: No smoking in dining room;
Air conditioning

Civil licence: 120
Accommodation: 21 rooms (21 en suite) ★ ★ ★
Directions: Signed from A64, W of Tadcaster

WEST WITTON
Map 8 SE08

Wensleydale Heifer Inn

The fabric of this attractive, white-painted inn has remained largely unchanged (except for modern facilities) since its construction in 1631. Log fires illuminate beamed ceilings and stone flagged floors with some magnificent scenery outside providing ample decoration. Quality English fayre such as casserole of pheasant seasoned with cranberries, cinnamon, nutmeg and port.

Style: Classic, Country-house
Smoking: No-smoking area; no pipes
Accommodation: 9 rooms (9 en suite) ★★
Directions: On the A684 (approx 4m west of Leyburn)

DL8 4LS
Tel: 01969 622322
Fax: 01969 624183
e heifer@daelnet.co.uk
Chef(s): Adrian Craig
Owner(s): Mr & Mrs Sharp
Cost: Alc £19. ☺ ☺
Times: Noon-2pm/6-9pm.
Additional: Sunday L. Bar food.
Children welcome.
Vegetarian by request only
Seats: 40

YARM
Map 8 NZ41

Judges Hotel

Kirklevington, TS15 9LW
Tel: 01642 789000
Fax: 01642 782878
Chef(s): Martin Horsley
Owner(s): Mr M Downs
Cost: Alc £30, set price L £14.95/
D £27.50. ☺ H/wine £13.25
Times: Noon-2pm/7-10pm.
Closed L Sat
Additional: Sunday L. Bar food L.
Children welcome
Seats: 60. Private dining room 40.
Jacket and tie preferred
Smoking: No smoking in dining room
Civil licence: 200
Accommodation: 21 rooms (21 en suite) ★★★
Directions: From A69 take A67 towards Kirklevington, hotel 1.5 miles on L.

This Victorian mansion with its fifteen acres of landscaped gardens and woodland walks offers a haven of calm and tranquillity. The dining room itself invites customers to sink into deep comfortable chairs amidst well spaced-out carved wooden tables, with the large conservatory ensuring that the delightful garden views are exploited to the full. The strength of the cuisine lies with the superb freshness of the ingredients. A Thai vegetable salad starter has yielded a real variety of distinctive flavours in successful contrasting combinations, with the likes of a crunchy green leaf salad accompanying a light feta and black olive tart making for a satisfying main course.

YORK
Map 8 SE65

Ambassador Hotel

123 The Mount, YO24 2DA
Tel: 01904 641316
Fax: 01904 640259
Telephone for further details

The rich burgundy reds of the décor coupled with ornate pictures, a grand piano and subdued and gentle lighting set a truly elegant note. Well produced dishes are produced with great dexterity - from good honest winter soup to roast vegetable, mozzarella and spinach wrap. Close to the main road but interesting views nonetheless.

Dean Court Hotel

A traditional and spacious hotel dining room with wonderful views towards York Minster. The menu includes a good selection from the chargrill and modern European dishes such

as marinated loin of venison with honey roast pear and celeriac rösti or pan fried sea bream with grilled aromatic vegetables and tomato and oregano butter.

Duncombe Place, YO1 2EF
Tel: 01904 625082
Fax: 01904 620305
e info@deancourt.co.uk
Chef(s): Peter Brown
Cost: Alc £28.50, set price L £14.50/D £25-£34.50. ☺ ☺
H/wine £11.95
Times: 12.30-2pm/7-9.30pm. Closed L 31 Dec, D 25 Dec
Additional: Sunday L. Bar food. Children 6yrs+ at D
Seats: 60. Private dining room 40
Style: Traditional
Smoking: No smoking in dining room
Civil licence: 50
Accommodation: 39 rooms (39 en suite) ★ ★ ★
Directions: City centre, directly opposite York Minster

The Grange Hotel

1 Clifton, YO3 6AA
Tel: 01904 644744
Fax: 01904 612453
e info@grangehotel.co.uk

The Grange Hotel has a lot to offer. The plush opulent dining room boasts fine art, comfortable seats, beautifully laid tables,

YORK *Continued*   Map 8 SE65

and attentive staff. On top of this, the menu is a kaleidoscope of both contemporary and classical with a loyalty to Northern British cuisine thrown in for good measure. There is also a strong emphasis on seasonal seafood. Grilled sea bass with a herb crust, saffron fondant potato, tomato and balsamic broth, olive purée and crisp Parma ham could be followed by pine nut and praline tart, coffee cream, and caramelised apple pearls.

Smoking: No smoking in dining room. **Civil licence:** 60
Accommodation: 30 rooms (30 en suite) ★ ★ ★
Directions: 400yds to N of city walls on A19

Chef(s): Michael Whiteley
Owner(s): Jeremy &
Vivien Cassel
Cost: *Alc* £27, set price L £11.50/
D £26. ☺ H/wine £10.50
Times: Noon-2pm/7-10pm.
Closed L Sat, D Sun
Additional: Sunday L.
Children welcome
Seats: 35. Private dining room 60
Style: Classic

Knavesmire Manor

302 Tadcaster Road,
YO24 1HE
Tel: 01904 702941
Fax: 01904 709274
e enquirie@knavesmire.co.uk
Chef(s): Andrew Hagan
Owner(s): Mr T Reid
Cost: *Alc* £17.50, set price L
£10.25/D £14.50-£16. ☺ ☺
H/wine £7.10
Times: 12.15-1.45pm/6-9pm.
Closed L Mon-Sat

Bistro-style restaurant in an attractive Georgian house (lots of wood panelling and striped wallpaper). The unfussy European-based menu includes classic meat dishes (steak, lamb shank with rosemary mash, pork glazed with mustard) and vegetarian options such as goats' cheese with toasted hazelnuts or filo parcels of spinach and ricotta. Good coffee.

Additional: Sunday L. Children welcome
Seats: 40. Private dining room 40
Style: Modern, French
Smoking: No smoking in dining room
Civil licence: 50
Accommodation: 21 rooms (21 en suite) ★ ★
Directions: A64 to York, then A1036 York-Bishopthorpe leads on to Tadcaster Rd, hotel on L (overlooking racecourse)

Melton's

7 Scarcroft Road,
YO23 1ND
Tel: 01904 634341
Fax: 01904 635115
e great-food@meltons-
restaurant.freeserve.co.uk
Chef(s): Michael Hjort,
Adam Holliday
Owner(s): Michael & Lucy Hjort

Successful enough to warrant a sequel (watch this space) and understandably so in an establishment where the cause of customer-care is given so much thought and commitment. Appealing set-price lunch and cut-price early-evening menus work well along side a varied and interesting *carte*. The culinary style is best described as Anglo/French with dishes such as mackarel kebabs with piccalilli, game torte with Madeira sauce (plus green cabbage with bacon and mustard mash) and hot pancake soufflé of Seville oranges, making a real impact. Vegetarians are equally well catered for - fennel mousse with saffron risotto and a tomato and pepper dressing for example.

Style: Modern, British
Smoking: No-smoking area; Air conditioning
Directions: From centre head south across Skeldergate Bridge, restaurant opposite Bishopthorpe Road car park

Cost: *Alc* £22.50, set price L £16/ D £21. ☺ ☺ H/wine £12.50
Times: Noon-4pm/5.30-midnight. Closed L Mon, D Sun, 1 wk Aug, 3 wks Xmas
Additional: Sunday L.
Children welcome
Seats: 30. Private dining room 16

Middlethorpe Hall

This stunningly restored William III house is a bastion of civilised country-house leisure. Built in 1699 Middlethorpe Hall is only a mile and a half from the centre of York. Restoration by Historic House Hotels has been sympathetic with everything on a grand scale; antiques and oil paintings abound. The restaurant divided into three rooms is oak panelled, less elaborate meals are served in the grillroom. Cooking can veer from the competent to the more inspired (pastry and desserts are a strength). Expect the general use of good quality ingredients with such luxuries as truffles, lobster and oysters in dishes such as scallops with sauce vierge and guinea fowl with pancetta. Service is friendly and effective and a varied wine list at prices that reflect the luxury of the location, though some commitment to economy is shown by a canny selection of bottles offered below £20.

Accommodation: 30 rooms (30 en suite) ★ ★ ★
Directions: 1.5miles S of York, beside York racecourse

Bishopthorpe Road, Middlethorpe, YO23 2GB
Tel: 01904 641241
Fax: 01904 620176
e info@middlethorpe.com
Chef(s): Martin Barker
Owner(s): Stuart McPherson
Cost: Set price L £19/D £36-£39.50. H/wine £14.50
Times: L from 12.30/7-late. Closed L 25 Dec, D 31 Dec, (L residents only 25 Dec & 31 Dec)
Additional: Sunday L. Children 8yrs+
Seats: 60. Private dining room 45. Jacket and tie preferred
Style: Traditional, Formal
Smoking: No smoking in dining room

Mount Royale

Georgian elegance is the hallmark of Mount Royale, not least in the formal restaurant which overlooks the delightful garden. Serving only dinner, the menu offers favourites such as halibut with king prawn, saffron and Champagne sauce or chicken liver parfait with tomato and apple chutney.

Accommodation: 23 rooms (23 en suite) ★ ★ ★
Directions: W on B1036, towards racecource

The Mount, YO24 1GU
Tel: 01904 628856
Fax: 01904 611171
e reservations@mountroyale.co.uk
Chef(s): Karen Brotherton
Times: Dinner only, 7.30-9.30pm

England

York Pavilion Hotel

45 Main Street, Fulford, YO10 4PT
Tel: 01904 622099
Fax: 01904 626939
e help@yorkpavilonhotel.co.uk
Chef(s): David Spencer
Owner(s): Irene & Andrew Cossins
Cost: *Alc* £25. ☺ ☺ H/wine £11.95
Times: Noon-2pm/6.30-9.30pm.
Additional: Sunday L.
Children welcome
Seats: 60. Private dining room
Style: English, Mediterranean
Smoking: No smoking in dining room
Civil licence: 90
Accommodation: 57 rooms (57 en suite) ★★★
Directions: S from York city centre on A19 (Selby), hotel 2 miles on L

Inviting brasserie-style restaurant in an attractive Georgian hotel. The menu changes regularly and features many daily specials such as chargrilled venison sausage with potato and parsnip pancake, red onion jam and marsala sauce. Robust main courses benefit from subtle touches such as a ragout of wild mushrooms and leeks to accompany venison steak with celeriac mash. The hotel stands in its own very attractive grounds making it an ideal place to escape the hustle and bustle of central York.

YORKSHIRE, SOUTH

CHAPELTOWN   Map 8 SK39

Greenhead House

A fine Georgian building with pretty gardens and a restaurant which retains its period charm. The cooking is equally stylish and refined. Classically based dishes might include timbale of lamb with juniper or grilled fillets of lemon sole with a lobster risotto and a lobster sauce. Desserts typically range from sticky toffee pudding to tropical fruit mille-feuille.

84 Burncross Road, S35 1SF
Tel: 0114 246 9004
Fax: 0114 246 9004
e allengreenhead@hotmail.com
Chef(s): Neil Allen
Owner(s): Mr & Mrs N Allen
Cost: Set price L £16/D £32. ☺ H/wine £12.90
Times: Noon-1pm/7-9pm.
Closed Sun-Tue, L Wed & Sat,
2 wks Easter, 2 wks end Aug,
Xmas-New Year

Additional: Children 7 yrs+
Seats: 32
Style: Country-house
Smoking: No smoking in dining room
Directions: M1 J35, follow signs to Chapeltown, straight across 2 rdbts onto Buncross Rd. Restaurant is on R, 200mtrs

ROTHERHAM   Map 8 SK49

The Consort Hotel   NEW

Modern hotel with an open plan arrangement for the Crown Restaurant and Bar, where a good choice is offered from comprehensive menus. A stuffing of apricots and cashews adds

Brampton Road, Thurcroft, S66 9JA
Tel: 01709 530022
Fax: 01709 531529
e info@consorthotel.com

England

interest to roast breast of duck, served tender and pink with a redcurrant sauce, and a ravioli of crab and avocado comes with a delicate home-made pasta.

Chef(s): Steve James
Owner(s): Mr D C Peat
Cost: Alc £19, set price L £8.95/ D £16.95. ☺ ☺ H/wine £9.50
Times: Noon-2pm/6-9pm
Additional: Sunday L. Bar food L. Children welcome. Vegetarian by request only
Seats: 70. Jacket and tie preferred
Style: Classic, Traditional
Smoking: No smoking in dining room; Air conditioning
Accommodation: 27 rooms (27 en suite) ★ ★ ★
Directions: Telephone for directions

SHEFFIELD

Map 8 SK38

Charnwood Hotel   NEW

10 Sharrow Lane, S11 8AA
Tel: 0114 258 9411
Fax: 0114 255 5107
📧 king@charnwood.force9.co.uk
Chef(s): Paul MacNeil
Owner(s): Mr C J King
Cost: Alc £25.60, set price L £15.25/D £15.25. ☺ ☺
Times: D only, 6.30-10.30pm. Closed Sun, BHs
Additional: Bar food. Children welcome
Seats: 70. Private dining room 40
Style: Traditional, Parisienne
Smoking: No pipes; no cigars
Civil licence: 90
Accommodation: 22 rooms (22 en suite) ★ ★ ★
Directions: M1 J33 & A621. 1.5 miles SW of city centre, off London Road

As the name suggests Brasserie Leo, has Parisian leanings with the requisite mirrors, lights, polished tables and a large bar counter. Good steaks are an option, or some decent fish dishes such as red bream with mango and coriander salsa. Amongst the desserts, a tangy upside down rhubarb cheesecake was appreciated.

Mosborough Hall Hotel

High Street, Mosborough, S20 5EA
Tel: 0114 248 4353
Fax: 0114 247 7042
📧 wllms9999@aol.co.uk
Chef(s): Ian Torpey
Owner(s): Mr G Williams
Cost: Alc £22.50/D £17.50. ☺ ☺ H/wine £10.80
Additional: Children welcome. Vegetarian not available
Seats: 75
Times: Noon-3pm/7-9.30pm. Closed D Sun

A 16th-century manor house and Grade II listed building close to the M1. Facilities include a galleried bar, conservatory lounge and vividly decorated dining room. Dishes are freshly prepared and satisfying. Some interesting combinations appear as in piperade risotto with coriander naan, while more traditional partnerships form the core of the menu in the likes of local pheasant breasts on spring onion champ.

Civil licence: 80
Accommodation: 23 rooms (23 en suite) ★ ★ ★
Directions: Hotel on A616, 5miles from M1 J30

SHEFFIELD *Continued*   Map 8 SK38

Rafters Restaurant

First floor restaurant with glass-topped tables, exposed brick walls, high ceilings and beams. The fixed-price menu offers around six dishes at each course. Home-made breads set the standard for a Thai soup with a potent fishy flavour, and tender lamb fillet with parsnip and rosemary crumble.

Times: Dinner only, 7-11pm. Closed Sun, Tue, 25-26 Dec, 1wk Jan, 2wks Aug
Additional: Children 5yrs+. **Seats:** 38
Style: Modern European. **Smoking:** No pipes; no cigars
Directions: Telephone for directions

220 Oakbrook Road,
Nethergreen, S11 7ED
Tel: 0114 230 4819
Fax: 0114 230 4819
Chef(s): J Bosworth, Marcus Lane
Owner(s): Mr J Bosworth &
Mrs J L Bosworth
Cost: Set price D £24.95. ☺
H/wine £9.95

Richard Smith at Thyme

34 Sandygate Road,
S10 5RY
Tel: 0114 2666096
Fax: 0114 2660279
 thyme@sheffield10.freeserve.co.uk
Chef(s): Richard Smith, Scott Wake
Owner(s): Richard & Victoria Smith
Cost: *Alc* £25, set price L £15. ☺ ☺
H/wine £10
Times: Noon-4pm/6-Midnight.
Additional: Sunday L. Children welcome. Vegetarian by request only
Seats: 70. Private dining room 24
Style: Bistro
Smoking: No smoking in dining room; Air conditioning
Directions: From Sheffield centre take A57; at Crosspool turn R onto Sandygate Road. 100yds on R

It used to be an Indian restaurant, but from the moment you step past the doorman into the busy, noisy bar thronged with colourful types it becomes evident that things have changed. Three floors later, having negotiated a second bar serving shared food - ribs of beef, huge chocolate puds etc - and up through a huge dining room with clay oven, chargrill and open kitchen, the quiet rooftop restaurant comes as a pleasant surprise. A bird's eye view replaces the hectic Smithfield streets, and here mainly Antipodean waitresses in red shirts and black trousers serve largely organic food gleaned from Islay, Pembroke, Somerset et al. The likes of lobster omelette with Thai basil and star anise demonstrates the accomplished cooking, while Islay sirloin with béarnaise uses top-notch meat, and comes with decent fat chips. Tuscan veal casserole with polenta mash and country bread, and the Thyme fishcake might also feature.

YORKSHIRE, WEST

BRADFORD   Map 7 SE13

Apperley Manor

The restaurant is elegant, the gardens are lush. Presentation is the keyword of this welcoming hotel, where the food comes prepared to complement the pretty Yorkshire landscapes. Menu

Apperley Lane, Apperley Bridge,
BD10 0PQ
Tel: 0113 250 5626
Fax: 0113 250 0075

England

choices are plentiful, and don't even think of leaving without trying the caramelised pineapple with a sweet butterscotch sauce and banana ice cream.

Seats: 100. Private dining room 20
Style: Traditional, Country-house
Smoking: No-smoking area; no pipes; no cigars
Accommodation: 13 rooms (13 en suite) ★ ★ ★
Directions: On A658 Bradford to HarrogateRoad

 anne@apperley-manor.co.uk
Chef(s): Matthew Colley
Owner(s): Anne Hodgson
Cost: Alc £25, set price L £12.50/ D £14.95-£16.95. ☺ ☺ H/wine £9.45
Times: Noon-2.30pm/6-9.30pm.
Additional: Sunday L. Bar food. Children welcome

DEWSBURY Map 8 SE22

Healds Hall Hotel

Leeds Road, Liversedge, WF15 6JA
Tel: 01924 409112
Fax: 01924 401895
 healdshall@ndirect.co.uk
Chef(s): P McVeagh, D Winter
Owner(s): Mr T Harrington
Cost: Alc £25/D £16-£24. ☺ ☺ H/wine £8.50
Times: Noon-2.30pm/6-midnight. Closed L Sat, D Sun (ex residents), BH Mons
Additional: Sunday L. Bar food L. Children welcome. Vegetarian by request only
Seats: 40. Private dining room 30
Style: Modern, Country-house
Smoking: No smoking in dining room; Air conditioning
Accommodation: 24 rooms (24 en suite) ★ ★
Directions: M1 J40, A638, then onto A62, 50yds on L

The hotel is a fine 18th-century building, and the restaurant has recently been re-sited in a comfortable modern space decorated in shades of pale gold. An interesting choice of dishes is offered and the food is capably cooked with an emphasis on presentation. Fillet of turbot and excellent crab dumplings with vibrant steamed vegetables have been amongst the successes.

HALIFAX Map 7 SE02

Holdsworth House Hotel

Holdsworth, HX2 9TG
Tel: 01422 240024
Fax: 01422 245174
 info@holdsworthhouse.co.uk
Chef(s): Neal Birtwell
Owner(s): Gail Moss, Tim Wynn

The juxtaposition of 16th-century elegance and a creatively cosmopolitan approach to cuisine works well. Candlelit intimacy amidst acres of polished woodwork and intriguing antiques is a luxury in itself but also serves to highlight the

England

HALIFAX *Continued*   **Map 7 SE02**

fresh, lively attitude apparent in dishes like beetroot jelly with smooth goats' cheese and a salad of carrot and walnuts. The effort and innovation displayed in such a starter is also reflected in main courses such as caramelised king prawns with bok choi and rice cake (accurate spicing displaying a particular flair for Far Eastern influence), or tournedos with foie gras, pommes Anna and Madeira jus.

Accommodation: 40 rooms (40 en suite) ★ ★ ★
Directions: From Halifax take A629 (Keighley), 2 miles turn R at garage to Holmfield, hotel 1.5 miles on R

Cost: *Alc* £27.25, set price L £13.
☺ ☺ H/wine £11.95
Times: Noon-1.45/7-9.30pm.
Closed L Sat-Sun, Xmas
Additional: Bar food. Children welcome
Seats: 45. Private dining room 120
Style: Traditional, Country-house
Smoking: No smoking in dining room
Civil licence: 120

Shibden Mill   NEW

Cosy inn that steers clear of routine pub food, with its vivid, up-to-date cooking. Seasonal produce shines through strikingly presented dishes prepared by a deft hand with a light touch. Technical skill is evident in simple dishes like succulent roast chicken with spiced cabbage and challenging desserts like chocolate tart with raspberry coulis and Malteser ice cream.

Shibden Mill Fold, Shibden,
HX3 7UL
Tel: 01422 365840
Fax: 01422 362971
✉ shibdenmillinn@zoom.co.uk
Chef(s): Neil Butterworth
Owner(s): Mr J D Heaton
Cost: *Alc* £20. ☺ ☺ H/wine £9.90
Times: Noon-2pm/6-9.30pm.
Closed 25 Dec, D 26 Dec & 31 Dec
Additional: Sunday L. Bar food.
Children welcome
Seats: 39
Style: Rustic
Civil licence: 70
Accommodation: 12 rooms (12 en suite) ♦♦♦♦
Directions: Telephone for directions

The Spring Rock   NEW ⊚

This bright and airy country restaurant delivers stylish contemporary dishes with flair and panache. Honest cooking allows the ingredients to speak for themselves in starters such as 'simply grilled' wild salmon or roast aubergine with peppers and goats' cheese. Main courses might include a ballotine of chicken stuffed with foie gras ('glorious') or chargrilled tuna with garlic sautéed king prawns.

Seats: 36. Private dining room 12
Style: Formal, Modern
Smoking: No smoking in dining room
Directions: 2.5 miles from Elland. 4 miles from M62 J24

Norland Road,
Upper Greetland, HX4 8PT
Tel: 01422 377722
Chef(s): Garry Saunders,
Andrew Riley
Owner(s): Gary Saunders,
Andrew Riley
Cost: *Alc* £23.50/D £13.95. ☺
H/wine £9.45
Times: Dinner only, 5.30-10pm.
Closed Mon, D Sun,
2wks after 26 Dec
Additional: Sunday L. Children welcome

HAWORTH

Map 7 SE03

Weavers Restaurant

Stuffed with bric a brac and strong on Yorkshire cheer, this restaurant occupies three weaver's cottages in the shadow of the Brontë parsonage museum. The food is copious, sourced locally and strong on tradition - expect the likes of steak and chips and steamed salmon with herb butter sauce followed by good old fashioned puddings.

Seats: 65
Style: Chic, Bistro-Style
Smoking: No smoking in dining room; Air conditioning
Accommodation: 3 rooms (3 en suite) ◆◆◆
Directions: From A629 take B6142 to Haworth centre, by Brontë Museum car park

15 West Lane, BD22 8DU
Tel: 01535 643822
Fax: 01535 644832
🄴 colinandjane@aol.com
Chef(s): Colin & Jane Rushworth
Owner(s): Colin & Jane Rushworth
Cost: Alc £25, set price D £15. ☺
H/wine £10.25
Times: Dinner only, 6.30-9pm.
Closed Sun-Mon, 1wk Xmas & 1wk June
Additional: Bar food D. Children welcome

HUDDERSFIELD

Map 7 SE11

The Lodge Hotel

This country house style restaurant may be traditional in terms of décor but specialises in modern British and European cuisine. The seasonally changing menu might include risotto, confit of duck (recommended) or tournedos of wild salmon. Service is attentive and friendly. Don't miss the quality coffee with petits fours.

Seats: 62. Private dining room 20
Style: Country-house
Smoking: No smoking in dining room
Accommodation: 12 rooms (12 en suite) ★ ★
Directions: M62 J24 (Huddersfield), L at 1st lights (Birkby Rd) then A629, R after Nuffield Hospital (Birkby Lodge Rd), 100yds on L

48 Birkby Lodge Road,
Birkby, HD2 2BG
Tel: 01484 431001
Fax: 01484 421590
Chef(s): Richard Hanson
Owner(s): Mr D G & Mr K J Birley
Cost: Alc £14.95, set price L £14.95/D £23.95-£26. ☺ ☺
H/wine £10.95
Times: Noon-2pm/7.30-9.45pm.
Closed L Sat, D Sun, BH Mons
Additional: Sunday L. Children welcome

The Weavers Shed Restaurant

Admirable set-up in this former woollen mill offering a menu of suitably rustic dishes in a setting of rough stone walls and flagstone floors. Much of the herbs, vegetables and fruit comes from their own kitchen garden and these do tend to shine, with radiant, earthy flavours served family-style alongside main-courses such as loin of Worsbrough venison or braised belly pork with its own accompaniment of Savoy cabbage, cider-roast potatoes and cider gravy. Amongst the starters twice-baked Stilton soufflé is a real success and the care extends to excellent bread and peripherals such as a velvety demi-tasse of pumpkin soup served as an amuse. Amongst the puds a baked ginger pudding with Armagnac and ginger sauce is a winner.

Smoking: No pipes; no cigars
Accommodation: 5 rooms (5 en suite) ◆◆◆
Directions: 3 miles W of Huddersfield, off A62

Acre Mill's, Knowl Road,
Golcar HD7 4AN
Tel: 01484 654284
Fax: 01484 650980
🄴 info@weavers-shed.demon.co.uk
Chef(s): I McGunnigle, R Jones, S Jackson, C Sill
Owner(s): Stephen & Tracy Jackson
Cost: Alc £23, set price L £13.95.
☺ ☺ H/wine £12.95
Times: Noon-2pm/7-10pm. Closed Sun, Mon, L Sat, 25 Dec, 31 Dec, 1 Jan, BHs
Additional: Children welcome
Seats: 65. Private dining room 30
Style: Traditional

England

ILKLEY

Map 7 SE14

Box Tree Restaurant

Just before we went to press Toby Hill brought his considerable talents to this special restaurant with its enviable reputation. Quite a combination and although there are no physical changes planned for the restaurant, the menu is likely to make a subtle move to a slightly lighter style whilst retaining many of the elements that it has become famous for. Intensity of flavour looks set to be a defining characteristic in dishes like roast fillet of sea bass with confit fennel and sauce vierge or red mullet with couscous, aubergine and essence of red peppers. Expect ravioli of lobster and coriander to come with super-thin pasta, "crammed to the gunwhales" with shellfish meat and a fathom-deep shellfish sauce. Fillet of Aberdeen Angus accompanied by a satisfying combination of fondant potato, confit shallots and whole garlic. Tarte Tatin here is pronounced "quite excellent" with the fruit just soft enough, terrific caramel and exemplary pastry. All in all an exceptionally encouraging start

35-37 Church Street,
LS29 9DR
Tel: 01943 608484
Fax: 01943 607186
e info@theboxtree.co.uk
Chef(s): Toby Hill
Cost: Alc £27.50, set price L £19.50/ D £19.50. ☺ H/wine £11.50
Times: Noon-2.30pm/7-9.30pm. Closed Mon, D Sun, Xmas-New Year, 1-15 Jan
Additional: Sunday L. Children welcome
Seats: 50. Private dining room 16. Jacket and tie preferred
Style: Formal
Smoking: No smoking in dining room

Directions: On A65, on the Skipton side of Ilkley near the church

Rombalds Hotel

An elegant Georgian townhouse situated on the edge of Ilkley Moor. The last visit found the kitchen in transition, but under a new chef, there are signs of a welcome emphasis on local, top-quality produce. The menu offers a range of elaborate and robust sounding combinations such as a starter of boudin blanc with butternut squash and sage jus or a main course of lamb loin with shitaki polenta and a rosemary jus.

11 West View, Wells Road,
LS29 9JG
Tel: 01943 603201
Fax: 01943 816586
e reception@rombalds.demon.co.uk
Chef(s): Matthew Brown
Owner(s): Colin & Jo Clarkson
Cost: Alc £24, set price L £9.95/ D £12.95-£21.95. ☺ ☺ H/wine £9.95
Times: Noon-2.30pm/6.30-9.30pm.
Additional: Sunday L. Bar food. Children welcome
Seats: 34. Private dining room 50
Style: Modern
Smoking: No smoking in dining room
Civil licence: 70
Accommodation: 15 rooms (15 en suite) ★ ★ ★

Directions: From Leeds take A65 to Ilkley. At 2nd lights turn L & follow signs for Ilkley Moor. At junction take Wells Rd, by HSBC bank. Hotel 600yds on L

KEIGHLEY

Map 7 SE04

The Harlequin Restaurant NEW

What a find! Slick service, cosmopolitan menus, and a stylish dining venue. An autumn lunch kicked off with freshly prepared prawn and vegetable spring rolls served with a sprightly nouccham dip. A traditional main course of "impressively tender" slow roasted lamb shank and a warm bitter chocolate fondant won praise, as did the value for money.

139 Keighley Road, Cowling, BD22 0AH
Tel: 01535 633277
Fax: 01535 633927
Chef(s): Terry Lee
Owner(s): Mr & Mrs S Robinson
Cost: Alc £25, set price L £12.50.
☺ ☺ H/wine £10.50
Times: Noon-2pm/6.30-9.30pm.
Closed Wed-Sun, Xmas for 4 days
Additional: Sunday L. Bar food. Children 6yrs+ at D. Vegetarian by request only

Seats: 42
Style: Modern
Smoking: No smoking in dining room
Directions: On A6068 in the village of Cowing, between Crosshills and Colne. (6 miles from M65)

LEEDS

Map 8 SE23

Brasserie Forty Four

44 The Calls, LS2 7EW
Tel: 0113 234 3232
Fax: 0113 234 3332
Chef(s): Jeff Baker
Owner(s): Michael Gill
Cost: Alc £23, set price L £12.25/ D £12.25. ☺ ☺ H/wine £10.65
Times: Noon-2pm/6-11pm.
Closed Sun, L Sat, BHs
Additional: Children welcome
Seats: 110. Private dining room 50
Style: Modern, Bistro Style
Smoking: No pipes; no cigars; Air conditioning

Converted from a redundant grain store in a trendy, regenerated area of the city, Brasserie Forty Four is a fun place to eat, with off-the-wall interior design and a vast collection of cookery books arrayed in glass cases. An engaging menu ranges through Catalan mussel broth, sweet onion and Parmesan tart, and griddled calves' liver on candied turnip. An excellent piece of the freshest Whitby cod comes simply cooked and served on a purée of fresh minted peas accompanied by gaufrette potatoes and a thin cordon of aged vinegar. Fish, chips and mushy peas as it's rarely seen in this part of Yorkshire.

Directions: From Crown Point Bridge, L past Church, L into High Court Road. On the river

Brio NEW

St George House, St George Street,
Tel: 0113 246 5225
Telephone for further details

'Brio' literally means brilliant, and both the vibrant décor and the trendy cooking live up to the name. This is punchy Italian food along the lines of fried polenta with proscuitto and dolcelatte, or linguini with Sardinian bottarga. Chocolate budino (like brownies) is a typical dessert.

England

Fourth Floor Café at Harvey Nichols

107/111 Briggate, LS1 6AZ
Tel: 0113 204 8000
Fax: 0113 204 8080
e simonpreston@harveynichols.co.uk
Chef(s): Richard Allen
Owner(s): Harvey Nichols and Co Ltd
Cost: *Alc* £26, set price L £16/
D £18. ☺ ☺
Times: Noon-3pm/6-10.30pm.
Closed D Sun-Wed, 25-26 Dec, 1 Jan
Additional: Sunday L. Bar food D.
Children welcome
Seats: 80
Style: Modern
Smoking: No-smoking area;
Air conditioning
Directions: In Harvey Nichols
department store

Take the sophisticated styling of this modern dining venue, add the slick, quick draw service of the well-heeled staff and prepare to be propelled into a theatre of abandoned short-order cooking. Reckless partnerships like seared halibut with roasted pork belly, and scallops with spiced aubergine and chilli dressing, create a frisson of excitement, along with a creditable banana Tatin.

Guellers   NEW

After a brief closure, Guellers reopened just as we went to press. Simon Gueller (well-known for his considerable achievements at Rascasse) is now firmly ensconced at the stove and has introduced new menus based on his style of modern classical cuisine with a particular emphasis on fish and shellfish. Deceptively simple dishes with authentic Mediterranean flavours look set to be the order of the day.

3 York Place, LS1 2DR
Tel: 0113 245 9922
Telephone for further details

Haley's Hotel

Shire Oak Road,
Headingley, LS6 2DE
Tel: 0113 278 4446
Fax: 0113 275 3342

Reminiscent of a Country House, yet within the city and close to the cricket ground, this conversion of a Victorian terrace is hidden away in a tree-lined cul-de-sac. There is nothing shy, however, about its confident and contemporary approach to food. Seared scallops, slightly charred and warmed through to the middle, were superb, whilst game pudding was "lip-smacking", with a well-flavoured jus and Parisienne potatoes. Consistency and flavour were evident in a hazlenut and coffee parfait. Well-crafted petits fours too.

Style: Modern, Country-house
Smoking: No smoking in dining room; Air conditioning
Civil licence: 52
Accommodation: 29 rooms (29 en suite) ★ ★ ★
Directions: 2m N of city centre off A660, between HSBC and Yorkshire Banks

 info@haleys.co.uk
Chef(s): Jon Vennell
Owner(s): John Appleyard
Cost: Alc £35, set price L £13.50/ D £25. ☺ ☺ H/wine £13.25
Times: Noon-2pm/7-9.30pm. Closed L Mon-Sat, D Sun, 26-30 Dec
Additional: Sunday L. Children welcome
Seats: 52. Private dining room 24. Jacket and tie preferred

Leeds Marriott

This is a large, modern hotel in a pedestrianised square in the city centre. The restaurant operation is now focused solely on the informal John T's where the menu is modern and fairly simple. Duck confit with crisp skin and tasty, tender meat works well with a sharp balsamic dressed salad.

4 Trevelyan Square,
Boar Lane, LS1 6ET
Tel: 0113 236 6366
Fax: 0113 236 6367
Telephone for further details

Pool Court at 42

With its gracefully cool interior, gleaming chrome and pale blond surfaces, the restaurant echoes a certain Milan-style chic and shares the same cool, sophisticated feel as the adjoining hotel, 42 The Calls, despite being independently operated. Menus provide a wide ranging choice; there is the tasting menu of seven imaginative courses, a *carte* containing up to five choices at each course with commendable focus on local produce, and speciality luncheon menus featuring a selection of Jeff Baker's favourite dishes. He cooks boldly, with some complex dishes that occasionally find flavours fighting for dominance. Typical is a starter of Whitby crabmeat canneloni with langoustine, pineapple and vanilla jus and a main dish comprising poached corn-fed chicken, timbale of chicken and foie gras, truffle fumet and sweetcorn kernels. Service is slick and some fine labels of global wine offer genuine value for money.

44 The Calls, LS2 7EW
Tel: 0113 244 4242
Fax: 0113 234 3332
 poolcourt@onetel.net.uk
Chef(s): Jeff Baker
Owner(s): Michael Gill
Cost: Set price L £19/D £30-£50. ☺ H/wine £11.45
Times: Noon-2pm/7-10pm. Closed Sun, L Sat, BHs
Additional: Children 3yr+
Seats: 38
Style: Chic, Minimalist
Smoking: No smoking in dining room; Air conditioning
Directions: From M1 follow A61 (Harrogate) into city centre, cross River Aire via Crown Point Bridge. 2nd L at rdbt on to Maude St and then The Calls

England

Rascasse

Named after an essential ingredient of bouillabaisse, Rascasse is a stylish, split-level restaurant housed in an old granary warehouse. Smooth wooden floors, linen covered tables and brightly upholstered chairs provide the perfect backdrop for the modern French based cooking. A meal might begin with confit of pig's cheek with choucroute coleslaw and cockle pickle, followed by magret of duck with ravioli, savoy cabbage, pear and vanilla purée. Equally stylish desserts could include a croquante of white chocolate and redcurrant with pineapple and raspberry ravioli and blackcurrant jus or caramelised peach tarte Tatin with honeycomb and clove ice cream.

Directions: 0.5 mile from M621 J3; follow signs to city centre, turn L Water Lane, then R on Canal Wharf. On Canal Basin. 4 min walk from railway station

Canal Wharf, Water Lane,
LS11 5PS
Tel: 0113 244 6611
Fax: 0113 244 0736
Chef(s): John Lyons
Owner(s): Nigel Jolliffe
Cost: *Alc* £32, set price L £18/D £18.
☺ ☺ H/wine £12
Times: Noon-2pm/6.30-10.30pm.
Closed Sun, L Sat, BH Mons,
Xmas, 1wk after Xmas
Additional: Children welcome
Seats: 100
Style: Modern, French
Smoking: No pipes; Air conditioning

Shear's Yard

Lively, fun dining in a converted riverside chandlery. Exposed brick walls, stone floors, an open fire and a large outdoor terrace make for an excellent venue to enjoy sound modern cooking such as pear, rocket and Parmesan tart served with a tomato fondue. A Tapas style menu is a welcome additional option.

Directions: From M1 follow signs for City Centre Loop. Cross over Crown Point Bridge & L for Waterfront. Restaurant on R at J15 of the Loop

The Calls, LS2 7EY
Tel: 0113 244 4144
Fax: 0113 244 8102
🄴 shearsyard@ydg.co.uk
Chef(s): Daniel Janes
Owner(s): Rob Noble &
Peter Connolly
Cost: *Alc* £23, set price L £13.95-
£20.95/D £13.95-£20.95. ☺ ☺
H/wine £11.95
Times: Noon-2.30pm/6-10.30pm.
Closed Sun, 1 wk Xmas, BH Mons
Additional: Bar food. Children
welcome
Seats: 70
Style: Rustic, Bistro-Style
Smoking: No-smoking area; Air
conditioning
Civil licence: 150

The finest wine lists

The AA wine awards recognise some of the finest wine lists in the country. As well as the winners for England, Scotland and Wales you will find this symbol throughout the guide indicating those restaurants who reached the final shortlist and others that were recognised for their excellence in specialist areas. The AA wine awards are sponsored by T&W wines of Thetford.

England

Teatro Leeds   NEW   ⊕⊕

Lesley Ash and Lee Chapman's modern and minimalist L-shaped restaurant in a stunning riverside location with windows overlooking a large terrace used for al fresco dining. Cuisine is modern European with one or two fusion influences and several adventurous combinations. Thinly sliced Parma ham is served with piccalilli and a poached egg, whilst sweet braised suckling pig comes with noodles, Pak Choi and shiitake mushrooms. Crème brûlée with Granny Smith sorbet is particularly impressive - great brûlée with good consistency and a nice thin crispy topping, and a blissful sorbet with a delightfully clear flavour. A strong selection of fine wines too.

The Quays,
Concordia Street,
LS1 4BJ
Tel: 0113 243 6699
Fax: 0113 243 2244
✉ teatro@teatroleeds.co.uk
Chef(s): Mark Anderson
Owner(s): Lee Chapman & Lesley Ash
Cost: Alc £26, set price L £13/D £13. ☺ ☺ H/wine £13.50
Times: Noon-3pm/9-10.45pm. Closed Xmas, BHs
Additional: Sunday L. Children welcome
Seats: 120. Private dining room 30
Style: Modern, Chic
Smoking: No pipes; Air conditioning
Directions: Telephone for directions

TODMORDEN   Map 7 SD92

The Old Hall   NEW   ⊕

Unlike many restaurants that bear little resemblance to their name the Old Hall is quite simply a hall that is old, but has recently been rejuvenated by a stylish, eclectic refurbishment. Cooking is strikingly straightforward - try black pudding with poached egg and chorizo or crispy duck and watercress salad.

OL14 7AD
Tel: 01706 815998
Fax: 01706 810669
Chef(s): Chris Roberts
Owner(s): Nick & Madeleine Hoyle
Cost: Alc £24. ☺ ☺ H/wine £10.50
Times: Noon-2pm/7-9.30pm. Closed Mon, D Sun, 25 Dec, 1 Jan, 1st wk Jan
Additional: Sunday L. Children welcome
Seats: 70. Private dining room 24
Style: Modern, Country-house
Smoking: No-smoking area; no pipes
Civil licence: 60
Directions: Near centre of town, up Hall St

WENTBRIDGE

Map 8 SE41

Wentbridge House Hotel

WF8 3JJ
Tel: 01977 620 444
Fax: 01977 620 148
e info@wentbridgehouse.co.uk
Chef(s): Steven Turner
Owner(s): Mr G Page
Cost: *Alc* £30, set price L £14.95/
D £23. ☺ ☺ H/wine £12.50
Times: 12.15-2pm/7.15-9.30pm.
Closed L 31 Dec, D 25 Dec
Additional: Sunday L. Bar food.
Children welcome
Seats: 60. Private dining room 24.
Jacket and tie preferred
Style: Classic, Country-house
Smoking: No pipes
Accommodation: 18 rooms (18 en
suite) ★ ★ ★
Directions: 0.5 mile off A1,
4 miles S of M62/A1 junction

Wentbridge house dates from 1700, two elegant rooms combine to form the wood-panelled restaurant. Traditional/classical cuisine in dishes such as steamed sea bass and mussels with lemongrass broth, braised endive and pasta or marinated venison with a parsnip and celeriac gratin. Chargrills also available.

WETHERBY

Map 8 SE44

Wood Hall Hotel

Trip Lane, Linton, LS22 4JA
Tel: 01937 587271
Fax: 01937 584353
e events.woodhall@arcadianhotels.
co.uk
Chef(s): Phillip Pomfret
Cost: *Alc* £32, set price L £15.95/
D £24.95. ☺ H/wine £12.50
Times: Noon-2pm/7-10pm.
Closed L Sat
Additional: Sunday L. Bar food.
Children welcome. Vegetarian by
request only
Seats: 35. Private dining room 100
Style: Country-house
Smoking: No smoking in dining room
Civil licence: 120

Destroyed in the civil war then rebuilt on its present site, all that remains of the original Wood Hall is the coat of arms in the entrance hall to this Georgian mansion. Its smart restaurant offers crisp white tablecloths, oil paintings and an open fire. Challenging classical dishes - such as an authentic fillet Rossini (something of a rarity) served with a foie gras parfait, are well executed. The same goes for more modern interpretations: red bream with chilli couscous and lime dressing, or roast salmon fillet with ratatouille vegetables, Thai crab cake and tomato olive oil. Good quality coffee and petits fours.

Accommodation: 43 rooms (43 en suite) ★ ★ ★
Directions: In town, take turning opposite Windmill pub signed Wood Hall and Linton

CHANNEL ISLANDS
GUERNSEY

CATEL   Map 16

Cobo Bay Hotel

A very popular hotel, not least for the lovely views of Cobo Bay that can be enjoyed from the balconies, restaurant and sun terrace. The Chesterfield bar (fully equipped with leather sofas and armchairs) is a relaxing place to begin an evening, served by a friendly, dedicated team of staff. The restaurant delivers an imaginative menu, which successfully combines the best of British and French cuisine. A meal might include oven baked brie with apple and prune compôte and a port wine sauce, followed by grilled medallions of beef on a spring onion and chive champ with a Guinness and grain mustard jus and confit of roasted baby onions.

Accommodation: 36 rooms (36 en suite)
Directions: From St Peter Port follow signs for Castel/Cobo/West Coast. At coast road turn R, Hotel 100m on R. Or from airport turn R, follow road to west coast, turn R for Cobo (approx 5 miles)

Cobo, GY5 7HB
Tel: 01481 257102
Fax: 01481 54542
e info@cobobayhotel.com
Chef(s): John Chapman
Owner(s): Mr D Nussbaumer
Cost: Alc £22-£18.50. ☺ ☺
H/wine £9
Times: Noon-2pm/7-9.30pm.
Closed L Mon-Sat,
Additional: Sunday L.
Children welcome
Seats: 120
Style: Modern, Classic
Smoking: Air conditioning

La Grand Mare Hotel

The Coast Road, Vazon Bay, GY5 7LL
Tel: 01481 256576
Fax: 01481 256532
Chef(s): Fergus Mackay
Owner(s): Vermeulen Family
Cost: Alc £25, set price L £12.95/D £19.95. ☺ ☺ H/wine £8.95
Times: noon-2pm/7-9.30pm.
Additional: Sunday L. Bar food L.
Children welcome
Seats: 70. Private dining room 30.
Jacket and tie preferred
Style: Classic

Emphasis on freshness and quality of produce rather than ostentatious construction. For instance - top quality king prawns simply cooked with garlic and lime butter and a simple mixed leaf accompaniment and a selection of al dente vegetables. The restaurant is fairly formal, though the conservatory area makes for a slightly more relaxed alternative.

Smoking: No-smoking area
Accommodation: 34 rooms (34 en suite)
Directions: 15 mins from both St Peter Port and the airport. Hotel is opposite Vazon Bay

England

Map 16

L'Atlantique Hotel

Perelle Bay, GY7 9NA
Tel: 01481 264056
Fax: 01481 63800
e patrick@perellebay.com
Chef(s): Richard Torode
Owner(s): Mr P K Lindley
Cost: *Alc* £24.50, set price L £13/
D £18.50. ☺ ☺ H/wine £8.85
Times: Noon-1.45pm/6.30-9.30pm.
Closed L Mon-Sat, 1 Jan-end Mar
Additional: Sunday L.
Children welcome
Seats: 50
Style: Modern, Classic
Smoking: No-smoking area; no pipes;
no cigars

Enjoy the sight and sound of the sea from this modern hotel, set in its own landscaped grounds beside the bay. Restaurant L'Atlantique is a traditionally decorated restaurant with beautiful views and a menu which neatly combines French, local and modern cuisine: dishes might include roast noisettes of English lamb with a tarragon and port wine reduction, served with gratin dauphinoise potatoes and aubergine and red pepper compôte. Also look out for supreme of chicken chargrilled with thyme and honey, served on steamed couscous with stir fried vegetables and a sweet chilli dressing.

Accommodation: 21 rooms (21 en suite) ★ ★ ★
Directions: Off West coast road overlooking Perelle Bay

Map 16

La Barbarie Hotel

Dating from the 17th century, this former priory combines modern comforts with carefully preserved character and charm. The beamed restaurant offers a wide range of dishes, from pan seared calves' liver with onion mash to pork tenderloin on wild rice with buttered Savoy cabbage and a balsamic jus.

Seats: 80. **Smoking:** No smoking in dining room
Accommodation: 23 rooms (23 en suite) ★ ★ ★
Directions: At traffic lights in St Martin take road to Saints Bay – hotel is on R at end of Saints Road

Saints Road, Saints Bay, GY4 6ES
Tel: 01481 235217
Fax: 01481 35208
e barbarie@guernsey.net
Chef(s): David Hayden
Cost: *Alc* £18, set price L £16/
D £16. ☺ H/wine £8.95
Times: Noon-2pm/6.15-9.30pm.
Additional: Sunday L. Bar food L.
Children welcome. Vegetarian by
request only

Idlerocks Hotel

From its cliff-top location, this family run hotel enjoys sea views of islands and the French coast. The choice of dining options includes Admirals restaurant, where the menu offers familiar but welcome combinations such as braised steak with root vegetables or grilled salmon with string beans and dill sauce.

Seats: 60. Private dining room 80. **Style:** Classic, Traditional
Smoking: No smoking in dining room
Accommodation: 28 rooms (28 en suite) ★ ★ ★
Directions: 5 mins drive from St Peter Port on main road

Jerbourg Point, GY4 6BJ
Tel: 01481 237711
Fax: 01481 35592
e info@idlerocks.com
Owner(s): Jan Hamill
Cost: Set price D £15.50. ☺ ☺
H/wine £9.90
Times: Noon-2pm/6.30-9pm.
Additional: Sunday L. Bar food.
Children welcome

St Margaret's Lodge

A popular hotel with many regular guests returning for both the quality of service and of the food. The menu has imaginatively presented traditional dishes using high quality ingredients - such as pan-fried local plaice with chives and white wine sauce, roasted Mediterranean tart with tarragon cream or chicken Milanese with tomato concasse and homemade pesto

Smoking: No smoking in dining room
Accommodation: 47 rooms (47 en suite)
Directions: Out of airport, turn L. Follow road for 1 mile. Hotel on L

Forest Road, GY4 6UE
Tel: 01481 235757
Fax: 01481 237594
🄴 smhotel@gtonline.net
Owner(s): C Stefani
Cost: Alc £29.50, set price L £15.95/ D £15.95. ☺ ☺ H/wine £9.50
Times: Noon-2.30pm/6.30-9.30pm.
Additional: Sunday L. Bar food. Children welcome
Seats: 80. Private dining room 100
Style: Traditional

ST PETER PORT Map 16

Da Nello

Popular Italian fish restaurant offering honest cooking, value for money and a relaxed ambience. A conservatory piazza has attractively extended the 500-year-old property. There are plenty of 'catches of the day' and a few chef's specials in addition to the extensive menu. Creditable efforts have included a good risotto with mushrooms and king prawn tails.

46 La Pollet, GY1 1WF
Tel: 01481 721552
Fax: 01481 724235
Chef(s): Tim Vidamour
Owner(s): Nello Ciotti
Cost: Set price L £10/D £17. ☺ ☺ H/wine £8.95
Times: Noon-2pm/6.30-10pm.
Additional: Sunday L. Children welcome
Seats: 90. Private dining room 20. Jacket and tie preferred
Style: Modern
Smoking: No-smoking area; no pipes; no cigars; Air conditioning
Directions: In town centre, 100yds from North beach car park.

La Frégate

Packed to the gunwhales on the likes of a wet and windy Tuesday night has to be some kind of recommendation.

continued

Les Cotils, GY1 1UT
Tel: 01481 724624
Fax: 01481 720443
🄴 lafregate@guernsey.net
Chef(s): Neil Maginnis
Owner(s): GSH Ltd
Cost: Alc £23, set price L £14.50/ D £20. ☺ ☺ H/wine £9.50
Times: L from 12.15/7-9.30pm.
Additional: Sunday L. Children 10yrs+
Seats: 70. Private dining room 30. Jacket and tie preferred
Style: Modern, Minimalist
Smoking: No pipes; no cigars; Air conditioning
Accommodation: 13 rooms (13 en suite) ★ ★ ★
Directions: Town centre, above St Julian's Avenue

ST PETER PORT *Continued*   Map 16

Spectacular views over Guernsey's capital are only part of the picture and it's the French biased cuisine that is winning many friends in a restaurant that manages to offer sea views from every table. On the food front it's the sea that dominates too with a truly classic lobster bisque (real chunks of lobster!) making up for the many disappointing examples to be found elsewhere. Top-notch sea bass has featured in combination with a mushroom duxelle and parsley crust - Dover sole, skate and plaice are also available with a choice of both cooking methods and sauces (a similar model applies for fillet steak too). The mix and match philosophy extends to a choice of around a dozen vegetables available as side orders. Pastry is a strength - caramelised carpaccio of pineapple with in a sweet pastry case with cinnamon ice cream being a prime example.

Merchant House Restaurant

Elegant 18th-century restaurant overlooking the High Street. A menu of gluten-free and dairy-free dishes has been introduced in addition to existing vegetarian and vegan alternatives. The general menu is varied, with options such as Cretan chicken, hot seafood melange, and chargrilled venison.

Additional: Bar food L. Children 6yrs+. Vegetarian by request only
Seats: 54. Private dining room 20
Style: Classic, Country-house
Smoking: No-smoking area. **Accommodation:** 2 rooms
Directions: Telephone for directions

38 High Street, GY1 2JU
Tel: 01481 728019
Fax: 01481 725875
e davidandgina@merchant-house.org.uk
Chef(s): David Mann
Owner(s): Mr & Mrs D Mann
Cost: *Alc* £26, set price L £13.50/ D £15.50. ☺ ☺ H/wine £10.50
Times: Noon-1.45pm/7-9.30pm. Closed Sun (winter only)

Le Nautique Restaurant

This converted stone warehouse enjoys a romantic seaside setting. The understated dining room offers an extensive, modern menu: a whole page of fish dishes might include Guernsey brill topped with a ragout of scampi, scallops and prawns in a light beurre blanc, whilst meat eaters might enjoy confit roast half duckling with caramelised apples and Calvados sauce.

Quay Steps, GY1 2LE
Tel: 01481 721714
Fax: 01481 721786
Chef(s): Gunter Botzenhardt
Owner(s): Gunter Botzenhardt
Cost: *Alc* £22, set price L £14.50/ D £20. ☺ ☺ H/wine £9.80
Times: Noon-2pm/6.30-10pm. Closed Sun, L Sat
Additional: Children welcome
Seats: 56. Private dining room 30
Style: Traditional
Smoking: No-smoking area; Air conditioning
Directions: Sea front opposite Harbour and Victoria Marina

Old Government House Hotel

When you visit this spacious, traditionally furnished restaurant, nearby France makes its presence felt in a good and well-described wine list and professional French staff. The quality of

Ann's Place, GY1 4AZ
Tel: 01481 724921
Fax: 01481 724429
e ogh@guernsey.net

the food is demonstrated by light ravioli filled with fresh lobster, French beans with a saffron and spring onion velouté followed by sea bass with good vegetables and a very fresh crème brûlée.

Seats: 130. Private dining room 20. Jacket and tie preferred
Style: Classic, Formal
Smoking: No-smoking area; no pipes; no cigars
Accommodation: 68 rooms (68 en suite) ★ ★ ★ ★
Directions: Telephone for directions

Chef(s): Kevin Buckley
Owner(s): Kenneth W McVey
Cost: *Alc* £25.75, set price D £18.75.
☺ ☺ H/wine £9.50
Times: Noon-2.30pm/7-10pm.
Closed L Mon-Sat
Additional: Sunday L. Bar food.
Children welcome

St Pierre Park Hotel

⊛⊛
Rohais, GY1 1FD
Tel: 01481 728282
Fax: 01481 712041
e enquiries@stpierrepark.co.uk
Chef(s): Austin Mitchell,
Kevin Hyde
Owner(s): Ann Street Brewery
Cost: *Alc* £28, set price L £12.50-
£14.50/D £19.50-£21.50. ☺ ☺
H/wine £10.50
Times: Noon-2.15pm/7-10.15pm.
Closed D Sun
Additional: Sunday L. Bar food.
Children welcome.
Vegetarian by request only
Seats: 70. Private dining room 24.
Jacket and tie preferred

A bold colour scheme adds a real element of luxury to this formal dining room. Further glamour is provided by the adjoining bar terrace overlooking an elegant water feature. A kitchen well skilled in classical techniques offers the likes of mosaic of fresh salmon and red mullet with fine beans and baby leeks set in a saffron jelly as tempting starters. Mains might include mille-feuille of skate wing with caper mash, crab and coriander mousse, and fresh plum tomato oil, or asparagus spears and poached egg glazed with a tarragon Hollandaise on an English muffin.

Style: Traditional
Smoking: No smoking in dining room
Accommodation: 131 rooms (131 en suite) ★ ★ ★ ★
Directions: 1 mile from town centre on route to west coast

The Absolute End

For a full-on seafood experience, The Absolute End is appropriately located ten yards from the Guernsey seafront. In addition to their extensive selection of fish dishes (plaice fillets baked with almonds, scampi provençale in a rich tomato sauce with garlic), they offer both vegetarian and meat options (veal escalopes a la crème).

Smoking: No-smoking area; no pipes; no cigars;
Air conditioning
Civil licence: 50
Directions: Less than 1 mile from town centre, going N on seafront road to St Sampson

Longstore, GY1 2BG
Tel: 01481 723822
Fax: 01481 729129
Chef(s): Antonio Folmi
Owner(s): Antonio Folmi
Cost: *Alc* £24, set price L £12.50.
☺ ☺
Times: Noon-2pm/7-10pm.
Closed Sun, Jan
Additional: Children welcome
Seats: 55. Private dining room 22
Style: Modern

England

HERM

HERM
Map 16

White House Hotel

⬡
GY1 3HR
Tel: 01481 722159
Fax: 01481 710066
✉ hotel@herm.island.com
Chef(s): Chris Walder
Owner(s): Sue Hester
Cost: Set price L £12.50-£17.50/ D £19.75-£21. ☺ ☺ H/wine £9.10
Times: 12.30-1.30pm/7-9pm. Closed Oct-Apr

Just a twenty minute boat ride from Guernsey, this attractive hotel enjoys a unique harbour setting with superb sea views. Savour these from the Conservatory restaurant, where dishes might include seared salmon with king prawns on saffron mash with a green pea sauce, or tournedos of beef fillet béarnaise on bubble and squeak with field mushroom and a truffled port wine sauce.

Additional: Sunday L. Bar food L. Children welcome
Seats: 100. Jacket and tie preferred
Style: Traditional, Formal
Smoking: No smoking in dining room
Accommodation: 39 rooms (39 en suite) ★★
Directions: By regular boat from St Peters Port, Guernsey

JERSEY

GOREY
Map 16

Jersey Pottery Restaurant

⬡⬡
Gorey Village, JE3 9EP
Tel: 01534 851119
Fax: 01534 856403
✉ admin@jerseypottery.com
Chef(s): Tony Dorris
Owner(s): Jones Family
Cost: A/c £23, set price L £14.50. ☺ H/wine £11.75
Times: Lunch only, noon-5.30pm. Closed Mon, Xmas 10 days
Additional: Sunday L. Bar food L. Children welcome.
Vegetarian by request only
Seats: 180. Private dining room 100
Style: Modern

Seafood platters so big you can hardly see your dinner partner are a speciality of this restaurant. Located in a vine-covered conservatory, it's packed with interesting pottery and features busy, helpful staff. Whilst modern seafood is the speciality, meat eaters should be satisfied by dishes such as pan-fried calves' liver or horseradish and peppered fillet steak with chips. Fish dishes range from pan-fried salmon fillet to grilled lobster with lemon, thyme and garlic butter. A huge array of desserts is displayed buffet-style for you to pick your own, and might include a tasty, fudge textured chocolate tart.

Smoking: No-smoking area; no pipes
Directions: In Gorey village, well signposted from main coast road

---

☺ Indicates a restaurant that has told us they offer a two-course lunch for less than £15

☺ Indicates a restaurant that has told us they offer a three-course dinner for less than £25

Suma's

Drop the anchor of your luxury yacht into the tranquil waters of Gorey harbour and enter a whitewashed vision of a restaurant for good food, wine and service. Yacht or not, you can take advantage of some accomplished modern British cooking. The scallops are superb - beautifully sweet and reverentially cooked. A high standard, matched by mains such as roast rump of lamb with a risotto of woodland mushrooms and desserts like dark chocolate fondant with rhubarb and peanut butter ice cream.

Gorey Hill, JE3 6ET
Tel: 01534 853291
Fax: 01534 851913
Chef(s): Shaun Rankin
Owner(s): Ms S Dufty & Mr M Lewis
Cost: Alc £30.50, set price L £16.50.
☺ ☺ H/wine £8.75
Times: Noon-2.30pm/6.30-10pm.
Closed D Sun (in winter only), 20 Dec-20 Jan
Additional: Sunday L.
Children welcome
Seats: 45
Style: Modern
Smoking: Air conditioning
Directions: Take A3 E from St Helier to Gorey. Restaurant 100yds before harbour on L

The Village Bistro

A delightfully informal restaurant with summer dining on the terrace, and good value eating all year round. The menu offers honest, straightforward cooking with plenty of natural flavours, served on polished tables against a backdrop of moons, stars and suns. Woodland mushroom risotto with rocket and Parmesan crisp might be followed by crispy duck leg confit with dauphinoise potatoes, bordelaise sauce, and a separate panache of vegetables. Sticky toffee pudding with vanilla ice cream was a delicious recent pudding, and espresso contains a generous hit of caffeine. A broad-reaching wine list includes a director's choice offering more expensive wines.

Gorey Village, JE3 9EP
Tel: 01534 853429
Telephone for further details

England

ROZEL BAY
Map 16

Château La Chaire

Rozel Bay, JE3 6AJ
Tel: 01534 863354
Fax: 01534 865137
e res@chateau-la-chaire.co.uk
Chef(s): Simon Walker
Owner(s): Hiscox Family
Cost: *Alc* £27.50, set price L £14.95/
D £27.50. ☺ ☺ H/wine £11.25
Times: noon-2pm/7-9.30pm.
Additional: Sunday L. Bar food L.
Children welcome
Seats: 60. Private dining room 28.
Jacket and tie preferred
Style: Country-house

Built as a gentleman's residence in 1843, Château La Chaire stands on the side of a wooded valley surrounded by five acres of terraced gardens. The interior retains plenty of country house charm, including some exquisite decorative plasterwork in the drawing room and a distinguished, oak panelled restaurant. The wide ranging menu includes classics - perhaps roast partridge with a girolle and roast shallot sauce - alongside internationally influenced dishes such as crispy confit duck with wok fried vegetables and oriental sauce or roast red mullet with pak choi, noodles and soy dressing.

Smoking: No-smoking area; no pipes
Accommodation: 14 rooms (14 en suite) ★ ★ ★
Directions: From St Helier NE towards Five Oaks, Maufant, then St Martin's Church & Rozel; 1st L in village, hotel 100 metres

ST AUBIN
Map 16

Somerville Hotel

Mont du Boulevard,
JE3 8AD
Tel: 01534 741226
Fax: 01534 746621
e somerville@dolanhotels.com
Chef(s): Martin Colis
Owner(s): Mr W Dolan
Cost: *Alc* £17, set price L £9.95-
£14.05/D £13-£17. ☺ ☺
H/wine £10.95
Times: 12.30-2pm/7-9pm.
Additional: Sunday L. Bar food L.
Children welcome. Vegetarian by
request only. **Seats:** 120
Style: Classic, Country-house
Smoking: No smoking in dining room;
Air conditioning
Accommodation: 59 rooms (59 en
suite) ★ ★ ★
Directions: From village follow
harbour, then take Mont du
Boulevard

Picture windows in the bar and restaurant make the most of spectacular views over St Aubin's bay. The menu offers four courses of imaginative cooking: familiar favourites might include fillet of salmon on a sauce of garden herbs, whilst global influences are seen in dishes such as breast of chicken on capsicum rice with a red Thai curry sauce.

ST BRELADE Map 16

The Atlantic Hotel

Le Mont de la Pulente, JE3 8HE
Tel: 01534 744101
Fax: 01534 744102
e info@theatlantichotel.com
Chef(s): Ken Healy
Owner(s): Patrick Burke
Cost: Alc £35, set price L £17.50/ D £30. ☺ H/wine £10.50
Times: L from 12.45pm/7.30pm-late. Closed Jan-Feb
Additional: Sunday L. Children welcome
Seats: 80. Private dining room 24. Jacket and tie preferred
Style: Classic, Formal
Smoking: No-smoking area; no pipes; no cigars

Quality and comfort are priorities in this recently refurbished hotel. The restaurant looks over gardens to the sea and offers a genuinely inspiring dining experience. All the staff are true professionals: the sommelier has excellent knowledge of his list, whilst the chef delivers assured, modern dishes such as pan-fried fillet of salmon on avocado guacomole with soya jus or duo of lamb and venison fillets with braised turnips and green peppercorn sauce. The pastry team are 'very much on the ball' so it's well worth sampling desserts such as chocolate tart with raspberry coulis or hot lemon soufflé.

Accommodation: 50 rooms (50 en suite) ★ ★ ★ ★
Directions: From St Brelade take the road to Petit Port, turn into Rue de Sergente and R again, signed to hotel

Hotel la Place

Route Du Coin, La Haule, JE3 8BT
Tel: 01534 744261
Fax: 01534 745164
e hotlaplace@aol.com
Chef(s): Robert McKillop
Cost: Alc £31. ☺ ☺ H/wine £12.75
Times: Noon-2.30pm/7.30-9.30pm. Closed L Mon-Sat
Additional: Sunday L. Bar food L. Children welcome

A peaceful hotel, centred around a 17th-century farmhouse in attractive landscaped gardens. The restaurant is a traditionally styled room with well spaced linen covered tables and comfortable seating. The menu has more than a hint of the modern: dishes such as pan-fried prawn creole might feature alongside familiar combinations such as roasted sirloin of beef with Yorkshire pudding or grilled halibut steak with buttered spinach, lemon and coriander butter. Dishes are consistently

ST BRELADE *Continued*   Map 16

well executed, attractively presented and make use of high quality ingredients. The wine list offers a comprehensive selection of French and New World wines.

Accommodation: 42 rooms (42 en suite) ★★★★
Directions: Telephone for directions

Seats: 80. Private dining room 50
Style: Traditional
Smoking: No smoking in dining room

Sea Crest Hotel

The sea can be heard as well as seen from this small modern hotel, situated in the secluded bay of Petit Port. The smart restaurant enjoys a high local reputation and makes particularly good use of local produce especially seafood. Although the menu has a modern feel it does not lose touch with tradition: dishes might include half a crispy duck with red cabbage, a sweetcorn pancake, fondant potato and a honey and lavender sauce or grilled turbot with wilted spinach, button onions, mushrooms, lardons and a red wine sauce. Welcoming staff and pretty garden views add to the relaxing atmosphere.

Accommodation: 7 rooms (6 en suite) ★★★
Directions: From Red Houses follow Route Orange, A13 to hotel, on R at bottom of dip

La Route Du Petit Port, JE3 8HH
Tel: 01534 746353
Fax: 01534 747316
🅔 seacrest@super.net.uk
Owner(s): Mr J Bernstein
Cost: *Alc* £38, set price L £15.50/ D £25. H/wine £11.75
Times: 12.30-2pm/7.30-10pm. Closed Mon, D Sun Oct-Apr
Additional: Sunday L. Bar food L. Children welcome
Seats: 60. Jacket and tie preferred
Style: Classic, Chic
Smoking: No pipes; no cigars; Air conditioning

Star Grill – Hotel L'Horizon

Overlooking the golden sands of St Brelade's Bay, the location of L'Horizon is superb. There are three restaurants and the option of eating al fresco in summer. The most serious choice is the art deco style grill. Naturally, seafood features strongly on the menu and sauces are well crafted and balanced. Langoustine ravioli, scallops, leek and herb cream sauce, or ham hock and potato terrine with an apricot compôte, are tempting starters. Main courses might be plum tomato and feta cheese tart with red onion jam or broiled lobster with coconut and coriander mash and Thai green curry sauce. A good selection of irresistible desserts.

Accommodation: 107 rooms (107 en suite) ★★★★
Directions: Overlooking St Brelade's Bay

St Brelade's Bay, JE3 8EF
Tel: 01534 43101
Fax: 01534 46269
🅔 hotellhorizon@jerseymail.co.uk
Chef(s): Paul Wells
Owner(s): Hand Picked Hotels
Cost: *Alc* £27.50, set price D £27. ☺ H/wine £12.50
Times: 12.30-2.30pm/7.30-10pm. Closed L Sun & Mon
Additional: Children 12 yrs+
Seats: 45. Private dining room 250. Jacket and tie preferred
Style: Modern, French
Smoking: No-smoking area; no pipes; no cigars; Air conditioning

England

ST CLEMENT

Map 16

Green Island Restaurant

Green Island, JE2 6LS
Tel: 01534 857787
Fax: 01534 619309
e amw@psilink.co.uk
Chef(s): Sarah Copp
Owner(s): Alan M Winch
Cost: Alc £25. ☺ ☺ H/wine £9.90
Times: Noon-2.30pm/7-9.30pm.
Closed Mon, D Sun, 2wks Nov,
Xmas week, 3 wks Feb/Mar
Additional: Sunday L. Children
welcome. Vegetarian by request only
Seats: 40
Style: Bistro-style, Rustic
Directions: Telephone for directions

Located next to the Green Island beach car park with its fast food kiosk, this gem of a restaurant could be mistakenly passed by. Diners can sit on the sun terrace in good weather, savouring colourful international dishes such as mild chicken and chickpea curry or oxtail braised with root vegetables, shallots and brown ale.

ST HELIER

Map 16

Grand Hotel

The Esplanade, JE4 8WD
Tel: 01534 722301
Fax: 01534 737815
e grand.jersey@devere-hotels.com
Chef(s): Lee Carroll
Owner(s): DeVere Group Plc
Cost: Alc £27.50, set price L £14.50/
D £23.50. ☺ ☺ H/wine £11.45
Times: 12.30-2.15pm/7-10pm.
Closed L Sat, D Sun, BHs
Additional: Sunday L. Children
welcome
Seats: 140. Private dining room 24.
Jacket and tie preferred
Style: French
Smoking: No-smoking area; no pipes;
no cigars; Air conditioning
Accommodation: 114 rooms (114 en
suite) ★ ★ ★ ★

Centrally placed for both the town and the beaches, this hotel offers plenty of lovely views along with a smart new leisure complex. Victoria's restaurant looks over the statue of Queen Victoria towards St Aubin, its light decor and comfy seating making it the perfect place to watch the sun set. The atmosphere is enhanced by a pianist playing tunes from the 40s and 50s. The imaginative menu offers colourful versions of classic dishes such as pan-fried calves' liver with roasted shallots and bacon lardons or rosemary marinated rack of lamb with Provençal potatoes and a leek and tarragon cream sauce.

Directions: On outskirts of town overlooking Victoria Park

ST HELIER *Continued*   Map 16

Pomme D'Or Hotel   NEW   ◉◉

Liberation Square, JE1 3UF
Tel: 01534 880110
Fax: 01534 737781
e enquiries@pommedorhotel.com
Chef(s): David Inwood
Owner(s): Seymour Hotels
Cost: *Alc* £24.50, set price L £15.50/
D £17.50. ☺ ☺ H/wine £9
Times: Noon-2pm/7pm-10pm.
Additional: Sunday L.
Children welcome
Seats: 140. Private dining room 250
Style: Traditional

A touch of faded glory adds a glamorous appeal to this first-floor hotel restaurant, with its elegant traditional décor. Tables are crisply clothed and set with neatly folded napkins, shiny silver and sparkling glassware, and service is all you could hope for. The food also delivers the promised flavours, and a set six course lunch offers real value for money when it's available. Ravioli of lobster with seared scallops and a shellfish cream sauce shows sensitive use of ingredients, while roast fillet of monkfish Niçoise, and pecan and almond tart with blueberry ice cream are sound choices.

Smoking: No-smoking area; Air conditioning
Accommodation: 141 rooms (141 en suite) ★★★
Directions: Telephone for directions

ST SAVIOUR   Map 16

Longueville Manor   ◉◉◉

JE2 7WF
Tel: 01534 725501
Fax: 01534 731613
e longman@itl.net
Chef(s): Andrew Baird
Owner(s): Malcolm Lewis
Cost: *Alc* £43, set price L £20-£22.50/
D £42-£70. H/wine £12
Times: 12.30-2pm/7-9.30pm.
Additional: Sunday L. Bar food.
Children welcome
Seats: 65. Private dining room 22.
Jacket and tie preferred
Style: Traditional, Country-house
Smoking: No-smoking area
Accommodation: 32 rooms (32 en
suite) ★★★★
Directions: From St Helier take A3 to
Gorey, hotel 0.75 miles on L

A very special place, with origins dating back to the 13th century, in 17 acres of grounds that include many fine specimen trees and a lake complete with black swans. Comfortable day rooms give guests an ideal excuse to relax over a light lunch or afternoon tea secure in the knowledge that nothing here is too much trouble in terms of service. In the heavily panelled dining-room, a well-travelled, polyglottic clientele particularly enjoys the native tastes of Jersey: warm salad of local scallops with globe artichoke and truffled beans; lobster risotto with asparagus; sea bass with sauce vierge and Jersey crab; and winter-berry soufflé. Good, fresh flavours and open textures are evident in calves' liver with dry-cured bacon and orange and onion marmalade and gratin of warm strawberries with a generous dash of Grand Marnier, rounded off with finely executed petits fours with coffee back in the lounge. Assured cooking, attentive service - despite, at times, some difficulty with the language - and an unusually comprehensive wine list continue to set standards that are the envy of these islands.

SARK

SARK   Map 16

La Sablonnerie

GY9 0SD
Tel: 01481 832061
Fax: 01481 832408
Owner(s): Elizabeth Perrée
Cost: Alc £21.80, set price L £19.80-£25.50/D £20.80-£26.50. ☺ ☺
H/wine £7.80
Times: noon-2.30pm/7-9.30pm.
Closed mid Oct-Easter
Additional: Sunday L. Bar food.
Children welcome
Seats: 39
Style: Chic, French
Smoking: No-smoking area; no pipes; no cigars
Accommodation: 22 rooms (12 en suite)
Directions: On southern part of island

A quaint, relaxing farmhouse hotel, packed from the croquet lawn to the beamed ceilings with traditional charm. The restaurant features whitewashed walls, polished wooden tables and leaded windows peering over the gardens - a source of many ingredients as well as a popular place to enjoy cream teas. A meal could begin with canapés in the bar (expect a roaring log fire in winter) followed by a starter of sea scallops with oriental spiced ratatouille and chive oil. Main courses might include fresh Sark lobster or home grown veal with redcurrant jelly.

England

MAN, ISLE OF

CASTLETOWN

Map 6 SC26

The Chablis Cellar

Overlooking the harbour and Castletown Castle, this remains an "in-place" to eat on the Isle, with an experienced new chef in place. Flowers are fresh and linen is crisp reflecting a precision and attention to detail also apparent in the likes of seared king scallops with caramelised soy sauce, tender veal with a pepper and cream reduction and warm bread-and-butter pudding with apricot glaze. Good strength coffee is freshly made and service is as attentive and professional as ever.

Style: Classic, French
Smoking: No-smoking area
Directions: Approach Castletown, bridge over harbour, 3 storey building on L. Small car park

21 Bank Street, IM9 1AT
Tel: 01624 823527
Fax: 01624 824016
Chef(s): Edward Pepper
Owner(s): Adrian Brown
Cost: Alc £28, set price L £15-£25.
☺ ☺ H/wine £12.50
Times: L from noon/D from 7pm.
Closed Tue (Winter only),
D Sun (Winter only)
Additional: Sunday L.
Children welcome
Seats: 52. Private dining room 22

PORT ERIN

Map 6 SC16

Bradda Glen Café

A traditional style restaurant whose window seats offer lovely views of Port Erin beach. The modern, European based menu might include slow roasted lamb with parsnip purée and mint jus or seared salmon with sweetened red cabbage and a saffron beurre blanc. Look out for local specialities such as Manx ice cream.

Smoking: No smoking in dining room
Directions: Follow signs from Promenade, then past hotels, entrance 450yds beyond

IM9 6PJ
Tel: 01624 833166
Chef(s): Ian Halstein
Owner(s): Mr & Mrs Halstein
Cost: Alc £18.50. ☺ H/wine £9.25
Times: Dinner only, 7-9pm.
Closed Mon, Oct & Mid Jan
Additional: Sunday L. Bar food L.
Children welcome
Seats: 36
Style: Chic, Classic

Restaurant Martin Wishart

Scotland

Sunshine on Leith. Restaurant Martin Wishart is located in the city's docklands makeover but would be "more than welcome anywhere in the city" according to one visitor. Cutting edge and minimalist – clean off-white walls, black blinds and a stone floor setting off the crisp white linen, and glassware - only large contemporary paintings bring a touch of colour to this chic and aspirational environment. The short (only four dishes in each course) daily-changing menu is equally to the point and is similarly well-contrasted and well-executed. The economy of the approach extends to the prices which are good value at all times but "exceptional" at lunch.

For your money you can expect some forceful starters that might include a roast saddle of French rabbit, carrot and cardamom purée and braised Belgian endive wrapped in Vantreche bacon ("a European tour of a dish"), or a satisfying roulade of foie gras with a compôte of Agen prunes and salad of mash & hazelnuts. Fish is handled particularly well with main courses that have included a "top-notch" fillet of sea bass with roasted paysanne of celeriac, salsify, turnip, pommes Parisiennes accompanied by oyster beignet and champagne velouté. It's not all mighty flavours though, there is a genuine deftness apparent especially in desserts like crème vanille with Champagne on peach, strawberry and pear or a lemon crème brûlée presented in a scooped-out lemon with a flashed sugar topping. Service is appropriately bright (in all senses of the word) and attentive. The wine list follows the flow by being brief but very well chosen and marked-up with restraint.

Martin Wishart

54 The Shore, Leith,   **MAP 11 NT27**
EDINBURGH, EH6 6RA
Tel: 0131 553 3557
Fax: 0131 467 7091
Email: info@martin-wishart.co.uk
Chef: Martin Wishart
Owners: Martin Wishart, Cecile Auvinet
Cost: Alc £32. Set-price L £13.50-£16.50 /
D £50 (seven courses) ☺
H/wine £11.50
Times: Noon-2pm /7-10pm. Closed L Sat,
Xmas, New Year, 2 wks Jan, 1 wk Jun
Seats: 33
Style: French, minimalist
Smoking: No pipes, no cigars
Directions: Telephone for directions

Scotland

ABERDEEN CITY

ABERDEEN   Map 15 NJ90

Ardoe House

Built in the 1870s for a wealthy manufacturer, Ardoe House still retains original features such as the oak fireplace in the dining room. The menu has some interesting combinations including fruity accompaniments. Among the starters may be a citrus salad partnering a terrine of smoked salmon and monkfish with caper dressing or potted Highland game with blueberry and orange marmalade. For a main course try a confit of duck leg with spiced fig compote in an orange and cassis sauce. Fish lovers will not be disappointed with seared fillet of halibut and roasted fennel and cherry tomatoes in balsamic jus.

Accommodation: 110 rooms (110 en suite) ★ ★ ★ ★
Directions: 3 miles from Aberdeen on B9077, on L

Blairs, South Deeside Road, AB1 5YP
Tel: 01224 867355
Fax: 01224 861283
e ardoe@macdonald-hotels.co.uk
Chef(s): Ivor Clark
Owner(s): Macdonald Hotels Plc
Cost: *Alc* £35 H/wine £15.50
Times: Noon-2pm/6.30-9.45pm.
Closed L Sat
Additional: Sunday L. Bar food.
Children welcome
Seats: 80. Jacket and tie preferred
Style: Traditional, Country-House
Smoking: No smoking in dining room

Maryculter House Hotel

With stone walls, an open fire and lovely grounds, the scene is set for a traditional meal made with quality local produce. The Priory restaurant can deliver the informal Poacher's bar both deliver the goods: Scottish salmon, Scottish lamb and Aberdeen Angus beef are all on the menu, and it's worth leaving room for the 'rather wicked' desserts.

Smoking: No smoking in dining room
Civil licence: 180
Accommodation: 23 rooms (23 en suite) ★ ★ ★
Directions: From Aberdeen City take B9077 (South Deeside Road) for 8 miles

AB12 5GB
Tel: 01224 732124
Fax: 01224 733510
e info@maryculterhousehotel.co.uk
Chef(s): Brian Emslie
Cost: *Alc* £25. ☺ H/wine £14.25
Times: Dinner only, 7-9.30pm.
Closed D Sun
Additional: Sunday L. Bar food.
Children 4yrs+
Seats: 40. Private dining room 30
Style: Traditional Country-House

Norwood Hall

Beautifully preserved Victorian mansion successfully retaining much of its original decor. Stained glass windows, tapestries and a finely carved ceiling, not to mention the delightful wooded grounds, provide an elegant and intimate setting. Expect the likes of breast of duck, with a leek, bacon and tomato confit with a rosemary and honey sauce.

Accommodation: 21 rooms (21 en suite) ★ ★ ★
Directions: Telephone for directions

Garthdee Road, Cults, AB15 9FX
Tel: 01224 868951
Fax: 01224 869868
e info@norwood-hall.co.uk
Chef(s): Alfie Murray
Cost: *Alc* £26. H/wine £11.75
Additional: Bar food.
Children welcome
Seats: 28. Private dining room 30

ABERDEENSHIRE

BALLATER   Map 15 NO39

Balgonie Country House

Intimate dining venue in an Edwardian country house set back from the main street. Creative cooking from a set-price seasonal menu encompasses rustic turnip and parsnip soup and a skilful Madeira crème brûlée. There's a choice of three dishes

Braemar Place, AB35 5NQ
Tel: 013397 55482
Fax: 013397 55482
e balgonie@lineone.net
Chef(s): John Finnie

at each stage, focusing around prime Scottish produce - fresh Dee salmon, east coast seafood, Aberdeen Angus beef and local game.

Style: Country-House
Smoking: No smoking in dining room
Accommodation: 9 rooms (9 en suite) ★ ★
Directions: On outskirts of Ballater, signposted off A93 (Ballater-Perth)

Owner(s): Mr J & Mrs P Finnie
Cost: Set price L £19.50/D £32.50. ☺
H/wine £17
Times: 12.30-2pm/7-9pm. L by reservation only, Closed 5 Jan-10 Feb
Additional: Sunday L. Children welcome. Vegetarian by request only
Seats: 30

Scotland

Darroch Learg Hotel

Expect to be visually enchanted and seduced by delicious aromatic flavours before tucking into the glorious food that is the pride of this Deeside country house hotel. Perhaps out of reverence to the cooking (and quite unasked) diners adopt a smart dress code, and in return for their appreciation, a couple of signature dishes - like ravioli of foie gras, and classic lemon

Braemar Road, AB35 5UX
Tel: 013397 55443
Fax: 013397 55252
e info@darrochlearg.co.uk
Chef(s): David Mutter
Owner(s): Mr N Franks
Cost: Set price L £20/D £35. ☺
H/wine £15
Times: 12.30-2pm/7-9pm.
Closed Xmas, last 3wks Jan
Additional: Sunday L. Bar food L. Children welcome
Seats: 48
Style: Traditional, Country-House
Smoking: No smoking in dining room
Accommodation: 18 rooms (18 en suite) ★ ★ ★
Directions: On A93 at the W end of village

tart - reappear by popular request. The menu is a feast of innovative Scottish creations, cruising through the likes of ham hock and foie gras terrine with pea purée and brioche, salad of Deeside hare en croute with butternut squash purée and cranberry sauce, breast of squab with mashed potato, apricots and sage sauce, and cep-roasted veal with cep purée and lentil sauce. The wine list matches the quality cooking, with several glasses and half-bottled pudding wines. Service flows smoothly in the conservatory restaurant, famous for its awesome mountain views.

Glen Lui Hotel

Watch the golfers play outside while savouring the modern British cooking at this friendly Deeside hotel. The menu is soundly based on fresh local ingredients, with the odd startling choice slipped in, like banana wrapped in bacon, grilled with mango chutney. There are plenty of orthodox dishes too, and imaginatively dressed old favourites such as crown roast of lamb with raspberry sauce.

Style: French, country-house
Smoking: No smoking in dining room
Accommodation: 19 rooms (19 en suite) ◆◆◆
Directions: Off A93 in the village of Ballater.

AB35 5RP
Tel: 013397 55402
Fax: 013397 55545
e infos@glen-lui-hotel.co.uk
Chef(s): Olivier Denis
Owner(s): Mr & Mrs Serge Geraud
Cost: Alc £22, set price L £11.50/D £22. ☺ ☺ H/wine £9.20
Times: Noon-2pm/6-9pm.
Additional: Sunday L. Children welcome
Seats: 35. Private dining room 30

BALLATER *Continued*　　　　　**Map 15 NO39**

Green Inn

The success of the Green Inn says much about the talent and application of chef/proprietors Jeff and Carol Purves, who have been here for 12 years. There is a fixed-price menu of two or three courses, with regional cheeses as an optional fourth. Dishes depend on the availability of fresh produce, mostly locally sourced and selected with an eye to the environment and sustainability. It would be easy to be sceptical of a dish like cheesecake of oak-smoked haddock and Highland cheddar with tarragon cream but there really is no need - it's a huge success. Loin of organic pork, "tender and full of flavour", comes served with choucroute and mustard cream.

Accommodation: 3 rooms (3 en suite)
Directions: On A93 in centre of Ballater on the Green

9 Victoria Road,
AB35 5QQ
Tel: 013397 55701
Fax: 013397 55701
📧 info@green-inn.com
Chef(s): J J Purves
Owner(s): Mr & Mrs Purves
Cost: *Alc* £33
Times: D only. Closed 2wks Oct, Sun-Mon from Mar-Oct
Additional: Children welcome
Seats: 30
Style: Traditional
Smoking: No cigars; Air conditioning

BANCHORY

Banchory Lodge

A striking, historic setting along the Rivers Feugh and Dee, with salmon fishing available from March to September. Try the fillet of salmon on black noodles with béarnaise sauce to honour the location, or a touch of the exotic with Bantry Bay mussels in a coriander, coconut and lemon cream.

Seats: 100. Private dining room 30
Style: Traditional, Country-house
Smoking: No smoking in dining room
Accommodation: 22 rooms (22 en suite) ★ ★ ★
Directions: Off A93 13miles W of Aberdeen

AB31 5HS
Tel: 01330 822625
Fax: 01330 825019
📧 enquiries@banchorylodge.co.uk
Chef(s): Cameron Kelly
Owner(s): Mrs M Jaffray
Cost: *Alc* £21, set price L £12.50-£15.50/D £22.50-£30. ☺ ☺
H/wine £10.75
Times: Noon-2.30pm/6-10pm
Additional: Sunday L. Bar food L. Children welcome

Raemoir House Hotel

Raemoir, AB31 4ED
Tel: 01330 824884
Fax: 01330 822171
📧 raemoirhse@aol.com
Chef(s): John Barber
Owner(s): Mr & Mrs R Bishop-Milnes
Cost: Set price L £16.50/D £23.50-£28.50. ☺ ☺ H/wine £13.60
Times: Noon-2pm/7-9pm

Fine dining in the elegant surroundings of the Oval Room, with Victorian tapestries covering the walls, an open fire in season, and the owner's magnificent orchids gracing the tables. Cooking majors on artistic presentation (which can be stunning) and innovative combinations - some more successful than others. Each item in a starter of chicken liver parfait, sun-dried Bretonne ham, and quail supreme with caramelised berry sauce was well executed and enjoyable, though they perhaps didn't entirely marry as a whole. The menu is priced for two or three courses, each with a choice of four dishes. A commendable wine list and refined service complete a happy experience.

Accommodation: 20 rooms (20 en suite) ★ ★ ★
Directions: A93 to Banchory then A980, hotel at crossroads after 2.5 miles

Additional: Sunday L. Bar food L. Children welcome
Seats: 40. Private dining room 35
Style: Country-House
Smoking: No smoking in dining room
Civil licence: 50

Tor-na-Coille Hotel

A fine Edwardian mansion set in tree-studded grounds, bringing a modern slant to classical dishes. The fixed-price two or three course menu includes smoked fish kedgeree topped with soft poached egg, supreme of guinea fowl on a potato cake with red onion relish and chasseur sauce, and white chocolate and Cointreau parfait.

AB31 4AB
Tel: 01330 822242
Fax: 01330 824012
e tornacoille@btinternet.com
Chef(s): Watson McNeil
Owner(s): Roxanne Sloan-Maris
Cost: Set price L £13.75-£15.75/ D £26.50-£29.50. ☺ ☺
H/wine £12.95
Times: Noon-2pm/6.30-9.30pm. Closed 24-27 Dec
Additional: Sunday L. Bar food. Children welcome
Seats: 65. Private dining room 100
Style: Classic, Country-House
Smoking: No smoking in dining room
Civil licence: 90
Accommodation: 22 rooms (22 en suite) ★ ★ ★
Directions: From Aberdeen take A93 (18 miles).

INVERURIE   Map 15 NJ72
Thainstone House Hotel

An imposing country mansion set in extensive grounds boasting a restaurant of true fine-dining calibre. The classic elegance of the decor is well matched to the cuisine that runs along the lines of risotto of field mushrooms with a spinach and ricotta ravioli. Main course options might include terrine of ham hock with sauce gribiche or seared medallions of beef with mushy pea fritter, red cabbage wafer and a port reduction. Artistic flair is given full rein in desserts such as glazed soft fruits served with an orange sorbet and Drambuie syrup, with the freshness and full flavour of the constituent fruits testifying to a devoted approach to sourcing.

AB51 5NT
Tel: 01467 621643
Fax: 01467 625084
Telephone for further details

NEWBURGH   Map 15 NJ92
Udny Arms Hotel

The upper section of the smart split-level restaurant takes full advantage of the very attractive estuary views. For those on the less panoramic ground level the sight of a provincial menu offering real modernity and choice is probably view enough. Sample mixed wild mushroom risotto with shaved Parmesan and truffle oil.

Main Street, AB41 6BL
Tel: 01358 789444
Fax: 01358 789012
e enquiry@udny.demon.co.uk
Chef(s): Scott Kinghorn
Owner(s): Mr & Mrs Craig

NEWBURGH *Continued* Map 15 NJ9

Cost: *Alc* £22. ☺ ☺ H/wine £12.95
Times: Noon-2.30pm/6.30-9.30pm.
Additional: Sunday L. Bar food. Children welcome
Seats: 50. Private dining room 28
Style: Country-House

Smoking: No smoking in dining room
Civil licence: 60
Accommodation: 26 rooms (26 en suite) ★★
Directions: Telephone for directions

PETERHEAD Map 15 NK14

Waterside Inn

A bright, modern, split-level restaurant with attractive views of the river. Seared scallops on an asparagus risotto are served up with a delicate and light mustard and cheese sauce - look out for a delicious dessert of choux bun filled with caramel ice cream and banana slices.

Fraserburgh Road, AB42 3BN
Tel: 01779 471121
Fax: 01779 470670
Telephone for further details

ANGUS

CARNOUSTIE Map 12 NO53

11 Park Avenue

A long-time fixture of Carnoustie, and a great location for getting in those golf rounds as the town is, once again, an Open Golf Championship venue. 11 Park Avenue offers comforting food with local touches as in, say, gratin of creamed Arbroath smokie with leek and Gruyère cheese.

Additional: Sunday L. Children welcome
Seats: 50. Jacket and tie preferred
Smoking: No smoking in dining room
Directions: From Dundee take A92 N (Arbroath). After 10-12 miles turn R to Carnoustie; at crossroads L, then R at mini-rdbt. Restaurant on L

11 Park Avenue, DD7 7JA
Tel: 01241 853336
Fax: 01241 859333
🄴 parkavenue@genie.co.uk
Chef(s): Stephen Collinson
Owner(s): Stephen Collinson
Cost: *Alc* £27.50, set price L £17.50.
☺ ☺ H/wine £11.50
Times: noon-2pm/7-10pm. Closed Mon, L Tue-Wed & Sat, D Sun, 1st wk in Jan

INVERKEILOR Map 15 NO64

Gordon's Restaurant

Originally constructed in the 1800s, this is a small and intimate restaurant with stained glass windows, sandstone walls, beamed ceilings and an open fire. Family-run, Gordon's is now well established in this East Coast fishing village. Cooking is fairly traditional with classical accompaniments, but presentation is pleasingly modern. Effective starters could include a smooth and rich chicken liver and foie gras parfait with spiced pear chutney and fruit loaf, while a char braised fillet of Angus beef with celeriac purée, crispy polenta, griddled asparagus and red wine reduction show that top class meat (as this is Angus what would one expect?) is treated with great respect.

Accommodation: 2 rooms (2 en suite)
Directions: Just off A92 (Arbroath to Montrose), follow Inverkeilor signs

Main Street, By Arbroath, DD11 5RN
Tel: 01241 830364
Fax: 01241 830364
Chef(s): Gordon Watson
Owner(s): Gordon & Maria Watson
Cost: *Alc* £29.50, set price L £17/D £29.50 ☺ H/wine £12.95
Times: Noon-1.45pm/7-9pm. Booking essential. Closed Mon, L Sat & Tue, D Sun, Jan
Additional: Sunday L. Children Dinner 6+
Seats: 24
Style: Rustic, Classical
Smoking: No smoking in dining room

ARGYLL & BUTE

ARDUAINE   Map 10 NM71

Loch Melfort Hotel

Probably one of the finest locations on the West coast of
Scotland, this popular family-run hotel has outstanding views
across Asknish Bay towards the islands of Jura, Scarba and
Shuna. The seafood served here may also be the freshest in
Scotland, having being caught in the waters viewed from the
restaurant then landed on the hotel's jetty. Ingredients are
sympathetically and precisely cooked so that the flavours speak
for themselves: a meal might include a fricassée of local
shellfish followed by roast fillet of turbot, brandade and a
Noilly Prat velouté. Service is relaxed and friendly.

PA34 4XG
Tel: 01852 200233
Fax: 01852 200214
e lmhotel@aol.com
Chef(s): Colin MacDonald
Owner(s): Kyle & Nigel Schofield
Cost: D £25-£30 H/wine £12.50
Times: Dinner only, 7.30-11pm
Additional: Sunday L. Bar food.
Children welcome
Seats: 75. Jacket and tie preferred
Style: Country-House
Smoking: No smoking in dining room
Accommodation: 27 rooms (27 en
suite) ★ ★ ★
Directions: From Oban, 20 miles S on
A816; from Lochgilphead, 19 miles N
on A816

BOWMORE   Map 10 NR35

The Harbour Inn   NEW

Standing by the water's edge and looking out towards Loch
Indaal and the Isle of Jura, this is something of a find. Under
the supervision of a new chef/proprietor, its "Tastes of Islay"
include pheasant, partridge and woodcock in various guises,
the finest local crab-fish cakes, Loch Gruinart oysters and a
special-recipe fish chowder. Start with hot peat-smoked salmon
or gamekeeper's terrine, then tuck into sea bass fillets with stir-
fried monkfish or haunch of hare with winter vegetables and a

The Square, Isle of Islay
PA43 7JR
Tel: 01496 810330
Fax: 01496 810990
e harbour@harbour-inn.com
Chef(s): Scott Chance
Owner(s): Scott Chance
Cost: Alc £25. ☺ ☺ H/wine £9.75
Times: Noon-2.30pm/6-9pm.
Closed L Sun, all Sun in winter

BOWMORE *Continued*   **Map 10 NR35**

rich game sauce. Steamed ginger sponge with butterscotch sauce has been described as "wicked" - a term that could in no way refer to the friendly, local staff.

Directions: Bowmore is situated approx 8 miles from both the ferry ports of Port Ellen and Port Askaig.

Additional: Bar food L.
Children welcome
Seats: 44
Style: Traditional
Smoking: No smoking in dining room
Accommodation: 7 rooms (7 en suite)

BRIDGE OF ORCHY   **Map 10 NN23**

Bridge of Orchy Hotel

Stop off on the road to Skye, take in the spectacular mountain scenery, and discover this popular restaurant, serving modern cuisine. The 'surprise' at the outset of the meal – a delicious fresh langoustine – is a worthier start than many a selection of canapés. Begin the meal proper with a selection of flavoursome

PA36 4AD
Tel: 01838 400208
Fax: 01838 400313
e bridgeoforchy@onyxnet.co.uk
Chef(s): Cameron Brown
Owner(s): Mr Coyle
Cost: *Alc* £25. ☺ ☺ H/wine £11
Times: Dinner only, 7-8.30pm.
Closed Dec
Additional: Sunday L. Bar food L.
Children welcome
Seats: 40
Style: Modern
Smoking: No smoking in dining room
Accommodation: 10 rooms (10 en suite) ★ ★
Directions: On A82, 6 miles N of Tyndrum on main Glasgow - Skye road

Scottish seafood poached in a light fish and tomato stock. Choose prime fillet of Scottish beef, again for its flavour and enjoy the perfectly complementary red wine and pickled walnut sauce. To finish, the tangy citrus tart, drizzled with chocolate sauce will fuel you for the remainder of your journey.

CLACHAN-SEIL   **Map 10 NM71**

Willowburn Hotel

Committed cooking with both flair and precision aimed at bringing out the flavour from locally sourced produce. Attention to detail is a keynote, from the freshly made canapés and choice of home-made breads through to the intricate dessert, a composite dish of nuts and chocolate presented together and separately in various forms (you need to see it). A starter of crab and avocado fishcake has been noted as "delightfully light", and the roast lamb "as good as any tasted this year". The restaurant itself is a charming room looking over the lawns to the tidal waters of Clachan Sound and the wooded hills beyond.

Accommodation: 7 rooms (7 en suite) ★ ★
Directions: 11 miles S of Oban via A816 and B844(Easdale) over Atlantic Bridge

PA34 4TJ
Tel: 01852 300276
Fax: 08152 300597
e willowburn.hotel@virgin.net
Chef(s): Chris Mitchell
Owner(s): Ms J Wolfe & Mr C Mitchell
Cost: Set price D £28. H/wine £12.50
Times: Dinner only, 7-8pm. Closed Jan-Feb
Additional: Children welcome
Seats: 24
Style: Classic
Smoking: No smoking in dining room

Scotland

DERVAIG
Map 13 NM45

Druimard Country House

Dipping into Scotland's abundant larder, for quality ingredients, the chef's enthusiasm is evident in her 5-course menu featuring innovative combinations. Quality, rather than choice - the necessity for which is delayed until dessert - stamps its mark here. A whisky-cured fillet of trout on a bed of leeks, laced with sliced smoked bacon works well to start and the fillet of Aberdeen Angus is moist and tender. An unusual banana and toffee crumble in a lovely pastry case, is a typically enticing dessert. Wendy and Haydn Hubbard, owners of this restored Victorian property, provide a friendly welcome and their establishment deserves its strong reputation.

Directions: From Craignure ferry turn R to Tobermory. Go through Salen, turn L at Aros, signposted Dervaig, hotel on right before village.

Isle of Mull,PA75 6QW
Tel: 01688 400345
Fax: 01688 400345
 druimard@hotels.
activebooking.com
Chef(s): Wendy Hubbard
Owner(s): Mr & Mrs Hubbard
Cost: Set price D £29.50. ☺
H/wine £9.95
Times: Dinner only, 7-8.30pm.
Closed Nov-Mar
Additional: Children welcome
Seats: 28
Style: Country-House
Smoking: No smoking in dining room
Accommodation: 7 rooms (6 en suite)
★★

DUNOON
Map 10 NS17

Chatters

A refreshingly honest cottage-style restaurant in the centre of Dunoon. A thoroughly modern style of cooking allows natural flavours to shine through with dishes such as fresh lemon sole (lightly grilled and simply served with a butter sauce) a real delight. Clarity of flavour is also evident in desserts such as a beautifully zesty lemon tart.

58 John Street, PA23 8BJ
Tel: 01369 706402
Telephone for further details

Enmore Hotel

A well thought out seating arrangement ensures that the majority of diners can enjoy excellent views over the Firth of Clyde. The temptation to over elaborate is firmly resisted and the resulting simplicity allows natural flavours to come through well. Tried and tested favourites such as Scotch beef fillet steak are as successful as ever.

Style: Country-House
Smoking: No smoking in dining room
Accommodation: 10 rooms (10 en suite) ★★
Directions: From Glasgow M8/A8 (Greenock) & ferry, or via Loch Lomond, A815 to Dunoon. Hotel on promenade btw 2 ferry terminals, 1 mile N of Dunoon

Marine Parade, Kirn, PA23 8HH
Tel: 01369 702230
Fax: 01369 702148
 enmorehotel@btinternet.com
Chef(s): David Wilson
Owner(s): Angela & David Wilson
Cost: Alc £25, set price L £18-£25/
D £20-£29. ☺ ☺ H/wine £14
Times: 12.30-2pm/6.30-9pm.
Closed Dec-Feb
Additional: Sunday L. Bar food.
Children welcome
Seats: 24. Private dining room 6

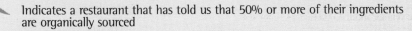

☺ Indicates a restaurant that has told us they offer a two-course lunch for less than £15

☺ Indicates a restaurant that has told us they offer a three-course dinner for less than £25

Indicates a restaurant that has told us that 50% or more of their ingredients are organically sourced

Prices quoted in the guide are for guidance only and are subject to change without notice

Scotland

ERISKA

Map 10 NM94

Isle of Eriska

Cross over the small bridge to the private island of Eriska, and enter a dream world of secluded beaches, protected wildlife and heart-stopping views. Best of all is the Victorian mansion itself where guests are welcomed spontaneously like friends, and treated to innovative food based on fresh seasonal produce, particularly local seafood and game. Beautifully-presented canapés and home-made breads herald seven set courses in the traditional dining room, with succulent starters like stuffed rabbit with herb ravioli and morels, and simple but mouth-watering middle courses of sautéed scallops and langoustine. Main roasts such as best end of lamb are formally carved at the table, or choose turbot with baby fennel, or farm-reared guinea fowl breast. The lightness of the cooking means little stamina is required to reach the dessert stage, where the choice might include filo-wrapped lemon sponge topped with lemon mousse. Retire to the hall for coffee and petit fours.

PA37 1SD
Tel: 01631 720371
Fax: 01631 720531
Chef(s): Robert MacPherson
Owner(s): Mr Buchanan-Smith
Cost: Set price D £38.50.
H/wine £9.20
Times: Dinner only, 8pm-9pm.
Closed Jan
Additional: Bar food L. Children welcome
Seats: 40. Jacket and tie preferred
Style: Country-House
Smoking: No smoking in dining room
Accommodation: 17 rooms (17 en suite) ★ ★ ★ ★
Directions: On private island with vehicular access

KILCHRENAN

Map 10 NN02

Ardanaiseig Hotel   NEW

Peerless location overlooking Loch Awe and in the shadow of Ben Cruachan. In many ways the archetypal Scottish country house with the impressive gardens open to the public. Classic cooking as one might expect but with a more modish edge than found in many similar venues. Take for example a really well-balanced starter of pan fried black bream with celeriac purée and vanilla sauce or a full-bodied main course of Aberdeen Angus with pancetta mash and wild mushrooms. Both a pre-dessert of coffee panacotta and an actual dessert of rhubarb soufflé with ginger anglaise have hit the mark. Great petits fours too.

PA35 1HE
Tel: 01866 833333
Fax: 01866 833222
📧 ardanaiseig@clara.net
Chef(s): Gary Goldie
Owner(s): Bennie Gray
Cost: Alc L £12.75.
Set price D £38.50
Times: 12.30-2pm/7-9pm.
Closed 2 Jan-10 Feb
Telephone for further details

Taychreggan Hotel

Awe-inspiring is an apt description of the views from Taychreggan, a lovely country house hotel, nestling on the shores of Loch Awe. Request a window table to make the most of the breathtaking scenery, whilst enjoying delicious dishes from the 5-course menu. Food, mainly locally sourced, is based on traditional recipes with a slightly modern Mediterranean slant. Mouthwatering canapés precede skilfully cooked quality main courses such as the corn-fed chicken supreme, served with haggis on a mustard potato blini, perfectly cooked puy lentils and a light whisky flavoured jus. Desserts live up to expectations.

Accommodation: 19 rooms (19 en suite) ★ ★ ★
Directions: W from Glasgow on A82 to Crainlarich. W on A85 to Taynuilt. S on B845 to Kilchrenan & Taychreggan

PA35 1HQ
Tel: 01866 833211
Fax: 01866 833244
📧 taychreggan@btinternet.com
Chef(s): Jerome Prodanu
Owner(s): Annie Paul
Cost: Set price L £22/D £35 ☺
H/wine £13.25
Times: D only, 7.30-8.45pm.
Closed L All Week
Additional: Bar food L. Children 14yrs+
Seats: 45. Private dining room 18
Style: Modern, Country-House
Smoking: No smoking in dining room

KILMARTIN

Map 10 NR89

Cairn Restaurant

A good example of a restaurant offering a 'total experience' with refreshingly unpretentious food and an atmosphere as friendly as one could wish to find. A main course of cannon of

PA31 8RQ
Tel: 01546 510254
Chef(s): Marion P Thomson
Owner(s): Mr I G Thompson

lamb offers accurately cooked meat that is moist and honest in flavour, with a sweet apricot relish and rosemary gravy.

Seats: 60 **Style:** Traditional, Rustic
Smoking: No pipes; Air conditioning
Directions: On A816 Lochgilphead-Oban road

Cost: *Alc* £25. ☺ ☺ H/wine £9.75
Times: noon-3pm/6.30-10pm. Closed L Nov-Mar, D Mon-Wed(Nov-Mar), 25 Dec, 1 Jan
Additional: Sunday L. Bar food. Children welcome (10yrs+ at D)

LOCHGILPHEAD
Map 10 NR88

Cairnbaan Hotel

The type of place where you simply switch off and watch the world go by. This is due in part to the attractive decor - dark green walls, polished wood floor, windows overlooking the garden and canal beyond - but mostly thanks to the seductive aromas emerging from the kitchen holding the promise of seared slices of Barbary duck in a raspberry dressing for instance.

Style: Modern, Chic. **Smoking:** No smoking in dining room
Civil licence: 120
Accommodation: 11 rooms (11 en suite) ★ ★ ★
Directions: From Lochgilphead on A816 2 miles. Hotel off B841

Crinan Canal, Cairnbaan, PA31 8SJ
Tel: 01546 603668
Fax: 01546 606045
e cairnbaan.hotel@virgin.net
Chef(s): David Galt
Owner(s): Darren & Christine Dobson
Cost: *Alc* £22. ☺ ☺ H/wine £10.50
Times: Noon-2.30pm/6-9.30pm.
Additional: Sunday L. Bar food. Children welcome. Vegetarian by request only
Seats: 40. Private dining room 30

OBAN
Map 10 NM82

Dungallan House Hotel

With such a stunning vista of the sea and islands from Oban, it's not surprising that fish should be a speciality here. Choose from a variety of fish dishes such as grilled or deep-fried sole or, if meat is your preference, try the grilled sirloin steak.

Additional: Sunday L. Bar food L. Children welcome. Vegetarian by request only
Seats: 45 **Smoking:** No smoking in dining room
Accommodation: 13 rooms (11 en suite) ★ ★
Directions: From Oban follow signs for Gallanach. Approx 0.5 miles

Gallanach Road, PA34 4PD
Tel: 01631 563799
Fax: 01631 566711
e welcome@dungallanhotel-oban. co.uk
Chef(s): Janice Stewart
Cost: Set price L £10-£20/D £25 H/wine £8.95
Times: 12.30-2pm/7.30-8.30pm. Closed Jan-Feb

Manor House Hotel

Wonderful views over Oban Bay and islands are a unique virtue, but even the most ardent sea gazer might be distracted by the likes of a decent tournedos of beef on a rösti with béarnaise sauce and crispy fried onion.

Gallanach Road, PA34 4LS
Tel: 01631 562087
Fax: 01631 563053
Chef(s): Patrick Freytas
Owner(s): Mr P.L. Crane
Cost: *Alc* £23, set price L £11.95-£16.95/D £23-£28.50. ☺ ☺ H/wine £11.95
Times: Closed Nov-Feb, Sun 3pm-Tue 3pm
Additional: Sunday L. Bar food L. Children 12yrs+
Seats: 30
Style: Traditional
Smoking: No smoking in dining room
Civil licence: 20
Accommodation: 11 rooms (11 en suite) ★ ★
Directions: 300 metres past Oban ferry terminal

Scotland

OBAN *Continued*   Map 10 NM82

Waterfront Restaurant

"From pier to pan - as fast as we can," reads the sign by the
kitchen and freshness of produce is certainly evident in this
speciality seafood restaurant. Situated on the Railway Pier, used
by the local fishing fleet and also the main ferry terminal for the
Western Isles, the restaurant has a fast-growing reputation: the
locals are hooked and now the nets are cast further afield.
Deliberately simple décor mirrors the approach to
commendable, straightforward cooking, where a tasty lobster and
crab bisque might lead nicely to meltingly fresh langoustines. An
extensive blackboard selection is supplemented by a short
printed menu - neither are exclusively seafood.

Directions: Telephone for directions

Railway Pier, PA34 4LW
Tel & Fax: 01631 563110
Chef(s): Alex Needham
Owner(s): Annie Paul
Cost: *Alc* £20, set price L £20. ☺ ☺
H/wine £10.75
Times: noon-2.15pm/5.30-9.30pm.
Closed New Year, Jan
Additional: Sunday L. Bar food L.
Children welcome
Seats: 78. **Style:** French, Bistro-style
Smoking: No cigars

PORT APPIN   Map 14 NM94

Airds Hotel

Enjoying the most stunning outlook over Loch Linnhe with the
mountains behind, this very special hotel is in a remote and
peaceful location far away from the modern world and its
pressures. Despite its splendid isolation, there is nothing
backward about its service, as a meal in the restaurant (with
breathtaking views) will demonstrate. The lightest of touches
can be detected in the compact menu: chicken liver terrine with
crab apple and orange jelly and toasted brioche to start with,
and then grilled calves' liver on a potato pancake with roasted
beetroot and a caper and parsley sauce, or fillet of turbot with a
leek risotto, trompette mushrooms and lobster sauce. There's a
different choice every evening, but desserts are never stinted
on. Expect date pudding with butterscotch sauce, orange and
grapefruit segments in a Grand Marnier jelly, or orange and
Cointreau ice cream, plus at least three other puds.

Directions: Leave A828 at Appin, hotel is 2.5 miles

PA38 4DF
Tel: 01631 730236
Fax: 01361 730535
✉ airds@airds-hotel.com
Chef(s): Steve MacCallum
Owner(s): Mr & Mrs Allen
Cost: Set-price D£45. H/wine £16.50
Times: D only, 7.30-8.30pm.
Closed 6-26 Jan
Additional: Children welcome.
Vegetarian by request only
Seats: 36. Jacket and tie preferred
Style: Classic
Smoking: No smoking in dining room
Accommodation: 16 rooms (16 en
suite) ★ ★ ★

STRACHUR   Map 10 NN00

Creggans Inn

This long established roadside inn has magnificent views over
Loch Fyne. The restaurant is smartly decorated (red walls and
white table linen) and delivers a modern, British based menu.
Dishes might include fillet of beef with potato rösti and

PA27 8BX
Tel: 01369 860279
Fax: 01369 860637
✉ info@creggans-inn.co.uk
Chef(s): Joe Simpson
Owner(s): Mr T A Robertson, Mr T A
Robertson Jnr & Mrs O Robertson
Cost: Set price D £28.50
H/wine £9.70
Times: Dinner only, 7-9pm.
Additional: Bar food. Children
welcome
Seats: 50
Style: Classic, Country House
Smoking: No smoking in dining room
Accommodation: 14 rooms (14 en
suite) ★ ★ ★

bordelaise sauce or grilled sea bass with a caper and chervil beurre blanc.

Directions: From Glasgow A82, along Loch Lomond, then W on A83, onto A815 to Strachur. Or by ferry from Gourock to Dunoon onto A815

TARBERT   Map 10 NR86

The Columba Hotel

A carefully restored Victorian building occupying a prime position in this pretty fishing village. Local and visiting diners come to both the bar and dining room for the freshest of seafood caught by local boats and some adventurous saucing. Simple fare like grilled sea bass and local langoustines with lemon, chive and butter sauce has won praise.

Style: Scottish **Smoking:** No smoking in dining room
Accommodation: 10 rooms (10 en suite) ★ ★
Directions: On A83 into Tarbert, L & around harbour, follow road for 0.5 mile. Hotel on R.

East Pier Road, PA29 6UF
Tel & Fax: 01880 820808
🄴 columbahotel@fsbdial.co.uk
Chef(s): Pasial Thizze
Owner(s): Mr & Mrs R Chicken
Cost: Set price D £21.50. ☺ ☺
H/wine £11.50
Times: Noon-2pm/6-9pm.
Closed 26 Dec
Additional: Bar food. Children welcome. **Seats:** 35

TIGHNABRUAICH   Map 10 NR97

Royal Hotel

The work of local artists displayed in the restaurant makes a valiant attempt to compete with superb views of the Kyles of Bute. Any remaining thoughts of art appreciation go firmly out the window when presented with fillet of Buccleuch beef served with king scallops resting on potato rösti and caramelised shallots.

Seats: 35 **Style:** Modern Scottish
Smoking: No smoking in dining room
Accommodation: 12 rooms (11 en suite) ★ ★
Directions: From Strachur, on A886, turn R onto A8003 to Tighnabruaich. Hotel on R at bottom of hill

Shore Road, PA21 2BE
Tel: 01700 811239
Fax: 01700 811300
🄴 royalhotel@btinternet.com
Chef(s): Roger McKie
Owner(s): Mr & Mrs R McKie
Cost: Set price L £26.95-£28.95/D
£26.95-£28.95 ☺ H/wine £12.95
Times: Dinner only, 7-9pm
Additional: Bar food. Children welcome

TOBERMORY   Map 13 NM55

Highland Cottage

Breadalbane Street, Isle of Mull, PA75 6PD
Tel: 01688 302030
Fax: 01688 302727
🄴 davidandjo@highlandcottage.co.uk
Chef(s): Josephine Currie
Owner(s): David & Josephine Currie
Cost: Set price D £24.50. ☺
H/wine £11.50
Times: Dinner only, 7pm-9pm.
Closed Mid Oct – Mid Nov, Xmas, part Jan-Feb
Additional: Children welcome
Seats: 24
Style: Traditional Country-House
Smoking: No smoking in dining room
Accommodation: 6 rooms (6 en suite) ★ ★
Directions: Opposite Fire Station. Main Street up Back Brae, turn at top by White House. Follow road to R, L at next junction.

Very attractive traditionally styled dining room in a small hotel in the upper part of Tobermory. A typical meal might include crab tart with tomato vinaigrette and leaves, braised shank of Glengorm lamb with olive mash and lamb gravy, and strawberry marquise to finish.

Scotland

AYRSHIRE, EAST

DARVEL

Map 11 NS53

Scoretulloch House

Simple dishes benefit from focused ingredients - well sourced meats and great seafood carefully and unfussily treated. The house is a lovely 500-year-old building with a grand, half-panelled dining room underneath enormous ceiling beams. A much more informal brasserie is also an appealing option and, when the weather obliges, a barbecue in the fabulous gardens is sure to be a particular treat. The formal dinner option might kick off with a well flavoured beetroot soup, followed perhaps by roasted Highland venison with garlic fondant potatoes, and finish with pannacotta or a brandy snap basket filled with wild berries.

Smoking: No smoking in dining room
Directions: Exit M74 J8 for A71. Hotel clearly signed 1 mile S of A71 (Strathaven-Kilmarnock), just E of Darvel

KA17 0LR
Tel: 01560 323331
Fax: 01560 323441
e mail@scoretulloch.com
Chef(s): Annie Smith
Owner(s): Donald & Annie Smith
Cost: Set price L £12-£15/D £29.50.
☺ H/wine £13.95
Times: Noon-2pm/7-9pm. Closed
Mon & Tues, D Sun, 25-26 Dec, 1 Jan
Additional: Sunday L. Bar food.
Children welcome
Seats: 36. Private dining room 12
Style: Country-House

AYRSHIRE, NORTH

BRODICK

Map 10 NS03

Auchrannie Country House

Isle of Arran, KA27 8BZ
Tel: 01770 302234
Fax: 01770 302812
e info@auchrannie.co.uk
Chef(s): Peter Wilson
Owner(s): Mr I Johnston
Cost: Set price D £22.50-£25. ☺ ☺
H/wine £11.95
Times: Dinner only, 6.30-9.30pm
Additional: Children welcome
Seats: 52. Private dining room 22.
Jacket and tie preferred
Style: Traditional Country-House
Smoking: No smoking in dining room
Civil licence: 100
Accommodation: 28 rooms (28 en suite) ★ ★ ★
Directions: From ferry terminal turn R and follow coast road through Brodick village, then take 2nd L past golf club

Stately island home and country club in six acres of landscaped grounds, formerly the home of the Dowager Duchess of Hamilton. A choice of bistro or conservatory restaurants await, the latter offering good, daily changing fixed-price menus. Minor weaknesses do not spoil what is consistently a pleasurable eating experience. Dishes are designed to suit the resort hotel clientele and are nicely presented, for example, 'delightfully tender' duck served cold, dusted with Cajun spices, accompanied by beetroot and pear chutney and yoghurt dressing.

Kilmichael Country House Hotel

Kilmichael's cuisine has a strong Italian influence and is served in a spacious, comfortable environment. At times a lighter touch in the cooking might be welcome, but dishes are often creative and can be absolutely delicious, like the wild garlic leaf soup or the sticky toffee pudding with pecan caramel sauce.

Seats: 18. Jacket and tie preferred
Style: Country-House
Smoking: No smoking in dining room
Accommodation: 7 rooms (7 en suite) ★ ★
Directions: Turn R on leaving ferry terminal, through Brodick & L at golf club. Continue past church & onto private drive

Glen Cloy, Isle of Arran, KA27 8BY
Tel: 01770 302219
Fax: 01770 302068
e enquiries@kilmichael.com
Chef(s): Antony Butterworth
Owner(s): G Botterill & A Butterworth
Cost: Alc £29.50, set price D £29.50.
☺ ☺ H/wine £11.95
Times: Dinner only, 7pm-Midnight.
Closed D Tue-Wed, Nov-Mar
Additional: Children 12yrs+

Scotland

DALRY Map 10 NS24

Braidwoods

People flock to this little white cottage along a country lane, and after just one mouthful of Keith Braidwood's astonishing food it is easy to understand the compulsion. From the tiny tasty appetisers to the home made chocolates and made-to-order ground coffee that top and tail a meal here, the cooking is almost flawless, with outstanding freshness and quality evident throughout. Even more impressive is that the chef works virtually on his own. Simplicity is the key to starters like rillettes of oak-smoked Marbury salmon, and layered terrine of potato and foie gras, while roast loin of Highland red deer needs little more than crushed root vegetables and wild mushroom sauce to complement it. Baked fillet of turbot and seared scallops exemplify freshness and skilful cooking. Stunning desserts sustain the momentum, and warm dark chocolate soufflé with a rocher of prune and Armagnac ice cream will trigger a crescendo of pure pleasure.

Directions: 1 mile from Dalry on the Saltcoats Road

Drumastle Mill Cottage,
KA24 4LN
Tel: 01294 833544
Fax: 01294 833553
e keithbraidwood@bt.
connect.co.uk
Chef(s): Keith Braidwood
Owner(s): Mr & Mrs Braidwood
Cost: Set price L £18/D £30-£32.50.
H/wine £13.95
Times: Noon-1.45pm/7-9pm. Closed L Mon-Tue, D Sun-Mon, 1st 3 wks Jan, 2 wks Sep
Additional: Sunday L. Children 12+.
Vegetarian by request only
Seats: 24
Style: Converted Miller's Cottage
Smoking: No smoking in dining room

KILWINNING Map 10 NS34

Montgreenan Mansion House

Gracious 17th-century mansion set amidst 48 acres of park and woods. Tranquillity indoors too where sumptuous day rooms, a drawing room, library and club-style bar await. Choose from a five-course fixed menu or brief carte. Classic sauces accompany myriad dishes from roast duck and sauté of lamb's liver to vegetable pasta.

Seats: 40. Private dining room 26. Jacket and tie preferred
Style: Traditional, Country-house
Smoking: No smoking in dining room
Civil licence: 110
Accommodation: 21 rooms (21 en suite) ★ ★ ★
Directions: 4 miles N of Irvine & 19 miles (20 minutes) S of Glasgow on A736.

Montgreenan Estate, KA13 7QZ
Tel: 01294 557733
Fax: 01294 850397
e enquiries@montgreenanhotel.
co.uk
Chef(s): Alan McCall
Owner(s): Crieff Hydro
Cost: Alc £26.50, set price L
£12.75/D £25.80. ☺ ☺ H/wine
£12.50
Times: Noon-2pm/7-9.30pm.
Additional: Sunday L. Bar food.
Children welcome. Vegetarian by request only

LARGS

Map 10 NS25

Brisbane House

NEW

14 Greenock Road, Esplanade,
KA30 8NF
Tel: 01475 687200
Fax: 01475 676295
Telephone for further details

Overlooking the bay towards the Isle of Cumbrae this well-established hotel has been modernised to great effect by the present owners. Eat in the formal restaurant or the more contemporary conservatory from a menu offering some imaginative combinations. Amongst the starters, wild mushroom tartlet with smoked salmon on red chard with quails eggs and a Champagne sabayon has worked well. Braised fillet of cod with a brandade of langoustine has succeeded amongst the main courses.

AYRSHIRE, SOUTH

ALLOWAY

Map 10 NS31

Ivy House

NEW

KN7 4NL
Tel: 01292 442336
Fax: 01292 445572
e theivyhousealloway@hotmail.com
Chef(s): Martin Ward & Joe Queen
Owner(s): George & Eli Whitlock
Cost: *Alc* £19.50, set price L £15/
D £28-£40. ☺ H/wine £12.95
Times: Noon-2.30pm/6.30-10pm.
Additional: Sunday L. Children welcome
Seats: 90. Private dining room 40
Style: Modern, Chic
Smoking: No smoking in dining room
Civil licence: 90

Robbie Burns' cottage may be just around the corner, but this smart restaurant has its eyes firmly fixed ahead. The modern style of cooking verges on the adventurous, with a lighter version of the dinner menu at lunchtime. Attentive staff serve dishes like chicken liver parfait with apricot chutney (smooth and rich), and lamb bourguignon with a spaghetti of spring vegetables and herb mash. Desserts range from crème brûlée, to warm sticky toffee pudding, and chilled coconut rice pudding, and there are tasty petit fours and good coffee. Meals are served in the Mediterranean-style conservatory with courtyard, or other cosy dining areas. Several wines by the glass.

Accommodation: 5 rooms (5 en suite)
Directions: From Glasgow exit M8 J20 towards Kilmarnock/ Prestwick Airport. Follow A77 to Ayr, then to Alloway. Through Alloway to T-Junct. Turn R, Ivy House 0.25 mile

AYR

Map 10 NS32

Fairfield House Hotel

12 Fairfield Road, KA7 2AR
Tel: 01292 267461
Fax: 01292 261456
e reservations@fairfieldhotel.co.uk
Chef(s): Brian Murphy
Cost: *Alc* £27. ☺ ☺ H/wine £12.95
Times: Dinner only, 7-9.30pm.
Additional: Sunday L. Bar food. Children welcome
Seats: 50. Private dining room 80. Jacket and tie preferred

Smart restaurant in a peaceful Victorian mansion. The menu is to the point, but 'quality not quantity' is an appropriate adage in this case with every dish demonstrating careful manipulation of quality produce. A beautifully tender fillet of Shetland lamb is one of a number of successful dishes from a kitchen showing significant promise.

Style: Traditional
Smoking: No smoking in dining room
Civil licence: 80
Accommodation: 44 rooms (44 en suite) ★ ★ ★ ★
Directions: Town centre, down Miller Rd to T-junction with traffic lights, filter L, immediately R into Fairfield Rd

Fouters Bistro

2A Academy Street, KA7 1HS
Tel: 01292 261391
Fax: 01292 619323

A warm welcome greets diners to this colourful, bustling basement bistro that is a veritable institution in the town.

Laurie Black is always keen to discuss what is best on the day, practising what he preaches in the use of finest flavours of Scotland. Smoked Finan haddock and Shetland mussels share the menu with chicken and mushroom country paté and baked mountain goats' cheese topped with tapenade. Prime local beef is cut and trimmed to order and served with hand-cut fries; alternatives include pan-roasted duck breast with apple and Calvados, braised hill lamb with rosemary sauce, a puff pastry of wild mushrooms and the best hand-picked catch fresh from Troon fish market.

Directions: Town centre, opposite Town Hall, down Cobblestone Lane

e qualityfood@fouters.co.uk
Chef(s): Laurie Black
Owner(s): Laurie & Fran Black
Cost: Alc £22.50. ☺ ☺
H/wine £11.95
Times: Noon-2pm/6-10pm. Closed Sun, Mon, 25-27 Dec, 1-3 Jan
Additional: Children welcome
Seats: 38. Private dining room 14
Style: Bistro-style
Smoking: No-smoking area; no cigars; Air conditioning

BALLANTRAE Map 10 NX08

Glenapp Castle NEW

KA26 0NZ
Tel: 01465 831212
Fax: 01465 831000
Telephone for further details

Booking is absolutely essential if you want to gain entry to the historic and lovingly restored castle with its fine grounds. "Pure luxury" is the defining characteristic with a wood panelled drawing room or the library the ideal places to take drinks before a dinner based on well-sourced ingredients. The set dinner is offered on an inclusive basis with wine and drinks, and changes daily. Fillet of turbot has come in the simple company of baby carrots and chervil sauce and lamb cutlets with tomato Provençal and fine beans has been judged a success. Expect canapés and an amuse (perhaps an asparagus feuilletté) amongst the add-ons.

GIRVAN Map 10 NX19

Wildings

Montgomerie Street, KA26 9HE
Tel: 01465 713481
Telephone for further details

Vibrant decor matches a tremendously lively atmosphere with the family run style making the whole place welcoming and comfortable. Good use is made of local produce such as prawns freshly landed at the nearby harbour, peeled in the kitchen, lightly sautéed so as to retain firmness and served simply with garlic butter.

MAYBOLE Map 10 NS20

Ladyburn

KA19 7SG
Tel: 01655 740585
Fax: 01655 740580
e jh@demon.co.uk
Chef(s): Jane Hepburn
Cost: Set price L £15/D £30.
H/wine £12
Times: 12.30-1.30pm/7.30-8.15pm.
Closed L Mon-Tue & Sun
Seats: 20. Jacket and tie preferred

Traditional and French cuisine provide the backbone to the menu at this charming country house. It is particularly noted for its delightful garden, part of Scotland's Garden Scheme. Both the fixed-price three-course lunch and dinner are carefully created from locally produced fish and game.

Style: Country-House **Smoking:** No smoking in dining room
Accommodation: 5 rooms (5 en suite) ★ ★
Directions: Telephone for directions

Scotland

Scotland

TROON

Map 10 NS33

Cellars

NEW

Part of the Anchorage Hotel with its popular bar and bar food operation. Cellars is an intimate basement restaurant with candlelight, deep blues and big band music. An admirable, rustic approach to the cooking with good home-made breads served with dipping oil and the likes of sautéed chicken livers with tomato brioche and redcurrant dressing. A hearty seafood stew (smoked halibut, lobster claw, monkfish and salmon), has come served with new potatoes at lunch. A coffee and chocolate terrine has proved a satisfying conclusion.

Style: Art Deco
Smoking: No smoking in dining room
Accommodation: 18 rooms (18 en suite)
Directions: Telephone for directions

147 Templehill, KA10 6BQ
Tel: 01292 317448
Fax: 01292 318508
🇪 anchor1812@aol.com
Chef(s): Robbie O' Keefe
Owner(s): Mr & Mrs Ronney
Cost: Alc £23.95, set price L £12.45/D £23.95. ☺ ☺
H/wine £11.50
Times: Noon-2.30pm/6-10pm.
Closed Tue, New Year
Additional: Sunday L. Children welcome
Seats: 38. Private dining room 35

Highgrove House

Refreshingly simple cooking that has kept pace with fashion and offers a sophisticated dining experience (booking essential). The split-level restaurant is an ideal setting, with its elegant, formally-set tables and near-unsurpassable views over Troon towards Ailsa Craig and Arran. Sauces complement dishes rather than overwhelm, as in pheasant breast mille-feuille with mushroom sauce, seared scallops with tomato dressing and leaves, and best end of lamb with wild mushrooms and orange and rosemary jus. Bread, butter and raspberry pudding was recently enjoyed, with good filter coffee and petit fours. Staff are pleasant, and wine knowledge is excellent.

Smoking: No cigars; Air conditioning
Accommodation: 9 rooms (9 en suite) ★ ★ ★
Directions: A77 from Ayr (Glasgow), L at Prestwick Airport, first R to Old Irvine. First L to Loans, R at mini rdbt to Highgrove.

Old Loans Road, KA10 7HL
Tel: 01292 312511
Fax: 01292 318228
🇪 highgrove@costley-hotels.co.uk
Chef(s): Laurent Labede
Owner(s): Bill Costley & Cath Costley
Cost: Alc £22, set price L £14.95/D £25.95. ☺ ☺ H/wine £9.95
Times: Noon-2.30pm/6-9.30pm
Additional: Sunday L. Bar food L. Children welcome
Seats: 80. Private dining room 14
Style: Traditional

Lochgreen House

A slightly colonial feel to the dining room that even with the finery and air of formality offers a fresh and appealing environment in which to dine. The menu makes the most of the opportunity presented by the enviable larder of the Scottish west coast. Whilst the produce tends towards the native, the cooking style tends towards the global with a creative selection of canapés including a cajun beef samosa and a warm scallop and caviar tartlet. Excellent scallops also on offer in combination with Ayrshire bacon, crayfish vinaigrette and (perhaps superfluously given the success of those) a coriander salad with orange and quail's eggs. Special praise for a "highly accomplished" dish of langoustines tails with fricassée of petit pois, button mushrooms and a creamed leek purée. Look out for the Lochgreen dessert, an assiette of tiny contrasting items presented in stunning, eye-catching fashion.

Monktonhill Road, Southwood, KA10 7EN
Tel: 01292 313343
Fax: 01292 318661
Telephone for further details

Piersland House Hotel

Like the remainder of the hotel, the stylish dining room retains all the original features of the home of Sir Alexander Walker,

Craigend Road, KA10 6HD
Tel: 01292 314747
Fax: 01292 315613

the wealthy Scotch whisky baron. A high standard of cuisine is achieved in the dinner menu which may offer pigeon breast on a black pudding scone accompanied by a red cabbage, apple and port essence, or loin of lamb with spinach and pimento served with onion marmalade in a tarragon and tomato jus. Vegetarian options have been an open puff pastry tartlet with caramelized onions and a provençale of vegetables topped with Brie.

e reservations@piersland.co.uk
Chef(s): John Rae
Owner(s): Mr. J Brown
Cost: Alc £25, set price L £10.95. ☺
☺ H/wine £10.95
Times: Noon-2.30pm/6.45-9.30pm.
Additional: Sunday L. Bar food.
Children welcome
Seats: 42. Private dining room 94
Style: Modern, Country-House
Smoking: No smoking in dining room

Civil licence: 73
Accommodation: 28 rooms (28 en suite) ★ ★ ★
Directions: Opposite Royal Troon Golf Club.

TURNBERRY

Map 10 NS20

Malin Court

KA26 9PB
Tel: 01655 331457
Fax: 01655 331072
e info@malincourt.co.uk
Chef(s): Andrea Beach
Cost: Set price L £10/D £20-£22.
☺ ☺ H/wine £11.95
Times: 12.30-2pm/7.30-9pm.
Additional: Sunday L. Bar food.
Children welcome
Seats: 80. Private dining room 70
Style: Modern
Smoking: No smoking in dining room
Accommodation: 18 rooms (18 en
suite) ★ ★ ★
Directions: On A719 one mile from
A77 on N side of village

Bright contemporary dining room overlooking the Clyde estuary with views out towards the island of Arran. The hotel is a rather unique institution - located at one end of a popular golf course and functioning in part as an exclusive retirement home. Nothing pedestrian or retiring about the cuisine however, take for example an excellent smoked haddock risotto - light, moist and full of flavour. A firm grasp of classic techniques is apparent in cooking typified by a refreshingly honest spinach soup, whilst an elaborate dish based around medallion of pork with a truffle and wild mushroom sauce demonstrated real creative flair.

DUMFRIES & GALLOWAY

Scotland

CASTLE DOUGLAS
Map 11 NX76

Plumed Horse Restaurant

Unexpected gem in a quiet village location. A light touch results in happy combinations such as fillets of salmon and sea bass with couscous and an orange and saffron sauce. The bread and butter pudding is one of the finest around, with pistachio

Main Street, Crossmicheal,
DG7 3AU
Tel: 01556 670333
Fax: 01556 670333
e plumed.horse@virgin.net
Chef(s): Tony Borthwick,
James Pearce
Owner(s): Tony Borthwick &
Charles Kirkbride
Cost: Alc £29.50, set price L £14.95-
£17.20. ☺ ☺ H/wine £10.99
Times: 12.30-1.30pm/7-9pm. Closed
Mon, L Sat, 1 wk Jan, 10 days Sept,
25-26 Dec, D Sun in winter
Additional: Sunday L. Children
welcome. Vegetarian by request only
Seats: 30. Private dining room 20
Style: Classic, Chic
Smoking: No smoking in dining room;
Air conditioning
Directions: 3.5 miles NW of Castle
Douglas on A713

ice cream and crème anglaise lifting the dish further. A separate vegetarian set menu offers a good range of dishes including cheddar soufflé and a charlotte of spiced aubergine. The dining space is fairly small and the decor stylish in its simplicity.

GATEHOUSE OF FLEET
Map 11 NX55

Cally Palace Hotel

An elegant dining room offers a grandiose charm in this Victorian shooting lodge. From cream of celery and Stilton soup to steamed medallions of monkfish on griddled provençal vegetables with sauce vierge, there is welcome steadiness to the cooking and no shortage of real flavour.

Style: Traditional
Smoking: No smoking in dining room; Air conditioning
Accommodation: 55 rooms (55 en suite) ★★★★
Directions: From M6 and A74(M) take A75, at Gatehouse take B727. Hotel on L

DG7 2DL
Tel: 01557 814341
Fax: 01557 814522
e info@callypalace.co.uk
Chef(s): Jamie Muirhead
Owner(s): H. McMillan
Cost: Alc £12-£25. H/wine £11.90
Times: Noon-1pm/6.45-9.15pm.
Closed Jan 3 – early Feb
Additional: Sunday L. Bar food L.
Children welcome
Seats: 130. Jacket and tie preferred

KIRKCUDBRIGHT
Map 11 NX65

Selkirk Arms Hotel

Once a hostelry frequented by Robbie Burns, this is now a smart, modern hotel noted for its friendly and attentive service. Food can be taken in the lounge bar bistro or in the restaurant, whose dinner menus are a touch classier, with good quality, locally sourced produce. Queenie scallop and prawn risotto is dressed with anchovy and Szechuan peppercorn butter, saddle of local roe deer with black pudding and apple compote, while quenelles of dark chocolate and ginger mousse with toasted

Old High Street,
DG6 4JG
Tel: 01557 330402
Fax: 01557 331639
e reception@selkirkarmshotel.co.uk
Chef(s): Ian Barron
Owner(s): E & S Morris
Cost: Set Price D £24. ☺
H/wine £8.95

almond and coconut flakes are followed by coffee and petit fours, served back in the cosy Burns Room.

Accommodation: 16 rooms (16 en suite) ★ ★ ★
Directions: 5 miles S of A75 junction with A711

Times: Dinner only, 7-9.30pm
Additional: Sunday L. Bar food. Children welcome
Seats: 60. Private dining room 22
Smoking: No smoking in dining room
Civil licence: 70

LOCKERBIE
Map 11 NY18

The Dryfesdale Country House

Fine views from the airy restaurant of this 17th-century country house hotel. Scottish flavours feature prominently, and a tartlet filled with Lockerbie haggis and mushrooms, topped by a poached egg and drizzled with whisky cream sauce is a house speciality. Other options include steaks, Solway salmon, and iced cranachan parfait set on traditional shortbread.

DG11 2SF
Tel: 01576 202427
Fax: 01576 204187
e reception@dryfesdalehotel.co.uk
Chef(s): Stuart Anold
Owner(s): Mr C Sturman
Cost: Alc £25, set price L £12-£14/ D £19.95-£21.50. ☺ ☺ H/wine £11
Times: Noon-2.30pm/7-9pm.
Additional: Sunday L. Bar food. Children welcome
Seats: 60. Private dining room 80
Style: Country-house
Smoking: No smoking in dining room
Civil licence: 90
Accommodation: 15 rooms (15 en suite) ★ ★ ★
Directions: M74 J17 (0.5 mile) to Lockerbie

MOFFAT
Map 11 NT00

Beechwood Country House

Freshly made canapés in the bar and home-made breads at the table hold plenty of promise for the five-course weekly changing set menu at Beechwood. The tenderness of the lamb and good vegetables have impressed in a dish of pan-fried lamb in red wine jus. The wine list, too, is of more than passing interest.

Harthope Place,
DG10 9RS
Tel: 01683 220210
Fax: 01683 220889
e info@beechwoodhousehotel.co.uk
Chef(s): Alan Mitchell
Owner(s): J P & L M Rogers

Scotland

MOFFAT *Continued*

Map 11 NT00

Cost: Set price L £15.50, set price D £25.50. H/wine £11
Times: Noon-2pm/7-8.45pm. Closed L Mon-Thu, 2 Jan-18 Feb
Additional: Sunday L. Children welcome
Seats: 20. Private dining room 10
Style: Traditional, Country-house

Smoking: No smoking in dining room
Accommodation: 7 rooms (7 en suite)
★★
Directions: At N end of High Street turn R

Moffat House Hotel   NEW

Spacious, elegant dining room in a fine listed Adam mansion in the centre of town. Unusual starters such as pan-fried grouse on crisp tattie scone prove successful, as does the fillet of pork with chestnut mushroom sauce. Lovely moist, full flavoured chocolate pudding with bitter chocolate sauce and home-made vanilla ice cream shows the same attention to detail.

High Street, DG10 9HL
Tel: 01683 220039
Fax: 01683 221288
Telephone for further details

Well View Hotel

This traditionally appointed hotel dining room is pretty enough but the food is the star, which is a tribute to Janet Schuckardt's accurate and original cooking. The 6-course tasting menu offers choice only at the dessert stage. Dishes are quite simple but

enjoyable for their focus on fresh ingredients and bold flavours, as in a vibrant chicken terrine with Cumberland sauce, and fillet of cod with tomato and basil sauce. There's a wide selection of wines, with quite a ritual attached to the service, with mein host tasting all wines from a silver cup.

Ballplay Road, DG10 9JU
Tel: 01683 220184
Fax: 01683 220088
e info@wellview.co.uk
Chef(s): Janet Schuckardt
Owner(s): John & Janet Schuckardt
Cost: Set price L £15/D £29.
H/wine £13
Times: 12.15-1.30pm/6.30-9pm.
Closed L Sat
Additional: Sunday L. Children 5yrs+ at D. Vegetarian by request only
Seats: 20. Private dining room 6.
Jacket and tie preferred
Style: Traditional, Country-House
Smoking: No smoking in dining room
Accommodation: 6 rooms
(6 en suite) ★
Directions: From Moffat take A708 (Selkirk); turn left after fire station in Ballplay Road

NEWTON STEWART

Map 10 NX46

Kirroughtree House

All change as we went to press with Ian Bennett departing and Rolf Mueller who achieved Three AA Rosettes at Kilfinan, arriving. It's an impressive venue for any chef with the 17th-century mansion set in eight acres of landscaped gardens. His style is described as Classical French with Scottish influences. The menu is set to include dishes along the lines of ravioli of quail and foie gras with celeriac purée and baked shallot sauce and breast of free range chicken with baby lobster and spinach.

Minnigaff,
DG8 6AN
Tel: 01671 402141
Fax: 01671 402425
e kirroughtree@n-stewart.demon.co.uk
Owner(s): Mr D McMillan
Cost: *Alc* £20, set price L £13.50/ D£30. ☺ H/wine £14.50

Smoking: No smoking in dining room
Accommodation: 17 rooms (17 en suite) ★ ★ ★
Directions: From A75 turn left into A712 (New Galloway), hotel entrance 300yds on left

Times: Noon-1.30pm/7-9pm.
Closed 3 Jan-mid Feb
Additional: Sunday L. Children 10+
Seats: 45. Jacket and tie preferred
Style: Formal

Scotland

PORTPATRICK   Map 10 NW95

Fernhill Hotel

Situated in a picture-postcard setting in the fishing village of Portpatrick, with views across the Irish Sea. The restaurant boasts its own lobster holding facility, providing freshly caught lobster in season. Local ingredients are top notch, although they could be treated with a little more sensitivity at times. Venison is 'melt-in-the-mouth' and Eccelfeccan tart is another excellent choice.

Smoking: No-smoking area
Accommodation: 23 rooms (23 en suite) ★ ★ ★
Directions: A77 from Stranraer, R before war memorial. Hotel 1st L

Heugh Road, DG9 8TD
Tel: 01776 810220
Fax: 01776 810596
e fernhill@portpatrick.demon.co.uk
Chef(s): John Henry
Owner(s): McMillan Hotels
Cost: Alc £24.70. Set price D £22.50.
☺ ☺ H/wine £9.50
Times: Noon-1.45pm/6.30-9.15pm
Additional: Sunday L. Bar food L.
Children welcome
Seats: 65. Private dining room 14
Style: Traditional, Informal

STOP PRESS
Change of Chef

STRANRAER   Map 10 NX06

Corsewall
Lighthouse Hotel   NEW

No surprise to find a nautical theme to the cosy dining room in this listed 19th-century lighthouse - and what better venue for a rounded meal? Corsewall's menu features locally sourced produce: quail, venison, salmon and Scotch beef, for example, appear as main courses. For flavour and texture, sample the game terrine served with Scottish oatcakes and don't overlook the Chocolate Nemesis - a beacon amongst the desserts!

Seats: 28
Style: Rustic, Country-House
Smoking: No smoking in dining room
Accommodation: 9 rooms (8 en suite) ★ ★ ★
Directions: From either A72 or A75 take B718, 12 miles W of Stranraer

Corsewall Point,
Kirkcolm, DG9 0QG
Tel: 01776 853220
Fax: 01776 854231
e corsewall_lighthouse@msn.com
Chef(s): Raymond McMurtrie,
Tony Corner
Owner(s): Gordon, Kay & Pamela Ward
Cost: Alc £23-£29.50. ☺ ☺
H/wine £12.95
Times: Noon-3pm/7-10pm.
Additional: Sunday L. Bar food L.
Children welcome

Scotland

STRANRAER *Continued* Map 10 NX06

North West Castle Hotel

Built for the Arctic explorer Sir John Ross in 1820 on the shores of Loch Ryan, North West Castle is a popular hotel which overlooks the bay and ferry terminal. During dinner, a pianist plays in the elegant dining room while you enjoy a set meal. Grilled fillet of Isle of Bute rainbow trout can be enjoyed, as well as the likes of pan-fried venison.

Style: Traditional, Formal. **Smoking:** No smoking in dining room. Jacket and tie preferred. **Civil licence:** 180
Accommodation: 73 rooms (73 en suite) ★ ★ ★ ★
Directions: Town Centre

DG9 8EH
Tel: 01776 704413
Fax: 01776 702646
e info@northwestcastle.co.uk
Chef(s): Bruce McLean
Owner(s): H C McMillan
Cost: *Alc* £19, set price D £21. ☺ ☺ H/wine £9.50
Times: Noon-2pm/7-9.30pm.
Additional: Sunday L. Bar food. Children welcome
Seats: 130. Private dining room 130

DUNBARTONSHIRE, WEST

BALLOCH Map 10 NS38

Cameron House Hotel

This much-extended mansion house that enjoys an unrivalled setting on the banks of Loch Lomond plays host to a variety of dining options, of which the Georgian Room is the hotel's flagship. Emphasis on Scotland's larder of fine fresh produce is much vaunted on the *à la carte* and gourmet menus, served in plush surroundings to the live accompaniment of piano or guitar. Ambitious in their approach to luxury ingredients and flavours, results at times can be a little over-elaborate. Nevertheless much credit for pan-fried roulade, crab meat with truffle pasta and tomato and pigeon breast poached in game consommé with wild mushrooms, chestnuts and parisienne potatoes. Refined desserts include the likes of a cleanly flavoured iced honey parfait with well balanced honey and ginger sauce. Service is friendly, well directed and professional.

Directions: M8/A82 to Dumbarton: take road to Luss, hotel signed 1 mile past Balloch on R

G83 8QZ
Tel: 01389 755565
Fax: 01389 759522
e devere.cameron@airtime.co.uk
Chef(s): Peter Fleming
Owner(s): De Vere Hotels
Cost: Set price D £43-£49
Times: Dinner only, 7-10pm.
Closed Monday
Additional: Children 14+
Seats: 42. Jacket and tie preferred
Smoking: No smoking in dining room; Air conditioning
Accommodation: 96 rooms (96 en suite) ★ ★ ★ ★ ★

CLYDEBANK Map 11 NS56

Beardmore Hotel

Beardmore Street, G81 4SA
Tel: 0141 951 6000
Fax: 0141 951 6018
e beardmore-hotel@hci.co.uk
Chef(s): Derek Donaldson
Cost: *Alc* £25. ☺ ☺ H/wine £13
Times: Dinner only, 7-10pm.
Closed Xmas
Additional: Sunday L.
Children 12yrs+
Seats: 60. Private dining room 16
Style: Chic
Smoking: No smoking in dining room; Air conditioning
Accommodation: 168 rooms (168 en suite) ★ ★ ★ ★

Well-placed for business guests and holidaymakers, the Beardmore Hotel is a tasteful, modern hotel that sits near the Erskine Bridge by the River Clyde. It's also a convenient twenty minutes from the city centre. Whilst no lunch is served in the main restaurant, dinner in the Citrus Restaurant can be chosen from a classical menu, with tournedos of duck and guinea fowl, shallot purée and roasted root vegetables amongst the options. Main courses major on prime cuts of meat and game from escalope of pork fillet to loin of highland venison or breast of goose.

Directions: M8 J19, follow signs for Clydeside Expressway to Glasgow Rd, then signs for Clydebank Business Park. Hotel on L within HCI International Medical Centre complex.

Scotland

DUNDEE CITY

DUNDEE
Map 11 NO43

Sandford Hotel

An elegant, pleasant restaurant, run by friendly staff. The varied menu places traditional Scottish fare such as fillet of Aberdeen Angus beef, Tay salmon and Loch Fyne scallops alongside, for example, a baked aubergine, tomato and goats' cheese gateau or, perhaps, Cambazola and fennel stuffed crêpes. A lunchtime bar menu offers good value dishes.

Style: Modern
Smoking: No smoking in dining room
Civil licence: 60
Accommodation: 16 rooms (16 en suite) ★ ★ ★
Directions: 4 miles south of Tay Bridge at jctn of A92 and B946

Newport Hill, Wormit,
DD6 8RG
Tel: 01382 541802
Fax: 01382 542136
e sandford.hotel@btinternet.com
Chef(s): Gordon Inglis
Cost: Set price D £25. ☺ H/wine £11
Times: Dinner only 6.30-9.30pm
Additional: Bar food. Children welcome
Seats: 30. Private dining room 50

EDINBURGH, CITY OF

EDINBURGH
Map 11 NT27

Atrium

10 Cambridge Street, EH1 2ED
Tel: 0131 228 8882
Fax: 0131 228 8808
Chef(s): Neil Forbes
Owner(s): Mr & Mrs Radford
Cost: Alc £25-£33, set price L £18/ D £25. ☺ ☺
Times: Noon-2pm/6.30-10.30pm. Closed Sun, L Sat, 25-26 Dec
Additional: Children welcome
Seats: 70
Style: Modern
Smoking: Air conditioning
Directions: From Princes St, turn into Lothian Rd, 2nd L & 1st R, by the Traverse Theatre

Striking in design, described by one staff member as a cross between Mad Max and the Flintstones, Atrium is situated within the Traverse theatre complex. Recycled railway sleepers to sit at, under concrete and sailcloth ceilings and flickering oil-lamps conspire to make a bold fashion statement, matched by consistent cooking that offers Mediterranean-style influences with touches of true flair. Flavour combinations work well in a

Scotland

starter of wild rabbit, truffled cannellini beans and red wine jus
and in a fine yet simple main dish comprising roast lamb rump,
whole tomatoes and delectably pulpy garlic cloves with a
niçoise salad, crispy beans and black olives that scored highly
for its quality of ingredients and intensity of flavours. A
sommelier's selection by the glass to accompany the alternative
set-price dinner menu is a welcome initiative.

Balmoral Hotel, Hadrians

Deliciously decorated in shades of pistachio, chocolate and
blue, Hadrian's is an upbeat, 1970s style brasserie. The menu
offers a generous, mix and match selection including soups,
salads, fish and meat dishes. A meal might begin with a terrine
of osso bucco and woodland mushroom, followed by a main
course of roast monkfish with ginger and garlic herb noodles.

Style: Chic, Art Deco
Smoking: No-smoking area; Air conditioning
Accommodation: 188 rooms (188 en suite) ★ ★ ★ ★ ★
Directions: Hotel at E end of Princes Street, Hotel is next to
Waverley Station

1 Princes Street, EH2 2EQ
Tel: 0131 557 5000
Fax: 0131 557 3747
e hadrians@thebalmoralhotel.com
Chef(s): Jeff Bland
Owner(s): R F Hotels
Cost: *Alc* £20, set price L £9.50. ☺ ☺
H/wine £13
Times: Noon-2.30pm/6.30-10.30pm.
Additional: Sunday L. Children
welcome
Seats: 88. Private dining room 30

Balmoral Hotel, Number One

Towering over the east end of Princes Street, Edinburgh's
Balmoral Hotel is imposing in its Edwardian grandeur. Guests
can take to the Roman-style health spa or the Palm Court Bar,
and dine in two restaurants of differing styles (see Hadrians
above). Experience haute dining at Number One where either a
carte menu or regularly changing market menu offer a good
selection of Scottish produce. Both the hotel and restaurant
offer a wealth of character and the cuisine majors on good,
simply handled local meats and seafood. Ranging from Scottish
beef and braised oxtail to Skye crab, which all feature strongly,
there is quality throughout

Directions: See entry above

1 Princes Street, EH2 2EQ
Tel: 0131 557 6727
Fax: 0131 557 8740
e numberone@thebalmoralhotel.
com
Chef(s): Jeff Bland
Owner(s): RF Hotels
Cost: *Alc* £37, set price L £15.50/
D £35. ☺ H/wine £16
Times: Noon-2pm/7-10pm.
Closed L Sat-Sun, 1-7 Jan
Additional: Children welcome
Seats: 50. Private dining room 50
Style: Modern, French
Smoking: No-smoking area; no pipes
or cigars; Air conditioning
Accommodation: 188 rooms (188 en
suite) ★ ★ ★ ★ ★

Bruntsfield Hotel

Bright conservatory restaurant offering imaginative dinner menus. Fish aficionados will be well served by duo of smoked halibut and salmon followed perhaps by grilled sea bass with couscous and a sweet pepper beurre noisette. Otherwise a fillet of Perthshire pork on Bramley apple compote scented with ginger might well appeal.

Additional: Sunday L. Bar food. Children welcome
Seats: 70. **Style:** Bistro
Smoking: No-smoking area
Accommodation: 75 en suite ★ ★ ★

69/74 Bruntsfield Place, EH10 4HH
Tel: 0131 229 1393
Fax: 0131 229 5634
e bruntsfield@queensferry-hotels.co.uk
Chef(s): Martyn Dixon
Owner(s): Mr & Mrs C Gwyn
Cost: Alc £28. Set price L £11.95/D £24.50. H/wine £9.95
Times: Noon-2pm/5.30-9.30pm.
Closed L Mon-Fri

Channings Restaurant

Occupying the lower ground floor of this Edwardian building, the older, traditional part of the restaurant leads into the light, bright contemporary conservatory. Modern Scottish food with a continental twist produces some adventurous, imaginative recipes: creamed artichoke and white port soup with rabbit boudins and white truffle oil to start, for instance. For a tasty main course, choose saddle of lamb à la sarladaise with wonderful 'candied' carrots and shallots and a cabbage parcel of shredded shank and vegetables. Tempting, innovative desserts make selecting a treat and the wine list includes a notable selection by the glass.

Directions: From Princes St follow signs to Forth Bridge (A90), cross Dean Bridge and take 4th R into South Learmonth Ave. Follow road to R at bottom of hill

South Learmonth Gardens, EH4 1EZ
Tel & Fax: 0131 315 2225
e restaurant@channings.co.uk
Chef(s): Richard Glennie
Owner(s): Mr P Taylor
Cost: Set price L £16/D £25. ☺ ☺ H/wine £14
Times: Noon-2pm/7-10pm.
Closed L Sun, 22-26 Dec
Additional: Bar food. Children welcome
Seats: 80. Private dining room 50
Style: Modern
Smoking: No smoking in dining room
Civil licence: 50
Accommodation: 46 rooms (46 en suite) ★ ★ ★ ★

Dalhousie Castle and Spa   NEW

Stunning 13th century castle set in beautiful parkland. The Dungeon restaurant makes no secret of its location providing an intimate fine dining setting. A welcome lightness of touch from the cooking which might feature the likes of a deft ravioli of confit of rabbit as a starter and confit of salmon with pancetta and lentils as a main. Puddings have featured a creditable assiette of peach desserts.

Style: Castle Dungeon
Smoking: Air conditioning. **Civil licence:** 90
Accommodation: 32 rooms (32 en suite) ★ ★ ★

Bonnybridge, EH19 3JB
Tel: 01875 820153
Fax: 01875 821936
e enquiries@dalhousiecastle.co.uk
Chef(s): Francois Graud, Charles Afrin
Cost: Alc £29.50, set price D £29.50. H/wine £12.40
Times: Dinner only, 7-9pm.
Closed Closed 2 wks Jan
Additional: Bar food. Children welcome
Seats: 44. Private dining room 100

Scotland

EDINBURGH *Continued*   **Map 11 NT27**

Duck's at Le Marché Noir

Fresh modern concepts guarantee interest and variety whilst a strong command of classical cooking styles and techniques (notably in a wonderfully textured chocolate and raspberry tart) ensures that justice is done to high quality ingredients. Tucked away just north of the city centre, so convenient but not too hectic.

Seats: 60. Private dining room 35
Smoking: No-smoking area
Directions: Follow the 'Mound' across Princes Street, George Street, Queen Street to bottom of Dundas Street

2/4 Eyre Place, EH3 5EP
Tel: 0131 558 1608
Fax: 0131 467 7230
🅱 bookings@ducks.co.uk
Chef(s): Brett Moreman
Owner(s): Mr M K Duck
Cost: *Alc* £29, set price L £15.50.
☺ ☺ H/wine £9.50
Times: Noon-2.30pm/7-10.30pm.
Closed L Sat-Sun, 25-26 Dec
Additional: Children welcome

George Inter-Continental

A short stroll from Princes Street finds you seated in the elegant Le Chambertin Restaurant - the fine dining option in this extensive hotel. The *carte* is extensive and features the likes of duck liver and morel parfait with brandied raisins and kumquat chutney. Buffet choice also available.

19-21 George Street, EH2 2PB
Tel: 0131 225 1251
Fax: 0131 226 5644
🅱 edinburgh@interconti.com
Chef(s): Klaus Knust
Cost: *Alc* £24. ☺ ☺ H/wine £13
Times: Noon-2.30pm/6.30-10pm.
Additional: Sunday L. Bar food. Children welcome
Seats: 150. Private dining room 20
Style: Modern Scottish
Smoking: No-smoking area; no pipes
Civil licence: 100
Accommodation: 195 rooms (195 en suite) ★★★★
Directions: At E end of George St, nr St Andrews Square

Haldanes

39A Albany Street, EH1 3QY
Tel: 0131 556 8407
Fax: 0131 557 2662
🅱 gkelso1547@aol.com
Chef(s): George Kelso
Owner(s): Mr and Mrs G Kelso
Cost: *Alc* £30, set price L £16.95. ☺
H/wine £12.75
Times: noon-1.30pm/6-9pm.
Closed L Sat-Mon
Additional: Children welcome
Seats: 50. Private dining room 20
Style: Traditional Country-House
Smoking: No smoking in dining room
Directions: Telephone for directions

Scotland

Situated in the elegant Georgian basement of The Albany Hotel, from which large windows overlook a small patio garden, Haldanes is a comfortable, pleasantly furnished restaurant offering a short lunch and more elaborate dinner menu. Try the crab cake starter, topped with crispy deep-fried leeks, and complemented by a hot chilli dressing, while the tenderness of the braised lamb main course is definitely worth a look. Look out for the chewy and crackly iced honey and praline parfait served with a mango and kiwi compote and roasted strawberries.

Holyrood Hotel

This is a hotel of modern construction next door to the new Scottish parliament, and the haunt of politicians and journalists as well as an international clientele. Flints restaurant, looking across to The Scotsman offices, is a sophisticated split-level affair, supremely comfortable with smart leather armchairs. Among the lunchtime options are pressed terrine of chicken and walnut with rosemary and grain mustard dressing, and seared supreme of duckling on braised red cabbage with little clusters of delicious apple and pear relish.

Civil licence: 120
Accommodation: 157 rooms (157 en suite) ★ ★ ★ ★
Directions: Edinburgh city centre near the Royal Mile

Holyrood Road, EH8 6AE
Tel: 0131 550 4500
Fax: 0131 550 4545
ⓔ info@holyrood.macdonald-hotels.co.uk
Chef(s): Steve Morrow
Owner(s): Macdonald Hotels
Cost: *Alc* £25-£30/D £18-£25. ☺ ☺
Times: 12.30-2pm/5-10pm
Additional: Bar food. Children welcome
Seats: 95. Private dining room 20
Style: Modern
Smoking: No smoking in dining room

Iggs

15 Jeffrey Street, EH1 1DR
Tel: 0131 557 8184
Fax: 0131 441 7111
Chef(s): Andy McQueen
Owner(s): Mr I Campos
Cost: *Alc* £29.50, set price L £12.
☺ H/wine £11.50
Times: Noon-3pm/6.30-1am.
Closed Sun
Additional: Children welcome
Seats: 50. Private dining room 40
Style: Modern
Smoking: No-smoking area;
Air conditioning
Directions: At the heart of Edinburgh's Old Town, just off the Royal Mile

Striking Spanish-style restaurant with mustard-coloured walls, big mirrors and creative lighting. The menu has a marked Spanish flavour despite the stray dish of tiger prawn wontons or aubergine and chickpea tagine, indeed there is an adjacent tapas bar. Tapas, as a starter, might comprise a generous selection of air-dried ham and chorizo sausage, a wedge of Spanish omelette, pork in red pepper sauce, and spiced sausage with diced potato sautéed in spices - all very tasty and different. Ragout of seafood is a simple but effective dish, with salmon, monkfish, mussels and whelks served in a saffron-scented fish stock with mini vegetables.

Le Café St Honore

French-style café in one of Edinburgh's cobbled back lanes. Buzzing at lunchtime, cosy and candlelit at night, with soft jazz playing in the background. The food is built on Scottish foundations, including some of the best grouse around - perfectly timed and delightfully tender, with a well-executed rösti, lentils and good jus. The thoughtful wine list offers a good selection by the glass.

Style: French
Smoking: No-smoking area
Directions: City centre

34 NW Thistle Street Lane, EH2 1EA
Tel: 0131 226 2211
Chef(s): Chris Colverson
Owner(s): Chris & Gill Colverson
Cost: *Alc* £16-£32. ☺ ☺
H/wine £10.50
Times: Noon-2.15pm/5-10pm.
Closed Sun, L Sat (ex Festival),
24-26 Dec, 3 days New Year
Additional: Children welcome
Seats: 56. Private dining room 18

Malmaison

One Tower Place, Leith, EH6 7DB
Tel: 0131 468 5001
Fax: 0131 468 5002
e edinburgh@malmaison.com
Chef(s): Stuart Muir
Owner(s): S.I.H/M.W.B
Cost: *Alc* £21, set price L £11.95/
D £12.95. ☺ ☺ H/wine £13.95
Times: Noon-2.30pm/6-11pm.
Closed 25 Dec (evening)
Additional: Sunday L. Bar food.
Children welcome
Seats: 66. Private dining room 40
Style: French
Smoking: Air conditioning
Accommodation: 60 rooms (60 en
suite) ★ ★ ★
Directions: From the city centre
follow Leith Docklands, through 3
sets of traffic lights and L into Tower
St

Contemporary style and charm combines with great food to produce a memorable night out. If you can stop yourself making mental notes of ideas for interior decoration you should find dishes such as grilled Toulouse sausage and mash with a Calvados jus to be equally rewarding to scrutiny.

Marriott Dalmahoy Hotel

Once home to William Douglas, who helped Mary Queen of Scots escape from Loch Levern Castle, this imposing mansion stands in extensive parklands. From its Pentland restaurant you can see the lake and Edinburgh Castle beyond. The elegant decor is appropriately traditional, and the menu mostly reflects this style: Scottish smoked salmon and Aberdeen Angus Beef make frequent appearances, but there is also the odd splash of international flavour, as seen in pan-fried langoustines with roasted vegetables and gazpacho dressing or a risotto of artichokes with roasted pepper. Staff are attentive and willing to please.

Accommodation: 215 rooms (215 en suite) ★ ★ ★ ★
Directions: Telephone for directions

Kirknewton, EH27 8EB
Tel: 0131 333 1845
Fax: 0131 333 1433
e dalmahoy@marriotthotels.co.uk
Chef(s): Alan Matthew
Cost: *Alc* £36, set price L £18/
D £22.50. ☺ ☺ H/wine £13
Times: Noon-2pm/7-10pm.
Closed L Sat
Additional: Sunday L.
Children welcome
Seats: 120. Private dining room 14
Style: Classic Country-House
Smoking: No smoking in dining room

Scotland

Martins Restaurant

Situated in the unlikeliest of places - in a quiet back lane tucked away from the lively buzz of the city. Yet Martins is a restaurant worth finding, where dependably good food emerges from the kitchen. Regulars return because they know just what they are getting - and the simple menus are a pleasure to order from. A modern European style is reflected in dishes that are well composed. Take, for example, a delightful panaché of chicken livers, avocado and chorizo - providing 'a Mediterranean overture on the palette' due to carefully chosen leaves and use of delicate, seasonal herbs. Other dishes show an equally considered approach to cooking.

Smoking: No smoking in dining room
Directions: North Lane is off Rose Street which runs parallel to and behind Princes Street

70 Rose Street, North Lane, EH2 3DX
Tel: 0131 225 3106
Fax: 0131 220 3403
Chef(s): David Romanis
Owner(s): Mr & Mrs Irons
Cost: Alc £32.25, set price L £17.25/D £25. ☺ ☺ H/wine £14
Times: Noon-2pm/7-10pm. Closed Sun-Mon, L Sat, 4 wks from 24 Dec, 1 wk May-Jun, 1 wk Oct
Additional: Children 8yrs+
Seats: 30. Private dining room 20
Style: Formal, Minimalist

Norton House Hotel

Elegant conservatory restaurant in fine dining style. This is a large country house dating back to 1833 now well set up to deal with large scale functions whilst managing to maintain the personal touch for private diners. A meal here might find you revelling in game terrine with winter berry compote before getting to grips with breast of Highland pheasant with crisp apples, chestnuts and sweet potato blini. A slightly lighter approach in the form of tomato, feta and apple salad followed by baked cod on sauté potatoes with a tapenade and herb crust is equally successful.

Civil licence: 200
Accommodation: 47 rooms (47 en suite) ★ ★ ★
Directions: M8 J2, off A8, 0.5 mile past Edinburgh Airport

Ingliston, EH28 8LX
Tel: 0131 333 1275
Fax: 0131 333 5305
🅴 events.nhh@arcadianhotels.co.uk
Chef(s): John Newton
Owner(s): Arcadian Hotels
Cost: Alc £32, set price L £17.70/D £28. ☺
Times: Noon-2pm/7-10pm. Closed L Sat
Additional: Sunday L. Bar food. Children welcome
Seats: 80. Private dining room 180
Style: Country-House
Smoking: No smoking in dining room

Off the Wall Restaurant   NEW

Climb the stone steps next to Bailie Fyfes Close and look out for the leaded windows - first-timers will need a keen eye to spot this city restaurant. Inside, modernity takes over with bright yellow walls, but there's smartness too in plush upholstery and classy table settings. David Anderson allows ingredients to speak for themselves, as in wild mushroom risotto (rich and creamy), fillet of beef with roast asparagus and shitake (succulent, melt-in-the-mouth), and lemon tart with raspberry coulis and crème Anglaise (ubiquitous but welcome). The beautifully presented dishes are never fussy, and the concise carte is particularly sought after in the evening.

Directions: On Royal Mile near John Knox House – Entrance via stairway next to Baillie Fyfes close (first floor)

🎖🎖
105 High Street, Royal Mile, EH1 1SG
Tel: 0131 558 1497
Fax: 0131 558 1497
🅴 otwedinburgh@aol.com
Chef(s): David Anderson
Cost: Alc £32, set price L £15/D £25. ☺ H/wine £13.75
Times: Noon-2pm/5.30-10pm. Closed Sun, 25-26 Dec
Additional: Children welcome
Seats: 44. Private dining room 20
Style: Classic, Chic
Smoking: No-smoking area

Scotland

Scotland

EDINBURGH *Continued*   **Map 11 NT27**

Restaurant at The Bonham

A contemporary style informs the decor and so black-and-white photos are more-or-less obligatory. However that extra bit of imagination is demonstrated with close-up stills of particular dishes throughout the various stages of preparation adorning the walls. The skill of the kitchen is equally manifest in successful dishes like grilled lamb cutlet with asparagus couscous.

35 Drumsheugh Gardens, EH3 7RN
Tel: 0131 623 9319
Fax: 0131 226 6080
e restaurant@thebonham.com
Chef(s): Michel Bouyer
Owner(s): Peter Taylor, The Town House Company
Cost: *Alc* £26, set price L £16. ☺ ☺ H/wine £15
Times: Noon-2.30pm/6.30-9.30pm. Closed 3-7 Jan
Additional: Sunday L. Children welcome
Seats: 60. Private dining room 24
Style: Modern
Smoking: No-smoking area
Accommodation: 48 rooms (48 en suite) ★ ★ ★ ★
Directions: Located to the W end of Princes St

Restaurant Martin Wishart
Restaurant of the Year for Scotland - see page 575 for entry

Rhodes & Co

Smart Edinburgh restaurant owned by the omnipresent champion of British cookery. Dark wood floors, light wood tables, leather and chrome come together to form a clean, sophisticated look. Menus are, as can be expected, easily recognisable with many of Rhodes' trademark ideas in evidence. Dishes like a creamy rocket risotto retaining some bite, are commendably good and although short, the menu tempts with additional ideas like braised shank of lamb with garlic, thyme, 'perfectly white' creamed potatoes, tomato and broad beans. Puds are dependably comforting.

3-15 Rose Street, EH2 2YJ
Tel: 0131 220 9190
Fax: 0131 220 9199
Chef(s): Will Hoy
Cost: *Alc* £16.50. Set price D £20.50. ☺ ☺ H/wine £11
Times: 11.30am-5pm/6-9.45pm. Closed D Sun, Xmas, New Year
Additional: Sunday L. Bar food L. Children welcome
Seats: 86. Private dining room 12
Style: Modern, Chic
Smoking: No pipes; Air conditioning
Directions: Telephone for directions

Roxburghe Hotel NEW

In the heart of the city overlooking Charlotte Square Gardens. The Melrose restaurant has a traditional feel but the menu is more contemporary than the surroundings suggest. Typical dishes being a bright and honest starter of vine tomatoes with mozzarella, mizuna and basil or an excellent wild mushroom risotto with deep fried rocket. Pistachio crème brûlée with marmalade ice cream has been noted as a winner amongst the desserts.

Smoking: No smoking in dining room; Air conditioning
Civil licence: 200
Accommodation: 197 rooms (197 en suite) ★ ★ ★ ★
Directions: Telephone for details

38 Charlotte Square, EH2 4HG
Tel: 0131 240 5500
Fax: 0131 240 5555
e info@roxburghe.macdonald-hotels.co.uk
Chef(s): Garham Shaw
Owner(s): Paragon Hotels
Cost: Set price L £12.25-£18.95/D £22-£32. ☺ ☺ H/wine £14.25
Additional: Sunday L. Bar food. Children welcome
Seats: 80. Private dining room

Stac Polly NEW

City centre eatery with the charm and atmosphere of a country restaurant. The decor is soft and welcoming with a light tartan motif and mossy coloured carpets. The approach is creative and modern with global touches - expect the likes of baked halibut set on buttered spinach with melting chorizo, garlic mash and balsamic syrup.

8-10 Grindlay Street, EH3 9AS
Tel: 0131 229 5405
Fax: 0131 557 9779
Chef(s): Steven Harvey
Owner(s): Roger Coulthard
Cost: Alc £28, set price L £15.95/D £28-£30. ☺ ☺ H/wine £12.95
Times: noon-2pm/6-midnight. Closed L Sat & Sun
Additional: Children welcome
Seats: 50. Private dining room 10
Style: Traditional
Smoking: No-smoking area; no cigars
Directions: In Town Centre. Situated beneath the castle, near Lyceum Theatre

The Sheraton Grand - The Grill Room

A makeover has transformed this modern hotel, with its marble entrance hall, grand central staircase and magnificent public

1 Festival Square, EH3 9SR
Tel: 0131 221 6422
Fax: 0131 229 6254
Chef(s): Nichola Laurent
Cost: Alc £40, set price L £27.50-£29 H/wine £16
Times: Noon-4.30pm/7-10.30pm. Closed Sun, L Sat
Additional: Children welcome
Seats: 45. Private dining room 16
Style: Traditional, French-Style
Smoking: No-smoking area; no pipes; Air conditioning
Accommodation: 260 rooms (260 en suite) ★ ★ ★ ★ ★
Directions: Off Lothian Road

Scotland

Scotland

EDINBURGH *Continued* Map 11 NT27

rooms. Despite the obvious homage paid to innovative architectural ideas, within the gleaming interior you will find a fine dining experience that pays tribute to the classical past. The Grill Room leaves no doubt as to the sort of food on offer: large leather-bound chairs, crisp linen-clad tables, large heavily-framed prints and classical music indicate a serious approach to dining, and the French cuisine duly obliges. Mosaic of Gressingham duck with caramelised parsnips and foie gras, and roast fillet of sea bass with truffle risotto, and langoustine are typical of the *carte*'s scope, and there are also vegetarian choices and grills. Gourmandise of chocolate with vanilla and chocolate sauce should satisfy any discerning chocoholic, while coupe of home made ice cream and sorbet with fruit coulis suggests a more restrained dessert. Good wines by the glass.

The Vintners Rooms

Whilst the vaults are ancient the main building dates back to 1785 and the exquisite interior is a reflection of the importance of the wine trade at that time. Although now on the other end of the wine trade the cellars are still in use with some 200 wines on offer to accompany robust and honest dishes such as casserole of venison with bitter chocolate.

Additional: Children welcome. **Seats:** 64
Style: Classic Bistro-Style
Smoking: No-smoking area
Directions: At the end of Leith Walk; L into Great Junction St, R into Henderson St. Restaurant is in old warehouse on R.

The Vaults,
87 Giles Street, Leith
EH6 6BZ
Tel: 0131 554 6767
Fax: 0131 467 7130
e tim@thevintnersrooms.demon. co.uk
Chef(s): James Baxter, Tim Cumming
Owner(s): A T & S C Cumming
Cost: *Alc* £30, set price L £15. ☺ ☺ H/wine £12
Times: noon-3.30pm/6-midnight. Closed Sun, 2wks Xmas

The Witchery by the Castle

Castlehill, Royal Mile,
EH1 2NF
Tel: 0131 225 5613
Fax: 0131 220 4392
e mail@thewitchery.com
Chef(s): Douglas Roberts
Owner(s): James Thomas
Cost: *Alc* £30, set price L £13.45.
☺ ☺ H/wine £13.50
Times: noon-6pm/5-11.30pm.
Closed 25, 26 Dec

A bagpipe-playing cherub may watch you eat, as the ceilings of The Witchery and its adjoining restaurant, are painted with striking heraldic and tarot-based designs. Bare timbers, tapestries and candlelight complete a scene fitting for a place whose name commemorates the hundreds of 'witches' burned on Castlehill during the reign of James VI. The British menu is unpretentious and makes good use of Scottish produce. Aberdeen Angus beef, wild salmon and seafood are simply but adeptly prepared, with the theatre supper (say, salmon omelette, baked crotin and sausages with mash) being particularly good value. Over 900 wines lurk in the cellar.

Accommodation: 2 rooms (2 en suite) ♦♦♦♦♦
Directions: At the gates of Edinburgh Castle, at the top of the Royal Mile

Tower Restaurant

Look out over the city rooftops from this smart and sophisticated brasserie-style restaurant occupying the top floor of the Museum of Scotland. The menus offer an eclectic choice ranging from sushi with pickled vegetables and wasabi, to good old fashioned fish and chips with pea purée.

Tel: 0131 225 3003
Fax: 0131 247 4220
 reservations@tower-restaurant.com
Chef(s): Steven Adair
Owner(s): James Thomson
Cost: Alc £27. ☺ ☺ H/wine £13.50
Times: noon-5pm/5pm-11pm. Closed 25-26 Dec
Additional: Sunday L. Children welcome
Seats: 96. Private dining room 90
Style: Modern, Chic
Smoking: No smoking in dining room;
Air conditioning
Directions: Located above the Landmark New Museum of Scotland at the corner of George IV bridge and Chambers St, on level 5

Museum of Scotland,
Chambers Street EH1 1JF

Additional: Sunday L. Children welcome
Seats: 120. Private dining room 70
Style: Chic, Classic
Smoking:; Air conditioning

Winter Glen

3A1 Dundas Street, EH3 6QG
Tel: 0131 477 7060
Fax: 0131 624 7087
Chef(s): Graham Winter
Owner(s): Graham Winter &
Blair Glen
Cost: Set price L £15/D £26.50 ☺
H/wine £13.25
Times: Noon-2pm/6-10pm.
Closed Sun, L Sun, Xmas, 1 Jan
Additional: Children 14 yrs+
Seats: 60. Private dining room 35
Style: Rustic
Directions: Telephone for directions

Two dining areas - one with exposed stone walls, the other with original large stone open fire places, both with a genuinely cosy, welcoming atmosphere. The food here goes from strength to strength with accurate flavours and a lightness of texture lifting a starter of spiced crab cake with cumin, coriander and a citrus lime caramel to notable culinary heights. With mains such as griddled halibut steak nicely marinated in olive oil and herbs with a tomato and chilli broth and an olive mash on offer a full set price dinner is a tempting prospect. This restaurant is also particularly notable for its commitment to quality at lunchtime.

FALKIRK

BANKNOCK
Map 11 NS77

Glenskirlie House Restaurant NEW

Kilsyth Road, FK4 1UF
Tel: 01324 840201
Fax: 01324 841054
e macaloneys@glenskirliehouse.com
Chef(s): John Thomson
Owner(s): John & Linda Macaloney
Cost: *Alc* £30, set price L £16.50. ☺
H/wine £11.50
Times: noon-2pm/6-9.30pm.
Closed D Mon, 26-27 Dec, 1-3 Jan
Additional: Sunday L. Bar food L.
Children welcome
Seats: 54. Private dining room 150
Style: Classic, Chic
Smoking: No pipes or cigars;
Air conditioning
Civil licence: 94
Directions: From Glasgow take A80
towards Stirling. At J4 take A803
towards Falkirk. At
Kilsyth/Bonnybridge turn R at T-
junction. Restaurant 1 mile on R

Family-run restaurant transformed from a 1920's residence in the village of Banknock, handy for the A80/M80. It has a good local following and customers come from south Glasgow, Stirling and Falkirk and many points between. The modern menu offers a varied choice, and tranche of salmon with herb and brioche crust and lemon cream sauce has been noted as a highlight.

GRANGEMOUTH
Map 11 NS98

Grange Manor

Le Chardon is the restaurant at this 19th-century country house hotel, providing an elegant setting for modern Scottish cooking offered from a choice of menus. A hands-on approach from the

Glensburgh, FK3 8XJ
Tel: 01324 474836
Fax: 01324 665861
e info@grangemanor.co.uk
Chef(s): Steven Ward
Owner(s): Mr W Wallace
Cost: *Alc* £25, set price L £13.50/
D £24.50. ☺ ☺ H/wine £12.50
Times: Noon-2pm/7-9.30pm.
Closed L Sat, 26 Dec, 1-2 Jan
Additional: Sunday L. Bar food L.
Children welcome
Seats: 70. Private dining room 40.
Jacket and tie preferred
Style: Classic, Country-House
Smoking: No-smoking area; no pipes;
Air conditioning
Accommodation: 37 rooms (37 en
suite) ★ ★ ★
Directions: M9 J6 200metres on right,
M9 J5 then A905 for 2 miles

Wallace family does much to enhance both the quality of service and the care taken with cuisine. Options from the *carte* might include roast loin of venison with elderflower jus and braised red cabbage, or grilled fillet of brill with courgette and lemon mousse together with a red wine jus. Good skill evident in the puds too with a glazed passion fruit tart with an effective citrus sorbet being a notable example.

Scotland

POLMONT

Map 11 NS97

Inchyra Grange

Very atmospheric hotel dining room with a Gothic, almost church-like aspect thanks to clever use of an old external wall. It's somehow appropriate that service is attentive, friendly and very correct. Skilful preparation is in evidence and full, strong flavours are the key in dishes such as ballotine of poussin with shitake mushrooms, dressed with rocket and truffle oil.

Style: Classic. **Civil licence:** 450
Smoking: No smoking in dining room; Air conditioning
Accommodation: 109 rooms (109 en suite) ★ ★ ★ ★
Directions: M9 J4 or 5. In Polmont, nr BP social club

Grange Road, FK2 0YB
Tel: 01324 711911
Fax: 01324 716134
e info@inchyra.macdonald-hotels.co.uk
Chef(s): David Murray
Cost: *Alc* £27.50, set price L £12.50.
☺ ☺ H/wine £14.50
Times: Noon-2pm/7-9.30pm.
Closed L Sat
Additional: Sunday L. Bar food.
Children welcome
Seats: 90. Private dining room

Scotland

FIFE

ANSTRUTHER

Map 12 NO50

Cellar Restaurant

"Well worth battling through fierce snowstorms to get to" was one recent verdict on Peter Jukes' longstanding venue. A warm welcome helps in these circumstances and with "charming" staff, candlelight and open fires, all the elements are in place for a hospitable ambience. Peripheral elements are well attended to, with canapés and amuse (sweet marinated herring for example) being well-chosen and carefully prepared and the in-house bread winning praise too. Fish is a real strength as in a starter of rich crayfish bisque glazed with cream and gruyère or a "good as it gets" grilled prime halibut with greens, pine nuts, smoky bacon and hollandaise sauce. Desserts might include the likes of a layered chocolate mousse, with dark white and milk chocolate elements and an orange liqueur custard. The wine list is realistic price wise and offers a good selection, especially amongst the whites.

24 East Green, KY10 3AA
Tel: 01333 310378
Fax: 01333 312544
Telephone for further details

CUPAR

Map 11 NO31

Eden House Hotel

2 Pitscottie Road,
KY15 4HF
Tel: 01334 652510
Fax: 01334 652277
e lv@eden.u-net.com
Chef(s): Alan Lunn
Owner(s): Laurence & Mary Vizan
Cost: *Alc* £24, set price L £16/D £20.
☺ ☺ H/wine £11
Times: Noon-2pm/6.30-9pm.
Closed L Sun, 25 Dec, 1 Jan
Additional: Bar food.
Children welcome
Seats: 70
Style: Traditional
Smoking: No-smoking area; no pipes
Accommodation: 11 rooms (11 en suite) ★ ★
Directions: Turn R after railway bridge in Cupar. Hotel is 100yds to R

Admirably honest, family-run hotel overlooking Haugh park. Strong cooking built on a foundation of best seasonal ingredients. Given that, the style is sensibly simple, allowing natural flavours to do the work in dishes such as rack of lamb with redcurrant sauce and almonds or a really good apple strudel.

CUPAR *Continued*   Map 11 NO31

Ostlers Close Restaurant

Bonnygate, KY15 4BU
Tel: 01334 655574
Chef(s): James Graham
Owner(s): James & Amanda Graham
Cost: *Alc* L £20/D £32. ☺
H/wine £12
Times: 12.15-2pm/7-9.30pm.
Closed Sun-Mon, L Tues-Thu,
25-26 Dec, 1-2 Jan, 2 wks May
Additional: Children 6+ at D.
Vegetarian dishes with prior notice
Seats: 26
Style: Informal, Traditional
Smoking: No pipes or cigars
Directions: In small lane off main
street A91 of Cupar

This is the kind of place where it's almost a relief that so little has changed; the cottage industry ambience, the garrulous warmth of Amanda Graham, and the nip and tuck cooking continues to set regional standards, as they have done for the last 20 years. The wine list is hand written and provides a global, reasonably priced selection to mix with the menu. From a vibrant amuse of a demi-tasse of smoked haddock soup through pan fried terrine of duck confit and potato served with duck livers to a classic fillet of Aberdeen Angus with a caramelised red onion and port sauce, sturdy flavours and deft execution are always in evidence. An accurately presented and astute assiette of chocolate has been noted as a success amongst the desserts with a particularly moreish bitter chocolate tart. Service is relaxed with staff doing their best to promote an atmosphere that the many regulars treat like a house party.

DUNFERMLINE   Map 11 NT08

Keavil House Hotel

Located in a manor house hotel, this smart conservatory restaurant specialises in carefully prepared Scottish specialities. A meal might begin with home smoked duck breast and orange vinaigrette before progressing to a main course of Perthshire beef with a sauté of field and forest mushrooms.

Style: Traditional Country-House
Smoking: No smoking in dining room. **Civil licence:** 100
Accommodation: 47 rooms (47 en suite) ★ ★ ★
Directions: M90 J3, 7 miles from Forth Rd Bridge, take A985, turning R after bridge. From Dunfermline, 2 miles W on A994

Crossford, KY12 8QW
Tel: 01383 736258
Fax: 01383 621600
📧 keavil@queensferry-hotels.co.uk
Chef(s): Volker Steinemann
Owner(s): Mark Simpkins
Cost: *Alc* £25, set price L £9.99/
D £22.50-£25. ☺ ☺ H/wine £9.95
Times: Noon-2pm/6-9pm.
Additional: Sunday L. Bar food L.
Children welcome
Seats: 65. Private dining room 22

GLENROTHES   Map 11 NO20

Rescobie House Hotel

Quietly tucked away off the main road, Rescobie House is a charming Edwardian building. The owners appreciate good food and the hotel boasts a restaurant with a high standard of cuisine. Traditional Scottish fare is of course important and home-cured local salmon may be served with a mustard and dill dressing or a

6 Valley Drive, Leslie,
KY6 3BQ
Tel: 01592 749555
Fax: 01592 620231
📧 rescobiehotel@compuserve.com
Chef(s): Ivan Lux

Scotland

char-grilled fillet of Scottish beef simply enhanced by a traditional béarnaise sauce. However, other influences impinge upon the menu with cream of courgette and fennel soup flavoured with a curry infusion or a delicious dessert of lasagnetta of chocolate mousse with marinated orange segments.

Owner(s): Andrew Davidson
Cost: *Alc* £22.95/D £22.95. ☺
H/wine £9.90
Times: Dinner only, 7-9pm. Closed Sun-Mon, 25-26 Dec, 31 Dec-2 Jan
Additional: Children 12yrs+
Seats: 20. Private dining room 10
Style: Country-House
Smoking: No smoking in dining room

Accommodation: 10 rooms (10 en suite) ★★
Directions: From A92 at Glenrothes take A911 to Leslie; at end of Leslie High St, straight ahead & 1st L

KIRKCALDY   Map 12 NT29

Dunnikier House Hotel

Dunnikier Park, KY1 3LP
Tel: 01592 268393
Fax: 01592 642340
e recp@dunnikier-house-hotel.co.uk
Chef(s): Stuart Archibald
Owner(s): Mr B Bridgens & Mrs K Garbutt
Cost: *Alc* £25, set price L £15.75.
☺ ☺ H/wine £9
Times: Noon-2pm/6-9pm.
Additional: Sunday L. Bar food. Children welcome
Seats: 24. Private dining room 12. Jacket and tie preferred

Dinner takes place in the Oswald Room restaurant at this 18th-century country house hotel. The best of fresh Scottish produce is served in dishes such as medley of East Neuk seafood, pan-fried sirloin of Aberdeen Angus, and medallions of wild venison with parsnip crumble, braised red cabbage and a port and prune sauce.

Style: Modern Country-House
Smoking: No smoking in dining room. **Civil licence:** 40
Accommodation: 14 rooms (14 en suite) ★★★
Directions: Turn off A92 at Kirkcaldy West, take 3rd exit at roundabout signed 'Hospital/Crematorium', then 1st L past school

---

LUNDIN LINKS   Map 12 NO40

Old Manor Hotel

All the elements of decent hotel dining in the Aithernie Restaurant - friendly service with the a judicious degree of formality, a good wine list, accurate cooking and pleasant surroundings. Enjoy views across the golf course towards the Firth of Forth and East Lothian. Local seafood, Scottish lamb and grilled Aberdeen Angus steaks are features of the *carte*. Seafood chowder comes with a fine velouté base and firm pieces of salmon, sole and haddock. Roast pheasant, powerfully flavoured, has come wrapped in bacon and served with red cabbage and pommes parisienne.

Leven Road, KY8 6AJ
Tel: 01333 320368
Fax: 01333 320911

LUNDIN LINKS *Continued*

Map 12 NO40

Directions: On A915 Leven St Andrews road in the village

Old Manor Hotel

 enquiries@oldmanorhotel.co.uk
Chef(s): Alan Brunt &
Roberta Drummond
Owner(s): Clark Family
Cost: Alc £29.50/D £27.50-£33.50.
H/wine £10.95
Times: Dinner only, 7-10pm
Additional: Sunday L. Bar food.
Children welcome
Seats: 36. Private dining room 50.
Jacket and tie preferred
Style: Formal Country-House
Smoking: No smoking in dining room
Civil licence: 100
Accommodation: 23 rooms (23 en
suite) ★ ★ ★

MARKINCH

Map 11 NO20

Balbirnie House

Balbirnie Park, KY7 6NE
Tel: 01592 610066
Fax: 01592 610529
balbirnie@breathemail.net
Chef(s): Alan Gibb
Owner(s): The Russell family
Cost: Set price L £14.50/D£31.50. ☺
H/wine £13.50
Times: Noon-2.30pm/7-9.30pm.
Additional: Sunday L. Children
welcome
Seats: 65. Private dining room 216
Style: Classic, Country-House
Smoking: No smoking in dining room
Civil licence: 200

Imposing country house hotel where the restaurant is primarily
based in the Orangery - a large, bright, airy room with a cluster
of potted citrus trees at its heart. This setting is also notable for
the splendid use it makes of the hotel's surroundings with views
onto the lovely gardens (including woods and a stream) filling
the restaurant with a truly bucolic atmosphere. Tastes of the
countryside are also available in the guise of cream of leek and
nutmeg soup with woodland mushrooms and crème fraiche, or
perhaps roast loin of venison with fondant potato and a red
wine and Dijon mustard game sauce.

Accommodation: 30 rooms (30 en suite) ★ ★ ★ ★
Directions: M90 J13, follow signs for Glenrothes and Bay
Bridge, R onto B9130 to Markinch and Balbirnie Park

The Peat Inn

Fife

WINE AWARD SCOTLAND WINNER

Few places engender as much affection and loyalty as David and Patricia Wilson's celebrated restaurant with rooms. Quietly situated six miles from St Andrews, the former coaching inn has a distinctly French air that extends from the warm terracottas and sunny yellows of the décor through to the classical foundation of the cooking. When it comes to the raw materials the emphasis is much closer to home: venison, lobster and scallops all feature strongly in a menu that majors on the local bounty and bows dutifully to the seasons. According to the time of year, flageolet beans might accompany spring lamb or young partridge might be roasted with wild mushrooms, braised leeks and cabbage. The restaurant which, with its low ceilings, fresh flowers and cutlery-sculpted candlesticks could serve as a reasonable definition for the word intimate, is the setting for precise and consistent cooking that makes the most of top quality produce. There is no lack of lively flavours either. An amuse of smoked fillet of fish with wild rocket, cherry tomatoes and a "lovely, vibrant" green herb vinaigrette for instance or a "generous" starter of lobster and prawn risotto in a vegetable bouillabaise. Fish is ultra-fresh and consequently hard to resist especially in well-judged combinations like fillet of turbot with medallions of lobster, artichoke hearts, timballe of wild mushrooms and a "terrific" lobster sauce. Desserts might include an equally deft caramel trio comprising a tiny crème caramel, caramel ice cream in a tuile basket and a "fabulous" apple tarte Tatin.

Cupar, PEAT INN, KY15 5LH **MAP 12 NO40**
Tel: 01334 840206
Fax: 01334 840530
E-mail: reception@thepeatinn.co.uk
Chef: David Wilson
Owners: Mr & Mrs D Wilson
Cost: Set price L £19.50/D £30 H/wine £16
Times: 12.30-1pm/7-9.30pm. Closed Sun-Mon, 25 Dec, 1 Jan
Additional: Children welcome
Seats: 48. Private dining room 24
Style: Traditional, French
Smoking: No smoking in the dining room
Accommodation: 8 rooms (8 en suite) ★ ★

The wine list, like much else here, is the work of an enthusiast. Although this is clearly a serious list, there is no hint of stuffiness or pretension and the imperative is simply to enjoy a great selection of wines. The approach is both accessible and democratic. Prices are remarkably fair and where appropriate, there are enlightening notes on the vintages and on particular estates. Once again the prevailing influence is French, although there are worthwhile forays into the New World and a particularly enlightened selection from Germany. There are particular strengths in Burgundy (both red and white) and some great older vintages amongst the clarets. It's also good to witness a half bottle selection that rises well above the merely token and a decent range of dessert wines too.

ST ANDREWS   Map 12 NO51

Road Hole Grill

The Road Hole Grill is a grand affair with oak panels, theatrical flower arrangements and views across the course to the surf beyond. It's aimed, pin-high, at classic dining and pretty much achieves it with discreet but professional service and some intricate but largely successful cooking. Luxury ingredients are to the fore with tarte tatin of red shallots coming with seared foie gras and a Madeira jus and crayfish tortellini with tomato consommé being a particular success. Desserts have included a highly competent assiette of chocolate (mousse, fondant and ice cream). Also at the Old Course Hotel, Sands Brasserie has picked up a Rosette this year for some modish cooking with a Pacific Rim bias in its less formal surroundings.

Old Course Hotel, KY16 9SP
Tel: 01334 474371
Fax: 01334 477668
e reservations@oldcoursehotel.co.uk
Telephone for further details

Rufflets Country House & Garden Restaurant

Strathkinness Low Road,
KY16 9TX
Tel: 01334 472594
Fax: 01334 478703
e reservations@rufflets.co.uk
Chef(s): Mark Pollock
Owner(s): Ann Russell
Cost: Set price L £20/D £34-£38.
H/wine £13
Times: 12.30-2pm/7-9pm.
Closed L Mon-Sat, 1-7 Jan
Additional: Sunday L. Bar food.
Children welcome. Vegetarian by
request only
Seats: 80. Private dining room 80
Style: Country-House

Fruit is a recurring theme in the Garden Restaurant - on the wallpaper, fabrics, crockery and even the menu (a hot passion fruit soufflé was absolutely spot on). Mark Pollock, the former sous chef, has taken control of the kitchen, and very capably so, with some touches of inspiration and the odd risky combination. Steamed salmon and langoustine teamed with broad bean purée and herb oil has been noted as visually especially impressive, and a roast rack of lamb featured good quality meat although a sharp herb and mustard crust rather dominated. Ravioli of wild mushrooms arranged on a surprise addition of wild mushroom risotto has been praised for some lovely flavours.

Smoking: No smoking in dining room
Civil licence: 30
Accommodation: 22 rooms (22 en suite) ★ ★ ★
Directions: 1.5m west of St Andrews on B939

Rusacks Hotel

The huge art deco windows of this hotel restaurant provide stunning views over the first and eighteenth tees and out to the sea. The modern interior includes wooden floors, crisp white linen and 'excellent' leather chairs. Dishes are equally up to

Pilmour Links, KY16 9JQ
Tel: 0870 4008128
Fax: 01334 477896
e heritagehotels-
standrews.rusacks@forte-hotels.com

Scotland

date, offering an appealing mixture of British and European flavours. A meal might begin with smoked haddock and monkfish terrine with a light scallop mousse and tomato and basil vinaigrette, before progressing to a canon of lamb encased in rosemary mousse, served with creamed celeriac, seared lambs kidneys and rosemary jus. Quality service is provided by the friendly, attentive staff.

Chef(s): Derek Anderson
Cost: Alc £32, set price L £12.50. ☺
H/wine £14.70
Times: Noon-6pm/7-10pm.
Additional: Sunday L. Bar food L.
Children welcome
Seats: 66. Private dining room 80
Style: Modern, Country-House
Smoking: No smoking in dining room;
Air conditioning
Civil licence: 60
Accommodation: 68 rooms (68 en suite) ★ ★ ★ ★
Directions: From M90 J8 take A91 to St Andrews. Hotel on L on entering the town

St Andrews Golf Hotel

40 The Scores,
KY16 9AS
Tel: 01334 472611
Fax: 01334 472188
📧 reception@standrews-golf.co.uk
Chef(s): Colin Masson
Owner(s): Justin Hughes
Cost: Alc £31, set price L £9.50/
D £31-£34 ☺ H/wine £13
Times: 12.30-2pm/7-9.30pm.
Closed 26 Dec
Additional: Sunday L. Bar food.
Children welcome
Seats: 60. Private dining room 20.
Jacket and tie preferred
Style: Traditional, Classic

Stylish Victorian hotel overlooking the bay, popular with locals and residents (especially golfers). The restaurant, lounge and cocktail bar are all inviting rooms which make it easy to spend an evening here. Menus show a good regard for seasonality and feature many local ingredients, such as loin of Perthshire lamb wrapped in cabbage leaf and Parma ham or Angus beef with stilton mousseline and veal jus. Technical skill and carefully chosen ingredients mean that the food is reliably good - and don't miss the wine list, clearly a passion of the proprietor. Accomplished service and warm hospitality complete an enjoyable experience.

Smoking: No smoking in dining room; Air conditioning
Accommodation: 22 rooms (22 en suite) ★ ★ ★
Directions: Enter town on A91, cross both mini rdbts, turn L at Golf Place and 1st R into The Scores. Hotel 200yds on R

ST ANDREWS *Continued*   Map 12 NO51

The Inn at Lathones

A lovely little country inn, parts of which date back 400 years. The friendly staff, real fires and beamed ceilings create a cosy atmosphere that attracts visitors from around the world. The French head chef has devised a modern menu which successfully combines classic French cooking with top quality local ingredients and a few ideas from further afield. A meal might include a warm salad of flaked pork with an Arran grain mustard sauce followed by grilled Angus ribeye with a Lagavulin smoked bacon and mushroom sauce. The impressive wine list includes helpful tasting notes by the proprietor.

Accommodation: 14 rooms (14 en suite) ★ ★
Directions: 5 miles S of St Andrews on A915. Inn 0.5mile before Largoward on L, just after hidden dip

Largoward, KY9 1JE
Tel: 01334 840494
Fax: 01334 840694
e lathones@theinn.co.uk
Chef(s): Marc Guibert
Owner(s): Mr N White
Cost: *Alc* £18, set price L £15/D £25-£35. ☺ ☺ H/wine £9.95
Times: Noon-2.30pm/6-9.30pm. Closed Xmas, 2wks in Jan
Additional: Sunday L. Bar food L. Children welcome
Seats: 35. Private dining room 40
Style: Country-House
Smoking: No smoking in dining room

ST MONANS   Map 12 NO50

The Seafood Restaurant

16 West End, KY10 2BX
Tel: 01333 730327
Fax: 01333 730327
e theseafood.restaurant@virginnet.co.uk
Chef(s): Craig Millar
Owner(s): The Butler Family
Cost: *Alc* £26, set price L £18. ☺ ☺ H/wine £12
Times: noon-4pm/6-midnight. Closed Mon, D Sun, Dec-Jan
Additional: Sunday L. Children welcome at L
Seats: 36
Style: Modern
Smoking: No smoking in dining room
Directions: Take A959 from St Andrews to Anstruther, then head W on A917 through Pittenweem. In St Monans to harbour then R

Perched this near the harbour walls, it wouldn't be surprising if the seafood simply strolled into the kitchen of this restaurant. Inside, the panoramic coastal views remain, thanks to floor-to-ceiling plate windows, but book in advance if you want to sit next to them - people make pilgrimages to eat here. Amongst the all-fresh dishes you might find lobster and crab brandade with chive gazpacho or seared hand dived scallops with langoustine tails, crab bisque and sea asparagus. For the determined flesh fanciers there are meat options - perhaps beef or guinea fowl. Presentation is simple (no tarting up necessary) and prices amazingly cheap.

GLASGOW, CITY OF

GLASGOW

Map 11 NS56

78 St Vincent Street

Striking features of the restored Phoenix Assurance building are the original marble staircase, unusual metalwork and a mural by Glasgow artist Donald McLeod. The modern menu has a strong Scottish flavour, with mosaic of west coast seafood, marinated Highland venison with potato soufflé and roast parsnips, and a vegetarian haggis with mash and rosemary cream.

Additional: Sunday L. Children welcome
Seats: 90. Private dining room 16
Style: Traditional French
Smoking: No-smoking area
Directions: Telephone for directions

78 St Vincent Street,
G2 5UB
Tel: 0141 248 7878
Fax: 0141 248 4663
e frontdesk@78stvincent.com
Chef(s): Stuart Wilson
Owner(s): Mike Conyers
Cost: Alc L £13/D £24.50. ☺ ☺
H/wine £12.95
Times: Noon-3pm/5-10.30pm.
Closed Xmas & New Year

Scotland

Amaryllis

All change at the famous Glasgow address of One Devonshire Gardens as we went to press. Gordon Ramsay has taken on the lease and brought young protégé David Dempsey from Restaurant Gordon Ramsay to head up the team. The increase in the restaurant's capacity to 70 covers will place some additional pressure on the kitchen but dinner will feature a *carte* along with a six-course *menu prestige* and a two-choice per course lunchtime option. Dishes will feature a number of familiar Ramsay offerings such as tortelllini of lobster and langoustines with fennel purée and baby spinach, velouté of haricots blanc with roasted ceps and canon of spring lamb with crushed potatoes with wild mushrooms and rosemary jus. Expect desserts with a similarly classic French slant like chocolate tart with fromage frais sorbet and chocolate shavings. Fiona Nairn of Braeval fame will oversee the front of house operation.

1 Devonshire Gardens, G12 0UX
Tel: 0141 337 3434
Fax: 0141 339 0047
e info@amaryllis1.demon.co.uk
Chef(s): David Dempsey
Owner(s): Gordon Ramsay
Cost: Alc £25, set price L £18-£21/ D £35
Times: Noon-2.30pm/6.45-11pm. Closed L Sat
Additional: Vegetarian by request only
Seats: 70. Private dining room 36
Style: Elegant, traditional
Smoking: No pipes or cigars
Accommodation: 27 rooms (27 en suite) ★ ★ ★ ★
Directions: From Great Western Road turn L at lights towards Hyndland, 200yds turn R and R again

Scotland

GLASGOW *Continued*　　　　Map 11 NS56

Amber Regent

Elegant Chinese restaurant, where the good value lunches don't stint on quality, and attract a loyal following from the surrounding offices. For a true taste of Canton the dinner *carte* will not disappoint, with dim sum for starters and several variations of the aromatic crispy dishes as house specialities.

50 West Regent Street,
G2 2QZ
Tel: 0141 331 1655
Fax: 0141 353 3398
Chef(s): K C Leung
Owner(s): Andy Chung
Cost: *Alc* £22, set price L £9.95/
D £26.95-£30.95. ☺ ☺
H/wine £12.95
Times: noon-2.15pm/5.30-11pm.
Closed Sun, Chinese New Year
Additional: Children welcome
Seats: 80
Style: Classic
Smoking: Air conditioning
Directions: Telephone for Directions

Carlton George Hotel　　NEW

Claiming to be the City's only rooftop restaurant, there are indeed fine views to the wooded southern suburbs. Especially good value at lunchtime and early evening, expect the likes of a decent chicken liver parfait with toasted brioche and best end of lamb with Dijon mustard crust, pommes dauphinoise and baby vegetables. Bitter chocolate mousse with a fondant sauce has impressed amongst the puds.

Style: Modern Bistro-Style
Smoking: No smoking in dining room; Air conditioning
Accommodation: 64 rooms (64 en suite) ★ ★ ★
Directions: Telephone for directions

44 West George Street, G2 1DH
Tel: 0141 353 6373
Fax: 0141 353 6263
e george@carltonhotels.co.uk
Chef(s): Kevin Breslin
Owner(s): Carlton Hotel Collection
Cost: *Alc* £25, set price L £13.95/
D £14.95. ☺ ☺ H/wine £13.95
Times: noon-3pm/5-10pm.
Additional: Sunday L. Children
welcome
Seats: 54. Private dining room 35

Eurasia

Slick city centre restaurant with an urbane crowd, and a positive mix of European and Asian flavours that are so popular with diners today. Some unusual and creative ideas come to the fore in such dishes as trio of Oriental hors d'oeuvres - essentially refreshing titbits in bamboo baskets including a spiced lentil broth, spring roll, and melon balls and lychee. Other appealing combinations could be beef carpaccio and daikon salad, lemon and cilantro dressing, while more traditional desserts like hot Christmas pudding soufflé come with distinctive accompaniments like cranberry ice cream, along with the usual brandy sauce.

Directions: Telephone for directions

150 St Vincent Street, G2 5NE
Tel: 0141 204 1150
Fax: 0141 204 1140
e info@eurasia-restaurant.co.uk
Chef & Owner: Ferrier Richardson
Cost: *Alc* £34.45, set price L
£16.95/D£31.50. H/wine £14.95
Times: Noon-2.30pm/7/11.30pm.
Closed Sun, L Sat, Bhs
Additional: Children welcome
Seats: 140. Private dining room 35

Farfelu　　NEW

A refreshingly no-nonsense approach at this first floor restaurant, part of a converted warehouse opposite the

89 Candleriggs, G1 1NP
Tel: 0141 552 5345
Telephone for further details

refurbished City Hall. Perfectly cooked fillets of sea bream came on wilted red chard, with black olive tapenade for a contrast of flavour. Lamb's liver and bacon was 'melt in the mouth', topped with caramelised red onion gravy and plenty of it. Mixed berry brûlée with soft fruit compote was freshly baked, rich in flavour and very smooth.

Gamba

225a West George Street, G2 2ND
Tel: 0141 572 0899
Fax: 0141 572 0896
e info@gamba.co.uk
Chef(s): Derek Marshall
Owner(s): Mr A C Tomkins &
Mr Marshall
Cost: *Alc* £30, set price L £14.95.
☺ ☺ H/wine £13.95
Times: noon-2.30pm/5-10.30pm.
Closed Sun, 25-26 Dec, 1-2 Jan,
Bh Mons
Additional: Children 14yrs+
Seats: 66
Style: Modern Spanish
Smoking: No cigars; Air conditioning
Directions: Near Blythswood Square

Given the movement in the Glaswegian gastronomic scene, Gamba provides a stable point of reference. It's a sleek basement restaurant with a Portuguese accent and seafood the speciality. If you go for the *carte* prices can quickly spiral, but the lunch menu is a relative bargain. The owner also runs a wine website so the good international wine list comes as no surprise.

Holiday Inn   NEW

A central location offers convenient proximity to the city's premier entertainment centres and shops. The Mediterranean-influenced menu offers real value and quality and the service is friendly and attentive. A ballotine of corn-fed chicken with field mushroom farcie looked good, tasted good and succinctly demonstrated what can be achieved with simple ingredients.

161 West Nile Street, G1 2RL
Tel: 0141 352 8300
Telephone for further details

Killermont Polo Club

Traditional Indian cuisine in the unlikely setting of a former manse, a few minutes' drive from the city centre. The club aims to create a renaissance both for the food and the polo as it was in the 1920s and 1930s at the time of the Raj, when the Maharaja of Jaipur and his team dominated the game internationally.

Additional: Sunday L. Children welcome
Seats: 80. Private dining room 30. **Style:** Country-House
Smoking: No smoking in dining room
Directions: Telephone for directions

2002 Maryhill Road,
Maryhill Park, G20 0AB
Tel: 0141 946 5412
Fax: 0141 946 0812
Chef(s): Belbir Farwaha
Owner(s): P Thapar
Cost: *Alc* £15, set price L £5.95/
D £12. ☺ ☺ H/wine £10.95
Times: noon-3.30pm/5-11pm.
Closed New Year

La Parmigiana

So Italian you'll expect Al Capone to burst in, guns blazing. The owners come and go, effusively greeting the regulars, there is the constant sound of Italian voices, and the menu bellows authenticity, from the cooked-to-order risotto (made with Italian brown rice) to the mixed fish zuppa with bruschetta. Don't expect the usual pizza and pasta dishes.

447 Great Western Road,
G12 8HH
Tel: 0141 334 0686
Fax: 0141 332 3533
Chef(s): Sandro Giovanazzi
Owner(s): Angelo & Sandro Giovanazzi

Scotland

GLASGOW *Continued* Map 11 NS56

La Parmigiana

Cost: *Alc* £25, set price L £9.10/
D £11.50. ☺ ☺ H/wine £12.10
Times: noon-2.30pm/6-11pm. Closed
Sun, 25-26 Dec, 1-2 Jan, Easter Mon
Additional: Children welcome
Seats: 60
Style: Classic
Smoking: No cigars; Air conditioning
Directions: Telephone for directions

Langs Hotel NEW

Contemporary mezzanine restaurant, serving Californian
cooking, with a good international wine list. Roast salad of
rabbit, with full-flavoured parsley purée and a tomato and
white wine sauce might be followed by seared turbot, on a
purée of celariac, accompanied by mashed potato with olive oil
and spinach. The very light chocolate fondant with crème
chantilly and chocolate sauce had a good bitter chocolate
flavour.

2 Port Dundas Place, G2 3LD
Tel: 0141 333 1500
Fax: 0141 333 5700
Telephone for further details

Lux

Dating back to 1896, the Kelvinside railway station has been
completely refurbished to house an informal restaurant/bar and
above it, the swankier Lux. The menu here is vibrantly
multinational, although Scottish pride shines through in dishes
such as Highland venison layered with game haggis and a dark
pickled nut jus.

Style: Minimalist
Smoking: No-smoking area; no cigars; Air conditioning
Directions: At the traffic lights signposted Gartnavel Hospital.

1051 Great Western Road, G12 0XP
Tel: 0141 576 7576
Fax: 0141 576 0162
Chef(s): Stephen Johnson
Owner(s): MBIC Ltd.
Cost: Set price D £28.50. H/wine £14
Times: Dinner only, 5.30pm-Late.
Closed D Sun, Mon,
25-26 Dec, 1-2 Jan
Additional: Children welcome
Seats: 64

Malmaison Hotel

The original Malmaison - a concept now transferred south of
the border as well - is built around a former church, with the

278 West George Street,
G2 4LL
Tel: 0141 572 1001
Fax: 0141 572 1000
 glasgow@malmaison.com
Chef(s): Richard Miller
Owner(s): Malmaison Hotels Ltd
Cost: *Alc* £30, set price L £12.95/
D £14.95. ☺ ☺ H/wine £13.95
Times: Noon-2.30pm/6-11pm.
Closed L Sat
Additional: Sunday L. Children
welcome
Seats: 96. Private dining room 20
Style: Traditional, French
Smoking: Air conditioning
Accommodation: 72 rooms (72 en
suite) ★ ★ ★

brasserie sited in the crypt. The menu reflects the stylish setting, offering classic French cooking with plenty of individual touches. Expect the likes of steak au poivre, grilled salmon and panfried calves' liver with bacon. Service is genuinely friendly.

Directions: From George Square take Vincent St to Pitt St – Hotel is on corner of this and West George St.

Nairns

13 Woodside Crescent, G3 7UL
Tel: 0141 353 0707
Fax: 0141 331 1684
e info@nairns.co.uk
Chef(s): Derek Blair
Owner(s): Nick & Christopher Nairn
Cost: Set price L £12/D £28.50 ☺
H/wine £14.50
Times: noon-2pm/6-9.45pm. Closed Sun, L Mon, 25-26 Dec, 1-2 Jan
Additional: Children welcome
Seats: 80. Private dining room 30
Style: Modern, Minimalist
Smoking: No cigars; Air conditioning
Accommodation: 4 rooms (4 en suite)

This Georgian townhouse has been refurbished in a sympathetic but modern style, with a wooden floor and charcoal walls adorned with trendy, understated artwork. The weekly changing menu is full of restyled classics: confit chicken and foie gras terrine with beetroot and shallot jam; char grilled rib eye with mustard and thyme potatoes and mushroom ragout; rump of lamb with basil crushed potatoes, French beans and Béarnaise. The approach works well: dishes are well timed, well seasoned and clearly make use of high quality ingredients. Desserts might include ginger tiramisu or glazed orange tart with spiced and steeped satsumas.

Directions: Telephone for directions

No Sixteen

16 Byres Road, G11 5JY
Tel: 0141 339 2544
Chef(s): Rupert Staniforth
Owner(s): Rupert & Aisla Staniforth
Cost: Alc £20.25. ☺ ☺
H/wine £10.50
Times: noon-2.30pm/5.30-10pm. Closed Sun, 24 Dec – 8 Jan
Additional: Children welcome
Seats: 45

Good food and a relaxed ambience make this a popular place to eat. The decor keeps things simple, and a similar style in the cooking brings out the natural flavours of quality ingredients. Expect modern interpretations of many favourites - perhaps ribeye steak on Parmesan polenta with garlic jus or poached halibut with saffron and smoked salmon risotto.

Style: Modern Bistro-Style
Smoking: No pipes or cigars
Directions: Two minutes walk from Kelvinshall tube station, at bottom of Byres Road

Papingo Restaurant　　NEW

104 Bath Street,
G2 2EN
Tel: 0141 332 6678
Fax: 0141 332 6549
e info@papingo.co.uk
Chef(s): David Clunas
Owner(s): Mr A Tomkins

Split-level basement restaurant, with blond wood flooring, rich blue table covers and parrot prints. Contemporary music sets the scene for a modern British *carte* supplemented by daily specials. The owner has consolidated the cooking team, with an executive chef in charge of both Papingo and its sister establishment, Gamba. Simplicity is still the keynote for honest

GLASGOW *Continued*   **Map 11 NS56**

dishes featuring lively flavours. A variation on a Chinese favourite, slices of tender roasted duck with spring onion and ginger served with an intense sauce and top-notch vegetables, served separately, has stood out.

Smoking: No-smoking area; no pipes; Air conditioning
Directions: Telephone for directions

Cost: *Alc* £25. ☺ ☺ H/wine £12.95
Times: noon-2.30pm/5-12pm. Closed L Sun, 25-26 Dec, 1-2 Jan, Bh Mons
Additional: Children welcome
Seats: 75
Style: Modern

Rococo

202 West George Street, G2 2NR
Tel: 0141 221 5004
Fax: 0141 221 5006
✉ res@rococoglasgow.com
Chef(s): Niall Murray
Owner(s): Alan & Audrey Brown
Cost: *Alc* £35, set price L £18/ D £32.50. ☺ ☺ H/wine £16
Times: noon-3pm/5-10pm.
Closed 1 Jan
Additional: Sunday L.
Children welcome
Seats: 60. Private dining room 18
Style: Modern, Chic

A relatively recent arrival in Glasgow, Rococo looks set to become one of its most popular restaurants. Italian limestone flooring, twinkling lights, chocolate leather armchairs and shades of cream provide the perfect backdrop for the vibrant artwork on the walls. The food lives up to the promise of the surroundings, offering a thoroughly modern mixture of quality local ingredients and exciting international flavours. A meal might include warm oriental style duck salad followed by loin of Highland venison with traditional neeps and tatties and whisky essence. Full flavours and perfectly timed dishes are complemented by a 'superb' wine list.

Smoking: No-smoking area; no pipes; Air conditioning
Directions: Telephone for directions

Sherbrooke Castle Hotel

Morrisons is a small restaurant - only nine tables -within a hotel celebrated for its banqueting facilities. The short, imaginative menu demonstrates that food really is taken seriously here. A twice-baked cheese soufflé of blue cheese wafers with tomato salad, toast and oil or local smoked salmon with a salad of buffalo Mozzarella, roast artichokes, orange fillets and a fresh herb vinaigrette may be offered as starters. These could be followed by a tender pan-fried fillet of beef on a foie gras croutin with a truffle jus or breast of Gressingham duck with braised red cabbage and a rich black cherry and Cointreau jus.

Smoking: No-smoking area; no pipes or cigars; Air conditioning
Accommodation: 25 rooms (25 en suite) ★ ★ ★
Directions: From city centre take M8 west to J23. Turn L into Dumbreck Rd, then 2nd L into Nithsdale Rd. Hotel 700m on R

11 Sherbrooke Avenue, Pollokshields, G41 4PG
Tel: 0141 427 4227
Fax: 0141 427 5685
✉ mail@sherbrooke.co.uk
Chef(s): Peter Cook
Cost: *Alc* £26.50, set price L £15/ D £26.50. ☺ ☺ H/wine £10.50
Times: 12.15-2.15pm/6.15-9.45pm
Additional: Sunday L. Bar food.
Children welcome
Seats: 40. Private dining room 18
Style: Traditional, Country-House

Shish Mahal

Park Road, G4 9JF
Tel: 0141 334 1057/334 7899
Fax: 0141 572 0800
🇪 reservations@shishmahal.co.uk
Chef(s): Mr S Ali
Owners: Ali A Aslam, Nasim Ahmed
Cost: Alc £15, set price L £5.25-
£6.50/ D £15-£25. ☺ ☺
H/wine £8.95
Times: Closed L Sun
Additional: Children 5yrs+
Seats: 95. Private dining room 14
Style: Modern, minimalist
Smoking: No-smoking area
Directions: Telephone for directions

Probably the best tandoori chicken tikka and vegetable pakora
in Scotland. This along with the friendly and attentive service of
the long standing family proprietors accounts for the continued
loyalty and enthusiasm of the clientele. Attention to detail is
also gratifying with the high standards extending to the basmati
rice and tandoori naan.

Stravaigin

30 Gibson Street, G12 8NX
Tel: 0141 334 2665
Fax: 0141 334 4099
Chef(s): Colin Clydesdale
Owner(s): Colin Clydesdale
Cost: Set price L £24.95/D £24.95.
H/wine £12.25
Times: noon-2.30pm/5-11pm. Closed
Mon, L Sun-Thu, 25-26 Dec, 1-2 Jan
Additional: Bar food. Children
welcome
Seats: 76
Style: Modern, Scottish
Smoking: No smoking in dining room;
Air conditioning
Directions: Next to Glasgow
University. 200yds from Kelvinbridge
underground

One of Glasgow's most innovative places, this unfussy
restaurant is cool and classy. The team cooks with complete
dedication in a cramped basement kitchen, producing freshly-
baked, glazed bread rolls and amuse-bouche as one chooses
between café/bar and fixed-price menus. Definitive Cullen skink
incorporates freshly seared salmon and smoked haddock,
followed by a roast breast of Barbary duck set on a tower of
potato pancake, beans and chorizo mash. Finish with a rich
Belgian chocolate mousse concoction on a "cushion" of crème
anglaise. Refined, contemporary décor, excellent filter coffee
and interesting wines.

The Devonshire Hotel of Glasgow

One of the city's most stylish hotels— a townhouse with
sumptuous furnishings in its day rooms and all the elegance
expected of a grand house. The restaurant is equally charming
with its log fire, big bay windows and high ceiling. Here the
Scottish menu is creative and inspiring with choices that work

5 Devonshire Gardens, G12 0UX
Tel: 0141 339 7878
Fax: 0141 339 3980
🇪 devonshir5@aol.com
Chef(s): Peter Lindsay
Owner(s): J Montgomery

GLASGOW *Continued*   **Map 11 NS56**

well, such as a 'tip top' foie gras terrine - smooth and rich in flavour, with a great texture, and served simply with rocket, olive oil, balsamic vinegar and truffle shavings. Fish might be a good main course option in the likes of roast fillet of turbot on mash with hazelnut dressing, baby asparagus and fennel, carrots and new potatoes - all quite satisfying.

Accommodation: 14 rooms (14 en suite) ★ ★ ★ ★
Directions: On Great Western Road turn L at lights towards Hyndland, 200 yds turn R and R again.

Cost: *Alc* £25, set price L £25-£30/ D £25-£35 H/wine £14.95
Times: 12.30-2.30pm/7-10pm. Closed L Sun & Sat
Additional: Bar food L. Children welcome
Seats: 16. Private dining room 50
Style: Modern
Smoking: No smoking in dining room

Ubiquitous Chip

12 Ashton Lane, G12 8SJ
Tel: 0141 334 5007
Fax: 0141 337 1302
e mail@ubiquitouschip.co.uk
Chef(s): Ronnie Clydesdale
Owner(s): Ronnie Clydesdale
Cost: *Alc* £32.95, set price L £23.95/D £32.95 H/wine £13.95
Times: Noon-2.30/5.30-11pm. Closed 1 Jan, 25 Jan
Additional: Sunday L. Children welcome
Seats: Private dining room 45
Smoking: Air conditioning
Directions: Telephone for directions

How could anyone visiting Glasgow miss out on the capable Scottish cooking at the Ubiquitous Chip? Moreover, the interior itself offers a surreal experience for diners stepping from the busy streets into a green, leafy setting that is more tropics than northern city. Come in to the glass-ceilinged arboretum where a bubbling water feature, stylish plank decking and plenty of flora and fauna will greet you. As for the menus - there are a multitude of them, but then, one can't complain about lack of choice. This restaurant pays proper homage to Scotland's bountiful larder and succeeds with fresh and smoky Cullen skink or oatmeal tart and its commendable range of regional cheeses.

HIGHLAND

ACHILTIBUIE   **Map 14 NC00**

The Summer Isles Hotel   NEW

IV26 2YG
Tel: 01854 622282
Fax: 01854 622251
e summerisleshotel@aol.com
Chef(s): Chris Firth-Bernard
Owner(s): Mark & Gerry Irvine
Cost: Set price D £40 ☺ H/wine £12.50
Times: 12.30-2pm/8-late. Closed Mid Oct-Easter

Idyllic is perhaps an over-used adjective but it's impossible to avoid in connection with the setting of this admirable small hotel. Set on the north-west coast of Scotland with views over the Summer Isles and across to the Hebrides, there is an inspired simplicity both to the elegance of the hotel and to the style of cooking. With access to some of the best seafood in the world there is no need for too much fussing around with langoustine and spiny lobster that might be simply served with

Scotland *(side tab)*

a salad at lunch. The five course dinner menu offers a choice at dessert only and whilst seafood dominates with the likes of Cullen skink and scallops with champ the meat is of similar quality with local lamb and beef having been praised. A weighty wine list offers everything from classic clarets to affordable New World and a good selection by the glass.

Directions: 10 miles N of Ullapool. Turn L off A835 onto single track road. 15 miles to Achiltibuie. Hotel 100yds after post office on L

Additional: Sunday L. Bar food.
Children 6yrs+. Vegetarian by request only
Seats: 28
Smoking: No smoking in dining room
Accommodation: 13 rooms (13 en suite)

ARISAIG — Map 13 NM68

Arisaig House

A delightful Scottish mansion peacefully nestling amid woodland and carefully-tended gardens in an outstandingly beautiful corner of the Highlands. Keep going past the hotel, and you'd end up in Mallaig en route for Skye and the Outer Hebrides. The spot may be remote, but the warm hospitality is all the more welcome for that. Dinner is a high point of any stay, and in the elegant wood-panelled dining room well-drilled staff appear on cue. The menu firmly places one foot in the classics and the other in a more forward-looking approach, with exciting results. Flawless timing and a quality marinade made gravadlax a strong recent starter, while crispy inshore codling with spring vegetables and light beurre blanc showed a clever balancing of flavours. The menu also embraces breast of Barbary duck, poached fillet of turbot, grilled king scallops and pan-fried fillet of Scotch beef, all from local sources and sympathetically married with top-quality ingredients.

Directions: On A830 Fort William to Mallaig road, 3 miles east of Arisaig

Beasdale, PH39 4NR
Tel: 01687 450622
Fax: 01687 450626
e arisaighse@aol.com
Chef(s): Duncan Gibson
Owner(s): Mr & Mrs J Smither
Cost: Alc L £16, D £40, set price L £25/D £28.50 (seasonal)-£55.
H/wine £15
Times: 12.30-2pm/7.15-8.45pm.
Closed Tues & Wed in Mar & Nov, 1 Dec-28 Feb
Additional: Sunday L. Bar food L.
Children 8 yrs+
Seats: 30. Jacket and tie preferred
Style: Classic, Formal
Smoking: No smoking in dining room
Accommodation: 12 rooms (12 en suite) ★ ★ ★

BOAT OF GARTEN — Map 14 NH91

Boat Hotel – The Capercaille

Deshar Road, PH24 3BH
Tel: 01479 831258
Fax: 01479 831414
e holidays@boathotel.co.uk
Chef(s): Peter Woods
Owner(s): Ian & Shona Tatchell
Cost: Set price D £29.50.
H/wine £11.50

Victorian railway hotel next door to what is now part of a steam railway running to and from Aviemore. In contrast to the rural/heritage aspect, the bold décor and striking oil paintings give the restaurant an element of city chic. The daily changing fixed-price dinner menu also follows the contemporary route with the likes of baked pork fillet with Stilton on a mustard-

Scotland

BOAT OF GARTEN *Continued*   **Map 14 NH91**

seed cream with braised paprika and coriander potatoes,
followed by orange and sultana bread and butter pudding on a
dark chocolate sauce with Amaretto ice cream. The latter
sounds ultra-rich but works really well - all the classical touches
but a light modern style.

Accommodation: 32 rooms (32 en suite) ★ ★ ★
Directions: Turn off A9 N of Aviemore onto A95. Follow signs
to Boat of Garten

Times: Dinner only, 7-9pm.
Closed Last 3 wks in Jan
Additional: Bar food.
Children welcome
Seats: 40. Private dining room 40
Style: Modern & Formal
Smoking: No smoking in dining room
Civil licence: 70

BREAKISH   **Map 13 NG62**

The Rendezvous Restaurant

Distinctive country house restaurant, with bags of enthusiasm
evident in both cooking and service. You're advised to go for
one of the more adventurous daily specials, not that there's
anything wrong with the popular seafood and meat dishes the
menu offers (charcoal grilled monkfish flambé with brandy and
a delicious prawn sauce for instance).

Additional: Sunday L. Children welcome
Seats: 32
Style: Country-Style
Smoking: No-smoking area; no pipes
Directions: 10 minutes N of Skye Bridge

Old School House,
Isle of Skye, IV42 8PY
Tel: 01471 822001
Fax: 01471 822986
Chef(s): Denis L C Woodtli
Owner(s): Denis L C Woodtli
Cost: *Alc* £17.50. ☺ ☺
H/wine £10.50
Times: 12.30-2.30pm/6.15-11pm.
Closed Tue, L Mon, Wed-Sat, 2wks
Oct, Jan, Feb

BRORA   **Map 14 NC90**

Royal Marine Hotel

The past and the present combine well in this distinctive, 1913
country house hotel. The traditional ambience of the elegant
dining room, still retaining many original features, is
complemented by a modern menu of dishes such as grilled
collops of local hot-smoked salmon with salsa, or baked breast
of chicken filled with hramsa cheese served with steamed
spinach and tomato coulis.

Style: Traditional, Country-House
Smoking: No smoking in dining room
Accommodation: 22 rooms (22 en suite) ★ ★ ★
Directions: Turn off A9 in village toward beach and golf course

Golf Road, KW9 6QS
Tel: 01408 621252
Fax: 01408 621181
e highlandescape@btinternet.com
Chef(s): Stevie Oglesby
Owner(s): Duncraggie Ltd
Cost: *Alc* £24. ☺ ☺ H/wine £10.95
Times: Noon-2pm/6.30-9pm
Additional: Sunday L. Bar food.
Children welcome
Seats: 50. Private dining room 12

The Links Hotel   **NEW**

Marvellous views over the golf course towards the North Sea
make this an enjoyable place to dine, as do the interesting
dishes available from the imaginative menu. These make
impressive use of local produce, as in the fillet of Brora Run
wild salmon on a bed of samphire or the slow cooked Rogart
lamb shank with a rosemary scented broth.

Seats: 60. **Smoking:** No smoking in dining room
Civil licence: 100
Accommodation: 22 rooms (22 en suite) ★ ★ ★
Directions: Turn off A9 at bridge in Brora towards the beach
and golf course.

Golf Road, KW9 6QS
Tel: 01408 621225
Fax: 01408 621181
e highlandescape@btinternet.com
Chef(s): Fiona Beattie
Owner(s): Duncraggie Ltd
Cost: *Alc* £24, set price D £24. ☺ ☺
H/wine £10.95
Times: Noon-2pm/6.30-9pm.
Closed Nov-Mar
Additional: Bar food L.
Children welcome
Style: Traditional Country-House

COLBOST   Map 13 NG24

The Three Chimneys

Isle of Skye, IV55 8ZT
Tel: 01470 511258
Fax: 01470 511358
e eatandstay@threechimneys.co.uk
Chef(s): Shirley Spear, Isabel Tomlin
Owner(s): Eddie & Shirley Spear
Cost: *Alc* £45, set price L £18/
D £35-£45 ☺ H/wine £14.95
Times: 12.30-2pm/6.30-9.30pm.
Closed L Sun & winter months,
3wks Jan
Additional: Children welcome
Seats: 30. Private dining room 20
Style: Rustic
Smoking: No-smoking area; no cigars
Accommodation: 6 rooms (6 en suite)
★ ★

Directions: Turn off A9 in village
toward beach and golf course

Prepare to be enchanted by this old crofter's cottage overlooking a sea loch, and luxury accommodation in the 'house-over-by'. Its growing international reputation bears testimony to the quality of the owners' vision. Superbly fresh local produce, much of it naturally from the sea, is simply prepared to devastating effect: flavours somehow contrive to be intense and subtle at the same time. Simply-prepared mussels and oysters might feature on the set lunch menu, with best Highland beef hotpot and curly kale mash, or scallop and monkfish brochette with lemon butter sauce to follow. Dinner is four courses of sheer bliss, from Loch Dunvegan langoustines and salad leaves, past say prawn and lobster bisque, to Highland venison collops with skirlie potato cake, juniper savoy, and beetroot and blueberry game gravy. After such sensational savouries, the likes of hot marmalade pudding and Drambuie custard do well to stand their ground.

CONTIN   Map 14 NH45

Coul House Hotel

IV14 9EY
Tel: 01997 421487
Fax: 01997 421945
e coulhouse@bestwestern.co.uk
Chef(s): Karl Taylor
Owner(s): Mr M A Hill
Cost: *Alc* £27/D £24.75-£30.50. ☺
H/wine £14.99
Times: Noon-2pm/7-9pm.
Additional: Sunday L. Bar food.
Children welcome
Seats: 40. Private dining room 16
Style: Traditional Country-House
Smoking: No smoking in dining room
Accommodation: 20 rooms (20 en
suite) ★ ★ ★
Directions: Telephone for directions

A lovely Victorian house whose regulars return for Taste of Scotland specialities, featured in the Mackenzie dining-room and a more informal bistro. At lunch, Scottish fromagerie and highland beef in whisky sauce; *carte* dinners perhaps adding west coast langoustine, salmon fillet with chive butter and quail with fresh herbs.

DINGWALL

Map 14 NH55

Kinkell House

From the restaurant a sweeping view of the Cromarty Firth and Wester Ross hills provides a delightful environment for a well-prepared daily-changing menu. Seasonal changes in fresh local produce keep the menu varied. Try char-grilled fillet of prime local beef with a rich wine jus or fresh salmon poached in Crabbies ginger wine.

Seats: 40
Style: Traditional, Country-House
Smoking: No smoking in dining room
Civil licence: 50
Accommodation: 9 rooms (9 en suite) ★ ★
Directions: On B9169 10 miles N of Inverness, 1 mile from A9 & A835.

Easter Kinkell,
Conon Bridge, IV7 8HY
Tel: 01349 861270
Fax: 01349 865902
e kinkell@aol.com
Chef(s): Douglas Hamilton
Owner(s): Ronnie &
Fiona Macdonald
Cost: *Alc* £25, set price L £17.50. ☺
H/wine £11
Times: Dinner only, 7-9.30pm
Additional: Sunday L. Children welcome

STOP PRESS Change of Owner

DORNOCH

Map 14 NH78

2 Quail Restaurant

An intimate atmosphere is created by two cosy dining rooms, once the front sitting room of this attractive Victorian house. Tastefully refurbished to retain their original character, the

rooms feature beautiful fireplaces, warm yellow walls and so many books you'll think you're in a library. The weekly changing menu delivers an accomplished selection of modern dishes such as quail stuffed with sweetbreads and a truffle sauce or corn fed chicken with pesto risotto and tomato and chilli salsa. Run by a husband and wife team, service is attentive but slightly leisurely if full. Still, who'd hurry from such a delightful setting?

Castle Street, Dornoch, Sutherland
IV25 3SN
Tel: 01862 811811
e reservations@2quail.com
Chef(s): Michael Carr
Owner(s): Mr & Mrs M Carr
Cost: Set price D £29.50.
H/wine £12.95
Times: Dinner only, 7.3-9.30pm.
Closed Sun & Mon, 2 wks Feb/Mar
Additional: Children welcome
Seats: 16. Private dining room 10
Style: Victorian Town House
Smoking: No-smoking area; no cigars
Accommodation: 2 rooms
Directions: 200yds past war memorial on L side of main street

DULNAIN BRIDGE

Map 14 NH92

Muckrach Lodge

A Victorian shooting lodge peacefully situated within attractive grounds. The well proportioned dining room maintains the classic elegance of the house, as does the cuisine - fillet of Highland beef topped with liver pâté on a port wine jus for example. Contemporary influences also feature as in a warm orange rice pudding with raspberry jam.

PH26 3LY
Tel: 01479 851257
Fax: 01479 851325
e info@muckrach.co.uk
Chef(s): Stephen Robertson
Owner(s): Dawn & James Macfarlane

Additional: Sunday L. Bar food. Children welcome
Seats: 28. Private dining room 60
Style: Modern. **Smoking:** No smoking in dining room
Accommodation: 14 rooms (13 en suite) ★★★
Directions: On A938, 0.5 mile from Dulnain Bridge.

Cost: Set price L £15.50/D £27.50. ☺
H/wine £12.50
Times: 12.15-2pm/7-8.30pm.
Closed all Mon, D Sun 1 Nov-31 Mar

DUNDONNELL   Map 14 NH08

Dundonnell Hotel

Little Loch Broom, IV23 2QR
Tel: 01854 633204
Fax: 01854 633366
e selbie@dundonnellhotel.co.uk
Chef(s): I Bellshaw, Graham Stewart
Owner(s): Selbie W Florence
Cost: Alc £25. ☺ H/wine £10.25
Times: Dinner only, 7-8.30pm.
Closed Jan-Feb
Additional: Bar food. Children
welcome
Seats: 70
Style: Traditional
Smoking: No smoking in dining room

A formal dining room with a lovely outlook over the sea and surrounding hills. The chef cooks with flair, giving an individual touch to many classic combinations and apparently enjoying arranging his dishes as 'towers'. Diners may get even more pleasure from dismantling such delights as confit of guinea fowl ('lovely, full of flavour') with stir fried cabbage, sautéed mushrooms, fondant potato and a red wine sauce. Though not big on trimmings such as canapés and petits fours, this is a reliably good restaurant with dishes to please everybody, from vegetarians to lovers of seafood.

Accommodation: 28 rooms (28 en suite) ★★★
Directions: On A832 Ullapool/Gairloch road, 14 miles from Braemore junction

FORT WILLIAM   Map 14 NN17

Inverlochy Castle Hotel

Stunning views of loch and hills, immaculate period furniture and table settings and slick, professional service from young Scottish and French staff all fulfil their promise at this world-famous hotel whose clientele has come to expect nothing but the best. Fine local produce including pristine sea-food and seasonal game makes a strong showing in dishes that demonstrate sound understanding and execution of modern British cooking. Pan-fried skate with slices of belly pork, capers and lemon works surprisingly well, while the Toulouse sausage and spinach that accompany roast monkfish is a gutsy, if rather less harmonious, combination. First class canapés and breads, excellent desserts and petits fours and an extensive wine list similarly deliver the goods.

Accommodation: 17 rooms (17 en suite) ★★★★
Directions: 3 miles N of Fort William on A82, just past the Golf Club

Torlundy, PH33 6SN
Tel: 01397 702177
Fax: 01397 702953
e info@inverlochy.co.uk
Chef(s): Matthew Gray
Cost: Set price L £28-£40/D £45-£55.
H/wine £17.50
Times: 12.30-1.30pm/7-9pm.
Closed Jan-Feb
Additional: Sunday L. Children
welcome
Seats: 40. Private dining room 20.
Jacket and tie preferred
Style: Classic
Smoking: No smoking in dining room

FORT WILLIAM *Continued*
Map 14 NN17

Moorings Hotel

Banavie, PH33 7LY
Tel: 01397 772797
Fax: 01397 772441
✉ reservations@moorings-fortwilliam.co.uk
Chef(s): Gordon McQueen
Owner(s): Mr S Leitch
Cost: Set price D £26. ☺
H/wine £9.95
Times: Dinner only, 7-9.30pm
Additional: Sunday L. Bar food.
Children welcome
Seats: 60. Private dining room 20
Style: Country-House
Smoking: No smoking in dining room
Accommodation: 21 rooms (21 en suite) ★ ★ ★
Directions: From A82 take A830 W for 1 mile. 1st R over Caledonian Canal on B8004

On clear days the panoramic views from this hotel extend as far as Ben Nevis. Situated alongside the Caledonian Canal at the famous Neptune's staircase, its Jacobean style dining room defies the building's modern exterior. Traditional style dishes might include garlic and clove studded loin of home cured ham or wild mushroom and chestnut faggots with roasted vegetables.

No 4 Cameron Square

4 Cameron Square, PH33 6AJ
Tel: 01397 704222
Fax: 01397 704448
Chef(s): Ross McCulloch
Owner(s): Mr S Leitch
Cost: *Alc* £21.50, set price L £8.50/D £21.50. ☺ ☺
Times: Noon-2.30pm/6.30-9.30pm
Additional: Children welcome. Vegetarian by request only
Seats: 55. Private dining room 40
Style: Traditional, Country-House
Smoking: No-smoking area; no cigars
Directions: Just off pedestrianised High Street, next to the Tourist Information Office.

Stylish restaurant serving modern British cooking. Dinner is the focal point (lunch is more snacky), and the three courses might include cod and parsley sausage, roast breast of duck on a wild mushroom risotto cake with a light cognac sauce, and vanilla and rum panacotta with balsamic ice cream.

GRANTOWN-ON-SPEY
Map 14 NJ02

Culdearn House

A welcoming little hotel with many regular customers, Culdearn's charm is evident in the restaurant, where guests receive a high level of personal attention from the proprietors. Careful treatment of quality raw ingredients guarantees an enjoyable meal. Dishes might include Angus steak with mushrooms and Drambuie cream or roast chicken with pan gravy.

Woodlands Terrace, PH26 3JU
Tel: 01479 872106
Fax: 01479 873641
✉ culdearn@globalnet.co.uk
Chef(s): Isobel Little
Owner(s): Mr A K & Mrs I Little
Cost: *Alc* £26, set price D £26. ☺
H/wine £11.50

Seats: 24. Jacket and tie preferred
Style: Traditional Country-House
Smoking: No smoking in dining room
Accommodation: 9 rooms (9 en suite) ★ ★
Directions: Enter Grantown from SW on A95, L at 30mph sign

Times: Dinner only, 6.30-9pm
(Bookings only). Closed Nov-14 Mar
Additional: Children 10yrs+.
Vegetarian by request only

Scotland

HALKIRK   Map 15 ND15

Ulbster Arms Hotel

A long established Highland hotel which proves particularly popular with sporting clientele - smoked salmon, gravadlax and prawn mille-feuille, or pan-fried collops of venison are on hand to counteract all that unseemly exercise. Excellent sticky toffee pudding too.

Seats: 50. Private dining room 12
Style: Modern Country-House
Smoking: No smoking in dining room
Accommodation: 10 rooms (10 en suite) ★ ★
Directions: Halkirk off A9, 3m N of Spittal

Bridge Street, KW12 6XY
Tel: 01847 831206
Fax: 01847 831206
e ulbster-arms@ecosse.net
Chef(s): Steven Robertson-Carswell
Owner(s): Lord Thurso
Cost: Set price D £22.50. ☺
H/wine £8.95
Times: Dinner only, 7-9pm.
Closed 25 Dec, 1&2 Jan
Additional: Children welcome

INVERGARRY   Map NH30

Glengarry Castle Hotel   NEW

A refreshingly uncomplicated style of cooking allows natural flavours to prosper unfettered. Innovative ideas such as thinly sliced oak-smoked halibut with a savoury and chilli dressing add interest to an otherwise reasonably traditional menu. Excellent views over the loch-side garden make for a worthwhile visit.

Style: Country-House
Smoking: No smoking in dining room
Accommodation: 26 rooms (25 en suite) ★ ★ ★
Directions: 25 miles N of Fort William on A82. Near junction of A82 & A87

PH35 4HW
Tel: 01809 501254
Fax: 01809 501207
e castle@glengarry.net
Chef(s): Michael Grahl
Owner(s): Mr & Mrs MacCallum
Cost: Alc £12.50, set price L
£10.50/D £26. ☺ ☺ H/wine £11
Times: Noon-1.45pm/7-8.30pm.
Closed early Nov to mid Mar
Additional: Sunday L. Bar food L.
Children welcome
Seats: 40

INVERMORISTON   Map 14 NH41

Glenmoriston Arms Hotel

A range of suitably Scottish tinged dishes appears on the set dinner menu at this welcoming hotel close to Loch Ness. Simplicity is the key to punchy dishes like carpaccio of beef with mushroom and shaved Parmesan, and timbale of west coast salmon and sole with scallop and salmon mousseline.

Seats: 28
Style: Country-house, Modern
Smoking: No smoking in dining room
Accommodation: 8 rooms (8 en suite) ★ ★
Directions: At the junction of A82 & A877

IV63 7YA
Tel: 01320 351206
Fax: 01320 351308
e scott@lochness-glenmoriston.co.uk
Chef(s): Carol Scott
Owner(s): Carol & Neil Scott
Cost: Alc £18, set price D £26.50. ☺
H/wine £11
Times: Noon-2pm/6.30-9.30pm.
Closed Jan & Feb
Additional: Sunday L. Bar food.
Children welcome

INVERNESS

Map 14 NH64

Bunchrew House Hotel

Baronial splendour with rich red carpet and curtains, candle-lit intimacy and genuine, professional service. The cooking offers honest flavours and lovely contrasting colours (a warm roulade of lobster and sole with pink caviar) not to mention top quality ingredients (pink and tender loin of Highland lamb for example.) These strengths apply throughout the menu with desserts such as dark chocolate and Tia Maria mousse - great quality in the central constituent with real variety in flavours and colours provided by the accompaniments (a 'Picasso sauce' and a chocolate cup filled with fresh fruit).

Smoking: No smoking in dining room
Civil licence: 120
Accommodation: 11 rooms (11 en suite) ★ ★ ★
Directions: 2.5 miles from Inverness on A862 towards Beauly

Bunchrew, IV3 6TA
Tel: 01463 234917
Fax: 01463 710620
e welcome@bunchrew-inverness.
co.uk
Chef(s): Walter Walker
Owner(s): Graham & Janet Cross
Cost:, set price L £23.50/D £29.50.
H/wine £14
Times: 12.30-2pm/7-9pm
Additional: Sunday L. Children
welcome
Seats: 40. Private dining room 14
Style: Classic Country-House

Glenmoriston Town House Hotel

Situated on the banks of the River Ness is this sophisticated hotel restaurant, known as Ristorante La Riviera. The menu offers a range of Mediterranean-influenced cuisine, including medallions of veal with Taleggio cheese, Parma ham, and a Marsala sauce, although there is variety for those who wish to depart from the high-quality and well-balanced Italian food (breast of duck with savoury cabbage, orange sauce and sweet red wine glaze, for example). Service is delivered by attentive and friendly staff. Stylish contemporary design blends well with the classical architecture.

Accommodation: 15 rooms (15 en suite) ★ ★ ★
Directions: 5 mins from town centre, on river opposite theatre.

20 Ness Bank, IV2 4SF
Tel: 01463 223777
Fax: 01463 712378
e glenmoriston@cali.co.uk
Chef(s): Steven Devlin
Owner(s): Mr A Pieraccini
Cost: Alc £25, set price L £15.50/
D £25-£32.50. ☺ ☺ H/wine £12.75
Times: Noon-2pm/6.30-9.30pm.
Additional: Sunday L. Children
welcome
Seats: 50. Private dining room 18
Style: Modern Italian
Smoking: No cigars

The Riverhouse

Former corner grocer's shop now combining stylish interior design with fine woodwork in a cosy relaxed environment. Try sautéed local monkfish and mussels in a cream saffron and spinach sauce, or loin of Caithness lamb on a bed of red onion marmalade with a red wine and garlic jus.

1 Greig Street, IV3 5PT
Tel: 01463 222033
Fax: 01463 220890
Chef(s): Marcus Blackwell
Owner(s): Marcus & Colleen
Blackwell
Cost: Alc £19, set price D £25.95 ☺
H/wine £11.50
Times: 12.15-2pm/6.30-9.30pm.
Closed Sun & Mon, Jan
Additional: Children 8yrs+
Seats: 26
Style: Classic
Smoking: No smoking in dining room
Directions: On corner of Huntly
Street and Greig Street

ISLE ORNSAY
Map 13 NG71

Duisdale Country House

Tranquillity and relaxation are promised at this old hunting lodge which snuggles cosily beside the Sound of Sleat. Blazing fires, plenty of books and a ready supply of malts are all conducive to calming the spirit, but satisfying the gastronome is another high priority. Owner Marie Campbell's culinary pedigree is evident from her innovative cooking based on the Highland's abundant produce. Her short but very sweet menus might offer prawns with garlic and lemon butter, then fresh tomato soup, baked sea bass with red pepper sauce, lemon cake with raspberries and sabayon, and Scottish cheeses. An epic voyage, but memorable.

Accommodation: 19 rooms (19 en suite) ★ ★ ★
Directions: 7miles N of Armadale Ferry, and 12miles south of Skye Bridge on A851

Sleat, Isle of Skye, IV43 8QW
Tel: 01471 833202
Fax: 01471 833404
e marie@duisdalehotel.demon.co.uk
Chef(s): Marie Campbell
Owner(s): Marie Campbell
Cost: Alc £26, set price D £26-£33. H/wine £11
Times: Dinner only, 7.30-10.30pm.
Closed Nov-Mar
Additional: Children 4yrs+
Seats: 40. Private dining room 12
Style: Country-House
Smoking: No smoking in dining room
Civil licence: 40

Hotel Eilean Iarmain

If you think romance is dead, perhaps a meal at Hotel Eilean Iarmain - voted one of the most romantic hotels in Britain - will change your mind. The restaurant (Celtic music, candlelight and lots of bare wood) lives up to the accolade and serves a seductive blend of modern and traditional Scottish-based cooking, all done with balance and finesse. A meal might include home-made lobster bisque, roasted duck with blueberry and port glaze, and vanilla creme brûlée. Other treats include a carefully chosen, themed wine list and (if you have the room) Scottish cheeses with home made oatcakes.

Sleat, Isle of Skye, IV43 8QR
Tel: 01471 833332
Fax: 01471 833275
e hotel@eilean-iarmain.co.uk
Chef(s): Andy Morrison
Owner(s): Sir Ian Andrew Noble
Cost: Alc £25, set price L £12-£16.50/ D £18.75-£31. ☺ ☺ H/wine £12
Times: Noon-2.30pm/7.30-9pm.
Closed L All week (ex bookings)
Additional: Sunday L. Bar food.
Children welcome
Seats: 40. Private dining room 22.
Jacket and tie preferred
Style: Traditional Country-House
Smoking: No smoking in dining room
Accommodation: 16 rooms (16 en suite) ★ ★
Directions: Overlooking harbour – cross bridge at Kyle of Lochalsh then take A850 and A851, then to harbour front.

Kinloch Lodge

Set in a stunning location on the shores of Loch Na Dal, this hotel's long history includes stints as a farmhouse and a sporting lodge. Now home to the well known Lord and Lady Macdonald, it has a welcoming, family house feel, with portraits on the walls and plenty of real fires in winter. A homely feel is also retained in the cooking, which makes good use of local produce. A meal might include Skye scallops pan-fried with lime, pink ginger and sesame oil followed by roast rack of Highland lamb with pinhead oatmeal and a cracked black peppercorn crust.

Isle of Skye, IV43 8QY
Tel: 01471 833214/833333
Fax: 01471 833277
e kinloch@dial.pipex.com
Chef(s): C MacDonald, P Macpherson
Owner(s): The Lord & Lady Macdonald
Cost: Set price D £37. ☺ H/wine £7
Times: Dinner only, 8-10pm.
Closed Xmas

continued

Scotland

ISLE OF ORNSAY *Continued*   Map 13 NG71

Accommodation: 14 rooms (14 en suite) ★★
Directions: 1 mile off main road, 6 miles S of Broadford on A851, 10 miles N of Armadale

Kinloch Lodge

Additional: Children 8yrs+.
Vegetarian not available
Seats: 30

KENTALLEN   Map 14 NN05

Holly Tree Hotel

With such stunning views of the loch, it is hardly surprising that this restaurant specialises in fish. The style is straightforward, allowing fresh ingredients to speak for themselves. Look out for the 'especially interesting' Rendezvous of Seafood, an encyclopaedic mixed platter. Meat, game and poultry dishes are also available.

Style: Bistro-Style
Smoking: No smoking in dining room
Accommodation: 10 rooms (10 en suite) ★★
Directions: 3miles south of Ballachulish on A828

Kentallen Pier, PA38 4BY
Tel: 01631 740292
Fax: 01631 740345
e stay@hollytreehotel.co.uk
Chef(s): Annette McFatridge
Owner(s): Annette McFatridge
Cost: *Alc* £25. ☺ H/wine £12.50
Times: Dinner only, 7-9.30pm.
Closed Dec-Feb
Additional: Children welcome.
Vegetarian by request only
Seats: 50

KINGUSSIE   Map 14 NH70

Osprey Hotel

Small, family-run hotel beside the Memorial Gardens at the south side of the town. A short fixed price dinner menu offers a variety of interesting choices - from Jamaica tilapia with a Bloody Mary sauce, to a range of carefully prepared Scottish specialities.

Smoking: No smoking in dining room
Accommodation: 8 rooms (8 en suite) ★★
Directions: South end of High Street off A9

Ruthven Road, PH21 1EN
Tel & Fax: 01540 661510
e aileen@ospreyhotel.freeserve.co.uk
Chef(s): Aileen Burrow
Owner(s): Mr & Mrs J. Burrow
Cost: £23. ☺ H/wine £9
Times: Dinner only, 7.30-8.30pm
Additional: Children 10yrs+.
Vegetarian by request only
Seats: 20. **Style:** Traditional

The Cross

The Cross is a converted and extended tweed mill alongside the river that formerly provided power for the mill. The friendly host with a dry sense of humour encourages guests to chat and relax prior to their meal — a precursor to an enjoyable visit for sure. A mammoth wine list purposely excludes French wines in earnest protest of the nation's nuclear testing in the Pacific a few years back. However, with so much choice, one need hardly worry about this omission. Instead, focus on the fresh flavours

Tweed Mill Brae, Ardbroilach Road, PH21 1LB
Tel: 01540 661166
Fax: 01540 661080
e fabulousfood@thecross.co.uk
Chef(s): Ruth Hadley,
Becca Henderson
Owners: Tony & Ruth Hadley
Cost: D £37.50. H/wine £12.50

and quality of the produce, as in the case of west coast prawns that are just hours out of the sea and served with perfectly ripe avocado and dressed leaves. Poached cod, just lightly smoked and served warm on flageolet bean salad, is also a much appreciated combination, judging from many admiring comments and cleared plates.

Accommodation: 9 rooms (9 en suite) ★ ★

Times: D only, 7-8.30pm.
Closed Tue, 1 Dec-28 Feb
Additional: Children 8yrs+.
Vegetarian by request only
Seats: 24
Smoking: No smoking in dining room

The Scot House Hotel

A warm welcome is assured at this family run village hotel. Meticulously maintained throughout, the public rooms include a cosy, relaxing restaurant decorated in warm peach and green. Good honest cooking, hearty portions and friendly service ensure an enjoyable meal. Dishes might include tournedos of beef Rossini or noisettes of Highland lamb pan fried with rosemary and brandy.

Seats: 24. **Style:** Traditional Country-House
Smoking: No smoking in dining room
Accommodation: 9 rooms (9 en suite) ★ ★
Directions: South end of the main street

Newtonmore Road, PH21 1HE
Tel: 01540 661351
Fax: 01540 661111
e shh@sirocco.globnet.co.uk
Chef(s): Andrew Woods
Owner(s): Mr & Mrs Gilbert & Mr & Mrs Mc Conachie
Cost: Alc £26/D £19.50. ☺ ☺
H/wine £9.50
Times: Dinner only, 7-8.45pm.
Closed 25-26 Dec
Additional: Sunday L. Bar food.
Children welcome

LOCHINVER   Map 14 NC02

Inver Lodge Hotel

Built high on a hillside with a backdrop of wilderness and mountains, this modern hotel offers spectacular views of the harbour and bay. These can be enjoyed from the restaurant, where the daily changing menu gives a contemporary slant to Scottish produce such as Inver Bay lobster with vermouth cream sauce or Grampian chicken roulade with creamed mash and tarragon jus.

Style: Traditional, Formal. **Smoking:** No smoking in dining room
Accommodation: 20 rooms (20 en suite) ★ ★ ★
Directions: A835 to Lochinver, L at village hall, private rd for 0.5 mile

IV27 4LU
Tel: 01571 844496
Fax: 01571 844395
e stay@inverlodge.com
Chef(s): Nicholas Gorton
Owner(s): Mr & Mrs Vestey
Cost: Set price D £30. H/wine £10.95
Times: Dinner only, 7-9pm.
Closed Nov – Apr
Additional: Bar food L.
Children 10yrs+
Seats: 50. Jacket and tie preferred

The Albannach   NEW

Baddidarroch, IV27 4LP
Tel: 01571 844407
Fax: 01571 844285
e the.albannach@virginnet.co.uk
Chefs & Owners: Lesley Crosfield & Colin Craig
Cost: Set price D £35. H/wine £9.50
Times: Dinner only, at 8pm. Closed Mon, Jan, Feb
Additional: Children 12 yrs+
Seats: 16. **Style:** Country-House
Smoking: No smoking in dining room
Accommodation: 5 rooms (5 en suite)
Directions: In Lochinver follow signs for Badiddarroch (Highland Stoneware). 0.5 mile

The owner enters the restaurant wearing full Highland dress at dinnertime, and unsurprisingly the food also veers towards the

LOCHINVER *Continued*   Map 14 NC02

wild lochs and mountains. Plenty of seafood is collected from
the nearby rocks and seas, and along with game in season and
locally-produced lamb and beef, it features heavily on the
menu. A cosy log fire warms the dining room, where at 8pm the
five-course dinner is served by candlelight: fillet of Highland
beef is a gourmet experience in itself, grazed on the moors and
tasting 'like it used to', and vegetables are organic where
possible. Expect also turbot, monkfish and scallops.

MUIR OF ORD   Map 14 NH55

The Dower House

The Dower House is more of a Highland cottage with bags of
charm in the personal touches and period memorabilia. The
restaurant, with its antique furnishings, sofa and piano, might
well have been the day room of the original house. Dinner is
7.30 for 8pm and Mena Aitchison looks after guests while
husband Robyn cooks the set three-course meal. His touch is
light and deft, with respect for the main ingredients - a perfectly
pitched dish of scallops with cod roe and bacon, generous cuts
of local beef, and a well-risen raspberry soufflé. The wine list -
including quality house wines - deserves study.

Accommodation: 8 rooms (5 en suite) ★
Directions: From Muir of Ord take A862 (Dingwall) 1 mile, L at
double bend

IV6 7XN
Tel: 01463 870090
Fax: 01463 870090
e aa@thedowerhouse.co.uk
Chef(s): Robyn Aitchison
Owner(s): Ms M Aitchison
Cost: Set price L £19.50/D £30.
H/wine £15
Times: 12.30-2pm/7.30-8pm. Closed
L All week (ex bookings), Xmas
Additional: Children 6yrs+.
Vegetarian by request only
Seats: 26
Style: Traditional, Country-House
Smoking: No smoking in dining room

NAIRN   Map 14 NH85

Boath House

A lovingly restored Georgian mansion, set in 20 acres of
mature wooded grounds. The inviting lounges feature open fires
and an impressive display of work by Highland artists. From the
airy dining room visitors can enjoy views of the trout stocked
lake. The menu is imaginative, bringing together traditional
ideas with a twist of the contemporary. Fresh, high quality
ingredients might include fillets of John Dory and squat lobster
served with salsify and asparagus spears or tender lamb, roasted
with a herb crust and served on a cassoulet of white beans and
pancetta. Cooking is slick, simple and honest, bringing out the
very best in the ingredients.

Auldearn, IV12 5TE
Tel: 01667 454896
Fax: 01667 455469
e wendy@boath-house.demon.co.uk
Chef(s): Charles Lockley
Owner(s): Mr & Mrs D Matherson
Cost: Set price L £22.50/D £35
Times: 12.30-2.30pm/7-9pm.
Closed L Mon-Wed, Xmas,
last wk Jan,1st wk Feb
Additional: Sunday L.
Children welcome
Seats: 28. Private dining room 8
Style: Country-House
Smoking: No smoking in dining room
Civil licence: 30
Accommodation: 7 rooms (7 en suite)
★ ★
Directions: 2 miles E of Nairn on A96
(Inverness to Aberdeen road)

Golf View Hotel

The conservatory provides an informal alternative to the more traditional restaurant. Either way the food is freshly made, well balanced and artistically presented - spiced oriental pork fillet with roast pineapple and a ginger and star anise sauce for example.

Directions: 15 miles SE of Inverness, 7 miles from airport on A96. In Nairn, turn L at church and continue to end of Seabank Road

Seabank Road, IV12 4HD
Tel: 01667 452301
Fax: 01667 455267
e scotland@morton-hotels.
demon.co.uk
Chef(s): George Mackay
Owner(s): Morton Hotels
Cost: Alc £15, set price D £26. ☺ ☺
H/wine £10.95
Times: Noon-9.15pm
Additional: Sunday L. Bar food.
Children welcome
Seats: 80. Private dining room 120
Style: Modern
Smoking: No smoking in dining room;
Air conditioning
Accommodation: 48 rooms (48 en suite) ★ ★ ★ ★

Scotland

Newton Hotel

The stunning setting in 21 acres of grounds overlooking the Moray Firth is one of the attractions at this welcoming business and leisure hotel. The other is the food, and the simply furnished restaurant adeptly turns out sturdy dishes like pot roasted loin of Highland venison with a creamy green peppercorn and cranberry sauce.

Inverness Road, IV12 4RX
Tel: 01667 453144
Fax: 01667 454026
e sales@morton-hotels.com
Chef(s): Steve McKenzie
Owner(s): Morton Hotels
Cost: Alc £26, set price L £15-
£18.50/D £27 ☺ H/wine £11
Times: Noon-2pm/7-9pm.
Additional: Sunday L. Bar food.
Children welcome
Seats: 70. Private dining room 45
Style: Traditional
Smoking: No smoking in dining room
Civil licence: 400
Accommodation: 57 rooms (57 en suite) ★ ★ ★ ★
Directions: West of the town centre

ONICH   Map 14 NN06

Allt-Nan-Ros Hotel

Colourful gardens set this friendly, tourist hotel apart, and its bright, spacious dining room commands stunning views over Loch Linnhe to the mountains across the way. All the public rooms are inviting, while the graciousness of the staff is a credit to the hotel. The dinner menu changes daily with choices such as parfait of chicken livers with garden leaves and onion

PH33 6RY
Tel: 01855 821210
Fax: 01855 821462
e reception@allt-nan-ros.co.uk
Chef(s): Thomas Petig
Owner(s): Mr & Mrs McLeod

Scotland

ONICH *Continued*

Map 14 NN06

marmalade - tasty with good texture and flavour, and rich chocolate cake with rum and raisin ice cream.

Allt-Nan-Ros Hotel

Cost: *Alc* £16, set price L £12.50/ D £29.95. ☺ ☺ H/wine £11.50
Times: Noon-1.30pm/7-8.30pm
Additional: Children welcome. Vegetarian by request only
Seats: 50
Style: Traditional
Smoking: No smoking in dining room
Accommodation: 20 rooms (20 en suite) ★ ★ ★
Directions: On shores of Loch Linnhe, 10 miles S of Fort William on A82

Onich Hotel

Genuine hospitality and lovely views of the loch make this a pleasant setting for a meal. The menu is both innovative and traditional, making good use of Scottish specialities: Angus beef might come with gnocchi, turnip purée and whisky jus; West Highland pheasant with Drambuie jus and potato rösti. Staff are smart and attentive.

PH33 6RY
Tel: 01855 821214
Fax: 01855 821484
✉ reservations@onich-fortwilliam.co.uk
Chef(s): Allan Donald
Owner(s): Mr S Leitch
Cost: *Alc* £16, set price D £16-£23. ☺ ☺ H/wine £10.75
Times: Dinner only, 7-9pm
Additional: Sunday L. Bar food. Children welcome. Vegetarian by request only
Seats: 50. Private dining room 24
Style: Traditional
Smoking: No smoking in dining room
Accommodation: 25 rooms (25 en suite) ★ ★ ★
Directions: Beside A82, 2miles N of Ballachulish Bridge

PLOCKTON

Map 14 NG83

Haven Hotel

Robust Scottish fare, supported by a carefully chosen list of wines from around the world. Home-baked soda bread, lovely fresh cod with cheesy crust and pesto sauce, robust lentil broth, and king scallops with lime and spring onion set the tone. Essential to look out for a delicious Ecclefechan tart.

Style: Traditional
Smoking: No smoking in dining room
Accommodation: 15 rooms (13 en suite) ★ ★
Directions: Turn off A87 just before Kyle of Lochalsh; after Balmacara look for sign to Plockton

Innes Street, IV52 8TW
Tel: 01599 544334
Fax: 01599 544467
Chef(s): Joanne Fenner
Owner(s): Mr & Mrs Dryburgh
Cost:, set price L £15-£17/D £27. ☺ ☺ H/wine £8.50
Times: Noon-2pm/7-8.30pm. Closed L (ex advanced booking), 20 Dec-1 Feb
Additional: Children 7yrs+
Seats: 40

POOLEWE   Map 14 NG88

Pool House Hotel

IV22 2LD
Tel: 01445 781272
Fax: 01445 781403
Telephone for further details

Fine views across the otter-friendly Loch can be enjoyed whilst sampling accomplished cuisine such as open tart of black pudding with sautéed leeks and poached egg. The loch-side location is also a boon for diver-caught scallops - superbly sweet and moist served wrapped in bacon and fried, with a rich langoustine sauce.

PORTREE   Map 13 NG44

Bosville Hotel

Bosville Terrace, Isle of Skye,
IV51 9DG
Tel: 01478 612846
Fax: 01478 613434
Telephone for further details

An attractive restaurant themed around a ship's chandlery which forms the focal point of this comfortable island hotel. Seafood is a speciality and genuine craft is evident in dishes such as lightly seared local scallops presented on a bed of saffron mash with wilted spinach.

Cuillin Hills Hotel

Isle of Skye, IV51 9LU
Tel: 01478 612003
Fax: 01478 613092
e office@cuillinhills.demon.co.uk
Chef(s): Jeff Johnston
Cost: Alc £24.50-£28. ☺
H/wine £10.95
Times: Dinner only (ex Sun), 6.30-11.30pm
Additional: Sunday L. Bar food. Children welcome. Vegetarian by request only
Seats: 48. Private dining room 20. Jacket and tie preferred
Style: Traditional, Country-House
Smoking: No smoking in dining room
Accommodation: 30 rooms (30 en suite) ★ ★ ★
Directions: 3.25 miles N of Portree on A855

Enjoy wonderful views across the bay to the Cuillins from the elegant restaurant. The set price menu offers starters along the lines of chicken liver parfait with citrus fruit salad, oatcakes and Cumberland sauce, and mains such as whole grilled rainbow trout with a caper, prawn and lemon butter sauce.

PORTREE *Continued*

Map 13 NG44

Rosedale Hotel

From its position on the upper level of this popular waterfront hotel, the attractive restaurant enjoys a superb outlook over Portree Bay and harbour. Attentive and extremely friendly staff serve some imaginative dishes fashioned from impressive quality ingredients with bold flavour combinations: pan fried local scallops with lasagne and red pepper sauce for example.

Smoking: No smoking in dining room
Accommodation: 23 rooms (23 en suite) ★ ★
Directions: On waterfront in Portree

Beaumont Crescent, Isle of Skye, IV51 9DB
Tel: 01478 613131
Fax: 01478 612531
Chef(s): Kirk Moir
Owner(s): Mr & Mrs P Rouse
Times: Dinner only, 7-8.30pm.
Closed 1 Nov-30 Apr
Additional: Children welcome.
Vegetarian by request only
Seats: 36
Style: Traditional

SHIELDAIG

Map 14 NG85

Tigh an Eilean Hotel

The bright airy dining room looks over Loch Sheldaig, so the menu naturally includes fresh seafood like spiny lobsters from nearby Sheild Eigg or Loch Torridon crab. But there is plenty of other local produce such as Blackface lamb or venison with roasted fennel or breast of pigeon enhanced by an apple and potato crush with port wine sauce.

Additional: Sunday L. Bar food. Children welcome. Vegetarian by request only
Seats: 24. **Style:** Classic
Smoking: No smoking in dining room
Accommodation: 11 rooms (11 en suite) ★
Directions: In centre of Shieldaig, at water's edge.

IV54 8XN
Tel: 01520 755251
Fax: 01520 755321
e tighaneileanhotel@shieldaig.
fsnet.co.uk
Chef(s): Christopher Field
Owner(s): Christopher &
Cathryn Field
Cost: Set price D £27. ☺
H/wine £9.75
Times: Dinner only, 7-late.
Closed end Oct-end Mar

SPEAN BRIDGE

Map 14 NN28

Old Pines Restaurant with Rooms

A unique style that makes for a unique place. First among the virtues a policy of encouraging children who can enjoy a high tea and then make for the playroom whilst the adults partake in the five course set menu. The emphasis on the local bounty is a further plus with the likes of Mallaig fish soup or roast haunch of venison with fresh pineapple thyme and juniper being prime examples. The desserts (lemon and raspberry posset or brown sugar meringues with grapes, kiwi fruit and elderflower ice cream for example) come with a recommended dessert wine by the glass.

Smoking: No smoking in dining room. **Civil licence:** 120
Accommodation: 8 rooms (8 en suite) ♦♦♦♦♦
Directions: Telephone for directions

PH34 4EG
Tel: 01397 712324
Fax: 01397 712433
e goodfood.at.oldpines.co.uk
Chef(s): Sukie Barber
Owner(s): Bill and Sukie Barber
Cost: *Alc* £15.50/D £24.50-£30. ☺ ☺
H/wine £10.50
Times: Open L all day. D at 8pm.
Closed D Sun (ex residents), all Mon
(ex BHs), 2 wks Winter
Additional: Sunday L. Children
welcome
Seats: 30
Style: Scottish, Country-House

STRONTIAN

Kilcamb Lodge Hotel

In a stunning loch-side setting with mountain views, this former hunting lodge has been sympathetically modernised. The restaurant is just the place to relax after a hard day's walking,

PH36 4HY
Tel: 01967 402257
Fax: 01967 402041
e kilcamblodge@aol.com

with its candles and flowers, and cooking based on local produce. Shellfish from the loch, other fish from the Sound of Mull, and venison from the garden might appear on the menu, alongside perhaps confit of duck, a hearty leek and potato soup, and rack of lamb with rosemary sauce. Desserts are a highlight, like lemon cheesecake terrine with fruit coulis. Service is quite natural, and there's a well-chosen wine list.

Smoking: No smoking in dining room
Accommodation: 11 rooms (11 en suite) ★ ★
Directions: Take the Corran ferry off A82. Follow A861 to Strontian. First L over bridge in centre of village.

Chef(s): Neil Mellis
Owner(s): Peter & Anne Blakeway
Cost: Set price D £20.50-£29.50 ☺
H/wine £9.75
Times: Noon-2pm/D at 7.30pm.
Closed Xmas, Jan, Feb
Additional: Children welcome
Seats: 26
Style: Modern

TAIN
Map 14 NH78

Glenmorangie House

Expect the best of Highland hospitality at Glenmorangie House, the distillery's 'Highland Home' overlooking the Moray Firth. Dishes from the short set-price menu are based on local seafood, Ross-shire beef and lamb, and fresh produce from the kitchen garden - perhaps baked salmon on garden kale topped with smoked salmon mousse and served with tarragon butter sauce.

Cadboll, Fearn, IV20 1XP
Tel: 01862 871671
Fax: 01862 871671
e relax@glenmorangieplc.co.uk
Chef(s): Anne Mackenzie
Cost: Set price L £15-£18/D £38.50
Additional: Sunday L. Children
welcome
Seats: 24. Private dining room.
Jacket and tie preferred
Style: Classic

Smoking: No smoking in dining room
Civil licence: 24
Accommodation: 9 rooms (9 en suite) ★ ★
Directions: N on A9 turn R onto B9175 (just before Tain) & follow signs for hotel

Mansfield House Hotel

Scotsburn Road, IV19 1PR
Tel: 01862 892052
Fax: 01862 892260
e mansfield@cali.co.uk
Chef(s): David Lauritsen
Owner(s): Mr N Lauritsen
Cost: Alc £25, set price L £11.75/
D £25. ☺ ☺ H/wine £14
Times: Noon-2pm/5-9pm.
Additional: Sunday L. Bar food.
Children 8yrs+ at D
Seats: 28. Private dining room 20
Style: Traditional Country-House
Smoking: No smoking in dining room
Civil licence: 45
Accommodation: 20 rooms (20 en
suite) ★ ★ ★
Directions: From S on A9, ignore 1st
turning to Tain and after 0.5 mile turn
R at sign for police station

Smack bang opposite the Royal Academy this impressive mansion house sits in its own grounds with impressive public rooms furnished in period style. The cooking, happily, doesn't overcomplicate and there is a refreshing simplicity to dishes like marinated seared duck on crisp leaves with its own crackling, that has consistently impressed. Some good strong flavours too in robust dishes like fillet of venison on a potato rösti with a wild mushroom duxelle and a game glaze. Good desserts along the lines of of a hot chocolate pudding with a mocca crème anglaise.

Scotland

TONGUE
Map 14 NC55

Ben Loyal Hotel

Main Street, IV27 4XE
Tel: 01847 611216
Fax: 01847 611212
✉ Thebenloyalhotel@btinternet.com
Chef(s): Elizabeth Warburton
Owner(s): Mr & Mrs P Lewis
Cost: Set price D £24. ☺
H/wine £10
Times: D only, 7-8.30pm.
Additional: Sunday L. Bar food.
Children welcome
Seats: 50. Private dining room
Style: Traditional
Smoking: No smoking in dining room
Accommodation: 11 rooms (11 en
suite) ★★
Directions: Hotel in centre of village
at junction of A836/A838

A welcoming hotel restaurant looking out over the Kyles of
Tongue and the ruins of Varrick Castle. Terrine of chicken
scented with sage and set on cranberry chutney proves a
delicate introduction to some sturdy main courses including
pan-fried gigot lamb steak with a mint and peppercorn glaze.

TORRIDON
Map 14 NG95

Loch Torridon
Country House Hotel

Originally the grand hunting lodge of the Earl of Lovelace
(architectural modesty was obviously not his strong point) this
is a sumptuous hotel in an enormously glamorous loch-side
setting. Largely traditional British cuisine is served up under
the ornate ceilings of a plushly furnished dining room. After
enjoying the likes of tartare of west coast scallops, smoked
salmon mousse with chopped tomato and dill and a good range
of tempting desserts, turn your attention to one or more of the
250 malt whiskies served in the wood-panelled bar.

Smoking: No smoking in dining room
Accommodation: 20 rooms (20 en suite) ★★★
Directions: From Inverness, follow signs to Ullapool (A835). At
Garve take A832 to Kinlochewe; take A896 to Torrido.
Do not turn off to Torridon Village – Hotel is 1mile on L

IV22 2EY
Tel: 01445 791242
Fax: 01445 791296
✉ enquiries@lochtorridonhotel.com
Chef(s): Neil Dowson
Owner(s): David & Geraldine
Gregory
Cost: Alc £38 H/wine £14.50
Times: Dinner only, 7-8.30pm
Additional: Bar food L. Children
12yrs+
Seats: 38. Private dining room 12.
Jacket and tie preferred
Style: Classic, Country-House

Give us your views!

All the restaurants in this guide have been visited by one of the AA's team
of professional inspectors but we want to hear from you too. Use the report
forms in the back of the guide or email us at lifestyleguides@theAA.com
with your comments on any of the establishments featured or other
restaurants that you feel are worthy of an entry. We would also be pleased
to receive your views on the guide itself and suggestions for any other
information you would like to see included.

ULLAPOOL

Altnaharrie Inn

Map 14 NH19

IV26 2SS
Tel: 01854 633230
Chef(s): Gunn Eriksen
Owner(s): Fred Brown &
Gunn Eriksen
Cost: Set price D £75. H/wine £11
Times: Dinner only, 8pm
Additional: Children 8yrs+.
Vegetarian with advance notice only
Seats: 16
Style: Country-House/Waterside
Smoking: No smoking in dining room
Accommodation: 8 rooms (8 en suite)
Directions: Telephone from Ullapool
for directions for the ferry

Crossing Loch Broom, with the lobster creel buoys bobbing gently in the wake of Mother Goose (the hotel's launch) has to be one of the great culinary pilgrimages of the world. It's rare to hear Altnaharrie talked about in anything but reverential terms and it's the all-pervading sense of harmony and serenity that seems to capture most hearts. In the end, Altnaharrie is very much an expression of Fred Brown and Gunn Eriksen's vision of the perfect retreat. Even items as mundane as water jugs have been selected with a real eye for the aesthetic and the absence of clutter seems designed to throw the spotlight upon Gunn's tapestries in the dining room and her ceramics in the upstairs drawing room. Prior to dinner, nibbles (not a word that does the freshest langoustine tails served with perfect mayonnaise much justice) are served to an eager band of diners who will occupy the half-a-dozen tables. The great thing about the cooking here is that there is the confidence to know when to stop and let the ingredients do the talking. An especially fruitful philosophy when the raw materials are of such exemplary quality. The near legendary lobster with two sauces (Champagne that actually tastes of Champagne, a pink blush made from lobster coral) continues to take the breath away with a sweet succulence that many find unsurpassed. Flavours can reach remarkable intensities as in an "amazing" morel soup with a pungent forest aroma and garnished with yet more langoustine tails. Roast fillet of calf has come with enoki mushrooms, trompettes de mort and a truffled ragout of artichokes and "the most amazing potatoes ever". The latter being a copper pan of velvety, aromatic truffled mash with parmesan. Puds tend to be a compilation featuring the likes of cloudberry ice cream with carpaccio of pineapple, and a "devastating" chocolate mousse. Couple all this with a terrific selection of well-kept cheeses, "damned fine" coffee and an enthusiasts wine list and the chances are you will be dreaming of making that crossing again almost as soon as you've left.

LANARKSHIRESHIRE, SOUTH

BIGGAR

Shieldhill Castle

Map 11 NT03

Quothquan, ML12 6NA
Tel: 01899 220035
Fax: 01899 221092
Telephone for further details

Fortified mansion house with peaceful views over rolling countryside and a wealth of historic features. The oak-panelled lounge and the high carved ceilings of the restaurant all make for a refined yet relaxing ambience. The cooking is creatively classical with many dishes and combinations rooted firmly in the past but taking on a modern feel thanks to imaginative presentation and a real delicacy of flavour. Spiced halibut fishcakes with seasonal leaves and a balsamic vinaigrette demonstrated real precision and superb freshness. Similarly a pan-seared fillet of Scottish beef which was further enhanced by an excellent truffle jus and fresh seasonal wild mushrooms.

EAST KILBRIDE   Map 11 NT03

Crutherland Country House

Renovated mansion set in its own grounds offering carefully prepared dishes and a wide range of imaginative menu choices. Both the restaurant and the service are formal, but comfortable and pleasant at the same time. The chicken liver and foie gras parfait, with a toasted brioche and fresh chutney comes recommended.

Strathaven Road, G75 0QZ
Tel: 01355 577000
Fax: 01355 220855
e info@crutherland.macdonald-hotels.co.uk
Chef(s): Stephan Frost
Owner(s): Macdonald Hotels Plc
Cost: *Alc* £29.50, set price L £18.50/D £26.50-£30. ☺
H/wine £14.50
Times: Noon-2.30pm/7-9.30pm.
Closed L Sat
Additional: Sunday L. Children welcome

Seats: 64. Private dining room 36. Jacket and tie preferred
Style: Traditional
Smoking: No smoking in dining room; Air conditioning
Civil licence: 250
Accommodation: 75 rooms (75 en suite) ★ ★ ★ ★
Directions: From E Kilbride take A726 towards Strathaven. 1.5 miles, & beyond Torrance roundabout, hotel on L

ROSEBANK   Map 11 NS84

Popinjay Hotel

Situated about 4 miles off the M74, the main England-Scotland motorway, the Popinjay Hotel, with its Tudor-style façade and picturesque gardens extending to the banks of The River Clyde, is a lovely venue. Look out towards the river, relax with the friendly, attentive service and tuck-in to traditional country-house cuisine.

Lanark Road, ML8 5QB
Tel: 01555 860441
Fax: 01555 860204
e sales@popinjayhotel.co.uk
Chef(s): James Queenan
Owner(s): Mr L Spence
Cost: *Alc* £30, set price L £9.95/D £15.95. ☺ ☺ H/wine £9.95
Times: Noon-2.30pm/6-10.30pm.
Additional: Sunday L. Bar food. Children welcome
Seats: 64. Private dining room 40

Style: Traditional, Country-House
Smoking: No-smoking area; Air conditioning
Civil licence: 160
Accommodation: 38 rooms (38 en suite) ★ ★ ★
Directions: On A72 between Hamilton & Lanark

LOTHIAN, EAST

DIRLETON   Map 12 NT58

The Open Arms Hotel

EH39 5EG
Tel: 01620 850241
Fax: 01620 850570
e openarms@clara.co.uk
Chef(s): John Kay

The rich red colours of the library dining room create a warm space in which to savour some traditional British food. Fixed price menus offer starters like marinated game parfait wrapped in air-dried ham with redcurrant and orange jelly, followed by the likes of maple and chilli roast rack of lamb on a celeriac and olive mash with a thyme and lemongrass jus.

Owner(s): Chris & Lyn Hansen
Cost: Set price L £18.50/D £29.50.
H/wine £11.50
Times: Noon-2.30pm/7-9pm.
Closed L Mon-Sat, D Sun
Additional: Sunday L. Children welcome. Vegetarian by request only
Seats: 30. Private dining room 30
Style: Classic, Traditional

Smoking: No smoking in dining room
Accommodation: 10 rooms (10 en suite) ★ ★ ★
Directions: From A1 (S) take A198 to North Berwick, then follow signs for Dirleton – 2 miles W. From Edinburgh take A6137 leading to A198

GULLANE
Map 12 NT48

Greywalls Hotel

Country house hotel already blessed in style but nevertheless working hard to produce high quality cuisine. The genuinely attractive, honey coloured building was built in 1901 under direction from the celebrated architect Edwin Lutyens, and is enclosed by an extensive series of walled gardens. The dining room shares in the style and comfort of the whole establishment and is particularly well placed to capitalise on dramatic views over the neighbouring golf course. The set price menu is carefully put together resulting in such successful progressions as langoustines salad followed by fillets of Port Seton seabass and ending with lemon and lime cheesecake.

Accommodation: 23 rooms (23 en suite) ★ ★ ★
Directions: From Edinburgh take A1 to North Berwick slip road, then follow A198 along coast to far end of Gullane – Greywalls in last road on L

Muirfield, EH31 2EG
Tel: 01620 842144
Fax: 01620 842241
🄴 hotel@greywalls.co.uk
Chef(s): Simon Burns
Owner(s): Mr & Mrs G Weaver
Cost: Set price L £20/D £40.
H/wine £15
Times: 12.30-2pm/7.30-9.30pm.
Closed Nov-Mar
Additional: Sunday L. Bar food L.
Children welcome
Seats: 40. Private dining room 20.
Jacket and tie preferred
Style: Modern
Smoking: No smoking in dining room

Scotland

LOTHIAN, WEST

LINLITHGOW
Map 11 NS97

Champany Inn

A smart, sophisticated restaurant with service to match, set around a small courtyard. The interior includes a tank of lobsters and oysters, but first and foremost this is a steak restaurant, renowned for the quality of its Aberdeen Angus beef - all hung, prepared in house and cut to order. Other dishes might include charcoal grilled salmon with lemon butter or breast of Gressingham duck with green lentils. Steak dishes come with a selection of mustards, including the house speciality, honey and whisky. An equally broad selection of accompaniments might include dauphinoise potatoes, French fries and wild mushrooms.

Style: Traditional, Formal
Accommodation: 16 rooms (16 en suite)
Directions: 2 miles NE of Linlithgow at junction of A904 & A803

EH49 7LU
Tel: 01506 834532
Fax: 01506 834302
🄴 reception@champany.com
Chef(s): C Davidson, D Gibson,
K Hope
Owner(s): Mr & Mrs C Davidson
Cost: Alc £39.50, set price L £16.75.
H/wine £14.50
Times: 12.30-2pm/7-10pm.
Closed Sun, L Sat, 25-26 Dec
Additional: Bar food. Children 8yrs+
Seats: 50. Private dining room 30.
Jacket and tie preferred

Livingston's Restaurant

52 High Street, EH49 7AE
Tel & Fax: 01506 846565
Chef(s): Julian Wright
Owner(s): Ronald &
Christine Livingston
Cost: Set price L £16.50/D £27.50. ☺
H/wine £12
Times: noon-2pm/6-9pm. Closed Sun-
Mon, 1 wk Jun, 1 wk Oct, 2wks Jan

Scotland

LINLITHGOW *Continued*   Map 11 NS97

Livingston's Restaurant

The semi-secret location (through an arch from the High Street), cottage stone walls and flickering candlelight add up to a great deal of charm and not a little romance. No surprise perhaps, to find the menu featuring the likes of Aberdeen Angus, hill lamb or Highland venison, but the treatments are less predictable. Venison has come with bitter chocolate sauce and goose-fat roast potatoes for example. Sometimes the finesse doesn't altogether match the level of ambition, but you're unlikely to be disappointed, especially by less complex offerings such as a loin of lamb with ratatouille and an exemplary roasted garlic and rosemary jus. Full marks also for a "classic" tarte au chocolat.

Additional: Children 8yrs+
Seats: 40. Jacket and tie preferred
Style: Traditional
Smoking: No-smoking area
Directions: Opposite post office

UPHALL   Map 11 NT07

Houstoun House Hotel

Steeped in character, with stone stairs leading from a vaulted bar to the elegant dining rooms, the three restaurants reflect the country house atmosphere of this sympathetically extended hotel. The main restaurant has an appetizing *carte* and attentive service, creating a very enjoyable dining experience. Roast rack of lamb sliced on to a thyme rösti with white pudding, roast shallots and baby vegetables, and pan-fried whole lemon sole with a caper and parsley sauce and a panaché of vegetables were recent main course suggestions. A towered apple tarte tatin with a crown of burnt sugar and home-made ice cream has been well recommended.

Style: Traditional, Country-House
Smoking: No smoking in dining room
Accommodation: 72 rooms (72 en suite) ★ ★ ★ ★
Directions: At junction between A89 and A899

@@
EH52 6JS
Tel: 01506 853831
Fax: 01506 854220
e events@houstoun.
macdonald-hotels.co.uk
Chef(s): David Veal & Peter Mackenzie
Owner(s): Macdonald Hotels
Cost: *Alc* £32, set price L £18.50/ D £26. ☺ ☺
Times: 12.30-2pm/7-9.30pm. Closed L Sat
Additional: Sunday L. Bar food L. Children welcome
Seats: 65. Private dining room 30. Jacket and tie preferred

MORAY

ARCHIESTOWN   Map 15 NJ24

Archiestown Hotel

This hotel has dominated the town square for a century or more, yet its restaurant is 21st-century bistro, with curios relating to fishing, whisky and wars-gone-by. Quality and careful shopping shine through in menus that encompass fish, shellfish, daily roasts and casseroles. A full-flavoured smoked mackerel paté perhaps precedes wonderfully fresh halibut in butter sauce with side dishes that might include stir-fried vegetables: then round off with a tangy lemon tart garnished with wild strawberries. This honest style of cooking is consistently robust and refreshingly uncomplicated.

Accommodation: 8 rooms (7 en suite) ★ ★
Directions: Turn off A95 onto B9102 at Craigellachie

@@
AB38 7QL
Tel: 01340 810218
Fax: 01340 810239
e judith.bulgar@btconnect.com
Chef(s): Judith Bulger
Owner(s): Mr & Mrs Bulger
Cost: *Alc* £27.50. ☺ ☺ H/wine £12
Times: Noon-2.30pm/6.30-10pm. Closed 1 Oct-9 Feb
Additional: Sunday L. Bar food L. Children welcome
Seats: 25. Private dining room 15
Style: Bistro-Style

CRAIGELLACHIE

Craigellachie Hotel

AB38 9SR
Tel: 01340 881204
Fax: 01340 881253
 sales@craigellachie.com
Chef(s): Anthony Allcott
Cost: Set price L £16.95/D £32 ☺
H/wine £9.95
Times: noon-4pm/6-12.30pm.
Additional: Sunday L. Bar food L.
Children welcome
Seats: 30. Private dining room 40
Style: Traditional
Smoking: No smoking in dining room;
Air conditioning
Civil licence: 40

Scotland

Arguably the premier hotel on Speyside, Craigellachie provides a fine dining experience, using quality Scottish ingredients in innovative, contemporary recipes. In the Ben Aigan Room, fishing and game memorabilia adorn the walls, whilst candle-lit tables are attractively tartan-clothed. A starter of west coast langoustines in a creamy dill sauce is beautifully presented and then you're spoilt for choice. Try baked fillets of Loch Duart salmon with fennel and orange duxelle, and the pancake of pear and orange with a Grand Marnier sauce and sugar-coated almonds is simply delicious. There's an extensive wine list and, in the Quaiche Bar, a mere 300 single malts from which to choose.

Accommodation: 26 rooms (26 en suite) ★ ★ ★
Directions: In the village centre

DRYBRIDGE

Map 15 NJ46

Old Monastery Restaurant

AB56 5JB
Tel: 01542 832660
Fax: 01542 839437

Worshippers of good food and drink flock to the 'Chapel dining room' so booking is advised for dinner. A small rural restaurant with big ideas - not least a very serious commitment to sourcing top quality produce. This shows in dishes such as wild boar terrine with a 'good honest flavour', delicious light sole filled with a delicate salmon mousseline with fresh crunchy steamed vegetables on the side, and exquisitely tangy lemon tart. The setting itself is also a strong pull - a converted church perched on the hillside above the fishing town of Buckie with views over the Moray Firth.

 buchanan@oldmonasteryrestaurant.freeserve.co.uk
Chef(s): K Mitchell, C Buchanan
Owner(s): Mr & Mrs C Buchanan
Cost: *Alc* £28.95. ☺ ☺ H/wine £11
Times: noon-2pm/7-8.45pm. Closed Sun-Mon,
3 wks Jan, 1wk Oct (Open L 1st Sun each month)
Additional: Children 8yrs+ at D. **Seats:** 42
Style: Modern
Smoking: No smoking in dining room
Directions: Leave A98 at Buckie junction onto Drybridge Road, continue for 2.5 miles (do not turn into Drybridge village). Restaurant on L at top of hill

Scotland

ELGIN
Map 15 NJ26

Mansion House Hotel

Much care has been put into the elegant, formal dining room with blues and greens setting a sophisticated note and recently acquired artwork adding much interest and character. The quality is consistently high with appetisers of smoked salmon with lemon, and mains of roast rack of lamb benefiting from an uncluttered approach to top quality produce.

Smoking: No smoking in dining room
Civil licence: 180
Accommodation: 23 rooms (23 en suite) ★ ★ ★
Directions: In Elgin turn off A96 into Haugh Rd; hotel at end of road by river

The Haugh, IV30 1AW
Tel: 01343 548811
Fax: 01343 547916
e reception@mhelgin.co.uk
Chef(s): Nicholas Nicholson
Owner(s): J & J Stirrat
Cost: Set price L £15.50/D £27. ☺ ☺
H/wine £12
Times: Noon-2pm/7-9pm.
Additional: Sunday L. Bar food. Children welcome
Seats: 50. Private dining room 30
Style: Classic

ORKNEY

ST MARGARET'S HOPE
Map 16 ND49

Creel Restaurant

A magical place. Situated on the seafront with fine views over St Margaret's Hope Bay, this is exactly the kind of (primarily) seafood restaurant you would dream of finding on the Island. The approach is commendably simple and rests on the twin pillars of freshness and sympathetic cooking. Nowhere is this more evident than in "Parton Bree" - fresh crab soup brimming with succulent claw meat and finished with just a swirl of cream. Supreme of organic salmon (farmed but fed on only natural salmon foods) comes as pale fleshed as nature intended and in the company of some brilliant roast cod, a spiced green lentil and fennel dressing and excellent mash. Puds tend to the calorie ridden - such as crushed meringue, crème caramel and chocolate mousse with a butterscotch sauce. Run with real enthusiasm and affection by chef Alan Craigie and wife Joyce.

Directions: 13 miles S of Kirkwall on A961, on seafront in village

⊛⊛
Front Road, KW17 2SL
Tel: 01856 831311
e alan@thecreel.freeserve.co.uk
Chef(s): Alan Craigie
Owner(s): Alan & Joyce Craigie
Cost: Set price D £28. H/wine £10.50
Times: Dinner only, 6.45-9pm. Closed Jan-Mar, Nov
Additional: Children welcome
Seats: 34. Private dining room 16
Style: Traditional
Smoking: No smoking in dining room
Accommodation: 3 rooms (3 en suite)

PERTH & KINROSS

ABERFELDY
Map 14 NN84

Guinach House Hotel

This little family-run hotel centres around the elegant restaurant, where the proprietor cooks in the French style and wise non-residents book ahead. The fixed-price four-course menu offers a balanced choice based around local produce along with herbs and vegetables from the hotel's own garden. Local flavour creeps into a dish of guinea fowl supreme with sweet heather honey on piquant sherry sauce, while the fishy option could be fillet of monkfish on a parsnip crumble edged with a red wine butter sauce. Finish with a platter of Scottish cheeses, if you can resist a dessert like Provence-style pine nut tart.

Accommodation: 6 rooms (6 en suite) ★ ★
Directions: From Aberfeldy: A826 (Crieff) hotel is on R

⊛⊛
'By The Birks', Urlar Road, PH15 2ET
Tel: 01887 820251
Fax: 01887 829607
Chef(s): Albert Mackay
Owner(s): Albert Mackay
Cost: Set price D £25. H/wine £9.95
Times: Dinner only, 7-9.30pm. Closed 25-28 Dec
Additional: Children welcome
Seats: 22. Private dining room
Style: French, Country-House
Smoking: No smoking in dining room

AUCHTERARDER
Map 11 NN91

Auchterarder House

As Victorian mansions go, Auchterarder House takes some beating. Not least because of its 17 acres of wooded and landscaped gardens or its ornate interior. Featuring amongst the latter is the imposing oak panelled dining room with its stained glass windows overlooking the gardens and log fire in the grate. The food has some performing to do to match the surroundings but it stands up very well indeed in dishes that require, and receive a deft touch from a skilled kitchen team. Canapés (lamb kebab, duck wonton, smoked salmon en croute) are a delicate foretaste of the dishes to come with a leek and smokie tart with parmesan and polenta being light and "beautifully balanced". Tellingly, fish is handled with precision, pan-fried halibut with a light broth of pasta, root vegetables and tomato being judiciously sauced and cooked to perfection. Similar accuracy and good timing apparent in a banana soufflé shot through with caramelised banana and partnered with top-notch rum and raisin ice cream. Petits fours are stunning. Serious and comprehensive wine list with fair mark-ups.

PH3 1DZ
Tel: 01764 663646
Fax: 01764 662939
e auchterarder@wrensgroup.com
Chef(s): William Deans
Owner(s): Wren's Hotels
Cost: Set price D £42. ☺
H/wine £24.50
Times: Noon-2pm/7-9.30pm.
Additional: Sunday L. Bar food L. Children welcome
Seats: 45. Private dining room 18. Jacket and tie preferred
Style: Modern, Country-house
Smoking: No smoking in dining room
Civil licence: 45
Accommodation: 15 rooms (15 en suite) ★ ★ ★
Directions: 1.5 miles N of Auchterarder on B8062

Scotland

Cairn Lodge

The clientele at this romantic little hotel are often fugitives from Gleneagles who prefer the more intimate surroundings. Cooking in the Capercaillie Restaurant is accomplished but while there is no doubt about the quality the menu tends to play safe. A fixed-price menu, with four choices at three courses, follows the seasons with starters like plump west coast scallops with lime and lemon butter sauce - simple but effective. A main course comprising two towers of pork and apple gateau topped with a savoury crumble and set on a Calvados sauce was reminiscent of nouvelle cuisine - small but perfectly formed.

Smoking: No smoking in dining room
Accommodation: 11 rooms (11 en suite) ★ ★
Directions: From A9 take A824 (Auchterader). Hotel at S end of town; on road to Gleneagles

Orchil Road, PH3 1LX
Tel: 01764 662634
Fax: 01764 664866
e email@cairnlodge.co.uk
Chef(s): M Riva
Owner(s): Mr A McDonald
Cost: Alc £29.50, set price L £18.95-£22.95/D £29.50. ☺ ☺
H/wine £13.50
Times: Noon-2.30pm/6.30-11pm.
Additional: Sunday L. Bar food. Children welcome
Seats: 50. Private dining room 32
Style: Country-House

Duchally Country Estate

PH3 1PN
Tel: 01764 663071
Fax: 01764 662464
Chef(s): Paul Higgin
Cost: Alc £21.27. ☺ ☺
H/wine £11.90
Times: 12.30-2.30pm/6.3-9.30pm.
Additional: Sunday L. Bar food L. Children welcome
Seats: 36. Jacket and tie preferred
Style: Classic Country-House
Smoking: No smoking in dining room
Accommodation: 13 rooms (13 en suite) ★ ★ ★

Country house going back to the 19th-century which has seen a recent complete refurbishment. A relaxed, panelled lounge

Scotland

AUCHTERARDER *Continued*   **Map 11 NN91**   *Duchally Country Estate*

bar, large bay windows with superb rural views and two old fireplaces all add to the grace and character of this manor house. Brevity prevails on the fixed price menu, which nevertheless offers imaginatively constructed dishes. Individual flavours particularly stand out in the likes of lemon sole and baby vegetable nage where a creamy broth is buoyant with al dente veg and nice chunks of fish. Meat too is handled tenderly as witnessed in succulent beef filled with white pudding - evidence of the care taken in some excellent cooking.

Directions: S from Auchterarder on A9 for 0.5m. Onto A823, bear L towards Dunfermline. L 0.5m at Duchally sign

The Gleneagles Hotel

Legendary resort hotel on the grand scale with championship golf courses and more country capers than you could shake a stick at, from falconry to an off-road four-wheel drive course. There's a choice of restaurants, but for fine dining head for the Strathearn, where as we went to press, Andrew Fairlie (who held Three Rosettes at One Devonshire Gardens) took up the reins. An exciting development for this famous venue.

Style: Classic
Smoking: No-smoking area; no pipes
Accommodation: 212 rooms (212 en suite) ★ ★ ★ ★ ★
Directions: Just off A9, well signposted.

PH3 1NF
Tel: 01764 662231
Fax: 01764 662134
e resort.sales@gleneagles.com
Cost: *Alc* £52, set price
D £42.50 H/wine £22
Times: 12.30-2.30pm/7-10.30pm.
Closed L Mon-Sat
Additional: Sunday L. Bar food L.
Children welcome
Seats: 196. Private dining room 300

STOP PRESS - Change of Chef

BLAIR ATHOLL   **Map 14 NN86**

The Loft Restaurant

Golf Course Road, PH18 5TE
Tel: 01796 481377
Fax: 01796 481511
Chef(s): Graham Horne
Owner(s): Mr S I Richardson
Cost: *Alc* £21.50. ☺ ☺ H/wine £9.95
Times: Noon-2.30pm/6-9.30pm.
Closed Mon-Tue (winter)
Additional: Sunday L. Children welcome
Seats: 36

Literally a former hayloft, pleasingly converted to retain its genuine characteristics of oak beams, stone walls and oak floors. The Loft has smartly dressed tables, effective spot lighting and French windows - this is no rustic room but an elegant space in which to dine. At lunch, only the bistro operates while reservations are recommended for dinner. A seasonal *carte* is backed up by a worldly wine list, on which New World options feature strongly. Combinations that work well include dishes like roasted sea bass with fennel, ginger,

couscous, green beans and chilli oil while a dark chocolate 'marie' makes a change from simple Chantilly.

Directions: Off A9, 6 miles N of Pitlochry. In the village turn sharp L at Tilt Hotel

Style: Rustic, French
Smoking: No smoking in dining room; Air conditioning
Accommodation: 5 rooms

BLAIRGOWRIE
Map 15 NO14

Kinloch House Hotel

A thoroughbred country house hotel, from its setting in extensive grounds and gardens to the antiques and wood panelling of the interior. The restaurant follows suit, decorated with deep green wallpaper and oil paintings. It's clear from the smartly dressed staff (and the proprietor, who usually wears a

kilt) that there is to be a sense of occasion to a meal here. Jacket and tie is the order of the day. The menu offers few innovations but can nevertheless be relied upon for a wide choice of dishes and excellent use of Scottish produce. This is, for example, a good place to sample Aberdeen Angus beef from the local butcher, pan fried and topped with Bearnaise sauce or served with braised oxtail on Savoy cabbage with fondant potatoes, diced vegetables and Madeira sauce. Other Scottish specialities include fresh seafood (lobster thermidor; prawns with garlic and caviar butter) and over 160 malt whiskies.

Directions: Three miles W of Blairgowrie on A923

PH10 6SG
Tel: 01250 884237
Fax: 01250 884333
e info@kinlochhouse.com
Chef(s): Bill McNicoll
Owner(s): Mr & Mrs D Shentall
Cost: Set price L £16.95/D £34. ☺
H/wine £16
Times: 12.30-2pm/7-9.15pm.
Closed 18-29 Dec
Additional: Sunday L. Bar food L.
Children 7yrs+
Seats: 55. Private dining room 16.
Jacket and tie preferred
Style: Modern Scottish
Smoking: No smoking in dining room
Accommodation: 20 rooms (20 en suite) ★ ★ ★

COMRIE
Map 11 NN72

Royal Hotel
NEW

Classically appointed dining room with a candlelit, intimate ambience in this 18th century hotel that has been beautifully upgraded. Much emphasis on the best of Perthshire produce with prime Scotch beef, lamb, venison and game featuring strongly, together with salmon, good sea fish and shellfish. Some interesting combinations and obvious technical skill in the kitchen.

Style: Chic, Classic
Smoking: No smoking in dining room
Accommodation: 11 rooms (11 en suite) ★ ★ ★
Directions: In main square

Melville Square, PH6 2DN
Tel: 01764 679200
Fax: 01764 679219
e reception@royalhotel.co.uk
Chef(s): David Milsom, Michael Ludgate
Owner(s): The Milsom Family
Cost: Alc £19/D £26.50. ☺ ☺
H/wine £9.50
Times: noon-2.30pm/6-9.30pm.
Additional: Sunday L. Bar food.
Children welcome
Seats: 60

CRIEFF
Map 11 NN82

The Bank Restaurant   NEW

Housed in a listed building (former high street bank) which retains its original wood panelling and décor. This small bistro-style eatery is bright and airy, and friendly in approach. Lunch can be a simple affair while the dinner menu is more adventurous. Try robust rib-eye beef on colcannon and red wine jus along with a light and tangy lemon tart.

Additional: Sunday L. Children welcome. **Seats:** 28
Style: Bistro-Style. **Smoking:** Air conditioning
Directions: Telephone for directions

32 High Street, PH7 3BS
Tel: 01764 656575
Fax: 01764 656575
🄴 bankrestaurant@talk21.co.uk
Chef(s): Bill McGuigan
Owner(s): Mr B & Mrs L McGuigan
Cost: Alc £22, set price L £18.50. ☺
☺ H/wine £11.95
Times: noon-2.30pm/7pm-10pm.
Closed Mon, D Sun, 2wks mid Jan,
24-26 Dec

DUNKELD
Map 11 NO04

Kinnaird

The splendid setting of this magnificent mansion cannot fail to impress, and the food is equally deserving of praise. Even jaded travellers find it hard to fault the place, experiencing a sense of well-being on arrival. Anticipate a warm welcome into plush reception rooms filled with rare antiques and fine paintings, including two beautiful dining rooms - one with frescoed wall panelling. The short menus change daily, concentrating on quality produce and a depth of flavour that doesn't falter. Diver scallops (seared, with vegetable risotto) feature alongside foie gras (pan-fried or ballotine with honey-roasted figs) and black truffle risotto, and salmon is smoked on the estate. Accurate cooking elevates an inspired assiette of four small terrines, and pan-fried monkfish medallions burst with flavour. Desserts maintain the soaring pace, as in a 'matchless' mille-feuille of meringue with passion fruit mousse and exotic fruits.

Directions: From A9 N take B898 for 4.5 miles. Hotel on R

Kinnaird Estate, PH8 0LB
Tel: 01796 482440
Fax: 01796 482289
🄴 enquiry@kinnairdestate.com
Chef(s): Trevor Brooks
Owner(s): Mrs C Ward
Cost: Set price L £30/D £45.
H/wine £18
Times: Noon-1.45pm/7-9.30pm.
Additional: Sunday L. Children 12yrs+. Vegetarian by request only
Seats: 35. Private dining room 20.
Jacket and tie preferred
Style: Classic, Country House
Smoking: No smoking in dining room
Accommodation: 9 rooms (9 en suite)
★ ★ ★

KILLIECRANKIE
Map 14 NN96

Killiecrankie Hotel

PH16 5LG
Tel: 01796 473220
Fax: 01796 472451
🄴 enquiries@killiecrankiehotel.co.uk
Chef(s): Mark Easton
Owner(s): Mr & Mrs C Anderson
Cost: Set price D £32. H/wine £13.20
Times: Dinner only, 7-8.30pm.
Closed Jan
Additional: Children 5yrs+.
Vegetarian not available
Seats: 34
Accommodation: 10 rooms (10 en suite) ★ ★
Directions: From A9 take B8079 for Killiecrankie, hotel on R just past village signpost

Carole and Colin Anderson have the business of running their delightful hotel down to a fine art. Standards have been consistently high for years, particularly in the hospitality, service

Scotland

and food departments. Dinner is a set price affair of three courses plus cheese, with a reasonable choice based on local produce. Take a robust example like pan-fried loin of hare and rabbit with cauliflower, fine beans, smoked bacon and date and port sauce, or a lighter grilled fillet of sea bass with herb couscous and roasted vegetables. A selection of dessert wines by the glass are suggested as a final touch.

KINCLAVEN
Map 11 NO13

Ballathie House Hotel

PH1 4QN
Tel: 01250 883268
Fax: 01250 883396
e email@ballathiehousehotel.com
Chef(s): Kevin MacGillivray
Cost: Set price L £18.50/D £32-£35. H/wine £12
Times: 12.30-2pm/7-9pm.
Additional: Sunday L. Bar food L. Children welcome
Seats: 70. Private dining room 32. Jacket and tie preferred
Style: Country-House
Smoking: No smoking in dining room
Civil licence: 60

This splendid mansion, overlooking the river Tay, combines the grandeur of a former age with every modern comfort: it is a venue for enjoyment at a premium. Fresh rolls and an amuse-bouche - perhaps a demi-tasse of carrot, honey and ginger soup - precede starters of Loch Fyne salmon or grilled Arran goats' cheese with herb leaves and orange segments. Honey-roast pork fillet on a light jus of cassis and juniper might be accompanied by braised red cabbage and raisins. Kumquats with a lemon and ricotta cheesecake may be overly sweet for some despite counter-balancing raspberries, slices of orange and a fruit sorbet.

Accommodation: 43 rooms (43 en suite) ★★★
Directions: Off A93 at Beech Hedges, follow signs for Kinclaven, approx 2 miles

KINNESSWOOD
Map 11 NO10

Lomond Country Inn

The magnificent Loch Leven vies with the food for attention at this formal hotel restaurant, and struggles to assert its natural dominance. The kitchen achieves distracting results with a short but innovative *carte* supported by bar menu and blackboard specials, and dishes such as smoked trout and dill pate with pear chutney, and shank of lamb with shallots. Good puds too.

Style: Traditional Country-House
Smoking: No smoking in dining room
Civil licence: 50
Accommodation: 12 rooms (12 en suite) ★★
Directions: On A911, 10mins from M90 J5 (Glenrothes) or J7 (Milnathort)

Main Street, KY13 9HN
Tel: 01592 840253
Fax: 01592 840693
e enquiries@lomandcountryinn.com
Chef(s): John McQueen
Owner(s): Martin & Rosemary Bald
Cost: *Alc* £17.50, set price L £12/D £16. ☺ ☺ H/wine £10.95
Times: Noon-2.15pm/6.30-9.30pm.
Additional: Sunday L. Bar food.
Children 12yrs+
Seats: 40

Scotland *(side tab)*

KINROSS
Croft Bank

Modern Scottish cooking is served at Croft Bank, a Victorian former private residence, in either the main dining room or the spacious Backroom Brasserie. The latter is located in a spacious strip-panelled room that has in previous incarnations been both a billiard room and a dance hall. The choice of menus and daily specials all offer good value for money. Lunch in the brasserie might offer a seafood chowder - "a meal in itself". A typically robust main course might be pheasant breast on garlic potato mash, piled high with lardons, cabbage and game sauce.

Smoking: No smoking in dining room
Accommodation: 3 rooms (3 en suite)
Directions: Just off M90 J6 towards Kinross

KY13 8TG
Tel: 01577 863819
Fax: 01577 863819
Chef(s): Bill Kerr
Owner(s): Bill Kerr
Cost: Alc £25, set price L £13.95-£18/D £25-£28.95. ☺ ☺
H/wine £10.95
Times: Noon-1.45pm/6.30-9pm.
Closed Mon, D Sun, 1-14 Sep
Additional: Sunday L. Children 3yrs+
Seats: 24. Private dining room 28.
Jacket and tie preferred
Style: Modern French

PERTH   Map 11 NO12
Huntingtower Hotel

Crieff Road, Almondbank, PH1 3JT
Tel: 01738 583771
Fax: 01738 583777
Telephone for further details

Imposing and tastefully upgraded mansion on the western outskirts of the city. Traditional fine dining in intimate, wood panelled surroundings. Some intricate cooking (galantine of barbary duckling with asparagus and green peppercorns with a pear and rosemary jelly) and a bent towards local produce (panaché of west coast seafood with tomato and basil nage and spaghetti of vegetables).

Kinfauns Castle

Relish the romance of sweeping staircases, stately galleries and Far Eastern artefacts at this early 19th-century castle overlooking the Tay. The oak-panelled library, embossed with the original family crest, is the atmospheric setting for a short fixed-price lunch or a slightly more comprehensive dinner menu. Quality ingredients come to the fore in dishes such as organic Highland beef on a shallot tatin with cocotte potato, savoy cabbage and a truffle infused jus, or west coast sea bass on a herb risotto with French beans and lobster cream sauce. A vegetarian menu of some interest is also offered.

Smoking: No smoking in dining room. **Civil licence:** 50
Accommodation: 16 rooms (16 en suite) ★ ★ ★
Directions: 2 miles from Perth on A90 Dundee road turn L at sign for Kinauns Castle

Kinfauns, PH2 7JZ
Tel: 01738 620777
Fax: 01738 620778
📧 email@kinfaunscastle.co.uk
Chef(s): Jeremy Brazelle
Owner(s): Mr J A Smith
Cost: Set price L £18.50-£20.50/D £32-£35. ☺ H/wine £13.95
Times: Noon-1.30pm/7-8.30pm.
Closed 4-26 Jan
Additional: Sunday L. Bar food L.
Children 12yrs+
Seats: 48. Private dining room 50.
Jacket and tie preferred
Style: Country-House

Let's Eat

A lifetime's experience is celebrated in this well-established restaurant run by a popular chef patron. It occupies a corner site and diners are attracted by the inviting sofas and wood-burning stove in the open-plan lounge, which leads through to the spacious restaurant. Tony Heath has moved with the times and produces modern Scottish cooking with flare but no fripperies. His secret is simple - quality ingredients treated with respect - amply demonstrated in a superb piece of Shetland salmon, pan-seared and served on roasted vegetables with a lemony herb couscous and coriander and tomato sauce.

Style: Traditional
Smoking: No smoking in dining room
Directions: On corner of Kinnoull Street and Atholl Street, close to North Inch

77/79 Kinnoull Street, PH1 5EZ
Tel: 01738 643377
Fax: 01738 621464
e enquiries@letseatperth.co.uk
Chef(s): Tony Heath
Owner(s): Mr T Heath &
Ms S Drysdale
Cost: Alc £24.95. ☺ ☺
H/wine £10.50
Times: Noon-2pm/6.30-9.45pm.
Closed Sun & Mon, 2 wks Jan,
2 wks Jul
Additional: Children welcome
Seats: 65

Let's Eat Again

Anyone would be happy to repeat the experience if a creamy risotto of wild mushrooms, soft herbs and lively spring onions is anything to go by. Although an off-shoot of 'Let's Eat' (see entry above) the cuisine is under sole control of chef Paul Burns and his enthusiasm and experience really shines through in striking combinations such as oven baked rock turbot with leek rarebit served on bubble and squeak. The uncompromising approach to food is echoed in the bold decor - green tinted walls with orange tablecloths - and the rejection of market trends of cheaper ingredients at lunchtime.

Style: Bistro-Style
Smoking: No-smoking area
Directions: Telephone for directions

33 George Street, PH1 5LA
Tel: 01738 633771
Fax: 01738 621464
e enquiries@letseatperth.co.uk
Chef(s): J Paul Burns
Owner(s): Mr T Heath,
Ms S Drysdale
Cost: Alc £20. ☺ ☺ H/wine £10
Times: noon-2pm/6-9.30pm.
Closed Sun & Mon, 2wks Jan & July,
3 days Xmas,3 days New Year
Additional: Children welcome
Seats: 36

Murrayshall Country House

New Scone,
PH2 7PH
Tel: 01738 551171
Fax: 01738 552595
Chef(s): Clive Lamb
Cost: Alc £24.95. ☺ ☺
H/wine £12.50

A fine restaurant named The Old Masters may be found within this impressive country mansion noted not only for its elegance but also for its two golf courses. A love of golf, however, is not compulsory in appreciating the splendid dining experience offered by the restaurant. You might detect the vicinity of Scotland's coastline by sampling the seared scallops with

PERTH *Continued*   Map 11 NO12

Shetland mussels and tarragon butter sauce or alternatively try
the likes of pan fried wood pigeon with ravioli of wild
mushrooms and a thyme jus. Service is discreet yet attentive.

Civil licence: 100
Accommodation: 41 rooms (41 en suite) ★ ★ ★
Directions: From Perth A94 (Coupar Angus) turn R signed
Murrayshall before New Scone

Times: Noon-2pm/7-9.30pm.
Closed L Mon-Sat
Additional: Sunday L.
Children welcome
Seats: 55. Private dining room 35
Style: Classic
Smoking: No smoking in dining room;
Air conditioning

The Seafood Restaurant & Wine Bar

168 South Street, PH2 8NY
Tel: 01738 449777
Fax: 01738 629893
e dine@keracher.net
Chef(s): Peter Keracher
Owner(s): Mr & Mrs P Keracher
Cost: *Alc* £21. ☺ ☺ H/wine £10.90
Times: Noon-3pm/6.30-11pm.
Closed Sun-Mon
Additional: Bar food L. Children
welcome
Seats: 56. Private dining room 12
Style: Classic, French
Smoking: No-smoking area; no cigars
Directions: Town centre, at corner of
Scott Street and South Street

A delightful aroma of seafood drifts down the stairs to greet
you on approaching this comfortable first-floor restaurant.
The high-ceilinged room's art deco appearance is set-off by
modern chrome and glass furniture. The chef/owners'

involvement in wholesale fish purchasing enables them to
source the very best. The quality of the dishes reflects this, as
in a trio of salmon with their own recipe gravad lax, hot-kiln
salmon and traditional cold smoked salmon is served simply
with a dill mayonnaise to let the full flavours come through.
The food is not exclusively fish and all dishes are well balanced
and precisely seasoned.

PITLOCHRY   Map 14 NN95

Green Park Hotel

Clunie Bridge Road,
PH16 5JY
Tel: 01796 473248
Fax: 01796 473520
e bookings@thegreenpark.co.uk
Chef(s): Chris Tamblin
Owner(s): Mr & Mrs McMenemie
Cost: Set price D £19.50-£23. ☺ ☺
H/wine £9
Times: Noon-2pm/6-8.30pm.
Additional: Children welcome

Green Park has functioned as a country retreat since 1866 but
its idyllic lochside frontage is a happy coincidence of the
building of Pitlochry Dam in 1951. A few metres higher and
you might never have had the chance to enjoy braised pheasant
with black cherries and bacon in the attractive dining room.

Seats: 70
Style: Country House
Smoking: No smoking in dining room
Accommodation: 39 rooms (39 en suite) ★ ★ ★
Directions: Off A9 at Pitlochry, follow signs

Knockendarroch House Hotel

A friendly, relaxed atmosphere in a delightful Victorian mansion standing high above the Tummel Valley. Fine skills and quality produce combine to create bright, fresh dishes. From the daily-changing set four courses expect the likes of warm terrine of spinach and mushroom, and roast guinea fowl stuffed with orange and thyme mousseline.

Style: Country-House
Smoking: No smoking in dining room
Accommodation: 12 rooms (12 en suite) ★ ★
Directions: On entering town from Perth, 1st R (East Moulin Road) after railway bridge, then 2nd L, last Hotel on L.

Higher Oakfield, PH16 5HT
Tel: 01796 473473
Fax: 01796 474068
e info@knockendarroch.co.uk
Chef(s): Jane Ross
Owner(s): Mr & Mrs A Ross
Cost:-Alc £23. ☺
Times: Dinner only, 6-8.30pm.
Closed Nov-Feb
Additional: Children 10yrs+
Seats: 24

Pine Trees Hotel

An impressive Victorian mansion whose delights include lovely panelling, ornate ceilings and a wonderful marbled staircase complete with stained glass window. Recent improvements have made the most of the hotel's charm, with the elegant Garden Restaurant providing a fitting setting for a menu which promises 'a taste of Scotland'. Dishes are created from an excellent array of local produce but often have an innovative, continental feel: a meal might include Highland game terrine followed by loin of lamb on a bed of sauerkraut with Lyonnaise potatoes and vanilla jus. Staff are friendly and willing to please.

Smoking: No smoking in dining room
Accommodation: 20 rooms (20 en suite) ★ ★ ★
Directions: N through Pitlochry to far end of town, turn R into Marchwood Road. Hotel on L just below golf course.

Strathview Terrace, PH16 5QR
Tel: 01796 472121
Fax: 01796 472460
e info@pinetreeshotel.co.uk
Chef(s): James McGowan
Cost: Set price L £14.75/
D £23.50-£27. ☺ ☺
Times: Noon-2pm/6.30-9pm.
Closed L Mon-Sat
Additional: Sunday L. Bar food L.
Children welcome
Seats: 50. Private dining room 12.
Jacket & tie preferred
Style: Classic

ST FILLANS   Map 11 NN62

The Four Seasons Hotel

Originally built in the 1880s for the manager of the limekilns, this attractive building also served as a schoolmaster's house before being extended and converted into a welcoming hotel. Its location at the edge of Loch Earn guarantees beautiful views and a peaceful atmosphere. The restaurant makes the most of the location and offers an appealing, daily changing menu of modern Scottish cooking. A meal might include Loch Fyne mussels with coriander and garlic followed by Highland venison steaks with plums, figs and button onions served with fresh ribbon pasta.

Chef(s): Campbell Cameron
Owner(s): Mr A Low
Cost: Alc £19.50, set price D £26.50. ☺ ☺ H/wine £12.50
Times: Noon-2.30pm/7-9.30pm. Closed Feb
Additional: Sunday L. Bar food. Children welcome
Seats: 60. Private dining room 20
Style: Modern Scottish
Smoking: No smoking in dining room
Accommodation: 12 rooms (12 en suite) ★ ★ ★
Directions: From Perth take A85 W, through Crieff & Comrie. Hotel at west end of village

Loch Earn, PH6 2NF
Tel: 01764 685333
Fax: 01764 685444
e info@thefourseasonshotel.co.uk

Scotland

SPITTAL OF GLENSHEE — Map 15 NO17
Dalmunzie House Hotel

Splendidly located beneath the mountains, this turreted Highland hotel promises a real touch of the Scottish country house experience. Local produce from the loch, rivers and hills feature large on a menu that offers plenty of fish and game. The dishes are carefully prepared from quality ingredients and include a variety of traditional Scottish dishes.

Style: Traditional
Smoking: No smoking in dining room
Accommodation: 16 rooms (16 en suite) ★ ★
Directions: Turn off A93 at Spittal of Glenshee, hotel 200 yds on L

PH10 7QG
Tel: 01250 885224
Fax: 01250 885225
🄴 dalmunzie@aol.com
Chef(s): Ronny McDonald
Owner(s): Mr S N Winton
Cost: Set price D £23-£28. ☺ ☺
H/wine £10
Times: 12.30-5pm/7.3-8.30pm.
Closed 1-28 Dec
Additional: Bar food L. Children welcome
Seats: 45. Jacket and tie preferred

RENFREWSHIRE

LANGBANK — Map 10 NS37
Gleddoch House Hotel

A regal mansion house enjoying spectacular views over the River Clyde to the hills of Loch Lomond beyond. The large, luxurious, rather formal dining room maintains the inherent romance of the setting, as does the largely classical menu. After perhaps a short stroll in the formal gardens you might consider opening proceedings with a smooth terrine of duck livers, chicken and foie gras studded with pine nuts and orange fillets, flavoured with cognac and served with a toasted lettuce scroll. Roast loin of Galloway veal on a rich Madeira sauce with woodland mushrooms might follow with a strawberry and mint cheesecake to round things off.

Directions: From Glasgow take M8 (Greenock) then B789 Houston/Langbank exit. Follow signs to hotel

PA14 6YE
Tel: 01475 540711
Fax: 01475 540201
🄴 gleddochhouse@ukonline.co.uk
Chef(s): Brian Graham
Cost: *Alc* £36.50, set price L £20/ D £35. H/wine £12.50
Times: 12.30-2pm/7-9pm
Additional: Sunday L. Children welcome
Seats: 120. Private dining room 30. Jacket and tie preferred
Style: Classic, Country-House
Civil licence: 150
Accommodation: 38 rooms (38 en suite) ★ ★ ★ ★

RENFREWSHIRE, EAST

UPLAWMOOR — Map 10 NS45
Uplawmoor Hotel   NEW

Enthusiastically run 18th-century coaching inn with a history of smuggling. Start with hearty seafood chowder, stuffed with mussels, trout and salmon in a creamy fish stock. Pan-seared breast of Gressingham duck might come with a roulade of chicken, stuffed with garlic and wild mushroom, on Puy lentil broth enriched by a strong, meaty glaze. Try orange mousse in a chocolate cup as a light end to a great value meal.

Neilston Road, G78 4AF
Tel: 01505 850565
Fax: 01505 850689
Telephone for further details

SCOTTISH BORDERS

GATTONSIDE
Map 12 NT53

Hoebridge Inn Restaurant

TD6 9LZ
Tel: 01896 823082
Fax: 01896 823082
 hoebridge@easynet.co.uk
Chef(s): Maureen Rennie
Owner(s): Mr & Mrs T Rennie
Cost: *Alc* £20, set price D £20. ☺
H/wine £10.25
Times: Dinner only, 6.30-9pm.
Closed Mon, 26 Dec, 1 Jan ,Feb
Additional: Children 6yrs+
Seats: 45. Private dining room 18
Style: Rustic, Italian
Smoking: No-smoking area; no pipes
Directions: Take B6360 from either
A7 or A68. Restaurant in village
centre

A stylish restaurant that is obviously intending to turn local, seasonal sourcing into an art form. If you have ever wondered what the difference in flavour between Highland, Dexter and Longhorn cattle is then you'd best make this place a regular feature in your diary. The cooking style is wisely simple but includes Mediterranean and some far-eastern influences.

JEDBURGH
Map 12 NT62

Jedforest Hotel

Camptown, TD8 6PJ
Tel: 01835 840222
Fax: 01835 840226
 mail@jedforesthotel.freeserve.
co.uk
Chef(s): Patrick Bardoulet
Owner(s): Mr & Mrs S Ferguson
Cost: *Alc* £28. ☺ ☺ H/wine £11.50
Times: Noon-2.15pm/7-9pm.
Additional: Sunday L. Bar food.
Children welcome
Seats: 40. Private dining room 24.
Jacket and tie preferred
Style: Country-House
Smoking: No smoking in dining room

Country manor set amidst 35 acres of land, with private fishing on the Jed Water which flows into the River Teviot and Tweed. While the brasserie/lounge bar offers good value dishes created with flair, the main dining room offers elegant surroundings and more serious cooking (full menu at dinner only). Technical skill prevails throughout a meal that could include such expertly prepared dishes as pressed terrine of smoked salmon with mixed confit peppers, salmon roe and yoghurt dressing or pan-fried saddle of border lamb with Dijon mustard and brioche crumb, Stilton and potato gratin. Desserts are equally gratifying.

Accommodation: 8 rooms ★★★
Directions: Just off A68, 3m S of Jedburgh

Scotland

KELSO
Map 12 NT73

The Roxburghe Hotel

TD5 8JZ
Tel: 01573 450331
Fax: 01573 450611
e hotel@roxburghe.net
Chef(s): Keith Short
Owner(s): Duke of Roxburghe
Cost: *Alc* £15, set price L £15/
D £25-£29. ☺ H/wine £15
Times: 12.3-2pm/7.3-9.45pm.
Closed Mon, Xmas
Additional: Sunday L. Children
welcome
Seats: 35. Private dining room 40
Style: Country-House
Smoking: No smoking in dining room

This impressive Jacobean mansion sits peacefully among acres
of parkland close to the river Teviot. It is a popular choice for
sporting guests, attracted by the fishing, shooting and golf.
Appropriately enough, the menu features many traditional
dishes such as roast mallard, Scottish beef and saddle of
venison. Occasionally inspiration is drawn from Europe, as
in haddock and mussel tagliatelli or seared foie gras with
caramelised oranges. Desserts might include toffee apple
crumble tart or steamed ginger pudding, after which guests are
invited to move to the comfortable Library Bar for drinks.

Civil licence: 50
Accommodation: 22 rooms (22 en suite) ★ ★ ★
Directions: From A68, 1 mile N of Jedburgh, take A698 for 5
miles to Heiton

MELROSE
Map 12 NT53

Burt's Hotel

The Square,
TD6 9PN
Tel: 01896 822285
Fax: 01896 822870
e burtshotel@aol.com
Chef(s): Gary Moore
Owner(s): The Henderson Family

Well-established hotel in Melrose's 18th century market square,
close to the banks of the Tweed. With a reputation for being
the place to go for a special occasion, the hotel offers
tranquillity and a fine setting in which to dine. There's no doubt
about the kitchen's artistic presentation skills, but sometimes

slightly more accurate cooking would allow it to reach greater heights. However, there is still plenty to please from a creative smoked chicken tartlet with Kelsae cheese and tomato and rosemary beurre blanc to generous main courses like cod atop a moist risotto with deep-fried vegetables.

Smoking: No smoking in dining room
Accommodation: 20 rooms (20 en suite) ★ ★ ★
Directions: Town centre

Cost: Set price L £19.50/D £27.75. ☺
☺ H/wine £11.95
Times: Noon-2pm/7-9pm.
Closed 26 Dec
Additional: Sunday L. Bar food.
Children 10yrs+
Seats: 50. Private dining room 20
Style: Country-House

PEEBLES   Map 11 NT24

Castle Venlaw Hotel

The turrets of this 18th century mansion penetrate the sky line high above the town. The fairy-tale romance is heightened by the dense but carefully sculpted woodland that falls away to the lush valley below. Cuisine is in the classical vein with the likes of grilled red snapper carefully and simply presented.

Style: Traditional, Country-House
Smoking: No smoking in dining room
Accommodation: 13 rooms (13 en suite) ★ ★ ★
Directions: From Peebles at east end of High Street, turn L at rdbt signposted A703 to Edinburgh. After 0.75 miles the hotel drive is signposted on R

Edinburgh Road, EH45 8QG
Tel: 01721 720384
Fax: 01721 724066
e enquiries@venlaw.co.uk
Chef(s): Alex Burns
Owner(s): Mr & Mrs J Sloggie
Cost: Set price D £23-£26.50. ☺ ☺
H/wine £10.95
Times: Noon-2.15pm/6-9pm
Additional: Sunday L. Bar food.
Children welcome
Seats: 35. Private dining room 30

Cringletie House Hotel

Beauty and functionality combine in the walled garden of this imposing baronial country house which provides much of the kitchens produce. When combined with a variety of other well-sourced local ingredients and treated with serious Caledonian culinary know-how a true taste of modern Scotland is assured. Quality seafood features alongside seasonal game.

EH45 8PL
Tel: 01721 730233
Fax: 01721 730244
e enquiries@cringletie.com
Chef(s): Addy Daggert
Cost: A/c £15.95, set price L
£15.95/D £32.50-£40. ☺ H/wine £16
Times: 12.30-2pm/7-9pm.
Additional: Sunday L. Bar food L.
Children welcome
Seats: 40. Private dining room 20.
Jacket and tie preferred
Style: Classic Country-House
Smoking: No smoking in dining room
Civil licence: 70
Accommodation: 14 rooms (14 en suite) ★ ★ ★
Directions: 2.5 miles N of Peebles on A703

ST BOSWELLS   Map 12 NT53

Dryburgh Abbey Hotel   NEW

This red sandstone mansion stands near the abbey and the river Tweed. The restaurant is decorated in traditional style, with heavily draped curtains framing views of the river. A surprisingly modern menu offers stylish, multinational dishes

TD6 0RQ
Tel: 01835 822261
Fax: 01835 823945
e enquires@dryburgh.co.uk
Chef(s): Hugh Miller

Scotland

ST BOSWELLS *Continued*   Map

such as sirloin steak with haggis crust, and a light whisky and pink peppercorn sauce.

Seats: 70. Private dining room 30. Jacket and tie preferred
Style: Formal, Traditional
Smoking: No smoking in dining room
Accommodation: 38 rooms (38 en suite) ★ ★ ★
Directions: Telephone for directions

Owner(s): Matthew Grose
Cost: Set price L £15.95/D £26. ☺ ☺
H/wine £9.75
Times: Noon-2.30pm/7.15-9.15pm
Additional: Sunday L. Bar food L.
Children welcome

SWINTON   Map 12 NT84

Wheatsheaf Restaurant with Rooms

Close to historic Berwick Upon Tweed and idyllically situated in the pretty Scottish borders. It naturally follows that the Wheatsheaf uses some fine local ingredients - salmon from the Tweed, border lamb, Tweed-side honey and seafood from the

Berwickshire coast, amongst other native bounty. Such top notch produce is treated lovingly, with dishes promising good textures and flavours. Expect large portions of nicely executed dishes like Thai spiced crab cake on chilli and butter sauce or expertly handled game and poultry like woodpigeon or corn-fed chicken. Desserts more than meet expectations too, with options like 'good as it gets' crème brûlée with blueberry compôte.

Main Street, TD11 3JJ
Tel: 01890 860257
Fax: 01890 860688
 reception@wheatsheaf-swinton.co.uk
Chef(s): Alan Reid
Owner(s): Alan & Julie Reid
Cost: *Alc* D £25. ☺ ☺
H/wine £10.85
Times: Noon-2.15pm/6.30-9.30pm.
Closed Mon (ex residents),
D Sun (in winter), 1-14 Jan
Additional: Sunday L. Bar food.
Children welcome
Seats: 26. Private dining room 18
Style: Traditional, Bistro-Style
Smoking: No smoking in dining room
Accommodation: 8 rooms (8 en suite)
◆◆◆◆
Directions: B6461 – halfway between Kelso and Berwick-upon-Tweed;
A6112 – halfway between Duns and Coldstream

STIRLING

BALQUHIDDER   Map 11 NN52

Monachyle Mhor

Monachyle Mhor maintains its reputation as a reliable hotel which always seems to offer a rewarding experience. Charm seeps out of all of its nooks and crannies, with a cosy snug bar, relaxed sitting room and warming open fires. The 2000 acres surrounding the house don't hurt either. In the conservatory restaurant, fine views and an imaginative fixed-price menu combine to ensure an enjoyable experience. Honest cooking and some innovative ideas are to be expected in the likes of

FK19 8PQ
Tel: 01877 384622
Fax: 01877 384305
 info@monachylemhor.com
Chef(s): Tom Lewis
Owner(s): Rob, Jean & Tom Lewis
Cost: *Alc* £20, set price L £20/D £34.
☺ H/wine £10

Times: Noon-2pm/7-9.30pm.
Closed Jan
Additional: Sunday L. Bar food L.
Children 12yrs+
Seats: 40. Private dining room 12.
Jacket and tie preferred
Style: Chic, Minimalist
Smoking: No smoking in dining room;
Air conditioning
Accommodation: 10 rooms (10 en
suite) ★ ★
Directions: On A84, 11 miles N
Callander turn R at Kingshouse Hotel.
Monarchyle Mhor 6 miles

home cured bresaola with speck, lardo and chorizo with
smoked aubergine. Leave room for a devilishly good bitter
chocolate tart with liquorice ice cream.

BRIDGE OF ALLAN   Map 11 NS79

Royal Hotel

Friendly and comfortable hotel close to the historic town of
Stirling. The restaurant is traditional yet informal, with a cosy
fire offering a warm welcome. The menu strikes classical notes
with some Scottish flavours, from oak smoked Shetland salmon
to updated croquette of haggis with turnip fondant.

Seats: 36. Private dining room 16.   **Style:** Traditional
Smoking: No smoking in dining room
Civil licence: 80
Accommodation: 32 rooms (32 en suite) ★ ★ ★
Directions: Telephone for directions

Henderson Street, FK9 4HG
Tel: 01786 832284
Fax: 01786 834377
 stay@royal-stirling.co.uk
Chef(s): Oscar Sinjorgo
Owner(s): Mr M McIlrath
Cost: Alc £28.50, set price L £14.95-
£18.95/D £22.50-£27.50. ☺ ☺
H/wine £12.50
Times: Noon-2pm/7-9.30pm.
Additional: Sunday L. Bar food.
Children welcome

CALLANDER   Map 11 NN60

Roman Camp
Country House

FK17 8BG
Tel: 01877 330003
Fax: 01877 331533
 mail@roman-camp-hotel.co.uk
Telephone for further details

A picture of serenity at this country house hotel set beside the
River Teith. Long, low and very pink on the outside, the
interior offers a wealth of charming public rooms including the

Scotland

CALLANDER *Continued*

Map 11 NN60   *Roman Camp Country House*

tapestry strewn dining room with its striking floral displays. A meal here is a genuine occasion, heightened by a menu not short on ambition and with an eye to dramatic presentation. Expect all the add-ons from imaginative canapés through an amuse (ballotine of duck with balsamic reduction for instance) to a pre-dessert that might be a stunning champagne jelly served in a demi-tasse. Combinations can be simple and to the point as in a starter of roast lobster with brandade cake and sauce Bercy or complex but no less impressive as in guinea fowl with truffled noodles, foie gras, and wild mushroom fumet that also incorporated asparagus and carrots. Desserts too tend to the elaborate, and it is a measure of the talent in the kitchen that there is rarely a slip. An architecturally striking (and ultimately delicious) praline bavarois (presented in a dark chocolate cone) came with satellite rings of latticed pastry and a dark chocolate sorbet. Extensive wine list offering a good range of halves.

DUNBLANE

Map 11 NN70

Cromlix House

Kinbuck, FK15 9JT
Tel: 01786 822125
Fax: 01786 825450
e reservations@cromlixhouse.com
Chef(s): Paul Devonshire
Owner(s): Mr & Mrs D Assenti
Cost: Set price L £27/D £40.
H/wine £16.50
Times: 12.30-1.15pm/7-8.30pm.
Closed 1-21 Jan (L by reservation Oct-Apr)
Additional: Sunday L.
Children 6yrs+ at D
Seats: 42. Private dining room 70
Style: Traditional, Country-House
Smoking: No smoking in dining room
Civil licence: 70

Despite the grandeur of this Edwardian mansion, and its location in the midst of a large working estate, the atmosphere is relaxing, with just the right degree of formality balanced by friendliness and good humour. There are two elegant dining rooms offering fixed-price menus with a choice of two dishes per course. Fresh local produce features - fillet of Angus beef with potato and carrot rösti, butternut squash purée, shallots and red wine jus, or steamed fillets of John Dory with pomme Elizabeth, spaghetti vegetables and roast tomato sauce. Dessert wine and port to accompany the cheese are offered by the glass.

Accommodation: 14 rooms (14 en suite) ★ ★ ★
Directions: From A9 take B8033 (Kinbuck), through village, 2nd L after small bridge.

KILLIN
Map

The Ardeonaig Hotel
NEW

Serene location on the south Loch Tay road with views towards Ben Lawers. Fine dining in style but not in any way stuffy with knowledgeable but friendly staff. An economical cooking style with not too much "mucking about" offers some lively flavours in dishes such as seared scallops with tomato cream and herb risotto or a successful main of Gressingham duck with salsify, parsnip and a truffle cream. A textbook lemon tart with raspberry sauce stood out amongst the puds.

South Loch Tay Side, FK21 8SU
Tel: 01567 820400
Telephone for further details

STIRLING
Map 11 NS79

Stirling Highland Hotel

Once the town's High School, now an impressive hotel, housing Scholars Restaurant. School themed room names including the 'Headmaster's Study' bar even extend to the 'Larder Dinner Menu' - a modest heading for a selection which could well include terrine of duck and lentil with pear chutney and a balsamic reduction followed by fillet of pork with wild mushrooms, fondant potato and Madeira sauce. Desserts are equally far removed from the average school dinner with heather-honey and cinnamon parfait or blueberry bread and butter pudding with hot maple syrup.

Civil licence: 100
Accommodation: 94 rooms (94 en suite) ★ ★ ★ ★
Directions: In road leading to Stirling Castle – follow Castle signs

Spittal Street, FK8 1DU
Tel: 01786 272727
Fax: 01786 472929
e stirling@paramount-hotels.co.uk
Chef(s): Danny McArdle
Cost: Alc £27.50, set price L £13.95/D £22.50-£25. ☺ ☺
H/wine £12.95
Times: 12.30-2.30pm/7-9.30pm.
Closed L Sat
Additional: Sunday L. Bar food.
Children welcome
Seats: 80. Private dining room 100
Style: Traditional
Smoking: No smoking in dining room

STRATHYRE
Map 11 NN51

Creagan House

Distinctive hotel of just five bedrooms created from a former farmhouse with an impressive baronial-style dining room. Cooking is bold and imaginative, strong on Scottish flavour with the likes of 'smokie in a pokie' and Gaelic fillet steak of local Aberdeen Angus beef. Great care is taken over the sourcing of quality ingredients, much of it grown specifically for the hotel by local producers. A dish that particularly made its mark was loin of venison set on a wild mushroom risotto with truffled juniper berry and Madeira sauce.

Seats: 15. Private dining room 6. Jacket and tie preferred
Smoking: No smoking in dining room
Accommodation: 5 rooms (5 en suite) ★
Directions: 0.25 miles N of village, off A84

FK18 8ND
Tel: 01877 384638
Fax: 01877 384319
e eatandstay@creaganhouse
Chef(s): Gordon Gunn
Owner(s): Gordon Gunn & Cherry Gunn
Cost: Set price D £23.75.
H/wine £9.75
Times: Dinner only, 7.30-8.30pm.
Closed L All week (ex parties), Feb & 1 wk Oct
Additional: Children 10yrs+.
Vegetarian by request only

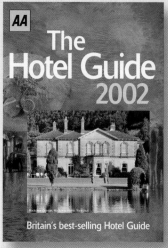

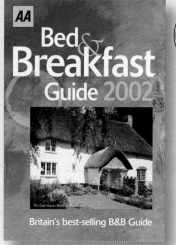

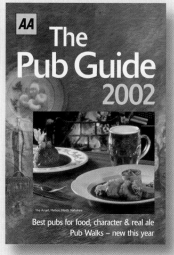
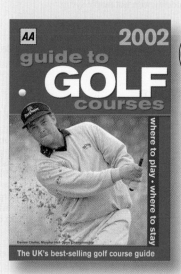

da Venditto

Contemporary Italian cuisine has arrived in the Welsh capital. About time too some would say given the long and historic Italian presence in South Wales. Tony Venditto has been part of that blend since arriving 25 years ago to work in one of Cardiff's better-known Italian venues. His eponymous restaurant occupies a discreet location just off the town centre with an interior that offers the kind of clean contemporary setting often found in London restaurants of a similar ilk. Impressive though the design is, it's the food that leads the way. The emphasis is placed firmly on quality raw materials and punchy flavours in intelligent and often classic combinations. Saffron and rocket risotto for instance arrived 'creamy-gold and perfectly timed' with good, peppery rocket. Adherence to things Italian is not slavish. Fillet of venison with bubble and squeak adds a modern British edge to proceedings with a porcini mushroom sauce giving extra depth of flavour. Desserts include the faithful (lemon and ricotta tart) and some original takes on the classics such as a surprisingly successful pairing of crème brûlée with a balsamic syrup. The wine list offers a varied selection of decent bins (some of which have been specially sourced and imported for the restaurant) with the expected emphasis on Italy. Service comes from a brigade of mainly Italian staff and is professional, relaxed and intelligent. A very welcome addition.

7-8 Park Place, CARDIFF **MAP 3 ST17**
CF10 3DP
Tel: 029 2023 0781
Fax: 029 2039 9949
E-mail: sherrytopo@aol.com
Chefs: Mark Freeman, Carl Hammett
Owner: Tony Venditto
Cost: *A/c* £30, Set-price L £13.50-£20.50/ D £17.50-£27.50. H/wine £12.50
Times: Noon-2.30pm /6-10.45pm. Closed Sun, Xmas, New Year, BHs
Style: Modern, Italian
Smoking: Air conditioning
Directions: City Centre. Opposite New Theatre

ANGLESEY, ISLE OF

BEAUMARIS
Map 6 SH67

Ye Olde Bulls Head Inn

Castle Street, LL58 8AP
Tel: 01248 810329
Fax: 01248 811294
📧 info@bullsheadinn.co.uk
Chef(s): Ernst von Halderen,
Jamie Williams
Owner(s): Rothwell & Robertson Ltd
Cost: Alc £31, set price D £28.75.
H/wine £13.75
Times: Dinner only, 7-9.30pm.
Closed Sun, 25-26 Dec, 1 Jan
Seats: 45
Style: Chic, Minimalist
Smoking: No smoking in dining room
Accommodation: 13 rooms (13 en
suite) ★ ★

Roaring log fires still blaze on cold evenings, and the bar remains a convivial meeting place, but Samuel Johnson and Charles Dickens, two former habitués, might have trouble recognizing this cheerful inn now. Modern British cooking is

served in the restaurant, where Keith Rothwell and his team attract a loyal following, and locally sourced produce underpins the quality of the food. Starters like marbled game terrine with bitter orange chutney show innovation, while medallions of venison with fresh fig confit offers interesting contrasts. Steamed rhubarb sponge with fudge ice cream should delight, and there are nearly 200 wines.

Directions: Town centre, main street

BRIDGEND

BRIDGEND
Map 3 SS97

Coed-Y-Mwstwr

🏛
Coychurch, CF35 6AF
Tel: 01656 860621
Fax: 01656 863122
📧 anything@coed-y-mwstwr.com
Chef(s): lenacio Vidales
Owner(s): Mr J Hitchcock
Cost: Alc £24, set price L £9.95/
D £22.95. ☺ ☺ H/wine £11.95
Times: Noon-2.30pm/7-10pm.
Additional: Sunday L. Bar food.
Children welcome
Seats: 44. Private dining room 24
Style: Traditional, Country-House

A sunny hotel dining room with an impressive domed ceiling and views over the hillside and gardens. Flavours are deftly handled by the kitchen as demonstrated by a pressed duck terrine with a cranberry and orange compôte - perfectly balanced with the duck shining through and the compôte neither too sweet nor too tart.

Smoking: No smoking in dining room
Civil licence: 120
Accommodation: 23 rooms (23 en suite) ★ ★ ★
Directions: M4 J35, A473 (Bridgend) into Coychurch, R at petrol station and up hill for 1 mile.

Wales

The Great House Restaurant

Originating from around 1550, local legend has it that the original house was a gift from Queen Elizabeth I to the Earl of Leicester, who used it a hunting lodge. Original mullioned windows, oak beams and inglenooks were retained in its restoration in 1986 and the name Leicester's bestowed on the restaurant. Assured cooking features throughout a dinner menu that makes good use of locally sourced and seasonal ingredients, for instance in terrine of duck confit and chicken livers and stuffed partridge with roast vegetables. A smaller bistro menu features daily fish dishes, local sausages and Scottish beef as well as lunchtime specials at kind prices.

Accommodation: 16 rooms (16 en suite) ★ ★ ★
Directions: M4 J35, A473 then A48 signed Porthcawl and Laleston

Laleston, CF32 0HP
Tel: 01656 657644
Fax: 01656 668892
e enquiries@great-house-laleston.co.uk
Chef(s): Neil Hughes, Stuart Bevan
Owner(s): Stephen and Norma Bond
Cost: ☺ ☺ H/wine £10.95
Times: Noon-2pm/6.45-10pm.
Closed D Sun, Xmas 3 days
Additional: Sunday L.
Children welcome
Seats: 50. Private dining room 40
Style: Country-house, Modern
Smoking: No smoking in dining room;
Air conditioning

Wales

CARDIFF

CARDIFF   Map 3 ST17

Armless Dragon   **NEW**

This hidden gem of a restaurant, 10 minutes' walk from the city centre, serves exciting modern Welsh food: expect cawl,

97 Wyvern Road, Cathays, CF2 4BG
Tel: 029 2038 2357
Fax: 029 2038 2055
e paul@thearmlessdragon.com
Chef(s): Paul Lane
Owner(s): Paul Lane
Cost: A/c £21, set price L £10. ☺ ☺
H/wine £8.90
Times: Noon-2pm/7-9.30pm. Closed
Sun, L Sat, Mon (except rugby
internationals), BHs
Additional: Children welcome
Seats: 46
Style: Modern
Smoking: No smoking in dining room
Directions: 10 mins walk from centre.
Adjacent to Senghennydd Rd

laverbread and lamb as you are unlikely to have seen them before. Dishes might include crab soup with Caerphilly croutons, seafood cawl with saffron potatoes or Pembrokeshire lamb with liver, beetroot and smoked garlic mash. Stylish, contemporary decor.

Copthorne Hotel Cardiff-Caerdydd

A lakeside setting for this oak-panelled restaurant in a modern hotel. The kitchen scores highly on home-made products and fresh ingredients, producing a pleasing corn-fed chicken with asparagus, noodles and champagne sauce, and choices like

Copthorne Way, Culverhouse Cross,
CF5 6DH
Tel: 029 2059 9100
Fax: 029 2059 9648
e sales.cardiff@mill-cop.com

flash-fried calves' liver with crispy bacon, parsley mashed potato, and a red onion marmalade.

Style: Traditional. **Smoking:** No-smoking area; Air conditioning
Civil licence: 180
Accommodation: 135 rooms (135 en suite) ★ ★ ★ ★
Directions: M4 J33 take A4232 (Culverhouse Cross), 4th exit at rdbt (A48). 1st left

Chef(s): John O' Reilly
Cost: *Alc* £25, set price L £15.50-£21/D £19.95-£27. ☺ ☺
H/wine £13.50
Times: 12.30-2pm/7-10pm
Additional: Bar food. Children welcome
Seats: 100. Private dining room 160

Cutting Edge   NEW

The ground floor of a legal firm with waterside views and a contemporary uncluttered feel. The approach is admirably to the point food-wise too, with carpaccio of beef coming with rocket salad, a nicely acidic balsamic dressing and shaved Parmesan. Amongst the mains, breast of duck on Savoy cabbage has been a success as has a delicate vanilla panacotta with strawberries.

Style: Modern, Minimalist
Smoking: No-smoking area; Air conditioning
Directions: Telephone for directions

Discovery House, Scott Harbour, Cardiff Bay
Tel: 029 2047 0780
Fax: 029 2044 0876
Chef(s): Peter Farrow
Owner(s): H Palser, R Crane, C Nott
Cost: *Alc* £27.50. ☺ ☺ H/wine £13
Times: Noon-2.30pm/7-9.30pm.
Closed Sun, Xmas, New Year, Easter
Additional: Children welcome
Seats: 45

da Venditto
Restaurant of the Year for Wales - see page 669 for entry

Gilby's Restaurant

With its reputation as one of the best seafood restaurants in Wales, Gilby's will appeal to fish fiends. Try squid fricassée or brodetto of red mullet, perhaps. If fish is not your thing, the meat and vegetarian choices, with a predominantly modern European influence, are similarly enticing, while the two-course set price lunch menu is a good value option. Situated on the Western edge of the city and well worth a diversion from the nearby M4.

Seats: 100. **Style:** Chic, Rustic. **Smoking:** No-smoking area
Directions: From M4 J33 follow signs for Airport/Cardiff West. Take A4050 Barry/Airport road and R at 1st mini rdbt

Old Port Road, Culverhouse Cross, CF5 6DN
Tel: 029 2067 0800
Fax: 029 2059 4437
✉ info@gilbysrestaurant.co.uk
Chef(s): M Cornock,A Armelin
Owner(s): Mr A Armelin
Cost: *Alc* £26.50, set price L £8.95/D £12.95. ☺ ☺ H/wine £10.95
Times: Noon-2.30pm/5.45-10.30pm.
Closed Mon, D Sun, Bhs, 1 wk Jan, 2 wks Sep. **Additional:** Sunday L. Children welcome

Izakaya Japanese Tavern   NEW

Mermaid Quay, Cardiff Bay, CF10 5BW
Tel: 02920 492939
Fax: 02920 492939
✉ info@izakaya-japanese-tavern.com
Chef(s): Yoshiko Evans, Peter Mansbridge
Owner(s): Iestyn and Yoshiko Evans
Cost: Set price L £10-£20/D £15-£25. ☺ ☺ H/wine £8.90
Times: Noon-2.30pm/6-11pm (Sun 1-10pm).
Closed Xmas, New Year
Additional: Children 6yrs+ at D
Seats: 85. Private dining room 20

Aggressively authentic taste of Japan in the heart of the thriving waterfront area of Cardiff. Authenticity is coupled with a hint of evangelism so the whole experience is very accessible with full English descriptions and even colour photos on the menu. It might look slightly tacky but importantly the food is good. Choose from up to sixty items including variations on sashimi, sushi, tempura and offerings such as skewered chicken liver, and grilled mackerel with Japanese radish.

Style: Japanese Izakaya
Smoking: No-smoking area
Directions: On the first floor of Mermaid Quay

Le Cassoulet

A popular neighbourhood restaurant specialising in regional French food. The proprietor's roots are firmly proclaimed in the decor, which incorporates his collection of champagne tops and

5 Romilly Crescent, Canton, CF11 9NP
Tel: 029 2022 1905
Fax: 029 2022 1905
📧 lecassoulet@ukonline.co.uk
Chef(s): Gilbert Viader, Joakim Hunarun
Owner(s): Mr & Mrs G Viader
Cost: Alc £25, set price L £13.50. ☺ ☺ H/wine £11.50
Times: Noon-2pm/7-10pm. Closed Sun & Mon, 2wk Xmas, 3 wks Aug
Additional: Children welcome
Seats: 40
Style: Formal
Smoking: No cigars; Air conditioning

photos of the Toulouse rugby team. Drapes are used to create a feeling of privacy, whilst shades of red and ochre make the room warm and inviting. The menu features familiar French classics (fillet Rossini, creme brûlée) alongside less familiar specialities such as cassoulet Toulousain (an earthenware dish of haricot beans, pork sausage and confit duck leg accompanied by chicory and apple salad). Naturally, the wine list is as French as the food and surroundings.

Directions: From M4 follow B4267 Canton, Restaurant is next to Post Office

Le Gallois

Striking a chord with foodies in Cardiff and beyond, this family-run restaurant is a modern neighbourhood eatery with a reputation that has spread rapidly. Recently, Le Gallois has seen a refurbishment, with seating for sixty on two levels, an extended bar and a reception area which seats twenty. It retains its slick minimalist decor, which also manages to exude warmth via warm yellow walls. Top notch ingredients and complex, modern European dishes match efficient service. Try dishes such as roasted monkfish with pea puree, brandade, pancetta and banyuls sauce with pepper fondue or prune and Armagnac soufflé. Friendly, knowledgeable service and a well-chosen wine list complete the picture at this special restaurant.

Smoking: No-smoking area; no cigars; Air conditioning
Directions: Telephone for directions

6-10 Romilly Crescent, CF11 9NR
Tel: 029 2034 1264
Fax: 029 2023 7911
📧 le.gallois@virgin.net
Chef(s): Padrig Jones
Owner(s): Graham & Anne Jones & family
Cost: Alc £40, set price L £12.95/ D £30-£35. ☺
Times: Noon-2.30pm/6.30-10.30pm. Closed Sun & Mon, Xmas, New Year, 3 wks Aug
Additional: Children welcome
Seats: 60. Jacket and tie preferred
Style: Modern, French-Style

Wales

CARDIFF *Continued*   Map 3 ST17

Manor Parc Country Hotel

Reliable cooking and a sensibly sized menu at this country hotel. Dishes are simple and accurate, with fish in particular being accurately cooked. Old school service stretches to the use of a dessert trolley. Nice garden views from the dining room.

Additional: Sunday L. Children welcome
Seats: 80
Style: Classic, Country -House
Smoking: No smoking in dining room
Civil licence: 80
Accommodation: 12 rooms (12 en suite) ★ ★ ★
Directions: off A469 Cardiff-Caerphilly road

Thornhill Road, Thornhill,
CF14 9UA
Tel: 029 2069 3723
Fax: 029 2061 4624
Chef(s): Giovanni Morabito
Owner(s): Mr E Cinus &
Mr S Salimeni
Cost: *Alc* £28, set price L £18/D £20.
H/wine £13.50
Times: Noon-2.15pm/7-9.45pm.
Closed D Sun, 24-26 Dec, 1 Jan

Metropolis Restaurant & Bar

Modern sculptures and paintings add to the swish, trendy feel of this city centre restaurant. The equally modern menu is British based, with touches from France, Italy and further afield: smoked haddock lasagne, moules marinère or crab fish cakes with honey and soy might feature alongside Welsh black beef, lamb shank or pheasant. Service is relaxed and friendly.

Seats: 75. Private dining room 50
Style: Modern,Chic
Smoking: Air conditioning
Directions: Telephone for directions

60 Charles Street, CF10 2GG
Tel: 029 2034 4300
Fax: 029 2066 6602
🅴 innactive@aol.com
Chef(s): Steven Brookes
Owner(s): David Williams
Cost: *Alc* £23. ☺ ☺ H/wine £11
Times: Noon-3pm-11pm. Closed
Sun, 25-26 Dec, 1 Jan, BHs
Additional: Bar food L. Children
welcome

New House Country Hotel

Situated in the hills above Cardiff, this hotel features an elegant, Regency style restaurant. Cooking is straightforward and British-based with a few ideas from further afield, such as hoi sin duck with noodles or calzone of vegetables and mozzarella. Panoramic views across the city.

Seats: 35. Private dining room 50
Style: Country-House
Smoking: No smoking in dining room
Civil licence: 200
Accommodation: 36 rooms (36 en suite) ★ ★ ★
Directions: Take A469 to the N of the city. Entrance on L shortly after crossing the M4 flyover

Thornhill, CF4 5UA
Tel: 029 2052 0280
Fax: 029 2052 0324
Chef(s): Ian Black
Owner(s): Mr J Hitchcock
Cost: *Alc* £30, set price L £12.95/
D £19.50. ☺ ☺ H/wine £11.95
Times: Noon-2pm/7-9.45pm.
Closed 26 Dec, 1 Jan
Additional: Sunday L. Bar food.
Children 8+

The St David's Hotel & Spa

In a period of transition as we went to press. Sir Rocco Forte's chic and minimalist waterfront hotel has bid goodbye to Martin Green and is to come under the wing of Marco Pierre White. Whoever takes the actual reins in the kitchen, expect a menu of MPW classics and cooking that attends to the really important

Havannah Street, Cardiff Bay,
CF10 5SD
Tel: 029 2045 4045
Fax: 029 2031 3075
🅴 reservations@thestdavidshotel.
com
Owner(s): RF Hotels

fundamentals like quality produce and honest flavours. Tides restaurant overlooks the (now permanently flooded) bay and aperitifs can be taken in the adjoining, seductively lit, bar.

Cost: *Alc* £32, set price L £19.50/ D £25
Times: 12.30-2.30pm/6.30-10.30pm.
Additional: Sunday L. Bar food. Children welcome
Seats: 98. Private dining room 40
Style: Modern

Smoking: No smoking in dining room; Air conditioning
Civil licence: 200
Accommodation: 132 rooms (132 en suite) ★ ★ ★ ★ ★
Directions: From M4 J33 take A432 9 miles to Cardiff Bay. At rdbt over Queens Tunnel take

Wales

Woods Brasserie

It's surprising to find an old stone house in the heart of the modern Cardiff Bay development. Less surprising, perhaps, to find that it houses a stylish bar and brasserie. Woods has a healthy bustle about it and offers a trendy selection of light bites, grills and seafood. Flavours are international, ranging from fish and chips to couscous filo parcels.

Seats: 90. Private dining room 36
Style: Modern, Minimalist
Smoking: No smoking in dining room; Air conditioning
Directions: From M4 J33, take A4232 towards Cardiff Bay for approx 8miles. Take turning signposted Techniquest Museum. Restaurant 500yds on R

Pilotage Building, Stuart Street, Cardiff Bay CF10 5BW
Tel: 029 2049 2400
Fax: 029 2048 1998
Chef(s): Martyn Peters
Owner(s): Martyn & Deborah Peters
Cost: *Alc* £25. ☺ ☺ H/wine £12.95
Times: Noon-2pm/7-10pm.
Closed Mon, D Sun, Xmas, New Year, Bhs
Additional: Sunday L. Children welcome

CREIGIAU   Map 3 ST08

Caesars Arms

Nothing is hidden in this friendly pub restaurant: a large open cooking area, help-yourself salads and an 'amazing display' of fresh fish, meats and game, all place an emphasis on personal choice and quality food. A meal here will not disappoint: the ever-changing blackboard menus might include a 'punchy' fish soup or a 'perfectly seasoned' lemon sole.

Seats: 150. Private dining room 60
Style: Traditional
Directions: 3 miles from M4 J34, take A411 (Cardiff). Turn L at Creigiau

Cardiff Road, CF15 9NN
Tel: 029 2089 0486
Fax: 029 2089 2176
Chef(s): Deborah Coleman
Owner(s): Steadychance Ltd
Cost: *Alc* £20. ☺ H/wine £9.95
Times: Noon-4pm/7-midnight.
Closed D Sun, 25-Dec
Additional: Sunday L. Children welcome

CARMARTHENSHIRE

BRECHFA
Map 2 SN53

Ty Mawr Country Hotel

Pretty stone-walled building in the heart of the village comprising of the village bakery and a delightful restaurant with a surprisingly art deco feel to it. The menu is sensibly to the point, allowing the kitchen to get the most out of the likes of pan-fried fillet of haddock with a sweet chilli pepper salsa.

SA32 7RA
Tel: 01267 202332
Fax: 01267 202437
Telephone for further details

CARMARTHEN
Map 2 SN42

The Four Seasons Restaurant

Simplicity is the virtue at this restaurant with rooms converted from Georgian farm buildings. Design, food and service share the same relaxed feel and reflect a desire to do the important things well. In food terms this equates to the likes of a delicate smoked haddock tartlet, fillet of Welsh Black beef with horseradish butter and an exemplary pear and almond tart. Creditable wine list too (a small wine merchant is part of the set-up).

Style: French, Chic. **Smoking:** No smoking in dining room
Accommodation: 6 rooms (6 en suite) ◆◆◆
Directions: From A40 turn onto B4310 at Nantgaredig; L up hill, 0.25 mile on R

Nantgaredig, SA32 7NY
Tel: 01267 290238
Fax: 01267 290808
e jen4seas@aol.com
Chef(s): M Wright & C Pasetti
Owner(s): M Wright & C Pasetti
Cost: Set price D £22.50. ☺
H/wine £10
Times: Dinner only, 7-9.30pm.
Closed Sun & Mon, Xmas (Variable)
Additional: Children 5+
Seats: 45

LAUGHARNE
Map 2 SN31

The Cors Restaurant

A whiff of bohemia. In striking contrast to the traditional exterior, the rooms of this former vicarage swing between vibrant, bold, colours and the almost gothic dark-crimson of the main dining room. The food is as exciting as the décor, using plenty of quality local ingredients such as black beef, smoked salmon and salt-marsh lamb. Ideas come from France, America and the Mediterranean, with an array of 'simple dishes done extremely well'. These might include moules marinière or herb crusted rack of lamb with caramelised shallots, 'awesome' gratin dauphinoise and a selection of vegetables. Service is informal and sometimes erratic but always endearing. Decent wine list too. Don't miss the extraordinary gardens on a summer's day.

Directions: From Carmarthen follow A40, L at St Clears, 4m to Laugharne

Newbridge Road,
SA33 4SH
Tel: 01994 427219
Chef(s): Nick Priestland
Cost: Alc £26. ☺ H/wine £10.50
Times: Dinner only, 7pm-Midnight.
Closed D Sun-Wed
Additional: Children 8 yrs+
No credit cards accepted
Seats: 24
Style: Modern, Country-House
Smoking: No smoking in dining room
Accommodation: 2 rooms (2 en suite)

LLANDEILO
Map 3 SN62

Cawdor Arms

Family-run hotel at the heart of a handsome and historic town above the River Towy. Dayrooms reflect its Georgian origins,

Rhosmaen Street, SA19 6EN
Tel: 01558 823500
Fax: 01558 822399

and menus demonstrate a serious approach with innovative and imaginative dishes that typically might include terrine of confit and smoked duck, roast rump of Carmarthenshire duck and hazelnut tart with white chocolate parfait. Lunch selections include a selection of soups, red mullet fillets with roasted fennel, Cox's apple crumble and a dependable selection of Welsh farmhouse cheeses.

Style: Modern, British
Smoking: No smoking in dining room
Accommodation: 17 rooms (17 en suite) ★ ★ ★
Directions: In town centre, at junction of A40 and A483

e cawdor.arms@btinternet.com
Chef(s): Jane Silver
Owner(s): John & Sylvia Silver
Cost: Alc £14.50, set price L £14.95-£16.95/D £21-£23.50. ☺ ☺
H/wine £10.10
Times: Noon-2pm/7.30-9pm.
Closed D Sun
Additional: Sunday L. Bar food L.
Children welcome
Seats: 90. Private dining room 12

CEREDIGION

ABERPORTH
Map 2 SN25

Penbontbren Farm

Suffused with genuine Welsh flavour, this country farmhouse is set in 90 acres of land, with converted buildings set around a courtyard. Smoked salmon from the Black Mountains, Pantysgawen goats' cheese, Welsh lamb and Welsh black steak all feature on the comprehensive set menu, along with wild mushrooms in a creamy wholegrain mustard sauce, and oak-smoked chicken and goose-breast slivers to start with, followed by supreme of guinea fowl with a rich red wine sauce. Decent desserts from the trolley, like rhubarb flapjack.

Directions: N from Cardigan on A487. 2nd R after Tan-y-Groes signposted Penbontbren

Glynarhten, SA44 6PE
Tel: 01239 810248
Fax: 01239 811129
e mglossop@compuserve.com
Owner(s): Mr & Mrs M Glossop
Cost: Alc £25/D £17.50-£22.50. ☺ ☺
H/wine £9.80
Times: Dinner only, 7pm-Midnight
Additional: Children welcome
Seats: 50. Jacket and tie preferred
Style: Traditional, Country-House
Smoking: No smoking in dining room
Accommodation: 10 rooms (10 en suite) ★ ★

ABERYSTWYTH
Map 6 SN58

Belle Vue Royal Hotel

Family owned hotel set on the Victorian promenade at the heart of Aberystwyth. The restaurant commands a view over Cardigan Bay and the pier, and its simple uncluttered décor steers clear of an overly formal atmosphere. Dishes are home cooked and generally very good although the presentation can be a little prosaic.

Marine Terrace, SY23 2BA
Tel: 01970 617558
Fax: 01970 612190
e reception@bellevueroyalhotelfsnet.co.uk
Chef(s): Mike Stagg
Owner(s): Mr & Mrs R A Davies
Cost: Alc £21, set price L £16/D £23. ☺ ☺ H/wine £9
Times: 12.30-2pm/6.30-9.30pm.
Closed 25-26 Dec (evening)
Additional: Sunday L. Bar food L.
Children welcome
Seats: 80. Private dining room 120
Style: Traditional
Smoking: No-smoking area; no cigars; Air conditioning
Accommodation: 34 rooms (34 en suite) ★ ★ ★
Directions: Overlooking Cardigan Bay

Wales

Conrah Hotel

This family-run hotel in 22 acres of grounds has been in the same hands for over twenty years. Its elegant Edwardian-style restaurant has glorious views towards the Welsh mountains across a mature garden that is a primary source of fresh herbs

Ffosrhydygaled, Chancery, SY23 4DF
Tel: 01970 617941
Fax: 01970 624546
e enquiries@conrah.co.uk
Chef(s): Stephen West
Owner(s): F J & P Heading
Cost: *Alc* L £18.50, set price D
£29.50-£32.50. ☺ H/wine £13
Times: Noon-2pm/7-9pm.
Closed 1 wk Xmas
Additional: Sunday L. Bar food L.
Children 5yrs+
Seats: 50
Style: Country-House, Modern
Smoking: No smoking in dining room
Civil licence: 60
Accommodation: 17 rooms (17 en suite) ★ ★ ★

and summer salad leaves. Cuisine that is classically based with modern influences draws on best local produce and continues to achieve high standards. Cardigan Bay crabmeat is used to good effect with a salad of flaked salmon and Puy lentils, followed perhaps by a fish course of lemon sole and filo pastry before main dishes that might be honey roast Welsh lamb or medallions of pork fillet with cider and rosemary sauce. Round off with a nicely tart and refreshing summer pudding or bitter chocolate tart.

Directions: On A487, 3 miles S of Aberystwyth

EGLWYSFACH   Map 6 SN69

Ynyshir Hall

SY20 8TA
Tel: 01654 781209
Fax: 01654 781366
e info@ynyshir-hall.co.uk
Chef(s): Les Rennie
Owner(s): Rob & Joan Reen
Cost: Set price L £23/D £40. ☺
H/wine £15

WINE AWARD FINALIST

On the very western edge of Wales and a favourite bolthole of television personalities, this fine country house hotel offers an intoxicating blend of peace and warm hospitality. Lovely gardens surround the house, and beyond is an unfolding range of mountains which creates a striking backdrop. Bold paintings of the local landscape by proprietor and artist Rob Reen adorn

the walls of the restaurant, where candle-lit dinners are part of the evening ritual. A gourmet menu (for the whole table) is offered alongside the fixed-price list, and much effort goes into appearances, with each dish a work of art in itself. The local hills are the source of main courses like cutlets of Brecon lamb with swede fondant, tomato and rosemary tortellini and lamb sauce, and roast fillet of Welsh black beef, root vegetables, braised button onions and red wine. A superb wine list covers all corners of the globe.

Times: 12.30-1.30pm/7-8.45pm. Closed Jan
Additional: Sunday L. Bar food L. Children 9yrs+
Seats: 30. Private dining room 16
Style: Modern
Smoking: No smoking in dining room
Civil licence: 40
Accommodation: 10 rooms (10 en suite) ★ ★ ★
Directions: On A487, 6 miles from Machunlleth

CONWY

Wales

ABERGELE
Map 6 SH97

Kinmel Arms

At the Kinmel Arms, local ingredients such as venison served with local elderberry sauce are often on the menu. The chef/owner of this 17th-century former coaching inn prefers to offer a short *carte* of fresh produce and dishes might include roast monkfish with Moroccan spices or pan-fried skate wings with caper butter.

Style: Informal
Smoking: No-smoking area
Directions: A5 towards Conway; L at top of hill, inn on L

St George, LL22 9BP
Tel: 01745 832207
Fax: 01745 832207
Chef(s): Gary Edwards
Owner(s): Gary Edwards
Cost: *Alc* £13.95, set price L £13.95/D £13.95. H/wine £8.95
Times: Noon-2pm/7-9pm. Closed 25 Dec
Additional: Children 4yrs+
Seats: 50

BETWS-Y-COED
Map 6 SH75

Tan-y-Foel Country House

Capel Garmon, LL26 0RE
Tel: 01690 710507
Fax: 01690 710681
🄴 enquiries@tyfhotel.co.uk
Chef(s): Janet Pitman
Owner(s): Mr & Mrs P Pitman
Cost: *Alc* £32. H/wine £15
Times: Dinner only, 7.30-8.15pm. Closed 14-27 Dec, 3 Jan-14 Feb

Perched on a wooded hillside looking down into the Conwy Valley, a 16th-century hotel with impeccably hospitable owners. The Pitman family go out of their way to please, and few would find fault with their efforts. The kitchen is an area of particular expertise, where vibrant, modern dishes are produced using organic produce wherever possible. In the green and stone restaurant, with its conservatory extension and wood-burning stove, the daily-changing menu offers lively interpretations of familiar dishes. Cappuccino of chicken livers (rich flavour), and

BETWS-Y-COED *Continued* Map 6 SH75

roast cod on a bed of pea purée with sesame-fried carrots (simple, well-executed) are two successful dishes, while a classic apple Charlotte with caramelised apple slices and Calvados cream achieved near perfection. The menu might also extend to butternut squash soup with herb dumplings, and Welsh venison loin on a leek and potato cake and buttered spring cabbage, with sweet potato crisps and Shrewsbury sauce.

Directions: A5 onto A470; 2 miles N towards Llantwst, then turning for Capel Garmon. Hotel on L before village

Additional: Booking essential. Children 7yrs+. Vegetarian by request only
Seats: 12
Style: Modern, French
Smoking: No smoking in dining room
Accommodation: 6 rooms (6 en suite)
★ ★

COLWYN BAY Map 6 SH87

Café Niçoise

Modern, French-style restaurant with terracotta-washed walls, a wooden floor and crisp, cream linen. Imaginative menus reflect the seasons and make use of fresh Welsh produce in, say, sirloin of Welsh beef with roast shallots, red wine and garlic mash or loin of Welsh lamb with parsnip purée and roast root vegetables. Home-made truffles with coffee follow classic desserts.

Style: Modern, French
Smoking: No-smoking area; no pipes
Directions: From A55 take old Colwyn exit, L at slip road, R at mini rdbt, R towards bay; Restaurant is on L

124 Abergele Road, LL29 7PS
Tel: 01492 531555
Fax: 01492 531555
 Lynne2000@fsmail.net
Chef(s): Carl Swift
Owner(s): Mr & Mrs C Swift
Cost: *Alc* £23.75, set price L £14.95/D £14.95. ☺ ☺ H/wine £9.95
Times: Noon-2pm/7-10pm. Closed Sun, L Mon-Tue, 25-26 Dec, 1 Jan, 1 wk Jan, 1 wk Jun,
Additional: Children 7yrs+ at D
Seats: 32

CONWY Map 6 SH77

The Castle Hotel NEW

16th-century hotel featuring Shakespeare's restaurant. A modish menu offers some bright, brasserie style cooking that commences with good home-made bread. Expect the likes of pressed terrine of ham hock and root vegetables with a poached egg and a mustard hollandaise as starter. Mains have included "beautifully fresh" pan fried fillet of baby halibut a creamy peppercorn sauce, leek and rosemary mash and deep fried pancetta.

High Street, LL32 8DB
Tel: 01492 592324
Telephone for further details

The Old Rectory Country House

A charming hotel with delightful gardens, overlooking the spectacular Conwy Estuary and the peaks of Snowdonia beyond. Antique furniture and classical interior design impart a homely, intimate ambience and the tiny restaurant (six tables) emphasises this pleasant sensation. Locally sourced ingredients of the highest quality go into the daily-changing dishes, and as choice is limited, dietary requirements or dislikes are ascertained at the time of booking. Herb-crusted fillet of halibut, scallop risotto, loin of Conwy lamb with olive mash, stuffed cabbage leaf and butternut squash, and spiced fillet of sea trout with boulangère potatoes show the imaginative food style, while the straightforward desserts might include pear and

Llanrwst Road,
Llansanffraid Glan
Conwy, LL28 5LF
Tel: 01492 580611
Fax: 01492 580544
 info@oldrectorycountryhouse.co.uk
Chef(s): Wendy Vaughan
Owner(s): M & W Vaughan
Cost: Set price D £29.50 H/wine £14.90
Times: Dinner only, 7.30 for 8.15pm. Closed Dec & Jan

Wales

chocolate tart, or chocolate ice cream. The wine list includes a selection of old favourites and some New World labels, and service is well paced and attentive to suit the relaxed mood of the restaurant.

Additional: Children 5yrs+.
Vegetarian by request only
Seats: 14. Jacket and tie preferred
Style: Modern British
Smoking: No smoking in dining room
Accommodation: 6 rooms (6 en suite)
★ ★
Directions: On A470, 0.5 mile S of junction with A55

LLANDUDNO
Map 6 SH78

Bodysgallen Hall

Perched loftily above the resort, Bodysgallen is an undoubted aristocrat amongst the hotels of North Wales. Expect serious service but not without humour in an often bustling restaurant

serving a surprisingly extensive menu of ambitious dishes. There is a welcome focus on local produce be it fish or meat. Pan fried brill has come with a crab risotto and loin of venison with red cabbage and a raspberry vinegar sauce. Amongst the desserts, bara brith and butter pudding with Calvados ice cream has been praised. Serious wine list.

Directions: From A55 take A470 (Llandudno). Hotel is 1 mile on the R

LL30 1RS
Tel: 01492 584466
Fax: 01492 582519
e info@bodysgallen.com
Chef(s): David Thompson
Owner(s): Historic House Hotels
Cost: Set price L £18-£24.50/ D £34.50 H/wine £14.50
Times: 12.30-1.45pm/7-9.30pm.
Additional: Sunday L. Bar food L. Children 8yrs+
Seats: 60. Private dining room 40. Jacket and tie preferred
Style: Traditional, Country-House
Smoking: No smoking in dining room; Air conditioning
Accommodation: 35 rooms (35 en suite) ★ ★ ★ ★

WINE AWARD FINALIST

Wales

Empire Hotel

Large terraced restaurant with white banisters, tiffany lamps and ornate mirrors - faintly reminiscent of a film set in fact. The menu concentrates on fresh home-made and local produce and is not afraid to offer old favourites such as Empire whole plaice, or roast loin of Welsh lamb with roast potato - simple but delicious.

Seats: 110. Private dining room 16. Jacket and tie preferred
Style: Modern, British
Smoking: No-smoking area; no cigars; Air conditioning
Accommodation: 58 rooms (58 en suite) ★ ★ ★
Directions: From Chester take A55 then A470 towards Llandudno. Follow signs to town centre, into Mostyn Street. Hotel at end

Church Walks, LL30 2HE
Tel: 01492 860555
Fax: 01492 860791
e reservations@empirehotel.co.uk
Chef(s): Michael Waddy & Gwyn Roberts
Owner(s): Len & Elizabeth Maddocks
Cost: *Alc* £24.50, set price L £14.50/D £24.50. ☺ ☺
H/wine £11.50
Times: 12.30-2pm/6.45-9.30pm. Closed L Mon-Sat, 25 Dec
Additional: Sunday L. Bar food. Children welcome. Vegetarian by request only

Imperial Hotel

Large seaside hotel located along Llandudno's Victorian promenade. The elegant Chantrey restaurant offers a monthly-changing menu that features local produce such as terrine of Welsh beef and pork with thyme dressing or Welsh lamb and leek sausage.

Style: Modern, Traditional
Smoking: No smoking in dining room
Civil licence: 150
Accommodation: 100 rooms (100 en suite) ★ ★ ★
Directions: On the Promenade

The Promenade, LL30 1AP
Tel: 01492 877466
Fax: 01492 878043
e imphotel@btinternet.com
Chef(s): Andy Goode
Owner(s): Greenclose Ltd
Cost: *Alc* £20, set price L £12.50/ D £20. ☺ ☺ H/wine £10
Times: 12.30-2.00pm/6.30-9.30pm.
Additional: Sunday L. Bar food L. Children welcome
Seats: 150

St Tudno Hotel

A riot of lime greens and daffodil yellows, exotic birds and flowers, and plenty of dazzling chinoiserie create an unforgettable impression at this far from routine Victorian seaside hotel restaurant. The bright air-conditioned room faces

The Promenade, LL30 2LP
Tel: 01492 874411
Fax: 01492 860407
e sttudnohotel@btinternet.com
Chef(s): David Harding
Owner(s): Mr & Mrs Bland
Cost: *Alc* £31.50, set price L £16/ D £36. ☺ H/wine £10.50
Times: 12.30-2pm/7-9.30pm.
Additional: Sunday L. Bar food L. No babies or toddlers at D
Seats: 60. **Style:** Formal

onto the midday sun, while in the evening rise-and-fall ceiling lights and table candles introduce intimacy and warmth. Local produce of impeccable quality features strongly on the menu, with Welsh lamb and beef, Conwy mussels and Trelough duckling given thoughtful treatment by the kitchen. Flavours are often intense, as in local fish soup with cod, haddock, bass and crab risotto, and just occasionally explosive, as in Great Orme lobster with crab sauce and baby vegetables which was a little besieged by a herb mash. Desserts range from the simple platter of fresh fruits and sorbets to extravagant poached pear with a dark chocolate sauce and Drambuie parfait. Good petit fours include home made Viennese and pecan biscuits, and some chocs. Impressive wine list too.

Smoking: No smoking in dining room; Air conditioning
Accommodation: 20 rooms (20 en suite) ★ ★
Directions: Town centre, on Promenade opposite the pier entrance

TREFRIW
Map 6 SH76

Princes Arms

Superb views over the Conwy Valley, with a restaurant overlooking old Trefriw Quay. Diners can choose to eat in the restaurant or informal brasserie. Either way, they're sure to be satisfied with the quality of home-cooking on offer. Tender and lean roast loin of pork with crispy crackling and summer pudding with Chantilly cream are top scorers.

Seats: 70. Private dining room 30
Style: Classic
Smoking: No smoking in dining room
Accommodation: 14 rooms (14 en suite) ★ ★
Directions: At far end of village on L

Betws-y-Coed,
LL27 0JP
Tel: 01492 640592
Fax: 01492 640559
e enquiries@princes-arms.co.uk
Chef(s): Ann Gordon
Owner(s): Ann Gordon
Cost: Alc £18, set price L £9.50/ D £18. ☺ ☺ H/wine £8.50
Times: Noon-2.30pm/6-9.30pm.
Additional: Sunday L. Bar food. Children welcome

Wales

DENBIGHSHIRE

LLANDEGLA
Map 7 SJ25

Bodidris Hall

Looking like something from a story book, this 15th-century manor house sits amid woods and gardens with ivy rambling over its walls and chimneys. The restaurant is a medieval style room, with a roaring fire, bare brickwork, exposed beams and golden yellow walls. There's even a stag's head and a suit of armour. The menu offers plenty of classic ingredients, many local, but breaks with tradition to create interesting modern interpretations: lamb, for example, might come with a Provençal crumb, thyme crust and braised couscous whilst breast of duck could be served with pink grapefruit marmalade, sarladaise potato and winter fruit sauce.

Accommodation: 9 rooms (9 en suite) ★ ★ ★
Directions: Llandegla is on A525 (Wrexham-Ruthin). In village (from Wrexham direction) turn R onto A5104. Hotel is signed 1 mile on L

LL11 3AL
Tel: 01978 790434
Fax: 01978 790335
e bodidrishall@fsnet.co.uk
Chef(s): Kevin Steel
Owner(s): W Farden
Cost: Set price £17.50-£35. H/wine £12.75
Times: Noon-2pm/7-9pm.
Additional: Sunday L. Children 14 yrs+. Vegetarian by request only
Seats: 40. Private dining room 22. Jacket and tie preferred
Style: Traditional, Country-House
Smoking: No smoking area
Civil licence: 65

LLANDRILLO
Map 6 SJ03

Tyddyn Llan Country Hotel

A jewel of a small hotel in a lovely wooded river valley. Georgian farmhouse, rough stone and slate roofed with striking grey blues and bright yellows on the interior perhaps pointing to Peter Kindred's artistic leanings. The restaurant is a panelled room with windows opening on to the verandah and

LL21 0ST
Tel: 01490 440264
Fax: 01490 440414
e tyddynllanhotel@compuserve.com
Chef(s): Matthew Haines
Owner(s): Mr & Mrs Kindred

LLANDRILLO *Continued*

Map 6 SJ03

Tyddyn Llan Country Hotel

garden. Tables are well-spaced and the linen and tableware are fine quality. The food is admirably unfussy and shorn of extraneous components. A main course of sea bass with asparagus and new potatoes and a smoked prawn sauce, defined by accuracy and clarity of flavours illustrates the style well. Puddings show a sure hand and a board of good farmhouse cheeses with home-made biscuits is always available. Thoughtful wine list with a good selection by the glass.

Directions: Take B4401 from Corwen to Llandrillo. Restaurant on R leaving village

Cost: *Alc* £20, set price D £25-£27.
☺ ☺ H/wine £13.50
Times: 12.30-2pm/7-9pm.
Closed L Mon, 2 wks Jan
Additional: Sunday L. Bar food L. Children welcome. Vegetarian by request only
Seats: 65. Private dining room
Style: Classic, Country-House
Smoking: No smoking in dining room
Civil licence: 35
Accommodation: 10 rooms (10 en suite) ★ ★

LLANGOLLEN

Map 7 SJ24

Bryn Howel Hotel

Serving traditional country-house fare, the spacious restaurant at Bryn Howel looks out on to attractive, well-tended gardens. The menu's mouth-watering descriptions include the rather civilised 'gathering' of various melon and grapefruit starters and the more robustly challenging 'mountain' of choux buns to finish. Lunch and dinner menus both provide tempting selections, designed to appeal to a variety of tastes.

Smoking: No smoking in dining room
Civil licence: 300
Accommodation: 36 rooms (36 en suite) ★ ★ ★
Directions: From M53 take A483 to Wrexham. On towards Ruabon & take A539 through Acrefair & Trevor. After 2 miles Hotel sign on L

LL20 7UW
Tel: 01978 860331
Fax: 01978 860119
🄴 hotel@brynhowel.co.uk
Chef(s): Dai Davies
Owner(s): Mr J & Miss A Lloyd
Cost: *Alc* £24.50-£14.95. ☺ ☺
H/wine £12.90
Times: Noon-2pm/7-9pm.
Closed L Sat
Additional: Sunday L. Bar food L. Children welcome
Seats: 90. Jacket and tie preferred
Style: Traditional, Country-House

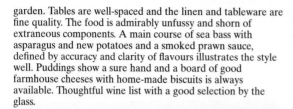

The finest wine lists

The AA wine awards recognise some of the finest wine lists in the country. As well as the winners for England, Scotland and Wales you will find this symbol throughout the guide indicating those restaurants who reached the final shortlist and others that were recognised for their excellence in specialist areas. The AA wine awards are sponsored by T&W wines of Thetford.

FLINTSHIRE

EWLOE Map 7 SJ36

De Vere St Davids Park

The elegant Fountains restaurant (one of a choice of eating options at this popular, modern hotel) offers both traditional and contemporary dishes: you might be tempted away from the grilled steak or roast lamb by an intriguing salmon and laverbread gateau or chicken with black pudding boudin, pancetta and pearl barley jus. Extensive wine list.

Directions: A494 Queensferry to Mold for 4 miles, then B5127 towards Buckley

St Davids Park, CH5 3YB
Tel: 01244 520800
Fax: 01244 520930
e reservations.st.davids@devere-hotels.com
Chef(s): Graham Wilson
Cost: *Alc* £29, set price L £19.50/ D £19.50. ☺ ☺ H/wine £12.50
Times: 12.30-2pm/7-10pm. Closed L Sat
Additional: Sunday L. Children welcome
Seats: 180. Private dining room 50
Style: Modern, Traditional
Smoking: No smoking in dining room; Air conditioning
Civil licence: 100
Accommodation: 145 rooms (145 en suite) ★ ★ ★ ★

Wales

HAWARDEN

The Brasserie

The local popularity of this super little brasserie speaks volumes. The place has a modern, fresh feel with its orange and blue, minimalist décor, while its friendly staff contribute to the welcoming ambience. The cooking is just as lively, from the baked goats' cheese croûtes, through moist seared fillet of cod, down to the smooth textured cappuccino brûlée. Good international wine list.

68 The Highway, CH5 3DH
Tel: 01244 536353
Fax: 01244 520888
Chef(s): Mark Jones
Owner(s): Neal Bates & Mark Jones
Cost: *Alc* £19, set price L £13.95-£15.25/D £13.95-£15.25. ☺ ☺
Times: Noon-2pm/6.45-9pm. Closed Sun, Mon, L Sat
Additional: Children welcome
Style: Modern, minimalist
Smoking: No cigars
Directions: From M56 take A55, through Queensferry, take road signed Ewloe & Buckley. Turn L, restaurant 1 miles on R

NORTHOP

Map 7 SJ26

Soughton Hall

CH7 6AB
Tel: 01352 840811
Fax: 01352 840382
Chef(s): Paul Wright
Owner(s): Mr & Mrs J Rodenhurst
Cost: Set price L £10.50-£12.50/
D £16-£18.95. ☺ ☺ H/wine £9.95
Times: Noon-3pm/6.30-11pm.
Additional: Sunday L. Bar food.
Children welcome
Seats: 120. Private dining room 100.
Jacket and tie preferred
Style: Modern
Smoking: No smoking in dining room
Civil licence: 80

Built as a bishop's palace in 1714, this truly elegant country house stands in 150 acres of magnificent grounds. The interior is furnished with tapestries, Baroque fireplaces and interesting antiques. Fine dining is available in the main house, whilst the adjacent stables offer a more relaxed, trendy environment. Décor includes wooden floors, open brickwork, bare beams and an open kitchen. Equally modern dishes might include tagliatelli of confit duck with chargrilled veg and honey or roasted halibut on cod brandade with Mediterranean veg. The wine list is good (not surprising as there is a wine shop on the premises).

Accommodation: 14 rooms (14 en suite) ★ ★ ★
Directions: Off A5119, 1mile S of Northop

GWYNEDD

ABERDYFI

Map 6 SN69

Penhelig Arms

LL35 0LT
Tel: 01654 767215
Fax: 01654 767690
e penheligarms@saqnet.co.uk
Chef(s): Jane Howkins
Owner(s): Mr & Mrs R Hughes
Cost: Set price L £14.50/D £23. ☺ ☺
H/wine £10
Times: Noon-2pm/7-9.30pm.
Closed 25-26 Dec
Additional: Sunday L. Bar food.
Children welcome
Seats: 36. Private dining room 22
Style: Modern
Smoking: No smoking in dining room;
Air conditioning
Accommodation: 14 rooms (14 en
suite) ★ ★
Directions: From Machynlleth take
A439 coastal route (9 miles)

With attractive views across the Dyfi estuary, Penhelig's cosy restaurant is a lovely environment in which to enjoy an impressive array of dishes. With up to 14 main courses from which to choose - around half of them fish or seafood - there's something for everyone. Fresh, complementary ingredients are tastily prepared and a meal here is unlikely to disappoint.

☺ Indicates a restaurant that has told us they offer a two-course lunch for less than £15

☺ Indicates a restaurant that has told us they offer a three-course dinner for less than £25

✎ Indicates a restaurant that has told us that 50% or more of their ingredients are organically sourced

Prices quoted in the guide are for guidance only and are subject to change without notice

Wales

ABERSOCH

Map 6 SN69

Neigwl Hotel

The reputation here for good food and warm hospitality is well deserved. Attractive sea and mountain views complement the eating experience, which might begin with smoked haddock fishcakes or Welsh lambs' kidneys chasseur. Try the brie in puff pastry complemented by a provençale sauce or the baked, herb-crusted fillet of cod as a main course.

Seats: 40. **Style:** Classic
Accommodation: 9 rooms (9 en suite) ★ ★ ★
Directions: A499 through Abersoch. The Neigwl is 400 yards on left overlooking the sea

Lon Sarn Bach, LL53 7DY
Tel: 01758 712363
Fax: 01758 712544
e relax@neigwl.com
Chef(s): Nigel Higginbottom
Owner(s): Gerry & Pat Heptonstall
Cost: Set price D £21-£26. ☺
H/wine £10
Times: Dinner only, 7-9pm.
Closed Jan
Additional: Children welcome.
Vegetarian by request only

Porth Tocyn Hotel

The Fletcher-Brewer family's epic stay at Porth Tocyn has rightly been the subject of much celebration. The current generation of the family deserve credit for continuing to move things forward whilst retaining the special character of what is a very individual country house hotel. One thing unlikely to ever change is the panoramic view of Cardigan Bay that can

conveniently be enjoyed from the restaurant windows. The menu, by contrast, changes completely every day but the accomplished cooking is generally rooted in simplicity and based on good quality ingredients. Pea & ham soup might feature as a starter for example, and mains might include poached lemon sole over braised red cabbage with saffron cream. Substantial puds are on offer together with a decent cheeseboard. The wine list is well thought out and covers most bases.

Bwlch Tocyn, LL53 7BU
Tel: 01758 713303
Fax: 01758 713538
e porthtocyn.hotel@virgin.net
Chef(s): L Fletcher-Brewer,
David Carney
Owner(s): Fletcher-Brewer family
Cost: Set price D £25.50-£32.
H/wine £12.50
Times: 12.15-2pm/7.30-9.30pm.
Closed L Mon-Sat, mid Nov,
wk before Easter
Additional: Sunday L. Bar food L.
Children 7yrs+ at D
Seats: 50
Style: Country-House
Smoking: No smoking in dining room
Accommodation: 17 rooms (17 en suite) ★ ★ ★
Directions: Situated 2 miles S of Abersoch, through Sarn Bach & Bwlch Tocyn. Follow brown highway signs

BALA

Map 6 SH93

Palé Hall Country House

This enchanting mansion was built in 1870 and overlooks beautiful wooded grounds. The fine entrance hall, with vaulted ceiling and a galleried oak staircase, leads to the library bar, two elegant lounges and the smart dining room. A remarkable setting with impressive carved fireplaces, tapestries and views of the grounds, it offers an equally distinctive menu: canapés might include a mini-cheeseburger, whilst the menu features restyled classics such as stilton soufflé with pear and red wine

Palé Estate, Llandderfel, LL23 7PS
Tel: 01678 530285
Fax: 01678 530220
e palehall@fsbdial.co.uk
Chef(s): Phillip Nahed
Owner(s): Mr & Mrs Sahed
Cost: Set price L £15.95/D £24.95. ☺
☺ H/wine £11.95
Times: Noon-1.45pm/7-8.30pm

Wales

BALA *Continued*   Map 6 SH93

jam or caramelised supreme of duck on a blini pancake with summer baby vegetables and blackcurrant sauce. Service is relaxed and informal.

Directions: Just off B4401, 4 miles from Llandrillo

Wales

BARMOUTH   Map 6 SH61

Ty'r Graig Castle

Gothic-style seaside hotel, with stained glass windows and wood-panelled walls. A good choice is offered from the set-price menu in the restaurant, and diners can take either two or three courses. Dishes range through roast Atlantic cod with Yorkshire pudding and shrimp gravy, local Welsh lamb, and haricot bean, shallot and roast vegetable stew with oatmeal dumplings.

Style: Country-House, Modern
Smoking: No smoking in dining room
Accommodation: 12 rooms (12 en suite) ★ ★
Directions: From Barmouth A496 for 0.75mile, hotel on left

BONTDDU   Map 6 SH61

Bontddu Hall

Palé Hall Country House

Additional: Sunday L. Bar food
Seats: 40. Private dining room 24.
Jacket and tie preferred
Style: Traditional, Country-House
Smoking: No smoking in dining room
Civil licence: 40
Accommodation: 17 rooms (17 en suite) ★ ★ ★

Llanaber Road, LL42 1YN
Tel: 01341 280470
Fax: 01341 281260
e tyrcraig.castle@btinternet.com
Chef(s): Christopher Wright
Owner(s): Mr & Mrs Holbrooke
Cost: *Alc* £23, set price L £13/ D £23-£30. ☺ ☺ H/wine £9
Times: 12.30-2pm/7-9pm.
Closed L Mon-Sat, D Sun, Jan
Additional: Sunday L. Children welcome. Vegetarian by request only
Seats: 24. Jacket and tie preferred

 ☺☺
LL40 2UF
Tel: 01341 430661
Fax: 01341 430284
e reservations@bontdduhall.co.uk
Chef(s): David Murphy
Owner(s): Mr M. Ball
Cost: *Alc* £25, set price L £14/D £25.
☺ ☺ H/wine £13.50
Times: Noon-2.30pm/7-9.30pm.
Closed Nov-Mar
Additional: Sunday L. Bar food.
Children 2yrs+
Seats: 60. Private dining room 30.
Jacket and tie preferred
Style: Classic
Smoking: No smoking in dining room

Overlooking the beautiful Mawddach estate, this 19th century Gothic style house is surrounded by 14 acres of landscaped gardens and wooded grounds. Once the home of Lord Birmingham, it is now an elegant country house hotel whose restaurant offers lovely views of the river and the mountains beyond. The menu offers a selection of regional and classical dishes such as timbale of smoked salmon risotto with lemon goujons or fillet of pork wrapped in bacon and served with a compote of apple and creamed leek. The chef makes good use of local produce including lamb, Meirionedd salmon and Barmouth lobster.

Civil licence: 150
Accommodation: 20 rooms (20 en suite) ★ ★ ★
Directions: From A470 1 mile N of Dolgellau take A496 to Barmooth, then 4 miles to Bontddu

CAERNARFON

Map 6 SH46

Seiont Manor

Authentic rural buildings in the heart of tranquil Welsh countryside house this splendid hotel, and the food is the genuine article too. Regional specialities share the menu with the traditionally British, and if the cooking is sometimes overcomplicated, kitchen skills remain solid. Expect fresh local produce such as pot-roasted lamb shanks or pan-fried pheasant breast, and decent international wines.

Civil licence: 100
Accommodation: 28 rooms (28 en suite) ★ ★ ★
Directions: From Bangor follow signs for Caenarfon. Leave Caenarfon on A4086. The hotel is 3 miles on L

Llanrug, LL55 2AQ
Tel: 01286 673366
Fax: 01286 672840
Chef(s): Martyn Williams
Owner(s): Hand Picked Hotels
Cost: Set price L £13.25-£15.20/D £23.50-£26.45. ☺ ☺ H/wine £13.50
Times: Noon-2pm/7-10pm
Additional: Sunday L. Bar food. Children welcome
Seats: 55. Private dining room 20
Style: Country House, Traditional
Smoking: No smoking in dining room

Ty'n Rhos Country Hotel

Wonderfully located between Snowdon and the Menai Straits this converted farmhouse continues to be the venue for some ambitious cooking with a heavy emphasis on the best of Welsh produce. Lynda Kettle's style is at once honest and accomplished with some vibrant flavours apparent in, for

Llanddeiniolen, LL55 3AE
Tel: 01248 670489
Fax: 01248 670079
✉ enquiries@tynrhos.co.uk
Chef(s): Lynda Kettle
Owner(s): Lynda & Nigel Kettle
Cost: Alc £27, set price L £12.95/D £19.50-£27.50. ☺ ☺ H/wine £11.50
Times: Noon-2pm/7pm-9pm. Closed 23-30 Dec
Additional: Sunday L. Children 6yrs+
Seats: 35. Private dining room 15
Style: Traditional
Smoking: No smoking in dining room
Accommodation: 14 rooms (14 en suite) ★ ★
Directions: In hamlet of Seion between B4366 & B4547

instance, salmon and smoked haddock fishcakes with a "proper" tartare sauce. Not surprising to find Welsh lamb featured in the happy company of a pea and lettuce casserole together with good ratatouille and top-notch croquette potatoes. Presentation, as in a tangy lemon tart with crushed nectarine, is much attended too without being over fussy.

DOLGELLAU
Map 6 SH71

Dolserau Hall

Views from the Winter Garden restaurant extend over the attractive grounds to the River Wnion. It is a Victorian property offering traditional British cooking from a short four-course set-price dinner menu, with options such as rolled fillets of lemon sole stuffed with mushrooms and spring onions, and roast duckling with apple compote and sherry sauce.

Style: Traditional, Country House
Smoking: No smoking in dining room
Accommodation: 15 rooms (15 en suite) ★ ★ ★
Directions: 1.5miles from town between A470/A494 to Bala

LL40 2AG
Tel: 01341 422522
Fax: 01341 422400
e aa@dhh.co.uk
Chef(s): Huw Roberts
Owner(s): Peter & Marion Kaye
Cost: Set Price D £21.95. ☺ H/wine £8.75
Times: Dinner only, 7-8.30pm. Closed Nov-mid Feb
Additional: Children 6yrs+
Seats: 40

Penmaenuchaf Hall

The oak-panelled dining room of this impressive 19th-century hall has wonderful views across the landscaped gardens and wooded hillside to the Arran mountains beyond. There are oriental rugs on the polished oak floor, and the tables are dressed with heavy linen and set with crystal and polished cutlery. At the time of writing a large conservatory was under construction, intended for dining use. Modern British dishes are offered from both set-price and *carte* menus, such as mousseline of sea scallops with crab and a coriander butter, and seared medallions of free-range local pork with roast quince and jasmine tea sauce.

Accommodation: 14 rooms (14 en suite) ★ ★ ★
Directions: From A470 take A493 (Tywyn/Fairbourne), entrance 1.5miles on L. by sign for Penmaenpool

Penmaenpool, LL40 1YB
Tel: 01341 422129
Fax: 01341 422787
e eat@penhall.co.uk
Chef(s): David Banks
Owner(s): Mark Watson
Cost: Alc £33.50, set price L £15.75/ D £27.50. ☺ H/wine £11.50
Times: Noon-2pm/7-9.30pm.
Additional: Sunday L. Children 6yrs+
Seats: 36. Private dining room 16. Jacket and tie preferred
Style: Country House, Modern
Smoking: No smoking in dining room
Civil licence: 50

Plas Dolmelynllyn

A 16th-century country house with a comfortable restaurant clad in traditional timber panelling. The menu changes emphasis with the seasons as fresh produce is de rigueur. So a summer selection may offer baked Teifi cheese and watercress pancakes, fillet of beef stuffed with beetroot and Parma ham on a Stilton sauce, and citrus posset with blueberries and rosemary shorties.

Style: Traditional, Country-House
Smoking: No smoking in dining room
Accommodation: 10 rooms (10 en suite) ★ ★ ★
Directions: Village centre on A4704 miles N of Dolgellau

Ganllwyd, LL40 2HP
Tel: 01341 440273
Fax: 01341 440640
e info@dolly-hotel.co.uk
Chef(s): Joanna Reddicliffe
Owner(s): Mr J Barkwith
Cost: Set price D £24.50. ☺ H/wine £10.50
Times: Dinner only, 7-11pm. Closed Nov-Mar
Additional: Bar food L. Children 8yrs+
Seats: 16

HARLECH
Map 6 SH53

Castle Cottage

This 16th-century building nestles amongst others of similar vintage, close to Harlech Castle. You will find informal and friendly service in the cottage style restaurant. Fresh, local produce is carefully prepared and might include Welsh salmon or Carmarthen air-dried ham. Seasonal vegetables are nicely

Pen Llech,
LL46 2YL
Tel: 01766 780479
Fax: 01766 780479
Chef(s): Glyn Roberts
Owner(s): Mr & Mrs G Roberts

cooked and the coffee crème brûlée makes a very agreeable dessert.

Smoking: No smoking in dining room
Accommodation: 6 rooms (4 en suite) ♦♦♦♦
Directions: Just off High Street (B4573) 100yds from Harlech Castle

Cost: Set price D £24. ☺ H/wine £10.50
Times: Dinner only, 7-9pm.
Closed 3 wks Feb
Additional: Children welcome
Seats: 45
Style: Cottage

LLANBERIS
Map 6 SH56

Y Bistro

The Welsh language menu provides English translations and reveals a firm commitment to local produce: lamb, beef, shellfish, trout and cheeses. Dishes are served attractively and the freshness of ingredients is evident. A main course of quail, stuffed with prunes and apricots, is moist and happily complemented by a selection of tasty vegetables. A good wine list includes some Welsh bins.

Smoking: No smoking in dining room
Accommodation: 3 rooms
Directions: In the centre of the village at the foot of Mount Snowdon by Lake Padam

Glandwr, 43-45 Stryd Fawr,
LL55 4EU
Tel: 01286 871278
Fax: 01286 871278
e ybistro@fsbdial.co.uk
Chef(s): Nerys Roberts
Owner(s): Danny & Nerys Roberts
Cost: Alc £26. ☺
Times: Dinner only, at 7.30pm.
Closed Sun, L Sun in winter
Additional: Children welcome
Seats: 32. Jacket and tie preferred
Style: Traditional

Wales

PORTMEIRION
Map 6 SH53

The Hotel Portmeirion

Frequented over the years by famous writers such as George Bernard Shaw, H.G.Wells and Bertrand Russell, the Hotel Portmeirion was one of the first stages of Clough Williams-Ellis' amazing Italianate village, famous as the setting for the cult Prisoner series. The airy restaurant enjoys estuary views and serves a selection of modern Welsh cuisine, using local ingredients wherever possible. A meal could begin with a starter of cabbage and sprout soup with bacon dumplings, followed by loin of Welsh lamb with a herb crust, pesto fondant and asparagus. Other specialities might include a dessert of bara brith and butter pudding with vanilla sauce.

Accommodation: 51 rooms (51 en suite) ★ ★ ★
Directions: Off A487 at Minffordd

LL48 6ET
Tel: 01766 770000
Fax: 01766 771331
e hotel@portmeirion-village.com
Chef(s): Colin Pritchard,
Billy Taylor, Steven Rowlands
Owner(s): Portmeirion Ltd
Cost: Alc £35, set price L £13.50-£15/D £35. ☺ H/wine £11
Times: Noon-2pm/7-9pm.
Closed L Mon, 7 Jan-4 Feb
Additional: Sunday L. Children welcome
Seats: 100. Private dining room 30
Style: Country-House
Smoking: No smoking in dining room
Civil licence: 100

PWLLHELI
Map 6 SH33

Plas Bodegroes

Delightful grounds and walled gardens create a charming, unspoilt setting around this Georgian manor house. Tear yourself away from this pretty picture for a rewarding meal in the fine dining room, a surprisingly contemporary corner of this 18th-century property. The fixed menu is bracketed by price, with three choices at each level. Dishes such as seafood hotpot with asparagus, chilli and coriander or chargrilled monkfish with roast vegetables and pesto demonstrate intelligence and imagination in their conception. The cooking is accomplished if sometimes a little fussy, with a perfectly cooked roast tenderloin of local pork with bacon and black pudding, and sage and onion sauce for instance, somewhat marred by an overly busy plate. Cinnamon biscuit with rhubarb, apple and elderflower custard has been described as "exceptional" however. An absorbing wine list offers a serious selection, and service is reliably attentive.

Directions: On A497, 1 mile W of Pwllheli

Nefyn Road, LL53 5TH
Tel: 01758 612363
Fax: 01758 701247
e gunna@bodegroes.co.uk
Chef(s): Chris Chown
Owner(s): Mrs G A Chown and Chris Chown
Cost: Alc £27, set price D £24.50.
☺ H/wine £12.50
Times: Noon-2pm/7-9pm.
Closed Mon, L Tue-Sat, Dec-Feb
Additional: Sunday L. Children welcome. Vegetarian not available
Seats: 40. Private dining room 16
Style: Modern, Chic
Smoking: No smoking in dining room
Accommodation: 11 rooms (11 en suite)

TALSARNAU
Map 6 SH63

Hotel Maes y Neuadd

Various additions over nearly seven hundred years have turned an original 14th-century property into a substantial stone-built house, enjoying fine views over the mountains and across the bay to the Llyn Peninsula. While one of its attractions is its position - good sea air and a terrific outlook - the other is its renowned cuisine based on the freshest local produce. Paintings (many by one of the owners) deck the walls of the traditional restaurant, and there's always a blazing fire when the weather calls for it. Dinner is an elaborate six-course affair, with only two choices for the starter and main course. Pan-fried fillet of trout with lemon and black butter sauce could start a meal, with fillet of beef with roasted shallots a sturdy and worthy main course. The policy of serving three different puddings, or two puds and a savoury, is highly popular. Enthusiastic, cheerful staff orchestrate the evening with some panache.

Directions: 3m NE of Harlech, signposted off B4573

LL47 6YA
Tel: 01766 780200
Fax: 01766 780211
e maes@neuadd.com
Chef(s): Peter Jackson
Owner(s): Mr & Mrs Slatter, Mr & Mrs Jackson
Cost: Set price D £28-£35. ☺ H/wine £11.95
Times: Noon-1.45pm/7-9pm.
Additional: Sunday L. Bar food L. Children welcome
Seats: 50. Private dining room 12
Style: Classic, Traditional
Smoking: No smoking in dining room
Civil licence: 65
Accommodation: 16 rooms (16 en suite) ★★

MONMOUTHSHIRE

ABERGAVENNY
Map 3 SO21

Llansantffraed Court

Decorated in traditional country house style and enjoying commanding views of the Brecon Beacons, this is a restful location for a meal. Dishes on the daily changing menu range from modern European (asparagus, herb and girolle mushroom risotto with butter bean purée and tomato and basil coulis) to traditional (loin of pork with parsnip mash and a coarse grain mustard sauce).

Llanvihangel Gobion, NP7 9BA
Tel: 01873 840678
Fax: 01873 840674
e reception@llch.co.uk
Chef(s): Kurt Fleming
Owner(s): Mr M Morgan
Cost: Alc £35, set price L £14.50/ D £27-£29 ☺ H/wine £12
Times: Noon-2pm/7-9pm.

Pantrhiwgoch Hotel & Riverside Restaurant

A welcoming hotel where the menu changes daily as everything depends on availability from mainly local suppliers. The owners are particularly keen to encourage the use of fresh, seasonal ingredients and obtain their meat from a local farmer and grow their own herbs. Loyal customers are particularly fond of both the 'own-recipe' batter and a gluten-free treacle tart.

Smoking: No smoking in dining room
Civil licence: 60
Accommodation: 18 rooms (18 en suite) ★ ★
Directions: On A40 midway between Abergavenny and Crickhowell

Walnut Tree Inn

The end of a quite remarkable era as Franco Taruschio left this jewel amongst British restaurants in early 2001. Signs of a bright new dynasty to come though with the talented Stephen Terry taking the helm behind the stove. The transition period saw the two men working at the stove together and the hand-over is eased further by a number of the dishes and much of the Italian authenticity being carried over to the new regime. From the new menu, baked crab tart (excellent pastry) has come with a radish salad, roast wood pigeon with sweet and sour pumpkin and barba di fratti. Desserts tend towards the familiar (but classic) including tiramisu and dark chocolate tart with tangerine sauce.

Smoking: Air conditioning
Directions: Three miles NE of Abergavenny on B4521.

CHEPSTOW   Map 3 ST59

Wye Knot Restaurant

Airy by day with a relaxed setting and calming décor, the whitewashed Wye Knot becomes a romantic, candlelit spot by night. It is also a 16th-century building overlooking the River Wye, and has a fascinating history to boot. A cosy lounge gives way to a spacious restaurant that attracts locals and foodies from further afield - which is always a good sign. The blackboard

---

Additional: Sunday L. Bar food. Children welcome. Vegetarian by request only
Seats: 50. Private dining room 30
Style: Country-House
Smoking: No smoking in dining room
Civil licence: 200
Accommodation: 21 rooms (21 en suite) ★ ★ ★
Directions: From junction of A40 & A465 at Abergavenny, take B4598 signed to Usk. Hotel 4.5 miles on L (with white gates). 0.5 mile along drive

Brecon Road, NP8 1EP
Tel: 01873 810550
Fax: 01873 811880
e info@pantrhiwgoch.co.uk
Owner(s): D & R Edwards, J & S Belcher
Cost: Alc £27. ☺ ☺ H/wine £9.95
Times: Noon-2.30pm/6.30pm-Midnight
Additional: Sunday L. Children welcome
Seats: 80. Jacket and tie preferred
Style: Traditional

NP7 8AW
Tel: 01873 852797
Fax: 01873 859764
e stephenandfrancesco@thewalnuttreeinn.com
Chef(s): Stephen Terry
Owner(s): Stephen Terry & Francesco Mattioli
Cost: Alc £30. ☺ ☺ H/wine £13.50
Times: Noon-3pm/6.30-11pm. Closed Sun-Mon, D BH Mon, 1wk Xmas
Additional: Children welcome
Seats: 70. Private dining room 40
Style: Italian, Country

The Back, NP16 5HH
Tel: 01291 622929
Chef(s): Kevin Brookes, Emma Williams
Owner(s): Kevin Brookes, Emma Williams

Wales

acts as sole menu here with a good range of options to choose from. Dishes work well, as in breast of chicken complemented by a black pudding stuffed ballotine of chicken leg, leaf spinach and a superbly robust reduction.

Wye Knot Restaurant

Cost: *Alc* £25, set price L £14.95/D £15.95. ☺ ☺ H/wine £11.95
Times: 12.30-2.30pm/7-10pm.
Closed Mon, L Sat, D Sun
Additional: Sunday L. Children welcome
Seats: 40
Style: Traditional, French
Smoking: No smoking in dining room
Directions: From M4 take M48, then onto Chepstow, following signs for Chepstow Castle & Riverbank

---

TINTERN   Map 3 SO50

Parva Farmhouse

Situated in a 17th-century farmhouse on the banks of the River Wye, this is a cosy, rustic restaurant with bare beams, fishing memorabilia and an inglenook fireplace. The menu features many traditional dishes, such as home-made parva pâté or Welsh venison in a port wine sauce with cranberry and apple.

Seats: 24
Style: Traditional.
Smoking: No smoking in dining room
Accommodation: 9 rooms (9 en suite) ★ ★
Directions: North end of Tintern on A466 alongside the Wye, 0.75 mile from the Abbey

NP16 6SQ
Tel: 01291 689411
Fax: 01291 689557
e parva-hoteltintern@hotmail.com
Chef(s): Dereck Stubbs
Owner(s): Mr & Mrs D R Stubbs
Cost: Set price D £19.50. ☺
H/wine £9.50
Times: Dinner only, 7-8.30pm
Additional: Children 4yrs+

Royal George Hotel

Dating back to 1598 when it was an iron master's cottage, the Royal George sits at the bottom of a gently sloping hillside in the picturesque Wye Valley. The restaurant is country house in demeanour, with traditional menus offering around seven starters and nine main courses. Try the likes of medallions of Welsh Black beef with smoked bacon, Stilton and walnuts.

Seats: 44. Private dining room 110
Style: Formal, Country-House
Smoking: No smoking in dining room
Accommodation: 16 rooms (16 en suite) ★ ★
Directions: On A486 Between Chepstow and Monmouth

NP6 6ST
Tel: 01291 689205
Fax: 01291 689448
e royalgeorgetintern@hotmail.com
Chef(s): Cliff Randall
Owner(s): Anthony & Maureen Pearce
Cost: *Alc* £22, set price L £12-£13.20/D £22. ☺ ☺ H/wine £9.75
Times: Noon-2pm/7-10pm.
Additional: Sunday L. Bar food. Children welcome

USK

Map 3 SO30

Three Salmons Hotel

Within this 18th-century coaching inn, the aptly named Ostlers restaurant offers an impressive selection of dishes, making good use of fresh, local ingredients. The recommended fish of the day is a safe choice for freshness and flavour - witness the cod with mustard mash and pesto. Stronger, perhaps, on savouries than desserts, Ostlers will certainly rustle up a satisfying meal.

Style: Modern
Civil licence: 100
Accommodation: 24 rooms (24 en suite) ★ ★ ★
Directions: M4 J24, A449 N, first L A472 to Usk. Hotel in centre of village

Bridge Street, NP15 1RY
Tel: 01291 672133
Fax: 01291 673979
e threesalmons.hotel@talk21.com
Chef(s): Nick Williams
Owner(s): Julian Hitchcock
Cost: Set price L £8.95/D £16.50.
☺ ☺
Times: L from Noon, D from 7pm.
Closed D Sun
Additional: Sunday L. Bar food.
Children welcome
Seats: 34. Private dining room 22

WHITEBROOK

Map 3 SO50

The Crown at Whitebrook

This small hotel - an 18th-century drover's inn - stands in the narrow, wooded Whitebrook valley, one mile from the river Wye and on the edge of Tintern forest. Its intimate restaurant makes good use of fresh Welsh ingredients such as laverbread, beef and lamb. A strong French influence is evident in dishes such as medallions of beef fillet layered with boudin blanc and served with a stout sauce or roast loin of venison with celeriac purée and caper sauce. Desserts might include warm chocolate tart with coffee bean ice cream and chocolate sauce or rhubarb tarte tatin with vanilla crème fraîche.

Accommodation: 11 rooms (11 en suite) ★ ★
Directions: Turn W off A66 immediately S of Bigsweir Bridge (5miles from Monmouth), 2miles on unclassified road

NP5 4TX
Tel: 01600 860254
Fax: 01600 860607
e crown@whitebrook.demon.co.uk
Chef(s): Mark Turton
Owner(s): Ms A Barbara & Ms E Barbara
Cost: Set price L £15.95/D £29.95. ☺ H/wine £10.95
Times: Noon-2pm/7-9pm.
Closed L Mon, 2 wks Jan, 2 wks Aug
Additional: Sunday L. Children 8yrs+
Seats: 32. Private dining room 12
Style: Modern, French
Smoking: No smoking in dining room

NEWPORT

NEWPORT

Map 3 ST38

Celtic Manor Resort

A peerless golfing and conference hotel of vast proportions, including capacity to house up to 1500 delegates and 800 residents. Executive dining takes place in a boldly stylish conservatory bedecked in unique Celtic artwork. Here, Owens menu is commendably prominent in Welsh produce such as Lady Llanover salt duck, home-smoked sea bass, salt marsh lamb and selected Celtic cheeses served with laverbread loaf and Welsh elderberry liqueur. Classic dishes in a modern idiom include pan-fried monkfish with wild mushroom Arborio rice, grilled salmon and Llanboidy cheese roulade and triple Pembrokeshire chocolate terrine. Largely polished service and an improved wine list.

Civil licence: 100
Accommodation: 400 rooms (400 en suite) ★ ★ ★ ★ ★
Directions: From M4 J24 take A48 towards Newport, turn after 100 metres

Coldra Woods, NP18 1HQ
Tel: 01633 413000
Fax: 01633 412910
e postbox@celtic-manor.com
Chef(s): Peter Fuchs
Owner(s): Dr T Matthews
Cost: Alc £22.50, set price L £18.50/D £23. ☺ ☺ H/wine £15
Times: 12.30-3pm/7-10.30pm.
Closed D Sun
Additional: Sunday L. Bar food.
Children welcome
Seats: 180. Private dining room 26
Style: Modern
Smoking: No-smoking area; no pipes; Air conditioning

Wales

NEWPORT *Continued*   Map 3 ST38

Junction 28

Not a motorway service station, but nevertheless a welcome diversion for travellers on the M4. Large throughput of customers allows for an extensive menu including warm salad of black pudding with bacon and apple crisps, pan-fried calves liver and Cajun seasoned seared halibut steak on a salsa of avocado, tomato and coriander.

Seats: 165. Private dining room 12
Style: Modern
Smoking: No smoking in dining room
Directions: M4 J28, follow signs Risca-Brymawr, then L in 0.5m signed Caephilly. R at mini-roundabout, then 1st L beyond St Basil's church

Station Approach, Bassaleg,
NP10 8LD
Tel: 01633 891891
Fax: 01633 895978
Chef(s): Jon West
Owner(s): Jon West, Richard Wallace
Cost: *Alc* £20/D £11.95. ☺ ☺
H/wine £9.95
Times: Noon-2pm/5.30-9.30pm.
Closed D Sun, Last wk July,
1st wk Aug
Additional: Bar food. Children welcome

The Inn at the Elm Tree   NEW

Modern, intimate restaurant situated in an early 19th century barn, with exposed stone wall panels juxtaposed with contemporary blue and grey decor. Welsh produce makes a strong mark from Welsh Black beef to game from nearby estates, and the restaurant makes a point of using local organic pork and free-range chicken. Plus, if you see caramelised rice pudding and apricot compôte on the menu, it's a real treat.

St Brides Wentlooge,
Wentlooge, NP10 8SQ
Tel: 01633 680225
Fax: 01633 681035
 inn@the-elm-tree.co.uk
Chef(s): Mike Thomas, Gareth Charles
Owner(s): Mike & Trish Thomas
Cost: *Alc* £23.50, set price L £13.50.
☺ ☺ H/wine £10
Times: Noon-1am. Closed D Sun in Winter
Additional: Sunday L. Bar food. Children 12 yrs+
Seats: 45. Jacket and tie preferred
Style: Modern, Minimalist
Smoking: No-smoking area; no cigars
Accommodation: 10 rooms (10 en suite) ♦♦♦♦
Directions: From M4 J28 take A48 towards Castleton. At 1st rdbt turn L (Morgan Way), turn R at T-junction onto B4239. Inn in 2.5 miles

PEMBROKESHIRE

FISHGUARD   Map 2 SM93

Tregynon Farmhouse Restaurant

Peter and Jane Heard's special Pembrokeshire retreat now offers self-catering cottages rather than rooms but the restaurant remains at the heart of things. Imaginative menus are based on the best of local produce and meticulously designed to offer variety for those staying more than one night. Grilled goats' cheese muffins, loin of local pork with prunes

Gwaun Valley, SA65 9TU
Tel: 01239 820531
Fax: 01239 820531
 tregynon@online-holidays.net
Chef(s): Peter & Jane Heard
Cost: *Alc* £23.50, set price D £23.50.
H/wine £11.50

Wales

Calvados and cream and lemon meringue roulade have all featured.

Times: D only, 7.30-8.30pm. Closed Sun, Thu (and some Wed), 3 wks in winter
Additional: Children 8yrs+
Seats: 24. Private dining room 12
Style: Traditional, Country-house
Smoking: No-smoking area
Directions: Telephone for directions

HAVERFORDWEST — Map 2 SM92

Wolfscastle Country Hotel

Wolf's Castle, SA62 5LZ
Tel: 01437 741225
Fax: 01437 741383
e andy741225@aol.com
Chef(s): Steve Brown
Owner(s): Mr A Stirling
Cost: Alc £18. ☺ ☺
Times: Noon-2pm/6.45-9.15pm. Closed D Sun, 24-26 Dec
Additional: Sunday L. Bar food. Children welcome
Seats: 55
Style: Country-House
Smoking: No smoking in dining room
Civil licence: 60
Accommodation: 20 rooms (20 en suite) ★ ★
Directions: From Haverfordwest take A40 towards Fishguard. Hotel in centre of Wolf's Castle

Once a vicarage, this stone-built Victorian property is home to an attractive restaurant, serving an impressive range of well-cooked dishes. Vegetarian and 'traditional' choices are separately listed, alongside up to ten other main courses. Expect the likes of chicken livers with grapes and port served with walnut bread croutes amongst the starters and baked fillet of cod on cabbage and bacon with a cheese sauce to be featured on the mains. Good range of classic puds like lemon tart served warm with raspberry coulis.

PEMBROKE — Map 2 SM90

Left Bank

The setting of an old bank in the centre of town gives an overall feeling of style and modernity. Whilst the lunch menu is simple and uncomplicated (but worthy nevertheless) a more serious, ambitious approach is taken at dinner yielding the likes of salmon with beurre blanc followed by an excellent pannacotta.

63 Main Street, SA71 4DA
Tel: 01646 622333
Telephone for further details

Wales

ST DAVID'S

Map 2 SM72

Morgan's Brasserie

20 Nun Street,
SA62 6NT
Tel: 01437 720508
Fax: 01437 720508
e morgans@stdavids.co.uk
Chef(s): Ceri Morgan
Owner(s): Ceri Morgan
Cost: Alc £24. ☺ H/wine £10.50
Times: Dinner only, 7-9pm.
Closed Sun, Jan-Feb (times may vary
out of season)
Additional: Children welcome
Seats: 32
Style: Traditional, Bistro-Style
Smoking: No smoking in dining room
Directions: 60 yards off Cross Square

Located in a side street close to the centre of St David's, Morgan's is an attractive, rustic setting with exposed brickwork and plain walls displaying colourful artwork. The cooking is as simple and unpretentious as the décor, allowing the quality local ingredients to shine. A few popular dishes stand firm on a frequently changing menu, which is supplemented by a daily board of fish specials. A meal might begin with 'beautifully plump and tender' Menai Mussels with tomato, garlic and herbs, followed by Welsh black fillet steak Rossini. Service is relaxed and friendly.

St Non's Hotel

Catherine Street, SA62 6RJ
Tel: 01437 720239
Fax: 01437 721839
e stnons@enterprise.net
Chef(s): Shane Morrissey
Owner(s): Peter Trier
Cost: Alc £18. ☺ ☺ H/wine £11
Times: Noon-2pm/6-9pm.
Closed Nov & Dec
Additional: Bar food. Children
welcome
Seats: 40

This modern hotel has grown up around an old whitewashed house on the path to St Non's well. The restaurant is unfussily decorated in pastel shades, and offers an imaginative selection of British based dishes. Local ingredients are put to good use, as in a main course of Black beef with brandy and peppercorn cream sauce.

Style: Modern, Bistro-Style
Smoking: No smoking in dining room
Accommodation: 20 rooms (20 en suite) ★ ★
Directions: Close to Cathedral and St Non's Retreat

Warpool Court

SA62 6BN
Tel: 01437 720300
Fax: 01437 720676
e warpool@enterprise.net
Chef(s): John Daniels
Owner(s): Peter Trier
Cost: Set price L £25-£37.
H/wine £12.50
Times: Noon-2pm/7-9.15pm.
Closed Jan
Additional: Sunday L. Bar food.
Children welcome. Vegetarian by
request only
Seats: 50. Private dining room 22
Style: Country-House
Smoking: No smoking in dining room

Once the old choir school for St David's Cathedral, Warpool Court commands impressive views over St Bride's Bay. Visit on a clear day to enjoy the vista from the glass-fronted restaurant. You will find the service attentive and professional and the food of good quality. This is genuinely imaginative and often intricate cooking, pork fillet medallions, pan-fried salmon, red mullet and beef fillet steak are typical main courses, the latter served with a goats' cheese glaze, roast vegetables and shallot sauce. From the sweet menu it's hard to resist the lure of warm scotch pancakes with crème fraîche, redcurrant compôte and aniseed cream. Now that's something to sing about!

Civil licence: 130. **Accommodation:** 25 rooms (25 en suite) ★ ★ ★
Directions: From Cross Square, left by Midland Bank into Goat St, at fork follow hotel signs

Panorama Hotel

A well dressed restaurant with sea views providing a classically intimate setting for a candlelit dinner. Where possible all the produce has been sourced in Pembrokeshire. This includes a good choice of seafood, an impressive vegetarian selection, and prime Welsh beef steaks served with a variety of sauces.

Smoking: No smoking in dining room
Accommodation: 7 rooms (7 en suite) ★ ★
Directions: From A478 follow South Beach & town centre signs, sharp L at mini-rdbt, under railway and up Greenhill Road. Go along South Pde to Esplanade

The Esplanade, SA70 7DU
Tel: 01834 844976
Fax: 01834 844976
e mail@panoramahotel.f9.co.uk
Chef(s): Robin Wright
Owner(s): Robin & Carol Wright
Cost: Alc £25, set price D £19.95. ☺
H/wine £8.95
Times: Dinner only, 7-9pm.
Closed Sun
Additional: Children welcome
Seats: 25
Style: Country House, Formal

Penally Abbey Country House

Charming old country house benefiting from scenic views over Tenby's golf course and the bay beyond it, not to mention a distinctively tranquil atmosphere, provided by its position elevated above the village. An elegant restaurant offers the likes of breast of chicken supreme with summer berries.

Style: Country House
Smoking: No smoking in dining room
Civil licence: 45
Accommodation: 12 rooms (12 en suite) ★ ★ ★
Directions: From Tenby take A4139 to Penally

Penally, SA70 7PY
Tel: 01834 843033
Fax: 01834 844714
e penally.abbey@btinternet.com
Chef(s): Mrs E Warren, Mrs M Doney
Owner(s): Mr & Mrs S T Warren
Cost: Alc £28, set price L £18-£22/
D £28. H/wine £12.95
Times: 12.30-2.30pm/7.30-9.30pm
Additional: Children 7yrs+
Seats: 46. Private dining room 16

POWYS

Best Western Castle of Brecon Hotel

Standing beside a ruined castle, this 19th century coaching inn has great views of the Usk Valley and the Brecon Beacons. Whilst the restaurant looks traditional, the food is full of striking international flavours - perhaps pork in cajun spices or chicken stuffed with mascarpone and basil. There is a welcome emphasis on quality produce, much of it local.

Smoking: No smoking in dining room
Civil licence: 40
Accommodation: 42 rooms (42 en suite) ★ ★
Directions: Follow signs to town centre. Turn opposite Boars Head towards Cradog Golf Club, turn R after 200yds in Castle Square

Castle Square, LD3 9DB
Tel: 01874 624611
Fax: 01874 623737
e hotel@breconcastle.co.uk
Chef(s): Lee Havard
Owner(s): Tim & Louise Eggins
Cost: Alc £22. ☺ H/wine £8.40
Times: Noon-2pm/7-9pm.
Closed Sun, L Mon-Sat
Additional: Sunday L. Bar food.
Children welcome
Seats: 70. Private dining room 30
Style: Traditional

Wales

BRECON *Continued*   Map 3 SO02

The Usk Inn   NEW

An exemplary village inn offering rooms and some robust honest cooking well-suited to the venue. The cooking has a welcome emphasis on the best of local produce including some top-quality meats. Menus are supported by a range of frequently changing blackboard specials and offer the likes of fishcakes made with salmon & cod served with tomato sauce and fresh cod fillet dipped in beer batter & deep fried.

Seats: 60
Style: Mediterranean Bistro
Smoking: No-smoking area; no pipes; Air conditioning
Accommodation: 11 rooms (11 en suite) ♦♦♦♦
Directions: 250yds off A40, 6 miles E of Brecon

Station Road, Talybont-on-Usk, LD3 7JE
Tel: 01874 676251
Fax: 01874 676392
e dine@uskinn.co.uk
Chef(s): Mike Taylor
Owner(s): Mike & Babara Taylor
Cost: *Alc* £28, set price L £9.95/ D £18.95. ☺ ☺ H/wine £8.35
Times: Noon-3pm/6.30-9pm. Closed Xmas
Additional: Sunday L. Bar food. Children welcome

The White Swan   NEW

They keep things simple here and it's all the better for it. A short menu with blackboard specials is pretty much in the

gastropub mould (duck confit with cucumber and oriental dressing, rack of lamb with wild mushroom risotto) offering dishes that are crisp and honest. Eat in the bar or the restaurant (crisp linen, decent glasses). Short but exceptionally well-chosen wine list.

LD3 7BZ
Tel: 01874 665276
Chef(s): Rod Lewis
Owner(s): Richard Griffiths
Cost: *Alc* £21. ☺ ☺ H/wine £11.95
Times: Noon-2pm/7-9.30pm. Closed Mon-Tue, D Sun, 25-26 Dec, 1 Jan
Additional: Sunday L. Bar food L. Children welcome
Seats: 60. Private dining room 40
Style: Traditional, Rustic
Smoking: No smoking in dining room
Directions: Situated 3 miles east of Brecon off A40. Take B4558 followings signs for Llanfrynach

BUILTH WELLS   Map 3 SO05

Caer Beris Manor

Once home to Lord Swansea, this delightful 16th-century manor hotel has extensive grounds and, in keeping with the setting, the dining room has original 16th-century panelling. The seasonally-changing menu offers local specialities such as gratinée of laver bread and fillet of Welsh Black beef, and for the finalé, a white chocolate mousse served with a dark chocolate sauce.

Civil licence: 100
Accommodation: 23 rooms (23 en suite) ★ ★ ★
Directions: Just off A483 on W side of Builth Wells

LD2 3NP
Tel: 01982 552601
Fax: 01982 552586
e caerberis.manor@btinternet.com
Chef(s): Valentine Bayona-Martinez
Cost: Set price D £25. H/wine £9.95
Times: Noon-2.30pm/7.30-9.30pm.
Additional: Children welcome
Seats: 40
Style: Country House
Smoking: No smoking in dining room

Wales

CRICKHOWELL   Map 3 SO21

Bear Hotel

NP8 1BW
Tel: 01873 810408
Fax: 01873 811696
e bearhotel@aol.com
Chef(s): Brian Simmonds
Owner(s): Mrs. J Hindermarsh
Cost: *Alc* £25. ☺ ☺ H/wine £8.95
Times: Noon-3pm/7pm-Midnight.
Closed D Sun, 25 Dec
Additional: Sunday L. Bar food.
Children welcome
Seats: 60. Private dining room 30
Smoking: Air conditioning
Accommodation: 35 rooms (35 en
suite) ★ ★ ★

Geographically and socially at the centre of the town, The Bear
is renowned for its character and friendliness. Its large
restaurant is divided into two parts: a lower section with bare
tables, beamed ceilings and flagged floors, and a more homely
upper level where floors are carpeted and the tables clothed in
lace. The menu makes good use of local ingredients, but gives
them an exciting international twist: if you order Welsh lamb, it
might appear on African couscous with an apricot sauce, whilst
venison could be served with braised red cabbage, celeriac
dauphinoise and caramelised chestnuts.

Directions: Town centre off A40

Gliffaes Country House

NP8 1RH
Tel: 01874 730371
Fax: 01874 730463
e calls@gliffaeshotel.com
Chef(s): Iain Sampson
Owner(s): Mr & Mrs Brabner &
Mr & Mrs Suter

If you want a country retreat with heaps of activities, Gliffaes
may be the place for you. Situated in an area famed for some of
the best fishing in the UK, the hotel offers guests 2.5 miles of
wild brown trout and salmon runs. One also has access to a golf
putting green, tennis court, croquet lawn and full-sized snooker

Wales

CRICKHOWELL *Continued*   Map 3 SO21

table. If you're knackered at the thought of it all, head for the restaurant instead. Menus offer traditional country house fare with interesting touches, in the likes of tomato and herb stuffed loin of rabbit with confit leg on saffron risotto with vegetable tagliatelle and game jus.

Style: Traditional, Country-House
Smoking: No smoking in dining room
Civil licence: 40
Accommodation: 22 rooms (22 en suite) ★ ★ ★
Directions: 1 mile off A40. 2.5 miles W of Crickhowell

Cost: *Alc* £25.35/D £25.35-£30.
☺ H/wine £12
Times: Noon-2.30pm/7.30-9.15pm.
Closed L Mon-Sat
Additional: Sunday L. Bar food L.
Children welcome
Seats: 70. Private dining room 35.
Jacket and tie preferred

Manor Hotel

Stunning hillside location in the manor house where Sir George Everest was born. The restaurant is decorated in warm browns and golds and looks out on the Usk valley. Though cooking sometimes lacks precision, this is a good place to sample classics such as rack of lamb with parsnip mash or rib eye steak with herb butter.

Additional: Sunday L. Bar food. Children welcome
Seats: 54. Private dining room 26
Style: Traditional
Smoking: No smoking in dining room
Civil licence: 250
Accommodation: 22 rooms (21 en suite) ★ ★ ★
Directions: 0.5 mile W of Crickhowell on A40 Brecon rd

Brecon Road, NP8 1SE
Tel: 01873 810212
Fax: 01873 811938
🄴 info@manorhotel.co.uk
Chef(s): Glyn Bridgeman,
Matthew Sussex
Owner(s): Mr G Bridgeman
Cost: *Alc* £19.95, set price D £19.95.
☺ ☺ H/wine £11.95
Times: Noon-2.30pm/7-9.30pm.
Closed D Sun

Nantyffin
Cider Mill Inn

Bustling roadside inn. Located in the old cider making area of the mill, the restaurant is on two levels with the cider press taking pride of place. The *carte* is supported by a choice of daily specials - perhaps roast rack of salt marsh lamb with herb crust and celeriac purée, or poached fresh haddock with saffron risotto and chive and mussel cream sauce.

Additional: Sunday L. Bar food. Children welcome
Seats: 65
Style: Traditional, Rustic
Smoking: No smoking in dining room
Directions: 1 mile west of Crickhowell on A40 at junction with A479

Brecon Road, NP8 1SG
Tel: 01873 810755
Fax: 01873 810775
🄴 nantyffin@aol.com
Chef(s): Sean Gerrard, Ian Powell
Owner(s): Glyn Brideman,
Sean Gerrard
Cost: *Alc* £21. ☺ ☺ H/wine £12.95
Times: Noon-2.30pm/6.30-9.30pm.
Closed Mon, 1wk Nov,1 wk Jan

KNIGHTON   Map 7 SO27

Milebrook House

Quality cooking and real attention to detail at this amicable hotel set in the Teme Valley. This is a relaxed environment in a setting where the hospitality of the staff really stands out. A

Milebrook, LD7 1LT
Tel: 01547 528632
Fax: 01547 520509
🄴 hotel@milebrook.kc3ltd.co.uk

typical meal might feature the likes of potato-apple rösti with smoked salmon and horseradish, or rack of local Welsh lamb with a niçoise olive sauce.

Chef(s): Beryl Marsden
Owner(s): Mr & Mrs R T Marsden
Cost: Alc £22, set price L £11.95-£17.90/D £20.50-£28. ☺ ☺
H/wine £10.95
Times: Noon-1.30pm/7-8.30pm.
Closed L Mon
Additional: Sunday L. Bar food L.
Children 8yrs+
Seats: 40. Private dining room 16
Style: Country House
Smoking: No smoking in dining room
Accommodation: 10 rooms (10 en suite) ★ ★
Directions: 2 miles E of Knighton on A4113 (Ludlow)

LLANFYLLIN
Map 7 SJ11

Seeds

Cosy cottage style restaurant with plenty of charm and character enhanced by exposed beams, stone-flagged floors and an abundance of bric-a-brac from around the world. Informal and friendly, it's an easygoing atmosphere in which to enjoy the likes of tomato and dolcelatte pastry, tender fillet of pork and a comforting treacle tart and cream.

Additional: Sunday L. Bar food L. Children welcome
Seats: 22. **Smoking:** No smoking in dining room
Directions: Village centre, on A490, 13 miles from Welshpool

5 Penybryn Cottage,
High Street, SY22 5AP
Tel: 01691 648604
Chef(s): Mark Seager
Owner(s): Ms F Seager & Mark Seager
Cost: Alc £17.50/D £19.95. ☺ ☺
H/wine £11
Times: 11am-2pm/7-9pm.
Closed Mon, L Tue in winter, D Sun,
2 wks Jan

LLANGAMMARCH WELLS
Map 3 SN94

Lake Country House

There's a feeling of grandeur about this spacious, elegant country house style restaurant. White linen and silver sit comfortably in the formal, traditional setting. Home-baked breads cut from the loaf at your table and tasty canapés set an encouraging tone. The warm scallop flan with caviar butter sauce proved an interesting, if rather rich starter, while the main course assiette of Welsh lamb, for example, brings a generous portion of tender, pink meat, together with kidneys and sweetbreads. Dessert, chosen from an imaginative selection, may be followed up with coffee and a variety of agreeable home-made petits fours.

Accommodation: 19 rooms (19 en suite) ★ ★ ★
Directions: A483 from Garth, turn L for Llangammarch Wells & follow signs to hotel

LD4 4BS
Tel: 01591 620202
Fax: 01591 620457
e info@lakecountryhouse.co.uk
Chef(s): Sean Cullingford
Owner(s): J Mifsud
Cost: Set price L £17.50/D £35.
H/wine £13.50
Times: 12.30-2.45pm/7.30-
Additional: Sunday L. Bar food L.
Children 8yrs+
Seats: 40. Private dining room 30.
Jacket and tie preferred
Style: Country-House
Smoking: No smoking in dining room
Civil licence: 70

Wales

Wales

LLANWDDYN

Map 6 SJ01

Lake Vyrnwy Hotel

Lake Vyrnwy, SY10 0LY
Tel: 01691 870692
Fax: 01691 870259
e res@lakevymwy.com
Chef(s): Shaun Mitchell
Owner(s): Bisiker family
Cost: Alc £32.50, set price L
£15.95/D £27.50. ☺ H/wine £12.95
Times: Noon-2pm/7-10pm
Additional: Sunday L. Bar food.
Children welcome
Seats: 80. Private dining room 120
Style: Modern, Country-House
Smoking: No smoking in dining room
Civil licence: 125
Accommodation: 35 rooms ★★★

This 'wonderful' country hotel stands in a 27,000 acre sporting estate, popular for shooting, fishing and even quad biking - but rest assured, no noise will interrupt your enjoyment of the breathtaking views. The restaurant looks over fairytale Lake Vyrnwy to the mountains beyond. Decorated in pretty, country house style, it is a relaxing, friendly place to dine. The cooking is simple but accomplished, making good use of local produce and striking a balance between old favourites (game terrine; lamb Wellington), and imaginative dishes such as grilled seabass with Thai shallots, wild rice and lime sauce.

Directions: Follow Tourist signs on A495/B4393, 200yds past dam at Lake Vyrnwy

LLANWRTYD WELLS

Map

Carlton House

Mary Ann Gilchrist really knows her stuff. Her intelligent, thoughtful cooking will leave you keen to return, so it's fortunate that Carlton House is a 'restaurant with rooms' and offers some great value all inclusive breaks. The restaurant retains its 19th-century wood panelling and is filled with interesting antiques. Its warm, inviting atmosphere is enhanced by the friendly manner of Mary Ann and her husband, who are clearly committed to satisfying everybody's expectations. Nowhere is this more evident than in the daily changing menu, which makes excellent use of seasonal and local produce. Swansea cod, for example, could appear as a starter in a crisp parcel of crab meat with seafood velouté, whilst local hill lamb might be roasted until 'tender, flavoursome and sublime' then served with crushed Jersey royals, leek fondue, asparagus and sauce Paloise. The equally intelligent wine list completes an exciting and always memorable experience.

Dolycoed Road,
LD5 4RA
Tel: 01591 610248
Fax: 01591 610242
e info@carltonrestaurant.co.uk
Chef(s): Mary Ann Gilchrist
Owner(s): Dr Gilchrist
Cost: Alc £34, set price D £24. ☺
H/wine £9.95
Times: Dinner only, 7-8.30pm.
Closed 10 Dec-10 Jan
Additional:. Vegetarian by request only
Seats: 14
Style: French
Smoking: No smoking in dining room
Accommodation: 7 rooms (7 en suite)
★★
Directions: In the town centre

LLYSWEN

Map 3 SO13

Llangoed Hall

The exterior of this imposing country house was remodelled by Clough Williams-Ellis of Portmeirion fame. The interior balances grandeur with comfort and interest: rooms contain open fires, deep cushioned sofas and a range of interesting

artwork and antiques. The restaurant is decorated with Laura Ashley fabrics and offers a menu to complement the opulent surroundings. A meal might include a starter of 'delicious' poached fillet of turbot with salmon ravioli and crème fraîche sauce, followed by a 'nicely flavoured' tenderloin of pork saltimbocca with Stilton tartlet and bittersweet jus. The efficient, friendly staff add to the enjoyment.

Accommodation: 23 rooms (23 en suite) ★ ★ ★ ★
Directions: On A470, 2 miles from Llyswen towards Builth Wells

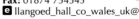

LD3 0YP
Tel: 01874 754525
Fax: 01874 754545
e llangoed_hall_co_wales_uk@
compuserve.com
Chef(s): Daniel James
Owner(s): Sir Bernard Ashley
Cost: Alc £45, set price L £17.50-£39.50. ☺ H/wine £15
Times: Noon-2pm/7-9.30pm
Additional: Sunday L. Bar food L. Children 8yrs+.
Vegetarian by request only
Seats: 50. Private dining room 100. Jacket and tie preferred
Style: Formal, Country-House
Smoking: No smoking in dining room
Civil licence: 60

MONTGOMERY

Map 7 SO29

Dragon Hotel

Market town hotel with a beamed restaurant and cosy tables. The comprehensive menu offers dishes based on fresh local produce, described as modern English and Welsh with a Mediterranean influence. These include crab mousse and scallops with a shallot and caper dressing.

Market Square, SY15 6PA
Tel: 01686 668359
Fax: 01686 668287
e reception@dragonhotel.com
Chef(s): James Riches
Owner(s): M & S Michaels
Cost: Alc £21.50, set price D £18.50. ☺ ☺ H/wine £9.25
Times: Noon-2pm/7-9pm.
Closed L All week (ex bookings),
Additional: Sunday L. Bar food.
Children welcome
Seats: 42
Smoking: No smoking in dining room
Accommodation: 20 rooms (20 en suite) ★ ★
Directions: Behind the town Hall

Wales

Wales

MONTGOMERY *Continued* Map 7 SO29

The Bricklayers Arms NEW

Bustling restaurant full of cottagey charm (think real fires, bare floorboards and bric-a-brac). The menu offers a good choice of modern British dishes: perhaps Welsh ribeye with a fondue of leek and Madeira jus or seared salmon with a cucumber salad and tomato butter sauce. Service is informal but attentive and efficient.

Chirbury Road, SY15 6QQ
Tel: 01686 668177
e robjennings6@hotmail.com
Chef(s): Robert Jennings
Owner(s): Robert Jennings and Sara Pezzack
Cost: *Alc* £23.45. ☺ ☺ H/wine £9.20
Times: Noon-2.30pm/7-9pm. Closed Mon, 1 Jan, 2wks Feb, 1 wk Sep
Additional: Sunday L. Children welcome
Seats: 40
Style: Traditional, Rustic
Smoking: No-smoking area; no cigars

Directions: From Welshpool take A438 bypass towards Newtown. After 8 miles at rdbt follow signs for Montgomery on B4388. On entering town turn L by war memorial onto B4386. Bricklayers Arms 300yds on L down hill

NANT-DDU Map 3 SO12

Nant Ddu Lodge

Within this 19th-century Georgian hotel, the colourful, continental-style bistro, with its polished wood tables, is a focal point. Nant Ddu's imaginative menu caters for a range of tastes, offering a vegetarian and 'old favourites' selection as well as a good choice of daily specials, all have an emphasis on good quality fresh produce. Friendly service in a bustling atmosphere.

Smoking: No smoking in dining room
Accommodation: 22 rooms (22 en suite) ★ ★ ★
Directions: 6 miles N of Merthyr Tydfil, and 12 miles S of Brecon on A470

Cwm Taf, Nant Ddu, CF48 2HY
Tel: 01685 379111
Fax: 01685 377088
e enquiries@nant-ddu-lodge.co.uk
Chef(s): Mark Coulton
Owner(s): Mr & Mrs D Ronson
Cost: *Alc* £22. ☺ ☺ H/wine £8.95
Times: Noon-3pm/6.30-11pm. Closed D Sun
Additional: Sunday L. Bar food. Children welcome
Seats: 80. Private dining room 16
Style: Bistro-Style

PWLLGLOYW Map

Seland Newydd NEW

17th century inn in the tongue-bending village of Pwllgloyw, just north of Brecon. The roaring log fire in the open plan bar, oak beams and warm, tasteful decoration throughout make a sojourn to Seland Newydd worthwhile. Here, local produce is treated respectfully, from Welsh lamb to wild local pheasant in season, and regional flavours may also crop up in the form of Welsh rarebit croutons or diced leeks flavouring a mussel broth.

LD3 9PY
Tel: 01874 690282
Fax: 01874 690282
Chef(s): Paul Thomasson
Owner(s): A F Savage, P Thomasson & M Thomasson
Cost: *Alc* £28, set price L £17.50. ☺ ☺ H/wine £10.95

Menus are to the point but interesting with sound ingredient combinations. The likes of a crisp tomato and basil tart with confit of peppers and a lightly dressed salad works in its simplicity and execution.

Smoking: No smoking in dining room
Accommodation: 3 rooms (3 en suite)
Directions: Telephone for directions

Times: Noon-2.30pm/7-9.30pm.
Closed Mon, D Sun
Additional: Sunday L. Bar food.
Children welcome
Seats: 35. Private dining room 6
Style: Classic, Traditional

THREE COCKS   Map 3 SO13

Three Cocks Hotel

The rugged countryside of the Brecon Beacons surrounds this stone-built 15th-century inn. Inside, original paintings, log fires and oriental rugs create a cosy atmosphere. Food is at centre of the operation, and the menu has a strong Belgian influence. Flavours shine through from the quality produce in dishes such as classic lobster bisque accompanied by a vibrant rouille; stunningly fresh fillet of gurnard with a fragrant herb sauce, and loin of Welsh lamb cooked with courgette and aubergine. Passion fruit mousse has made a top-notch finish with a brunoise of mango and paw paw and a coconut tuile.

Directions: On A438 in the village of Three Cocks, 4 miles from Hay-on-Wye, 11 miles from Brecon

@@
LD3 0SL
Tel: 01497 847215
Fax: 01497 847339
Chef(s): Michael & Thomas Winstone
Owner(s): Mr & Mrs M Winstone
Cost: Alc £33/D £28. ☺
H/wine £8.95
Times: Noon-1.30pm/7-9pm.
Closed Tue, L Sun, Dec-Jan
Additional: Bar food L. Children welcome. Vegetarian by request only
Seats: 30. Jacket and tie preferred
Smoking: No cigars
Accommodation: 7 rooms (6 en suite)
★★

Wales

RHONDDA CYNON TAFF

MISKIN   Map 3 ST08

Miskin Manor

Lush, country pile conveniently located along the M4 corridor, close to Cardiff. Inside, the old-world charm is intact, bar a gas fire in the restaurant where an authentic one would blend in with fine surroundings. Food preparation and service conforms to good standards, and the menu highlights such local flavours as Gower mussels and Welsh Black beef.

Seats: 50. Private dining room 6. Jacket and tie preferred
Style: Country-House
Smoking: No smoking in dining room
Accommodation: 43 rooms (43 en suite) ★★★★
Directions: 8 miles W of Cardiff. M4 J34, follow hotel signs

@
Groes Faen, CF72 8ND
Tel: 01443 224204
Fax: 01443 237606
🄴 info@miskin-manor.co.uk
Chef(s): Richard Jones
Owner(s): Mr & Mrs Rosenberg
Times: Noon-2pm/7-9.45pm.
Closed L Sat
Additional: Sunday L. Bar food.
Children welcome

SWANSEA

REYNOLDSTON
Map 2 SS48

Fairyhill

Wine Award Winner for Wales – *see* opposite page for entry

SWANSEA
Map 3 SS69

Dermott's Restaurant

Don't let the neighbourhood put you off. Swansea's High Street may feel more like a back street, but Dermott's oozes real sophistication. A bright, modern restaurant whose understated décor includes fascinating photos of old Swansea, it has proved an exciting addition to the town's restaurant scene. The menu injects new life into traditional combinations (braised shank of Welsh lamb with puréed minted peas, caramelised parsnips, Parmesan crackling and rosemary jus) and travels the world with dishes such as croquettes of crab with fresh ginger served on black bean couscous, fried pak choi and choi sum with a sour and sweet lime syrup

Directions: M4 J45 onto A4118 to city centre, to Railway Station. With station on L, 150 mtrs along High Street

219 High Street, SA1 1NN
Tel: 01792 459050
Fax: 01792 459050
Chef(s): Dermott Slade
Owner(s): Dermott Slade & Wendy Slade
Cost: Set price D £23.50-£29.75. ☺ H/wine £11
Times: Dinner only, 7.30-late. Closed Sun & Mon, 2 wks from 23 Dec, 2 wks from 14 Jul
Additional: Children welcome
Seats: 40
Style: Modern
Smoking: No-smoking area; no cigars

Windsor Lodge Hotel

Food is taken seriously here, a restaurant which prides itself on simplicity of style and fresh, good quality produce. A layered chicken terrine to start might be followed by fillet of salmon with creamy savoy cabbage. There is no lack of imagination in the well-balanced dinner menu and accomplished cooking is much in evidence.

Mount Pleasant, SA1 6EG
Tel: 01792 642158
Fax: 01792 648996
Chef(s): Tina Stewart, Stuart Chambers
Owner(s): Ron & Pam Rumble
Cost: *Alc* £22.50, set price L £12/ D £22.50. ☺ ☺ H/wine £8.95
Times: Noon-2.30pm/6.30pm-Midnight. Closed Sun, L by prior arrangement, 25-26 Dec
Additional: Bar food. Children welcome. Vegetarian by request only
Seats: 45
Style: Country-House
Smoking: No smoking in dining room
Accommodation: 19 rooms (19 en suite) ★★
Directions: Town centre, L at station R immediately after 2nd set of lights

Wales

Fairyhill

Swansea

Small but perfectly formed, Fairyhill is the kind of hotel where care and attention to detail define every aspect of the operation. Whilst it has many of the trappings associated with luxury country house hotels, it lacks the stiff formality sometimes found in these venues and with just eight bedrooms, the owning partners play a weighty role in the day to day running. There is no question though that the restaurant is the hub. The conservatory dining room introduces an element of contemporary chic and is an appropriate setting for food that has progressively moved towards a highly focussed modern European style. There is a genuine and unforced emphasis on local Welsh produce in combinations that make a virtue of simplicity and are intelligently conceived. Starters include a healthy selection of seafood that may feature seared scallops with

black fettucini and saffron sauce feuillantine of crab with spring onion, ginger and lime dressing. Welsh lamb, unusually, appears amongst the starters in a slow-cooked version, wrapped in filo and served with organic minted yoghurt. Amongst the main courses sea bass might come seared with wilted greens and a laverbread butter sauce and loin of Brecon venison comes in the company of tempura apple and a red wine jus. Desserts are often classic and sturdy with the likes of apricot and frangipane crumble with vanilla sauce and there is the welcome inclusion of a savoury in apple and Llanboidy rarebit with spiced apple chutney.

Reynoldston, SWANSEA, SA3 1BS **MAP 2 SS48**
Tel: 01792 390139
Fax: 01792 391358
E-mail: postbox@fairyhill.net
Chefs: Paul Davies, Adrian Coulthard
Owners: Mr Hetherington, Mr Davies &
Mr Camm
Cost: Set price L £17.50/D £35 ☺
H/wine £13.50
Times: 12.30-1.45pm/7.30-9pm
Additional: Sunday L. Children 8yrs+
Style: Country-house, modern
Smoking: No smoking in the dining room
Accommodation: 8 rooms (8 en suite)★ ★
Directions: Just outside Reynoldston, off
A4118 from Swansea

The wine list is a tour de force. Predominantly French but with creditable selections from the New World and Spain in particular, the list is prefaced with an admirable selection by the glass and a useful selection of bins that fall below the £20 mark. Bordeaux, Burgundy and Rhône offer a tremendous selection of vintages from quality estates and there are some great dessert wines from Austria. The half bottle list is also extensive. A marvellous achievement.

VALE OF GLAMORGAN

Wales

BARRY
Map 3 ST16

Egerton Grey Country House

A formal setting but nothing staid about the cooking despite being located in a former rectory. Local produce figures prominently on both the *carte* and fixed-price menus. Terrine of guinea fowl with pork and cashew nuts has proved a worthwhile combination with a subtle pepper coulis and soft leek bread.

Porthkerry, Rhoose, CF62 3BZ
Tel: 01446 711666
Fax: 01446 711690
e info@egertongrey.co.uk
Chef(s): Nigel Roberts
Owner(s): Mr A Pitkin
Cost: *Alc* £25, set price L £14.50-£23.50/D £18-£27. ☺ ☺
H/wine £11.50
Times: Noon-2pm/7-9.30pm.
Additional: Sunday L. Bar food L.
Children welcome
Seats: 40. Private dining room 18.
Jacket and tie preferred
Style: Modern
Smoking: No smoking in dining room
Civil licence: 60
Accommodation: 10 rooms (10 en suite) ★ ★ ★
Directions: M4 J33, follow signs for Airport then Porthkerry, L at hotel sign by thatched cottage

WREXHAM

LLANARMON DYFFRYN CEIRIOG
Map 7 SJ13

West Arms Hotel

A short, fixed-price daily menu is offered in the pleasing restaurant of this 16th-century establishment, based as far as possible on locally sourced produce. Choose from a selection of home-made breads, followed by the likes of good smoked salmon drizzled with a herby hollandaise, and lean medallions of beef cooked rare with wild mushrooms and a robust horseradish and shallot sauce.

LL20 7LD
Tel: 01691 600665
Fax: 01691 665622
e gowestarms@aol.com
Chef(s): Grant Williams
Owner(s): Mr & Mrs G Leigh-Ford
Cost: *Alc* £15, set price L £15/D £21.90-£24.90. ☺ ☺
H/wine £11.50
Times: Noon-2pm/7-9pm.
Closed L Mon-Sat
Additional: Sunday L. Bar food.
Children welcome
Seats: 34. Private dining room 12.
Jacket and tie preferred
Style: Traditional, Country-House
Smoking: No smoking in dining room
Civil licence: 70
Accommodation: 15 rooms (15 en suite) ★ ★
Directions: Exit A483 (A5) at Chirk and follow signs for Ceiriog Valley (B4500) – 11 miles

ROSSETT   Map 7 SJ35

Rossett Hall

Chester Road, LL12 0DE
Tel: 01244 571000
Fax: 01244 571505
e info@rossetthallhotel.co.uk

Oscar's bistro is a slick, modern affair with a traveller's tale of a
menu. Stir fry, risotto, cajun chicken and rack of lamb all get a
mention. The kitchen copes skilfully with the variety:
ingredients are high quality and flavours clear. Simpler meals
such as sausages and mash or char grilled steaks are also
available.

Smoking: No-smoking area; Air conditioning
Civil licence: 110
Accommodation: 30 rooms (30 en suite) ★★★
Directions: M56, take M53 to Wrexham- (becomes A55). Take
A483 Chester/Wrexham exit to Tosset (B5445). Hotel in centre
of village

Chef(s): Stephen Rawlinson
Owner(s): Darryl Shaw, Paul Burt
Cost: Alc £17. ☺ ☺ H/wine £8.95
Times: Open all day until 9.30pm
Additional: Sunday L. Bar food.
Children welcome
Seats: 100. Private dining room 110
Style: Modern

WREXHAM

Cross Lanes Hotel & Restaurant

Brasserie option in a late 19th-century country house hotel
standing in six acres of beautiful grounds. The style is
traditional with period furnishings and bric-a-brac. Goujons of
Scotch Beef rolled in paprika proved a tender and flavoursome
dish.

Cross Lanes, Bangor Road,
Marchwiel LL13 0TF
Tel: 01978 780555
Fax: 01978 780568
e guestservices@crosslanes.co.uk
Chef(s): John Bevan
Owner(s): Michael Kagan
Cost:. ☺ ☺ H/wine £9.85
Times: noon-2.30pm/6.30-9.30pm.
Closed 25 Dec evening, 26 Dec
Additional: Sunday L. Bar food.
Children welcome
Seats: 50. Private dining room 60
Style: Rustic, Bistro
Smoking: No-smoking area; no cigars
Civil licence: 140
Accommodation: 16 rooms (16 en
suite) ★★★
Directions: On A525, Wrexham to
Whitchurch Rd, between Marchweil
and Bangor-on-Dee

Wales

Give us your views!

All the restaurants in this guide have been visited by one of the AA's team
of professional inspectors but we want to hear from you too. Use the report
forms in the back of the guide or email us at lifestyleguides@theAA.com
with your comments on any of the establishments featured or other
restaurants that you feel are worthy of an entry. We would also be pleased
to receive your views on the guide itself and suggestions for any other
information you would like to see included.

NORTHERN IRELAND
CO ANTRIM

BALLYMENA   Map 1 D5

Galgorm Manor

What could be more enjoyable than an excellent meal after a
hard days' riding or fishing? Galgorm Manor, set beside the
River Maine, offers plenty of facilities to ensure a good appetite
for its fine cuisine. The elegant restaurant, with its Waterford
chandeliers, fine paintings and attentive service, recreates the
atmosphere of an 18th-century gentleman's residence. Tempting
dishes may include gateau of peppered strawberries and melon
with a crispy pineapple wafer, perhaps followed by medallions
of beef served with a filo basket of wild mushroom in a
Madeira jus with a horseradish cream.

Smoking: Air conditioning
Accommodation: 24 rooms (24 en suite) ★ ★ ★ ★
Directions: 1 mile outside Ballymena, on A42 between
Galgorm and Cullybackery

BT42 1EA
Tel: 028 2588 1001
Fax: 020 2588 0080
📧 mail@galgorm.com
Owner(s): Nicholas & Paul Hill
Cost: Alc £24/D £19.50-£27.50. ☺
H/wine £11.50
Times: Noon-2.30pm/7-9.30pm.
Closed Mon, L Tue-Sat
Additional: Sunday L. Bar food.
Children welcome. Vegetarian by
request only
Seats: 70. Private dining room 16
Style: Classic

STOP PRESS Change of Chef

CARNLOUGH   Map 1 D6

Londonderry Arms

Old world charm at this endearing coastal town hotel. Cooking
of disarming honesty allows the quality of the locally sourced
ingredients to speak for itself. Daily specials add excitement to
the menu - local asparagus with ham and Parmesan, turbot with
spinach and saffron sauce, and pannacotta with spiced oranges.

Additional: Sunday L. Bar food. Children welcome
Seats: 80. Private dining room 14
Style: Traditional Country-House
Smoking: No-smoking area
Accommodation: 35 rooms (35 en suite) ★ ★ ★
Directions: 14 miles N of Larne on coast road

20 Harbour Road, BT44 0EU
Tel: 028 2888 5255
Fax: 028 2888 5263
📧 lda@glensofantrim.com
Chef(s): Manus Jamieson
Cost: Alc £22, set price L £14.50/
D £22.50. ☺ ☺ H/wine £9.75
Times: 12.30-3pm/7-9pm.
Closed 25 Dec

PORTRUSH   Map 1 C6

Ramore Restaurant

Stylishly furnished with a modern, nautical theme to match its
harbour setting, this trendy restaurant and wine bar is well
endowed with creativity and technical prowess. A flan of
langoustines and bacon displayed a light touch with delicious
flaky pastry and fresh, tender prawns blending well with a
fragrant herb velouté.

The Harbour, BT56 8DF
Tel: 028 7082 4313
Fax: 028 7082 3194
Telephone for further details

Ireland

CO BELFAST

BELFAST   Map 1 D5

Beatrice Kennedy   NEW

Stylish city centre restaurant close to the university. Modern fusion dishes alongside more traditional offerings. Chilli squid has been carefully handled and roast cod with sauce vierge and crushed potatoes judged a real success. Amongst the desserts, a chocolate tart with burnt orange ice cream has impressed.

Seats: 75. Private dining room 25
Style: Bistro-Style
Directions: Situated adjacent to Queens University

44 University Road, BT7 1NJ
Tel: 028 9020 2290
Fax: 028 9020 2291
Chef(s): Jim McCarthy & Tony O'Neill
Owner(s): Jim McCarthy
Cost: Alc £23. H/wine £10
Times: 12.30-2.30pm/5-10.30pm. Closed Mon, L Tue-Sat
Additional: Sunday L. Children welcome

Cayenne

Paul Rankin seems to be seriously enjoying himself. Cayenne finds him steering ever further away from the fine dining confines of the Roscoff moniker and into an ever more surreal and sometimes inspired take on global cuisine. The scene is pretty much set by the crazed abstract décor and even the chilli popcorn in the bar gives a fairly stern clue as to what is to come. A starter of crispy duck confit with kimchee (Japanese red cabbage soused in red wine vinegar) and sweet and sour apple relish won't disappoint and seared skate wing with béarnaise and wok fried noodles has been described as a "brilliant, bold statement". Similar plaudits for a fairly outlandish Indian spiced bread and butter pudding featuring coconut milk, a pinch of curry and cardamom. Great food, great entertainment.

Directions: At top of Belfast's 'Golden Mile'

7 Lesley House, Shaftesbury Square, BT2 7DB
Tel: 028 9033 1532
Fax: 028 9031 2093
Chef(s): Paul & Jeanne Rankin
Owner(s): Paul & Jeanne Rankin
Cost: Alc £22. ☺ ☺ H/wine £12.95
Times: Noon-2.30pm/6-11.15pm. Closed Sun, L Sat, 25-26 Dec,1 Jan, 12-13 July, Easter Mon/Tue
Additional: Bar food. Children welcome
Seats: 80. Private dining room 100
Style: Modern, Chic
Smoking: No-smoking area; Air conditioning

Malone Lodge

The experience of the chef tells in this innovative, modern menu. Cauliflower and white bean soup with sesame oil, followed, possibly, by rack of lamb served with dauphinoise potatoes, aubergine caviar and a confit of leeks give a flavour of what's on offer before moving on to the alluring desserts. Enjoy the comfortable, bright, formal atmosphere.

Seats: 49. Private dining room 16
Style: Modern
Smoking: No-smoking area; no cigars; Air conditioning
Accommodation: 51 rooms (51 en suite) ★ ★ ★
Directions: At hospital rdbt exit towards Bouchar Road. L at 1st rdbt, R at lights, 1st L into Eglantine Ave

60 Eglantine Avenue, BT9 6DY
Tel: 028 9038 8000
Fax: 028 9038 8088
✉ info@malonelodgehotel.com
Chef(s): Dean Butler
Cost: Alc £25, set price L £14.50/ D £22.50-£27.50. ☺ ☺ H/wine £10.75
Times: Noon-2pm/6.30-9.45pm. Closed L Sat, 24-30 Dec, 9-15 Jul
Additional: Sunday L. Bar food. Children welcome

Ireland

BELFAST *Continued*   Map 1 D5

Restaurant Michael Deane

Negotiate your way through the healthy buzz of the ground floor brasserie to the first floor where Michael Deane's fine dining restaurant continues to set the pace for Northern Ireland cuisine. This may be the quieter of the two eating options here, but the gothic theatricality of the décor is garrulous enough and it is a suitably original environment in which to experience cooking that is consistently innovative, sometimes complex and always flavour intensive. Bread is always a pretty good indicator of things to come and a creditable warmed selection has featured caramelised onion, focaccia and soda. Freshness, vibrancy and "spot-on seasoning" have been apparent in cappuccino cauliflower soup with truffle that came as an amuse, whilst "remarkable dexterity" was on display in a plate of salmon offerings – which included a "delectable salmon mousse," a smoked salmon parcel of tartar and a poached roundel all topped with quails eggs cooked three different ways. Seafood is treated with due reverence with "the sweetest" langoustines and "perfectly cooked" monkfish in a delicate lasagne of the two. Expect the likes of mango mousse, coconut parfait and a coconut mousse amongst the desserts along with intense espresso and "delicious" chocolate truffles. Slick but cheerful service and a serious wine list.

38/40 Howard Street, BT1 6PD
Tel: 028 9033 1134
Fax: 028 9056 0001
Chef(s): Michael Deane
Owner(s): Michael Deane
Cost: *Alc* £39.50/D £36.50-£39.50.
H/wine £16
Times: Dinner only, 7-9.30pm.
Closed Sun-Tues, Xmas, New Year,
1 wk Jan, Easter, 2 wks Jul
Additional: Children welcome
Seats: 35
Style: Classic, Formal
Smoking: No cigars; Air conditioning
Directions: Telephone for directions

Shu   NEW

253 Lisburn Road, BT9 7EN
Tel: 028 9038 1655
Telephone for further details

Fusion, of a kind, is clearly alive and well on the Lisburn Road. Soft suedes and dark leathers set the tone and the healthy buzz of business is enough evidence that this is currently the in place to be. Nevertheless, the cooking is a real attraction in itself. Variety is a key component and alongside the imaginative, Asian-tinged dishes are more prosaic sounding offerings like egg and bacon salad or bangers and mash. At lunchtime a versatile light menu of 18 dishes offers most in starter or main course proportions. Good breads come with dipping oil and can be followed by the likes of a crisp and incisive Asian salad with beef or punchy soy marinated salmon with pickled ginger and sticky rice. Amongst the puds a chocolate and hazelnut mousse has stood out.

The Crescent Townhouse   NEW

Smartly-presented Regency town house next to the botanic gardens, with a trendy split-level brasserie serving good modern food. Care and subtlety goes into authentic crab chowder, monkfish with red curry risotto, and traditional desserts such as a deep chocolate tart. A popular eating place with reasonable prices.

Seats: 72
Style: Modern, Bistro-Style
Smoking: No-smoking area; no pipes; Air conditioning
Accommodation: 11 rooms (11 en suite) ★ ★ ★
Directions: Just off Botanic Avenue in Belfast City Centre.

13 Lower Crescent,
BT7 1NR
Tel: 028 9032 3349
Fax: 028 9032 0646
e info@crescentownhouse.co.uk
Chef(s): Aaron Loughran
Owner(s): Wine Inns Ltd.
Cost: *Alc* £20, set price L £12-£16/
D £20-£32. ☺ ☺ H/wine £10
Times: Noon-3pm/6-10pm.
Closed 25 Dec, L Sun-Tues, D Sun,
Additional: Bar food L. Children
welcome

CO DOWN

BANGOR

Map 1 D5

Shanks

At the heart of Blackwood Golf Centre, a Conrad-designed building of cosmopolitan sophistication that enjoys the irony, from its warm interior, of overlooking those golf fanatics who trudge rain-soaked into the clubhouse. The split-level restaurant has a stylish 1970s feel throughout, to which Robbie Millar's seasonal menus bring a touch of European style and flair. Fashionable combinations such as seared foie gras with carrot purée, toasted brioche and poached grapes in Sauternes jus and peppered loin of estate venison with red cabbage, chestnuts and wild mushrooms amply illustrate the balance of carefully sourced ingredients with an ambitious, thoughtful approach. Presentation in the modern idiom, knowledgeable, unpretentious service and a global wine list notable for quality and value are amongst added bonuses.

Directions: From A2 turn R onto Ballysallagh Rd 1 mile before Bangor, 1st L after 0.5 mile to Blackwood Golf Centre

The Blackwood,
Crawfordsburn Road,
BT19 1GB
Tel: 028 9185 3313
Fax: 028 9185 2493
Chef(s): Robbie Millar
Owner(s): Mr & Mrs R Millar
Cost: Set price L £19.95/D £35
H/wine £12.50
Times: 12.30-2.30pm/7-10pm.
Closed Sun-Mon, L Sat, 25-26 Dec
and Easter Tue
Additional: Children welcome
Seats: 70. Private dining room 36
Style: Modern, Minimalist
Smoking: No-smoking area; no cigars;
Air conditioning

CRAWFORDSBURN

Map 1 D5

Old Inn

NEW

15 Main Street, BT19 1JH
Tel: 028 9185 3255
Fax: 028 9185 2775
e info@theoldinn.com
Telephone for further details

Ireland

1614 is the fine dining option here - a wood panelled, candlelit, split-level affair with the theatrical sweep of heavy curtains and coats of arms on the wall. It's the setting for some ambitious food with a menu that might set some alarm bells ringing but a quality of cooking that will soon reassure you. Classic principles are coupled with a fusion tinge in dishes like boudin of smoked cod "brilliantly light" with langoustine bok choi and a chive beurre blanc or seared scallops with hoi sin sauce and herb risotto. Special praise for a balanced and flavour-packed, main course of monkfish with Singapore noodles and black bean sauce. Look out for a creditable ganache of chocolate with vanilla bean ice cream.

PORTAFERRY

Map 1 D5

Portaferry Hotel

10 The Strand, BT22 1PE
Tel: 028 4272 8231
Fax: 028 4272 8999
e info@portaferry.com
Chef(s): Ann Truesdale
Cost: *Alc* £25 H/wine £13.50
Times: 12.30-2.30pm/7-9pm.
Additional: Sunday L. Bar food (ex Sunday). Children welcome
Seats: 70
Style: Classic
Smoking: No pipes
Accommodation: 14 rooms (14 en suite) ★ ★ ★
Directions: Opposite Strangford Lough Ferry terminal at Portaferry

Can scallops get any fresher than at Portaferry Hotel? Straight out of beautiful Strangford Lough, which lies in front of the hotel, the pan-fried scallops with bacon and garlic are a menu favourite. An alternative choice from a good selection of dishes may be confit of duck with stir-fried vegetable or a dessert of prune and Armagnac tart with crème fraîche.

The Narrows

8 Shore Road, BT22 1JY
Tel: 028 4272 8148
Fax: 028 4272 8105
Telephone for further details

A modern conversion in the truly enviable position of sitting on the shore of Strangford Lough. There is some serious cooking going on here blending contemporary classics with some bold fusion dishes that keep pace with fashion. The style is precise and focussed with starters like seared foie gras on hazelnut brioche with a balsamic reduction finding favour for their crisp textures and lightness of touch. Amongst the mains cornfed chicken with Parmesan risotto has impressed and there is a choice of side orders to accompany (rocket salad for instance). Highlight of one meal was a "super" chocolate tart in the Marco Pierre White vein with ultra-thin pastry and a great vanilla anglaise. There's a fun kids menu too.

CO LONDONDERRY

LIMAVADY

Map 1 C5

Radisson Roe Park Hotel

BT49 9LB
Tel: 028 7772 2222
Fax: 028 7772 2313
e reservations@radissonroepark.com
Telephone for further details

The Courtyard restaurant boasts an ambitious menu that combines regional, contemporary and classical gastronomy. A secluded location is ideal to enjoy the likes of fillet of Irish beef with a well balanced Madeira jus, alongside well executed desserts such as chocolate Bakewell tart with a Baileys sauce.

The Lime Tree

Relaxed owner-run restaurant, with Stanley Matthews in the kitchen and wife Marie out front. Competitively priced menus, including an award-winning business lunch and daily specials. Lunch is very good value with the likes of caesar salad, confit of duck leg with plus sauce, and a fruit crumble flan with crème anglaise.

Seats: 30, **Style:** Rustic. **Smoking:** No cigars
Directions: Entering Limavady from the Derry side, restaurant is on right on a small slip road

60 Catherine Street, BT49 9DB
Tel: 028 7776 4300
Chef(s): Stanley Matthews
Owner(s): Mr & Mrs S Matthews
Cost: Set price L £6.95-£12.95/ D £12.95. ☺ ☺ H/wine £9.75
Times: Noon-2pm/6-9pm. Closed Mon-Tue , L Sat, 1 wk Nov,1 wk end Feb-beg Mar, 1 wk Jul
Additional: Sunday L. Children welcome

LONDONDERRY   Map 1 C5
Beech Hill Country House

Once the billiard room of this fascinating house, the Ardmore restaurant has an ornate glass ceiling and overlooks extensive gardens. The menu includes a page of vegetarian options and has a distinctly French feel: paté de foie gras, braised pig's trotter and noisettes of lamb 'en crepenette' might feature alongside red onion tartlet or green pea and herb risotto. Good wine list.

Seats: 90. Private dining room 80
Style: Classic, French
Smoking: No smoking in dining room
Accommodation: 27 rooms (27 en suite) ★ ★ ★
Directions: A6 Londonderry to Belfast road, turn off at Faughan Bridge. 1 mile further to Ardmore Chapel. Hotel entrance is opposite

32 Ardmore Road,
BT47 3QP
Tel: 028 7134 9279
Fax: 028 7134 5366
e info@beech-hill.com
Chef(s): Adrian Catterall
Owner(s): Mr S Donnelly
Cost: *Alc* £32, set price L £17.95-£18.95/D £20.95-£27.95. ☺ ☺
H/wine £12.95
Times: Noon-2.30pm/6-9.45pm. Closed 24-25 Dec
Additional: Sunday L. Bar food. Children welcome

Ireland

 CO TYRONE

OMAGH   Map 1 C5
Hawthorn House   NEW

The chef here cooks from the hip, and the stylish cosmopolitan dishes are a bit of a surprise in this country house setting. Excellent seafood is a feature, and a grill of hake, scallops and langoustine with chilli oil made for a palette-tingling main course with fresh and delicate flavours combining well.

72 Old Mountfield Road, BT79 7EN
Tel: 028 8225 2005
Fax: 028 8225 2005
e information@hawthornhouse.co.uk
Chef(s): Michael Gaine
Owner(s): Michael Gaine
Cost: *Alc* £22.50, set price L £10/ D £17.50. ☺ ☺ H/wine £9.75
Times: 12.15-2.30pm/6.30-9.30pm.
Additional: Sunday L. Bar food L. Children welcome
Seats: 64. Private dining room 15
Style: Country-House
Smoking: No-smoking area
Accommodation: 5 rooms (5 en suite)
♦♦♦
Directions: Telephone for details

REPUBLIC OF IRELAND

The Republic of Ireland hotel-restaurants listed below have built their reputations on the quality of their food; all have earned our coveted Rosette Award. The information is supplied by AA Hotel Services, Dublin.

Please note that the area codes given apply only within the Republic. If dialling from outside you should check the telephone directory. Area codes for numbers in Britain and Northern Ireland cannot be used directly from the Republic.

CO CARLOW

Dolmen Hotel
CARLOW   0503 42002

CO CAVEN

Slieve Russell Hotel Golf and Country Club
BALLYCONNELL   049 9526 444

Kilmore Hotel
CAVAN   049 4332288

The Park Hotel
VIRGINIA   049 8547235

CO CLARE

Gregans Castle
BALLYVAUGHAN   065 7077 005

Fitzpatrick Bunratty Hotel
BUNRATTY   061 361177

Temple Gate Hotel
ENNIS   065 6823300

Sheedys Restaurant & Hotel
LISDOONVARNA   065 7074026

Dromoland Castle Hotel
NEWMARKET-ON-FERGUS   061 368144

CO CORK

Bay View Hotel
BALLYCOTTON   021 4646746

Sea View Hotel
BALLYLICKEY   027 50073

Baltimore Harbour Hotel & Leisure Centre
BALTIMORE   028 20361

Casey's of Baltimore Hotel
BALTIMORE   028 20197

The Lodge & Spa at Inchydoney Island
CLONAKILTY   023 33143

Arbutus Lodge Hotel
CORK   021 501237

Hayfield Manor
CORK   021 315600

Rochestown Park Hotel
CORK   021 892233

The Kingsley Hotel
CORK   021 4800500

Courtmacsherry
COURTMACSHERRY   023 46198

Castlehyde Hotel
FERMOY   025 31865

Garryvoe Hotel
GARRYVOE   021 4646718

Innishannon House Hotel
INNISHANNON   021 4775121

Actons Hotel
KINSALE   021 4772135

Trident Hotel
KINSALE   021 4772301

Castle Hotel
MACROOM   026 41074

Longueville House Hotel
MALLOW   022 47156

Midleton Park ◎◎★★★
MIDLETON 021 631767

Eldon Hotel ◎★★
SKIBBEREEN 028 22000

**Devonshire Arms Hotel
and Restaurant** ◎★★
YOUGHAL 024 92827

CO DONEGAL

Kee's Hotel ◎◎★★★
BALLYBOFEY 074 31018

Ostan Gweedore ◎◎◎★★★
BUNBEG 075 31177

**Harvey's Point Country
Hotel** ◎◎◎◎★★★
DONEGAL 073 22208

Fort Royal Hotel ◎◎◎★★★
RATHMULLAN 074 58100

Sand House Hotel ◎◎◎★★★
ROSSNOWLAGH 072 51777

CO DUBLIN

Bewley's Hotel Ballsbridge ◎★★★
DUBLIN 01 6681111

Buswells Hotel ◎★★★
DUBLIN 01 6146500

**Clarion Stephen's Hall
All-Suite Hotel** ◎◎◎★★★
DUBLIN 01 6381111

Clontarf Castle Hotel ◎★★★★
DUBLIN 01 8332321

Herbert Park Hotel ◎◎★★★★
DUBLIN 01 6672200

Jurys Hotel Dublin ◎★★★★
DUBLIN 01 6605000

Longfield's Hotel ◎◎★★★
DUBLIN 01 6761367

Marine Hotel ◎◎★★★
DUBLIN 01 8390000

**Radisson SAS St Helen's
Hotel** ◎◎★★★★★
DUBLIN 01 2186000

Red Cow Moran Hotel ◎★★★★
DUBLIN 01 4593650

Shelbourne Meridien Hotel ◎★★★★
DUBLIN 01 6634500

The Clarence ◎◎★★★★
DUBLIN 01 4070800

The Fitzwilliam Hotel ◎◎◎★★★★
DUBLIN 01 4787000

The Hibernian Hotel ◎◎◎★★★
DUBLIN 01 6687666

The Merrion Hotel ◎◎◎◎★★★★★
DUBLIN 01 6030600

The Plaza Hotel ◎◎★★★★
DUBLIN 01 4624200

The Schoolhouse Hotel ◎◎★★★
DUBLIN 01 6675014

**Portmarnock Hotel
& Golf Links** ◎◎★★★★
PORTMARNOCK 01 8460611

CO GALWAY

Ballynahinch Castle ◎◎★★★★
BALLYNAHINCH 095 31006

Cashel House Hotel ◎◎★★★
CASHEL 095 31001

Zetland Country House Hotel ◎◎★★★
CASHEL 095 31111

Abbeyglen Castle Hotel ◎◎★★★
CLIFDEN 095 21201

Alcock & Brown Hotel ◎★★★
CLIFDEN 095 21206

Ardagh Hotel & Restaurant ◎◎◎★★★
CLIFDEN 095 21384

**Rock Glen Country
House Hotel** ◎◎◎★★★
CLIFDEN 095 21035

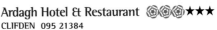

Ireland

Ireland

Ardilaun House Hotel ★ ★ ★ ★
GALWAY 091 521433

Glenlo Abbey Hotel ★ ★ ★ ★
GALWAY 091 526666

Westwood House Hotel ★ ★ ★ ★
GALWAY 091 521442

Galway Bay Golf & Country Club Hotel ★ ★ ★
ORANMORE 091 790500

Ross Lake House Hotel ★ ★ ★
OUGHTERARD 091 550109

Lough Inagh Lodge Hotel ★ ★ ★
RECESS 095 34706

Eldons Hotel ★ ★
ROUNDSTONE 095 35933

CO KERRY

The White Sands Hotel ★ ★ ★
BALLYHEIGE 066 7133 102

Dingle Skellig Hotel ★ ★ ★
DINGLE 066 9150200

Dromquinna Manor ★ ★ ★
KENMARE 064 41657

Park Hotel Kenmare ★ ★ ★ ★
KENMARE 064 41200

Sheen Falls Lodge ★ ★ ★ ★
KENMARE 064 41600

Aghadoe Heights Hotel ★ ★ ★ ★
KILLARNEY 064 31766

Arbutus Hotel ★ ★ ★
KILLARNEY 064 31037

Cahernane Hotel ★ ★ ★
KILLARNEY 064 31895

Killarney Park Hotel ★ ★ ★ ★
KILLARNEY 064 35555

Muckross Park Hotel Ltd ★ ★ ★ ★
KILLARNEY 064 31938

Great Southern Hotel ★ ★ ★ ★
PARKNASILLA 064 45122

Butler Arms Hotel ★ ★ ★
WATERVILLE 066 9474144

CO KILDARE

Leixlip House Hotel ★ ★ ★
LEIXLIP 01 6242268

Moyglare Manor ★ ★ ★
MAYNOOTH 01 6286351

Keadeen Hotel ★ ★ ★
NEWBRIDGE 045 431666

Barberstown Castle ★ ★ ★
STRAFFAN 01 6288157

The Kildare Hotel & Country Club ★ ★ ★ ★ ★
STRAFFAN 01 6017200

CO KILKENNY

Kilkenny Ormonde Hotel ★ ★ ★ ★
KILKENNY 056 23900

Kilkenny River Court Hotel ★ ★ ★ ★
KILKENNY 056 23388

Mount Juliet Hotel ★ ★ ★ ★
THOMASTOWN 056 73000

CO LEITRIM

The Landmark ★ ★ ★ ★
CARRICK-ON-SHANNON 078 22222

CO LIMERICK

Dunraven Arms Hotel ★ ★ ★
ADARE 061 396633

Castle Oaks House Hotel ★ ★ ★
CASTLECONNELL 061 377666

Castletroy Park Hotel ★ ★ ★ ★
LIMERICK 061 335566

Limerick Ryan Hotel ★ ★ ★
LIMERICK 061 453922

South Court Business & Leisure Hotel ★ ★ ★
LIMERICK 065 6823000

CO MAYO

Cill Aodain Hotel ✿★★
KILTIMAGH 094 81761

Belmont Hotel ✿★★★
KNOCK 094 88122

Ardmore Country House Hotel ✿★★★
WESTPORT 098 25994

The Atlantic Coast Hotel ✿★★★
WESTPORT 098 29000

The Olde Railway Hotel ✿★★★
WESTPORT 098 25166

CO MONAGHAN

Nuremore Hotel ✿✿★★★★
CARRICKMACROSS 042 9661438

CO SLIGO

Markree Castle ✿★★★
COLLOONEY 071 67800

Silver Swan Hotel ✿★★
SLIGO 071 43231

CO TIPPERARY

Cahir House Hotel ✿★★★
CAHIR 052 42727

Minella Hotel ✿★★★
CLONMEL 052 22388

Abbey Court Hotel ✿★★★
NENAGH 067 41111

CO WATERFORD

Ballyrafter House Hotel ✿★★
LISMORE 058 54002

Dooley's Hotel ✿★★★
WATERFORD 051 873531

Granville Hotel ✿★★★
WATERFORD 051 305555

Waterford Castle Hotel ✿✿★★★★
WATERFORD 051 878203

CO WESTMEATH

Hodson Bay Hotel ✿★★★
ATHLONE 0902 92444

CO WEXFORD

**Dunbrody Country House
& Restaurant** ✿✿★★★
ARTHURSTOWN 051 389600

Courtown Hotel ✿★★
COURTOWN HARBOUR 055 25210

Marlfield House Hotel ✿✿★★★
GOREY 055 21124

**Clarion Brandon House Hotel
and Leisure Centre** ✿★★★
NEW ROSS 051 421703

Kelly's Resort Hotel ✿✿★★★★
ROSSLARE 053 32114

Danby Lodge Hotel ✿★★
ROSSLARE HARBOUR 053 58191

Ferrycarrig Hotel ✿✿★★★★
WEXFORD 053 20999

**Talbot Hotel Conference
& Leisure Centre** ✿★★★
WEXFORD 053 22566

Whitford House Hotel ✿★★★
WEXFORD 053 43444

CO WICKLOW

Downshire House Hotel ✿★★★
BLESSINGTON 045 865199

Brooklodge at MacCreddin ✿✿★★★★
MACREDDIN 0402 36444

Hunter's Hotel ✿★★★
RATHNEW 0404 40106

**Tinakilly Country House &
Restaurant** ✿✿★★★
RATHNEW 0404 69274

Woodenbridge Hotel ✿★★★
WOODENBRIDGE 0402 35146

Ireland

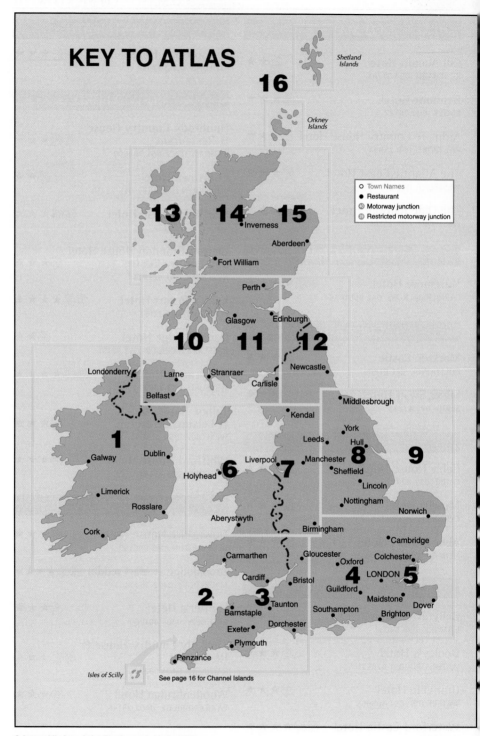

KEY TO ATLAS

16 Shetland Islands

Orkney Islands

Legend:
- ○ Town Names
- ● Restaurant
- Ⓜ Motorway junction
- ⓡ Restricted motorway junction

13 **14** **15**
- Inverness
- Aberdeen
- Fort William

10 **11** **12**
- Perth
- Glasgow
- Edinburgh
- Newcastle
- Stranraer
- Carlisle

Londonderry • Larne
Belfast
Middlesbrough
Kendal

8 **9**
- York
- Leeds
- Hull
- Manchester
- Sheffield
- Lincoln

1
- Galway
- Dublin
- Liverpool
- Nottingham
- Norwich
- Holyhead
- Limerick
- Rosslare
- Aberystwyth
- Birmingham
- Cambridge
- Cork

6 **7**
- Carmarthen
- Gloucester
- Colchester
- Oxford
- Cardiff
- Bristol
- LONDON

2 **3** **4** **5**
- Guildford
- Maidstone
- Dover
- Barnstaple
- Taunton
- Southampton
- Brighton
- Exeter
- Dorchester
- Plymouth
- Penzance

Isles of Scilly
See page 16 for Channel Islands

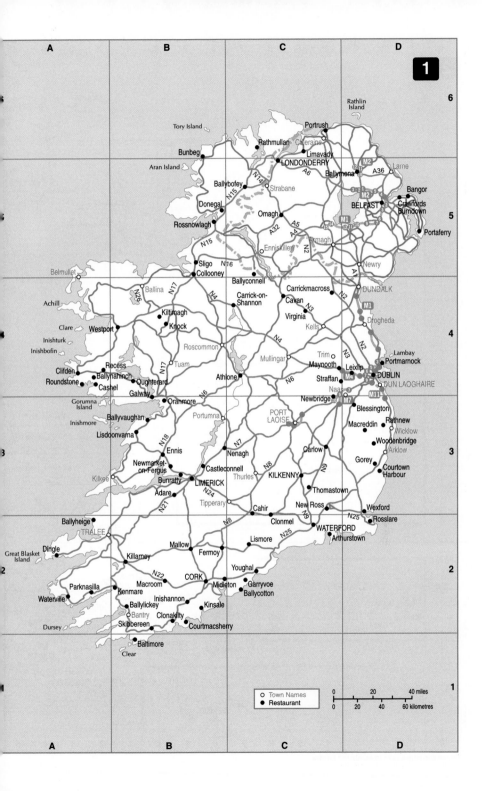

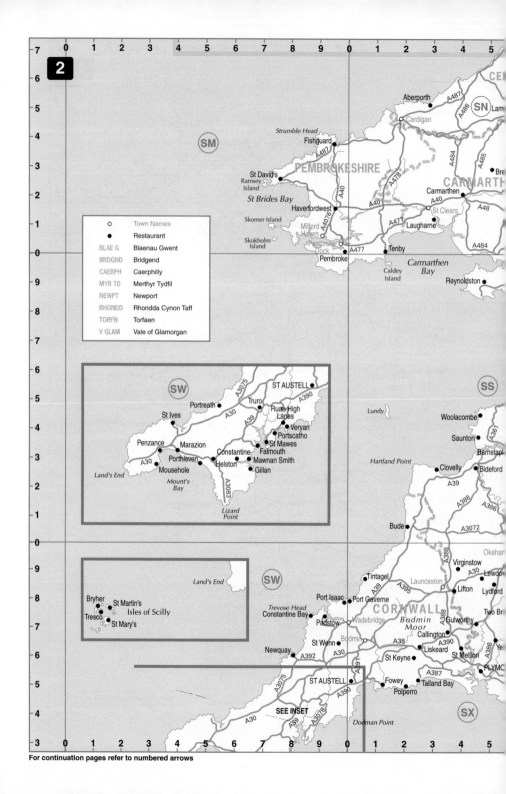

	Town Names
●	Restaurant
BLAE G	Blaenau Gwent
BRDGND	Bridgend
CAERPH	Caerphilly
MYR TD	Merthyr Tydfil
NEWPT	Newport
RHONDD	Rhondda Cynon Taff
TORFN	Torfaen
V GLAM	Vale of Glamorgan

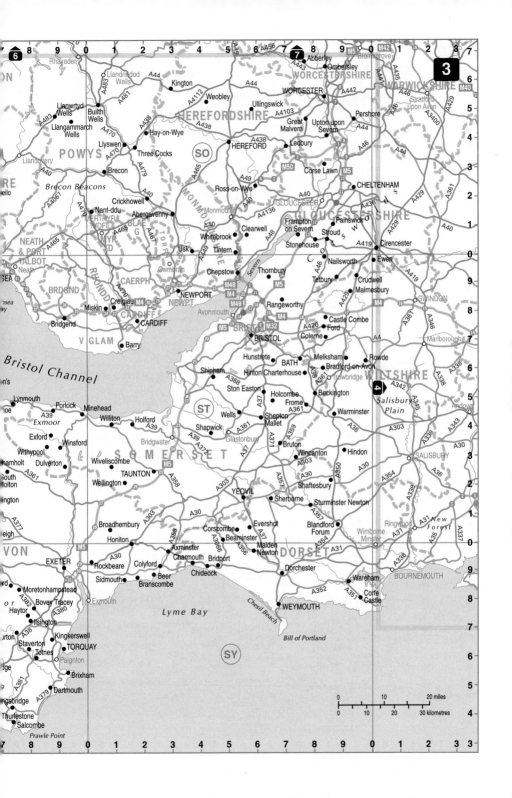

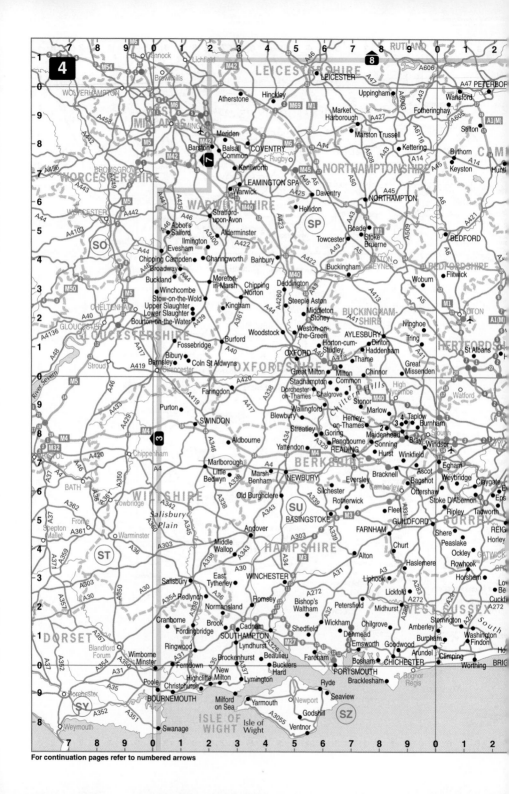

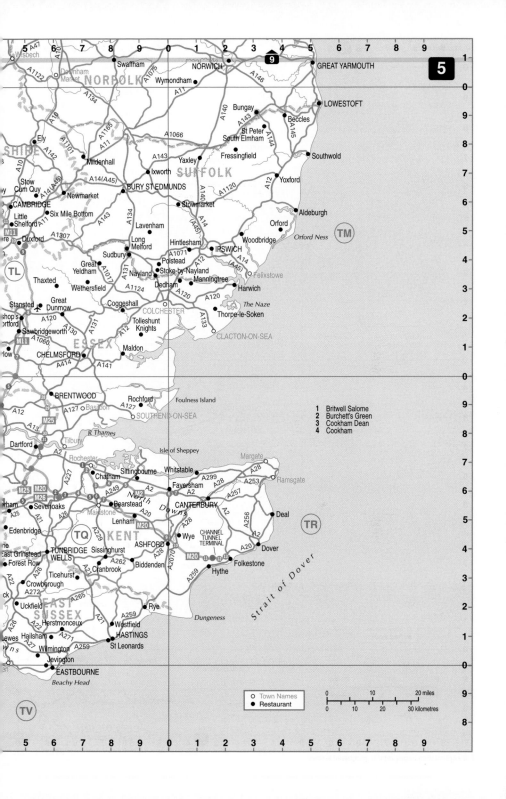

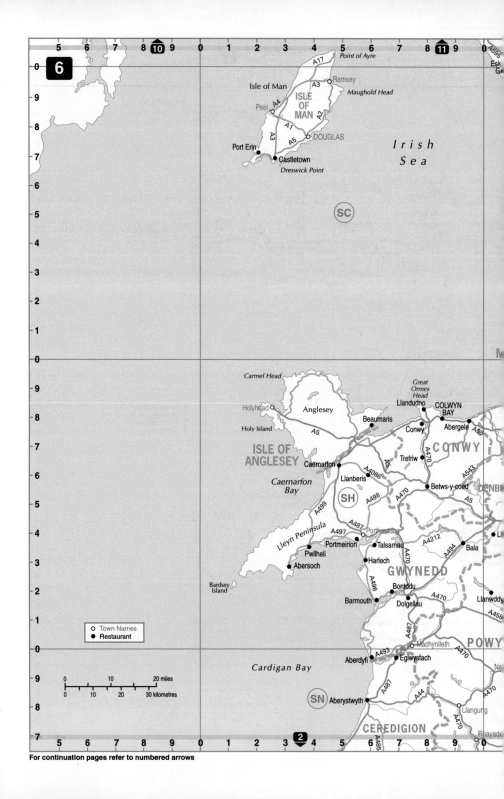

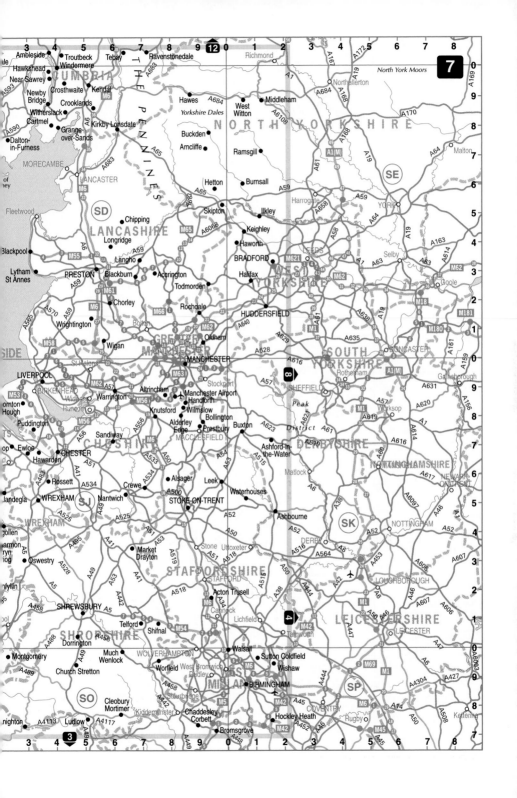

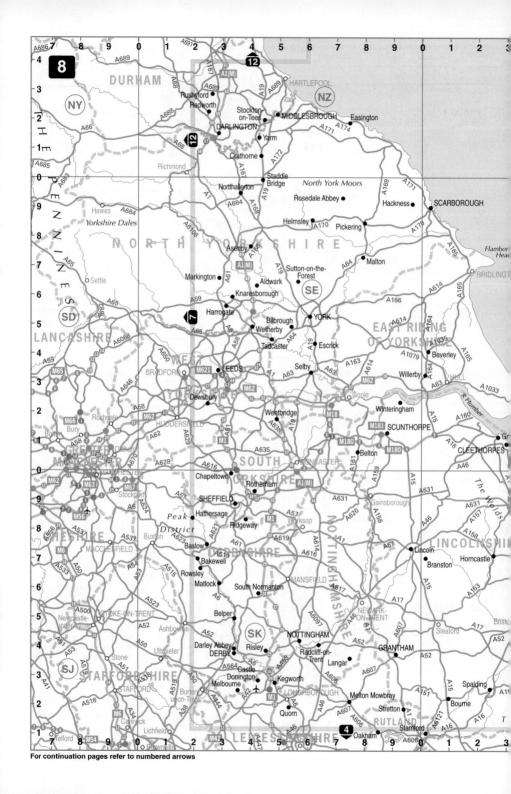

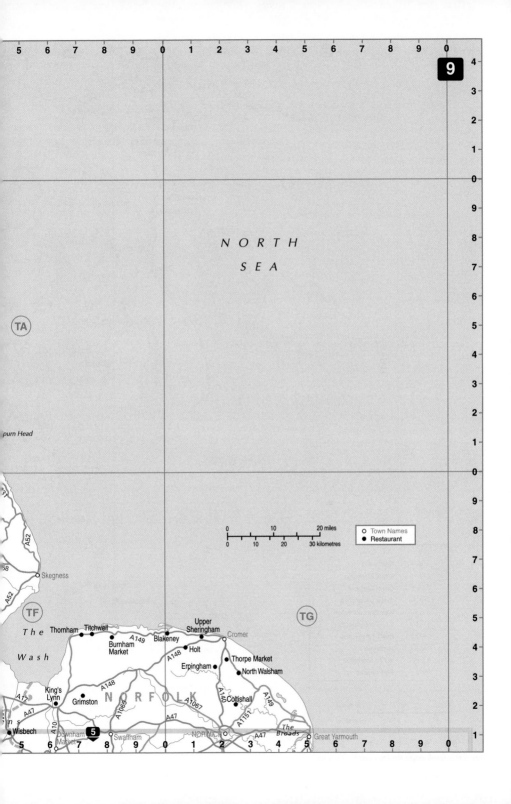

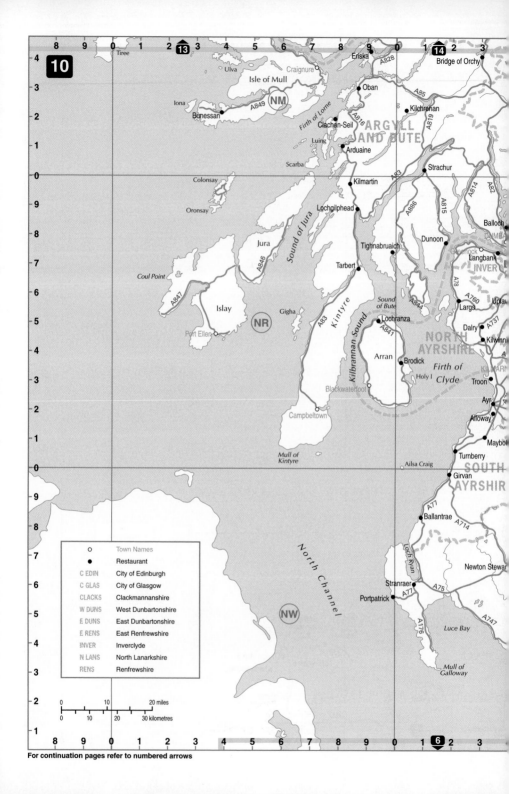

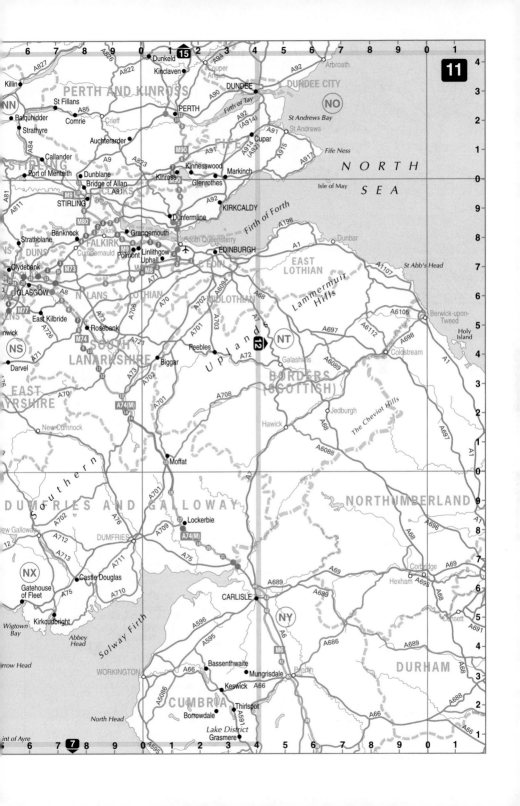

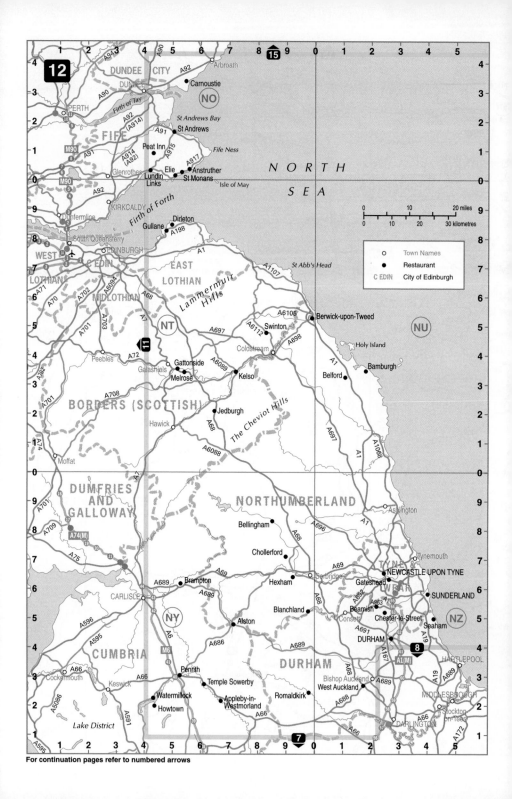

For continuation pages refer to numbered arrows

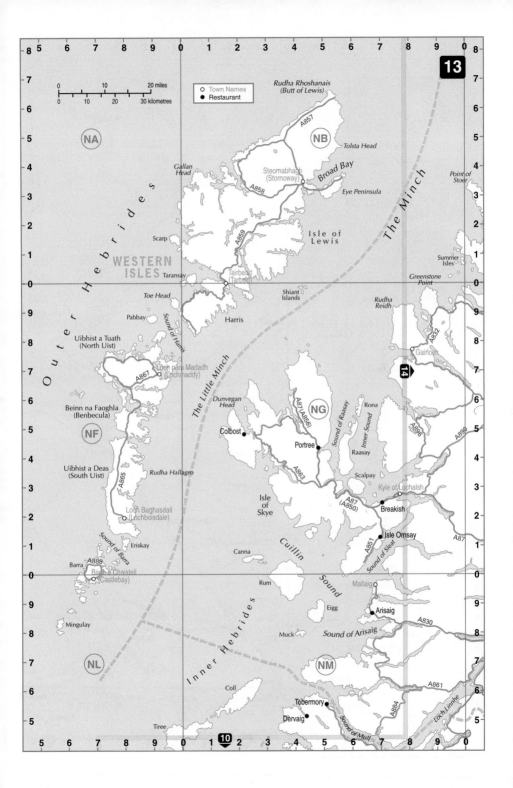

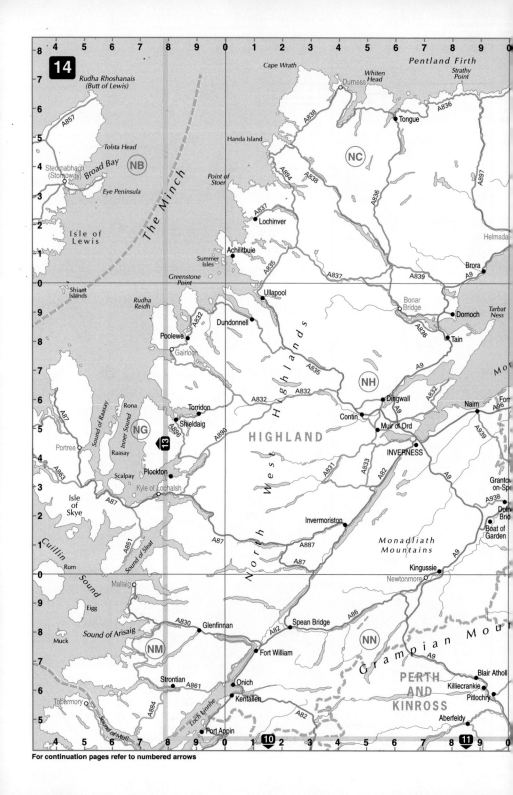

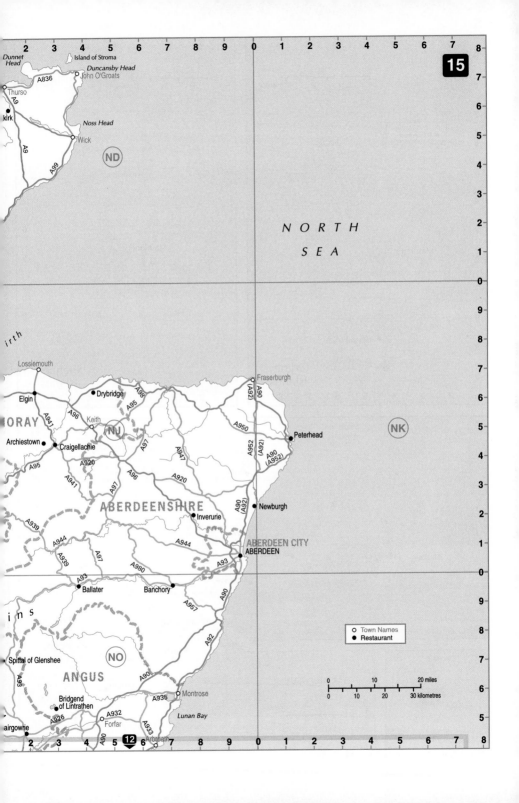

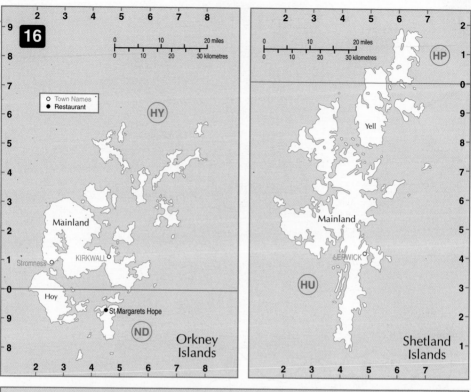

16

Town Names
Restaurant

20 miles
30 kilometres

HY

Mainland

Stromness   KIRKWALL

Hoy

St Margarets Hope

ND

Orkney Islands

HP

Yell

Mainland

LERWICK

HU

Shetland Islands

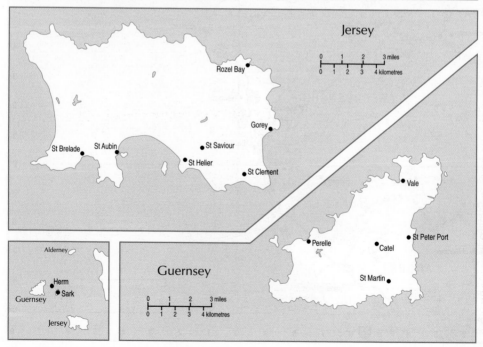

Jersey

Rozel Bay

Gorey

St Brelade   St Aubin   St Saviour
St Helier
St Clement

Vale

St Peter Port
Catel
Perelle

St Martin

Alderney

Herm
Sark

Guernsey   Guernsey

Jersey

Greater London

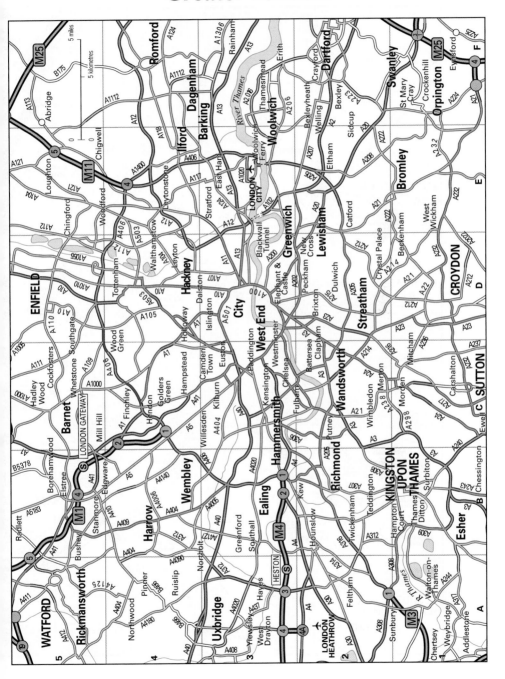

Central London

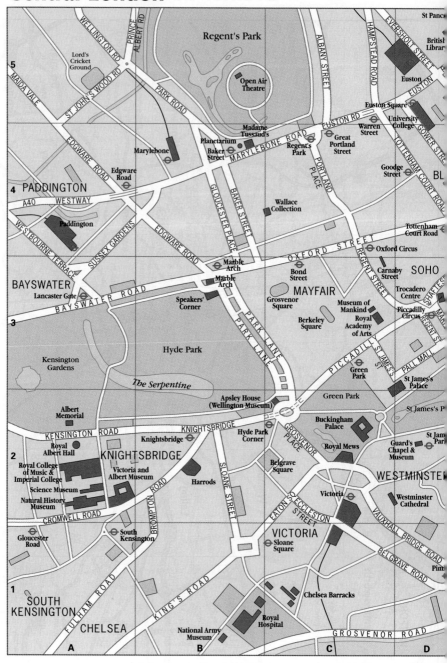

Regent's Park

St Panc

Britist
Librar

Euston

WELLINGTON RD
PRINCE ALBERT RD
ALBANY STREET
HAMPSTEAD ROAD
EVERSHOLT STREET

5

Lord's
Cricket
Ground

Open Air
Theatre

Euston Square

University
College

MAIDA VALE
ST JOHN'S WOOD RD
PARK ROAD
EUSTON RD
EUSTON

Madame
Tussaud's

Warren
Street

Great
Portland
Street

Goodge
Street

BL

EDGWARE ROAD

Marylebone

Planetarium

Regent's
Park

Edgware
Road

Baker
Street

MARYLEBONE ROAD
BAKER STREET
PORTLAND PLACE
GOWER STREET
TOTTENHAM COURT ROAD

4 PADDINGTON

Edgware
Road

Wallace
Collection

Tottenham
Court Road

A40 WESTWAY

Paddington

GLOUCESTER PLACE
EDGWARE ROAD

OXFORD STREET

Oxford Circus

WESTBOURNE TERRACE
SUSSEX GARDENS

Marble
Arch

Bond
Street

Carnaby
Street

SOHO

BAYSWATER

Marble
Arch

MAYFAIR

Trocadero
Centre

Lancaster Gate

Speakers'
Corner

Grosvenor
Square

Museum of
Mankind

Piccadilly
Circus

REGENT STREET
SHAFTE

3

BAYSWATER ROAD

Berkeley
Square

Royal
Academy
of Arts

REGENT S

Hyde Park

PARK LANE

PICCADILLY
ST JAMES'S
PALL MALL

Kensington
Gardens

Green
Park

St James's
Palace

The Serpentine

Apsley House
(Wellington Museum)

Green Park

St James's P

Albert
Memorial

Buckingham
Palace

St Jam
Par

KENSINGTON ROAD
KNIGHTSBRIDGE

Hyde Park
Corner

Guard's
Chapel &
Museum

Royal
Albert Hall

Knightsbridge

GROSVENOR PLACE

Royal Mews

2

Royal College
of Music &
Imperial College

Victoria and
Albert Museum

WESTMINSTER

Science Museum

Harrods

Belgrave
Square

Natural History
Museum

BROMPTON ROAD
SLOANE STREET

Victoria

Westminster
Cathedral

CROMWELL ROAD

Victoria

VAUXHALL BRIDGE ROAD

Gloucester
Road

South
Kensington

EATON SQUARE
ECCLESTON STREET

VICTORIA

Sloane
Square

BELGRAVE ROAD

Pim

1

SOUTH
KENSINGTON

FULHAM ROAD
KING'S ROAD

Chelsea Barracks

CHELSEA

National Army
Museum

Royal
Hospital

GROSVENOR ROAD

A   **B**   **C**   **D**

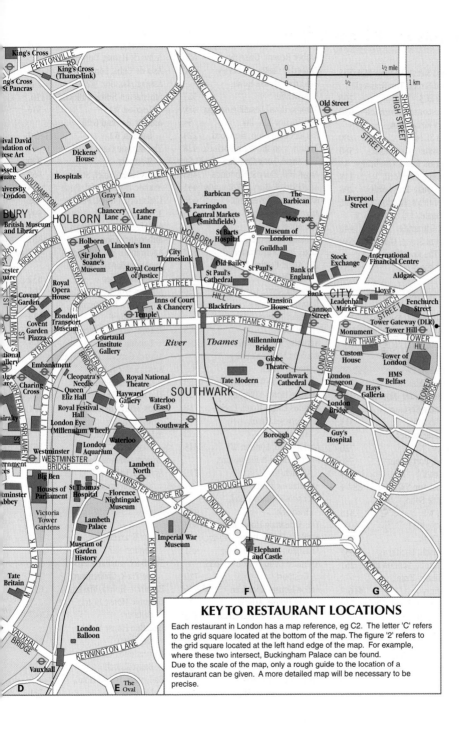

King's Cross
PENTONVILLE RD
CITY ROAD
ng's Cross
(Thameslink)
ng's Cross
St Pancras
Old Street
ROSEBERY AVENUE
GOSWELL ROAD
OLD STREET
GREAT EASTERN STREET
SHOREDITCH HIGH STREET

ival David
idation of
ese Art
Dickens'
House
Hospitals
CLERKENWELL ROAD
ssell
uare
iversity
London
THEOBALD'S ROAD
Gray's Inn
Barbican
The Barbican
Liverpool Street
CITY ROAD
MOORGATE
BISHOPSGATE

BURY
HOLBORN
British Museum
and Library
Chancery
Lane
Leather
Lane
Farringdon
Central Markets
(Smithfields)
Moorgate
Museum of
London
ALDERSGATE ST

HIGH HOLBORN
HOLBORN
HOLBORN VIADUCT
St Barts
Hospital
Guildhall

RD
HIGH HOLBORN
Holborn
Lincoln's Inn
City
Thameslink
Stock
Exchange
International
Financial Centre

ester
uare
Sir John
Soane's
Museum
Royal Courts
of Justice
Old Bailey
St Paul's
St Paul's
Cathedral
Bank of
England
Aldgate

MONMOUTH ST
ST MARTIN'S
Royal
Opera
House
KINGSWAY
FLEET STREET
LUDGATE
HILL
CHEAPSIDE
Bank
CITY
Lloyd's

Covent
Garden
Inns of Court
& Chancery
Blackfriars
Mansion
House
Leadenhall
Market
FENCHURCH STREET
Fenchurch
Street

tional
allery
London
Transport
Museum
STRAND
ALDWYCH
Temple
Cannon
Street
Monument
Tower Gateway (DLR)
Tower Hill

Covent
Garden
Piazza
EMBANKMENT
UPPER THAMES STREET
LWR THAMES ST
TOWER
HILL

Courtauld
Institute
Gallery
River
Thames
Millennium
Bridge
Custom
House
Tower of
London

Embankment
WATERLOO BRIDGE
Globe
Theatre
LONDON BRIDGE
HMS
Belfast

algar
are
Charing
Cross
Cleopatra's
Needle
Queen
Eliz Hall
Royal National
Theatre
Tate Modern
Southwark
Cathedral
London
Dungeon
Hays
Galleria

iralty
Royal Festival
Hall
Hayward
Gallery
Waterloo
(East)
SOUTHWARK
London
Bridge
TOWER BRIDGE

London Eye
(Millennium Wheel)
Southwark
Guy's
Hospital

Westminster
WESTMINSTER
BRIDGE
London
Aquarium
Waterloo
WATERLOO ROAD
Borough
BOROUGH HIGH STREET
GREAT DOVER STREET
TOWER BRIDGE ROAD

ernment
es
VICTORIA
Lambeth
North
LONG LANE

Big Ben
Houses of
Parliament
St Thomas'
Hospital
Florence
Nightingale
Museum
WESTMINSTER BRIDGE RD
BOROUGH RD

tminster
bbey
Victoria
Tower
Gardens
Lambeth
Palace
LONDON RD
NEW KENT ROAD
OLD KENT ROAD

Museum of
Garden
History
Imperial War
Museum
ST GEORGE'S RD
Elephant
and Castle

Tate
Britain
MILLBANK
KENNINGTON ROAD
F
G

London
Balloon

KEY TO RESTAURANT LOCATIONS

Each restaurant in London has a map reference, eg C2. The letter 'C' refers
to the grid square located at the bottom of the map. The figure '2' refers to
the grid square located at the left hand edge of the map. For example,
where these two intersect, Buckingham Palace can be found.
Due to the scale of the map, only a rough guide to the location of a
restaurant can be given. A more detailed map will be necessary to be
precise.

Vauxhall
VAUXHALL BRIDGE
KENNINGTON LANE
D
E The
Oval

Index

1 Lombard Street, London EC3 265
1 Lombard Street, The Brasserie,
  London EC3 266
2 Quail Restaurant, Dornoch 630
3 Monkeys Restaurant,
  London SE24 280
11 Park Avenue, Carnoustie 580
22 Chesterton Road, Cambridge 53
22 Mill Street, Chagford 118
36 On The Quay, Emsworth 208
40° at Veronica's, London W2 346
42 Churchgate,
  Bury St Edmunds 442
78 St Vincent Street, Glasgow 619
947AD at The Royalist,
  Stow-on-the-Wold 187

A

Abbey Court Hotel, Nenagh 721
Abbeyglen Castle Hotel, Clifden 719
The Absolute End,
  St Peter Port 565
The Acorn Inn, Evershot 149-50
Actons Hotel, Kinsale 718
Adlard's Restaurant, Norwich 375
The Admiralty Restaurant 357
Agaric, Ashburton 113
Aghadoe Heights Hotel,
  Killarney 720
Airds Hotel, Port Appin 586
aka, London E4 357
Al Duca, London SW1 280-1
Alastair Little Soho,
  London W1 314
Alastair Little W11,
  London W11 354
The Albannach, Lochinver 637
Alba Restaurant, London EC1 261
Albright Hussey Hotel,
  Shrewsbury 416-7
Alcock & Brown Hotel, Clifden 719
Alderley Edge Hotel,
  Alderley Edge 59-60
Aldwark Hotel, Aldwark 527
Alexander House, Turners Hill 481
Alloro, London W1 315
Allt-nan-Ros Hotel, Onich 639-40
Altnaharrie Inn, Ullapool 645
Alton Grange Hotel, Alton 200
Alverton Manor, Truro 84

Amaryllis, Glasgow 619
Ambassador Hotel, York 544-5
Amber Regent, Glasgow 620
Amberley Castle, Amberley 470
Amerdale House Hotel,
  Arncliffe 527
Amor's, Royal Leamington Spa 489
The Anchor Inn, Ely 54
Ancient Camp Inn, Hereford 224
Andrew's on the Weir, Porlock 428
The Angel, Long Crendon 49-50
Angel Hill, Bury St Edmunds 443
Angel Hotel, Bury St Edmunds 441
Angel Hotel, Lavenham 446
Angel Inn, Hetton 535
The Angel Inn,
  Stoke-by-Nayland 451
Angel Inn, Warminster 517
The Angel Posting House,
  Guildford 456
Anglesea Arms, London W6 350
L'Anis, London W1 315
Annesley House Hotel,
  Norwich 375
Apperley Manor, Bradford 550-1
Appleby Manor Country
  House Hotel,
  Appleby-in-Westmorland 87
Arbutus Hotel, Killarney 720
Arbutus Lodge Hotel, Cork 718
Archiestown Hotel,
  Archiestown 648
Archipelago, London W1 315
Ardagh Hotel & Restaurant,
  Clifden 719
Ardanaiseig Hotel, Kilchrenan 584
Ardencote Manor Hotel,
  Warwick 495
The Ardeonaig Hotel, Killin 667
Ardilaun House Hotel, Galway 719
Ardington Hotel, Worthing 481
Ardmore Country House Hotel,
  Westport 720
Ardoe House, Aberdeen 576
Arisaig House, Arisaig 627
Ark Restaurant, Erpingham 373
Armandier et Bistro Daniel,
  London W2 346
Armathwaite Hall,
  Bassenthwaite 88
Armless Dragon, Cardiff 671
Aroma II, London W1 316
Arundell Arms, Lifton 127
Ashburn Hotel, Fordingbridge 210

Ashdown Park Hotel,
  Forest Row 465
Ashwick House, Dulverton 425
Asia de Cuba, London WC2 358
Assaggi, London W2 346
Athenaeum Hotel, Bullochs @ 116,
  London W1 316
Atlantic Bar and Grill,
  London W1 316-7
The Atlantic Coast Hotel,
  Westport 720
The Atlantic Hotel, St Brelade 568
Atlantic House Hotel, Bude 68
L'Atlantique Hotel, Perelle 562
Atrium, Edinburgh 599
Auberge du Lac, Welwyn 233
Aubergine, London SW10 307
Auchrannie Hotel, Brodick 588
Auchterarder House,
  Auchterarder 651
Audleys Wood, Basingstoke 201
Augustine's Restaurant,
  Canterbury 234
Aurora, Great Eastern Hotel,
  London EC2 263-5
Aurora Garden Hotel, Windsor 40
Austin's Bar & Bistro,
  Chester-le-Street 160
The Avenue, London SW1 281
Avins Bridge Restaurant,
  Ardingly 471
Axis, One Aldwych,
  London WC2 361
Aynsome Manor Hotel, Cartmel 90
Ayudhya Thai,
  Kingston upon Thames 367

B

Babur Brasserie,
  London SE23 279-80
The Bacchanalian at The Hotel on
  the Park, Cheltenham 178
Balbirnie House, Markinch 614
Balgonie House Hotel,
  Ballater 576-7
Ballathie House Hotel,
  Kinclaven 655
Ballynahinch Castle,
  Ballynahinch 719
Ballyrafter House Hotel,
  Lismore 721
Balmer Lawn Hotel,
  Brockenhurst 203

Balmoral Hotel, Hadrian's,
Edinburgh   600
Balmoral Hotel, Number One,
Edinburgh   600
Banchory Lodge Hotel,
Banchory   578
Bank, Birmingham   497
The Bank Restaurant, Crieff   654
Bank Restaurant, London WC2   358
Bank Westminster & Zander Bar,
London SW1   281
Banks Bistro,
Bishop's Waltham   202-3
La Barbarie Hotel, St Martin   562
Barberstown Castle, Straffan   720
Barnard's Restaurant,
Denmead   207
Barnsdale Lodge Hotel,
Oakham   406
Bartley Lodge, Cadnam   206-7
Barton Cross Hotel, Exeter   121
Bath Priory, Bath   419
Bath Spa Hotel, Bath   419-20
Baumann's Brasserie,
Coggeshall   165
The Bay Tree, Burford   389
The Bay Tree, Melbourne   111
Bay View Hotel, Ballycotton   718
Beamish Park Hotel, Beamish   160
Bear Hotel, Crickhowell   701
The Bear Hotel, Woodstock   405
Beardmore Hotel, Clydebank   598-9
Beatrice Kennedy, Belfast   713
Beaujolais Restaurant,
Cheltenham   175
Beaulieu Hotel, Beaulieu   202
Bedford Hotel, Tavistock   135
Bedford Lodge Hotel,
Newmarket   449
Beech Hill Hotel, Londonderry   717
Beech Hill Hotel, Windermere   102
Beeches Hotel & Victorian
Gardens, Norwich   376
Beechleas Restaurant,
Wimborne Minster   159
Beechwood Country House,
Moffat   595-6
Beechwood Hotel,
North Walsham   374-5
Beiderbecke's Hotel,
Scarborough   541
Belair House, London SE21   279
Belfry House Hotel, Handforth   63
Bell Inn, Brook   206
Bell Inn Hotel, Stilton   58

Belle Vue Royal Hotel,
Aberystwyth   677
Bells Diner, Bristol   42
Belmont Hotel, Knock   720
Belmont House, Leicester   252
Belmore Hotel, Sale   200
Belton Woods Hotel, Belton   254
Belvedere, London W8   351
Ben Loyal Hotel, Tongue   644
Bentley's, London W1   317
The Berkeley, La Tante Claire,
London SW1   296
The Berkeley, Vong,
London SW1   296-7
The Berners Hotel, London W1   317
Bertie's, Romsey   217
Bertie's, Winchester   221
Bert's Restaurant,
Great Missenden   48
The Best Western Castle of Brecon,
Brecon   699
Best Western Lee Wood Hotel,
Buxton   109
Best Western Yew Lodge Hotel,
Kegworth   251
Bewley's Hotel Ballsbridge,
Ballsbridge   719
Bibendum, London SW3   298
Bibury Court, Bibury   172
Bice, London W1   318
Bignell Park Hotel, Bicester   388
Billesley Manor Hotel,
Stratford-upon-Avon   492
Bindon House, Wellington   432
Birmingham Marriott,
Birmingham   497-8
Bishop's Table Hotel, Farnham   455
Bishopstrow House,
Warminster   517
Biskra Beach Hotel, Ryde   504
Bistro 21, Durham   161
Bistro on the Beach,
Bournemouth   142
Bistro on the Bridge,
Christchurch   146-7
Bistro 190, London SW7   305
Black Chapati, Brighton   462
Black Horse Inn, Bourne   254-5
The Black Swan, Helmsley   534
The Black Truffle,
London NW1   269
Blackaller Hotel,
Moretonhampstead   129
Blewbury Inn, Blewbury   388-9
Blue Bell Hotel, Belford   383

Blue Goose Restaurant , Bristol   42
Blue Print Café, London SE1   274
Bluebird, London SW3   298
Blues Bistro & Bar,
London W1   318
Blunsdon House Hotel,
Swindon   516
Boar's Head Hotel, Harrogate   532
Boat Hotel, Boat of Garten   627-8
The Boath House, Nairn   638
Bodidris Hall, Llandegla   683
Bodysgallen Hall Hotel,
Llandudno   681
Boisdale, London SW1   281
Bombay Bicycle Club,
London SW12   310
Bontddu Hall Hotel,
Bontddu   688-9
Boringdon Hall, Plymouth   130
Borrowdale Gates Country House
Hotel, Borrowdale   88-9
Bosville Hotel, Portree   641
Botleigh Grange, Southampton   219
Bournemouth Highcliff Marriott
Hotel, Bournemouth   143
Les Bouviers,
Wimborne Minster   159
Bowlish House, Shepton Mallet 429
Box Tree Restaurant, Ilkley   533
Bradda Glen Café, Port Erin   574
Braidwoods, Dalry   589
Branston Hall Hotel, Branston   255
Brasserie 21, Sunderland   486
Brasserie Forty Four, Leeds   555
The Brasserie, Hawarden   685
Brazz, Taunton   430
The Bricklayers Arms,
Montgommery   706
Bridge House Hotel,
Beaminster   142
Bridge of Orchy Hotel,
Bridge of Orchy   582
Bridgewood Manor Hotel,
Chatham   235
Brio, Leeds   555
Brisbane House, Largs   590
Bristol Marriott City Centre,
Bristol   42
Bristol Marriott Royal Hotel,
Bristol   42-3
Broadoaks Country House,
Troutbeck   100
Brockencote Hall,
Chaddesley Corbett   519-20
Brocks, Padstow   75

Brooklands Grange Hotel,
Coventry 501
Brooklodge at MacCreddin,
Macreddin 721
Brownlands Hotel, Sidmouth 134
Browns Hotel & Brasserie,
Tavistock 136
Brown's Hotel, Restaurant 1837,
London W1 319
Brown's Restaurant, Worcester 525
Bruerne's Lock Restaurant,
Stoke Bruerne 382
Brummells Seafood Restaurant,
Norwich 376
Bruntsfield Hotel, Edinburgh 601
Bryce's Seafood Restaurant,
Ockley 457
Bryn Howel Hotel, Llangollen 684
Buck Inn Hotel, Buckden 529
Buckland Manor, Buckland 174
Buckland-Tout-Saints,
Kingsbridge 126
Budock Vean - The Hotel on the
River, Mawnan Smith 72
The Bull Auberge, Yaxley 452
Bullochs @ 116, Athenaeum Hotel,
London W1 316
Bunchrew House Hotel,
Inverness 634
Burnham Beeches, Burnham 47
Burpham Country House,
Arundel 471
Burt's Hotel, Melrose 662-3
Burythorpe House Hotel,
Malton 537
Bush Hill, Hatfield 230
Buswells' Hotel, Dublin 719
Butler Arms Hotel, Waterville 720
Butlers Wharf Chop House,
London SE1 274
Buxted Park, Uckfield 469
By Appointment, Norwich 376

C

The Cadogan Hotel,
London SW1 282
Caer Beris Manor, Builth Wells 700
Caesars Arms, Creigiau 675
Café 21, Newcastle-upon-Tyne 483
Café 21 Newcastle,
Newcastle-upon-Tyne 483
Le Café du Marché,
London EC1 262
Café Niçoise, Colwyn Bay 680

Le Café St Honore, Edinburgh 604
Cahernane Hotel, Killarney 720
Cahir House Hotel, Cahir 721
Cairn Lodge, Auchterarder 651
Cairn Restaurant, Kilmartin 584-5
Cairnbaan Hotel, Lochgilphead 585
Calcot Manor, Tetbury 188
Callow Hall, Ashbourne 107
Cally Palace Hotel,
Gatehouse of Fleet 594
Cambio de Tercio,
London SW5 304
Cambridge Quy Mill Hotel,
Cambridge 52
Cameron House Hotel, Balloch 598
Cannizaro House,
London SW19 313
Canterbury Hotel, Canterbury 235
Cantina del Ponte, London SE1 275
Cantina Vinopolis, London SE1 275
The Capital, London SW3 298
Le Caprice, London SW1 282
Captain's Table, Woodbridge 452
Caraffini, London SW1 282-3
Carbis Bay Hotel, St Ives 79
Carey's Manor Hotel,
Brockenhurst 203
Carlton George Hotel, Glasgow 620
Carlton House Hotel,
Llanwrtyd Wells 704
Carlyon Bay Hotel, St Austell 78-9
Carved Angel Restaurant,
Dartmouth 119-20
Casey's of Baltimore Hotel,
Baltimore 718
Cashel House Hotel, Cashel 719
Le Cassoulet, Cardiff 673
Castle Cottage, Harlech 690-1
The Castle Green Hotel, Kendal 96
Castle Hotel, Conwy 680
Castle Hotel, Lincoln 256
Castle Hotel, Macroom 718
Castle Hotel, Taunton 431
Castle Hotel, Windsor 40
Castle House, Hereford 224-5
Castle Inn, Castle Combe 507
Castle Oaks House Hotel,
Castleconnell 720
Castle Restaurant, Hurst 34-5
The Castle Rock Hotel,
Port Isaac 77
Castle Venlaw Hotel, Peebles 663
Castlehyde Hotel, Fermoy 718
Castleman Hotel,
Blandford Forum 142

Castletroy Park Hotel,
Limerick 720
Catch, London SW5 304
The Cavendish, St James's,
London SW1 283
Caviar House, London W1 319
Cawdor Arms Hotel,
Llandeilo 676-7
Cayenne, Belfast 713
Cecconi's, London W1 320
Cellar Restaurant, Anstruther 611
Cellars, Troon 592
Celtic Manor Resort, Newport 695
The Chablis Cellar, Castletown 574
Chalk Lane Farm, Epsom 455
Champany Inn, Linlithgow 647
Le Champignon Sauvage,
Cheltenham 175-6
Champor Champor,
London SE1 275
Channings Restaurant,
Edinburgh 601
Chapel House Hotel,
Atherstone 488
Chapter One, Bromley 364
Chapter Two, London SE3 278-9
Charingworth Manor Hotel,
Charingworth 174-5
Charlton House,
Shepton Mallet 429
Charnwood Hotel, Sheffield 549
Chase Hotel, Ross-on-Wye 226-7
Château La Chaire, Rozel Bay 567
Chatters, Dunoon 583
Chauntry House Hotel, Bray 31
Chav Brasserie,
Chipping Norton 392
Chavignol at the Old Mill,
Shipston on Stour 491
The Chequers Inn Restaurant,
Fowlmere 55
The Chequers Inn, Rowhook 479
Chequers Hotel, Pulborough 479
The Chesil Rectory, Winchester 221
The Chester Crabwall Manor Hotel,
Chester 61
Chester Grosvenor Hotel,
Chester 61-2
Chesterfield Hotel, London W1 320
Chewton Glen Hotel,
New Milton 215
Chez Bruce, London SW17 313
Chez Max, London SW10 308
Chez Moi, London W11 354
Chez Nous, Plymouth 130-1

cheznico, London W1 320
Chideock House Hotel,
    Chideock 146
Chilston Park Hotel, Lenham 240
Chimneys Restaurant,
    Long Melford 447
Chine Hotel, Bournemouth 143
Chinon Restaurant,
    London W14 356
The Chiswick, London W4 348
Chor Bizarre, London W1 321
La Chouette, Dinton 48
Christopher's, London WC2 358
Chung Ying Garden,
    Birmingham 498-9
Churchill Arms, Paxford 186
Churchill Inter-Continental,
    London W1 321
Chutney Mary Restaurant,
    London SW10 308
Cibo, London W14 356
Cigala, London W14 357
Cill Aodain Hotel, Kiltimagh 720
City Rhodes Restaurant,
    London EC4 266
Clare House, Grange-over-Sands 91
The Clarence, Dublin 719
Claridge's, London W1 321
Clarion Brandon House Hotel,
    New Ross 721
Clarion Stephen's Hall All-Suite
    Hotel, Dublin 719
Clarke's, London W8 351
Cley Hall Hotel, Spalding 258
Cliffords Cottage Restaurant,
    Bracklesham 472
Cliveden, The Terrace Dining
    Room, Taplow 51-2
Cliveden, Waldo's Restaurant,
    Taplow 51
Clontarf Castle Hotel, Dublin 719
Close Hotel, Tetbury 189
Club Gascon, London EC1 262
Cobo Bay Hotel, Catel 561
Cock Inn, Polstead 450
Coed-y-Mwstwr, Bridgend 670
The Collection, London SW3 299
Columba Hotel, Tarbert 587
Colwall Park Hotel, Malvern 521
Combe Grove Manor Hotel,
    Bath 420
Combe House at Gittisham,
    Honiton 125
Comme Ça, Chichester 473
The Compleat Angler, Marlow 50-1

Congham Hall, Grimston 373
Coniston Hall Lodge, Skipton 542
The Connaught, London W1 322
Conrad International London,
    London SW10 308
Conrah Hotel, Aberystwyth 678
The Consort Hotel,
    Rotherham 548-9
The Cookhouse, Ludlow 410
Copper Inn, Pangbourne 38
Coppid Beech, Bracknell 30
Copthorne Birmingham,
    Birmingham 499
Copthorne Hotel Cardiff-Caerdydd,
    Cardiff 671-2
Copthorne London Gatwick,
    Copthorne 474
Copthorne Manchester,
    Manchester 192-3
Corbyn Head Hotel, Orchid
    Restaurant, Torquay 138
Corisande Manor Hotel,
    Newquay 74
Cornish Range, Mousehole 73
Cornwallis Country Hotel,
    Brome 440
The Cors Restaurant,
    Laugharne 676
Corse Lawn House Hotel,
    Corse Lawn 182
Corsewall Lighthouse Hotel,
    Stranraer 597
Cotswold House,
    Chipping Campden 179
Cotswold Lodge Hotel, Oxford 398
The Cottage in the Wood,
    Malvern 522
Cottons Hotel, Knutsford 63
Coul House Hotel, Contin 629
Coulsdon Manor, Croydon 364
Country Friends Restaurant,
    Dorrington 409
Courtmacsherry,
    Courtmacsherry 718
Courtown Hotel,
    Courtown Harbour 721
The Courtyard, Harrogate 532
The Courtyard, Ludlow 410
Crab & Lobster Restaurant,
    Asenby 528
Craigellachie Hotel,
    Craigellachie 649
Crathorne Hall Hotel,
    Crathorne 530
Craxton Wood, Puddington 65

The Crazy Bear Hotel,
    Stadhampton 401
The Crazy Bear Hotel, Thai Thai,
    Stadhampton 401
Creagan House, Strathyre 667
Creel Restaurant,
    St Margaret's Hope 650
Creggans Inn, Strachur 586-7
The Crescent Townhouse,
    Belfast 714
Crewe Hall, Crewe 62
Cringletie House Hotel,
    Peebles 663
Critchards Seafood Restaurant,
    Porthleven 77
The Criterion, London W1 322
Croft Bank House, Kinross 656
Cromlix House Hotel,
    Dunblane 666
Crooklands Hotel, Crooklands 91
Croque-en-Bouche Restaurant,
    Malvern 522
The Cross, Kingussie 636
Cross Lanes Hotel, Wrexham 711
Crossways Hotel, Wilmington 470
Crouchers Bottom Country Hotel,
    Chichester 473
The Crown & Castle, Orford 449-50
The Crown of Crucis,
    Cirencester 180-1
Crown Hotel, Exford 425
The Crown Inn,
    Cleobury Mortimer 409
Crown Lodge Hotel, Wisbech 59
The Crown, Southwold 450
The Crown at Whitebrook,
    Whitebrook 695
Crowne Plaza London - Heathrow,
    London 366
Crowne Plaza Manchester -
    The Midland, Manchester 193
Crowthers Restaurant,
    London SW14 311
Crutherland Country House,
    East Kilbride 646
Cucina, London NW3 271
Cuillin Hills Hotel, Portree 641
Culdearn House,
    Grantown-on-Spey 632
Cumberland Hotel, Norwich 376
Cutting Edge, Cardiff 672

D

Da Nello, St Peter Port 563
da Venditto, Cardiff 669
The Daffodil, Cheltenham 176
Dakota, London W11 354-5
Dale Head Hall, Keswick 96
Dale Hill Hotel, Ticehurst 469
Dales Country House Hotel,
Upper Sheringham 379
Dalhousie Castle and Spa,
Edinburgh 601
Dalmunzie House,
Spittal of Glenshee 660
Danby Lodge Hotel,
Rosslare Harbour 721
Danesfield House, Marlow 50
Daneswood House Hotel,
Shipham 430
Dans Restaurant, London SW3 300
Daresbury Park Hotel,
Warrington 66
Darleys Restaurant,
Darley Abbey 110
Darroch Learg Hotel, Ballater 577
Dartmoor Inn, Lydford 128
The De Vere Belfry, Wishaw 495
De Vere St David's Park, Ewloe 685
De Vere Slaley Hall, Hexham 384
Dean Court Hotel, York 545
The Depot Waterfront Brasserie,
London SW14 311
Dermott's Restaurant, Swansea 708
Desports,
Stratford-upon-Avon 492-3
Les Deux Garçons, Horsham 477
Devonshire Arms,
Bolton Abbey 529
Devonshire Arms Hotel and
Restaurant, Youghal 719
The Devonshire Hotel of Glasgow,
Glasgow 525
Dew Pond, Old Burghclere 215-16
Dexters Restaurant,
Deddington 392
Dial House Hotel,
Bourton-on-the-Water 173-4
Dicken's Restaurant,
Wethersfield 171
Dingle Skellig Hotel, Dingle 720
Dinham Hall Hotel, Ludlow 410-11
The Dining Room,
Boroughbridge 529
The Dining Room, Reigate 459
Dolmen Hotel, Carlow 718

Dolserau Hall, Dolgellau 690
The Don, London EC4 266-7
Donnington Valley Hotel,
Newbury 36
Dooley's Hotel, Waterford 721
The Dorchester, Grill Room,
London W1 322
The Dorchester, The Oriental,
London W1 323
The Dormy, Ferndown 150-1
Dormy House Hotel, Broadway 518
The Dove, Canterbury 235
Dower House Hotel,
Knaresborough 536
The Dower House,
Muir of Ord 638
Downshire House Hotel,
Blessington 721
Dragon Hotel, Montgomery 705
Drewe Arms, Broadhembury 117
Dromoland Castle Hotel,
Newmarket-on-Fergus 718
Dromquinna Manor, Kenmare 720
Drones, London SW1 283
Druimard Country House,
Dervaig 583
Drunken Duck Inn, Ambleside 86
Dryburgh Abbey Hotel,
St Boswells 663-4
Dryfesdale Hotel, Lockerbie 595
Duchally Country Estate,
Auchterarder 651-2
Duck's at Le Marché Noir,
Edinburgh 602
Duisdale Hotel, Isle Ornsay 635
Duke of Cornwall Hotel,
Plymouth 131
Dukes' Hotel & Fitzroys, Bath 421
Dunbrody Country House &
Restaurant, Arthurstown 721
Dundonnell Hotel, Dundonnell 631
Dungallan House Hotel, Oban 585
Dunkenhalgh Hotel,
Accrington 246
Dunkerley's Hotel, Deal 237
Dunnikier House Hotel,
Kirkcaldy 613
Dunraven Arms Hotel, Adare 720
Dunstone Hall, Torquay 136
Durant Arms Restaurant,
Totnes 139
Durham Marriott Hotel, Royal
County, Durham 161-2
Dusty Miller, Harrogate 532

Duxford Lodge Hotel,
Duxford 53-4

E

Earsham Street Café, Bungay 440
East Lodge Hotel, Rowsley 113
Eastbury Hotel, Sherborne 155
Eastwell Manor, Ashford 233
Eden House Hotel, Cupar 611
Edgemoor Hotel, Bovey Tracey 115
Edgwarebury Hotel, Elstree 229
Egerton Grey Country House,
Barry 710
Egypt Mill Hotel, Nailsworth 184
Elderton Lodge Hotel,
Thorpe Market 378-9
Eldon Hotel, Skibbereen 718
Eldons Hotel, Roundstone 720
Empire Hotel, Llandudno 682
English Garden Restaurant,
London SW3 300
Enmore Hotel, Dunoon 583
L'Escargot - The Ground Floor
Restaurant, London W1 323
L'Escargot - The Picasso Room,
London W1 324
Eslington Villa Hotel,
Gateshead 482
Esseborne Manor, Andover 201
Etrop Grange Hotel,
Manchester Airport 197
Ettington Park Hotel,
Alderminster 487
Eurasia, Glasgow 620
The Evesham Hotel, Evesham 520

F

Fairfield House Hotel, Ayr 590
The Fairlawns at Aldridge,
Walsall 504
Fairwater Head Hotel,
Axminster 114
Fairyhill, Reynoldston 709
Falcon Inn, Fotheringhay 380
Fallowfields Country House Hotel,
Oxford 398
Farfelu, Glasgow 620-1
Farlam Hall Hotel, Brampton 89
The Fat Duck, Bray 32
Fat Olives, Emsworth 207
Fawsley Hall, Daventry 380
Fayrer Garden House,
Windermere 102

Feathers Hotel, Ledbury 226
Feathers Hotel, Woodstock 405
Femi's, Norwich 377
Fernhill Hotel, Portpatrick 597
Ferrycarrig Hotel, Wexford 721
Feversham Arms Hotel,
  Helmsley 534
Fifehead Manor,
  Middle Wallop 213
The Fifth Floor Restaurant,
  London SW1 284
Findon Manor Hotel, Worthing 482
Fire Station, London SE1 276
Fischer's, Baslow Hall,
  Baslow 108-9
Fisherbeck Hotel, Ambleside 86
Fisherman's Lodge,
  Newcastle-upon-Tyne 483-4
Fishermans Wharf, Sandwich 241
Fish Market, Great Eastern Hotel,
  London EC2 265
Fitzpatrick Bunratty Hotel,
  Bunratty 718
The Fitzwilliam Hotel, Dublin 719
Five Lakes Hotel,
  Tolleshunt Knights 171
La Fleur de Lys, Shaftesbury 154
Fleur de Sel, Storrington 480
Floriana, London SW3 300-1
Foley Arms Hotel, Malvern 523
Food for Thought, Fowey 70
Forest Pines Hotel, Scunthorpe 258
Fort Royal Hotel, Rathmullan 719
La Fosse at Cranborne,
  Cranborne 148-9
Fossebridge Inn,
  Fossebridge 182-3
Four Seasons Hotel, Canary Wharf,
  London E14 261
Four Seasons Hotel,
  London W1 324
Four Seasons Hotel, St Fillans 659
Four Seasons Restaurant,
  Carmarthen 676
The Fourth Floor Café at Harvey
  Nichols, Leeds 556
Fouters Bistro, Ayr 590-1
Fowey Hall, Fowey 70
Fowey Hotel, Fowey 70-1
Fox and Goose,
  Stratford-upon-Avon 493
Fox and Goose Inn,
  Fressingfield 443
Fox & Hounds Country Inn,
  Pickering 539

The Fox Inn, Corscombe 148
The Fox Reformed,
  London N16 269
Foxhills, Ottershaw 458
Francine's Restaurant, Maldon 169
Frederick's Restaurant,
  London N1 267
Fredrick's Hotel, Maidenhead 35
La Frégate, St Peter Port 563-4
The French Horn, Sonning 39
The French House Dining Room,
  London W1 324
Frère Jacques,
  Kingston upon Thames 367
Friends Restaurant, Pinner 368

G

Galgorm Manor, Ballymena 712
Le Gallois, Cardiff 673
Galway Bay Golf & Country Club
  Hotel, Oranmore 720
Gamba, Glasgow 621
Garrack Hotel & Restaurant,
  St Ives 79-80
Garryvoe Hotel, Garryvoe 718
The Gate, London W6 350
Gaudi Restaurante,
  London EC1 262-3
Le Gavroche Restaurant,
  London W1 324-5
Gee's Restaurant, Oxford 399
Gemini, Tadworth 461
General Tarleton Inn,
  Knaresborough 536
George & Dragon, Burpham 472
George & Dragon, Rowde 514-5
The George at Hathersage,
  Hathersage 110-11
George Hotel,
  Dorchester-on-Thames 393
George Hotel, Yarmouth 506
George Inter-Continental,
  Edinburgh 602
George of Stamford Hotel,
  Stamford 258
Georgian Lodge,
  Bradford-on-Avon 506-7
Gibbon Bridge Hotel, Chipping 247
Gidleigh Park, Chagford 117-18
Gilbey's, London W5 349
Gilby's Restaurant, Cardiff 672
Gilpin Lodge Hotel,
  Windermere 103

The Gingerman Restaurant,
  Brighton 462
Glass Boat Restaurant, Bristol 43
Glass House Restaurant,
  Worcester 525
The Glasshouse, Kew 366
Glazebrook House Hotel,
  Ivybridge 126
Gleddoch House, Langbank 660
Glenapp Castle, Ballantrae 591
Glen Lui Hotel, Ballater 577
The Gleneagles Hotel,
  Auchterarder 652
Glengarry Castle Hotel,
  Invergarry 633
Glenlo Abbey Hotel, Galway 719
Glenmorangie House, Tain 643
Glenmoriston Arms Hotel,
  Invermoriston 633
Glenmoriston Town House Hotel,
  Inverness 634
Glenskirlie House Restaurant,
  Banknock 610
Glewstone Court, Ross-on-Wye 227
Gliffaes Hotel, Crickhowell 701-2
Gold Rill Hotel, Grasmere 92
The Golden Lion,
  Northallerton 538
Goldstone Hall,
  Market Drayton 413
Golf View Hotel, Nairn 639
The Goose, Britwell Salome 389
Goose Fat & Garlic,
  Sawbridgeworth 231
Gordon's Restaurant,
  Inverkeilor 580
Goring Hotel, London SW1 284-5
La Gousse d'Ail, Oxford 399
Grafton Manor Restaurant,
  Bromsgrove 518
Grand Hotel, Eastbourne 464
Grand Hotel, St Helier 571
Grand Hotel, Swanage 157
Grand Hotel, Torquay 136
La Grande Mare Hotel, Catel 561
Grange Hotel, Sherborne 156
Grange Hotel, York 545-6
Grange Hotel, Grangemouth 610
Granita, London N1 267
Granville Hotel, Waterford 721
Grapevine Hotel,
  Stow-on-the-Wold 186-7
Grasmere Hotel, Grasmere 92
Gravetye Manor Hotel,
  East Grinstead 476

Great Eastern Hotel, Aurora,
London EC2   264
Great eastern Hotel, Fish Market,
London EC2   265
The Great House, Bridgend   671
Great House Restaurant,
Lavenham   446
Great Southern Hotel,
Parknasilla   720
Green Dragon, Haddenham   48-9
Green Inn, Ballater   578
Green Island Restaurant,
St Clement   571
Green Olive, London W9   353
Green Park Hotel, Pitlochry   658
Greenhead House, Chapeltown   548
Greenhouse Restaurant,
London W1   325
Greens Bistro, Lytham St Annes   249
Green's Restaurant & Oyster Bar,
London SW1   285
The Greenway, Cheltenham   177
Gregans Castle, Ballyvaughan   718
Gresslin's, London NW3   272
Greywalls Hotel, Gullane   647
The Grill Room, The Dorchester
Hotel, London W1   322-3
Grinkle Park Hotel, Easington   531
Grissini, Hyatt Carlton Tower Hotel,
London SW1   285
Grosvenor Arms, Hindon   510
Grosvenor Hotel, Mima's
Restaurant, Torquay   137
Grovefield Hotel, Burnham   47
Guellers, Leeds   556
Guinach House Hotel,
Aberfeldy   650
The Gurkha Square, Fleet   210

H

Hackness Grange Country House,
Hackness   531
Haigs Hotel, Balsall Common   496
Hakkasan, London W1   325
Halcyon Hotel, London W11   355
Haldanes, Edinburgh   602-3
Haley's Hotel, Leeds   556-7
The Halfway Inn, Stroud   188
The Halkin Hotel, Nahm,
London SW1   290
Hall Garth Hotel, Darlington   160-1
Hallidays, Chichester   473
Halmpstone Manor, Barnstaple   114
Hambleton Hall, Oakham   406

Hamilton's Restaurant,
Stow-on-the-Wold   187
Hanover International,
Bromsgrove   519
Hanover International Hotel,
Basingstoke   202
Hanover International Hotel ,
Warrington   66
The Harbour Inn, Bowmare   581-2
The Harlequin Restaurant,
Keighley   555
Harris' Restaurant, Penzance   76
Harrogate Brasserie Hotel,
Harrogate   533
Harrow Inn, Little Bedwyn   511
Harry's Place, Grantham   255-6
Hart's Restaurant, Nottingham   385
Hartwell House, Aylesbury   46
Harvey's Point Country Hotel,
Donegal   719
Harveys Restaurant, Bristol   43-4
Harvey's Restaurant, Grimsby   256
Haven Hotel, Plockton   640
Haven Hotel, Poole   152
Hawthorn House, Omagh   717
Haxted Mill & Riverside Brasserie,
Edenbridge   238
Haycock Hotel, Wansford   58-9
Haydon House Hotel,
Stoke-on-Trent   438
Hayfield Manor, Cork   718
Hazlewood Castle, Tadcaster   543
Headlam Hall Hotel,
Darlington   161
Healds Hall Hotel, Dewsbury   551
Heddon's Gate Hotel,
Heddon's Mouth   124
Hell Bay Hotel, Bryher   68
Hempstead House Country Hotel,
Sittingbourne   242
Herbert Park Hotel, Dublin   719
Hibernian Hotel, Dublin   719
Hibiscus, Ludlow   411
High Moor Inn, Wrightington   250
Highbullen Hotel,
Chittlehamholt   119
Highfield Hotel, Keswick   96
Highfield House Country Hotel,
Hawkshead   95
Highgrove House, Troon   592
Highland Cottage, Tobermory   587
Hilaire, London SW7   305-6
Hintlesham Hall, Hintlesham   444
Hipping Hall, Kirkby Lonsdale   97
Hob Green Hotel, Markington   537

Hodson Bay Hotel,
Hodson Bay   721
Hoebridge Inn Restaurant,
Gattonside   661
The Hogarth, London SW5   304
Holbeck Ghyll, Windermere   103-4
Holbrook House Hotel,
Wincanton   434
Holdfast Cottage, Malvern   523
Holdsworth House Hotel,
Halifax   551-2
Holiday Inn, Glasgow   621
Holly Tree Hotel, Kentallen   636
The Holt Hotel, Steeple Aston   402
Holyrood Hotel, Edinburgh   603
Homewood Park,
Hinton Charterhouse   426
Honours Mill Restaurant,
Edenbridge   238
Hooked, Dartmouth   120
Horn of Plenty, Gulworthy   123-4
Horse and Farrier Inn, Keswick   96
The Horse and Groom,
Malmesbury   511
Horsted Place, Uckfield   469
Hoste Arms, Burnham Market   372
Hotel Barcelona, Exeter   121
Hotel des Clos, Nottingham   386
Hotel du Vin & Bistro, Bristol   44
Hotel du Vin & Bistro,
Royal Tunbridge Wells   242
Hotel du Vin & Bistro,
Winchester   222
Hotel Eilean Iarmain,
Isle Ornsay   635
Hotel Inter-Continental London -
Le Soufflé, London W1   325-6
Hotel Kandinsky, Café Paradiso,
Cheltenham   177
Hotel Maes y Neuadd,
Talsarnau   692
Hotel la Place, St Brelade   569
Hotel l'Horizon, Star Grill,
St Brelade   570
Hotel on the Park, The
Bacchanalian, Cheltenham   178
Hotel Portmeirion,
Portmeirion   691
Hotel Renouf, Rochford   170
Hotel Smokies Park, Oldham   198
Hotel Tresanton, St Mawes   82
Hour Glass, Fordingbridge   210
The House, London SW3   301
Houston House Hotel, Uphall   648
The Howard Arms, Atherstone   488

Howard's House Hotel,
Salisbury   515
Howards Restaurant, Bristol   44
Hundred House Hotel,
Norton   414-5
The Hundred House Hotel,
Ruan High Lanes   78
Hungry Monk Restaurant,
Jevington   467
Hunsdon Manor Hotel,
Ross-on-Wye   227
Hunstrete House Hotel,
Hunstrete   427
Hunter's Hotel, Rathnew   721
Huntingtower Hotel, Perth   656
Hurtwood Inn Hotel, Peaslake   458
Hush, Lomdon W1   326
Hyatt Carlton Tower Hotel,
Grissini, London SW1   285
Hylands Hotel, Coventry   501
Hythe Imperial Hotel,
Hythe   239-40

I

Ibbetson's, Bishop's Stortford   229
Idlerocks Hotel, St Martin   562
Idle Rocks Hotel, St Mawes   82
Iggs, Edinburgh   603
Il Convivio, London SW1   285
Il Forno, London W1   326
Il Punto, Ipswich   444-5
Ilsington Country Hotel,
Ilsington   125
Imperial Hotel,
Great Yarmouth   373
Imperial Hotel, Llandudno   682
Imperial Hotel, Torquay   137
Inchyra Grange, Polmont   611
Incognico, London WC2   358-9
Indigo, One Aldwych,
London WC2   361
Inishannon House Hotel,
Inishannon   718
Inn at Lathones, St Andrews   618
The Inn at the Elm Tree,
Newport   696
Inn For All Seasons, Burford   390
Inn on the Green,
Cookham Dean   34
Inver Lodge Hotel, Lochinver   637
Inverlochy Castle Hotel,
Fort William   631
Island Hotel, Tresco   84
Isle of Eriska, Eriska   584

Isola, London SW1   286
Ivy House, Alloway   590
Ivy House Farm, Lowestoft   448
Ivy House Hotel, Marlborough   513
The Ivy, London WC2   359
Izakaya Japanese Tavern,
Cardiff,   672-3

J

J. Sheekey, London WC2   359
The Jack In The Green Inn,
Rockbeare   133
Jak's, London SW1   286-7
Jedforest Hotel, Jedburgh   661
Jeremy's at Borde Hill,
Haywards Heath   477
Jerichos, Windermere   104
Jersey Arms Hotel,
Middleton Stoney   397
Jersey Pottery Restaurant,
Gorey   566
The Jew's House, Lincoln   257
John Burton-Race,The Landmark,
London NW1   269-70
Jonathan's at the Angel,
Burford   390
JSW, Petersfield   216
Judges Hotel, Yarm   544
The Jumble Room Cafe,
Grasmere   92
Junction 28, Newport   696
Juniper, Altrincham   192
Jurys Hotel Dublin, Dublin   719
Just St James, London SW1   286

K

Kai Mayfair, London W1   326-7
Karslake House, Winsford   434
Kastoori, London SW17   313
Keadeen Hotel, Newbridge   720
Keavil House Hotel,
Dunfermline   612
Kee's Hotel, Ballybofey   719
Kelly's Resort Hotel, Rosslare   721
Kemps Country House Hotel,
Wareham   157
Kennel Holt Hotel, Cranbrook   236
Kensington Place, London W8   351
Kenwick Park Hotel, Louth   257
Kettering Park Hotel, Kettering   381
Kilcamb Lodge Hotel,
Strontian   642-3

The Kildare Hotel & Country Club,
Straffan   720
Kilkenny Ormonde Hotel,
Kilkenny   720
Kilkenny River Court Hotel,
Kilkenny   720
Killarney Park Hotel, Killarney   720
Killermont Polo Club, Glasgow   621
Killiecrankie Hotel,
Killiecrankie   654-5
Kilmichael Country House Hotel,
Brodick   589
Kilmore Hotel, Cavan   718
Kinfauns Castle, Perth   656
Kinghams, Shere   460
Kings Head, Coltishall   372
The King's Head, Ivinghoe   49
Kings Head Hotel and Inn,
Keswick   97
Kings Head Inn, Woodstock   406
The Kingsley Hotel, Cork   718
Kings Lodge Hotel, Durham   162
Kingsway Hall, London WC2   359
Kingsway Hotel, Cleethorpes   255
Kinkell House, Dingwell   630
Kinloch House Hotel,
Blairgowrie   653
Kinloch Lodge, Isle Ornsay   635-6
Kinmel Arms, Abergele   679
Kinnaird, Dunkeld   654
Kirroughtree House,
Newton Stewart   596-7
Kitley House Hotel, Plymouth   131
Knavesmire Manor Hotel, York   546
Knife & Cleaver, Bedford   28
Knockendarroch House Hotel,
Pitlochry   659
Knoll House Hotel,
Malmesbury   511-2
Kwizeen, Blackpool   246-7

L

Ladyburn, Maybole   591
Laicram Thai, London SE3   279
Lainston House Hotel,
Winchester   222
Lake Country House,
Llangammarch Wells   703
Lake Isle Hotel, Uppingham   408
Lake Vyrnwy Hotel, Llanwddyn   704
Lakeside Hotel, Newby Bridge   99
The Lamb at Buckland,
Faringdon   393
Lamb at Hindon Hotel, Hindon   510

Lamb Inn, Burford   391
Lambs of Sheep Street,
    Stratford-upon-Avon   493
Landgate Bistro, Rye   468
The Landmark,
    Carrick-on-Shannon   720
The Landmark, John Burton Race,
    London NW1   269
The Lanesborough,
    London SW1   287
Langar Hall, Langar   385
Langdale Chase Hotel,
    Windermere   104
Langdon Court Hotel,
    Plymouth   132
Langley House Hotel,
    Wiveliscombe   435
Langley Wood Restaurant,
    Redlynch   514
Langrish House, Petersfield   216
Langs Hotel, Glasgow   622
Langshott Manor, Horley   457
Langtry Manor Hotel,
    Bournemouth   143
Langtry's at The Birmingham
    Marriott, Birmingham   498
Lansdowne Hotel,
    Leamington Spa   490
Launceston Place Restaurant,
    London W8   352
Lea Hill Hotel, Axminster   114
Leamington Hotel and Bistro,
    Leamington Spa   490
Leaping Hare Restaurant,
    Bury St Edmunds   422
The Leatherne Bottel, Goring   394
Leeds Marriott Hotel, Leeds   557
Leeming House, Watermillock   100
Left Bank, Pembroke   697
Leftbank, Birmingham   499
Leixlip House Hotel, Leixlip   720
Lemonia, London NW1   270
Les Trois Garçon, London E1   260
Let's Eat, Perth   657
Let's Eat Again, Perth   657
Levant, London W1   327
Lewtrenchard Manor,
    Lewdown   127
Lickfold Inn, Lickfold   477
Lifeboat Inn, Thornham   378
Lighthouse, Aldeburgh   439
The Lighthouse Restaurant,
    London SW19   314
The Lime Tree, Lenham   241
The Lime Tree, Limavady   717

Limerick Inn Hotel, Limerick   720
Lindeth Fell Hotel,
    Windermere   104-5
Lindsay House Restaurant,
    London W1   327
The Links Hotel, Brora   628
The Linnet, Trowbridge   516
Linthwaite House Hotel,
    Windermere   105
Little Barwick House, Yeovil   435
Little Yang Sing, Manchester   193
Liverpool Marriott City Centre,
    Liverpool   370
Livingston's Restaurant,
    Linlithgow   647-8
Llangoed Hall, Llyswen   705
Llansantffraed Court,
    Abergavenny   692-3
Loch Melfort Hotel, Arduaine   581
Loch Torridon Hotel, Torridon   644
Lochgreen House, Troon   592
The Lodge Hotel, Huddersfield   553
The Lodge & Spa at Inchdoney
    Island, Clonakilty   718
The Loft Restaurant,
    Blair Atholl   652-3
Lola's, London N1   267-8
Lomond Country Inn,
    Kinnesswood   655
London Heathrow Marriott Hotel,
    London   366
London Marriott Hotel County Hall,
    London SE1   276
London Marriott Grosvenor Square,
    London W1   328
Londonderry Arms, Carnlough   712
Longfield's Hotel, Dublin   719
Longueville House Hotel,
    Mallow   718
Longueville Manor, St Saviour   572
The Lord Bute Restaurant,
    Highcliffe   151
Lord Haldon Hotel, Exeter   122
Lords of the Manor,
    Upper Slaughter   190-1
Lough Inagh Lodge Hotel,
    Recess   720
Lovelady Shield House, Alston   85
Low Wood Hall Hotel,
    Nether Wasdale   99
Low Wood Hotel, Windermere   105
Lower Brook House, Blockley   173
Lower Slaughter Manor,
    Lower Slaughter   183
Lowry Hotel, Manchester   194

Lucknam Park, Colerne   508-9
Lux, Glasgow   622
Lygon Arms, Broadway   518
Lysses House Hotel, Fareham   209
Lythe Hill Hotel, Haslemere   456-7

M

McCoys (Tontine Inn),
    Staddle Bridge   542
Magenta's, Carlisle   89-90
The Magpie Room,
    Newcastle-upon-Tyne   484
Magpies Restaurant,
    Horncastle   256
Maison Bleue,
    Bury St Edmunds   442
Maison Novelli, London EC1   263
Makeney Hall Hotel, Belper   109
Malik's, Cookham   33-4
Malin Court, Turnberry   593
Mallory Court Hotel,
    Leamington Spa   490-1
Malmaison, Edinburgh   604
Malmaison Hotel, Glasgow   622
Malmaison Hotel,
    Newcastle-upon-Tyne   485
Malone Lodge Hotel, Belfast   713
The Malt House,
    Chipping Campden   179
The Malt Shovel, Barston   497
Mandarin Oriental Hyde Park,
    London SW1   288
Manna, London NW3   272
Le Manoir Aux Quat'Saisons,
    Great Milton   395
Manor Hotel, Crickhowell   702
Manor Hotel, Meriden   502
The Manor House, Beverley   526
Manor House Hotel, Alsager   60
Manor House Hotel,
    Castle Combe   508
Manor House Hotel,
    Moreton-in-Marsh   184
Manor House Hotel,
    Moretonhampstead   129-30
Manor House Hotel, Oban   585
Manor House, West Auckland   164
Manor Parc Country Hotel,
    Cardiff   674
Mansfield House Hotel, Tain   643
Mansion House Hotel, Elgin   650
Mansion House Hotel, Poole   152-3
Marco's Restaurant, Norwich   377
Margot's, Padstow   75

La Marinade, Brighton   463
Marine Hotel, Dublin   719
The Market Place Hotel, Wells   433
Markree Castle, Collooney   721
Markwicks, Bristol   45
Marlborough Hotel, Ipswich   445
Marlfield House Hotel, Gorey   721
Marriott Dalmahoy, Edinburgh   604
Marriott Forest of Arden Hotel,
    Meriden   503
Marriott Goodwood Park Hotel,
    Goodwood   476-7
Marriott Hotel, Gosforth Park   485
Marriott Hanbury Manor Hotel,
    Ware   232
Marriott Meon Valley Hotel,
    Shedfield   218
Marriott Sprowston Manor,
    Norwich   377
Marriott Worsley Park Hotel,
    Manchester   194
Marsh Goose Restaurant,
    Moreton-in-Marsh   184
Martin's Restaurant, Edinburgh   605
Maryculter House Hotel,
    Aberdeen   576
Marygreen Manor, Brentwood   165
Mash, London W1   328
The Masons Arms,
    Branscombe   116
Master Builders House Hotel,
    Bucklers Hard   206
Matsuri, London SW1   288
Mauro's Restaurant,
    Bollington   60-1
Mayfair Inter-Continental, Opus 70,
    London W1   329
Mayfield House Hotel,
    Malmesbury   512
Maypool Park, Brixham   116
McClements Restaurant,
    Twickenham   369
Mela, London WC2   360
Meliá White House Regents Park,
    London NW1   270
Melton's, York   546-7
Memories of China Restaurant,
    London SW1   289
Menzies Avant Hotel,
    Oldham   198-9
Menzies Carlton Hotel,
    Bournemouth   144
Menzies Flitwick Manor,
    Flitwick   28-9

Menzies Mickleover Court Hotel,
    Derby   110
The Merchant House, Ludlow   411
Merchant House Restaurant,
    St Peter Port   564
Merchant's Restaurant,
    Nottingham   386
Mere Court Hotel, Knutsford   63
Le Meridien Piccadilly - The Oak
    Room, London W1   329
Le Meridien Piccadilly - The
    Terrace, London W1   329-30
Le Meridien Waldorf,
    London WC2   360
The Mermaid Inn, Rye   468
The Merrion Hotel, Dublin   719
Metropolis Restaurant & Bar,
    Cardiff   674
Mezzo, London W1   330
Michael Caines at the Royal
    Clarence, Exeter   122
Michael's Nook Country House
    Hotel, Grasmere   93
Michel's Restaurant, Ripley   459-60
Middlethorpe Hall, York   547
Midleton Park, Midleton   718
Midsummer House, Cambridge   53
Milburn Arms Hotel,
    Rosedale Abbey   540
Milebrook House Hotel,
    Knighton   702
Milford Hall Hotel, Salisbury   516
Mill End Hotel, Chagford   118
The Mill Hotel, Mungrisdale   98
Mill House Hotel, Kingham   396
Millennium Hotel London Mayfair,
    London W1   330
Millennium Knightsbridge, Mju,
    London SW1   289
Millennium Madejski Hotel,
    Reading   38-9
Miller Howe Hotel,
    Windermere   106
Millstone Hotel, Blackburn   246
Millstream Hotel, Bosham   472
Milsom's, Dedham   166
Mims, London EN4   363
Minella Hotel, Clonmel   721
Mirabelle, London W1   330-31
Miskin Manor Hotel, Miskin   707
Mitsukoshi, London SW1   289
Mju at Millennium Knightsbridge,
    London SW1   289
Moat House, Stafford   437
The Mock Turtle, Dorchester   149

Moffat House Hotel, Moffat   596
Momo, London W5   349
Mon Plaisir, London WC2   360
Monachyle Mhor,
    Balquhidder   664-5
Monkey Island Hotel, Bray   33
Monsieur Max, Hampton   365
Montagu Arms Hotel, Beaulieu   202
Montcalm-Hotel Nikko London,
    London W1   331
Montgreenan Mansion House
    Hotel, Kilwinning   589
Monte's, London SW1   290
The Moody Goose, Bath   421
Moonfleet Manor, Weymouth   158
Moorings Hotel, Fort William   632
Moortown Lodge Hotel,
    Ringwood   216
Morgan's Brasserie, St David's   698
Moro, London EC1   263
Morston Hall, Blakeney   371
Mortons House Hotel,
    Corfe Castle   148
Mortons, London W1   331
Mosborough Hall Hotel,
    Sheffield   549
Moss Nook, Manchester   194-5
Mottram Hall Hotel, Wilmslow   67
Mount Haven Hotel, Marazion   72
Mount Juliet Hotel,
    Thomastown   720
Mount Royale, York   547
Mount Somerset Hotel,
    Taunton   432
Moyglare Manor, Moyglare   720
Mr Underhills, Ludlow   412
Muckrach Lodge Hotel,
    Dulnain Bridge   630-1
Muckross Park Hotel,
    Killarney   720
Mulberry House Hotel,
    Torquay   137
The Mulberry Tree,
    Wrightington   250
Mullion Cove, Mullion   74
Murrayshall Hotel, Perth   657

N

Nahm, The Halkin Hotel,
    London SW1   290
Nailcote Hall,
    Balsall Common   496
Nairns, Glasgow   623

Nanny Brow Country House,
Ambleside   86
Nansloe Manor, Helston   71
Nant Ddu Lodge Hotel,
Nant-Ddu   706
Nantyffin Cider Mill Inn,
Crickhowell   702
Nare Hotel, Veryan   85
The Narrows, Portaferry   716
Le Nautique Restaurant,
St Peter Port   564
Neal Street Restaurant,
London WC2   361
Neat, London SE1   277
Neigwl Hotel, Abersoch   687
New Emperor, Manchester   195
New Hall, Sutton Coldfield   503
New House Country Hotel,
Cardiff   674
New Inn, Tresco   84
New Inn at Coln,
Coln St Aldwyns   181-2
New Mill, Eversley   209
New Park Manor,
Brockenhurst   204
New World, London W1   332
Newick Park Country Estate,
Newick   468
Newton Hotel, Nairn   639
Nico Central, London W1   332
Nico Central, Manchester   195
Nicole's, London W1   332
Nightingales,
Richmond upon Thames   368
Nine The Square, Winchester   222-3
Nipa Thai Restaurant, London   347
Nippon Kan, Old Thorns Hotel,
Liphook   211-12
No 4 Cameron Square,
Fort William   632
No 5 Bistro, Bath   422
No Sixteen, Glasgow   623
Noble Rot, London W1   332
Nobu, London W1   333
Noel Arms Hotel,
Chipping Campden   179-80
Norfolk Mead Hotel, Coltishall   372
North West Castle Hotel,
Stranraer   598
Northampton Marriott,
Northampton   381
Northcote Manor, Burrington   117
Northcote Manor, Langho   247-8
Norton House Hotel,
Edinburgh   605

Norwood Hall, Aberdeen   576
Number Twenty Four,
Wymondham   380
Nunsmere Hall, Sandiway   65
Nuremore Hotel,
Carrickmacross   721
Nutfield Priory, Redhill   459
Nuthurst Grange Hotel,
Hockley Heath   501-2
Nutter's, Rochdale   199

O

The Oaks Hotel, Porlock   428
The Oak Room, Le Meridien
Piccadilly, London W1   329
Oatlands Park Hotel,
Weybridge   461
L'Odéon, London W1   333
Odettes, London NW1   270
Off the Wall Restaurant,
Edinburgh   605
Old Bank Hotel, Oxford   400
Old Beams Restaurant with Rooms,
Waterhouses   438
Old Bell Hotel, Malmesbury   512
Old Bridge Hotel, Huntingdon   55
Old Church Hotel,
Watermillock   101
Old Coastguard Inn, Mousehole   74
Old Course Hotel, Road Hole Grill,
St Andrews   616
Old Custom House Inn, Pescadou
Restaurant, Padstow   75
Old Fire Engine House, Ely   54
Old Forge, Storrington   480
Old Government House Hotel,
St Peter Port   564-5
The Old Hall, Todmorden   559
Old House Hotel, Wickham   220-1
Old Inn, Crawfordsburn   715
The Old House Restaurant,
Copthorne   474-5
Old Manor Hotel,
Lundin Links   613-4
Old Manor House Restaurant,
Romsey   217
Old Monastery Restaurant,
Drybridge   649
Old Pines Restaurant with Rooms,
Spean Bridge   642
The Old Rectory, Conwy   680-1
The Old Rectory, Crudwell   509
Old Rectory Hotel, Martinhoe   129
Old Rectory, Norwich   377

The Old Rectory, St Keyne   80
Old Thorns Hotel, Thorns
Restaurant, Liphook   212
The Old Vicarage, Ridgeway   112
Old Vicarage Hotel, Worfield   418-9
The Olde Railway Hotel,
Westport   721
The Olive Branch Brasserie,
Thorpe-le-Soken   171
The Olive Tree at the Queensberry
Hotel, Bath   422
One Aldwych - Axis,
London WC2   361
One Aldwych - Indigo,
London WC2   361
One Paston Place, Brighton   463
Onich Hotel, Onich   640
Open Arms Hotel, Dirleton   646
Opus 70, May Fair Inter-
Continental, London W1   329
L'Oranger, London SW1   290-1
Orchid Restaurant, Torquay   138
Orestone Manor Hotel,
Torquay   138
Organic Café, London NW6   272
The Orient, London W1   333
The Oriental, The Dorchester,
London W1   323
The Orrery, London W1   334
Orsino, London W11   355
Orso Restaurant, London WC2   362
Orton Hall Hotel, Peterborough   57
Osborne Hotel, Torquay   138-9
'Oscars' at the Royal Bath Hotel,
Bournemouth   144
Osprey Hotel, Kingussie   636
Ostan Gweedore, Bunbeg   719
Osteria Antica Bologna, SW11   309
Ostlers Close Restaurant,
Cupar   612
Overton Grange Hotel,
Ludlow   412-3
The Oxford Belfry,
Milton Common   397
The Oxo Tower Restaurant,
London SE1   276-7
Ozer, London W1   334

P

Painswick Hotel, Painswick   185
Palé Hall Country House,
Bala   687-8
Panorama Hotel, Tenby   699

Pantrhiwgoch Hotel & Riverside
Restaurant, Abergavenny 593
Papingo Restaurant, Glasgow 623-4
Parade, London W5 349-50
Paris House Restaurant,
Woburn 29
The Parisienne Chop House,
London SW3 302
Park Hotel Kenmare, Kenmare 720
The Park Hotel, Virginia 718
Park House Hotel, Shifnal 416
The Park Lane Hotel,
London W1 335
Parkmore Hotel,
Stockton-on-Tees 164
Park Restaurant, London W2 347
La Parmigiana, Glasgow 621-2
The Parsonage Hotel, Escrick 531
Parva Farmhouse Hotel,
Tintern 694
Passione, London W1 335
Paul Heathcote's Restaurant,
Longridge 248
The Peacock Inn,
Tenbury Wells 524
The Pear Tree at Purton,
Purton 513-4
The Pear Tree, Whitley 517
The Peat Inn, Peat Inn 615
Pedn-Olva Hotel, St Ives 80
Pen-y-Dyffryn Country Hotel,
Oswestry 415
Penally Abbey Hotel, Tenby 699
Penbontbren Farm Hotel,
Aberporth 677
Pencraig Court Hotel,
Ross-on-Wye 227
Pendley Manor, Tring 232
Pengethley Manor,
Ross-on-Wye 228
Penhaven Country House,
Parkham 130
Penhelig Arms, Aberdyfi 686
Penmaenuchaf Hall, Dolgellau 690
Pennyhill Park Hotel,
Bagshot 453-4
People's Palace, London SE1 277
Peppers Bar & Bistro,
Bishop's Waltham 203
Percy's Country Hotel & Restaurant,
Virginstow 140-1
Periton Park Hotel, Minehead 427
Perry's Restaurant,
Weymouth 158-9
Pescatori, London W1 335

Le Petit Blanc, Birmingham 499
Le Petit Blanc, Cheltenham 178
Le Petit Blanc, Manchester 195
Le Petit Blanc, Oxford 400
Le Petit Canard,
Maiden Newton 151-2
Le Petit Pierrot Restaurant,
Claygate 454
Pétrus, London SW1 27
Pharmacy Restaurant,
London W11 356
Pheasant Inn, Keyston 55
Pheasants Restaurant,
Sherborne 156
Phoenix Bar & Grill,
London SW15 312
Pied à Terre, London W1 336
Pier at Harwich, Harwich 168-9
Piersland House Hotel, Troon 592
Pine Trees Hotel, Pitlochry 659
The Pink Geranium,
Melbourn 56-7
Pitt House Restaurant,
Kingskerswell 126
Plas Bodegroes, Pwllheli 692
Plas Dolmelynllyn, Dolgellau 690
The Plaza Hotel, Dublin 719
Plough at Clanfield, Clanfield 392
Plumber Manor,
Sturminster Newton 156-7
Plumed Horse Restaurant,
Castle Douglas 594
Pomme D'Or Hotel, St Helier 572
Le Pont de la Tour,
London SE1 278
Pool Court at 42, Leeds 557
Pool House Hotel, Poolewe 641
Pophams, Winkleigh 141
Popinjay Hotel, Rosebank 646
Port Gaverne Hotel,
Port Gaverne 76-7
Portaferry Hotel, Portaferry 716
La Porte des Indes,
London W1 336-7
Porth Tocyn Hotel, Abersoch 687
Porth Veor Manor Hotel,
Newquay 75
Porthminster Beach Restaurant,
St Ives 80
Portmarnock Hotel and Golf Links,
Portmarnock 719
Le Poussin at Parkhill,
Lyndhurst 213
Powder Mills Hotel, Battle 462
Preston House Hotel, Saunton 134

Pride of the Valley Hotel, Churt 454
The Priest House on the River,
Castle Donington 251
Prince Hall Hotel,
Two Bridges 139-40
Princes Arms Hotel, Trefriw 683
Priory Bay Hotel, Seaview 505
Priory Hotel, Bury St Edmunds 443
Priory Hotel, Wareham 157
Priory House, Yeovil 436
Pug, London W4 348
The Punchbowl, Crosthwaite 91
The Purple Onion,
Middlesbrough 538
The Purple Sage, London W1 337
Putney Bridge, London SW15 312

Q

Q brasserie, Lytham St Anne's 249
Quaglino's, London SW1 291
Quality Chop House,
London EC1 263
Quayside Hotel, Brixham 116-17
Queens Court Hotel, Exeter 122-3
Queen's Head Hotel,
Troutbeck 100
Queens Hotel, Bournemouth 144
Quentin's, Hove 466
Quincy's Restaurant,
London NW2 271
Quo Vadis, London W1 337
Quorn Country Hotel, Quorn 254

R

Radisson Edwardian Berkshire
Hotel, London W1 337
Radisson Edwardian Mountbatten
Hotel, London WC2 362
Radisson Edwardian Vanderbilt
Hotel, London SW7 306
Radisson Roe Park Hotel,
Limavady 716
Radisson SAS Hotel Manchester
Airport, Manchester Airport 198
Radisson SAS St Helen's Hotel,
Dublin 719
Raemoir House Hotel,
Banchory 578
Raffles Restaurant, Aldbourne 506
Rafters Restaurant, Sheffield 550
Rain, London W10 354
Ram Jam Inn, Stretton 407
Ramore Restaurant, Portrush 712

Rampsbeck Hotel,
Watermillock 101-2
Rankins, Sissinghurst 242
Ransome's Dock,
London SW11 309-10
Rasa Sumudra, London W1 338
Rasa W1, London W1 338
Rascasse, Leeds 558
Raven Hotel, Much Wenlock 414
Read's Restaurant, Faversham 239
The Real Greek, London N1 268
Red Cow Morans Hotel, Dublin 719
The Red Cube, London WC2 362
Red House, Marsh Benham 36
Red Lion Hotel, Burnsall 530
Red Lion Hotel, Clovelly 119
Red Lion Hotel,
Henley-on-Thames 395
Red Lion Inn, Chalgrove 391
The Red Pepper, London W9 353
The Red Room, London W1 338
Red Snapper Restaurant, Bristol 45
Redmond's, London SW14 311
Redworth Hall Hotel,
Redworth 162
Reeves Restaurant, Felsted 166-7
Regatta Restaurant, Aldeburgh 439
Regency Park Hotel, Newbury 37
Regent Hotel, Ambleside 87
Renaissance Derby/Nottingham
Hotel, South Normanton 113
Renaissance Restaurant,
Bakewell 108
Rendezvous Restaurant,
Breakish 628
Rescobie House Hotel,
Glenrothes 612
Restaurant at The Bonham,
Edinburgh 606
Restaurant Bosquet,
Kenilworth 488
Restaurant Gordon Ramsay,
London SW3 302
Restaurant le Clos, Bath 420
Restaurant Lettonie, Bath 423
Restaurant Martel, Selby 542
Restaurant Martin Wishart,
Edinburgh 575
Restaurant Michael Deane,
Belfast 714
Restaurant One-O-One, Sheraton
Park Tower, London SW1 294
Restaurant on the Green,
Frampton-on-Severn 183
Restaurant 755, London SW6 305

Restaurant Twentyfour,
London EC2 265
Rhinefield House,
Brockenhurst 204
Rhodes & Co, Edinburgh 606
Rhodes & Co, Manchester 196
Rhodes in the Square,
London SW1 291
Riber Hall, Matlock 111
Richard Smith at Thyme,
Sheffield 550
Richmond Gate Hotel,
Richmond-upon-Thames 368-9
Right on the Green,
Royal Tunbridge Wells 243
The Ring O'Roses Country Inn, 426
Rising Sun Hotel, Lynmouth 129
Rising Sun Hotel, St Mawes 82-3
Risley Hall Hotel, Risley 112
Riso Restaurant, London W4 348
Ristorante L'Incontro,
London SW1 292
The Ritz, London W1 339
Riva Restaurant, London SW13 310
La Rive, Hereford 225
River Café, London W6 350-1
Riverdale Hall Hotel,
Bellingham 383
The Riverhouse, Inverness 634
The River Room, The Savoy,
London WC2 363
Riverside Hotel, Evesham 520
Riverside Hotel, Mildenhall 448
Riverside House Hotel,
Ashford-in-the-Water 107-8
Riverside Restaurant, Bridport 145
Riverstation, Bristol 45
Riviera Hotel, Sidmouth 134-5
RK Stanleys, London W1 339
Road Hole Grill, Old Course Hotel,
St Andrews 616
Roade House Restaurant,
Roade 381
Rochestown Park Hotel,
Douglas 718
Rock Glen Country House Hotel,
Clifden 719
Rock Inn, Haytor Vale 124
Rockfield Hotel, Warrington 67
Rococo, Glasgow 624
Rococo, King's Lynn 374
Roebuck Inn Restaurant,
Ludlow 413
Roman Camp Country House,
Callander 665-6

Romans Hotel, Silchester 218-9
Rombalds Hotel, Ilkley 554
Romford House, Swaffham 378
Rookery Hall, Nantwich 64
Rose & Crown,
Sutton on the Forest 543
Rose & Crown, Winkfield 41
Rose and Crown Hotel,
Romaldkirk 163
Rosedale Hotel, Portree 642
Rosehill Manor,
Market Drayton 413
Röser's Restaurant,
Hastings & St Leonards 465
Rosevine Hotel, Portscatho 78
Rosmarino, London NW8 273
Ross Lake House Hotel,
Oughterard 720
Rossett Hall Hotel, Rossett 711
Rothay Garden Hotel,
Grasmere 93-4
The Rouille Restaurant,
Milford on Sea 214
Roussillon, London SW1 293
Rowhill Grange, Dartford 237
Rowton Castle Hotel,
Shrewsbury 417
Roxburghe Hotel, Edinburgh 607
The Roxburghe Hotel, Kelso 662
Royal Berkshire Hotel, Ascot 30
Royal Chase Hotel,
Shaftesbury 154-5
Royal Crescent Hotel, Pimpernels,
Bath 423
Royal Duchy Hotel, Falmouth 69
Royal & Fortescue, The Bank,
Barnstaple 114-15
Royal Garden Hotel, Tenth Floor
Restaurant, London W8 352-3
Royal George Hotel, Tintern 694
Royal Horseguards,
London SW1 293
Royal Hotel, Bridge of Allan 665
Royal Hotel, Comrie 563
Royal Hotel, Tighnabruaich 587
The Royal Hotel, Ventnor 505
Royal Hotel, Winchester 223
Royal Lancaster Hotel, Nipa Thai
Restaurant, London W2 347
Royal Lancaster Hotel, Park
Restaurant, London W2 347
Royal Marine Hotel, Brora 628
Royal Oak Hotel, Sevenoaks 241
Royal Oak Hotel, Yattendon 41
Royal Oak Inn, Withypool 434

Royal Wells Inn,
Royal Tunbridge Wells 243
RSJ, The Restaurant on the South
Bank, London SE1 278
The Rubens at the Palace,
London SW1 293
Rudding Park House,
Harrogate 533
Rufflets Country House,
St Andrews 616
Runnymede Hotel, Egham 454-5
Rusacks Hotel, St Andrews 616-7
Rutland Arms Hotel, Bakewell 108
Rutland Square Hotel by the Castle,
Nottingham 387

S

La Sablonnerie, Sark 573
Sabras Restaurant,
London NW10 274
St Andrews Golf Hotel,
St Andrews 617
St Benedicts Restaurant,
Norwich 378
The St David's Hotel & Spa,
Cardiff 674-5
St John, London EC1 264
St Margaret's Lodge, St Martin 563
St Martin's on the Isle,
St Martin's 81
St Mellion International Hotel,
St Mellion 83
St Michael's Manor,
St Albans 230-1
Saint Michel, Bournemouth 144-5
St Non's Hotel, St David's 698
St Olaves Hotel & Restaurant,
Exeter 123
St Peter's Hall, Bungay 441
St Petroc's House, Padstow 76
St Pierre Park Hotel,
St Peter Port 565
St Quentin Brasserie,
London SW3 303
St Tudno Hotel, Llandudno 682-3
Salford Hall Hotel,
Abbot's Salford 487
Salloos Restaurant,
London SW1 294
Salterns Hotel, Poole 153
The Salt House, London NW8 273
The Salutation Inn, Weobley 228
Sand House Hotel,
Rossnowlagh 719

Sandbanks Hotel, Poole 153-4
Sandford Hotel, Dundee 599
Sandgate Hotel, Restaurant La
Terrasse, Folkestone 239
Santini, London SW1 294
Sartoria, London W1 339
Satis House Hotel, Yoxford 453
Sauce, London NW1 271
The Savoy Grill, London WC2 362-3
The Savoy, River Restaurant,
London WC2 363
Sawrey House Country Hotel,
New Sawrey 98
The Schoolhouse Hotel,
Dublin 719
Scoretulloch House, Darvel 588
The Scot House Hotel,
Kingussie 637
Scott's Brasserie, Ipswich 445
Scotts, London W1 340
Scutchers Restaurant,
Long Melford 447
Sea Crest Hotel, St Brelade 570
Sea Trout Inn, Staverton 135
Sea View Hotel, Ballylickey 718
The Seafood Restaurant,
Padstow 76
The Seafood Restaurant & Wine
Bar, Perth 658
The Seafood Restaurant,
St Monans 618
Seaham Hall Hotel, Seaham 164
Seaview Hotel, Seaview 505
Sebastian's Hotel & Restaurant,
Oswestry 415
Seckford Hall Hotel,
Woodbridge 452
Seeds, Llanfyllin 703
Seiont Manor Hotel,
Caernarfon 689
Seland Newydd, Pwllgloyw 706-7
Selkirk Arms Hotel,
Kirkcudbright 594-5
Selsdon Park Hotel, Croydon 365
Severnshed, Bristol 45
Seymour House Hotel,
Chipping Campden 180
The Shakespeare,
Stratford-upon-Avon 493-4
Shanks, Bangor 715
Shapwick House Hotel,
Shapwick 428-9
Sharrow Bay, Howtown 95
Shaw Country Hotel,
Melksham 513

Shaw Hill Hotel, Chorley 247
Shear's Yard, Leeds 558
Sheedy's Restaurant & Hotel,
Lisdoonvarna 718
Sheen Falls Lodge, Kenmare 720
Sheene Mill, Melbourn 57
Shelbourne Meridien Hotel,
Dublin 719
Shelleys Hotel, Lewes 467
Shepherds, London SW1 294
The Sheraton Grand, The Grill
Room, Edinburgh 607-8
Sheraton Park Tower, Restaurant
One-O-One, London SW1 295
Sherbrooke Castle Hotel,
Glasgow 624
Shibden Mill, Halifax 552
Shieldhill Hotel, Biggar 645
Shillingford Bridge Hotel,
Wallingford 403
Shimla Pinks, Birmingham 500
The Ship Hotel, Chichester 473
Shish Mahal, Glasgow 625
Shu, Belfast 714
Signor Franco,
Royal Tunbridge Wells 244
Silver Swan Hotel, Sligo 721
Simonstone Hall Hotel, Hawes 534
Simply Heathcotes, Liverpool 370
Simply Heathcotes, Manchester 196
Simply Heathcotes, Preston 249-50
Simply Nico, London SW1 295
Simply Poussin, Brockenhurst 205
Simpsons, Kenilworth 489
Singapore Garden Restaurant,
London NW6 273
Sir Charles Napier, Chinnor 391
Sir Christopher Wren Hotel,
Windsor 40-1
Six-13, London W1 340
60 Hope Street, Liverpool 370-1
Sketchley Grange Hotel,
Hinckley 251
Slieve Russell Hotel,
Ballyconnell 718
Smiths of Smithfield,
London EC1 264
Snooty Fox, Tetbury 189
Soar Mill Cove Hotel,
Salcombe 133
Soho South, Cranbrook 236
Sol Restaurant, Shrewsbury 417-8
Solent Hotel, Fareham 209
Solo, Royal Leamington Spa 491
Somerville Hotel, St Aubin 568

Sonny's, Nottingham 387
Sonny's Restaurant,
  London SW13 310
Sopwell House Hotel, St Albans 231
Soufflé Restaurant, Bearsted 234
Soughton Hall Hotel, Northop 686
South Court Business & Leisure
  Hotel, Limerick 720
South Lawn Hotel,
  Milford on Sea 214
South Lodge Hotel, The Camellia
  Restaurant, Lower Beeding 478
Southdowns Country Hotel,
  Midhurst 478
The Spa Hotel,
  Royal Tunbridge Wells 244
Spencers, Emsworth 208
Spiga, London W1 340
La Spighetta, London W1 340-1
Splinters, Christchurch 147
Spoon + at Sanderson,
  London W1 341
Spread Eagle Hotel, Thame 403
The Spring Rock, Halifax 552
Springs Hotel, Wallingford 404
The Square, London W1 341
Stac Polly, Edinburgh 607
Stade Court, Hythe 240
The Stafford, London SW1 295
The Stagg Inn and Restaurant,
  Kington 226
Stanneylands Hotel, Wilmslow 67
Stanwell House Hotel,
  Lymington 212-13
Stapleford Park,
  Melton Mowbray 253
Star Castle Hotel, St Mary's 81
Star Grill - Hotel l'Horizon,
  St Brelade 570
Star Inn, East Tytherley 207
Star Inn, Helmsley 534-5
Starr Restaurant,
  Great Dunmow 167
Stephen Bull Restaurant,
  London W1 341
The Stepping Stone,
  London SW8 307
Stirling Highland Hotel,
  Stirling 667
Stirrups Country House Hotel,
  Bracknell 31
Stock, Manchester 197
Ston Easton Park, Ston Easton 430
Stonehouse Court, Stonehouse 186
Stonor Arms Hotel, Stonor 402

Storrs Hall Hotel, Windermere 106
Stour Bay Café, Manningtree 169
Stratfords, London W8 353
Stravaigin, Glasgow 625
The Strawberry Tree,
  Milton Ernest 29
Stretton Hall Hotel,
  Church Stretton 408
String of Horses Country House
  Hotel, Sway 220
The Studio, Church Stretton 409
Studley Priory Hotel,
  Horton-cum-Studley 396
Sudbury House Hotel,
  Faringdon 394
The Sugar Club, London W1 342
Suma's, Gorey 566-7
The Summer Isles Hotel,
  Achiltibuie 626-7
Summer Lodge, Evershot 150
The Sun Inn, Marston Trussell 381
Sundial Restaurant,
  Herstmonceux 466
Suntory Restaurant,
  London SW1 296
Swag & Tails, London SW7 306
Swallow Churchgate Hotel,
  Harlow 168
Swallow Eden Arms Hotel,
  Rushyford 163
Swallow George Hotel,
  Chollerford 384
Swallow Hotel, Sunderland 486
Swallow International Hotel,
  London SW5 304
Swallows Eaves, Colyford 119
The Swan, West Malling 245
The Swan at Tetsworth, Thame 403
Swan Diplomat Hotel, Streatley 39
Swan Hotel, Bibury 172-3
Swan Hotel, Southwold 450
Swan House, Beccles 440
Swynford Paddocks,
  Six Mile Bottom 58
Sycamore House, Little Shelford 56

T

Tabb's Restaurant, Portreath 77
The Tagore,
  Royal Tunbridge Wells 244
Tai Pan, Manchester 197
Tajine, London W1 342
Le Talbooth Restaurant,
  Dedham 166

Talbot Hotel Conference & Leisure
  Centre, Wexford 721
Talbot Inn Restaurant, Frome 426
Talland Bay Hotel, Talland Bay 83
Tamarind, London W1 342
Tan-y-Foel Hotel,
  Betws-y-Coed 679-80
Tanners Restaurant, Plymouth 132
La Tante Claire, The Berkeley,
  London SW1 296
Taps, Horning 374
Tatsuso Restaurant,
  London EC1 264
Taychreggan Hotel, Kilchrenan 584
Taylors Barn Restaurant,
  Cuckfield 475
Teatro, Leeds 559
Teatro, London W1 343
Teca, London W1 343
Temple Gate Hotel, Ennis 718
Temple Sowerby House Hotel,
  Temple Sowerby 99-100
Tenth Floor Restaurant, Royal
  Garden Hotel, London W8 352
The Terrace, Le Meridien
  Piccadilly, London W1 329-30
Terre à Terre, Brighton 463
Thackeray's House Restaurant,
  Royal Tunbridge Wells 245
Thai Edge Restaurant,
  Birmingham 500
Thai Thai, Stadhampton 401
The Thai Garden, London E2 260
Thainstone House, Inverurie 579
Thatch Lodge Hotel,
  Charmouth 146
Thatched Cottage Hotel,
  Brockenhurst 205
Theobalds Restaurant,
  Ixworth 445-6
Thornbury Castle, Thornbury 190
Three Chimneys Restaurant,
  Colbost 629
Three Cocks Hotel,
  Three Cocks 707
The Three Hares Country Inn,
  Bilbrough 528
Three Horseshoes Inn, Leek 436
Three Horseshoes Restaurant,
  Madingley 56
The Three Lions,
  Fordingbridge 211
Three Salmons Hotel, Usk 695
Three Swans Hotel,
  Market Harborough 253

The Three Tuns, Northallerton 539
Three Ways House,
  Chipping Camden 180
Thurlestone Hotel, Thurlestone 136
Thyme & Plaice, Callington 68
Tickton Grange Hotel, Beverley 526
Tico Tico, Bristol 46
Tides Reach Hotel, Salcombe 133-4
The Tiffin, Leicester 252
Tigh an Eilean Hotel, Shieldaig 642
Tillmouth Park Hotel,
  Cornhill-on-Tweed 384
Tinakilly Country House &
  Restaurant, Rathnew 721
Tinhay Mill Restaurant, Lifton 128
Titchwell Manor Hotel,
  Titchwell 379
The Tollgate Inn, Kingham 397
Toorak Hotel, Torquay 139
Tor-Na-Coille Hotel, Banchory 579
La Toque d'Or, Birmingham 500
Tot Hill House, Stowmarket 451
Tower Restaurant, Edinburgh 609
Treacle Moon,
  Newcastle upon Tyne 485
Trebrea Lodge, Tintagel 83
Tregildry Hotel, Gillan 71
Treglos Hotel, Constantine Bay 69
Tregynon Farmhouse Restaurant,
  Fishguard 696-7
Trelawne Hotel, Mawnan Smith 73
Trengilly Wartha Inn,
  Constantine 68-9
Trident Hotel, Kinsale 718
La Trompette, London W4 348-9
The Trouble House, Tetbury 190
Truffles, Bruton 425
Tudor Farmhouse Hotel,
  Clearwell 181
Tufton Arms Hotel,
  Appleby-in-Westmorland 87
Turners Restaurant,
  London SW3 303
Two Bridges Hotel,
  Two Bridges 140
Ty Mawr Country Hotel,
  Brechfa 676
Tyddyn Llan Country House,
  Llandrillo 683-4
Tylney Hall, Rotherwick 218
Ty'n Rhos Country Hotel,
  Caernarfon 689
Ty'r Graig Castle Hotel,
  Barmouth 688

U

Ubiquitous Chip, Glasgow 626
Ubon by Nobu, London E14 261
Udny Arms Hotel,
  Newburgh 579-80
Ulbster Arms Hotel, Halkirk 633
Underscar Manor, Keswick 97
Uplands Hotel, Cartmel 90
Uplawmoor Hotel, Uplawmoor 660
The Usk Inn, Brecon 700

V

Valley Hotel, Telford 418
Vama, London SW10 309
Vasco & Piero's Pavilion,
  London W1 343
Veeraswamy Restaurant,
  London W1 344
La Ventura Restaurant,
  London N4 268-9
The Venture In Restaurant,
  Ombersley 524
Vermont Hotel,
  Newcastle-upon-Tyne 486
Victoria Hotel, Bamburgh 383
Victoria Hotel, Sidmouth 135
Viet-Hoa, London E2 260
The Village Bistro, Gorey 567
The Village Pub, Barnsley 172
Villandry, London W1 344
Villiers Hotel, Henry's Restaurant,
  Buckingham 46-7
Vine House Restaurant,
  Towcester 382
Vineyard at Stockcross,
  Newbury 37-8
The Vintners Room, Edinburgh 608
Vong, London SW1 296-7

W

Wallett's Court, Dover 237-8
Walnut Tree Inn, Abergavenny 693
Warpool Court Hotel,
  St David's 698
Washbourne Court Hotel,
  Lower Slaughter 183-4
The Waterdine,
  Llanfair Waterdine 410
Waterford Castle Hotel,
  Waterford 721
Waterford House,
  Middleham 537-8

Waterford Lodge Hotel,
  Christchurch 147
Waterfront Restaurant, Oban 586
Waterman's, Nailsworth 185
Waterside Inn, Bray 33
Waterside Inn, Peterhead 580
Watersmeet Hotel,
  Woolacombe 141
Watsons Restaurant & Bar,
  Leicester 252-3
Wayfarers Restaurant,
  Shaftesbury 155
Weavers Restaurant, Haworth 553
Weavers Shed Restaurant,
  Huddersfield 553
Welcombe Hotel,
  Stratford-upon-Avon 494
Well House Hotel, Liskeard 71-2
Well View Hotel, Moffat 596
Wensleydale Heifer Inn,
  West Witton 544
Wentbridge House Hotel,
  Wentbridge 560
Wentworth Hotel, Aldeburgh 439
Wapping Food, London E1 260
Wesley House, Winchcombe 191
West Arms Hotel,
  Llanarmon Dyffryn Ceiriog 710
West House Restaurant,
  Biddenden 234
West Lodge Park Hotel,
  Hadley Wood 365
Westbury Hotel, London W1 344
The Westleton Crown,
  Westleton 451
Westmorland Hotel, Tebay 99
Weston Manor Hotel,
  Weston-on-the-Green 404
Westover Hall,
  Milford on Sea 214-15
Wheatsheaf Restaurant with Rooms,
  Swinton 664
Whipper-in Hotel, Oakham 407
White Hart, Great Yeldham 168
White Hart Hotel,
  Dorchester-on-Thames 393
White Hart Inn, Ford 509
White Hart Inn, Nayland 448-9
White Hart Inn, Oldham 199
White Horse Inn, Chilgrove 474
White House Hotel, Herm 566
White House Hotel, Williton 433
White House Restaurant,
  Prestbury 64-5

White Lion Hotel,
    Upton upon Severn   525
White Moss House, Grasmere   94
White Onion, London N1   268
The White Sands Hotel,
    Ballheige   720
The White Swan, Brecon   700
White Swan, Pickering   539
Whitehall Hotel, Stanstead   170
Whitford House Hotel,
    Wexford   721
Whitley Ridge Hotel,
    Brockenhurst   205-6
Whytes, Brighton   464
Wife of Bath Restaurant, Wye   245
Wig & Mitre, Lincoln   257
Wild Boar Hotel, Windermere   106
Wild Duck Inn, Ewen   182
Wildings, Girvan   591
The Wild Mushroom Restaurant,
    Westfield   470
Willerby Manor Hotel, Willerby 527
Willowburn Hotel, Clachan-Seil 582
Wiltons, London SW1   297
Windsor Lodge Hotel, Swansea   708
Winter Glen, Edinburgh   607
Winteringham Fields,
    Winteringham   259
Witchery by the Castle,
    Edinburgh   608-9
Wolfscastle Country Hotel,
    Haverfordwest   697
Wood Hall Hotel, Wetherby   560
Wood Norton Hall, Evesham   520-1

Woodenbridge Hotel,
    Woodenbridge   721
Woodland Park Hotel,
    Altrincham   192
Woodlands Lodge Hotel,
    Southampton   219-20
Woodlands Manor Hotel,
    Bedford   28
Woodlands Park Hotel,
    Stoke d'Abernon   461
Woods Brasserie, Cardiff   675
Woods Restaurant, Bath   424
Woolley Grange,
    Bradford-on-Avon   507
Woolpack Inn, Beckington   424
Wordsworth Hotel, Grasmere   94
Worsley Arms Hotel,
    Hovingham   536
Wrea Head Country Hotel,
    Scarborough   541
Wrightington Hotel, Wigan   200
Wroxton House Hotel, Banbury   388
Wyck Hill House Hotel,
    Stow-on-the-Wold   187
Wye Knot Restaurant,
    Chepstow   693-4
Wykeham Arms, Winchester   223
Wynnstay Hotel, Oswestry   416

Y

Y Bistro, Llanberis   691
Yalbury Cottage, Dorchester   149
Ye Olde Bell Hotel, Maidenhead 36

Ye Olde Bulls Head Inn,
    Beaumaris   670
Yeoldon Country House Hotel,
    Bideford   115
Yeovil Court Hotel, Yeovil   436
Yetman's, Holt   374
The Yew Trees,
    Radcliffe on Trent   387
YMing, London W1   345
Ynyshir Hall, Eglwysfach   678-9
York Pavilion Hotel, York   548
Yorke Arms, Ramsgill   540
Yumi Restaurant, London W1   345

Z

Zafferano, London SW1   297
Zaika, London SW3   303
Zetland Country House Hotel,
    Cashel   719
Ziba, Liverpool   371

Please send this form to:
  Editor, The Restaurant Guide,
  Lifestyle Guides,
  The Automobile Association,
  Fanum House,
  Basingstoke RG21 4EA

or fax: 01256 491647
or e-mail: lifestyleguides@theAA.com

Readers' Report form

Please use this form to tell us about any restaurant you have visited, whether it is in the guide or not currently listed. Feedback from readers helps us to keep our guide accurate and up to date. Please note, however, that if you have a complaint to make during a visit, we strongly recommend that you discuss the matter with the restaurant management there and then so that they have a chance to put things right before your visit is spoilt. The AA does not undertake to arbitrate between you and the restaurant management, or to obtain compensation or engage in correspondence.

Date:

Your name (block capitals)

Your address (block capitals)

....

....

....

.... e-mail address:

Comments (If you are recommending a new restaurant please enclose a menu or note the dishes that you had).

....

....

....

....

....

....

....

(please attach a separate sheet if necessary)

Please tick here if you DO NOT wish to receive details of AA offers or products

Readers' Report Form

	YES	NO

Have you bought this guide before? ☐ ☐

Have you bought any other restaurant, pub, accommodation or food guides recently? If yes, which ones?

....

....

What are your main reasons for visiting restaurants (circle all that apply)

business   entertaining   business travel   trying famous restaurants

family celebrations   leisure travel   trying new food

enjoying not having to cook yourself   to eat food you couldn't cook yourself

other ....   because I enjoy eating out regularly

How often do you visit a restaurant for lunch or dinner? (circle one choice)

more than once a week   once a week   once a fortnight

once a month   once in six months

Please answer these questions to help us make improvements to the guide:

Do you use the location atlas?..

Do you generally agree with the rosette ratings at the restaurants you visit in the guide? (if not please give examples)

Who is your favourite chef? ....

Which is your favourite restaurant? ....

Which type of cuisine is your first choice e.g. French, Indian, Chinese:

....

Which of these factors are most important when choosing a restaurant?

Price   Service   Location   Type of food   Awards/ratings

Decor/surroundings   Other (please state):....................................

Which elements of the guide do you find most useful when choosing a restaurant?

Description   Photo   Rosette rating

Please send this form to:
    Editor, The Restaurant Guide,
    Lifestyle Guides,
    The Automobile Association,
    Fanum House,
    Basingstoke RG21 4EA

    or fax: 01256 491647
    or e-mail: lifestyleguides@theAA.com

Readers' Report form

Please use this form to tell us about any restaurant you have visited, whether it is in the guide or not currently listed. Feedback from readers helps us to keep our guide accurate and up to date. Please note, however, that if you have a complaint to make during a visit, we strongly recommend that you discuss the matter with the restaurant management there and then so that they have a chance to put things right before your visit is spoilt. The AA does not undertake to arbitrate between you and the restaurant management, or to obtain compensation or engage in correspondence.

Date:

Your name (block capitals)

Your address (block capitals)

....

....

....

.... e-mail address:

Comments (If you are recommending a new restaurant please enclose a menu or note the dishes that you had).

....

....

....

....

....

....

....

(please attach a separate sheet if necessary)

Please tick here if you DO NOT wish to receive details of AA offers or products

Readers' Report Form

	YES	NO
Have you bought this guide before?	☐	☐

Have you bought any other restaurant, pub, accommodation or food guides recently? If yes, which ones?

....

....

What are your main reasons for visiting restaurants (circle all that apply)

business   entertaining   business travel   trying famous restaurants

family celebrations   leisure travel   trying new food

enjoying not having to cook yourself   to eat food you couldn't cook yourself

other ....   because I enjoy eating out regularly

How often do you visit a restaurant for lunch or dinner? (circle one choice)

more than once a week   once a week   once a fortnight

once a month   once in six months

Please answer these questions to help us make improvements to the guide:

Do you use the location atlas?...

Do you generally agree with the rosette ratings at the restaurants you visit in the guide? (if not please give examples)

Who is your favourite chef? ....

Which is your favourite restaurant? ....

Which type of cuisine is your first choice e.g. French, Indian, Chinese:

....

Which of these factors are most important when choosing a restaurant?

Price   Service   Location   Type of food   Awards/ratings

Decor/surroundings   Other (please state):.......................................

Which elements of the guide do you find most useful when choosing a restaurant?

Description   Photo   Rosette rating

Readers' Report form

Please send this form to:
  Editor, The Restaurant Guide,
  Lifestyle Guides,
  The Automobile Association,
  Fanum House,
  Basingstoke RG21 4EA

or fax: 01256 491647
or e-mail: lifestyleguides@theAA.com

Please use this form to tell us about any restaurant you have visited, whether it is in the guide or not currently listed. Feedback from readers helps us to keep our guide accurate and up to date. Please note, however, that if you have a complaint to make during a visit, we strongly recommend that you discuss the matter with the restaurant management there and then so that they have a chance to put things right before your visit is spoilt. The AA does not undertake to arbitrate between you and the restaurant management, or to obtain compensation or engage in correspondence.

Date:

Your name (block capitals)

Your address (block capitals)

....

....

....

.... e-mail address:

Comments (If you are recommending a new restaurant please enclose a menu or note the dishes that you had).

....

....

....

....

....

....

....

(please attach a separate sheet if necessary)

Please tick here if you DO NOT wish to receive details of AA offers or products

☐

PTO

Readers' Report Form

	YES	NO

Have you bought this guide before? ☐ ☐

Have you bought any other restaurant, pub, accommodation or food guides recently? If yes, which ones?

....

....

What are your main reasons for visiting restaurants (circle all that apply)

business   entertaining   business travel   trying famous restaurants

family celebrations   leisure travel   trying new food

enjoying not having to cook yourself   to eat food you couldn't cook yourself

other ....   because I enjoy eating out regularly

How often do you visit a restaurant for lunch or dinner? (circle one choice)

more than once a week   once a week   once a fortnight

once a month   once in six months

Please answer these questions to help us make improvements to the guide:

Do you use the location atlas?...

Do you generally agree with the rosette ratings at the restaurants you visit in the guide? (if not please give examples)

Who is your favourite chef? ....

Which is your favourite restaurant? ....

Which type of cuisine is your first choice e.g. French, Indian, Chinese:

....

Which of these factors are most important when choosing a restaurant?

Price   Service   Location   Type of food   Awards/ratings

Decor/surroundings   Other (please state):....................................

Which elements of the guide do you find most useful when choosing a restaurant?

Description   Photo   Rosette rating

Please send this form to:
  Editor, The Restaurant Guide,
  Lifestyle Guides,
  The Automobile Association,
  Fanum House,
  Basingstoke RG21 4EA

  or fax: 01256 491647
  or e-mail: lifestyleguides@theAA.com

Readers' Report form

Please use this form to tell us about any restaurant you have visited, whether it is in the guide or not currently listed. Feedback from readers helps us to keep our guide accurate and up to date. Please note, however, that if you have a complaint to make during a visit, we strongly recommend that you discuss the matter with the restaurant management there and then so that they have a chance to put things right before your visit is spoilt. The AA does not undertake to arbitrate between you and the restaurant management, or to obtain compensation or engage in correspondence.

Date:

Your name (block capitals)

Your address (block capitals)

....

....

....

.... e-mail address:

Comments (If you are recommending a new restaurant please enclose a menu or note the dishes that you had).

....

....

....

....

....

....

....

(please attach a separate sheet if necessary)

Please tick here if you DO NOT wish to receive details of AA offers or products

PTO

Readers' Report Form

YES   NO

Have you bought this guide before? ☐ ☐

Have you bought any other restaurant, pub, accommodation or food guides recently? If yes, which ones?

....

....

What are your main reasons for visiting restaurants (circle all that apply)

business   entertaining   business travel   trying famous restaurants

family celebrations   leisure travel   trying new food

enjoying not having to cook yourself   to eat food you couldn't cook yourself

other ....   because I enjoy eating out regularly

How often do you visit a restaurant for lunch or dinner? (circle one choice)

more than once a week   once a week   once a fortnight

once a month   once in six months

Please answer these questions to help us make improvements to the guide:

Do you use the location atlas?..

Do you generally agree with the rosette ratings at the restaurants you visit in the guide? (if not please give examples)

Who is your favourite chef? ....

Which is your favourite restaurant? ....

Which type of cuisine is your first choice e.g. French, Indian, Chinese:

....

Which of these factors are most important when choosing a restaurant?

Price   Service   Location   Type of food   Awards/ratings

Decor/surroundings   Other (please state):......................................

Which elements of the guide do you find most useful when choosing a restaurant?

Description   Photo   Rosette rating

Please send this form to:
  Editor, The Restaurant Guide,
  Lifestyle Guides,
  The Automobile Association,
  Fanum House,
  Basingstoke RG21 4EA

Readers' Report Form

or fax: 01256 491647
or e-mail: lifestyleguides@theAA.com

Please use this form to tell us about any restaurant you have visited, whether it is in the guide or not currently listed. Feedback from readers helps us to keep our guide accurate and up to date. Please note, however, that if you have a complaint to make during a visit, we strongly recommend that you discuss the matter with the restaurant management there and then so that they have a chance to put things right before your visit is spoilt. The AA does not undertake to arbitrate between you and the restaurant management, or to obtain compensation or engage in correspondence.

Date:

Your name (block capitals)

Your address (block capitals)

....

....

....

.... e-mail address:

Comments (If you are recommending a new restaurant please enclose a menu or note the dishes that you had).

....

....

....

....

....

....

....

(please attach a separate sheet if necessary)

Please tick here if you DO NOT wish to receive details of AA offers or products

Readers' Report Form

YES   NO

Have you bought this guide before? ☐   ☐

Have you bought any other restaurant, pub, accommodation or food guides recently? If yes, which ones?

....

....

What are your main reasons for visiting restaurants (circle all that apply)

business   entertaining   business travel   trying famous restaurants

family celebrations   leisure travel   trying new food

enjoying not having to cook yourself   to eat food you couldn't cook yourself

other ....   because I enjoy eating out regularly

How often do you visit a restaurant for lunch or dinner? (circle one choice)

more than once a week   once a week   once a fortnight

once a month   once in six months

Please answer these questions to help us make improvements to the guide:

Do you use the location atlas?...

Do you generally agree with the rosette ratings at the restaurants you visit in the guide? (if not please give examples)

Who is your favourite chef? ....

Which is your favourite restaurant? ....

Which type of cuisine is your first choice e.g. French, Indian, Chinese:

....

Which of these factors are most important when choosing a restaurant?

Price   Service   Location   Type of food   Awards/ratings

Decor/surroundings   Other (please state):...

Which elements of the guide do you find most useful when choosing a restaurant?

Description   Photo   Rosette rating